Michael Miller

The General Electric **A** Course
ENGINEERING ANALYSIS

The General Electric **A** Course
ENGINEERING ANALYSIS

DONALD R. MACK
General Electric Company

General Electric Company
Advertising and Sales Promotion Operations
Norwalk, Connecticut 06856

 Printed in the United States of America by The Saybrook Press, Inc., Old Saybrook, Connecticut. Library of Congress Catalog Card Number 82-81434.

PREFACE

In 1923 Robert E. Doherty founded the Advanced Course in Engineering in the General Electric Company. His initials in Greek letters adorn the bar sinister of the ACE shield on the cover of this book.

Recognizing that Steinmetz and a few other central oracles were mortal, Doherty intended that the ACE would teach young engineers how to solve the real engineering problems of industry. At first the curriculum was informal, determined by the priority of the Company's current engineering problems. Soon a structured curriculum developed, and gradually a body of text material. The homework continued to be real engineering problems, some new but most already solved.

In 1953 the ACE staff compiled the notes for the first year or **A** Course into three volumes titled *Fundamentals of Engineering Analysis*. That staff's successors published a second edition in 1957.

This new volume, *Engineering Analysis*, can be considered as a third edition of FOEA, updated and thoroughly revised. Like its predecessors, the new volume includes a wide variety of topics in electrical and mechanical engineering. In a typical **A** Class of graduate electrical and mechanical engineers about half of the material is review for each student and the other half is unfamiliar enough to be considered new. A 20-hour homework problem accompanies each chapter.

Engineers not taking the **A** Course may find that because of its ecumenical range of topics, *Engineering Analysis* is a useful reference book and review of electrical and mechanical engineering.

Several chapters contain original material. The useful and little-known Trick of Papoulis for inverting Laplace transforms with complex poles is explained in Chapter 2, and an original extension to z transforms appears in Chapter 12. Chapter 14 is an explanation of Jay Forrester's System Dynamics in the language of electrical engineering. A detailed discussion of Kirchhoff's law is included in Chapter 29 on Radiant Heat Transfer to correct the impression that $\varepsilon = \alpha$. Chapter 30 on Convective Heat Transfer contains a proof of Buckingham's Pi Theorem that is absent from Buckingham's original 1914 paper and the subsequent literature.

Engineering Analysis is intended as a model for the technical writing that has always been a part of ACE. The book is free of first-person pronouns (Let us turn our attention . . .), redundant words (The receiver system is itself essentially stable . . .), and dangling participles (Combining these equations, the result is . . .). The book is dedicated to the proposition that problem solving and technical writing are taught most effectively in the same course. The book is also dedicated to the several thousand heros who have solved and written up all of the 20-hour-or-more problems of the **A** Course.

Donald R. Mack

CONTENTS

Chapter 1

CLASSICAL SOLUTIONS OF ORDINARY DIFFERENTIAL EQUATIONS

1.1 Introduction

An electrical or mechanical engineer must sometimes add the voltages around a loop in a circuit, the currents entering a junction, or the forces on a moving body. The sum of the terms is a differential equation. It is called *ordinary* because it contains total derivatives but no partial derivatives. The *order* of a differential equation is the order of the highest derivative in the equation. The differential equations mentioned above are of second order. If a circuit has several loops or nodes, or if several interconnected bodies are moving, the system is represented by differential equations of higher order. They are usually of a class called *linear*, because fortunately resistances, capacitances, inductances, masses, spring constants, and damping constants are often very nearly constant. If these parameters vary, the differential equations may be nonlinear. Then the methods of solution become approximate, numerical instead of analytical, or applicable to only limited cases. This chapter will consider only linear differential equations. Classical methods of solution will be demonstrated, that are frequently tedious and can often be avoided by the use of Laplace transforms, state-transition matrices, and eigenvectors. These glamorous methods will be explained later. The pedestrian classical methods deserve attention now, because they are often the only tools with which a solution can be obtained.

1.2 Test for Linearity of Systems

Differential equations describe the operation of systems. For example, Fig. 1.1 shows an R-C circuit for which

$$v(t) = R\,i(t) + \frac{1}{C}\int_{-\infty}^{t} i(x)dx \tag{1.1}$$

and

$$y(t) = \frac{1}{C}\int_{-\infty}^{t} i(x)dx\,. \tag{1.2}$$

Then

$$\frac{dy}{dt} = \frac{1}{C}\,i(t) \tag{1.3}$$

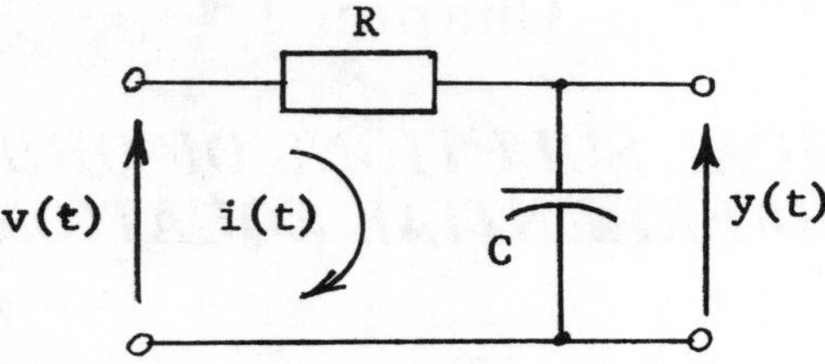

Fig. 1.1. R-C electrical circuit.

and

$$v(t) = RC\frac{dy}{dt} + y\,. \tag{1.4}$$

The differential equation representing the circuit is therefore

$$RC\frac{dy}{dt} + y = v(t)\,. \tag{1.5}$$

The right side $v(t)$, called the *forcing* or *driving function*, can be considered as the input to the system, and the dependent variable $y(t)$ as the output, as shown in Fig. 1.2.

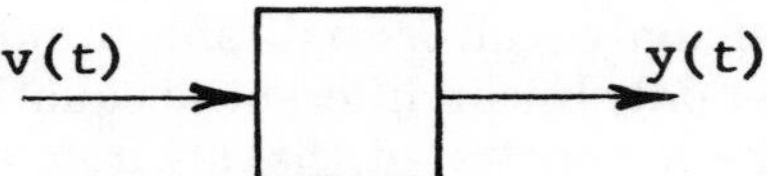

Fig. 1.2. Input and output of a system.

Fig. 1.3. shows a mass m supported by a spring and a damper, whose only allowable motion is vertical translation. The force $v(t)$ applied to the mass causes the deflection $y(t)$. If the forces exerted upward on the mass by the spring and damper are ky and $c\dot{y}$, the sum of forces on the mass is

$$m\ddot{y} + c\dot{y} + ky = v(t)\,. \tag{1.6}$$

The applied force is the driving function, and may be considered to be the input of the system. If the deflection is the output, the system is represented by Fig. 1.2.

A system with input $v(t)$ and output $y(t)$ can be described by several adjectives, the first of which is "linear." Suppose that the response of a system to the input $v_1(t)$ is $y_1(t)$, and the response to $v_2(t)$ is $y_2(t)$. Apply the input

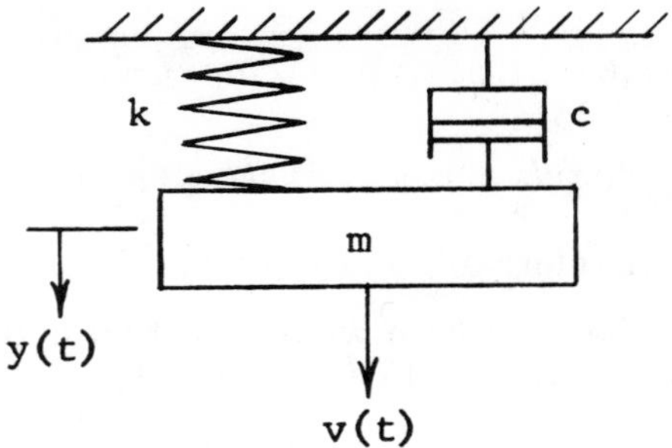

Fig. 1.3. Moving mass.

$$v(t) = c_1 v_1(t) + c_2 v_2(t) , \tag{1.7}$$

where c_1 and c_2 are constants. The system is *linear* if the output is

$$y(t) = c_1 y_1(t) + c_2 y_2(t) . \tag{1.8}$$

Another statement of the definition will provide a useful test. Let L represent the operation that the system performs on the input to produce the output:

$$y(t) = L[v(t)] . \tag{1.9}$$

A system is linear iff (if and only if)

$$\begin{aligned} L[c_1 v_1(t) + c_2 v_2(t)] &= c_1 L[v_1(t)] + c_2 L[v_2(t)] \\ &= c_1 y_1(t) + c_2 y_2(t) . \end{aligned} \tag{1.10}$$

This equation is a statement of the *superposition principle*. Many systems are linear within engineering accuracy, over a limited range of v_1, v_2, c_1, and c_2. Eq. (1.10) can be used to test some common subsystems for linearity, with unexpected results.

Integrator. For the integrator shown in Fig. 1.4,

$$y(t) = \int_{-\infty}^{t} v(x)dx . \tag{1.11}$$

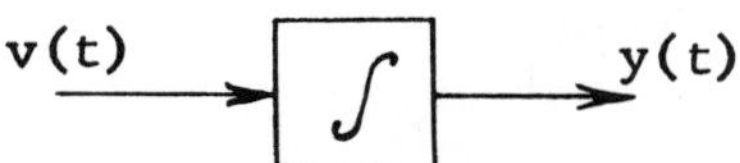

Fig. 1.4. An integrator.

Then

$$L[c_1v_1(t) + c_2v_2(t)] = \int_{-\infty}^{t} [c_1v_1(x) + c_2v_2(x)]dx$$

$$= c_1 \int_{-\infty}^{t} v_1(x)dx + c_2 \int_{-\infty}^{t} v_2(x)dx = c_1y_1(t) + c_2y_2(t)\ . \qquad (1.12)$$

An integrator is therefore a linear system.

Differentiator. For a system whose function is to differentiate its input n times and multiply it by a constant k,

$$y(t) = k\frac{d^n v(t)}{dt^n}\ . \qquad (1.13)$$

Then

$$L[c_1v_1 + c_2v_2] = k\frac{d^n}{dt^n}(c_1v_1 + c_2v_2)$$

$$= c_1k\frac{d^nv_1}{dt^n} + c_2k\frac{d^nv_2}{dt^n} = c_1y_1 + c_2y_2\ , \qquad (1.14)$$

which proves that differentiation is a linear operation.

Time-varying coefficient. The system

$$y(t) = f(t)\frac{d^nv}{dt^n}\ , \qquad n = 0, 1, 2, \ldots \qquad (1.15)$$

appears in engineering work with various coefficients $f(t)$. In stress analysis the independent variable might be distance x instead of time t. Is the system linear? Again, apply the weighted sum of two inputs. The result is

$$L[c_1v_1 + c_2v_2] = f(t)\frac{d^n}{dt^n}[c_1v_1 + c_2v_2]$$

$$= c_1f(t)\frac{d^nv_1}{dt^n} + c_2f(t)\frac{d^nv_2}{dt^n} = c_1y_1 + c_2y_2\ . \qquad (1.16)$$

Perhaps counter to intuition, a differentiator with a time-varying coefficient is linear.

Coefficient a function of the input. If the coefficient of the derivative term is a function of the driver,

$$y(t) = f(v)\frac{d^nv}{dt^n}\ . \qquad (1.17)$$

Now

$$L[c_1v_1 + c_2v_2] = f(c_1v_1 + c_2v_2)\frac{d^n}{dt^n}(c_1v_1 + c_2v_2)$$

$$= c_1 f(c_1 v_1 + c_2 v_2) \frac{d^n v_1}{dt^n} + c_2 f(c_1 v_1 + c_2 v_2) \frac{d^n v_2}{dt^n} . \tag{1.18}$$

For this system, the right side of Eq. (1.10) is

$$c_1 y_1 + c_2 y_2 = c_1 f(v_1) \frac{d^n v_1}{dt^n} + c_2 f(v_2) \frac{d^n v_2}{dt^n} . \tag{1.19}$$

The system of Eq. (1.17) fails the test, and is therefore nonlinear. It can be linear only if the coefficient is a constant or a function of the independent variable.

The reader can readily prove that a series connection of linear subsystems, shown in Fig. 1.5, constitutes a linear system. For this connection,

$$x(t) = L_1[v(t)] \quad \text{and} \quad y(t) = L_2[x(t)] .$$

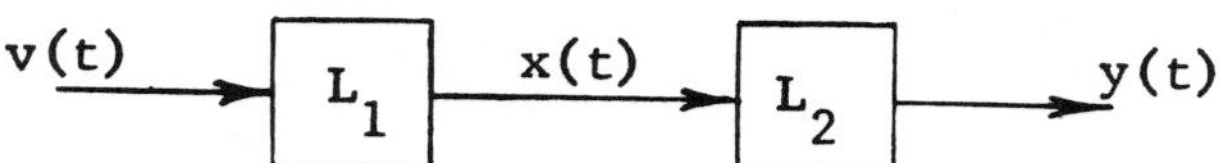

Fig. 1.5. Series connection of linear subsystems.

Likewise, a parallel connection of linear subsystems, as in Fig. 1.6, is a linear system. For this connection,

$$y(t) = L_1[v(t)] + L_2[v(t)] .$$

In fact, a system composed of linear components that are interconnected in any way is linear.

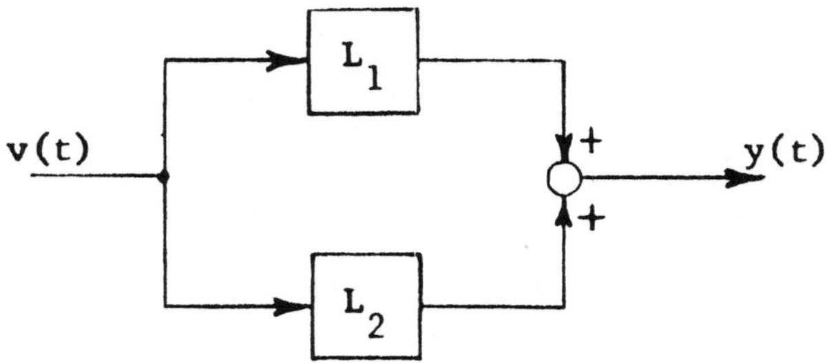

Fig. 1.6. Parallel connection of linear subsystems.

1.3 Test for Time Invariance

A system is *time invariant* or *fixed* if the relationship between the input and output is independent of time. If a given input $v(t)$ applied to such a system now produces the output $y(t)$, the same input applied λ seconds from now will produce the same output, also delayed by λ seconds. In other words, if

$$L[v(t)] = y(t)\,, \tag{1.20}$$

the system is fixed if

$$L[v(t-\lambda)] = y(t-\lambda)\,. \tag{1.21}$$

Two of the subsystems will be tested for time variance.

Time-varying coefficient. For the linear system described by the equation

$$y(t) = f(t)\,\frac{d^n v(t)}{dt^n}\,, \tag{1.22}$$

the left side of Eq. (1.21) is

$$L[v(t-\lambda)] = f(t)\,\frac{d^n v(t-\lambda)}{dt^n}\,. \tag{1.23}$$

The right side is

$$y(t-\lambda) = f(t-\lambda)\,\frac{d^n v(t-\lambda)}{d(t-\lambda)^n}\,. \tag{1.24}$$

Since in general $f(t) \neq f(t-\lambda)$, the two sides of Eq. (1.21) are not equal. Eq. (1.22) therefore describes a time-varying, linear operation.

Coefficient a function of the input. For the nonlinear operation

$$y(t) = f[v(t)]\,\frac{d^n v(t)}{dt^n}\,, \tag{1.25}$$

the left side of Eq. (1.21) is

$$L[v(t-\lambda)] = f[v(t-\lambda)]\,\frac{d^n v(t-\lambda)}{dt^n}\,. \tag{1.26}$$

The right side is

$$y(t-\lambda) = f[v(t-\lambda)]\,\frac{d^n v(t-\lambda)}{d(t-\lambda)^n}\,. \tag{1.27}$$

Since differentiation with respect to $t-\lambda$ or t is the same, the last two results are equal. Surprisingly, the nonlinear operation of Eq. (1.25) is time invariant. The reader is invited to show that an integrator and a differentiator are time invariant.

A system is *nonanticipative* or *causal* if the present output does not depend on future values of the input. Then $y(0)$ is determined by the structure of the system and $v(t)$ for times prior to $t = 0$, but not for $t > 0$. Physical systems cannot predict the future and are causal. The term "causal" has a slightly different meaning when it is applied to a mathematical function. A function $f(t)$ is said to be causal if it is zero for negative t.

A system is *realizable* if it is causal and all real inputs $v(t)$ produce real (not complex) outputs $y(t)$. Physical systems are realizable. The name is somewhat misleading, because there may be no known way to build a given realizable system. The analysis of a physical system is aided by the knowledge that it is realizable. For example, if the calculated response to the real input $v(t) = \sin \omega t$ contains an imaginary term, the analyst knows that the calculation is wrong.

1.4 Representation of Systems by Differential Equations

A system is linear and time invariant if all of its components are linear and time invariant. If any of the components is nonlinear or time variant, the system is also. Differential equations are classified in the same way as the system they represent. The differential equation

$$\frac{d^2y}{dt^2} + t\frac{dy}{dt} + 3y = v(t) \tag{1.28}$$

represents the system in Fig. 1.7, all of whose components are linear. Since one of them is time variant, the system and the differential equation are linear and time variant. Please classify these differential equations:

1. The van der Pol equation, $\ddot{y} - k(1 - y^2)\dot{y} + y = 0$.
2. $\sqrt{t}\,\dfrac{d^2y}{dt^2} + \dfrac{1}{\ln t}\,\dfrac{dy}{dt} + (1 - t^2)y = \operatorname{sgn}(t)$.
3. Eq. (1.6), $m\ddot{y} + c\dot{y} + ky = v(t)$.

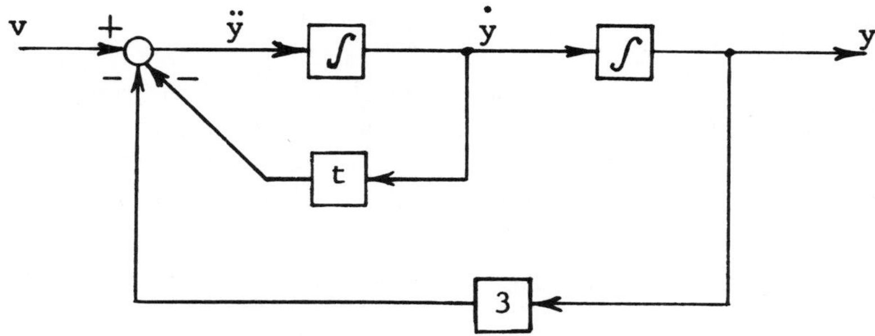

Fig. 1.7. Time-variant, linear system.

If a system is fixed and linear, the differential equation relating its input and output can be derived with relative ease. An example is provided by the electrical circuit of Fig. 1.8. The equation relating the input $v_1(t)$ to the output $v_3(t)$ is found by summing currents at the nodes. The sum of currents leaving node 1 is

$$C_1 \frac{d(v_2 - v_3)}{dt} + \frac{v_2 - v_3}{R_2} + \frac{v_2 - v_1}{R_1} = 0$$

or

$$\left[C_1 \frac{dv_2}{dt} + \left(\frac{1}{R_2} + \frac{1}{R_1}\right) v_2\right] - \left[C_1 \frac{dv_3}{dt} + \frac{v_3}{R_2}\right] = \frac{1}{R_1} v_1 . \tag{1.29}$$

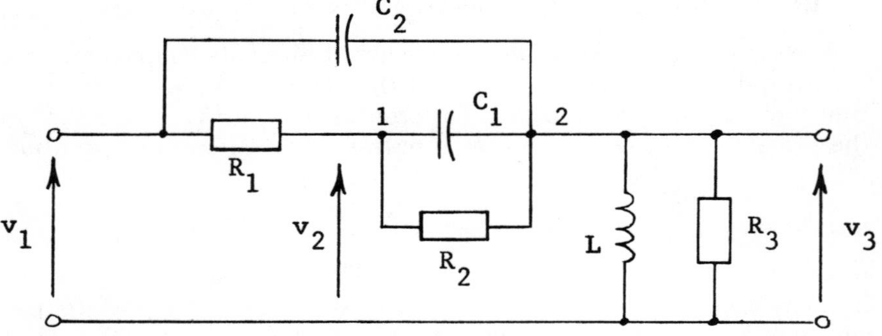

Fig. 1.8. R-L-C electrical circuit.

The sum of currents leaving node 2 is

$$-\left[C_1 \frac{dv_2}{dt} + \frac{1}{R_2} v_2\right] + \left[(C_1 + C_2)\frac{dv_3}{dt} + \left(\frac{1}{R_2} + \frac{1}{R_3}\right)v_3 + \frac{1}{L}\int_{-\infty}^{t} v_3(x)dx\right] = C_2 \frac{dv_1}{dt} . \tag{1.30}$$

The last two equations show that if the C's, R's and L are constant, the system is linear and fixed. For this special case the manipulations may be simplified by letting $p = d/dt$. If the second equation is differentiated once to remove the integral sign, and each C, R, and L is 1 farad, ohm, or henry, the two equations become

$$(p + 2)v_2 - (p + 1)v_3 = v_1 \tag{1.31}$$

$$-(p^2 + p)v_2 + (2p^2 + 2p + 1)v_3 = p^2 v_1 . \tag{1.32}$$

Cramer's rule can be used to find v_3 in terms of v_1:

$$v_3 = \frac{\begin{vmatrix} p+2 & v_1 \\ -(p^2+p) & p^2 v_1 \end{vmatrix}}{\begin{vmatrix} p+2 & -(p+1) \\ -(p^2+p) & 2p^2+2p+1 \end{vmatrix}} \tag{1.33}$$

or

$$(p^3 + 4p^2 + 4p + 2)v_3 = (p^3 + 3p^2 + p)v_1 \, . \tag{1.34}$$

The differential equation relating the input and output of the electrical circuit is therefore

$$\dddot{v}_3 + 4\ddot{v}_3 + 4\dot{v}_3 + 2v_3 = \dddot{v}_1 + 3\ddot{v}_1 + \dot{v}_1 \, . \tag{1.35}$$

In general, a dynamic system can be described by a set of simultaneous differential equations. If the system is fixed and linear, they can be reduced by Cramer's rule to a single fixed , linear differential equation relating the input $v(t)$ and output $y(t)$, whose form is

$$a_n \frac{d^n y}{dt^n} + a_{n-1} \frac{d^{n-1} y}{dt^{n-1}} + \ldots + a_1 \frac{dy}{dt} + a_0 \, y = b_m \frac{d^m v}{dt^m} + \ldots + b_1 \frac{dv}{dt} + b_0 v \tag{1.36}$$

in which the a_i's and b_i's are constants. The driving function $f(t)$ is the entire right side of the differential equation. Thus

$$a_n \frac{d^n y}{dt^n} + \ldots + a_1 \frac{dy}{dt} + a_0 \, y = f(t) \, . \tag{1.37}$$

Notice that the driving function is not in general the input $v(t)$ but is a function of $v(t)$.

In the example above, the equation $p^3 + 4p^2 + 4p + 2 = 0$ is called the *characteristic equation* of the differential equation. If Eqs. (1.31) and (1.32) are solved for v_2 instead of v_3, a differential equation relating v_2 and v_1 is obtained. It has the same left side as Eq. (1.35), and the same characteristic equation. In general, a set of simultaneous, fixed, linear differential equations has a single characteristic equation, which can be called the characteristic equation of the system. If the system is linear and time varying, the differential equations describing it contain time varying coefficients. Then the method used in the example to relate the input to the output does not work, because operators like tp^2 cannot be treated as algebraic quantities. For time varying systems and for nonlinear systems too, a single equation relating the input and output cannot usually be obtained.

1.5 First-Order Linear Differential Equations

Any first-order linear differential equation can be written in the form

$$\dot{y}(t) + a(t)y(t) = f(t) \tag{1.38}$$

by dividing by the coefficient of $\dot{y}(t)$, if there is one. Equations like this are important for two reasons: (1) they appear in engineering work, and (2) any set of simultaneous, linear differential equations can be written in the comparable vector form

$$\dot{\mathbf{y}}(t) + \mathbf{A}(t)\mathbf{y}(t) = \mathbf{f}(t)$$

in which $\mathbf{A}(t)$ is a matrix , $\mathbf{y}(t)$ is a vector of dependent variables, and $\mathbf{f}(t)$ is a vector of driving functions. The method of solution of the scalar equation, which will be developed, can be extended to solve the vector equation, which represents scalar equations of any order.

Eq. (1.38) will be solved by the *adjoint* method. One initial condition must be known:

$$y(t_0) = y_0 \ . \tag{1.39}$$

The adjoint equation of Eq. (1.38) is

$$\dot{x} - a(t)x = 0 \ . \tag{1.40}$$

The initial condition of the new variable x is $x(t_0) = x_0$. It need not be know, because it will not appear in the final solution. To solve the adjoint equation, write it as

$$\frac{1}{x}\ \frac{dx}{dt} = a(t) \ . \tag{1.41}$$

Now

$$\frac{d}{dt}\,(ln\ x) = \frac{1}{x}\ \frac{dx}{dt} \ . \tag{1.42}$$

Therefore

$$\frac{d}{dt}\,(ln\ x) = a(t) \ . \tag{1.43}$$

The integral of this equation is

$$ln\ x\Big|_{x_0}^{x} = ln\ \frac{x}{x_0} = \int_{t_0}^{t} a(z)dz \ . \tag{1.44}$$

Then

$$\frac{x}{x_0} = \mathrm{e}^{\int_{t_0}^{t} a(z)dz} \tag{1.45}$$

and

$$x(t) = x_0\, e^{\int_{t_0}^{t} a(z)dz} . \tag{1.46}$$

This is the solution of the adjoint equation. Now to solve the original differential equation, observe that

$$\frac{d(xy)}{dt} = x\dot{y} + \dot{x}y = x[f(t) - a(t)y] + [a(t)x]y = xf(t) . \tag{1.47}$$

The integral is

$$xy\Big|_{x_0,y_0}^{x,y} = xy - x_0y_0 = \int_{t_0}^{t} x(z)f(z)dz . \tag{1.48}$$

Therefore

$$y = \frac{x_0y_0}{x(t)} + \frac{1}{x(t)}\int_{t_0}^{t} x(z)f(z)\mathrm{dz} . \tag{1.49}$$

Substituting the solution of the adjoint equation into this equation produces the result

$$y(t) = \frac{\displaystyle\int_{t_0}^{t} f(z)e^{\int_{t_0}^{z} a(u)du}\, dz + y_0}{e^{\int_{t_0}^{t} a(z)dz}} . \tag{1.50}$$

This is the solution of any first-order linear differential equation. The integrals can be evaluated numerically if necessary.

As an example, solve the differential equation

$$t\,\frac{dy}{dt} + 5y = 6t^2 \tag{1.51}$$

with the initial condition $y(1) = 3$. To reduce the equation to the form of Eq. (1.38), divide by t:

$$\frac{dy}{dt} + \frac{5}{t}\,y = 6\mathrm{t} . \tag{1.52}$$

For this problem

$$a(t) = \frac{5}{t}\,, \quad f(t) = 6t\,, \quad t_0 = 1\,, \quad \text{and } y_0 = 3 .$$

Now

$$\int_{t_0}^{t} a(z)dz = \int_{1}^{t} \frac{5}{z}\, dz = 5\, ln\, z\Big|_{1}^{t} = 5\, ln\, t \qquad (1.53)$$

and

$$e^{\int_{t_0}^{t} a(z)dz} = e^{5\, ln\, t} = t^5 \,. \qquad (1.54)$$

Eq. (1.50) becomes

$$y(t) = t^{-5}\left(\int_1^t 6z^6 dz + 3\right) = t^{-5}\left(\frac{6}{7}\, z^7\right)_1^t + 3t^{-5}$$

$$= \frac{15}{7}\, t^{-5} + \frac{6}{7}\, t^2 \,. \qquad (1.55)$$

1.6 Properties of Linear Differential Equations

The concept of linear independence of functions is needed for an understanding of differential equations. If the functions $y_1(t), y_2(t), \ldots, y_n(t)$ are *linearly independent,* no one of them can be expressed as a linear combination of the others. If in the equation

$$c_1y_1 + c_2y_2 + \ \ldots\ + c_ny_n = 0 \qquad (1.56)$$

the constants are not all zero, the functions are *linearly dependent.* If two or more constants are not zero, one function can be expressed as a linear combination of the others. The case of only one nonzero constant c_i does nct arise, because then $c_iy_i = 0$. This statement contradicts the fact that y_i is a function of t. To find out whether all the constants in Eq. (1.56) are zero, write out the equation and its first $n-1$ derivatives:

$$\begin{array}{llll} c_1y_1 & + c_2y_2 & + \ldots + c_ny_n & = 0 \\ c_1\dot{y}_1 & + c_2\dot{y}_2 & + \ldots + c_n\dot{y}_n & = 0 \\ \cdot & & & \\ \cdot & & & \\ \cdot & & & \\ c_1y_1^{(n-1)} & + c_2y_2^{(n-1)} & + \ldots + c_ny_n^{(n-1)} & = 0 \ . \end{array} \qquad (1.57)$$

According to Cramer's rule, all the constants are zero unless

$$W = \begin{vmatrix} y_1 & y_2 & \ldots y_n \\ \dot{y}_1 & \dot{y}_2 & \dot{y}_n \\ \cdot & \cdot & \cdot \\ \cdot & \cdot & \cdot \\ \cdot & \cdot & \cdot \\ y_1^{(n-1)} & y_2^{(n-1)} & \ldots y_n^{(n-1)} \end{vmatrix} = 0 \ . \qquad (1.58)$$

This determinant is called the *Wronskian*, after the Polish mathematician G. Wronski (1778–1853). If the Wronskian is not zero, each of the constants is zero, and the functions are linearly independent. If the Wronskian is zero, Cramer's rule provides the uncertain information that each constant is 0/0. The reader who is familiar with the geometric interpretation of matrices (to be covered in Chapter 7) can get better information. Write Eqs. (1.57) as the vector equation

$$\mathbf{W}\,\mathbf{c} = \mathbf{0} \tag{1.59}$$

where $\mathbf{W}$ is the matrix whose determinant is W and $\mathbf{c}$ is the vector of constants. Eq. (1.59) is satisfied by a nonzero vector $\mathbf{c}$ only if matrix $\mathbf{W}$ is singular. If the Wronskian is zero, matrix $\mathbf{W}$ is singular, and constants can be chosen that are not all zero. Therefore if the Wronskian is zero, the functions are linearly dependent.

Now the study of linear differential equations can continue. They have the form

$$a_n(t)\,\frac{d^n y}{dt^n} + a_{n-1}(t)\,\frac{d^{n-1}y}{dt^{n-1}} + \ \ldots\ + a_1(t)\,\frac{dy}{dt} + a_0(t)y = f(t)\,. \tag{1.60}$$

If the right size is zero, the equation is called *homogeneous*. The homogeneous equation has n linearly-independent solutions $y_1, y_2, \ldots, y_n$. Their linear combination

$$y_c = c_1y_1 + c_2y_2 + \ \ldots\ + c_ny_n \tag{1.61}$$

is called the *complementary* or *transient* solution. If contains n arbitrary constants c_i. The function y_p that satisfies the nonhomogeneous equation (1.60) is called the *particular* or *steady-state* solution. The particular solution contains no arbitrary constant. The general or complete solution of the linear differential equation (1.60) is

$$y = y_c + y_p\,. \tag{1.62}$$

The n constants in y_c can be evaluated if n initial conditions are known, by substituting them into Eq. (1.62).

Eq. (1.50) is the complete solution of the first-order linear differential equation (1.38). Notice that the solution contains $n{=}1$ arbitrary constant that is evaluated by one initial condition. The reader is invited to identify the complementary and particular solutions.

As an example of the use of the Wronskian, consider the homogeneous differential equation $\ddot{y} + k^2y = 0$. It should have two linearly-independent solutions. However, the functions

$$\begin{aligned} y_1 &= \sin kt \\ y_2 &= \cos kt \\ y_3 &= e^{jkt} \end{aligned} \tag{1.63}$$

are all solutions. The Wronskian of the three functions is

$$W = \begin{vmatrix} \sin kt & \cos kt & e^{jkt} \\ k \cos kt & -k \sin kt & jke^{jkt} \\ -k^2 \sin kt & -k^2 \cos kt & -k^2 e^{jkt} \end{vmatrix} = 0 \,. \qquad (1.64)$$

Therefore the three functions are linearly dependent. Since the Wronskian of any two of the functions is nonzero, any two are linearly independent, and constitute the solution. For example,

$$y = c_1 \sin kt + c_2 e^{jkt} \,. \qquad (1.65)$$

1.7 Solution of the Homogeneous Differential Equation

For homogeneous linear differential equations with time-varying coefficients there is no general method of solution. If the coefficients are constant, as they often are in practice, a straightforward method is available. The differential equation is

$$a_n y^{(n)} + a_{n-1} y^{(n-1)} + \ldots + a_1 \frac{dy}{dt} + a_0 y = 0. \qquad (1.66)$$

Assume a solution of the form

$$y = e^{rt} \,, \qquad (1.67)$$

where r is a constant. Then

$$y^{(n)} = r^n e^{rt} \qquad (1.68)$$

and the differential equation becomes

$$a_n r^n e^{rt} + a_{n-1} r^{n-1} e^{rt} + \ldots + a_1 r e^{rt} + a_0 e^{rt} = 0 \qquad (1.69)$$

or

$$a_n r^n + a_{n-1} r^{n-1} + \ldots + a_1 r + a_0 = 0. \qquad (1.70)$$

This is the characteristic equation, which of course can be written by inspection of the differential equation. This polynomial of degree n has n roots, which can be called $r_1, r_2, \ldots, r_n$. These are the values of r for which Eq. (1.67) satisfies the differential equation. The linear combination

$$y_c = c_1 e^{r_1 t} + c_2 e^{r_2 t} + \ldots + c_n e^{r_n t} \qquad (1.71)$$

is also a solution. If the roots are distinct (all different), the n solutions are linearly independent, and Eq. (1.71) is the general solution. If two roots are the same, say $r_1 = r_2$, then

$$y_1 = e^{r_1 t} \qquad \text{and} \qquad y_2 = te^{r_1 t} \qquad (1.72)$$

are independent solutions. If r_1 is repeated k times, the complementary solution is

$$y_c = c_1 e^{r_1 t} + c_2 t e^{r_1 t} + \ldots + c_k t^{k-1} e^{r_1 t} + c_{k+1} e^{r_2 t} + \ldots + c_n e^{r_{n-k+1} t} . \tag{1.73}$$

For practice, find the solution of the differential equation

$$\ddot{y} + 2\dot{y} + y = 0 . \tag{1.74}$$

For differential equations that represent real systems, the coefficients a_i in the characteristic polynomial are real numbers. The roots are therefore either real or occur in complex pairs. The complementary solution y_c is a real function of time. For this reason if it contains a complex pair of exponents r_1 and r_2, their coefficients c_1 and c_2 are also a complex pair. For example, if

$$r_1 = \alpha + j\beta \qquad \text{and} \qquad r_2 = \alpha - j\beta , \tag{1.75}$$

the part of the solution for these two roots is

$$\begin{aligned} c_1 e^{r_1 t} + c_2 e^{r_2 t} &= e^{\alpha t}(c_1 e^{j\beta t} + c_2 e^{-j\beta t}) \\ &= e^{\alpha t}[(c_1 + c_2)\cos \beta t + j(c_1 - c_2)\sin \beta t] \\ &= e^{\alpha t}(A \cos \beta t + B \sin \beta t) = K e^{\alpha t} \sin(\beta t + \theta) . \end{aligned} \tag{1.76}$$

This is a more convenient form because it avoids complex coefficients and exponents. The constants α, β, A, B, K, and θ are all real numbers, and

$$K = \sqrt{A^2 + B^2} \qquad \text{and} \qquad \theta = \tan^{-1} \frac{A}{B} . \tag{1.77}$$

An illustration of the method is provided by calculation of the displacement y of the undriven spring-mass-damper in Fig. 1.9, whose

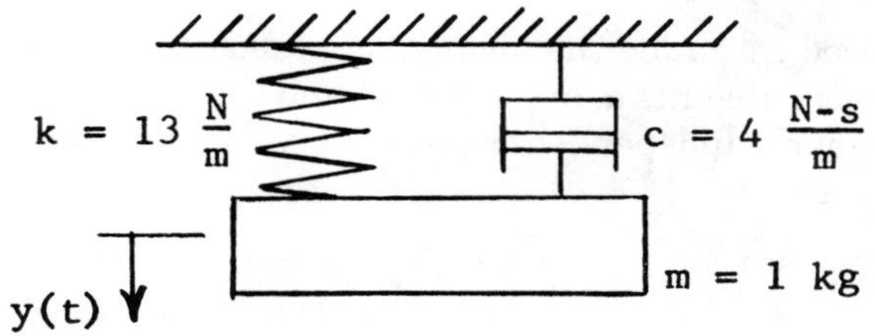

Fig. 1.9. Mass vibrating freely.

initial displacement and velocity are $y(0) = 1$ meter and $\dot{y}(0) = 0$. The sum of forces on the mass provides the homogeneous differential equation

$$\ddot{y} + 4\dot{y} + 13y = 0 . \tag{1.78}$$

The characteristic equation

$$r^2 + 4r + 13 = 0 \tag{1.79}$$

has the roots

$$r = -2 \pm j3 . \tag{1.80}$$

Therefore

$$y = K\, e^{-2t} \sin(3t + \theta) \tag{1.81}$$

and

$$\dot{y} = -2K\, e^{-2t} \sin(3t + \theta) + 3K\, e^{-2t} \cos(3t + \theta) . \tag{1.82}$$

The initial conditions give

$$1 = K \sin\theta \qquad \text{and} \qquad 0 = -2K \sin\theta + 3K \cos\theta \tag{1.83}$$

or

$$\theta = \tan^{-1}\frac{3}{2} = 0.983 \text{ rad} \qquad \text{and} \qquad K = \frac{\sqrt{13}}{3} = 1.202 . \tag{1.84}$$

Therefore

$$y = 1.202\, e^{-2t} \sin(3t + 0.983) \qquad \text{meters.} \tag{1.85}$$

1.8 The Method of Undetermined Coefficients

Now consider ways of finding the particular solution y_p of a linear differential equation whose right side is not zero:

$$a_n(t)y^{(n)} + a_{n-1}(t)y^{(n-1)} + \ldots + a_1(t)\frac{dy}{dt} + a_0(t)y = f(t) . \tag{1.86}$$

A simple procedure called the *method of undetermined coefficients* can be used if the coefficients a_i are constant and the driver $f(t)$ has a finite number of linearly-independent derivatives. For example, $f(t)$ could be $t \sin 3t$, because

$$f(t) = t \sin 3t , \qquad \dot{f}(t) = \sin 3t + 3t \cos 3t \tag{1.87}$$

and

$$\ddot{f}(t) = 6 \cos 3t - 9t \sin 3t . \tag{1.88}$$

The Wronskian of f, $\dot{f}$, and $\ddot{f}$ is nonzero. Higher derivatives repeat the terms in the first three. If a column for the third derivative is included in the Wronskian, the determinant is zero. Other forms of $f(t)$ that qualify are a polynomial with positive powers of t, or a combination of exponentials, sines, cosines, or hyperbolic functions. The method does not work if, for example, $f(t)$ is $ln\ t$ or $\sqrt{t}$. To find y_p, assume that it is a linear combination of the terms in $f(t)$ and their derivatives, each term being multiplied by an undetermined coefficient. Substitute the assumed y_p and its derivatives into the differential equation (1.86), and evaluate the coefficients by equating the coefficients of like terms. As an example, determine the current $i(t)$ in the circuit of Fig. 1.10. A sinusoidal

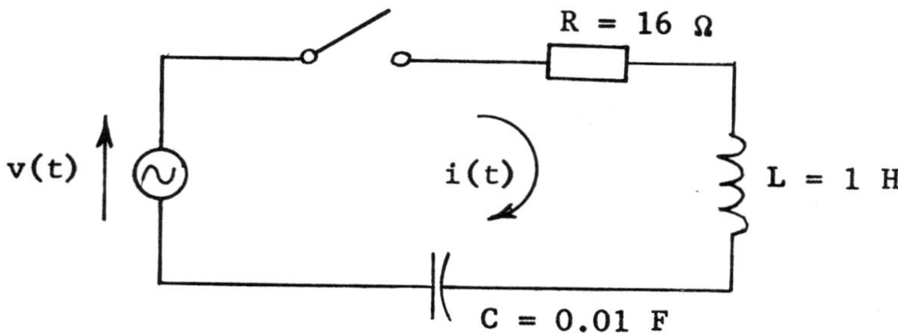

Fig. 1.10. Circuit driven by a sinusoidal voltage.

power supply delivers 64 volts peak-to-peak at a frequency of 10 rad/s. The capacitor is initially uncharged. The switch is closed at the instant the voltage passes thru zero on the way up. The sum of voltages around the circuit is

$$100 \int_{-\infty}^{t} i(x)dx + 16i + \frac{di}{dt} = 32 \sin 10t \tag{1.89}$$

or

$$\frac{d^2i}{dt^2} + 16\frac{di}{dt} + 100i = 320 \cos 10t\ . \tag{1.90}$$

When the switch is closed at $t = 0$, the inductance prevents a step change in current. Therefore $i(0) = 0$. Since there is no initial voltage across the resistor or the capacitor, the initial voltage $L\ di/dt$ across the inductor is also zero. Therefore

$$\frac{di(0)}{dt} = 0\ . \tag{1.91}$$

To find the complementary solution, write the characteristic equation

$$r^2 + 16r + 100 = 0 . \tag{1.92}$$

Its roots are

$$r = -8 \pm j6 . \tag{1.93}$$

The complementary solution is

$$i_c = K e^{-8t} \sin(6t + \theta) . \tag{1.94}$$

To find the particular solution by the method of undetermined coefficients, assume that it is a linear combination of the term in $f(t)$ and its derivative:

$$i_p = A \sin 10t + B \cos 10t . \tag{1.95}$$

Then

$$\frac{di_p}{dt} = 10A \cos 10t - 10B \sin 10t \tag{1.96}$$

and

$$\frac{d^2 i_p}{dt^2} = -100A \sin 10t - 100B \cos 10t . \tag{1.97}$$

Substituting these values into the differential equation (1.90) yields

$$\begin{aligned} &-100A \sin 10t - 100B \cos 10t + 160A \cos 10t - 160B \sin 10t \\ &+ 100A \sin 10t + 100B \cos 10t = 320 \cos 10t . \end{aligned} \tag{1.98}$$

Collecting the coefficients of sin $10t$ and then of cos $10t$ produces the two equations

$$-100A - 160B + 100A = 0 \tag{1.99}$$

and

$$-100B + 160A + 100B = 320 . \tag{1.100}$$

Thus $B = 0$, $A = 2$, and Eq. (1.95) becomes

$$i_p = 2 \sin 10t . \tag{1.101}$$

The complete solution is

$$i = i_c + i_p = K e^{-8t} \sin(6t + \theta) + 2 \sin 10t . \tag{1.102}$$

The two arbitrary constants K and θ can now be evaluated from the two initial conditions. Since $i(0) = 0$ and $di(0)/dt = 0$,

$$0 = K \sin \theta \tag{1.103}$$

and

$$0 = -8K \sin\theta + 6K \cos\theta + 20 \tag{1.104}$$

or

$$K = -\frac{10}{3} \quad \text{and} \quad \theta = 0\,. \tag{1.105}$$

The complete solution becomes

$$i = -\frac{10}{3} e^{-8t} \sin 6t + 2 \sin 10t \quad \text{amperes}\,. \tag{1.106}$$

The complementary solution justifies the name "transient" because it dies out. The particular or steady-state current remains and has the same form as the driving voltage.

The method of undetermined coefficients must be modified if any of the terms in the assumed particular solution y_p is already in the complementary solution. Multiply each term in the family of the duplicating term in y_p by t enough times to eliminate the duplication. For example, if

$$\ddot{y} + 2\dot{y} + y = t\,e^{-t} + \sin 2t\,, \tag{1.107}$$

the complementary solution is

$$y_c = c_1 e^{-t} + c_2 t\, e^{-t}\,. \tag{1.108}$$

As the particular solution, first assume the form

$$y_p = A\,t\,e^{-t} + B\,e^{-t} + C \sin 2t + D \cos 2t\,. \tag{1.109}$$

Since the terms e^{-t} and te^{-t} are also in y_c, that family must be multiplied by t^2 to avoid the duplication. The correct form is

$$y_p = A\,t^3 e^{-t} + B\,t^2 e^{-t} + C \sin 2t + D \cos 2t\,. \tag{1.110}$$

When this solution and its derivatives are substituted into the differential equation (1.107), the coefficients can be evaluated. The result is

$$y_p = \frac{1}{6} t^3 e^{-t} - \frac{3}{25} \sin 2t - \frac{4}{25} \cos 2t\,. \tag{1.111}$$

1.9 The Method of Variation of Parameters

Another method of finding the particular solution of a linear differential equation is available, that works even if the coefficients are time varying, and places no restriction on the driving function $f(t)$. It is called the method of variation of parameters. It requires more work than the method of undetermined coefficients, and the complementary solution must be known before it can be used. The latter requirement limits its usefulness for time varying systems. The method is valuable for solving fixed linear differential equations with unusual driving functions. In addition, a study of the method is valuable because it has other uses, such as reducing the order of a linear homogeneous differential equation by one, when one solution is known. The method will be illustrated for a second-order equation:

$$a_2\ddot{y} + a_1\dot{y} + a_0 y = f(t) \tag{1.112}$$

whose coefficients a_i may be time varying. First calculate the complementary solution

$$y_c = c_1 y_1 + c_2 y_2 \,. \tag{1.113}$$

Then assume the particular solution

$$y_p = u_1 y_1 + u_2 y_2 \tag{1.114}$$

where u_1 and u_2 are undetermined functions of t. To evaluate u_1 and u_2, substitute the assumed solution back into the differential equation. The result is a complicated expression that imposes one condition to be satisfied by the two unknown functions. Another condition is needed. For example, either u_1 or u_2 might be chosen arbitrarily. A more convenient procedure is to choose another equation relating u_1 and u_2 to simplify the complicated expression. The two equations allow calculation of the two parameters u_1 and u_2. Since Eq. (1.114) satisfies the differential equation (1.112), it is the particular solution. To start this process, calculate

$$\dot{y}_p = u_1\dot{y}_1 + \dot{u}_1 y_1 + u_2\dot{y}_2 + \dot{u}_2 y_2 \,. \tag{1.115}$$

Choose the simplifying condition

$$\dot{u}_1 y_1 + \dot{u}_2 y_2 = 0 \,. \tag{1.116}$$

Then

$$\ddot{y}_p = u_1\ddot{y}_1 + \dot{u}_1\dot{y}_1 + u_2\ddot{y}_2 = \dot{u}_2\dot{y}_2 \,. \tag{1.117}$$

Substitution of y_p and its derivatives into Eq. (1.112) gives

$$a_2(\dot{u}_1\dot{y}_1 + \dot{u}_2\dot{y}_2) + u_1(a_2\ddot{y}_1 + a_1\dot{y}_1 + a_0 y_1) + u_2(a_2\ddot{y}_2 + a_1\dot{y}_2 + a_0 y_2) = f(t) \,. \tag{1.118}$$

Since y_1 and y_2 both satisfy the homogeneous differential equation, the second and third terms of this equation are zero. Thus

$$\dot{u}_1\dot{y}_1 + \dot{u}_2\dot{y}_2 = \frac{f(t)}{a_2} \,. \tag{1.119}$$

This equation and (1.116) are the two conditions needed to evaluate the two unknown functions. Their simultaneous solution is

$$\dot{u}_1 = \frac{-y_2 f(t)}{a_2 \begin{vmatrix} y_1 & y_2 \\ \dot{y}_1 & \dot{y}_2 \end{vmatrix}}, \qquad \dot{u}_2 = \frac{y_1 f(t)}{a_2 \begin{vmatrix} y_1 & y_2 \\ \dot{y}_1 & \dot{y}_2 \end{vmatrix}}. \tag{1.120}$$

Notice that since y_1 and y_2 are linearly-independent functions, the denominators of these two expressions are never zero, and $\dot{u}_1$ and $\dot{u}_2$ can always be found. The two expressions are integrated, numerically if necessary, to obtain u_1 and u_2. Then the particular solution (1.114) of the differential equation is known, and can be added to the complementary solution (1.113) to obtain the complete solution. If the constants of integration are included in the integration, Eq. (1.114) becomes the complete solution. The method of variation of parameters works for linear differential equations of any order n, like Eq. (1.86). In general,

$$\dot{u}_i = \frac{W_{ni}(t) f(t)}{a_n W(t)} \tag{1.121}$$

where $W(t)$ is the Wronskian determinant of the n solutions of the homogeneous differential equation, and $W_{ni}(t)$ is the ni-th cofactor.

To illustrate the method, recompute the particular solution of Eq. (1.90),

$$\frac{d^2 i}{dt^2} + 16\frac{di}{dt} + 100i = 320 \cos 10t\,. \tag{1.122}$$

The complementary solution (1.94) can be written as

$$i_c = c_1 e^{-8t} \sin 6t + c_2 e^{-8t} \cos 6t\,. \tag{1.123}$$

The Wronskian of the two functions in this solution is

$$W = \begin{vmatrix} e^{-8t} \sin 6t & e^{-8t} \cos 6t \\ -8e^{-8t} \sin 6t + 6e^{-8t} \cos 6t & -8e^{-8t} \cos 6t - 6e^{-8t} \sin 6t \end{vmatrix}$$

$$= -6e^{-16t}\,. \tag{1.124}$$

The terms needed for Eqs. (1.120) are

$$a_2 = 1\,, \quad i_1 = e^{-8t} \sin 6t\,, \quad i_2 = e^{-8t} \cos 6t\,, \quad f(t) = 320 \cos 10t\,.$$

Then

$$\dot{u}_1 = \frac{-i_2 f(t)}{a_2 W(t)} = -\frac{(e^{-8t} \cos 6t)(320 \cos 10t)}{-6e^{-16t}} = \frac{160}{3} e^{8t} \cos 6t \cos 10t \tag{1.125}$$

and

$$\dot{u}_2 = \frac{i_1 f(t)}{a_2 W(t)} = \frac{(e^{-8t} \sin 6t)(320 \cos 10t)}{-6e^{-16t}} = -\frac{160}{3} e^{8t} \sin 6t \cos 10t \, . \tag{1.126}$$

Integration of these two expressions produces the two parameters. With the constants of integration omitted,

$$u_1 = \frac{80}{3}\left[\frac{e^{8t}}{8^2+4^2}(8 \cos 4t + 4 \sin 4t) + \frac{e^{8t}}{8^2+16^2}(8 \cos 16t + 16 \sin 16t)\right] \tag{1.127}$$

$$u_2 = \frac{80}{3}\left[\frac{e^{8t}}{8^2+4^2}(8 \sin 4t - 4 \cos 4t) - \frac{e^{8t}}{8^2+16^2}(8 \sin 16t - 16 \cos 16t)\right]. \tag{1.128}$$

The particular solution is

$$\begin{aligned} i_p &= u_1 i_1 + u_2 i_2 \\ &= \frac{1}{3}(8 \cos 4t \sin 6t + 4 \sin 4t \sin 6t) \\ &+ \frac{1}{12}(8 \cos 16t \sin 6t + 16 \sin 16t \sin 6t) \\ &+ \frac{1}{3}(8 \sin 4t \cos 6t - 4 \cos 4t \cos 6t) \\ &- \frac{1}{12}(8 \sin 16t \cos 6t - 16 \cos 16t \cos 6t) \\ &= 2 \sin 10t \, , \end{aligned} \tag{1.129}$$

which agrees with Eq. (1.101), obtained by the method of undetermined coefficients.

1.10 The Euler Equation

There is no standard method for obtaining the complementary solution of a linear differential equation with time-varying coefficients of order higher than 1. For some of these equations, however, special solutions are available. One important example is the *Euler* or *Cauchy* equation, in which each coefficient includes the independent variable raised to the same power as the order of the derivative:

$$a_n t^n \frac{d^n y}{dt^n} + a_{n-1} t^{n-1} \frac{d^{n-1} y}{dt^{n-1}} + \ldots + a_1 t \frac{dy}{dt} + a_0 y = f(t) . \qquad (1.130)$$

It arises in second-order form in the product solutions of partial differential equations, such as the solution of Laplace's equation in polar coordinates. It can be converted to a linear differential equation with constant coefficients by the substitution

$$t = e^z . \qquad (1.131)$$

Then

$$\frac{dy}{dz} = \frac{dy}{dt}\frac{dt}{dz} = t\frac{dy}{dt} . \qquad (1.132)$$

The time-varying term $t\, dy/dt$ has been converted to the fixed term dy/dz. To convert the next term, write

$$\frac{d^2y}{dz^2} = \frac{d}{dz}\left(\frac{dy}{dz}\right) = \left[\frac{d}{dt}\left(\frac{dy}{dz}\right)\right]\frac{dt}{dz} = \left[\frac{d}{dt}\left(t\frac{dy}{dt}\right)\right]t = t\left(t\frac{d^2y}{dt^2} + \frac{dy}{dt}\right) \qquad (1.133)$$

or

$$t^2 \frac{d^2y}{dt^2} = \frac{d^2y}{dz^2} - t\frac{dy}{dt} = \frac{d^2y}{dz^2} - \frac{dy}{dz} . \qquad (1.134)$$

Adopting the operator

$$D = \frac{d}{dz} \qquad (1.135)$$

permits writing Eqs. (1.132) and (1.134) as

$$t\frac{dy}{dt} = Dy \quad \text{and} \quad t^2\frac{d^2y}{dt^2} = D^2y - Dy = D(D-1)y . \qquad (1.136)$$

In general,

$$t^n \frac{d^n y}{dt^n} = D(D-1)(D-2)\ldots(D-n+1)y . \qquad (1.137)$$

For example, solve the Euler equation

$$t^2\frac{d^2y}{dt^2} + 3t\frac{dy}{dt} + 4y = 0 . \qquad (1.138)$$

Let $t = e^z$ and $D = d/dz$. Then the differential equation becomes

$$[D(D-1) + 3D + 4]y = 0 \qquad (1.139)$$

or

$$(D^2 + 2D + 4)y = \frac{d^2y}{dz^2} + 2\,\frac{dy}{dz} + 4y = 0\,. \tag{1.140}$$

This fixed equation can be solved easily. Its characteristic equation is

$$r^2 + 2r + 4 = 0 \tag{1.141}$$

and has the roots $r = -1 \pm j\sqrt{3}$. The solution is

$$y = e^{-z}(c_1 \sin \sqrt{3}\,z + c_2 \cos \sqrt{3}\,z)\,. \tag{1.142}$$

To convert back to the original independent variable, let $z = ln\,t$. Then

$$y = \frac{1}{t}\,[c_1 \sin(\sqrt{3}\,ln\,t) + c_2 \cos(\sqrt{3}\,ln\,t)]\,. \tag{1.143}$$

1.11 Simultaneous Linear Differential Equations

Many linear systems, such as the one in Fig. 1.8, are represented by simultaneous, fixed, linear differential equations. The classical method of solving them will be illustrated by a simple example. Suppose that a system is described by the two homogeneous first-order equations

$$\frac{dx}{dt} + y = 0 \tag{1.144}$$

$$x + \frac{dy}{dt} = 0 \tag{1.145}$$

with the initial conditions $x(0) = 1$, $y(0) = 1$. One dependent variable could be eliminated by differentiating the first equation and subtract the second equation from the first. The same result can be obtained more easily by adopting the operator $p = d/dt$. The equations become

$$\begin{aligned} px + y &= 0 \\ x + py &= 0\,. \end{aligned} \tag{1.146}$$

Then

$$x = \frac{\begin{vmatrix} 0 & 1 \\ 0 & p \end{vmatrix}}{\begin{vmatrix} p & 1 \\ 1 & p \end{vmatrix}}$$

and

$$(p^2 - 1)x = 0 \qquad \text{or} \qquad \frac{d^2x}{dt^2} - x = 0\,. \tag{1.147}$$

Similarly,

$$\frac{d^2y}{dt^2} - y = 0\,. \tag{1.148}$$

The solutions are

$$x_c = k_1e^t + k_2e^{-t}$$
$$y_c = k_3e^t + k_4e^{-t}\,. \tag{1.149}$$

The number of arbitrary constants equals the degree of the characteristic equation, namely two. But apparently there are four. To eliminate two constants, substitute the solutions into one of the differential equations, say Eq. (1.144). Then

$$k_1e^t - k_2e^{-t} + k_3e^t + k_4e^{-t} = 0 \tag{1.150}$$

or

$$k_3 = -k_1 \qquad \text{and} \qquad k_4 = k_2\,. \tag{1.151}$$

There are only two arbitrary constants. Eq. (1.149) can be written

$$y_c = -\,k_1e^t + k_2e^{-t}\,. \tag{1.152}$$

Now give the system a driver so that the differential equations are nonhomogeneous:

$$\dot{x} + y = \sin t \tag{1.153}$$
$$x + \dot{y} = 0\,. \tag{1.154}$$

According to the method of undetermined coefficients, the assumed particular solutions are linear combinations of all the driving functions and their derivatives:

$$x_p = A\sin t + B\cos t$$
$$y_p = C\sin t + D\cos t\,. \tag{1.155}$$

To evaluate the coefficients, substitute the assumed solutions into both differential equations. The result is

$$A\cos t - B\sin t + C\sin t + D\cos t = \sin t$$
$$A\sin t + B\cos t + C\cos t - D\sin t = 0\,. \tag{1.156}$$

The coefficients, found by equating coefficents of like terms, are

$$A = D = 0\,, \qquad C = \frac{1}{2}\,, \qquad B = -\,\frac{1}{2}\,. \tag{1.157}$$

Therefore

$$x_p = -\frac{1}{2}\cos t\,, \qquad y_p = \frac{1}{2}\sin t\,. \tag{1.158}$$

The particular solutions can also be obtained by deriving differential equations for x and y separately, using Cramer's rule. Eqs. (1.153) and (1.154) can be written as

$$px + y = \sin t \tag{1.159}$$

$$x + py = 0\,. \tag{1.160}$$

Then

$$x = \frac{\begin{vmatrix} \sin t & 1 \\ 0 & p \end{vmatrix}}{\begin{vmatrix} p & 1 \\ 1 & p \end{vmatrix}} = \frac{p\ \sin t}{p^2 - 1} \tag{1.161}$$

and

$$(p^2 - 1)x = \cos t \qquad \text{or} \qquad \ddot{x} - x = \cos t\,. \tag{1.162}$$

Similarly,

$$\ddot{y} - y = -\sin t\,. \tag{1.163}$$

The assumed particular solutions are given by Eqs. (1.155). Substituting each of them into its differential equation and equating coefficients of like terms reproduces Eqs. (1.158). The complete solutions of the two simultaneous differential equations are

$$x = x_c + x_p = k_1 e^t + k_2 e^{-t} - \frac{1}{2}\cos t \tag{1.164}$$

$$y = y_c + y_p = -k_1 e^t + k_2 e^{-t} + \frac{1}{2}\sin t\,. \tag{1.165}$$

The constants in the complementary solutions are evaluated by applying the initial conditions. Thus

$$1 = k_1 + k_2 - \frac{1}{2} \tag{1.166}$$

and

$$1 = -k_1 + k_2\,. \tag{1.167}$$

Accordingly,

$$k_1 = \frac{1}{4}\,, \qquad k_2 = \frac{5}{4}\,,$$

and

$$x = \frac{1}{4} e^t + \frac{5}{4} e^{-t} - \frac{1}{2} \cos t \tag{1.168}$$

$$y = -\frac{1}{4} e^t + \frac{5}{4} e^{-t} + \frac{1}{2} \sin t\,. \tag{1.169}$$

1.12 A Trap to Avoid

With simultaneous as well as single differential equations, the method of undetermined coefficients must be modified if any of the terms in the driving functions or their derivatives is included in the complementary solutions. For example, let

$$\dot{x} + y = \sin t \tag{1.170}$$

$$x + \dot{y} = e^{-t}\,. \tag{1.171}$$

The complementary solutions are given by Eqs. (1.149), and are

$$x_c = k_1 e^t + k_2 e^{-t} \tag{1.172}$$

$$y_c = k_3 e^t + k_4 e^{-t}\,. \tag{1.173}$$

Two of the four arbitrary constants have already been evaluated by substituting these solutions into one of the differential equations in its homogeneous form. As a result,

$$y_c = -\,k_1 e^t + k_2 e^{-t}\,. \tag{1.174}$$

The assumed particular solutions are initially linear combinations of all the terms in the driving functions and their derivatives. Notice, however, that the driving term e^{-t} is also in the complementary solution. According to the rule for single differential equations, the duplication is eliminated by writing the particular solutions as

$$x_p = A \sin t + B \cos t + C\, t\, e^{-t}$$

$$y_p = D \sin t + E \cos t + F\, t\, e^{-t}\,. \tag{1.175}$$

The next step is to substitute these assumed solutions into the differential equations and equate the coefficients of like terms. When this is done, the latter equations contradict each other and do not yield values for the coefficients. Something is wrong.

As a second attempt, derive differential equations for x and y separately. Eqs. (1.170) and (1.171) become

$$px + y = \sin t$$

$$x + py = e^{-t}\,. \tag{1.176}$$

The variables are separated with the help of Cramer's rule. Then

$$\ddot{x} - x = \cos t - e^{-t} \tag{1.177}$$

and

$$\ddot{y} - y = -\sin t - e^{-t}. \tag{1.178}$$

When the assumed particular solutions (1.175) are substituted into these differential equations, the coefficients can be evaluated. The results are

$$x_p = -\frac{1}{2}\cos t + \frac{1}{2}\, t\, e^{-t}. \tag{1.179}$$

$$y_p = \frac{1}{2}\sin t + \frac{1}{2}\, t\, e^{-t}. \tag{1.180}$$

Something is still wrong, because these particular solutions do not satisfy the original differential equations (1.170) and (1.171). The complete solutions obtained by adding the particular solutions to the complementary solutions (1.172) and (1.174) are

$$x = x_c + x_p = k_1 e^{t} + k_2 e^{-t} - \frac{1}{2}\cos t + \frac{1}{2}\, t\, e^{-t} \tag{1.181}$$

$$y = y_c + y_p = -k_1 e^{t} + k_2 e^{-t} + \frac{1}{2}\sin t + \frac{1}{2}\, t\, e^{-t}. \tag{1.182}$$

Clearly these are also wrong because they do not satisfy the original differential equations.

Either method can be modified to produce the correct solution. When the particular solutions are determined simultaneously, the rule for eliminating conflicts with the complementary solutions is changed. As before, include all of the driving terms and their derivatives in the assumed particular solutions. If any term duplicates a term in the complementary solutions, multiply each term in the family of the duplicating term by t enough times to eliminate the duplication. Now, however, retain all of the duplicated terms. Instead of Eqs. (1.175), assume the particular solutions

$$x_p = A\sin t + B\cos t + C\, t\, e^{-t} + D\, e^{-t}$$

$$y_p = E\sin t + F\cos t + G\, t\, e^{-t} + H\, e^{-t}. \tag{1.183}$$

When these are substituted into the original differential equations, the result is

$$x_p = -\frac{1}{2}\cos t + \frac{1}{2}\, t\, e^{-t} + D\, e^{-t}$$

$$y_p = \frac{1}{2}\sin t + \frac{1}{2}\, t\, e^{-t} + \left(D - \frac{1}{2}\right)e^{-t}. \tag{1.184}$$

These particular solutions satisfy the original differential equations. The complementary solutions (1.172) and (1.174) can be added to obtain the complete solution:

$$x = k_1e^t + k_2e^{-t} - \frac{1}{2}\cos t + \frac{1}{2}\,t\,e^{-t} + D\,e^{-t}$$

$$y = -\,k_1e^t + k_2e^{-t} + \frac{1}{2}\sin t + \frac{1}{2}\,t\,e^{-t} + (D - \frac{1}{2})e^{-t}\,. \tag{1.185}$$

Let k_2+D be renamed k_2. Then

$$x = k_1e^t + k_2e^{-t} - \frac{1}{2}\cos t + \frac{1}{2}\,t\,e^{-t}$$

$$y = -\,k_1e^t + (k_2 - \frac{1}{2})e^{-t} + \frac{1}{2}\sin \mathrm{t} + \frac{1}{2}\,t\,e^{-t}\,. \tag{1.186}$$

When the particular solutions are obtained individually using differential equations for x and y alone, the original rule for avoiding conflicts applies. Eqs. (1.179) and (1.180) are the correct particular solutions. Since they do not satisfy the original differential equations, adding to them the complementary solutions (1.172) and (1.174) that satisfy the homogeneous differential equations will not produce the complete solution. Instead, add the complementary solutions before eliminating half of their arbitrary constants:

$$x = x_c + x_p = k_1e^t + k_2e^{-t} - \frac{1}{2}\cos t + \frac{1}{2}\,t\,e^{-t}$$

$$y = y_c + y_p = k_3e^t + k_4e^{-t} + \frac{1}{2}\sin t + \frac{1}{2}\,t\,e^{-t}\,. \tag{1.187}$$

Since these complete solutions must satisfy the nonhomogeneous differential equations, substitute them into Eq. (1.170) or (1.171) to eliminate two of the constants. Equating the coefficients of like terms shows that

$$k_3 = -\,k_1 \qquad \text{and} \qquad k_4 = k_2 - \frac{1}{2}\,. \tag{1.188}$$

Finally,

$$x = k_1e^t + k_2e^{-t} - \frac{1}{2}\cos t + \frac{1}{2}\,t\,e^{-t}$$

$$y = -\,k_1e^t + (k_2 - \frac{1}{2})e^{-t} + \frac{1}{2}\sin t + \frac{1}{2}\,t\,e^{-t}\,. \tag{1.189}$$

These solutions agree with Eqs. (1.186). Since they satisfy the original differential equations and contain two arbitrary constants, they must be the complete solution.

The cause of the trouble can be seen now. The particular solution for y needs the term $-(1/2)e^{-t}$, which is not provided in Eq. (1.175). In the first method, this term is added in Eq. (1.183). In the second method, the term is borrowed from the complementary solution in Eq. (1.189). The next chapter shows that if simultaneous, fixed, linear differential equations are solved with Laplace transforms, no special rule is needed. Any duplication of terms in the particular and complementary solutions is handled automatically. Laplace transforms, however, produce numerical results only if the right initial conditions are known. For this example they are $x(0)$ and $y(0)$. The solutions obtained by the classical method, Eqs. (1.189), yield numerical results if any two initial conditions are known, such as $x(3)$ and $\dot{x}(2)$.

1.13 Exercises

The reader is invited to test his or her understanding of this chapter by solving these problems.

1. Fig. 1.11 shows the equivalent circuit of a transformer with a capacitor connected across the secondary terminals. Currents flowing into the dotted terminals produce flux in the core in the same direction. Derive a differential equation relating the primary and secondary voltages v_1 and v_2.

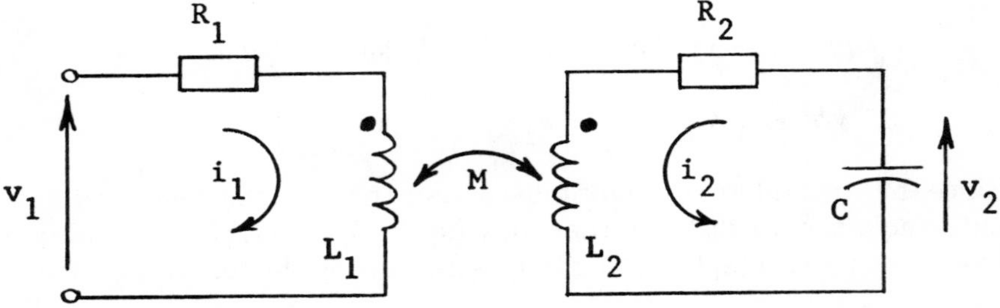

Fig. 1.11. Equivalent circuit of a transformer.

2. Fig. 1.12 shows two masses that can vibrate horizontally between three springs. Derive the equations for the deflections y_1 and y_2 with a total of four arbitrary constants.

3. Solve the differential equation

$$t^3 \frac{dy}{dt} + 2y = t^3 + 2t$$

with the initial condition $y(1) = 1+e$. Note that

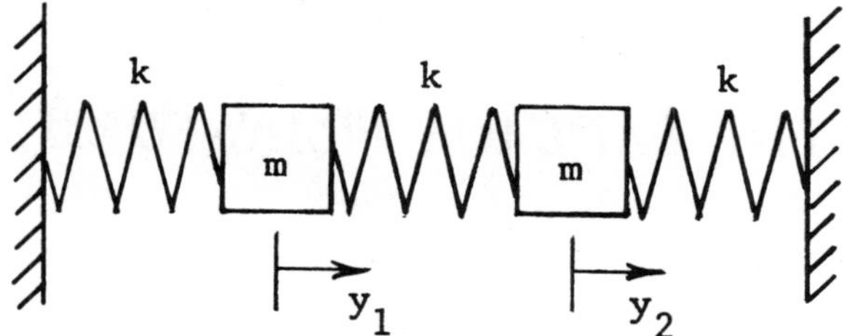

Fig. 1.12. System of springs and masses.

$$\frac{d}{dz}\left(ze^{-1/z^2}\right) = e^{-1/z^2}\left(1 + \frac{2}{z^2}\right)$$

4. Solve the linear differential equation

$$t^2 \frac{d^2y}{dt^2} + 4t \frac{dy}{dt} + 2y = \frac{1}{t}$$

with the initial conditions $y(1) = \dot{y}(1) = 1$.

Chapter 2

THE LAPLACE TRANSFORM

2.1 The Wonderful World of s

Laplace transforms provide transportation from the time domain to the s domain. In that world differential equations reduce to algebraic equations, and difficult convolution integrals become simple products. Analog-computer block diagrams contain no derivatives and no integral signs. Instead, the variables are multiplied and divided by s. Time does not exist in the s domain. Clocks, if they had any use there, would probably tell us what s it is.

The s domain is a good place in which to solve differential equations and analyze linear systems. Inverse Laplace transforms are available for transportation back to the real world, so that the results can be expressed as functions of time.

The *two-sided Laplace transform* of a function of time $f(t)$ is defined as

$$F(s) = \mathcal{L}[f(t)] = \int_{-\infty}^{\infty} f(t)e^{-st}dt \ , \tag{2.1}$$

where s is the complex variable $s=\sigma+j\omega$. Usually the time function is causal (zero for negative time), permitting use of the simpler *one-sided Laplace transform*

$$F(s) = \int_{0}^{\infty} f(t)e^{-st}dt \ . \tag{2.2}$$

The latter will be used throughout most of this chapter.

2.2 Use of Laplace Transforms to Solve Differential Equations

Most of the differential equations encountered by engineers are ordinary and linear with constant coefficients. Laplace transforms reduce this type to algebraic equations, and include the initial conditions automatically. To illustrate the process, solve the differential equation

$$\frac{d^2y}{dt^2} + 5\,\frac{dy}{dt} + 6y = e^{-4t} \tag{2.3}$$

with the initial conditions

$$y(0) = 0 \qquad \text{and} \qquad \dot{y}(0) = 1 \ . \tag{2.4}$$

First form the Laplace transform of both sides:

$$\int_0^\infty \frac{d^2y}{dt^2}\, e^{-st}dt + 5\int_0^\infty \frac{dy}{dt}\, e^{-st}dt + 6\int_0^\infty ye^{-st}dt = \int_0^\infty e^{-4t}e^{-st} \quad . \quad (2.5)$$

The last term is

$$\int_0^\infty e^{-(4+s)t}\, dt = -\left.\frac{e^{-(4+s)t}}{4+s}\right|_0^\infty = \frac{1}{s+4}\,, \qquad Re(s) > -4\,. \quad (2.6)$$

Notice that the integral converges, and the Laplace transform therefore exists, only if the real part of s is greater than -4. In general, if a is a constant, positive or negative,

$$\mathscr{L}[e^{-at}] = \frac{1}{s+a}\,, \qquad Re(s) > -a\,. \quad (2.7)$$

In work with one-sided Laplace transforms, the values of s for which the transform exists is not a concern.

The Laplace transform of $y(t)$ will be called $Y(s)$. The third term of Eq. (2.5) is therefore $6Y(s)$. To evaluate the second term, observe that

$$\mathscr{L}\left[\frac{dy}{dt}\right] = \int_0^\infty \frac{dy}{dt}\, e^{-st}dt = \int_0^\infty e^{-st}\, dy\,. \quad (2.8)$$

The last of these terms can be integrated by parts. Let

$$u = e^{-st}\,, \qquad du = -se^{-st}\, dt\,, \qquad v = y\,, \qquad dv = dy\,.$$

Then

$$\int_0^\infty u\, dv = uv\Big|_0^\infty - \int_0^\infty v\, du = e^{-st}\, y(t)\Big|_0^\infty + \int_0^\infty y(t)\, s\, e^{-st}\, dt$$

$$= e^{-st}\, y(t)\Big|_0^\infty + s\, Y(s) \quad . \quad (2.9)$$

If the Laplace transform $Y(s)$ exists, its integrand $y(t)e^{-st}$ must approach zero as t approaches infinity. Then Eq. (2.9) becomes

$$\mathscr{L}\left[\frac{dy}{dt}\right] = sY(s) - y(0)\,. \quad (2.10)$$

To evaluate the Laplace transform of d^2y/dt^2, substitute dy/dt for y in Eq. (2.10):

$$\mathscr{L}\left[\frac{d}{dt}\left(\frac{dy}{dt}\right)\right] = s[sY(s) - y(0)] - \dot{y}(0)$$

$$= s^2Y(s) - sy(0) - \dot{y}(0)\,. \quad (2.11)$$

Eq. (2.5) can now be written as the algebraic equation

$$s^2Y(s) - sy(0) - \dot{y}(0) + 5sY(s) - 5y(0) + 6Y(s) = \frac{1}{s+4}$$

or

$$(s^2+5s+6)Y(s) = \frac{1}{s+4} + 1 = \frac{s+5}{s+4} \tag{2.12}$$

in which the initial conditions are included automatically. Thus

$$Y(s) = \frac{s+5}{(s+2)(s+3)(s+4)} \, . \tag{2.13}$$

Is there a way to return to the time domain? A convenient path consists of expanding Eq. (2.13) into partial fractions, to put it into the form of Eq. (2.7):

$$Y(s) = \frac{s+5}{(s+2)(s+3)(s+4)} = \frac{3}{2}\cdot\frac{1}{s+2} - 2\cdot\frac{1}{s+3} + \frac{1}{2}\cdot\frac{1}{s+4} \, . \tag{2.14}$$

Since the integration performed in calculating a Laplace transform is a linear process, the Laplace transform of a sum of time functions is the sum of their individual transforms:

$$\mathscr{L}[f_1(t) + f_2(t) + \ldots] = F_1(s) + F_2(s) + \ldots \tag{2.15}$$

Accordingly, the inverse Laplace transform of $Y(s)$ is the sum of the inverses of the three transforms on the right side of Eq. (2.14):

$$y(t) = \frac{3}{2}\,e^{-2t} - 2e^{-3t} + \frac{1}{2}\,e^{-4t} \, . \tag{2.16}$$

This is the solution of the differential equation, Eq. (2.3). Ordinary linear differential equations with constant coefficients can usually be solved faster by Laplace transforms than by classical methods.

The reader is invited to verify that the solution of the first-order differential equation

$$\frac{dy}{dt} + 3y = 2\sinh t \, , \qquad y(0) = 0$$

is

$$y(t) = \frac{1}{4}\,(e^{t} - 2e^{-t} + e^{-3t}) \quad .$$

2.3 Some Useful Laplace Transforms

Several common time functions and their Laplace transforms are listed in Table 2.1 at the end of this chapter. A few of these deserving special mention will be derived here.

Unit Step. A unit step occurring at $t=a$ $(a \geqslant 0)$ as in Fig. 2.1 is defined as

$$f(t) = U(t-a) = \begin{cases} 1, & t \geqslant a \\ 0, & t < a\,. \end{cases} \tag{2.17}$$

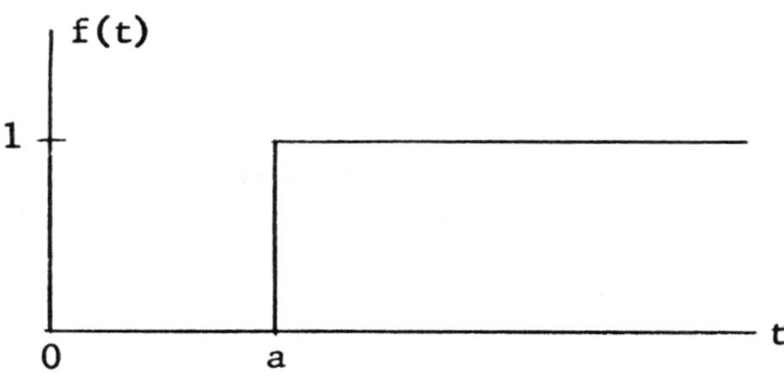

Fig. 2.1. Unit step.

Its Laplace transform is

$$F(s) = \int_0^\infty U(t-a)e^{-st}\,dt = \int_a^\infty e^{-st}\,dt = \frac{e^{-as}}{s}\,. \tag{2.18}$$

If the unit step occurs at $t=0$,

$$f(t) = U(t) \qquad \text{and} \qquad F(s) = \frac{1}{s}\,. \tag{2.19}$$

Note that the function $f(t) = U(t+a)$ is not causal and does not have a meaningful one-sided Laplace transform.

Unit Impulse. A unit impulse occurring at $t=a$ as in Fig. 2.2 is called $\delta(t-a)$. It is a special kind of a function called a *generalized function* or *distribution*. It can be regarded as a pulse of infinite height and zero width. The area under the pulse is 1:

$$\int_0^\infty \delta(t-a)dt = 1\,. \tag{2.20}$$

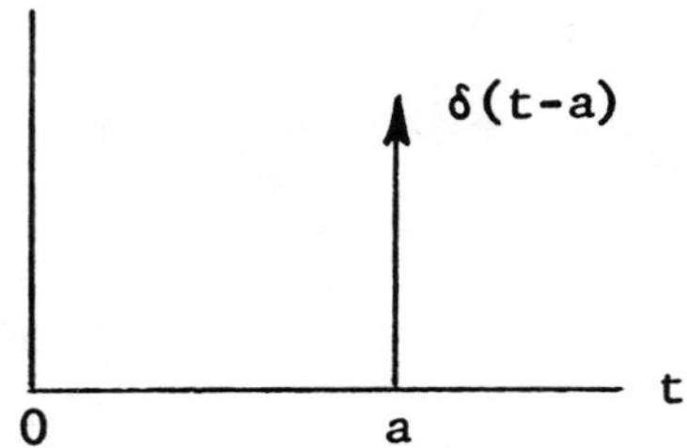

Fig. 2.2. Unit impulse.

The unit impulse can be defined rigorously in terms of the effect it has on any function $g(t)$:

$$\int_0^\infty g(t)\delta(t-a)dt = g(a) \ . \tag{2.21}$$

To show that these properties are compatible, draw an approximate representation of the unit impulse as in Fig. 2.3, together with a function $g(t)$. During the short time dt when the impulse is turned on, $g(t)$ has

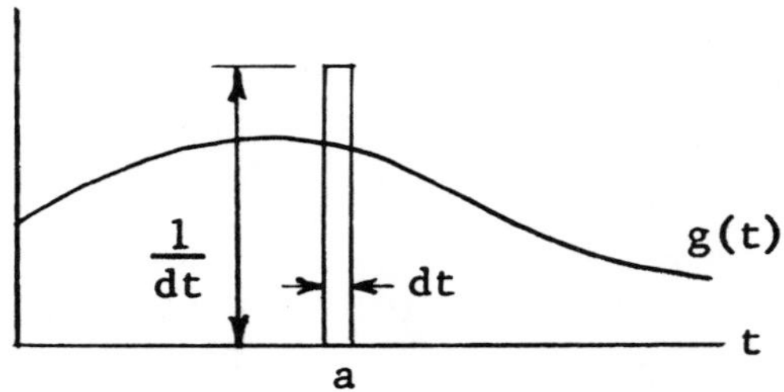

Fig. 2.3. Approximation of a unit impulse.

only the value $g(a)$. Therefore the left side of Eq. (2.21) becomes

$$\int_0^\infty g(t)\delta(t-a)dt = \int_0^\infty g(a)\delta(t-a)dt = g(a)\int_0^\infty \delta(t-a)dt = g(a) \ . \tag{2.22}$$

Letting $g(t) = e^{-st}$ in Eq. (2.21) produces the Laplace transform of the unit impulse:

$$\int_0^\infty \delta(t-a)e^{-st}\,dt = \mathscr{L}[\delta(t-a)] = e^{-as} \ . \tag{2.23}$$

If the unit impulse occurs at $t=0$,

$$f(t) = \delta(t) \qquad \text{and} \qquad F(s) = 1 \ . \tag{2.24}$$

Time Shift. Fig. 2.4 shows a typical causal time function $f(t)U(t)$, whose Laplace transform is $F(s)$. Fig. 2.5 shows the function $f(t-a)U(t-a)$, whose Laplace transform is

$$\mathscr{L}[f(t-a)U(t-a)] = \int_a^\infty f(t-a)e^{-st}dt \quad . \tag{2.25}$$

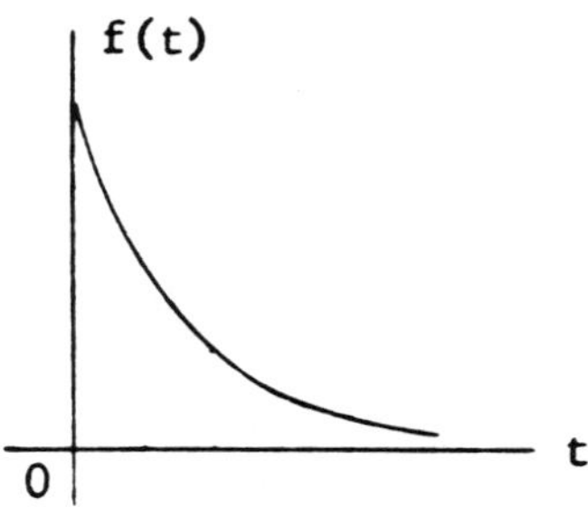

Fig. 2.4. A causal function.

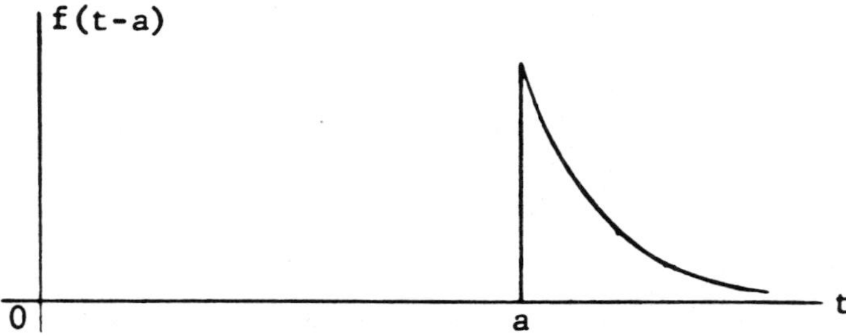

Fig. 2.5. The same function delayed.

Let $x=t-a$. Then

$$\mathscr{L}[f(t-a)U(t-a)] = \int_0^\infty f(x)e^{-s(x+a)}dx = e^{-as}\int_0^\infty f(x)e^{-sx}\,dx = e^{-as}F(s) \,. \tag{2.26}$$

Thus if a function is delayed by the time $t=a$, its Laplace transform is multiplied by e^{-as}. For example, if

$$F(s) = \frac{e^{-2s}}{s+3}\,, \tag{2.27}$$

$$f(t) = e^{-3(t-2)}\,U(t-2) \tag{2.28}$$

which looks like Fig. 2.5, with $a=2$.

Integral. Integrals of the form

$$g(t) = \int_{-\infty}^{t} f(u)\, du \,, \tag{2.29}$$

with a fixed lower limit of integration and a variable upper limit, appear in engineering practice. An example is the voltage across a capacitor of capacitance C:

$$v(t) = \frac{1}{C}\int_{-\infty}^{t} i(u)du \,. \tag{2.30}$$

To calculate the Laplace transform of $g(t)$, observe that if $f(u)$ is the ordinate of the curve in Fig. 2.6, the integral $g(t)$ is the area under the curve up to $u=t$. The rate of change of the area is

$$\frac{d}{dt}\, g(t) = f(t) \,. \tag{2.31}$$

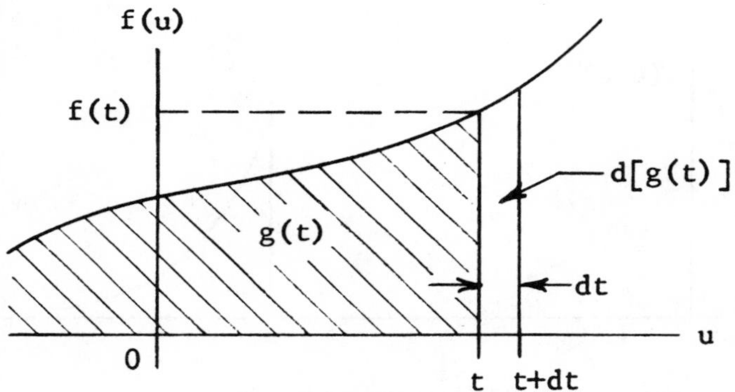

Fig. 2.6. Integral of a non-causal function.

According to Eq. (2.10),

$$\mathscr{L}\left[\frac{dg}{dt}\right] = s\mathscr{L}[g(t)] - g(0) \,. \tag{2.32}$$

Rearrangement of this equation to the form

$$\mathscr{L}[g(t)] = \frac{1}{s}\mathscr{L}\left[\frac{dg}{dt}\right] + \frac{1}{s}\, g(0) \tag{2.33}$$

and the definition

$$f^{-1}(0) = g(0) = \int_{-\infty}^{0} f(t)dt \tag{2.34}$$

produce the result

$$\mathcal{L}[g(t)] = \frac{1}{s}\,\mathcal{L}[f(t)] + \frac{1}{s}\,f^{-1}(0)\,, \tag{2.35}$$

and finally,

$$\mathcal{L}\left[\int_{-\infty}^{t} f(u)du\right] = \frac{1}{s}\,[F(s) + f^{-1}(0)]\,, \tag{2.36}$$

where $F(s)$ is the Laplace transform of $f(t)$. As Fig. 2.6 shows, $f(u)$ is not required to be a causal function. The term $f^{-1}(0)$ appears in Eq. (2.36) to account for the portion of the integral of $f(u)$ to the left of the origin. If $f(u)$ is causal, Eq. (2.36) becomes

$$\mathcal{L}\left[\int_{0}^{t} f(u)du\right] = \frac{1}{s}\,F(s)\,. \tag{2.37}$$

The usefulness of Eq. (2.36) is illustrated by a calculation of the current in the R-C circuit of Fig. 2.7 that flows after the switch is thrown. The capacitor is initially charged to voltage V. The initial charge is

$$\int_{-\infty}^{0} i(t)dt = i^{-1}(0) = CV\,. \tag{2.38}$$

After the switch is thrown,

$$Ri(t) + \frac{1}{C}\int_{-\infty}^{t} i(u)du = 0\,. \tag{2.39}$$

The Laplace transform of this equation, obtained with the help of Eq. (2.36), is

$$RI(s) + \frac{1}{Cs}\,[I(s) + i^{-1}(0)] = 0 \tag{2.40}$$

or

$$RI(s) + \frac{1}{Cs}\,[I(s) + CV] = 0\,. \tag{2.41}$$

Then

$$I(s) = -\frac{V/R}{s + \dfrac{1}{RC}}\,. \tag{2.42}$$

According to Eq. (2.7),

$$i(t) = -\frac{V}{R} e^{-t/RC} . \tag{2.43}$$

The first minus sign indicates that the current flows opposite to the direction indicated in Fig. 2.7.

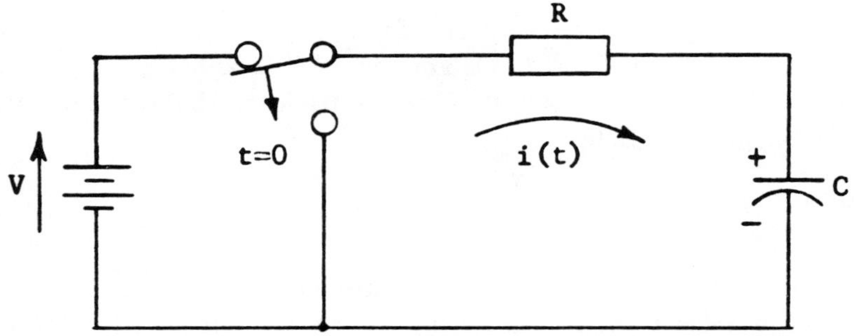

Fig. 2.7. Battery-powered R-C circuit.

Transform Differentiation. Notice that since

$$F(s) = \int_0^\infty f(t)\, e^{-st} dt \ , \tag{2.44}$$

Then

$$\frac{d}{ds} F(s) = \int_0^\infty -tf(t)e^{-st} dt \ . \tag{2.45}$$

Therefore

$$\mathscr{L}[tf(t)] = -\frac{dF(s)}{ds} . \tag{2.46}$$

This result can be used to take another step:

$$\mathscr{L}[t^2 f(t)] = \mathscr{L}[t\{tf(t)\}] = -\frac{d}{ds}\left[-\frac{dF(s)}{ds}\right] = \frac{d^2F(s)}{ds^2} . \tag{2.47}$$

A little inductive reasoning shows that if n is any positive integer,

$$\mathscr{L}[t^n f(t)] = (-1)^n \frac{d^nF(s)}{ds^n} . \tag{2.48}$$

This transform shows the futility of using Laplace transforms to solve linear differential equations with time-varying coefficients, such as

$$t \frac{d^2y}{dt^2} + \frac{dy}{dt} + 3y = 1 , \tag{2.49}$$

with

$$y(0) = \dot{y}(0) = 0 . \tag{2.50}$$

The Laplace transform of the equation is

$$-\frac{d}{ds}[s^2Y(s)] + sY(s) + 3Y(s) = \frac{1}{s} \tag{2.51}$$

or

$$s^2 \frac{dY(s)}{ds} + (s-3)Y(s) = -\frac{1}{s} . \tag{2.52}$$

The transformation has led nowhere. It has produced another linear differential equation with variable coefficients, whose initial conditions are unknown.

2.4 Application to Fixed Linear Systems

An example will illustrate the fundamental notions of impulse response and system function. Fig. 2.8 shows an R-L-C circuit in which the initial current $i(0)$ and the initial charge on the capacitor $i^{-1}(0)$ are zero. The sum of voltages around the left loop is

$$\frac{di}{dt} + 6\int_{-\infty}^{t} i(u)du + 5i = v(t) , \tag{2.53}$$

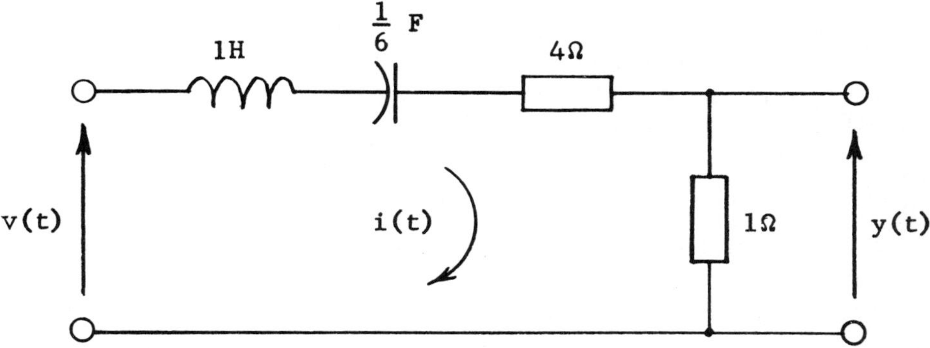

Fig. 2.8. R-L-C circuit.

where $v(t)$ is the input voltage. The Laplace transform is

$$sI(s) - i(0) + 6\,\frac{I(s)}{s} + 6\,\frac{i^{-1}(0)}{s} + 5I(s) = V(s)\ . \tag{2.54}$$

Since

$$i(0) = i^{-1}(0) = 0\ , \tag{2.55}$$

$$\left(s + \frac{6}{s} + 5\right) I(s) = V(s)\ . \tag{2.56}$$

Since the output voltage $y(t)$ is across a one-ohm resistor,

$$y(t) = i(t) \qquad \text{or} \qquad Y(s) = = I(s)\ , \tag{2.57}$$

and

$$\left(s + \frac{6}{s} + 5\right) Y(s) = V(s)\ . \tag{2.58}$$

Because the two initial conditions contribute nothing to the right side of Eq. (2.58), $Y(s)$ is zero if $V(s)$ is zero. Such a system, whose output $y(t)$ is zero as long as no input $v(t)$ is applied, is said to be *initially inert*. A fixed, linear system is initially inert if all of the initial conditions needed by the Laplace transforms of its differential equations are zero.

According to Eq. (2.58),

$$\frac{Y(s)}{V(s)} = \frac{s}{s^2+5s+6} = \frac{s}{(s+2)(s+3)} = \frac{3}{s+3} - \frac{2}{s+2}\ . \tag{2.59}$$

The ration of the Laplace transforms of the output $Y(s)$ and input $V(s)$ of a fixed, initially-inert linear system, $H(s)$, is called the *system function* or *transfer function*:

$$H(s) = \frac{Y(s)}{V(s)}\ . \tag{2.60}$$

It is determined by the parameters of the system, and is independent of the input and output signals. Notice that the ratio $y(t)/v(t)$ is not unique, but depends on the input signal $v(t)$. When the system function has been calculated, the response of the initially-inert system to any input can be calculated:

$$Y(s) = V(s)H(s)\ . \tag{2.61}$$

In the form of a block diagram, the Laplace transforms of the signals are related as shown in Fig. 2.9. For example, if the input to the system of Fig. 2.8 is the step

$$v(t) = 2U(t)\ , \tag{2.62}$$

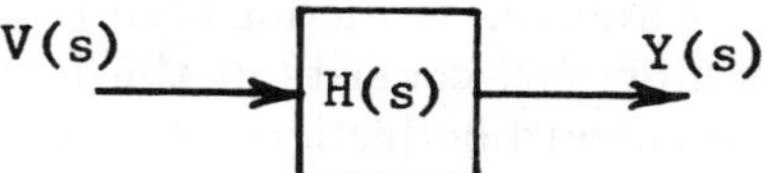

Fig. 2.9. Block diagram.

then

$$V(s) = \frac{2}{s} , \tag{2.63}$$

and

$$\begin{aligned} Y(s) = V(s)H(s) &= \frac{2}{s} \cdot \frac{s}{s^2+5s+6} = \frac{2}{s^2+5s+6} \\ &= \frac{2}{(s+2)(s+3)} = \frac{2}{s+2} - \frac{2}{s+3} . \end{aligned} \tag{2.64}$$

The output of the system is therefore

$$y(t) = 2(e^{-2t} - e^{-3t}) . \tag{2.65}$$

If a fixed, linear system is not initially inert, the output depends upon the initial conditions as well as the input and the parameters of the system. Eq. (2.61) cannot be used. Instead, the differential equation or equations describing the system, such as Eq. (2.53), must be solved. Eq. (2.54) is the first step of the solution.

If the input to a fixed, initially-inert linear system is the unit impulse $v(t) = \delta(t)$, for which $V(s) = 1$, the output is

$$Y(s) = V(s)H(s) = H(s) . \tag{2.66}$$

If the inverse Laplace transform of $H(s)$ is called $h(t)$,

$$y(t) = h(t) . \tag{2.67}$$

The output of the system in response to a unit-impulse input is $h(t)$, which is appropriately called the *impulse response.* The system function $H(s)$ is the Laplace transform of the impulse response. The impulse response of the circuit of Fig. 2.8, according to Eq. (2.59), is

$$h(t) = 3e^{-3t} - 2e^{-2t} . \tag{2.68}$$

The impulse response of the circuit could be observed experimentally by applying a narrow voltage pulse $v(t)$, and observing the output voltage $y(t)$ on an oscilloscope. The impulse response of a mechanical system such as a drop forge could be determined by striking the anvil with a hammer to produce an impulse of applied force, and measuring the resulting deflection of the anvil as a function of time. For example, assume that if the hammer blow $f(t)$ consists of the impulse shown in Fig. 2.10, the resulting downward deflection $x(t)$ has the simple (although unrealistic) form shown in Fig. 2.11. The impulse response of the drop forge is

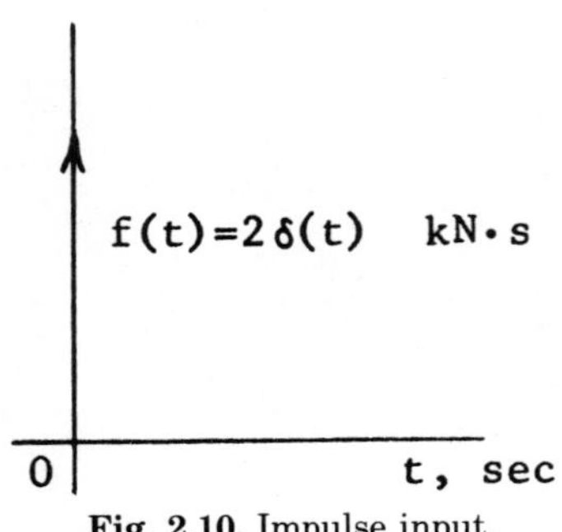

Fig. 2.10. Impulse input.

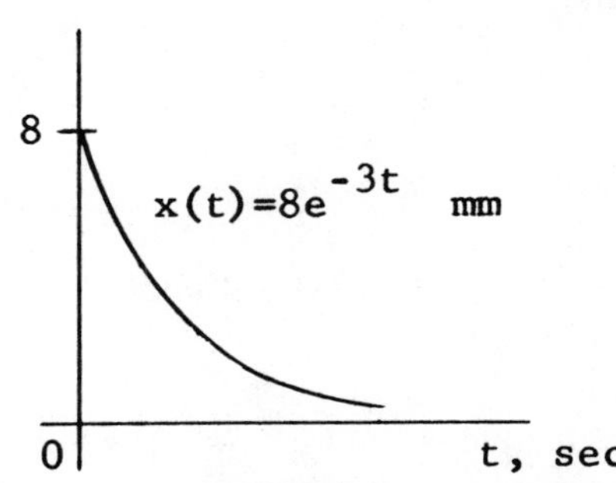

Fig. 2.11. Resulting response.

$$h(t) = 4e^{-3t} \qquad \frac{\text{mm}}{\text{kN·s}}, \tag{2.69}$$

and the system function is

$$H(s) = \frac{4}{s+3} . \tag{2.70}$$

Now the response to any applied force can be calculated. One such input is the square pulse shown in Fig. 2.12, whose formula is

$$f(t) = U(t) - U(t-2) , \tag{2.71}$$

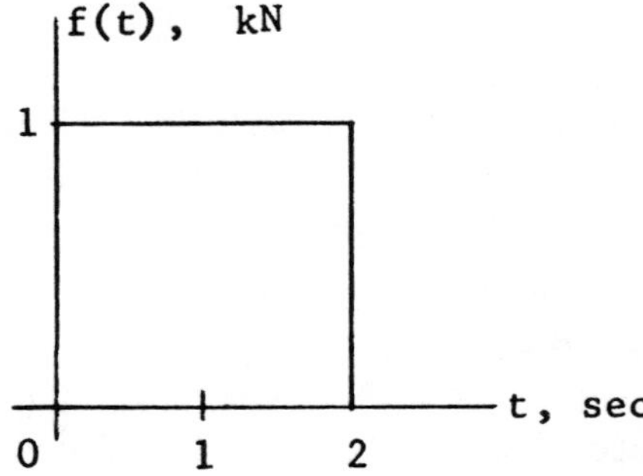

Fig. 2.12. Pulse input.

the Laplace transform of which is

$$F(s) = \frac{1}{s} - \frac{e^{-2s}}{s} . \tag{2.72}$$

The Laplace transform of the resulting deflection is

$$X(s) = F(s)H(s) = \frac{4}{s+3}\left(\frac{1-e^{-2s}}{s}\right) , \tag{2.73}$$

and the response to the square pulse of force is

$$x(t) = \frac{4}{3}\,(1-e^{-3t}) - \frac{4}{3}\,[1-e^{-3(t-2)}]U(t-2) \quad \text{mm} \quad , \tag{2.74}$$

shown in Fig. 2.13. The impulse response $h(t)$ of any physical system is causal, i.e., zero for negative t, because (1) the system is causal and therefore produces no output before the input appears, and (2) the input impulse occurs at $t=0$.

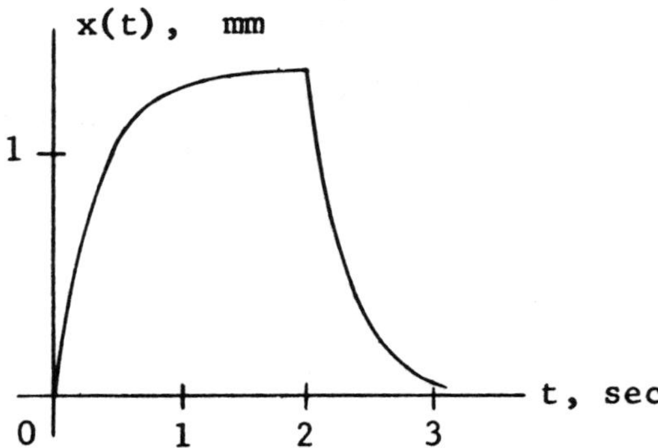

Fig. 2.13. Response to pulse input.

2.5 Convolution

An important Laplace-transform pair used frequently in the analysis of linear systems is

$$f(t) = \int_{-\infty}^{\infty} f_1(x)f_2(t-x)dx , \tag{2.75}$$

$$F(s) = F_1(s)F_2(s) . \tag{2.76}$$

Eq. (2.75) is the *convolution integral* of the two functions $f_1(t)$ and $f_2(t)$. Its Laplace transform is the product of the Laplace transforms of $f_1(t)$ and

$f_2(t)$. To prove that Eqs. (2.75) and (2.76) are a transform pair, use Eq. (2.1) to calculate the two-sided Laplace transform of the convolution integral:

$$F(s) = \int_{t=-\infty}^{\infty} \left[\int_{x=-\infty}^{\infty} f_1(x) f_2(t-x) dx \right] e^{-st} dt \ . \tag{2.77}$$

This can be rearranged to the form

$$F(s) = \int_{x=-\infty}^{\infty} f_1(x) \left[\int_{t=-\infty}^{\infty} f_2(t-x) e^{-st} dt \right] dx \ . \tag{2.78}$$

The integral within the brackets can be evaluated by letting $y = t-x$. Thus

$$\int_{t=-\infty}^{\infty} f_2(t-x) e^{-st} dt = \int_{y=-\infty}^{\infty} f_2(y) e^{-s(y+x)}\, dy = e^{-xs} \int_{-\infty}^{\infty} f_2(y) e^{-sy} dy$$

$$= e^{-xs}\, F_2(s) \ . \tag{2.79}$$

Eq. (2.78) becomes

$$F(s) = F_2(s) \int_{-\infty}^{\infty} f_1(x) e^{-xs}\, dx = F_1(s) F_2(s) \ , \tag{2.80}$$

which confirms Eq. (2.76). If $f_1(t)$ is causal, the lower limit of integration in the convolution integral (2.75) can be raised to 0. If $f_2(t)$ is casual, the upper limit can be lowered to t. Then Eq. (2.75) becomes

$$f(t) = \int_0^t f_1(x) f_2(t-x) dx \, . \tag{2.81}$$

The proof of Eq. (2.76) is unaffected by this change. Either Eq. (2.81) or (2.75) is abbreviated as

$$f(t) = f_1(t) * f_2(t) \ . \tag{2.82}$$

Thus

$$\mathscr{L}[f_1(t) * f_2(t)] = F_1(s) F_2(s) \ . \tag{2.83}$$

Since the Laplace transform of the output of a fixed, initially-inert linear system, according to Eq. (2.61), is

$$Y(s) = V(s) H(s) \ , \tag{2.84}$$

the output is

$$y(t) = v(t) * h(t) = \int_0^t v(x) h(t-x) dx = \int_0^t v(t-x) h(x) dx \ . \tag{2.85}$$

This convolution can be used, for example, to calculate the output of the first-order delay of Fig. 2.14, when the input is the unit step $v(t) = U(t)$. The impulse response of the delay is

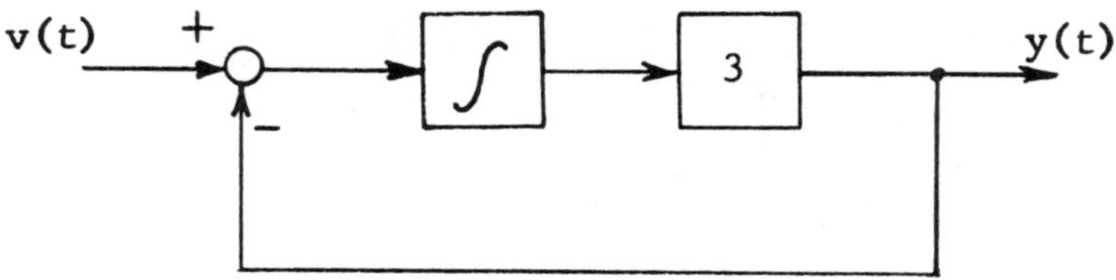

Fig. 2.14. First-order delay.

$$h(t) = 3e^{-3t}. \tag{2.86}$$

According to the first form of Eq. (2.85), the output is

$$y(t) = \int_0^t U(x) \cdot 3e^{-3(t-x)}\, dx = 3e^{-3t} \int_0^t e^{3x} dx = 1 - e^{-3t}. \tag{2.87}$$

Although this calculation of the output is simple, the calculation using Laplace transforms according to Eq. (2.84) is even simpler. The reader is invited to verify this assertion.

Eqs. (2.84) and (2.85) indicate a remarkable fact: in order to calculate the output of a fixed, initially inert, linear system resulting from a known input, all one needs to know about the system is either its system function or its impulse response. This fact is used, for example, to predict the vibration of a turbine bucket produced by the fluctuating blasts of steam encountered in service. Resistance strain gages are mounted at several locations on the bucket. When the bucket is given an impulse of force by striking it with a hammer, the output voltages of the strain-gage bridges, which are impulse responses, are converted from analog to digital signals and stored in a computer memory. Then when a voltage simulating any input steam force: sinusoidal, random, etc., is applied to the computer, it computes the deflection shape of the bucket and displays it as a moving picture.

2.6 Systems in Cascade

The response of two or more subsystems is cascade is easily calculated with the help of Laplace transforms. Fig. 2.15 shows two such subsys-

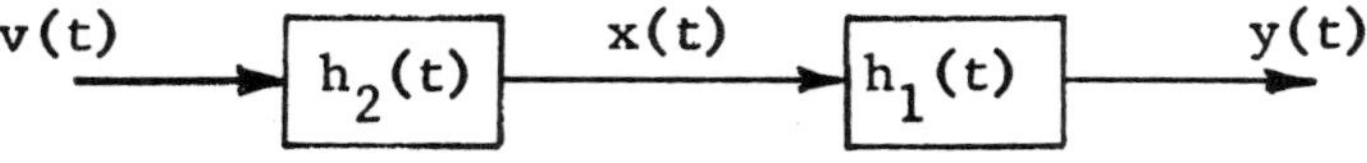

Fig. 2.15. Two subsystems in cascade.

tems with impulse responses $h_1(t)$ and $h_2(t)$ and system functions $H_1(s)$

and $H_2(s)$. The Laplace transform of the output is

$$Y(s) = \frac{Y(s)}{X(s)} \cdot \frac{X(s)}{V(s)} \cdot V(s) = H_1(s)H_2(s)V(s) . \tag{2.88}$$

The overall transfer function is therefore

$$H(s) = H_1(s)H_2(s) . \tag{2.89}$$

According to Eq. (2.83), the overall impulse response of the two subsystems is

$$h(t) = h_1(t)*h_2(t) . \tag{2.90}$$

The impulse response of a cascade of fixed, linear systems is the convolution of their individual impulse responses.

The reader can test his or her understanding by solving this problem: In the system of Fig. 2.15, if

$$v(t) = \delta(t) , \qquad x(t) = e^{-2t} , \tag{2.91}$$

and if

$$x(t) = \delta(t) , \qquad y(t) = e^{-3t} . \tag{2.92}$$

Then if

$$v(t) = U(t) , \quad \text{what is } y(t) \text{ ?}$$

2.7 Step Response

If the input to a system is the unit step $v(t) = U(t)$, the output is the *step response*, sometimes designated as $a(t)$. Its Laplace transform is $A(s)$. Since the Laplace transform of the input is $V(s) = 1/s$, and the Laplace transform of the output is $V(s)H(s)$,

$$A(s) = \frac{H(s)}{s} , \tag{2.93}$$

and according to Eq. (2.37),

$$a(t) = \int_0^t h(u)du . \tag{2.94}$$

This result shows that the step response of a fixed, linear system is the integral of the impulse response.

An *integrator* is a device whose output is the integral of its input:

$$y(t) = \int_0^t v(u)du . \tag{2.95}$$

Then

$$Y(s) = V(s)H(s) = \frac{V(s)}{s}\,. \tag{2.96}$$

This equation shows that the system function of an integrator is

$$H(s) = \frac{1}{s}\,. \tag{2.97}$$

The integrator is designated in a block diagram by an integral sign or by its system function, as shown in Fig. 2.16. The upper diagram in Fig. 2.17 shows an integrator in cascade with a fixed, linear subsystem

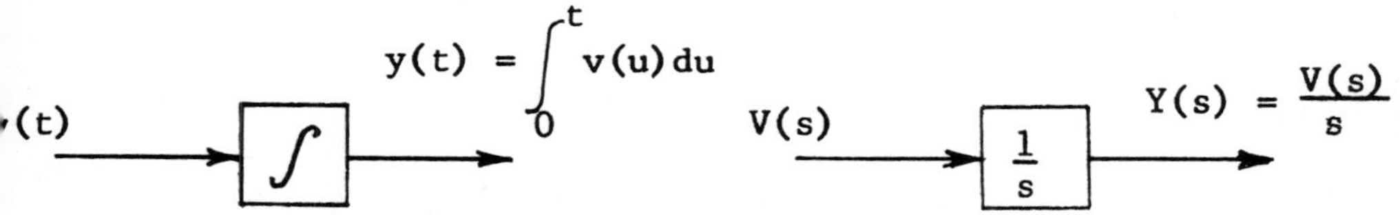

Fig. 2.16. Designation of an integrator.

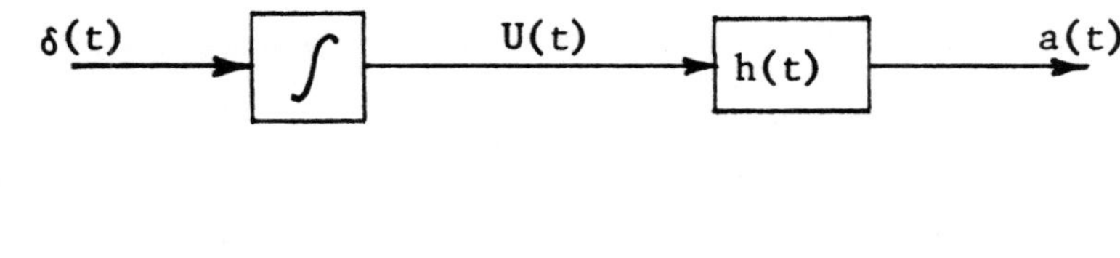

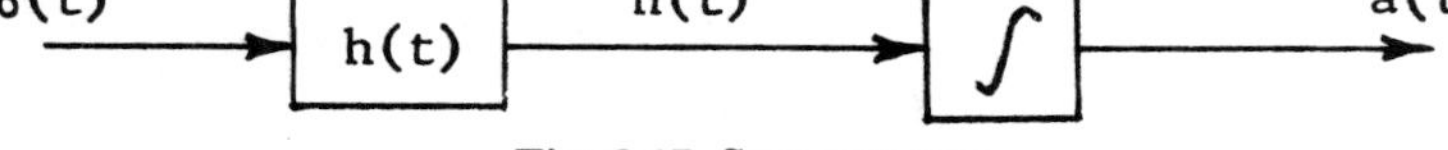

Fig. 2.17. Step response.

whose impulse response is $h(t)$. If the input to the integrator is a unit impulse $\delta(t)$, its output is the unit step $U(t)$. The output of the subsystem is its step response $a(t)$. In the lower diagram, the integrator and subsystem are interchanged. Since each is a fixed, linear device, the overall system function is unchanged. If the input is again $\delta(t)$, the output of the cascade is again $a(t)$. The output of the subsystem is its impulse response, $h(t)$. This is the input to the integrator. The lower diagram shows that $a(t)$ is the integral of the impulse response of the subsystem. In the upper diagram, $a(t)$ is defined as the step response of the subsystem. This argument constitutes a second proof that the step response of a fixed, linear system is the integral of its impulse response.

2.8 Graphical Convolution

Convolution integrals such as Eq. (2.81) can be performed graphically as well as analytically. Fig. 2.18 shows plots of a typical causal function

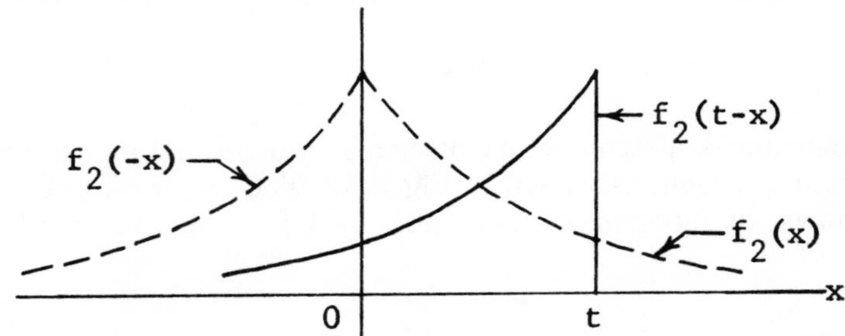

Fig. 2.18. Plot of $f_2(t-x)$.

$f_2(x) = e^{-ax}$, and the two modifications $f_2(-x)$ and $f_2(t-x)$, for a fixed value of t. Fig. 2.19 shows the same function $f_2(t-x)$ and another typ-

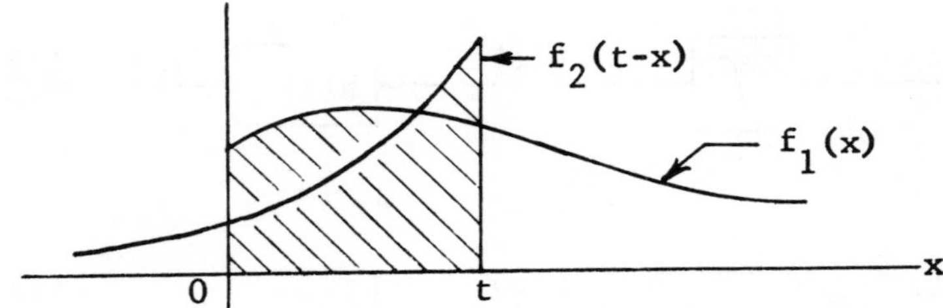

Fig. 2.19. Graphical convolution.

ical causal function $f_1(x)$. The convolution integral

$$f(t) = \int_0^t f_2(t-x) f_1(x) dx \tag{2.98}$$

is the integral of the product of the ordinates of the two curves over the interval of x from zero to t. To obtain $f(t)$ for another value of t, slide the curve of $f_2(t-x)$ to the new value of t, and repeat the integration. This graphical method is useful if the curves of the functions are simple. An example is the following calculation of the impulse response of two averaging circuits in cascade. An averaging circuit is shown in Fig. 2.20. The input signal $v(t)$ is integrated and multipled by $1/T$. From the result is then subtracted a version of itself that has been delayed by T

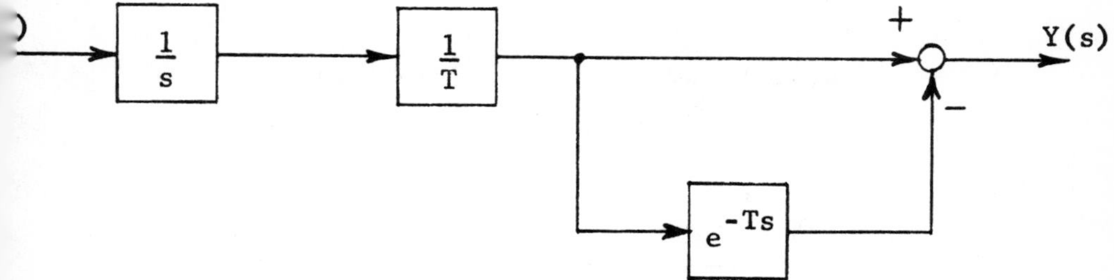

Fig. 2.20. Averaging circuit.

seconds, to produce the output $y(t)$. The overall system function is

$$H(s) = \frac{Y(s)}{V(s)} = \frac{1}{Ts}\,(1-e^{-Ts}) \quad , \tag{2.99}$$

and the impulse response is

$$h(t) = \frac{1}{T}\,[U(t) - U(t-T)] \ . \tag{2.100}$$

If $T=1$, the impulse response is the square pulse shown in Fig. 2.21.

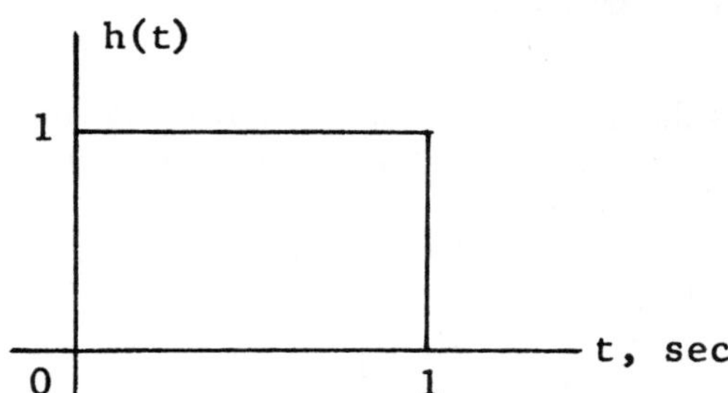

Fig. 2.21. Impulse response of an averaging circuit.

The overall impulse response $h_o(t)$ of two such averaging circuits in cascade, according to Eq. (2.90), is the convolution of $h(t)$ with itself:

$$h_o(t) = \int_0^t h(t-x)h(x)dx \ . \tag{2.101}$$

The graphical convolution indicated in Fig. 2.22 shows that

$$h_o(t) = \begin{cases} t\,, & 0 \leqslant t \leqslant 1 \\ 2-t\,, & 1 \leqslant t \leqslant 2 \\ 0\,, & t \geqslant 2 \end{cases} \quad . \tag{2.102}$$

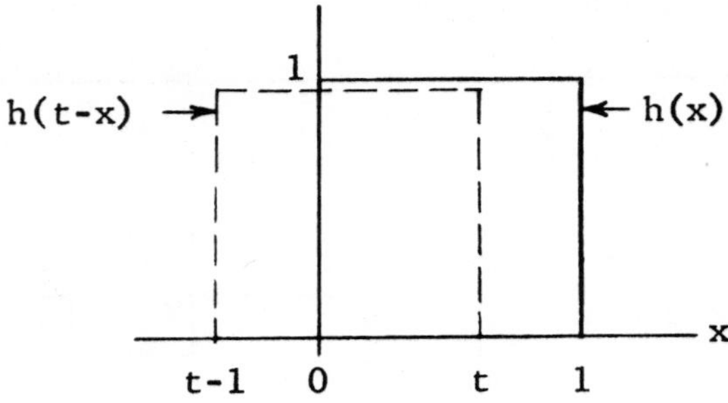

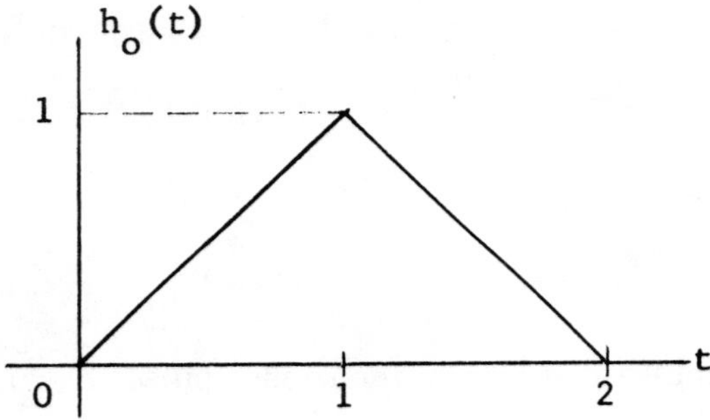

Fig. 2.22. Convolution of a square pulse with itself.

These equations describe the triangular pulse shown in Fig. 2.22. The astute reader is invited to calculate the impulse response of *three* averaging circuits in cascade.

Why is the circuit of Fig. 2.20 called an averaging circuit? Notice that since its system function is

$$H(s) = \frac{1}{T}\left(\frac{1}{s} - \frac{e^{-Ts}}{s}\right), \tag{2.103}$$

the Laplace transform of the output is

$$Y(s) = V(s)H(s) = \frac{1}{T}\left[\frac{V(s)}{s} - \frac{V(s)e^{-Ts}}{s}\right]. \tag{2.104}$$

If the input $v(t)$ is causal, the output is

$$y(t) = \frac{1}{T}\left[\int_0^t v(u)du - \int_0^{t-T} v(u)du\, U(t-T)\right]. \tag{2.105}$$

Fig. 2.23 shows a curve whose slope is $v(x)$, and whose ordinate is

$$f(x) = \int_0^x v(u)du \ . \tag{2.106}$$

At the abscissa $x=t$, the ordinate is

$$f(t) = \int_0^t v(u)du \ . \tag{2.107}$$

The same curve delayed by the time T is also shown. Its ordinate can be written as

$$f(x-T) = \int_0^{x-T} v(u)du \ U(x-T) \ , \tag{2.108}$$

the unit step at $x=T$ being a reminder that $f(x-T)$ is zero for $x<T$. At the abscissa $x=t$, the ordinate is

$$f(t-T) = \int_0^{t-T} v(u)du \ U(t-T) \ . \tag{2.109}$$

The ordinates in Eqs. (2.107) and (2.109) are the two terms on the right side of Eq. (2.105). Fig. 2.23 shows that their difference is the integral of $v(x)$ from $t-T$ to t. The output of the circuit can therefore be written as

$$y(t) = \frac{1}{T}\int_{t-T}^{t} v(x)dx \ . \tag{2.110}$$

At any time t, the output $y(t)$ is the average of the input $v(t)$ over the preceding time interval T.

2.9 Partial Fractions

When an ordinary differential equation with fixed coefficients is solved by Laplace transforms, the Laplace transform of the solution, such as that given by Eq. (2.13), is usually a ratio of polynomials. Similarly, when the output of a fixed, linear system is calculated by the formula $Y(s) = V(s)H(s)$, the Laplace transform of the output $Y(s)$ is usually a ratio of polynomials. (Delays such as the one in Fig. 2.20 add only a minor complication.) The solution of the differential equation, or the output of the system, is obtained by resolving the ratio of polynomials into partial fractions, and finding the inverse transform of each partial fraction. A summary of the rules for making partial fractions will expedite this process.

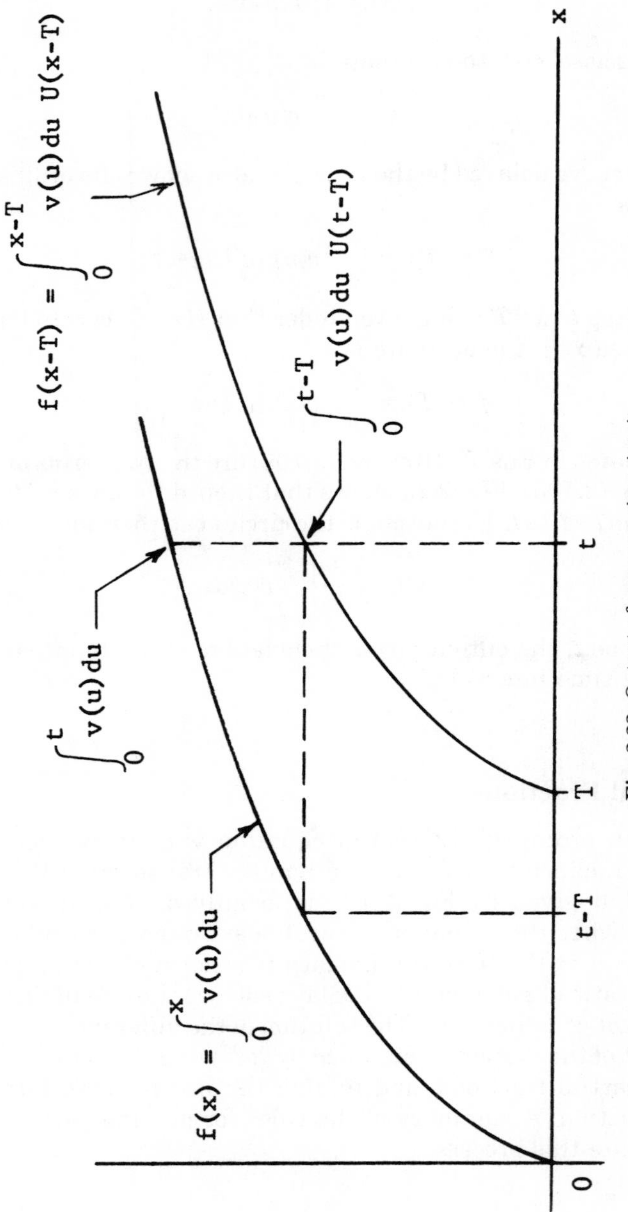

Fig. 2.23. Output of an averaging circuit.

1. *Denominator has distinct real roots.* If the polynomial in the numerator is $N(s)$ and the polynomial in the denominator is $(s-s_1)(s-s_2)$ . . . , and the roots s_1, s_2, . . . are all real, write

$$F(s) = \frac{N(s)}{(s-s_1)(s-s_2)(s-s_3)\ \dots} = \frac{A}{s-s_1} + \frac{B}{s-s_2} + \frac{C}{s-s_3} + \ \dots \tag{2.111}$$

To evaluate A, multiply both sides by $s-s_1$ and let $s=s_1$. Then

$$A = [(s-s_1)F(s)]_{s=s_1} = \frac{N(s_1)}{(s_1-s_2)(s_1-s_3)\ \dots} . \tag{2.112}$$

For example, if

$$F(s) = \frac{s+1}{(s+4)(s+5)} = \frac{A}{s+4} + \frac{B}{s+5} , \tag{2.113}$$

then

$$A = \frac{-4+1}{-4+5} = -3 , \qquad \text{and} \qquad B = \frac{-5+1}{-5+4} = 4 , \tag{2.114}$$

and

$$F(s) = -\frac{3}{s+4} + \frac{4}{s+5} . \tag{2.115}$$

2. *Denominator has a repeated real root.* Establish a partial fraction for every lower integral power of the repeated factor. If for example a root s_1 is of order 3, write

$$\begin{aligned} F(s) &= \frac{N(s)}{(s-s_1)^3(s-s_2)(s-s_3)\ \dots} \\ &= \frac{A_1}{s-s_1} + \frac{A_2}{(s-s_1)^2} + \frac{A_3}{(s-s_1)^3} + \frac{B}{s-s_2} + \frac{C}{s-s_3} + \ \dots \end{aligned} \tag{2.116}$$

The coefficients for the repeated root are evaluated by these formulas:

$$A_3 = [(s-s_1)^3F(s)]_{s=s_1} \tag{2.117}$$

$$A_2 = \left[\frac{d}{ds}\{(s-s_1)^3F(s)\} \right]_{s=s_1} \tag{2.118}$$

$$A_1 = \frac{1}{2}\left[\frac{d^2}{ds^2}\{(s-s_1)^3F(s)\} \right]_{s=s_1} . \tag{2.119}$$

In general, if the repeated root s_1 is of order r,

$$A_{r-k} = \frac{1}{k!}\left[\frac{d^k}{ds^k}\{(s-s_1)^rF(s)\} \right]_{s=s_1} , \quad k = 0, 1, \ \dots, r-1. \tag{2.120}$$

The coefficient A_1 is called the *residue* of the function $F(s)$ at the point $s{=}s_1$. As an example, let

$$F(s) = \frac{s+3}{(s+2)^2(s+1)} = \frac{A_1}{s+2} + \frac{A_2}{(s+2)^2} + \frac{B}{s+1}. \tag{2.121}$$

Please evaluate A_1, A_2, and B.

An alternate method consists of putting all of the partial fractions over their common denominator, and equating like powers of s. Eq. (2.121) becomes

$$\frac{s+3}{(s+2)^2(s+1)} = \frac{A_1(s+1)(s+2) + A_2(s+1) + B(s+2)^2}{(s+2)^2(s+1)}. \tag{2.122}$$

Please complete the calculation of A_1, A_2, and B.

3. *Denominator has a quadratic root* $s = -\alpha \pm j\beta$. One method consists of writing the partial fractions in the form

$$F(s) = \frac{N(s)}{[(s+\alpha)^2+\beta^2](s-s_2)(s-s_3)\ldots}$$

$$= \frac{A_1s+A_2}{(s+\alpha)^2+\beta^2} + \frac{B}{s-s_1} + \frac{C}{s-s_2} + \ldots \tag{2.123}$$

Put all of the partial fractions over their common denominator, and equate like powers of s. Please evaluate A_1, A_2, and B in this example:

$$F(s) = \frac{s+2}{(s^2+2s+5)(s+1)} = \frac{A_1s+A_2}{s^2+2s+5} + \frac{B}{s+1}. \tag{2.124}$$

An interesting alternate method, that produces the inverse of the quadratic partial fraction directly in a more convenient form, is the *trick of Papoulis.** Write the ratio of polynomials as

$$F(s) = \frac{N(s)}{D_1(s)[(s+\alpha)^2+\beta^2]} = \frac{A_1s+A_2}{(s+\alpha)^2+\beta^2} + \text{terms for } D_1(s)\,, \tag{2.125}$$

where $D_1(s)$ is the portion of the denominator not including the quadratic factor. The partial fraction for the quadratic factor can be ignored. Make the definition

$$Me^{j\theta} = \left.\frac{N(s)}{D_1(s)}\right|_{s=-\alpha+j\beta}. \tag{2.126}$$

* Dr. Athanasios Papoulis, Professor of Electrical Engineering at the Polytechnic Institute of New York.

The inverse Laplace transform is then

$$f(t) = \frac{M}{\beta} e^{-\alpha t} \sin(\beta t + \theta) + \text{the terms from } D_1(s) \ . \qquad (2.127)$$

As an example, let

$$F(s) = \frac{s+2}{(s+1)(s^2+2s+5)} = \frac{s+2}{(s+1)[(s+1)^2+(2)^2]} = \frac{A_1 s + A_2}{s^2+2s+5} + \frac{B}{s+1} \ . \qquad (2.128)$$

A use of Eq. (2.112) shows quickly that $B = 1/4$. According to Eq. (2.126),

$$Me^{j\theta} = \left.\frac{s+2}{s+1}\right|_{s=-1+j2} = \frac{-1+j2+2}{-1+j2+1}$$

$$= \frac{1+j2}{j2} = 1 - j\,\frac{1}{2} = \frac{\sqrt{5}}{2}\, e^{-j\tan^{-1}(1/2)} \ . \qquad (2.129)$$

Since

$$M = \frac{\sqrt{5}}{2}, \quad \alpha = 1, \quad \beta = 2, \quad \text{and} \quad \theta = -\tan^{-1}\frac{1}{2},$$

$$f(t) = \frac{\sqrt{5}}{4} e^{-t} \sin\left(2t - \tan^{-1}\frac{1}{2}\right) + \frac{1}{4} e^{-t} \ . \qquad (2.130)$$

Notice that the inverse transform of the quadratic partial fraction appears as a single sine term whose magnitude and phase shift are displayed. The common-denominator method of inverting $F(s)$ produces a sine term and a cosine term, whose combined magnitude must be computed separately.

4. *Denominator has two different pairs of quadratic roots.* If the ratio of polynomials has the form

$$F(s) = \frac{N(s)}{[(s+\alpha_1)^2 + \beta_1^2][(s+\alpha_2)^2 + \beta_2^2](s-s_1)(s-s_2)\ldots}, \qquad (2.131)$$

write

$$F(s) = F_1(s) + F_2(s) + \frac{B}{s-s_1} + \frac{C}{s-s_2} + \ldots, \qquad (2.132)$$

where $F_1(s)$ and $F_2(s)$ are the partial fractions for the first and second quadratic factors. To invert them, perform the trick of Papoulis twice. To use Eq. (2.126) for calculating $f_1(t)$, let

$$D_1(s) = [(s+\alpha_2)^2 + \beta_2^2](s-s_1)(s-s_2)\ldots \qquad (2.133)$$

For calculating $f_2(t)$, let

$$D_1(s) = [(s+\alpha_1)^2 + \beta_1^2](s-s_1)(s-s_2) \ldots \tag{2.134}$$

5. *Denominator has a repeated quadratic root.* As for a repeated real root, establish a partial fraction for every lower integral power of the repeated quadratic factor. If for example the quadratic root is of order 2, write

$$\begin{aligned} F(s) &= \frac{N(s)}{[(s+\alpha)^2+\beta^2]^2(s-s_2)(s-s_3)\ldots} \\ &= \frac{A_1s+A_2}{(s+\alpha)^2+\beta^2} + \frac{B_1s+B_2}{[(s+\alpha)^2+\beta^2]^2} + \frac{C}{s-s_2} + \frac{D}{s-s_3} + \ldots \end{aligned} \tag{2.135}$$

To evaluate the coefficients, put all of the partial fractions over their common denominator and equate like powers of s.

2.10 Solution of Simultaneous Differential Equations

The solution of simultaneous, ordinary, linear differential equations with constant coefficients by the classical methods is a tedious process. A special rule must be followed if any of the terms in the particular solution duplicates a term in the complementary solution. Laplace transforms simplify the solution, because they reduce the differential equations to a set of simultaneous algebraic equations that can be solved easily. To illustrate the usefulness of Laplace transforms, solve the simultaneous differential equations

$$\dot{x} + y = \sin t \tag{2.136}$$

$$x + \dot{y} = e^{-t}, \tag{2.137}$$

with the initial conditions $x(0) = y(0) = 1$. The second term in the complementary solution

$$x_c = k_1 e^t + k_2 e^{-t} \tag{2.138}$$

duplicates one of the driving functions. No trouble appears, however, when Laplace transforms are used. The transforms of Eqs. (2.136) and (2.137) are

$$sX(s) - 1 + Y(s) = \frac{1}{s^2+1} \tag{2.139}$$

and

$$X(s) + sY(s) - 1 = \frac{1}{s+1}, \tag{2.140}$$

or

$$sX(s) + Y(s) = \frac{1}{s^2+1} + 1 = \frac{s^2+2}{s^2+1} \qquad (2.141)$$

and

$$X(s) + sY(s) = \frac{1}{s+1} + 1 = \frac{s+2}{s+1} . \qquad (2.142)$$

Then according to Cramer's rule,

$$X(s) = \frac{\begin{vmatrix} \frac{s^2+2}{s^2+1} & 1 \\ \frac{s+2}{s+1} & s \end{vmatrix}}{\begin{vmatrix} s & 1 \\ 1 & s \end{vmatrix}} = \frac{\frac{s^3+2s}{s^2+1} - \frac{s+2}{s+1}}{s^2-1}$$

$$= \frac{s^4+s-2}{(s^2+1)(s^2-1)(s+1)} . \qquad (2.143)$$

A similar equation is written for $Y(s)$. From here on the solution consists of calculating partial fractions and applying the trick of Papoulis.

Notice that Laplace transforms can be used to solve differential equations only if the required initial conditions are available. The solution of Eqs. (2.136) and (2.137) requires $x(0)$ and $y(0)$. If $\dot{x}(0)$, $y(1)$, etc. are known instead, the tedious classical methods must be used to solve the differential equations.

2.11 Steady-State and Transient Response

The usefulness of Laplace transforms will be illustrated once more by a calculation of the current $i(t)$ in the R-C circuit of Fig. 2.24. The solution will help to answer two important questions about fixed, linear systems and the linear differential equations with constant coefficients that describe them:

1. When a differential equation is solved with Laplace transforms, how can the transient (or complementary) solution and the steady-state (or particular) solution be identified?

2. How can the initial conditions be chosen so that no transient occurs?

In the circuit of Fig. 2.24, the initial voltage on the capacitor is

$$\frac{1}{C}\int_{-\infty}^{0} i(t)dt = v_c(0) . \qquad (2.144)$$

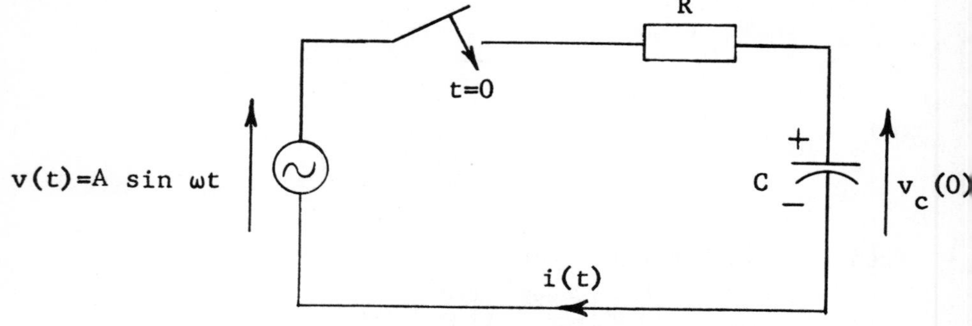

Fig. 2.24. R-C circuit with sinusoidal input.

The input voltage is $v(t) = A \sin \omega t$, and the switch is closed when t=0. Thereafter,

$$Ri(t) + \frac{1}{C}\int_{-\infty}^{t} i(u)du = A \sin \omega t \,. \tag{2.145}$$

Then

$$RI(s) + \frac{1}{Cs}\,I(s) + \frac{v_c(0)}{s} = \frac{A\omega}{s^2+\omega^2}\,, \tag{2.146}$$

$$\left(R + \frac{1}{Cs}\right) I(s) = \frac{R}{s}\left(s + \frac{1}{RC}\right) I(s) = -\,\frac{v_c(0)}{s} + \frac{A\omega}{s^2+\omega^2}\,, \tag{2.147}$$

and

$$\begin{aligned} I(s) &= \frac{s}{R}\left[-\,\frac{v_c(0)}{s\left(s + \dfrac{1}{RC}\right)} + \frac{A\omega}{(s^2+\omega^2)\left(s + \dfrac{1}{RC}\right)}\right] \\ &= -\,\frac{v_c(0)}{R}\cdot\frac{1}{s + \dfrac{1}{RC}} + \frac{A\omega}{R}\cdot\frac{s}{(s^2+\omega^2)\left(s + \dfrac{1}{RC}\right)} \\ &= -\,\frac{v_c(0)}{R}\cdot\frac{1}{s + \dfrac{1}{RC}} + \frac{k_1}{s + \dfrac{1}{RC}} + \frac{k_2 s + k_3}{s^2 + \omega^2}\,, \end{aligned} \tag{2.148}$$

the last step being an expansion into partial fractions. To evaluate k_1, use Eq.(2.112) to get

$$k_1 = -\,\frac{A\omega}{R^2C}\cdot\frac{1}{\left(\dfrac{1}{RC}\right)^2 + \omega^2} = -\,\frac{A}{\omega C}\cdot\frac{1}{R^2 + \dfrac{1}{(\omega C)^2}}\,. \tag{2.149}$$

The last term on the right side of Eq. (2.148) can be inverted directly with the trick of Papoulis. If

$$F(s) = \frac{N(s)}{D_1(s)(s^2+\omega^2)} = \frac{A\omega}{R} \cdot \frac{s}{\left(s+\dfrac{1}{RC}\right)(s^2+\omega^2)}, \tag{2.150}$$

let $\alpha=0$, $\beta=\omega$, and

$$Me^{j\theta} = \left.\frac{N(s)}{D_1(s)}\right|_{s=j\omega} = A\omega \left.\frac{1}{R+\dfrac{1}{Cs}}\right|_{s=j\omega}$$

$$= \frac{A\omega}{R - \dfrac{j}{\omega C}} = \frac{A\omega}{\sqrt{R^2 + \dfrac{1}{(\omega C)^2}}} e^{j\tan^{-1}(1/\omega RC)} . \tag{2.151}$$

This result shows that

$$M = \frac{A\omega}{\sqrt{R^2 + \dfrac{1}{(\omega C)^2}}} \quad \text{and} \quad \theta = \tan^{-1}\frac{1}{\omega RC} \cdot \tag{2.152}$$

Then

$$\frac{M}{\beta} e^{-\alpha t} \sin(\beta t+\theta) = \frac{A}{\sqrt{R^2 + \dfrac{1}{(\omega C)^2}}} \sin\left(\omega t + \tan^{-1}\frac{1}{\omega RC}\right) . \tag{2.153}$$

Finally, the inverse of the Laplace transform $I(s)$ given by Eq. (2.148) is

$$i(t) = \frac{A}{\sqrt{R^2 + \dfrac{1}{(\omega C)^2}}} \sin\left(\omega t + \tan^{-1}\frac{1}{\omega RC}\right) - \left[\frac{v_c(0)}{R} + \frac{A}{\omega C} \cdot \frac{1}{R^2+\dfrac{1}{(\omega C)^2}}\right] e^{-t/RC} . \tag{2.154}$$

This is the current flowing in the circuit of Fig. 2.24.

In order to answer the two questions asked above, observe that if the input to the system is $v(t)$, the output is $i(t)$, and the system is initially inert, then

$$v(t) = Ri(t) + \frac{1}{C}\int_0^t i(u)du , \tag{2.155}$$

and

$$V(s) = RI(s) + \frac{1}{Cs} I(s) = \left(R + \frac{1}{Cs}\right) I(s)\ . \tag{2.156}$$

The system function is

$$H(s) = \frac{I(s)}{V(s)} = \frac{1}{R + \dfrac{1}{Cs}}\ . \tag{2.157}$$

If s is replaced by $j\omega$,

$$H(j\omega) = \frac{1}{R + \dfrac{1}{j\omega C}} = \frac{1}{\sqrt{R + \dfrac{1}{(\omega C)^2}}}\, e^{j\tan^{-1}(1/\omega RC)}\ . \tag{2.158}$$

If the system function is written as a magnitude and a phase angle:

$$H(j\omega) = |H(j\omega)|e^{j\theta}\ , \tag{2.159}$$

the magnitude is

$$|H(j\omega)| = \frac{1}{\sqrt{R + \dfrac{1}{(\omega C)^2}}} \tag{2.160}$$

and the phase angle is

$$\theta = \tan^{-1} \frac{1}{\omega RC}\ . \tag{2.161}$$

If the input to any fixed, linear system with the system function $H(j\omega) = |H(j\omega)|\ e^{j\theta}$ is the sinusoidal function $v(t) = A \sin\omega t$, the steady-state portion of the output $i(t)$ is

$$i_{ss}(t) = A|H(j\omega)|\sin(\omega t + \theta)\ . \tag{2.162}$$

In Eq. (2.154), the steady-state current is the first term on the right side. When the response of any fixed, linear system to any input is calculated with Laplace transforms, the steady-state response is the inverse of the partial fractions whose denominators are contributed by the driving function. The steady-state output of the system has the same general form as the driving function. In Eq. (2.148), the partial fraction whose denominator is $s^2+\omega^2$ is the Laplace transform of the steady-state response. The other partial fractions, whose denominators are contributed by the system parameters, are the Laplace transform of the transient response. The form of the transient output of the system is determined by the parameters of the system. The magnitudes of the terms in the transient response are determined by the driving function and the initial conditions. In Eq. (2.154), the transient current is the second term on the right side.

Now the second question can be answered. To eliminate the transient current in Fig. 2.24, set the bracketed term in Eq. (2.154) equal to zero. Then

$$v_c(0) = -\frac{AR}{\omega C}\cdot\frac{1}{R^2+\dfrac{1}{(\omega C)^2}}. \tag{2.163}$$

This initial voltage on the capacitor will allow the current to start in steady state when the switch is closed.

TABLE 2.1. ONE-SIDED LAPLACE TRANSFORMS

No.	$f(t)$	$F(s)$
1	$\delta(t)$	1
2	$U(t)$ or 1	$\frac{1}{s}$
3	t	$\frac{1}{s^2}$
4	e^{-at}	$\frac{1}{s+a}$
5	$e^{-at}f(t)$	$F(s+a)$
6	te^{-at}	$\frac{1}{(s+a)^2}$
7	$\sin \omega t$	$\frac{\omega}{s^2+\omega^2}$
8	$\cos \omega t$	$\frac{s}{s^2+\omega^2}$
9	$e^{-at} \sin \omega t$	$\frac{\omega}{(s+a)^2+\omega^2}$
10	$tf(t)$	$-\frac{dF(s)}{ds}$
11	$t^n f(t)$	$(-1)^n \frac{d^nF(s)}{ds^n}$
12	$f(t-a)U(t-a)$	$e^{-as}F(s)$
13	$\frac{df(t)}{dt}$	$sF(s)-f(0)$
14	$\frac{d^2f(t)}{dt^2}$	$s^2F(s)-sf(0)-\dot{f}(0)$
15	$\int_0^t f(u)du$	$\frac{F(s)}{s}$
16	$\int_{-\infty}^t f(u)du$	$\frac{F(s)}{s}+\frac{f^{-1}(0)}{s}$
17	$\int_0^t f_1(x)f_2(t-x)dx$	$F_1(s)F_2(s)$

Chapter 3

FIXED LINEAR SYSTEMS

3.1 Introduction

Someone has said that happiness is believing that systems are linear. Much of the real world is nonlinear and therefore difficult to handle mathematically. Fortunately the nonlinearities and time variance in many important electrical and mechanical systems are small enough so that the systems may be assumed to be linear and fixed. Since this assumption makes them amenable to mathematical analysis, much has been written about fixed linear systems. The next several chapters will explain some of the methods, both ancient (before 1955) and modern, that have proved useful for analyzing them.

3.2 Block Diagrams

The differential equations representing any dynamic system, linear or nonlinear, can be displayed pictorially by a *block diagram*. An example is provided by the fixed linear system of Fig. 3.1, represented by the

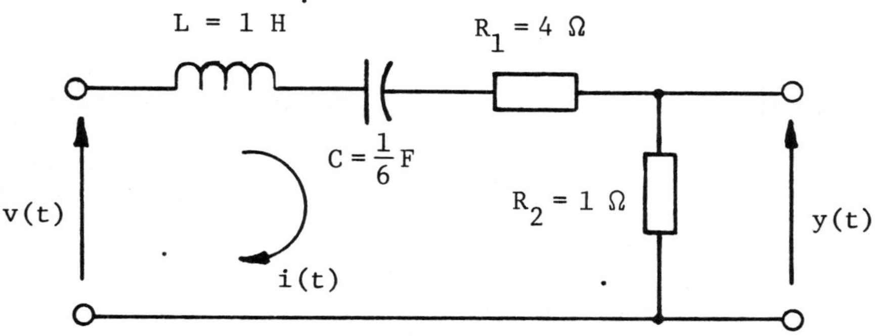

Fig. 3.1. A fixed linear system.

differential equation

$$\frac{dy}{dt} + 6\int_{-\infty}^{t} y(u)du + 5y = v(t)\ . \tag{3.1}$$

Solve for the highest derivative,

$$\frac{dy}{dt} = v(t) - 6 \int_{-\infty}^{t} y(u)du - 5y \tag{3.2}$$

and construct the block diagram of Fig. 3.2, in which the variables are

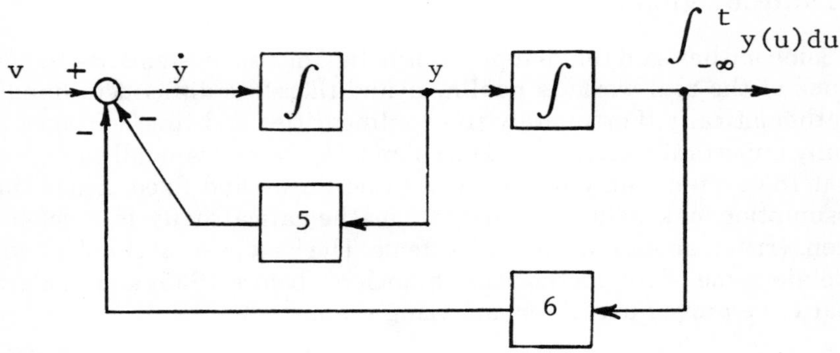

Fig. 3.2. A time-domain block diagram.

functions of time. The Laplace transforms of the time variables can also be shown in the block diagram. If the system is initially inert, the Laplace transform of Eq. (3.2) is

$$sY(s) = V(s) - 6\,\frac{Y(s)}{s} - 5\,Y(s)\,. \tag{3.3}$$

The block diagram now appears as in Fig. 3.3. A block diagram contains

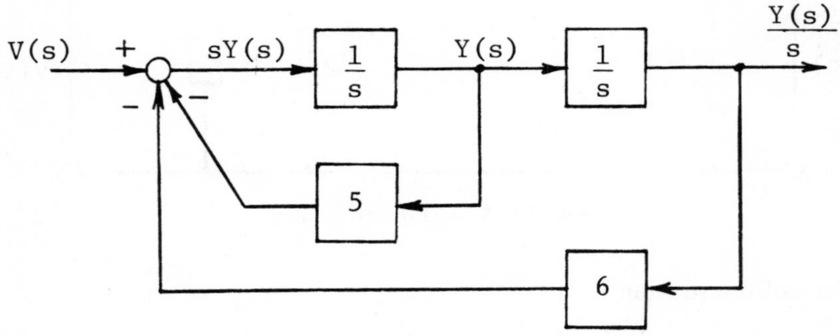

Fig. 3.3. An s-domain block diagram.

all the information that is in the differential equations. If a system is represented by several simultaneous differential equations, the block diagram has the extra advantage of showing the relationships between the variables. For example, suppose a system is represented by the two differential equations

$$\dot{y} - 2x = v_1(t) \tag{3.4}$$

and

$$\dot{x} + 3y = v_2(t)\ . \tag{3.5}$$

The block diagram in Fig. 3.4 shows that this system has two inputs and two outputs.

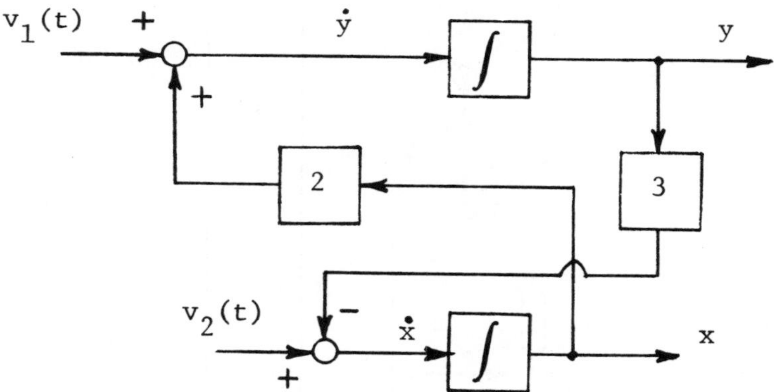

Fig. 3.4. A block diagram of two differential equations.

The concept of initial inertness, introduced in the preceding chapter, can now be explained differently. When a system is represented by individual integrators as in Fig. 3.2, 3.3, or 3.4, the system is initially inert if the initial output of each integrator is zero.

3.3 Components of a Block Diagram

When the block diagram representing a physical system is drawn, some of the intermediate work of writing the differential equations can be avoided if the transfer functions of some of the components are known. An example is provided by the position control in Fig. 3.5, which drives the output shaft so that its angular position θ_o is as nearly as possible proportional to that of the input shaft θ_i. A potentiometer on the input shaft produced a voltage v_i proportional to θ_i, which is compared at a summing junction to the voltage v_o proportional to θ_o. The difference is

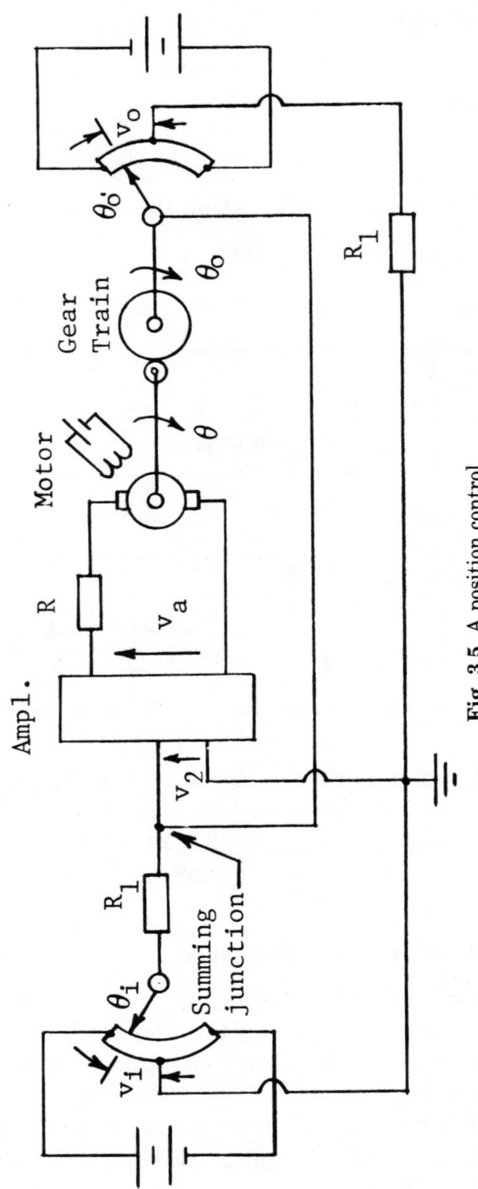

Fig. 3.5. A position control.

amplified and applied to the armature of a separately-excited DC motor. The motor drives a reduction gear, which turns the output shaft. In preparation for drawing the block diagram of the position control, the transfer function of each component will be retrieved from memory or derived.

Summing Junction. The operation of the summing junction or summer is shown in Fig. 3.6, in which v_i and v_o are represented by batteries. Since

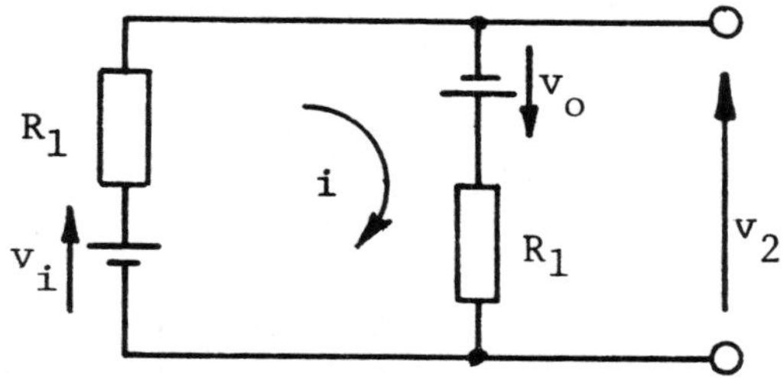

Fig. 3.6. Summing junction.

$$v_2 = v_i - iR_1 \tag{3.6}$$

and

$$v_i - 2iR_1 + v_o = 0, \tag{3.7}$$

then

$$iR_1 = \frac{v_i + v_o}{2} \tag{3.8}$$

and

$$v_2 = v_i - \frac{v_i + v_o}{2} = \frac{v_i - v_o}{2}. \tag{3.9}$$

The transfer function of the summing junction is therefore

$$\frac{V_2(s)}{V_i(s) - V_o(s)} = 0.5 . \tag{3.10}$$

The summing junction compares the input and feedback voltages, and applies a fraction of their difference to the amplifier input.

Amplifier. Many amplifiers have a transfer function of the form

$$\frac{V_a(s)}{V_2(s)} = \frac{A}{\dfrac{s}{\omega_c} + 1} \tag{3.11}$$

where A is the DC gain and ω_c is a constant called the *break frequency*. For the amplifier in Fig. 3.5, choose

$$\frac{V_a(s)}{V_2(s)} = \frac{6}{s+5} \, . \tag{3.12}$$

Motor. The circuit of a separately-excited DC motor is shown in Fig. 3.7. If R and L are the resistance and inductance of the armature

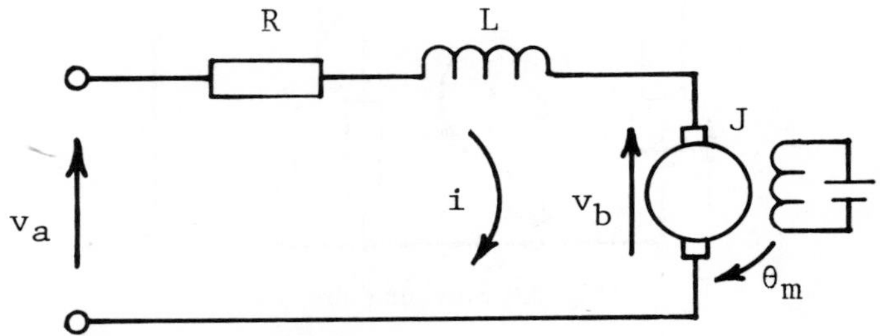

Fig. 3.7. Circuit of a separately-excited DC motor.

winding, i is the armature current, and v_b is the back emf generated by the motor, the voltage applied to the armature is

$$v_a = Ri + L\frac{di}{dt} + v_b \, . \tag{3.13}$$

Because the field excitation is constant, the back emf is proportional to the motor speed:

$$v_b = K_1 \, \omega \, , \tag{3.14}$$

where ω is the angular velocity of the rotor, and K_1 is the back-emf constant in volts per rad/sec. If the armature has N conductors of length L moving with velocity V at radius R, and the magnetic flux density at the conductors is B, the back emf is

$$v_b = N\,B\,L\,V = N\,B\,L\,R\,\omega \, . \tag{3.15}$$

Therefore

$$K_1 = N\,B\,L\,R. \tag{3.16}$$

Again, because the field excitation is constant, the torque exerted by the motor is proportional to the armature current:

$$T = K_2 i \,, \tag{3.17}$$

where K_2 is the torque constant in N·m/A. Since

$$T = N\,B\,i\,L\,R \,, \tag{3.19}$$

$$K_2 = N\,B\,L\,R \,. \tag{3.20}$$

The interesting conclusion is that $K_1 = K_2$. The two constants are both called the *motor constant, K.*

If the load on the motor is frictionless and consists only of the inertia J of the armature and any gears or wheels on the shaft, the motor torque is used only to accelerate the load, and

$$Ki = J\frac{d^2\theta}{dt^2} \,, \tag{3.21}$$

where θ is the angular displacement of the shaft. Eq. (3.13) can be written as

$$v_a = \frac{RJ}{K}\ddot{\theta} + \frac{LJ}{K}\dddot{\theta} + K\dot{\theta} \,. \tag{3.22}$$

If the motor is initially inert, so that $\theta(0) = \dot{\theta}(0) = \ddot{\theta}(0) = 0$,

$$V_a(s) = \left(\frac{LJ}{K}s^3 + \frac{RJ}{K}s^2 + Ks\right)\Theta(s) \,. \tag{3.23}$$

If the armature inductance is negligible compared to the resistance, the transfer function of the motor is

$$\frac{\Theta(s)}{V_a(s)} = \frac{1}{s\left(\frac{RJ}{K}s + K\right)} \quad \text{rad/volt.} \tag{3.24}$$

Assume that the motor in Fig. 3.5 has negligible armature inductance, a load that is purely inertial, and the transfer function

$$\frac{\Theta(s)}{V_a(s)} = \frac{0.7}{s(s+1)} \quad \text{rad/volt.} \tag{3.25}$$

Potentiometers and Gear Train. The transfer functions of the potentiometers and gear train are

$$\frac{V_i(s)}{\Theta_i(s)} = 3 \text{ v/rad}, \qquad \frac{V_o(s)}{\Theta_o(s)} = 150 \text{ v/rad}, \qquad \frac{\Theta_o(s)}{\Theta(s)} = 0.2 \,. \tag{3.26}$$

3.4 Block Diagram of the Position Control

The calculated transfer function of a component is incorrect if loading by the following component is neglected. For example, the input resistance R_2 of the amplifier might alter the transfer function of the summing junction. As Fig. 3.8 shows, this resistance is connected across the

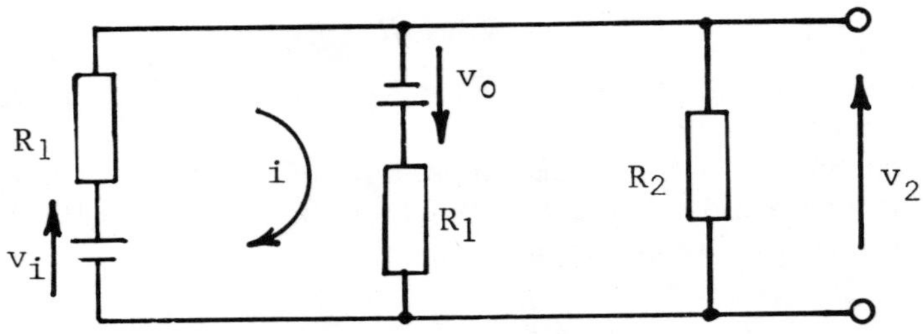

Fig. 3.8. Effect of amplifier input resistance R_2.

output terminals of the circuit of Fig. 3.6. The transfer function of the summing junction is now

$$\frac{V_2(s)}{V_i(s)-V_o(s)} = \frac{1}{\dfrac{R_1}{R_2}+2} . \tag{3.27}$$

It reduces to the value given by Eq. (3.10) only if R_2 is negligibly high. Similarly, the motor will affect the output voltage v_a of the amplifier and alter its transfer function unless the output resistance of the amplifier is negligibly low.

If the loading of each component by its following neighbor is negligible or accounted for in the transfer functions, the transfer functions can be connected in cascade. Fig. 3.9 shows the connections for the components of the position control. The next step is to put the block diagram into the standard form of Fig. 3.10. The summing junction in Fig. 3.9 must be moved upstream around the gain of 3. The gain of 150 must be divided by 3, because

$$V_2(s) = 0.5\,[3\,\Theta_i(s) - 150\,\Theta_o(s)] = 1.5\,[\Theta_i(s) - 50\,\Theta_o(s)] . \tag{3.28}$$

In general, if a summing junction is moved upstream around a component, the transfer function of each of the other components connected into the summer must be divided by the transfer function of that compo-

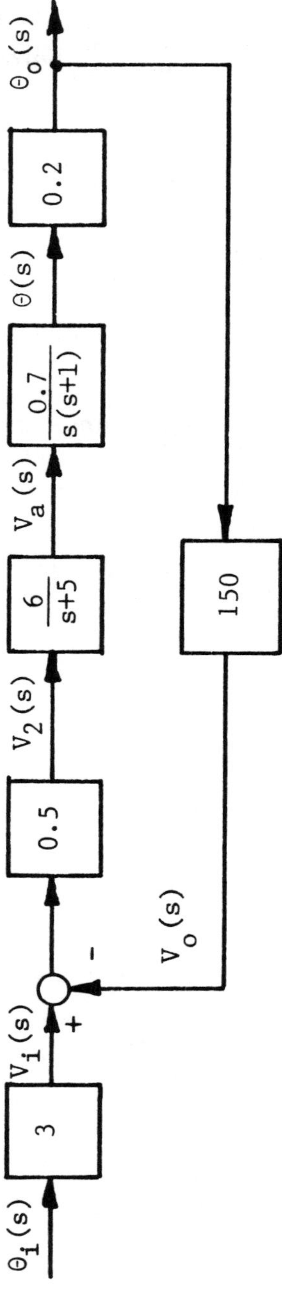

Fig. 3.9. Block diagram of the position control.

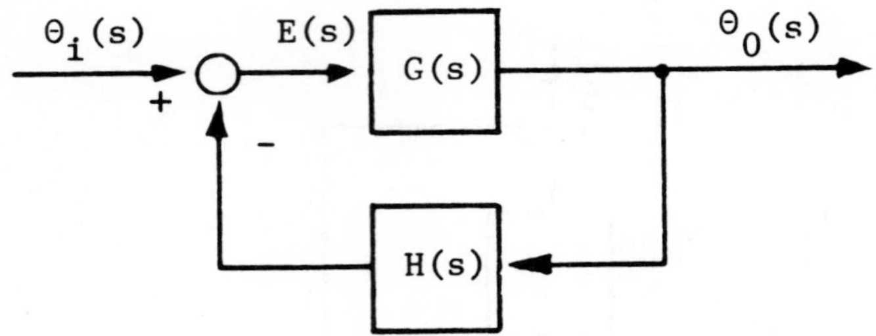

Fig. 3.10. Standard block diagram.

nent. Fig.3.9 can be redrawn as Fig. 3.11, and then in the standard form of Fig. 3.10, in which

$$G(s) = \frac{1.26}{s(s+1)(s+5)} \qquad \text{and} \qquad H(s) = 50\ . \tag{3.29}$$

The transfer function of the system in standard form can be derived easily. Since the error signal is

$$E(s) = \Theta_i(s) - H(s)\,\Theta_o(s) \tag{3.30}$$

and

$$\Theta_o(s) = G(s)\,E(s)\ , \tag{3.31}$$

then

$$\Theta_o(s) = G(s)\,\Theta_i(s) - G(s)\,H(s)\,\Theta_o(s) \tag{3.32}$$

and

$$\frac{\Theta_o(s)}{\Theta_i(s)} = \frac{G(s)}{1 + G(s)H(s)}\ . \tag{3.33}$$

Notice that $H(s)$ designates the feedback block here, and the system function in the preceding chapter. This duplication is unfortunate, but is well established in the literature.

3.5 Signal-Flow Graphs

An alternative to the block diagram as a representation of a system is the *signal-flow graph*. In the latter, the blocks are replaced by *branches*, and the signals by *nodes*. Fig. 3.12 is the signal-flow graph corre-

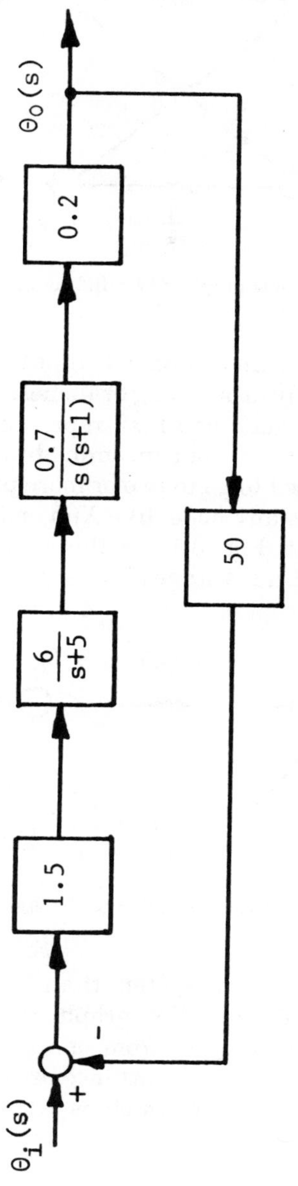

Fig. 3.11. Simplified block diagram.

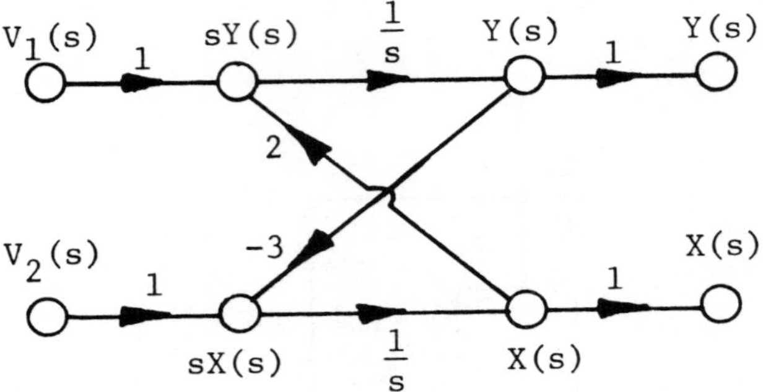

Fig. 3.12. Signal-flow graph of two differential equations.

sponding to the block diagram of Fig. 3.4. Input signals such as $V_1(s)$ and $V_2(s)$ are connected only to outgoing branches. A node having two or more incoming branches, such as $sY(s)$, represents a summer in the block diagram. A node with only one incoming branch, like $Y(s)$, represents a signal that is tapped to go to two or more places. A branch with unity gain can be added to any node, like $X(s)$ and $Y(s)$, to identify the node as an output signal. Fig. 3.13 is the signal-flow graph corresponding to Fig. 3.10. A disadvantage of the signal-flow graph is that it

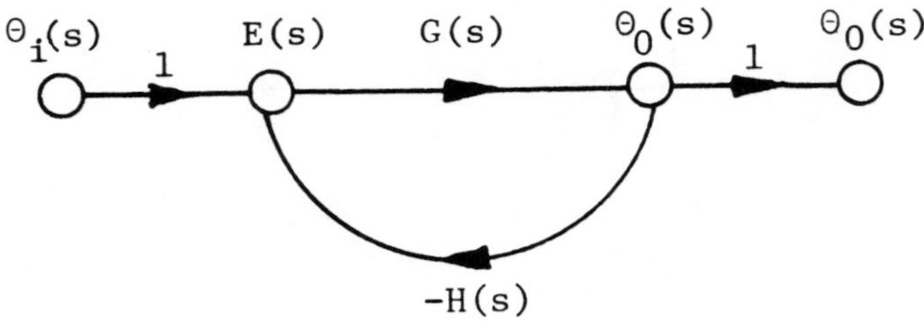

Fig. 3.13. Signal-flow graph corresponding to the standard block diagram.

looks less like a blueprint of the system than the block diagram does. The main advantage of the signal-flow graph is the ease with which the transfer function or *transmittance* from one point to another in the system can be calculated. The transmittance between any variable $X(s)$ and any other variable $Y(s)$ in the system is calculated by *Mason's loop rule*:

$$T = \frac{Y(s)}{X(s)} = \frac{\sum_k P_k \Delta_k}{\Delta} \tag{3.34}$$

where P_k is the transmittance along the kth direct path from $X(s)$ to $Y(s)$, Δ is the *determinant* of the graph, defined as

$$\Delta = 1 - \Sigma L_i + \Sigma L_i L_j - \Sigma L_i L_j L_k + \dots \quad (3.35)$$

and L_i is the transmittance around the ith loop in the graph. A loop is a closed path along which the arrows point in the same direction, that does not touch the same node twice. Eq. (3.35) means that Δ is 1 minus the sum of all loop transmittances, plus the sum of all combinations of products of transmittances around loops that do not touch each other (i.e., do not share any node in common), minus the products of transmittances of non-touching loops taken three at a time, etc. The *cofactor* Δ_k of path P_k is the value of Δ with the transmittance around each loop touching path P_k set equal to zero.

To illustrate the use of Mason's loop rule, calculate the transmittance from X_1 to X_7 in the system represented by Fig. 3.14. There are two paths:

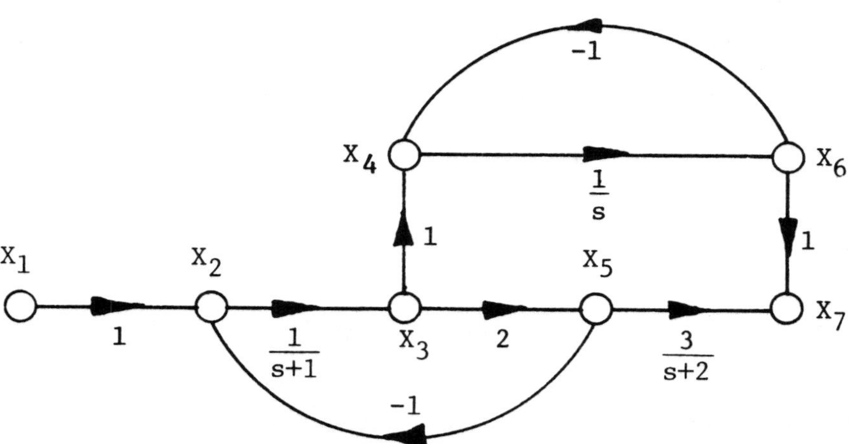

Fig. 3.14. Signal-flow graph with two loops.

$$P_1 = \frac{6}{(s+1)(s+2)} \quad \text{and} \quad P_2 = \frac{1}{s(s+1)} \quad (3.36)$$

and two loops:

$$L_1 = -\frac{2}{s+1} \quad \text{and} \quad L_2 = -\frac{1}{s}. \quad (3.37)$$

Since the loops do not touch each other, the graph determinant is

$$\Delta = 1 - L_1 - L_2 + L_1L_2 = 1 + \frac{2}{s+1} + \frac{1}{s} + \frac{2}{s(s+1)} = \frac{s^2+4s+3}{s(s+1)}. \tag{3.38}$$

The cofactors are

$$\Delta_1 = 1 + \frac{1}{s} \quad \text{and} \quad \Delta_2 = 1\,. \tag{3.39}$$

Then according to Eq. (3.34), the transmittance is

$$\frac{X_7(s)}{X_1(s)} = \frac{\dfrac{6}{(s+1)(s+2)}\left(1+\dfrac{1}{s}\right) + \dfrac{1}{s(s+1)}}{\dfrac{s^2+4s+3}{s(s+1)}} = \frac{7s+8}{(s^2+4s+3)(s+2)}$$

$$= \frac{7s+8}{s^3+6s^2+11s+6}. \tag{3.40}$$

Similarly, to calculate the transmittance between X_1 and X_3, write

$$P_1 = \frac{1}{s+1}, \qquad \Delta_1 = 1 + \frac{1}{s},$$

and

$$\frac{X_3(s)}{X_1(s)} = \frac{P_1\Delta_1}{\Delta} = \frac{\dfrac{1}{s+1}\left(1+\dfrac{1}{s}\right)}{\dfrac{s^2+4s+3}{s(s+1)}} = \frac{s+1}{s^2+4s+3}. \tag{3.41}$$

The denominator of a transmittance is called the *characteristic polynomial*. For the transmittance of Eq. (3.41) the *characteristic equation*, formed by setting the characteristic polynomial equal to zero, is

$$s^2 + 4s + 3 = 0\,. \tag{3.42}$$

The characteristic equation of the transmittance of Eq. (3.40) contains an extra factor, because that transmittance includes the branch $3/(s+2)$. If each branch in the paths of a transmittance has either no pole or is included in a loop transmittance, the denominator of the transmittance is the numerator of the graph determinant Δ. The transmittance $X_3(s)/X_1(s)$ fulfills this requirement, but $X_7(s)/X_1(s)$ does not. In some systems such as the one in Fig. 3.12, every possible transmittance fulfills the requirement. They all have the same denominator, and the differential equations relating the various pairs of variables all have the same characteristic equation.

3.6 Stability

To demonstrate the meaning of stability, calculate the response of the position control in Fig. 3.5 to a step input. According to Eqs. (3.29), the transfer function between the input and output is

$$\frac{\Theta_o(s)}{\Theta_i(s)} = \frac{G(s)}{1 + G(s)H(s)} = \frac{1.26}{s^3 + 6s^2 + 5s + 63}$$

$$= \frac{1.26}{(s + 6.67)\,[(s - 0.33)^2 + (3.06)^2]} \tag{3.43}$$

and the characteristic equation is

$$s^3 + 6s^2 + 5s + 63 = 0\,. \tag{3.44}$$

If the input is the step

$$\theta_i(t) = 0.1\;U(t)\,, \tag{3.45}$$

then

$$\Theta_i(s) = \frac{0.1}{s} \tag{3.46}$$

and the output is

$$\Theta_o(s) = \frac{0.126}{s(s + 6.67)\,[(s - 0.33)^2 + (3.06)^2]}\,, \tag{3.47}$$

whose inverse Laplace transform is of the form

$$\theta_o(t) = K_1 + K_2 e^{-6.67t} + K_3 e^{0.33t} \sin{(3.06t + \Phi)}\,. \tag{3.48}$$

The first term on the right side of this equation is the steady-state response, whose form is dictated by the input. The remaining two terms are the transient response, whose form is determined by the transfer function of the system. For any input, the transient response consists of the same two terms. Thus if any input $\theta_i(t)$ is applied to the system, the output $\theta_o(t)$ contains a sine wave whose amplitude increases exponentially until the potentiometer on the output shaft reaches the end of its travel. Mathematically, the output increases without limit. Such a system, whose response to a bounded input is unbounded, is said to be *unstable*. Specifically, a fixed linear system is *stable* iff (if and only if) all the roots of its characteristic equation (the poles of its transfer function) lie in the left half of the complex plane. The locations of the roots of Eq. (3.44) are shown in Fig. 3.15.

What if the characteristic equation of a system has a root at the origin or a pair of imaginary roots on the $j\omega$ axis? According to the

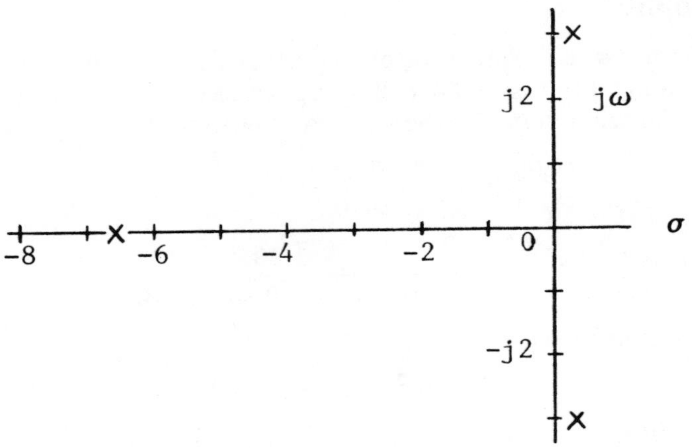

Fig. 3.15. Poles of the transmittance of an unstable system.

above definitions, the system is neither stable nor unstable. Its transient response includes a step or an undamped sinusoid, which may or may not be desirable, depending on the intended application.

3.7 The Routh-Hurwitz Stability Criterion

If a computer terminal is not available, a characteristic equation such as Eq. (3.44) cannot be factored easily. A look at Eq. (3.44) does not reveal whether the system is stable. Following are some rules developed in pre-computer days, for determining whether the equation

$$a_0 s^n + a_1 s^{n-1} + a_2 s^{n-2} + \ldots + a_{n-1} s + a_n = 0 \qquad (3.49)$$

has any roots with positive real parts.

1. If all the coefficients a_i are positive and a term is missing, a root is present having a non-negative real part (it may be on the $j\omega$ axis).
2. If a coefficient is negative, there is a root in the right-half plane.
3. If all the coefficients are present and positive, the Routh-Hurwitz criterion can be used. Make this array:

$$\begin{array}{lllll}
a_0 & a_2 & a_4 & a_6 & \ldots \\
a_1 & a_3 & a_5 & a_7 & \ldots \\
b_1 & b_3 & b_5 & \ldots & \\
c_1 & c_3 & \ldots & & \\
d_1 & d_3 & \ldots & & \\
e_1 & \ldots & & & \\
f_1 & \ldots & & &
\end{array}$$

where

$$b_1 = \frac{a_1 a_2 - a_0 a_3}{a_1} \qquad b_3 = \frac{a_1 a_4 - a_0 a_5}{a_1}$$

$$c_1 = \frac{b_1 a_3 - a_1 b_3}{b_1} \qquad c_3 = \frac{b_1 a_5 - a_1 b_5}{b_1}, \tag{3.50}$$

etc. The system is stable iff all the terms in the left column are positive. The number of sign changes in the left column is the number of roots with positive real parts. The reader is now invited to test the usefulness of the Routh algorithm. The transfer function of the position control in Fig. 3.5 can be written as

$$\frac{\Theta_0(s)}{\Theta_i(s)} = \frac{1.26}{s^3 + 6s^2 + 5s + 0.42\, k_o} \tag{3.51}$$

where k_o is the gain of the potentiometer on the output shaft, 150 v/rad. For what range of k_o is the system stable?

The three rules mentioned above tell only whether a fixed linear system is stable or not. Several techniques have been developed which not only tell whether a system is stable, but also provide information about its behavior and straightforward methods of improving the system performance. One of the most useful is the root-locus technique.

3.8 Root-Locus Plots

The root-locus method was developed by Walter R. Evans, a graduate of the General Electric 1944 C Class. It is a graphical procedure that enables the designer to put the poles of the transfer function where he or she wants them. To understand the method, first suppose that the standard system of Fig. 3.10 has

$$G(s) = \frac{k}{s(s+2)} \qquad \text{and} \qquad H(s) = 1 \tag{3.52}$$

where k is a parameter that can be varied, such as an amplifier gain. What happens to the poles of the transfer function as k increases from zero to infinity? The transfer function is

$$\frac{\Theta_o(s)}{\Theta_i(s)} = \frac{k}{s^2 + 2s + k}. \tag{3.53}$$

Its poles, which are the roots of the characteristic equation

$$s^2 + 2s + k = 0, \tag{3.54}$$

are

$$s = -1 \pm \sqrt{1 - k}\,. \tag{3.55}$$

Their loci, as k increases from zero to infinity, are plotted in Fig. 3.16.

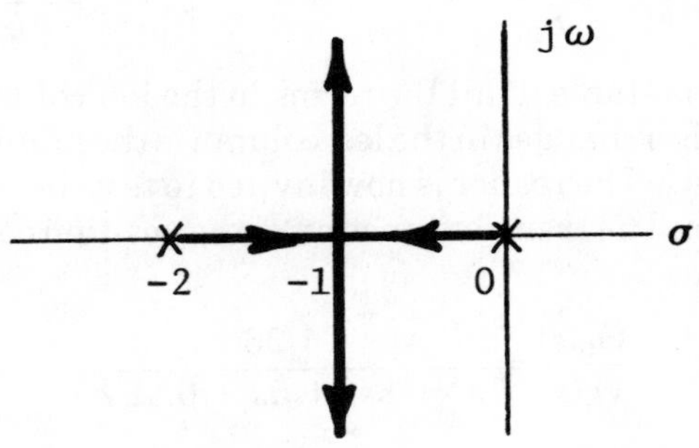

Fig. 3.16. Root loci.

They show that the system is stable for all values of k. If the characteristic polynomial is of higher degree, it cannot be factored easily. The root-locus method was developed to keep track of the roots of a polynomial of any degree that contains a parameter k, as k is varied. The polynomial must be written in the form

$$D(s) + k\,N(s) = 0 \tag{3.56}$$

or

$$k\,\frac{N(s)}{D(s)} = -1\,. \tag{3.57}$$

For example, if the polynomial is

$$s^3 + ks^2 + 3s + 4k = 0\,, \tag{3.58}$$

then

$$N(s) = s^2 + 4 \qquad \text{and} \qquad D(s) = s^3 + 3s\,. \tag{3.59}$$

A study of Eq. (3.57) reveals eight rules that govern the behavior of the root loci as k increases from zero in infinity.

1. Start of Loci. When $k = 0$, $D(s)$ must be zero. Therefore the root loci start at the zeros of $D(s)$. If

$$G(s) = \frac{kN_1(s)}{D_1(s)} \qquad \text{and} \qquad H(s) = \frac{N_2(s)}{D_2(s)}\,, \tag{3.60}$$

the transfer function of the standard feedback system in Fig. 3.10 is

$$\frac{G(s)}{1 + G(s)H(s)} = \frac{k\,N_1(s)D_2(s)}{D_1(s)D_2(s) + k\,N_1(s)N_2(s)}. \tag{3.61}$$

The characteristic equation is

$$D_1(s)D_2(s) + k\,N_1(s)N_2(s) = 0 \tag{3.62}$$

or

$$k\frac{N_1(s)N_2(s)}{D_1(s)D_2(s)} = G(s)H(s) = -1\,, \tag{3.63}$$

which has the same form as Eq. (3.57). The term $G(s)H(s)$ is called, for lack of a better name, the *open-loop transfer function*. Eq. (3.63) shows that if the root-locus method is applied to the standard feedback system, the loci of the poles of the closed-loop transfer function (the roots of the characteristic equation) start at the *open-loop poles*, namely the poles of $G(s)H(s)$. Fig. 3.17 shows the loci of the roots of the characteristic

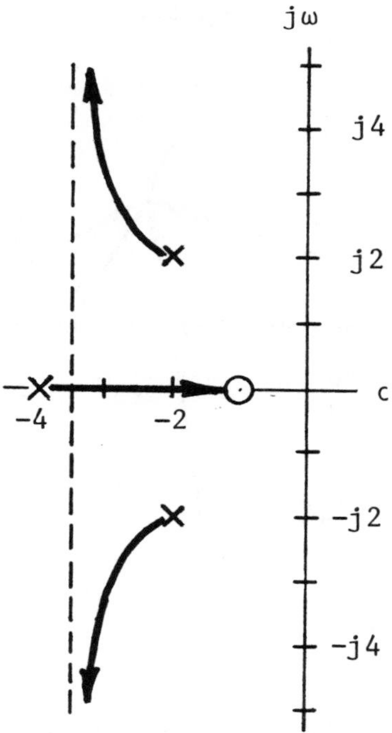

Fig. 3.17. Departure of root loci.

equation of the system for which

$$G(s)H(s) = \frac{k(s+1)}{(s+4)\,[(s+2)^2+(2)^2]} = \frac{k(s+1)}{(s+4)(s+2+j2)\,(s+2-j2)}\,. \tag{3.64}$$

The three open-loop poles are designated by X's, and the open-loop zero by a O. Notice that the root loci start at the open-loop poles.

2. Termination of Loci. When k is infinite, Eq. (3.57) is satisfied only if $N(s)$ is zero or $D(s)$ is infinite. The root loci therefore terminate either at the open-loop zeros or at $s = \infty$. If the degree of $D(s)$ is m higher than the degree of $N(s)$, m of the loci terminate at infinity. In Fig. 3.17, m is two.

3. Loci on the Real Axis. What portion of the real axis is occupied by the root loci? To answer this question, consider Fig. 3.18, that shows

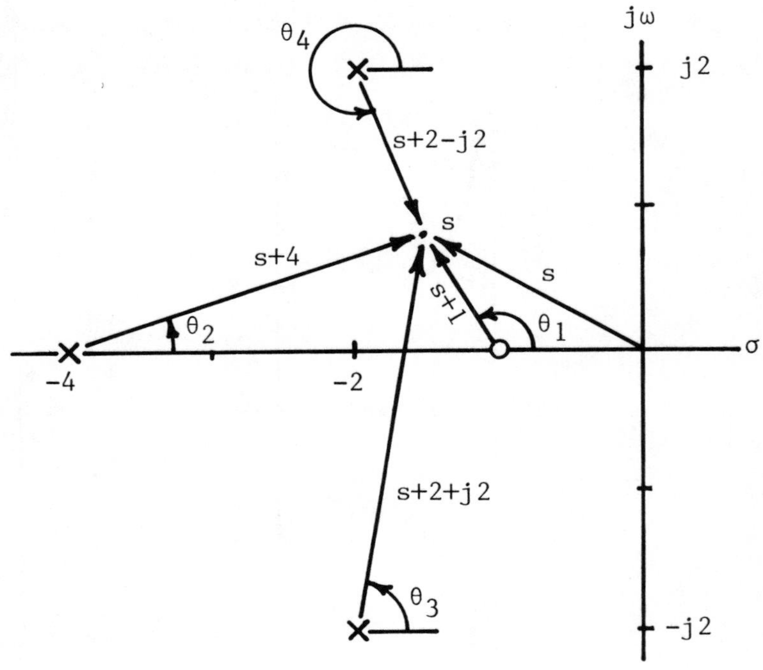

Fig. 3.18. Open-loop constellation.

again the constellation of open-loop poles and zeros of the system of Eq. (3.64). If s is a point in the complex plane, the vector drawn to it from the origin can also be designated as s. Each factor in Eq. (3.64) represents a vector drawn from an open-loop pole or zero to point s. If each of these vectors is represented by a magnitude P (for pole) or Z (for zero) and a phase angle θ drawn from the positive real axis, Eq. (3.64) can be written in the form

$$G(s)H(s) = \frac{kZ_1e^{j\theta_1}}{P_1e^{j\theta_2}P_2e^{j\theta_3}P_3e^{j\theta_4}} = \frac{k\,Z_1}{P_1P_2P_3}\,e^{j(\theta_1-\theta_2-\theta_3-\theta_4)}\;. \tag{3.65}$$

If the point s lies on the real axis, the angles of the vectors from the poles and zeros on the real axis are zero or 180°. The angles of vectors from a complex pair of poles add up to 360°. The phase angle of $G(s)H(s)$ is then

$$\theta_1 - \theta_2 - \theta_3 - \theta_4 = 0 \text{ or } \pm 180°\;. \tag{3.66}$$

If the point s on the real axis is also on a root locus,

$$G(s)H(s) = -1 = e^{\pm j180°} \tag{3.67}$$

and the phase angle of $G(s)H(s)$ must be $\pm 180°$, not zero. Accordingly, the left side of Eq. (3.66) must contain an odd number of ± 180-degree angles. This restriction establishes the third rule for root-locus plots: the portions of the real axis that are part of the root loci lie to the left of an odd number of open-loop poles and zeros. Notice that the loci in Fig. 3.17 obey this rule.

4. Angles of Asymptotes. What happens to the loci that approach infinity in the complex plane as k increases? As s approaches infinity, Eq. (3.64) becomes

$$\lim_{s\to\infty} \frac{k\,(s+1)}{(s+4)\,[(s+2)^2 + (2)^2]} = \frac{k}{s^2}\;. \tag{3.68}$$

In general, if N and D are the degrees of $N(s)$ and $D(s)$,

$$\lim_{s\to\infty} k\,\frac{N(s)}{D(s)} = k\,s^{N-D}. \tag{3.69}$$

Eq. (3.57) can be written as

$$\lim_{s\to\infty} k\,\frac{N(s)}{D(s)} = k\,s^{N-D} = -1 = e^{j(2n+1)\pi}, \quad n = 0,1,2,\ldots \tag{3.70}$$

or

$$s = k^{1/(D-N)}\,e^{j(2n+1)\pi/(N-D)}\;. \tag{3.71}$$

According to this equation, the root loci approach $D-N$ asymptotes that make the angles $(2n+1)\pi/(N-D)$ with the positive real axis. For example, if the degree of the denominator of $kN(s)/D(s)$ or $G(s)H(s)$ is three higher than that of the numerator, the angles corresponding to $n = 0, 1$ and 2 are $-\pi/3$, $-\pi$, and $-5\pi/3$ radians. Higher values of n duplicate these angles. Fig. 3.19 shows the asymptotes for the first four values of $D-N$. The two asymptotes for the system of Eq. (3.64) appear as dotted lines in Fig. 3.17.

5. Centroid of Asymptotes. The asymptotes start at the point on the real axis where

$$\sigma = \frac{\sum \text{Open-loop pole positions} - \sum \text{Open-loop zero positions}}{D-N} . \qquad (3.72)$$

This point is called the *centroid* of the asymptotes. For the example of Eq. (3.64),

$$\sigma = \frac{-4-2-2+1}{2} = -3.5 . \qquad (3.73)$$

A proof of Eq. (3.72) is given in Ref. 22, pages 135−136.

6. Coalescence Points. Some of the root loci, such as those in Fig. 3.16, coalesce on either the real or imaginary axis. The *coalescence* or *breakaway point* is one of the roots of the equation

$$\frac{dk}{ds} = 0 , \qquad (3.74)$$

where

$$k = -\frac{D(s)}{N(s)} . \qquad (3.75)$$

The proof is in Ref. 22, pages 139−140. An example is provided by the system of Eqs. (3.52). Points on the root loci satisfy the equation

$$G(s)H(s) = k\frac{N(s)}{D(s)} = \frac{k}{s(s+2)} = -1 , \qquad (3.76)$$

for which

$$k = -s^2 - 2s . \qquad (3.77)$$

According to Eq. (3.74),

$$\frac{dk}{ds} = -2s - 2 = 0 , \qquad (3.78)$$

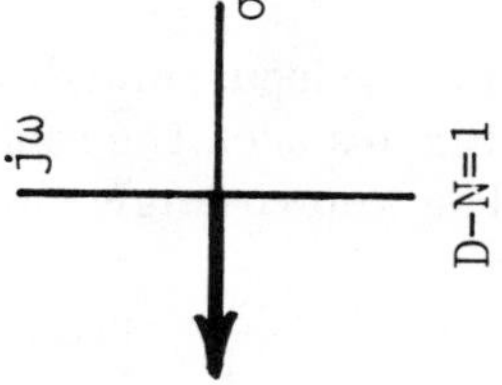

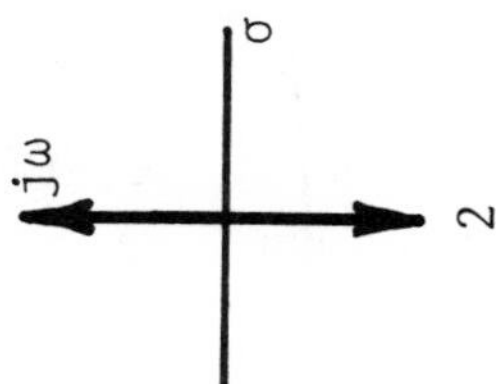

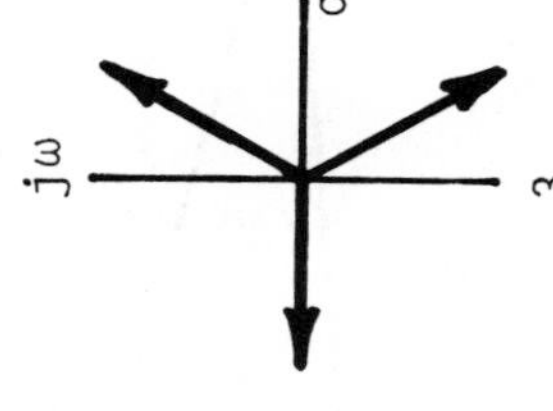

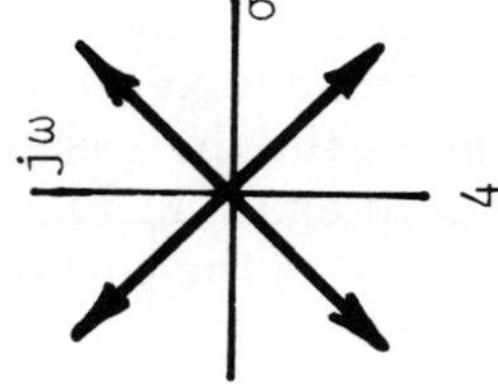

Fig. 3.19. Asymptotes for root loci.

and the breakaway point is at $s = -1$, as shown in Fig. 3.16. Frequently Eq. (3.74) has extraneous roots. The analyst must decide which one to use.

7. Angle of Departure. At what angle does a root locus depart from an open-loop pole? Consider again the system of Eq. (3.64), whose pole-zero constellation is shown again in Fig. 3.20. To determine the angle of departure of the locus from the pole at $-2 + j2$, move a short

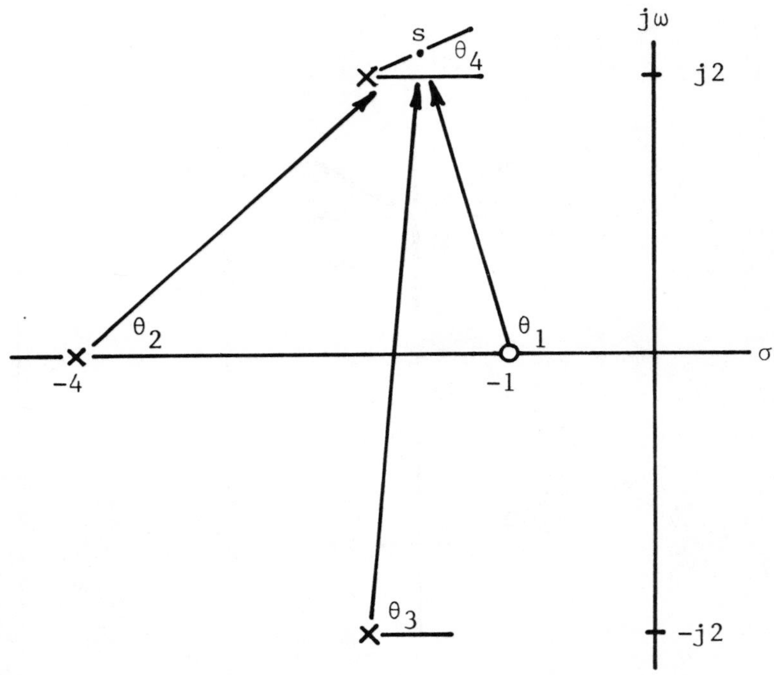

Fig. 3.20. Angle of departure.

distance away to a point s on the locus, and draw vectors to it from the open-loop poles and zeros. Since s is on the root locus, the angles of the vectors add up to $\pm 180°$. The known angles are

$$\theta_1 = \tan^{-1} \frac{2}{-1} = 116.6° \tag{3.79}$$

$$\theta_2 = \tan^{-1} \frac{2}{2} = 45° \tag{3.80}$$

$$\theta_3 = 90^\circ . \qquad (3.81)$$

Since

$$\theta_1 - \theta_2 - \theta_3 - \theta_4 = \pm 180^\circ , \qquad (3.82)$$

the angle of departure of the locus from the upper complex pole is

$$\theta_4 = 116.6 - 45 - 90 + 180 = 161.6^\circ , \qquad (3.83)$$

as shown in Fig. 3.17.

8. Calculation of Gain. The value of k at any point on a root locus is found by drawing the vectors to that point from the open-loop poles and zeros. These vectors satisfy the equation

$$k \frac{Z_1 e^{j\theta_1} Z_2{}^{j\theta_2} \ldots}{P_1 e^{j\theta_3} P_2 e^{j\theta_4} \ldots} = -1 = e^{\pm j\pi} . \qquad (3.84)$$

Therefore

$$k = \frac{P_1 P_2 \ldots}{Z_1 Z_2 \ldots} . \qquad (3.85)$$

The gain k is the product and quotient of the vector lengths, and can be determined by measuring the vectors with the edge of a piece of paper. Notice that the σ and $j\omega$ axes of the root-locus plot must have the same scale.

Computer programs are available to determine points on the root loci of any fixed linear system for which $G(s)$ and $H(s)$ are known. These programs of course give more accurate results than those obtained by plotting the loci by hand. However, the eight rules are in the repertory of every competent control engineer, and can frequently be used to obtain quick approximate answers. The reader is invited to become a more competent control engineer by solving three problems:

1. Plot the loci of the poles of the transmittance of the system in Fig. 3.10 with

$$G(s)H(s) = \frac{k(s+1)}{s(s+3)[(s+2)^2+1]} . \qquad (3.86)$$

(Hint: $\tan^{-1} 0.5 = 26.6^\circ$.) Using either Rule 8 or a Routh test, find the value of k at which the system becomes unstable.

2. Do the same for

$$G(s)H(s) = \frac{k}{s(s+1)(s+3)} . \qquad (3.87)$$

If a lead network with transmittance $(s + 2)/(s + 20)$ is included in the forward block $G(s)$, how high can k be raised before the system becomes unstable?

3. Plot the root loci of the pathological system for which

$$G(s)H(s) = \frac{1}{s^2(s^2 + 100)}. \tag{3.88}$$

Calculating the coalescence points will help.

Chapter 4

SECOND-ORDER LINEAR SYSTEMS

4.1 Introduction

The *order* of a linear system is the degree of its characteristic equation. Nature provides many systems, such as R-L-C circuits, vibrating masses, and Helmholtz resonators, that can be assumed to be linear and of second order. In addition, many feedback-control systems of higher order behave like second-order linear systems. For these reasons the control engineer should include in his bag of tricks a knowledge of the techniques for analyzing these simple but important systems.

4.2 Step Response of Second-Order Systems

The study of second-order linear systems begins with a calculation of their response to a step input. The results will show how the parameters of the system affect its performance, and will also make clear the meaning of several of the terms used to describe vibrations. Figs. 4.1 and 4.2 show two fixed, linear systems. The second-order linear differential equations describing their operation are

$$m\ddot{y} + c\dot{y} + ky = f(t) \tag{4.1}$$

for Fig. 4.1, and

$$L\ddot{q} + R\dot{q} + \frac{1}{C}q = v(t) \tag{4.2}$$

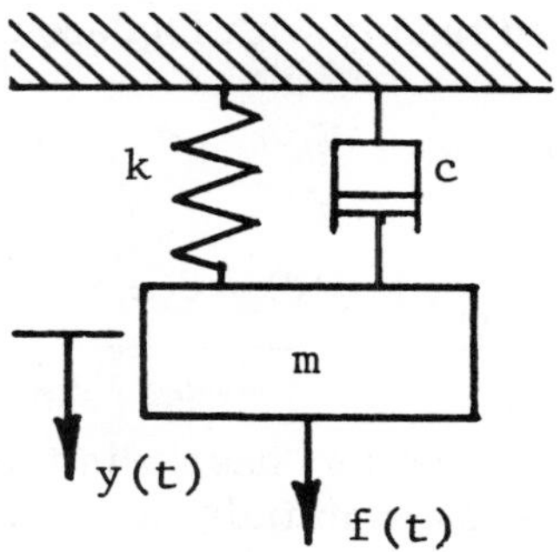

Fig. 4.1. Mechanical second-order system.

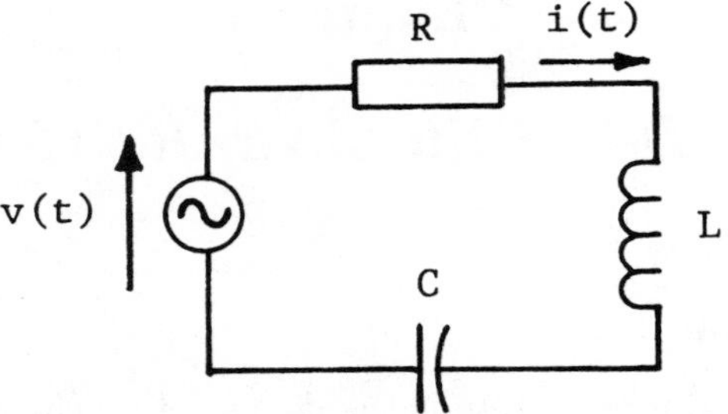

Fig. 4.2. Electrical second-order system.

for Fig. 4.2, where

$$i = \frac{dq}{dt}. \tag{4.3}$$

Since these equations have one dependent variable, the systems they represent are said to have one degree of freedom. All such second-order equations can be reduced to the standard form

$$\ddot{x} + 2\,\zeta\omega_n\dot{x} + \omega_n^2 x = z(t) \tag{4.4}$$

where x and t are the dependent and independent variables, and $z(t)$ is the driving function. For example, if

$$\omega_n = \sqrt{\frac{k}{m}} \quad \text{and} \quad \zeta = \frac{c}{2\sqrt{mk}}, \tag{4.5}$$

Eq. (4.1) becomes

$$\ddot{y} + 2\zeta\omega_n\dot{y} + \omega_n^2 y = \frac{f(t)}{m}. \tag{4.6}$$

The solution is obtained readily with Laplace transforms. First,

$$s^2Y(s) - sy(0) - \dot{y}(0) + 2\zeta\omega_n sY(s) - 2\zeta\omega_n y(0) + \omega_n^2 Y(s) = \frac{F(s)}{m} \tag{4.7}$$

or

$$Y(s) = \frac{\dfrac{F(s)}{m} + sy(0) + 2\zeta\omega_n y(0) + \dot{y}(0)}{s^2 + 2\zeta\omega_n s + \omega_n^2}. \tag{4.8}$$

If the spring-mass-damper system has the initial conditions $y(0) = \dot{y}(0) = 0$, it can be considered as an initially-inert linear system with input

$F(s)$, output $Y(s)$, and system function

$$H(s) = \frac{1}{m(s^2 + 2\zeta\omega_n s + \omega_n^2)} . \tag{4.9}$$

Then

$$Y(s) = H(s)\,F(s) . \tag{4.10}$$

If the applied force is the unit step $f(t) = U(t)$,

$$Y(s) = \frac{1}{ms(s^2 + 2\zeta\omega_n s + \omega_n^2)} . \tag{4.11}$$

According to Fig. 4.1 the steady-state deflection of the mass, namely the deflection remaining after the transient has subsided, is

$$y(\infty) = \frac{1}{k} = \frac{1}{m\omega_n^2} .$$

The same result is obtained by applying the final-value theorem to Eq. (4.11):

$$\lim_{t\to\infty} y(t) = \lim_{s\to 0} sY(s) = \frac{1}{m\omega_n^2} . \tag{4.12}$$

Now the deflection can be written in the normalized form

$$\frac{Y(s)}{y(\infty)} = \frac{\omega_n^2}{s(s^2 + 2\zeta\omega_n s + \omega_n^2)} = \frac{\omega_n^2}{s[(s + \zeta\omega_n)^2 + (\omega_n\sqrt{1 - \zeta^2})^2]} . \tag{4.13}$$

The parameter ζ is called the *damping ratio*. If it is greater than 1, the quadratic factor has two real zeros, and the deflection consists of a step and two exponentially-decreasing terms. The system does not oscillate, and is said to be *overdamped*. If ζ is less than 1, the system is *underdamped*. To calculate the step response of an underdamped second-order system, solve Eq. (4.13) with the help of the trick of Papoulis, explained in Chapter 2. According to this useful procedure, if a Laplace transform has a pair of complex poles at $s = -\alpha \pm j\beta$, write it as

$$F(s) = \frac{N(s)}{D_1(s)[(s + \alpha)^2 + \beta^2]} = \frac{As + B}{(s + \alpha)^2 + \beta^2} + \text{terms for } D_1(s) . \tag{4.14}$$

Make the definition

$$Me^{j\theta} = \left.\frac{N(s)}{D_1(s)}\right|_{s=-\alpha+j\beta} . \tag{4.15}$$

Then

$$f(t) = \frac{M}{\beta} e^{-\alpha t} \sin(\beta t + \theta) + \text{the terms from } D_1(s) . \quad (4.16)$$

When the trick is used on Eq. (4.13) with $\zeta < 1$,

$$-\alpha + j\beta = -\zeta\omega_n + j\omega_n \sqrt{1-\zeta^2} , \quad (4.17)$$

$$\frac{N(s)}{D_1(s)} = \frac{\omega_n^2}{s} , \quad (4.18)$$

and

$$Me^{j\theta} = \frac{\omega_n^2}{\omega_n(-\zeta + j\sqrt{1-\zeta^2})} = \omega_n e^{j(\pi + \cos^{-1}\zeta)} . \quad (4.19)$$

Therefore

$$\frac{y(t)}{y(\infty)} = 1 - \frac{1}{\sqrt{1-\zeta^2}} e^{-\zeta\omega_n t} \sin(\omega_n\sqrt{1-\zeta^2}\, t + \cos^{-1}\zeta) . \quad (4.20)$$

This equation is the step response of the spring-mass-damper system in Fig. 4.1, or any second-order system governed by Eq. (4.4). The step response is plotted in Fig. 4.3, and for several values of the damping ratio ζ in Fig. 4.4. The *undamped natural frequency* of the vibration is ω_n, and the *damped natural frequency* is

$$\omega_d = \omega_n \sqrt{1-\zeta^2} . \quad (4.21)$$

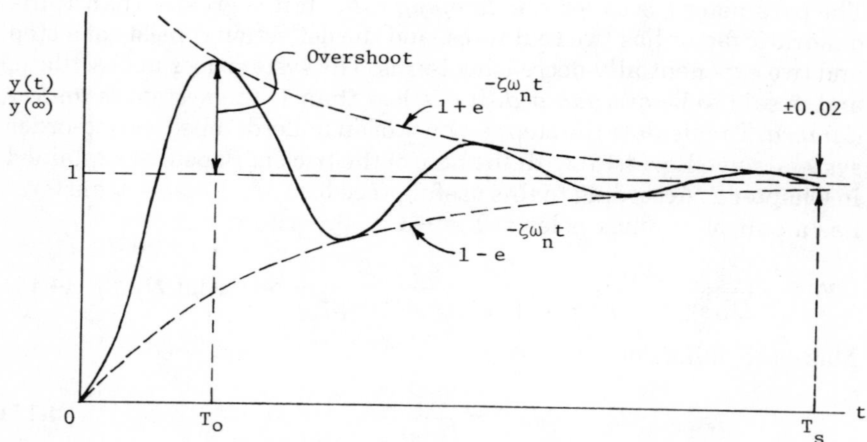

Fig. 4.3. Step response and its envelopes.

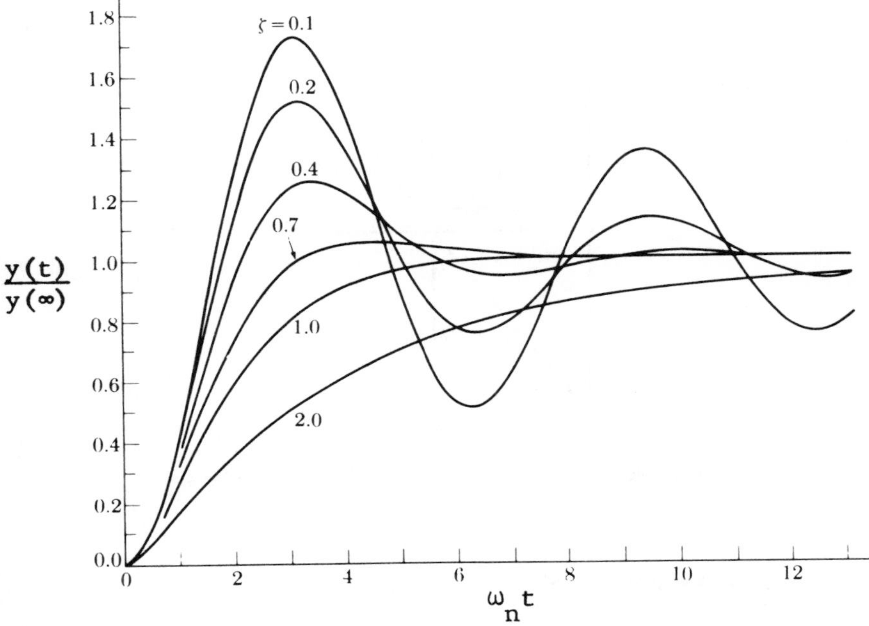

Fig. 4.4. Step response of a second-order system. (Reprinted by special permission from Richard C. Dorf, *Modern Control Systems*, 1967, Addison-Wesley, Reading, Mass.).

Fig. 4.5 shows the two poles of the transfer function $H(s)$ of the system in the s plane. Their location determines the damped and undamped natural frequencies and the damping ratio, and therefore provides all the information needed to calculate the step response of the system according to Eq. (4.20). Fig. 4.5 gives useful information about the transient response to any input. The transient term of the output has the form shown in Eqs. (4.16) and (4.17), for which ω_n and ζ are determined by the locations of the two poles in Fig. 4.5. If the poles are close to the imaginary axis, ζ is low and the transient oscillation dies out slowly. If the poles are close to the real axis, the frequency of the oscillation ω_d is low. If the poles are on the real axis, ζ is greater than 1 and the system is overdamped.

Fig. 4.3 shows the way in which the step response of the second-order system overshoots its final deflection. The maxima and minima are obtained by differentiating Eq. (4.20) and setting the derivative equal to

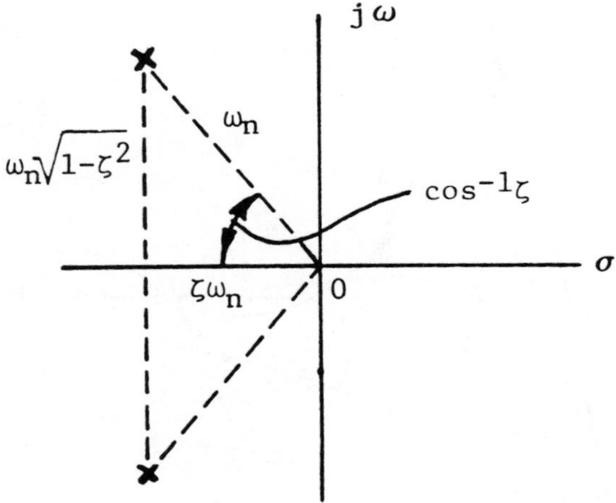

Fig. 4.5. Poles of the transfer function of a second-order system.

zero. The peaks occur at

$$\omega_n t = \frac{n\pi}{\sqrt{1 - \zeta^2}}, \quad n = 1, 2, \ldots \tag{4.22}$$

the maxima when n is odd and the minima when n is even. The time of the first overshoot, T_o, is

$$\omega_n T_o = \frac{\pi}{\sqrt{1 - \zeta^2}}, \tag{4.23}$$

and the height of the first overshoot is

$$\frac{y(t)}{y(\infty)} - 1 = e^{-\zeta\pi/\sqrt{1-\zeta^2}}. \tag{4.24}$$

The height of the overshoot as a function of the damping ratio is plotted in Fig. 4.6.

Settling time T_s is the time required for the envelopes of the underdamped step response to subside to within ±2 percent of the steady-state value. Substituting Eq. (4.22) into (4.20) shows that the exponential curves whose heights are $1 \pm \exp(-\zeta\omega_n t)$ pass thru the peaks of the step response, as in Fig. 4.3. Although these curves are not exactly tangent to the peaks, they are very nearly the envelopes of the step response. Therefore to calculate the settling time, let

$$e^{-\zeta\omega_n T_s} = 0.02\,. \tag{4.25}$$

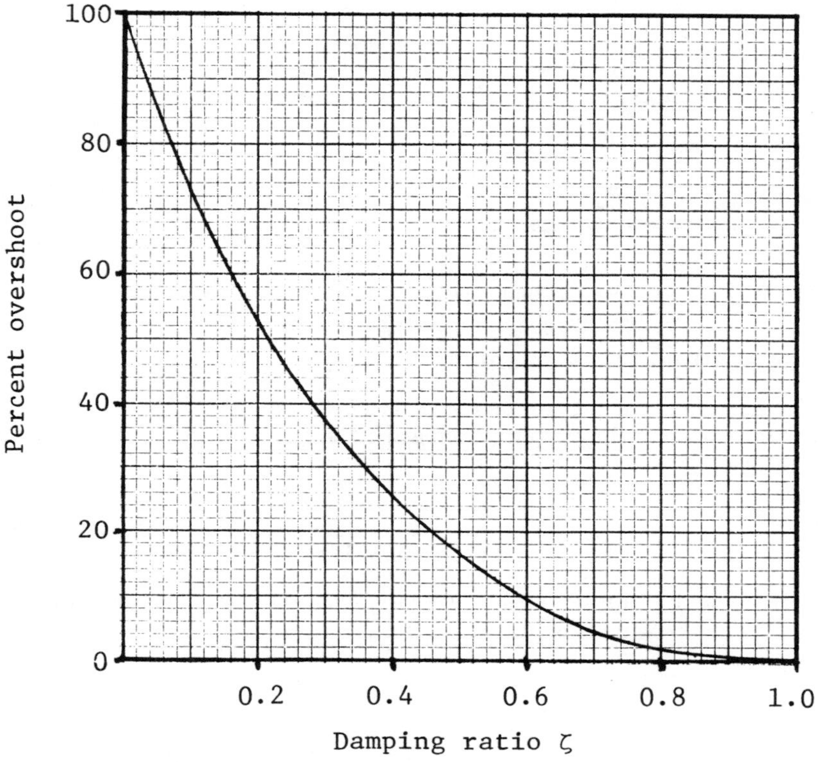

Fig. 4.6. Overshoot of a second-order system.

Then

$$T_s = \frac{3.91}{\zeta\omega_n} \quad \text{sec.} \tag{4.26}$$

Notice that the step response subsides to within ±2 percent of its steady-state value a little sooner than its envelopes.

Eq. (4.21) shows that the relationship between ω_d/ω_n and ζ is the circle

$$\left(\frac{\omega_d}{\omega_n}\right)^2 + \zeta^2 = 1 \tag{4.27}$$

shown in Fig. 4.7. If $\zeta = 0.2$, $\omega_d/\omega_n = 0.98$. Most vibrating systems such as turbine buckets, shafts, and masses on springs have damping ratios smaller than 0.2. For this reason the damped and undamped natural frequencies may usually, but not always, be assumed to be equal.

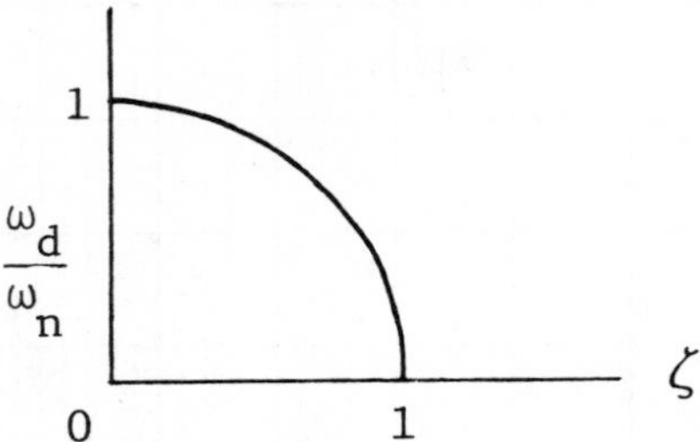

Fig. 4.7. Damped and undamped natural frequencies are not equal.

4.3 Logarithmic Decrement

The damping ratio ζ can be measured conveniently if an oscillogram of the vibration of the system, such as Fig. 4.3, is available. The period of the vibration is

$$T = \frac{2\pi}{\omega_d} = \frac{2\pi}{\omega_n\sqrt{1-\zeta^2}} . \tag{4.28}$$

The ratio of the amplitudes of any two successive positive peaks, measured from the steady-state deflection, is

$$\frac{\dfrac{y(a)}{y(\infty)} - 1}{\dfrac{y(a+T)}{y(\infty)} - 1} = \frac{e^{-\zeta\omega_n a}}{e^{-\zeta\omega_n(a+T)}} = e^{\zeta\omega_n T} = \exp\left(\frac{2\pi\zeta}{\sqrt{1-\zeta^2}}\right) \tag{4.29}$$

where a is the time of the first of the two peaks. The *logarithmic decrement* is defined as

$$\delta = \ln\frac{y(a) - y(\infty)}{y(a+T) - y(\infty)} = \frac{2\pi\zeta}{\sqrt{1-\zeta^2}} . \tag{4.30}$$

If $\zeta << 1$,

$$\delta = 2\pi\zeta . \tag{4.31}$$

The ratio of the amplitudes of two peaks m cycles apart is

$$\frac{y(a) - y(\infty)}{y(a+mT) - y(\infty)} = \frac{e^{-\zeta\omega_n a}}{e^{-\zeta\omega_n(a+mT)}} = e^{m\zeta\omega_n T} = \exp\left(\frac{2\pi m\zeta}{\sqrt{1-\zeta^2}}\right)$$

and

$$\ln\frac{y(a) - y(\infty)}{y(a+mT) - y(\infty)} = \frac{2\pi m\zeta}{\sqrt{1-\zeta^2}} = m\delta . \tag{4.32}$$

Thus

$$\delta = \frac{1}{m} \ln \frac{y(a) - y(\infty)}{y(a+mT) - y(\infty)} . \tag{4.33}$$

The amplitudes of peaks on an oscillogram can be measured easily, and the logarithmic decrement δ can be calculated by Eq. (4.30) or (4.33). Then the damping ratio ζ can be found by Eq. (4.30) or (4.31). Note that the overshoot given by Eq. (4.24) can be conveniently written as

$$\frac{y(t)}{y(\infty)} - 1 = e^{-\delta/2} . \tag{4.34}$$

An example of an oscillogram obtained experimentally appears in Fig. 4.8. A resistance strain gage was glued to the base of one of the buckets of a steam-turbine wheel. The wheel was mounted on a shaft in a test box that was evacuated to reduce windage, thereby reducing the power required to turn the wheel. A stationary steam jet was aimed at the buckets to give each one an impulse of force once per revolution. The lead wires of the strain gage were brought down to the hollow shaft and out thru a slipring at the end of the shaft to the instrumentation.

Any natural frequency of the bucket would be excited if it were an integral multiple of the wheel speed, because the bucket would then be pushed at the right times to reinforce the vibration. In a similar way, the natural frequency of a child's swing is excited if that frequency is an integral multiple of the frequency of pushes. The turbine bucket had a known natural frequency of about 245 Hz. The instrumentation included a band-pass filter set to pass a narrow band around 245 Hz, to remove the extraneous noise from the signal. Fig. 4.8 shows the filtered strain signal proportional to the amplitude of vibration, present at a wheel speed of 35 rps. The 1-per-revolution blips, provided by a magnetic pickup, confirm that the vibration frequency was 7 times the wheel speed. Before time A, the bucket was vibrating at its natural frequency of 245 Hz, and was being struck once every 7 cycles.

The amplitude of vibration might be expected to be the highest when the bucket passes the steam jet, and then decay exponentially until the next pass. The oscillogram before time A shows that instead, the amplitude increased in anticipation of the jet. The reason is that the wheel was flexible, allowing the bucket to feel the vibration of the buckets ahead of it. At time A the steam jet was tripped off. Thereafter the decrease in amplitude of vibration was approximately exponential. If the bucket is assumed to be a second-order system, its free vibration about its final position is governed by the same differential equation (4.4) as the vibration in Fig. 4.3, and the logarithmic decrement can be

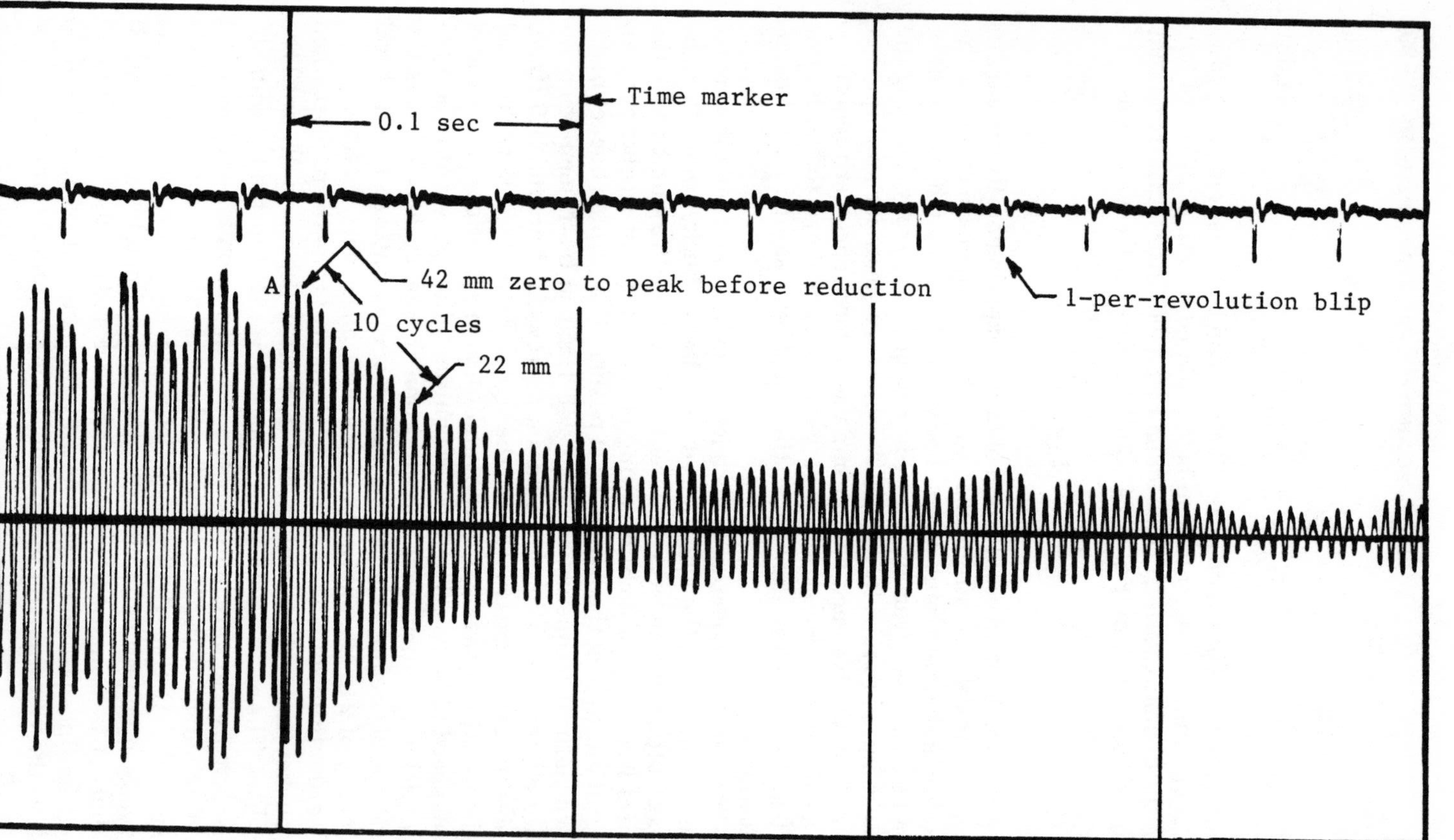

Fig. 4.8. Vibration of a turbine bucket turning at 35 rps.

calculated by the same formula, Eq. (4.33). The amplitudes of vibration measured 10 cycles apart on the original oscillogram before its size was reduced were 42 and 22 mm. The logarithmic decrement is therefore

$$\delta = \frac{1}{10} \ln \frac{42}{22} = 0.065 \,, \tag{4.35}$$

and the damping ratio is

$$\zeta = \frac{\delta}{2\pi} = 0.0103 \,. \tag{4.36}$$

This small amount of damping is typical of steel turbine buckets, and is a source of concern to their designers. Low damping is an advantage for tuning forks and chimes, but not for turbine buckets.

The irregularity in the decrease of bucket vibration after time A was caused by residual excitation. Although the steam was shut off, the wheel and shaft were still vibrating.

4.4 Frequency Response of Second-Order Systems

As important as the step response of a second-order linear system is its *frequency response*, namely, its steady-state response to a sinusoidal input. To reveal the importance, first calculate the steady-state response of a fixed, linear system of any order with system function $H(s)$, when the input is the sinusoidal force

$$f(t) = F_0 \sin \omega t \,. \tag{4.37}$$

Eq. (4.10) becomes

$$Y(s) = H(s)\, F(s) = \frac{F_0\, \omega\, H(s)}{s^2 + \omega^2} = \frac{A_1 s + A_2}{s^2 + \omega^2} + \text{terms for } H(s) \,. \tag{4.38}$$

The steady-state output is the inverse of the partial fraction whose denominator $s^2 + \omega^2$ is contributed by the driving force. It can be found readily with the trick of Papoulis. First,

$$\frac{N(s)}{D_1(s)} = F_0\, \omega\, H(s) \,. \tag{4.39}$$

Also,

$$\alpha + j\beta = 0 + j\omega \,. \tag{4.40}$$

Then

$$Me^{j\theta} = \left. \frac{N(s)}{D_1(s)} \right|_{s=-\alpha+j\beta} = F_0\, \omega\, H(j\omega) = F_0\, \omega |H(j\omega)| e^{j\theta} \tag{4.41}$$

where θ is the phase angle of $H(j\omega)$. Finally, the steady-state output is

$$y(t) = \frac{M}{\beta} e^{-\alpha t} \sin(\beta t + \theta) = F_0 |H(j\omega)| \sin(\omega t + \theta) . \tag{4.42}$$

This familiar result says that if the input to a fixed, linear system is a sine wave, the steady-state output is also a sine wave, whose amplitude and phase are found by replacing s in the system function by $j\omega$.

For the spring-mass-damper system in Fig. 4.1,

$$H(s) = \frac{1}{m(s^2 + 2\zeta\omega_n s + \omega_n^2)} . \tag{4.43}$$

Then

$$H(j\omega) = \frac{1}{m[(\omega_n^2 - \omega^2) + j2\zeta\omega_n\omega]} = \frac{e^{j\theta}}{m\omega_n^2 \sqrt{\left[1 - \left(\frac{\omega}{\omega_n}\right)^2\right]^2 + \left(2\zeta\frac{\omega}{\omega_n}\right)^2}} \tag{4.44}$$

where

$$\theta = -\tan^{-1} \frac{2\zeta\frac{\omega}{\omega_n}}{1 - \left(\frac{\omega}{\omega_n}\right)^2} . \tag{4.45}$$

The peak deflection of the mass at very low frequencies is

$$y_0 = \frac{F_0}{k} . \tag{4.46}$$

Combining Eqs. (4.46), (4.44), and (4.42) produces the steady-state output in normalized form:

$$\frac{y(t)}{y_0} = \frac{1}{\sqrt{\left[1 - \left(\frac{\omega}{\omega_n}\right)^2\right]^2 + \left(2\zeta\frac{\omega}{\omega_n}\right)^2}} \sin(\omega t + \theta) = k|H(j\omega)| \sin(\omega t + \theta) . \tag{4.47}$$

This is the frequency response of the spring-mass-damper system, or any second-order system whose equation of motion has the form of Eq. (4.4). The amplitude and phase angle of the frequency response are plotted in Figs. 4.9 and 4.10 for several values of the damping ratio ζ. Notice that the phase angle is $-90°$ when the driving frequency ω equals the undamped natural frequency ω_n, for all values of ζ. If ζ is small, the phase angle jumps abruptly from zero to $-180°$ when the driving fre-

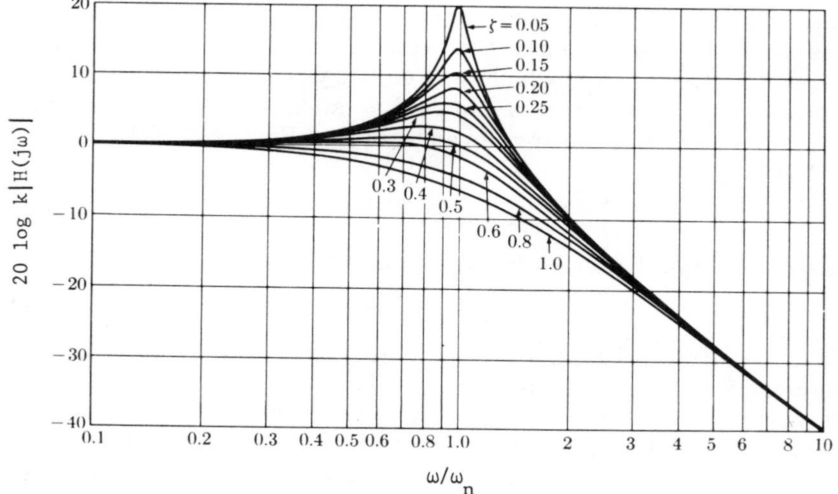

Fig. 4.9. Amplitude of the frequency response of a second-order system.

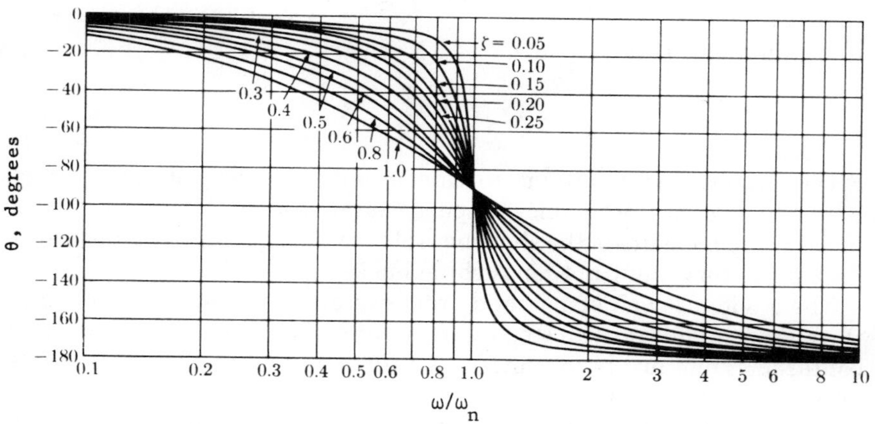

Fig. 4.10. Phase angle of the frequency response of a second-order system. (Figs. 4.9 and 4.10 are reprinted by special permission from Richard C. Dorf, *Modern Control Systems*, 1967, Addison-Wesley, Reading, Mass.).

quency passes thru ω_n. This fact can be demonstrated dramatically by suspending a weight on the lower end of a spring, and moving the upper end up and down sinusoidally.

The frequency-response amplitude curve is easily obtained for many electrical systems such as loudspeakers, oscillograph galvanometers, and amplifiers by driving them with a sine-wave oscillator, and measuring the amplitude of the acoustical, mechanical, or electrical output. The frequency at which the frequency-response amplitude curve reaches its maximum or *resonant peak* is called the *resonant frequency*. It is found by differentiating the amplitude in Eq. (4.47) with respect to ω, and is

$$\omega_r = \omega_n \sqrt{1 - 2\zeta^2} \tag{4.48}$$

which is different from the damped natural frequency

$$\omega_d = \omega_n \sqrt{1 - \zeta^2} \; . \tag{4.49}$$

Note that if $\zeta > 0.707$, the resonant frequency is imaginary, and the frequency-response curve has no peak. Thus if ζ is between 0.707 and 1, the system has no resonant peak, but still exhibits *underdamped* transient response. The height of the resonant peak, sometimes called the *figure of merit Q*, is found by substituting the resonant frequency for ω in the amplitude term of Eq. (4.47), and is

$$Q = \frac{1}{2\zeta\sqrt{1 - \zeta^2}} \; . \tag{4.50}$$

If the damping ratio ζ is low,

$$Q \approx \frac{1}{2\zeta} \; . \tag{4.51}$$

Either of these two equations provides a convenient way of calculating ζ if an experimental frequency-response curve is available. The figure of merit Q is a measure of the sharpness of resonance. A high Q is desirable for tuning forks, but not for turbine buckets.

The resonant peak of a second-order system, given by Eq. (4.50), and the overshoot following a step input, given by Eq. (4.24), are sometimes confused. They are both plotted as functions of ζ in Fig. 4.11. For ζ between 0.4 and 0.707, the two are approximately equal.

Bandwidth is the frequency of the sinusoidal driving force at which the frequency response is down 3 db from (to 0.707 of) its low frequency value. Fig. 4.9 shows that the bandwidth is high if the damping ratio is low. Oscillograph galvanometers are manufactured with $\zeta = 0.64$, which provides a reasonable compromise between large bandwidth, low resonant peak, and low overshoot following a step input.

4.5 Determination of Frequency Response in the s Plane

The frequency response of a fixed linear system can be computed conveniently in the *s* plane. According to Eq. (4.47), the phase angle of

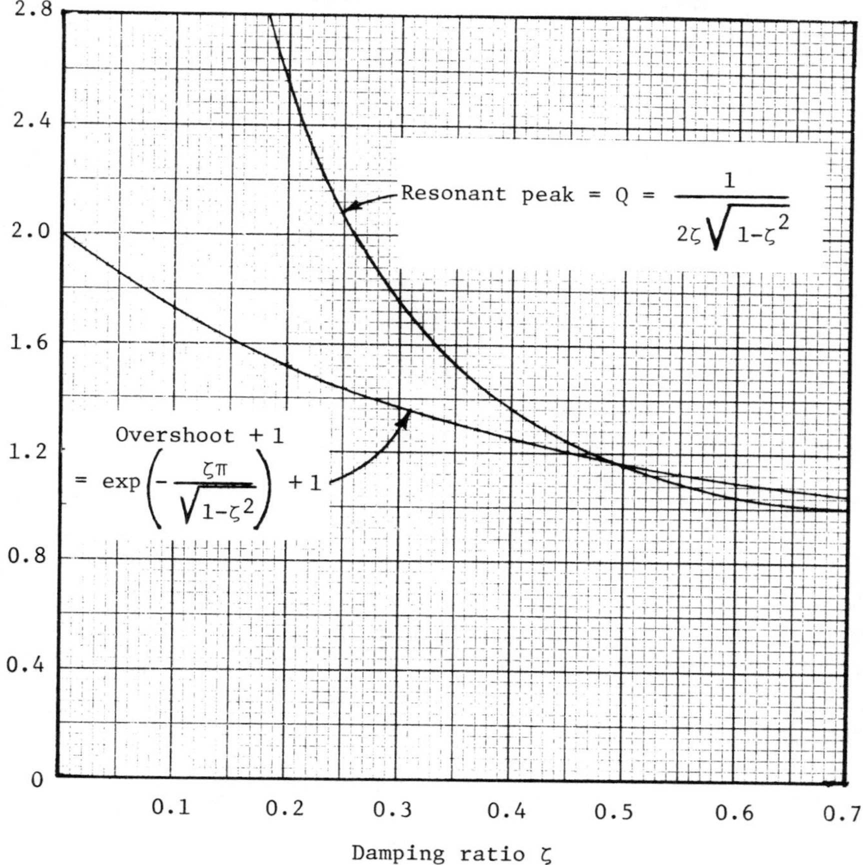

Fig. 4.11. Overshoot and resonant peak of a second-order system.

the frequency response is the phase angle θ of the system function $H(j\omega)$, and the amplitude of the frequency response is a known multiple of the amplitude of the system function. For the spring-mass-damper system,

$$H(j\omega) = \left.\frac{1}{m(s^2 + 2\zeta\omega_n s + \omega_n{}^2)}\right|_{s=j\omega}$$

$$= \frac{1}{m(j\omega + \zeta\omega_n - j\omega_n\sqrt{1-\zeta^2})(j\omega + \zeta\omega_n + j\omega_n\sqrt{1-\zeta^2})}. \tag{4.52}$$

Fig. 4.12 shows the two poles of the system function $H(s)$ in the s plane.

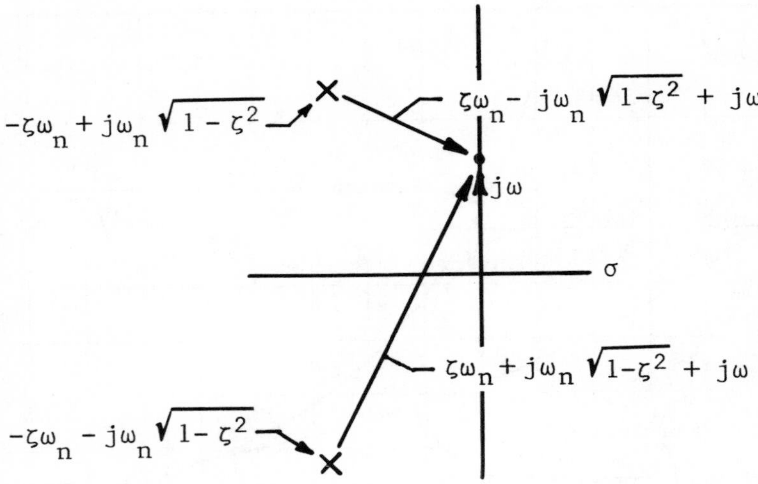

Fig. 4.12. Vectors to a point on the $j\omega$ axis.

Notice that the vectors from the two poles to a point $j\omega$ on the imaginary axis are the two terms in the denominator of Eq. (4.52). These two vectors are identified in Fig. 4.13 by their lengths L_1 and L_2, and their

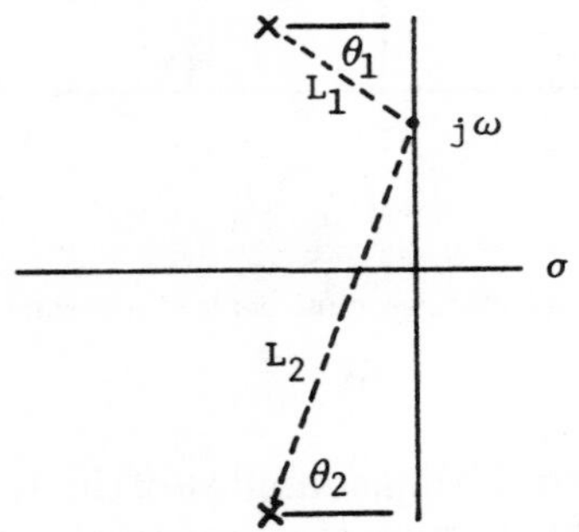

Fig. 4.13. Determination of frequency response.

angles with the real axis, θ_1 and θ_2. Eq. (4.52) can be expressed in the simpler form

$$H(j\omega) = \frac{1}{mL_1L_2} e^{-j(\theta_1+\theta_2)} . \qquad (4.53)$$

To plot amplitude and phase-angle frequency-response curves, choose values of ω, measure the lengths and angles of the two vectors, and compute $H(j\omega)$. If the semicircle drawn thru the two poles intersects the $j\omega$ axis as in Fig. 4.14, the shortening of vector L_1 as ω increases gives

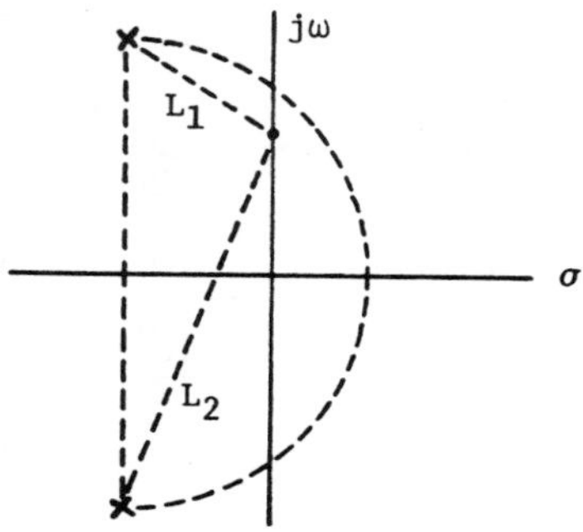

Fig. 4.14. Test for resonance of a second-order system.

the amplitude curve a resonant peak. As ω continues to increase, both vectors lengthen, and the frequency response drops off. If $\zeta > 0.707$ the semicircle does not intersect the $j\omega$ axis and the amplitude curve does not peak, but decreases monotonically as shown in Fig. 4.9.

If the system function of any fixed linear system is known, its frequency response can be obtained by this graphical method. For example, suppose that a root-locus plot shows that the closed-loop transfer function of a system with unity feedback is

$$H(s) = \frac{G(s)}{1 + G(s)} = \frac{k(s+2)}{(s+6)[(s+1)^2+3]} \tag{4.54}$$

where k is known. The constellation of poles and zeros is plotted in Fig. 4.15. The lengths and angles of the vectors to the point $j1$ on the $j\omega$ axis are

$$6 + j1 = 6.08 \,\underline{/9.5^\circ}$$

$$2 + j1 = 2.24 \,\underline{/26.6^\circ}$$

$$1 - j0.732 = 1.240 \,\underline{/-36.2^\circ}$$

$$1 + j2.732 = 2.91 \,\underline{/69.9^\circ}$$

Then

$$H(j1) = \frac{k\,(2.24 \,\underline{/26.6^\circ})}{(6.08 \,\underline{/9.5^\circ})(1.240 \,\underline{/-36.2^\circ})(2.91 \,\underline{/69.9^\circ})} = 0.1021k \,\underline{/-16.6^\circ}\,. \tag{4.55}$$

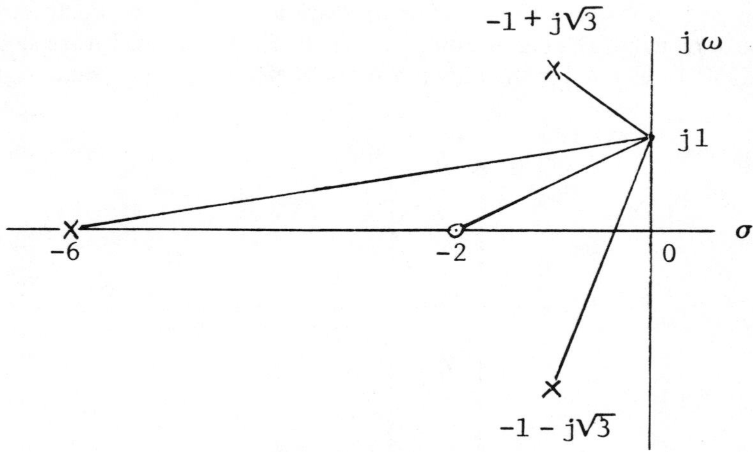

Fig. 4.15. Constellation of poles and zeros.

According to Eq. (4.42), if the input to the system is the sine wave $F_0 \sin \omega t$, the steady-state output at $\omega = 1$ rad/sec is

$$y(t) = 0.1021\, k\, F_0 \sin\,(t - 16.6°)\,. \tag{4.56}$$

If a similar calculation is made at other frequencies, frequency-response amplitude and phase-angle curves can be drawn.

4.6 The Second-Order Tendency Principle

The detailed study of second-order systems in the preceding sections is important because many higher-order feedback-control systems act like second-order systems. The reason is the fact, explained in Chapter 3, that as the open-loop gain increases, the closed-loop poles approach either the open-loop zeros or infinity. For example, Fig. 4.16 is the root-locus plot of a system with the open-loop transfer function

$$G(s) = \frac{k(s + 1.5)}{s(s + 1)(s + 6)(s + 10)}\,, \qquad H(s) = 1\,. \tag{4.57}$$

As k increases, one closed-loop pole moves toward minus infinity, one moves toward the zero at $s = -1.5$, and the other two are complex. When $k = 250$, the closed-loop transfer function is

$$\frac{G(s)}{1 + G(s)} = \frac{250\,(s + 1.5)}{(s + 1.66)(s + 12.77)[(s + 1.29)^2 + (4.01)^2]}\,. \tag{4.58}$$

The step response is

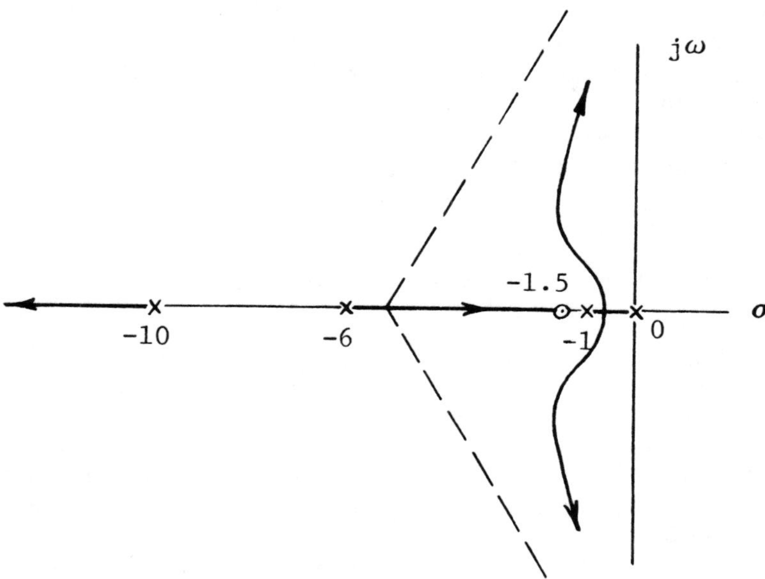

Fig. 4.16. Illustration of the second-order tendency.

$$Y(s) = \frac{250\,(s + 1.5)}{s(s + 1.66)(s + 12.77)[(s + 1.29)^2 + (4.01)^2]}$$

$$= \frac{A}{s} + \frac{B}{s + 1.66} + \frac{C}{s + 12.77} + \frac{Ds + E}{(s + 1.29)^2 + (4.01)^2} \tag{4.59}$$

or

$$y(t) = 1 + 0.13e^{-1.66t} - 0.13e^{-12.77t} + 1.21e^{-1.29t}\sin(4.01t - 2.18)\,. \tag{4.60}$$

The residue

$$B = [(s + 1.66)\,Y(s)]_{s=-1.66} = 0.13 \tag{4.61}$$

is small because the pole at $s = -1.66$ is close to the zero at $s = -1.5$, making the term $-1.66 + 1.5$ in the numerator of $Y(s)$ small. The residue

$$C = [(s + 12.77)\,Y(s)]_{s=-12.77} = -0.13 \tag{4.62}$$

is small because when $s = -12.77$, the denominator of $Y(s)$ is large. Furthermore, the term $\exp(-12.77t)$ dies out quickly because its time constant is small. The only other poles contributing to the transient response are the complex pair at $s = -1.29 \pm j4.01$. These are called *dominant poles*, since they dominate the transient portion of the step response and the transient response to other inputs. In general, closed-loop poles that are close to zeros or remote from the origin contribute little to the transient response.

The frequency response of the system to the input $f(t) = \sin \omega t$, according to Eq. (4.58), is

$$y(t) = \left| \frac{250\,(j\omega + 1.5)}{(j\omega + 1.66)(j\omega + 12.77)[(j\omega + 1.29)^2 + (4.01)^2]} \right| \sin(\omega t + \theta) \tag{4.63}$$

where θ is the phase angle of $G(j\omega)/[1 + G(j\omega)]$. The vectors from $s = -1.5$ and $s = -1.66$ to a point $s = j\omega$ on the imaginary axis have nearly the same length and direction, and therefore nearly cancel each other in the calculation of frequency response as in Eq. (4.55). The vector from $s = -12.77$ to $s = j\omega$ is long, and does not change much in length or direction over the operating range of ω. The frequency response is nearly the same as if only the dominant poles were present. In general, closed-loop poles that are near zeros or remote from the origin contribute little to the shape or phase angle of the frequency response. The result is expressed in the *second-order tendency principle: at the operating value of forward gain k, many higher-order systems have a closed-loop transfer function with a dominant pair of poles, and therefore behave like second-order systems.* This fact is the basis for the usefulness of Nyquist and Bode diagrams, which will be explained in the next chapter.

An example of the second-order tendency principle is provided by the system of Eqs. (4.57), whose step response is given by Eq. (4.60). How does this response compare to that of a second-order system with the same pair of dominant poles at $s = -1.29 \pm j4.01$? The latter system has the transfer function

$$H(s) = \frac{A}{(s + 1.29)^2 + (4.01)^2} \tag{4.64}$$

and the step response

$$Y(s) = \frac{A}{s[(s + 1.29)^2 + (4.01)^2]}\,. \tag{4.65}$$

For comparison, make the steady-state value of the step response the same as that for the actual system, namely 1. According to the final-value theorem,

$$y(\infty) = \lim_{s \to 0} sY(s) = \frac{A}{(1.29)^2 + (4.01)^2} = 1\,. \tag{4.66}$$

Therefore

$$A = 17.74\,. \tag{4.67}$$

The step response of the second-order system is therefore

$$Y(s) = \frac{17.74}{s[(s + 1.29)^2 + (4.01)^2]} \tag{4.68}$$

or

$$y(t) = 1 + 1.05\, e^{-1.29t} \sin\,(4.01t - 1.88)\,. \tag{4.69}$$

The step responses of the actual system and its second-order approximation are compared in Fig. 4.17. Clearly the poles of the system function at $s = -1.66$ and -12.77 contribute little to the step response.

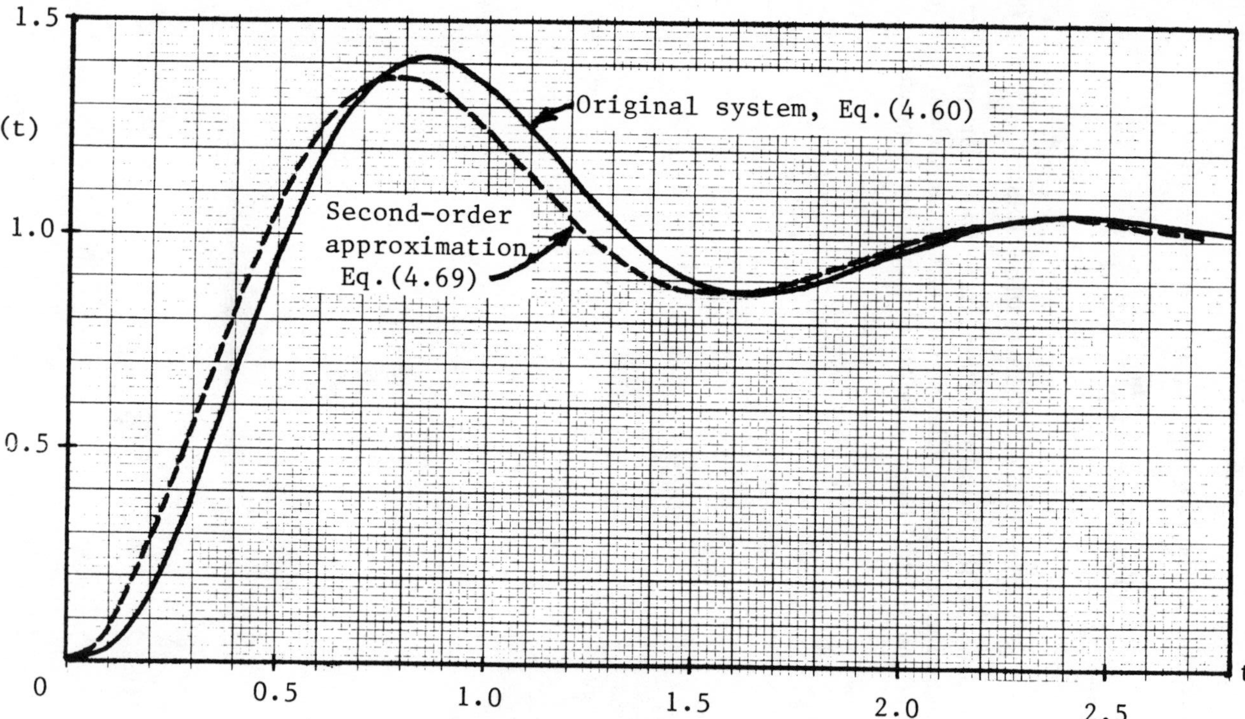

Fig. 4.17. Illustration of the second-order tendency principle.

Chapter 5

CLASSICAL CONTROL THEORY

5.1 Introduction

The preceding two chapters have shown the advantages of Evans' root-locus method of analyzing fixed linear systems. The method produces a graphical display of the poles and zeros of a system transfer function. This display permits either a quick, approximate estimation of the behavior of the system, or an accurate calculation of either its transient response or sinusoidal steady-state response. Methods of analysis developed earlier by H. Nyquist and H. W. Bode are also useful for calculating the behavior of linear systems. The older methods are somewhat cumbersome compared to Evans' method, but have the advantage of allowing the straightforward choice of compensating networks to improve system performance. The classical or "ancient" methods complement the root-locus method and are too useful to be neglected by modern control engineers.

5.2 The Nyquist Criterion of Stability

Nyquist's criterion is a method of determining the stability of a linear, time-invariant system when its open-loop poles and zeros are known, but its closed-loop poles are not. The block diagram of the system must be reducible to the standard form of Fig. 5.1. To understand the method, first let

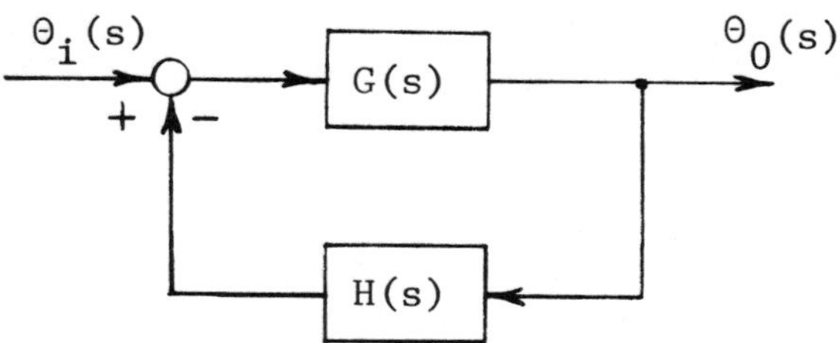

Fig. 5.1. Standard block diagram.

$$G(s) = \frac{N_1(s)}{D_1(s)} \quad \text{and} \quad H(s) = \frac{N_2(s)}{D_2(s)} . \tag{5.1}$$

The open-loop transfer function is

$$G(s)H(s) = \frac{N_1(s)N_2(s)}{D_1(s)D_2(s)}\,. \tag{5.2}$$

Also

$$1 + G(s)H(s) = \frac{N_1(s)N_2(s) + D_1(s)D_2(s)}{D_1(s)D_2(s)} \tag{5.3}$$

and the closed-loop transfer function is

$$\frac{G(s)}{1 + G(s)H(s)} = \frac{N_1(s)D_2(s)}{N_1(s)N_2(s) + D_1(s)D_2(s)}\,. \tag{5.4}$$

The stability of the system is determined by the roots of the characteristic equation

$$N_1(s)N_2(s) + D_1(s)D_2(s) = 0 \tag{5.5}$$

which are the poles of the closed-loop transfer function, or the *zeros* of $1 + G(s)H(s)$. The *poles* of $1 + G(s)H(s)$ are the same as those of the open-loop transfer function $G(s)H(s)$, and are usually know, as for example in the system of Fig. 3.11. Consider now Nyquist's unique way of determining whether any of the roots of the characteristic equation have positive real parts.

Eq. (5.3) is of the form

$$1 + G(s)H(s) = \frac{k(s-z_1)(s-z_2)(s-z_3)\ldots}{(s-p_1)(s-p_2)(s-p_3)\ldots} \tag{5.6}$$

in which the p_i are the known poles and the z_i are the unknown zeros. Fig. 5.2 is a typical plot of this constellation in the s plane. The factor $s-z_i$ is a vector from the ith zero to a point s, as shown in the figure. Similarly, $s-p_i$ is a vector from the ith pole to point s. Suppose that the point s starts at $s = 0-j\infty$, moves up the $j\omega$ axis to $s = 0+j\infty$, and then goes clockwise around the dotted circle of infinite radius, for which

$$s = \lim_{R\to\infty} Re^{j\theta}\,, \quad \frac{\pi}{2} \geqslant \theta \geqslant -\frac{\pi}{2}\,. \tag{5.7}$$

This closed path is called the *Nyquist contour*. Each of the six vectors follows the point s during this maneuver. When the circuit is complete, each vector from a pole or zero in the right-half plane has rotated clockwise one revolution. If Z and P are the numbers of zeros and poles of $1 + G(s)H(s)$ in the right-half plane, the vector $1 + G(s)H(s)$ has rotated

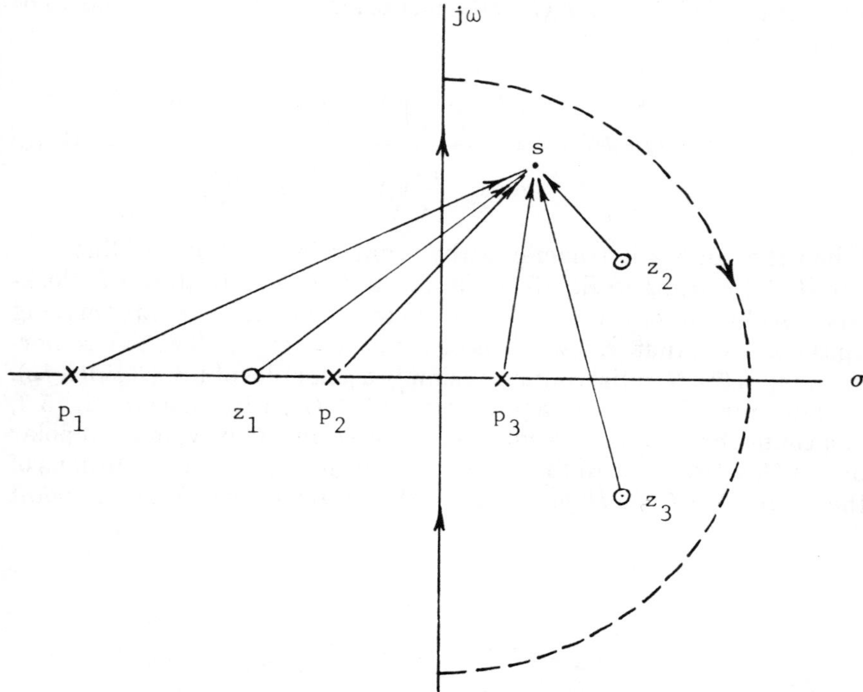

Fig. 5.2. The Nyquist contour.

clockwise $Z-P$ revolutions. The number P is known. The goal now is to find Z.

The revolutions of $1 + G(s)H(s)$ can be counted by plotting the complex variable

$$u + jv = 1 + G(s)H(s) \tag{5.8}$$

while the complex variable

$$s = \sigma + j\omega \tag{5.9}$$

describes the Nyquist contour. The plotting of $u + jv$, called a *conformal transformation* or *conformal mapping,* is simplified by a property of real systems. In any real system the open-loop frequency response $G(j\omega)H(j\omega)$ must decrease or approach a constant as the frequency of the sinusoidal driving force increases. Therefore the denominator of $G(s)H(s)$ is of the same or higher degree than the numerator. Then according to Eq. (5.3), $1 + G(s)H(s)$ has as many poles as zeros. Eq. (5.6) can be written as

$$1 + G(s)H(s) = k\,\frac{\left(1 - \frac{z_1}{s}\right)\left(1 - \frac{z_2}{s}\right)\left(1 - \frac{z_3}{s}\right)\cdots}{\left(1 - \frac{p_1}{s}\right)\left(1 - \frac{p_2}{s}\right)\left(1 - \frac{p_3}{s}\right)\cdots}. \tag{5.10}$$

When the point s is traversing the semicircle of infinite radius, $1 + G(s)H(s)$ according to Eq. (5.10) is constant. Therefore the $Z-P$ clockwise revolutions of $1 + G(s)H(s)$ must occur while the point s is moving up the $j\omega$ axis, that is, for values of $s = j\omega$ for $-\infty \leqslant \omega \leqslant \infty$. The conformal map of the Nyquist contour is simply a polar plot of $1 + G(j\omega)H(j\omega)$. To determine $Z-P$, make a polar plot of $1 + G(j\omega)H(j\omega)$ as in Fig. 5.3, and count the clockwise revolutions. More conveniently, make a polar plot of $G(j\omega)H(j\omega)$ as in Fig. 5.4 and count the clockwise revolutions of the vector $1 + G(j\omega)H(j\omega)$, namely the vector drawn from the point

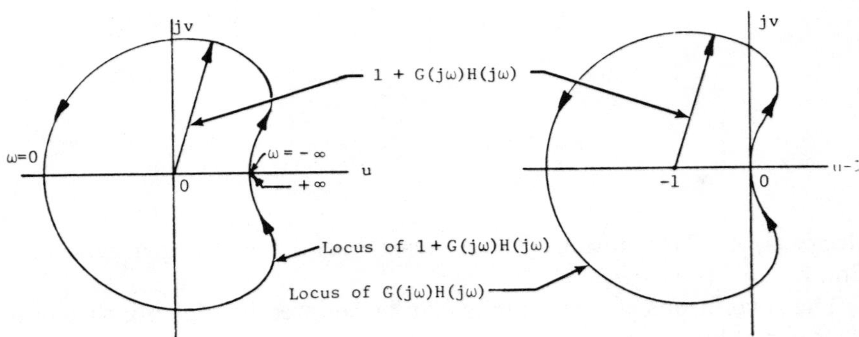

Fig. 5.3. Polar plot of $1 + G(j\omega)H(j\omega)$.

Fig. 5.4. Polar plot of $G(j\omega)H(j\omega)$.

$-1 + j0$ to the point $G(j\omega)H(j\omega)$. Calculate $G(j\omega)H(j\omega)$ for only the positive values of ω, to produce half of the polar plot. The other half, for negative values of ω, is the reflection of the first half about the horizontal axis.

The reasoning can be summarized as follows. The number of times the locus of $G(j\omega)H(j\omega)$ encircles the point $-1 + j0$ clockwise is $Z-P$. The number of poles of $G(s)H(s)$ in the right-half plane is P. The number of poles of the closed-loop transfer function in the right-half plane is Z. Accordingly, the *Nyquist criterion* states that a fixed, linear system is stable iff the number of *counterclockwise* encirclements of the point $-1 + j0$ by the vector $G(j\omega)H(j\omega)$ equals the number of poles of $G(s)H(s)$ with positive real parts.

To illustrate the use of Nyquist's criterion, investigate the stability of the system for which

$$G(s)H(s) = \frac{k(s + 1)}{(s - 0.5)(s + 3)}. \tag{5.11}$$

This equation shows that $P = 1$. The polar plot of $G(j\omega)H(j\omega)$ is represented by Fig. 5.4, which shows that $Z-P = -1$. Therefore $Z = P-1 = 0$, and the system is stable. If the gain k is lowered, the polar plot of $G(j\omega)H(j\omega)$ looks like Fig. 5.5. Now $Z-P = 0$. Hence $Z = P = 1$. The

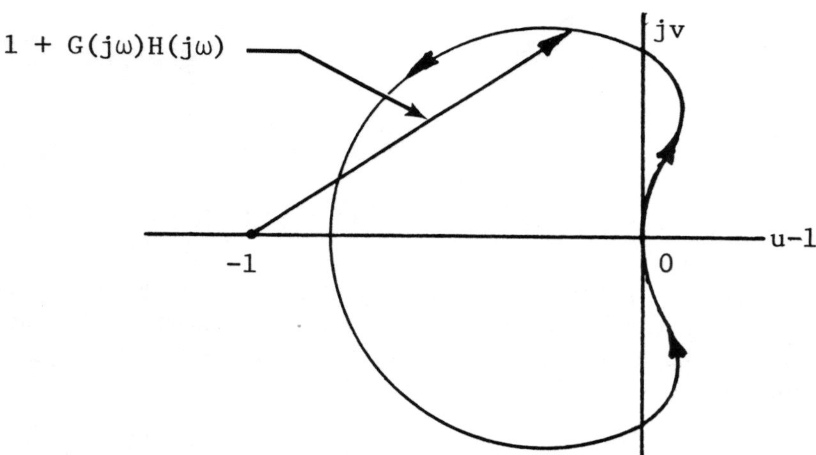

Fig. 5.5. Illustration of the Nyquist criterion.

closed-loop transfer function has a pole in the right-half plane, and the system is therefore unstable.

Another interesting example of the use of the Nyquist criterion is provided by a system for which

$$G(s)H(s) = \frac{k(s + a)(s + b)}{s(s + c)(s + d)(s + e)(s + f)} \tag{5.12}$$

in which all the poles and zeros are on the negative real axis. (The justification for including the pole at the origin in this category will be explained soon.) The zeros lie to the left of three of the poles, and to the right of two. Now $P = 0$. For one value of gain k, the locus of $G(j\omega)H(j\omega)$ appears as in Fig. 5.6. Here $Z-P = 2$, $Z = 2$, and the system is un-

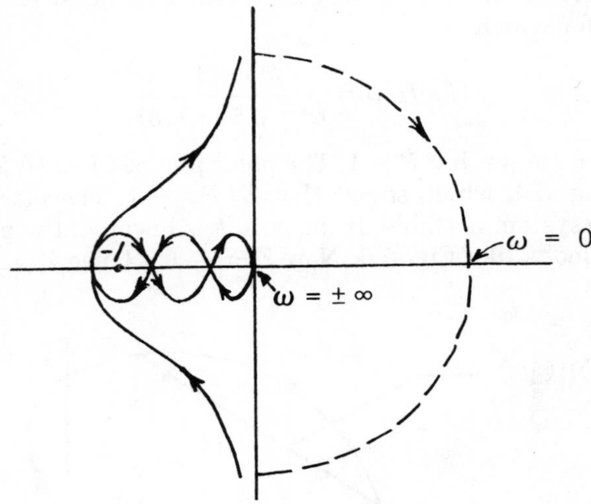

Fig. 5.6. Polar plot with low gain.

stable. When k is increased, the polar plot looks like Fig. 5.7. Now $Z-P = 0$, and the sytem is stable. When k is increased again, the plot of $G(j\omega)H(j\omega)$ appears as in Fig. 5.8. Now $Z-P = 2, Z = 2$, and the system is unstable again.

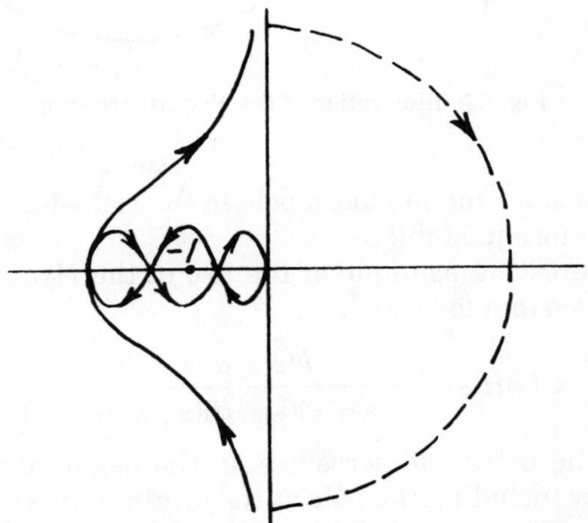

Fig. 5.7. Polar plot with intermediate gain.

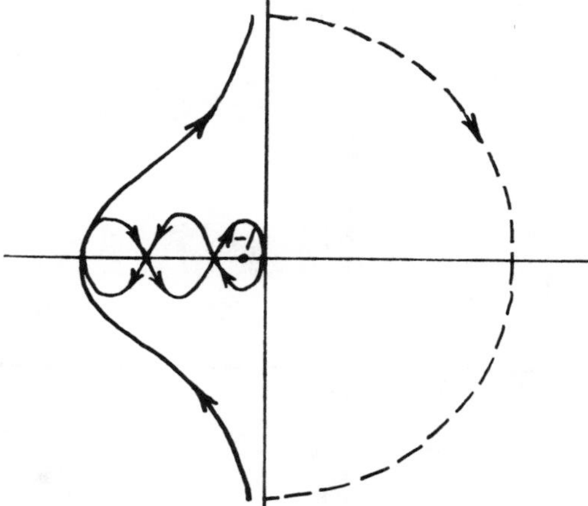

Fig. 5.8. Polar plot with high gain.

5.3 Poles and Zeros on the Imaginary Axis

The derivation of the Nyquist criterion did not consider the possibility that $1 + G(s)H(s)$ might have poles or zeros on the $j\omega$ axis. Suppose a pair of poles lie on the $j\omega$ axis as in Fig. 5.9. In traversing the Nyquist contour, the point s has two alternatives:

1. Detour to the *right* around each imaginary pole, along a semicircle of small radius, as shown in Fig. 5.9. These poles are now excluded from the closed contour, and contribute nothing to P or $Z-P$. Eq. (5.6) shows that while the moving point s is detouring *counterclockwise* around an imaginary pole, the polar plot of $1 + G(s)H(s)$ is moving *clockwise* around a semicircle of large radius, which must be included in the Nyquist polar plot. An example is shown in Fig. 5.6. The polar plot includes a large clockwise semicircle, generated when the point s detours around the pole of $1 + G(s)H(s)$ at the origin.
2. Detour to the *left* around each imaginary pole, thereby including these poles in the closed contour. For the system of Fig. 5.9, this change in the contour decreases $Z-P$ by 2, and adds 2 to P. During this detour, the polar plot of $1 + G(s)H(s)$ is moving *counterclockwise* around a semicircle of large radius. The Nyquist polar plot will look different from that produced by the first procedure, and will encircle the point $-1 + j0$ clockwise two times fewer.

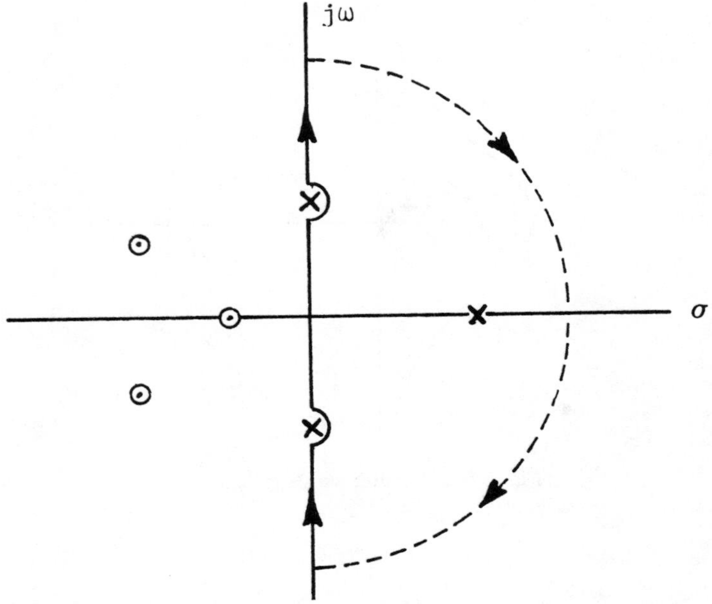

Fig. 5.9. Poles of $1 + G(s)H(s)$ on the imaginary axis.

Either method gives the right answer. The former is the one generally used.

If $1 + G(s)H(s)$ has a *zero* on the $j\omega$ axis, the point s can detour around it either way. If the detour is counterclockwise, it excludes the zero from the closed contour. The zero then contributes nothing to $Z-P$. Eq. (5.6) shows that the locus of $1 + G(s)H(s)$ then detours around the origin, or the locus of $G(s)H(s)$ detours around the point $-1 + j0$, counterclockwise along a small semicircle. When this small semicircle is included in the Nyquist polar plot, an accurate count can be made of the number of clockwise rotations of the vector $1 + G(s)H(s)$ as s makes its circuit in the s plane.

Notice that zeros of $1 + G(s)H(s)$ on the $j\omega$ axis, which are not in the left half of the complex plane, prevent the system from being classified as stable. If in addition $1 + G(s)H(s)$ has no zero in the right-half plane, it is not *unstable* either. The Nyquist polar plot described above will detect any zero in the right-half plane, and therefore determine whether the system is unstable or just oscillatory.

5.4 Systems with Open-Loop Stability

The Nyquist criterion of stability is simplified if the components of the system being considered are individually stable. Many systems consist of motors, amplifiers, passive R-L-C circuits, etc., all of whose poles lie in the left half of the s plane. For such a system all of the poles of $G(s)H(s)$ lie in the left-half plane, and the system is therefore stable when the feedback loop is open. Since P is now zero, $Z-P = Z$. Therefore the number of times the locus of $G(s)H(s)$ encircles the point $-1 + j0$ clockwise while mapping the Nyquist contour is Z, the number of roots of the characteristic equation in the right-half plane. Counterclockwise encirclement is not possible, because Z cannot be a negative number. For a system in the form of Fig. 5.1 that is open-loop stable, the Nyquist criterion can now be stated more simply: the system is closed-loop stable if the locus of $G(j\omega)H(j\omega)$ does not encircle the point $-1 + j0$.

Fig. 5.10 shows a typical Nyquist polar plot of a system for which

$$G(j\omega)H(j\omega) = \frac{k}{(j\omega + a)(j\omega + b)(j\omega + c)} \tag{5.13}$$

in which a, b, and c are positive, real numbers. The plot is typical of those for many systems with stable $G(s)H(s)$, in that as ω increases from zero, the magnitude or *gain* of the open-loop transfer function $G(j\omega)H(j\omega)$ decreases, and its phase shift $\phi(\omega)$ becomes more negative. A useful measure of the relative stability of these systems is the *phase margin* γ, defined as $\gamma = 180° + \phi_c$, where ϕ_c is the phase shift of $G(j\omega)H(j\omega)$ when its magnitude has decreased to 1. The phase margin is shown in Fig. 5.10. In general, if the phase margin is between 30 and 50 degrees,

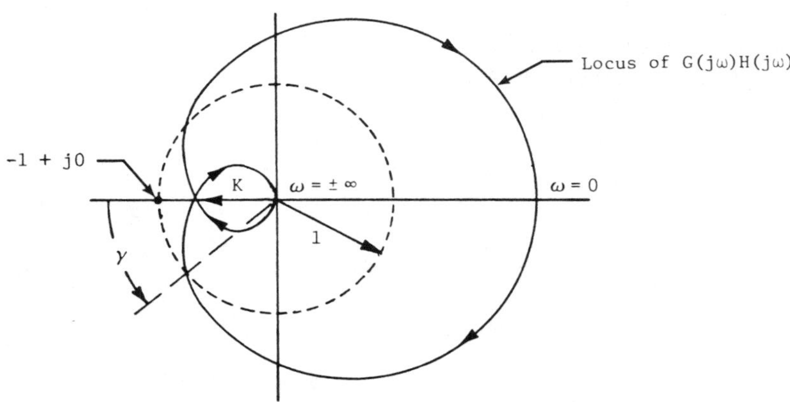

Fig. 5.10. Typical polar plot for a system that is open-loop stable.

the system performs well. If γ is smaller, the transient response has a large overshoot. If γ is larger, the response of the system is sluggish. If γ is negative, the system is unstable. A similar indicator of relative stability is the *gain margin*, $1/K$, where K is the magnitude of $G(j\omega)H(j\omega)$ when $\phi(\omega) = 180°$. Typically, $1/K$ is between 6 and 15 db.

5.5 Bode Diagrams

A Nyquist diagram is a polar plot of the gain and phase angle of the open-loop transfer function $G(j\omega)H(j\omega)$ of the standard feedback system in Fig. 5.1. The driving frequency ω is a parameter that does not appear in the diagram. The information can be plotted more easily, and can be used more conveniently to estimate performance and to modify the system, if the logarithm of the gain and the phase angle are plotted separately on rectangular-coordinate paper, each as a function of ω. These are called *Bode diagrams*, for H. W. Bode whose book (Ref. 6) was a major contribution to control theory. The rules for making Bode diagrams for systems that are open-loop stable will now be developed.

A typical stable, open-loop transfer function of a feedback system is

$$G(s)H(s) = \frac{k_1(s - z_1)(s - z_2)(s - z_3)}{(s - p_4)(s^2 + 2\zeta\omega_n s + \omega_n^2)} . \tag{5.14}$$

Since the system is open-loop stable, none of the poles of $G(s)H(s)$ is in the right half of the s-plane. In addition, specify that none of the zeros lies in the right-half plane. Then $G(s)H(s)$ is said to be a *minimum-phase* transfer function. This description is used because if one of the zeros is reflected about the $j\omega$ axis into the right-half plane, the total phase shift as ω increases from zero to infinity is greater than before. The sinusoidal open-loop transfer function is

$$\begin{aligned} G(j\omega)H(j\omega) &= \frac{k_1(j\omega + \omega_1)(j\omega + \omega_2)(j\omega + \omega_3)}{(j\omega + \omega_4)(-\omega^2 + j2\zeta\omega_n\omega + \omega_n^2)} \\ &= \frac{k_2\left(1 + j\dfrac{\omega}{\omega_1}\right)\left(1 + j\dfrac{\omega}{\omega_2}\right)\left(1 + j\dfrac{\omega}{\omega_3}\right)}{\left(1 + j\dfrac{\omega}{\omega_4}\right)\left[1 + j2\zeta\dfrac{\omega}{\omega_n} - \left(\dfrac{\omega}{\omega_n}\right)^2\right]} \end{aligned} \tag{5.15}$$

where $\omega_1 = -z_1$, etc., each of the ω_i's is a positive number, and

$$k_2 = \frac{\omega_1\omega_2\omega_3}{\omega_4\omega_n^2} k_1 . \tag{5.16}$$

Each first-degree factor in Eq. (5.15) represents a vector in the complex plane, and the quadratic factor represents two vectors. If the vectors are displayed in polar form, the equation becomes

$$G(j\omega)H(j\omega) = \frac{k_2 M_1 e^{j\phi_1} M_2 e^{j\phi_2} M_3 e^{j\phi_3}}{M_4 e^{j\phi_4} M_5 e^{j\phi_5} M_6 e^{j\phi_6}} \tag{5.17}$$

where M_i and ϕ_i are the magnitude and phase angle of the ith vector. Then

$$G(j\omega)H(j\omega) = \frac{k_2 M_1 M_2 M_3}{M_4 M_5 M_6} \; e^{j(\phi_1+\phi_2+\phi_3-\phi_4-\phi_5-\phi_6)} \; . \tag{5.18}$$

If the phase angle of $G(j\omega)H(j\omega)$ is $\phi(\omega)$,

$$G(j\omega)H(j\omega) = |G(j\omega)H(j\omega)|e^{j\phi(\omega)} \; . \tag{5.19}$$

Then

$$\log_{10}|G(j\omega)H(j\omega)| = \log k_2 + \log M_1 + \log M_2 + \log M_3 - \log M_4 - \log M_5 - \log M_6 \tag{5.20}$$

and

$$\phi(\omega) = \phi_1 + \phi_2 + \phi_3 - \phi_4 - \phi_5 - \phi_6 \; . \tag{5.21}$$

The logarithmic gain of $G(j\omega)H(j\omega)$ is the sum of the logarithmic gains of its factors, and the phase shift of $G(j\omega)H(j\omega)$ is the sum of the phase shifts of its factors. The gains of $G(j\omega)H(j\omega)$ and its factors are commonly plotted in decibels on a linear scale, against frequency ω on a logarithmic scale.

5.6 Bode Diagrams of the Factors

The work of making Bode plots is further simplified by the ease with which the gains and phase angles of the factors can be obtained. First the gain in decibels, namely $20 \log|G(j\omega)|$, and the phase angle $\phi(\omega)$ will be computed for each of the factors that can appear in an open-loop transfer function.

1. *Pole or zero at the origin.* If a factor is of the form

$$G(s) = \frac{1}{s} \tag{5.22}$$

then

$$G(j\omega) = \frac{1}{j\omega} = \frac{1}{\omega} \, e^{-j90^\circ} \; . \tag{5.23}$$

The gain is

$$20 \log|G| = -20 \log \omega \tag{5.24}$$

and the phase angle is constant at

$$\phi = -90° . \tag{5.25}$$

The Bode gain curve appears as in Fig. 5.11. It has a slope of exactly −20

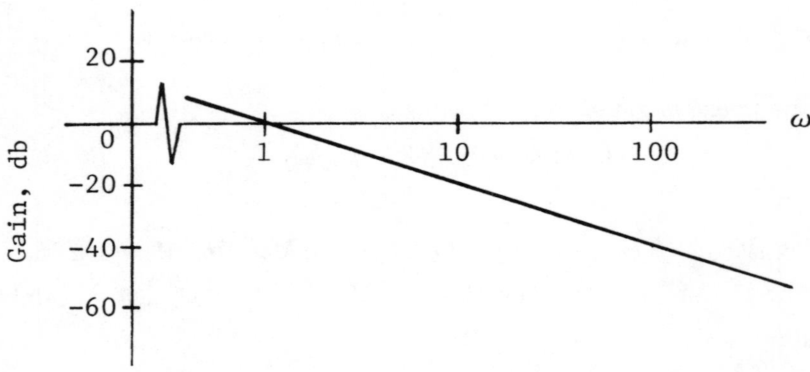

Fig. 5.11. Gain curve for a pole at the origin.

db/decade, or approximately −6 db/octave.

A zero at the origin in $G(s)H(s)$ contributes a factor

$$G(s) = s \qquad \text{or} \qquad G(j\omega) = j\omega . \tag{5.26}$$

Then

$$20 \log|G| = 20 \log \omega \qquad \text{and} \qquad \phi = 90° . \tag{5.27}$$

The gain curve is the reflection of Fig. 5.11 about the ω axis.

2. *Constant gain.* The constant k_2 in Eq. (5.15) contributes 20 log k_2 to the logarithmic gain of $G(j\omega)H(j\omega)$, and nothing to its phase angle. For the combination of factors

$$G(j\omega) = \frac{k}{j\omega} , \tag{5.28}$$

the gain is

$$20 \log|G| = 20 \log k - 20 \log \omega . \tag{5.29}$$

The gain curve is that of Fig. 5.11, raised 20 log k decibels.

3. *Real pole or zero.* If the open-loop transfer function of Eq. (5.14) has a real, negative pole at $s = p_o = -\omega_o$, Eq. (5.15) has a factor of the form

$$G(j\omega) = \frac{1}{1 + j\dfrac{\omega}{\omega_o}} . \tag{5.30}$$

Then

$$20 \log|G| = -20 \log|1 + j\omega/\omega_o| \tag{5.31}$$

and

$$\phi = -\tan^{-1} \frac{\omega}{\omega_o} . \tag{5.32}$$

At low frequencies the term $j\omega/\omega_o$ is small compared to 1, and

$$20 \log|G| \approx 0 .$$

At high frequencies,

$$20 \log|G| \approx -20 \log \frac{\omega}{\omega_o} = 20 \log \omega_o - 20 \log \omega , \tag{5.33}$$

which is a straight line with a slope of −20 db/decade, that intersects the ω axis at $\omega = \omega_o$. The gain curve for Eq. (5.30) can therefore be drawn approximately as the solid line in Fig. 5.12. At the break the true gain is

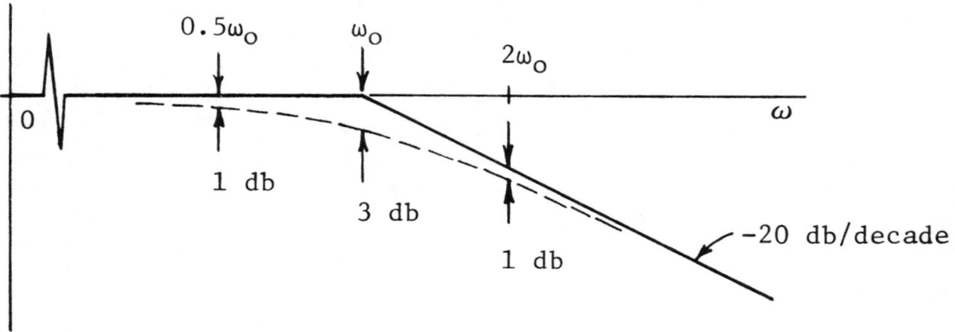

Fig. 5.12. Single downward break.

$$20 \log|G| = -20 \log|1 + j1| = -3\ db . \tag{5.34}$$

Therefore the straight-line or asymptotic approximation to the gain curve is in error by 3 db at the break frequency. The error is 1 db at half and twice the break frequency. The exact gain curve is the dotted line. A pole of $G(s)H(s)$ on the negative real axis is said to contribute a *single downward break* to the Bode gain plot.

If $G(s)H(s)$ has a *zero* on the negative real axis, then $G(j\omega)H(j\omega)$ has a factor of the form

$$G(j\omega) = 1 + j\frac{\omega}{\omega_o} \tag{5.35}$$

which contributes a single *upward* break to the Bode gain plot. The gain curve is the reflection of Fig. 5.12 about the ω axis. The phase angle of $G(j\omega)$ is

$$\phi = \tan^{-1}\frac{\omega}{\omega_o}. \tag{5.36}$$

Notice that the phase shift contributed by a single upward or downward break, given by Eq. (5.36) or (5.32), is 45° or −45° at the break frequency, approaches zero at low frequencies, and approaches 90° or −90° at high frequencies. The work of calculating $\phi(\omega)$ for each value of ω is simplified by the servomechanism scale of Fig. 5.13. The scale is intended for use with General Electric FN-265-A or FN-522-B semilog paper, and is the correct size when dimension A is 9.2 in. or 23.4 cm. To use the scale, fold the paper to make a ruler of the 3 CYCLE PHASE or 4 CYCLE PHASE divisions. Using the corresponding semilog paper, lay the ruler parallel to the ω axis, with the arrow (at 45°) at the frequency ω. The contribution of any single upward break to the phase angle at ω is the scale number at the break frequency. The phase angle contributed by a single downward break is the negative of the scale number. The phase angle contributed by a pole or zero at the origin, shown by the scale and verified by Eqs.(5.25) and (5.27), is minus or plus 90°. The reader is invited to draw a single downward break at $\omega = 5$ rad/sec, and confirm that the phase shifts contributed by this break at $\omega = 2$ and $\omega = 10$ rad/sec are approximately −22° and −64°.

4. *Multiple real pole or zero.* If $G(j\omega)H(j\omega)$ has the factor

$$G(j\omega) = \frac{1}{\left(1 + j\dfrac{\omega}{\omega_o}\right)^2} \tag{5.37}$$

the gain of the factor is

$$20 \log|G| = -40 \log|1 + j\omega/\omega_o| \tag{5.38}$$

which contributes a double downward break to the Bode gain plot of $G(j\omega)H(j\omega)$. The asymptotic approximation has a slope of −40 db/decade

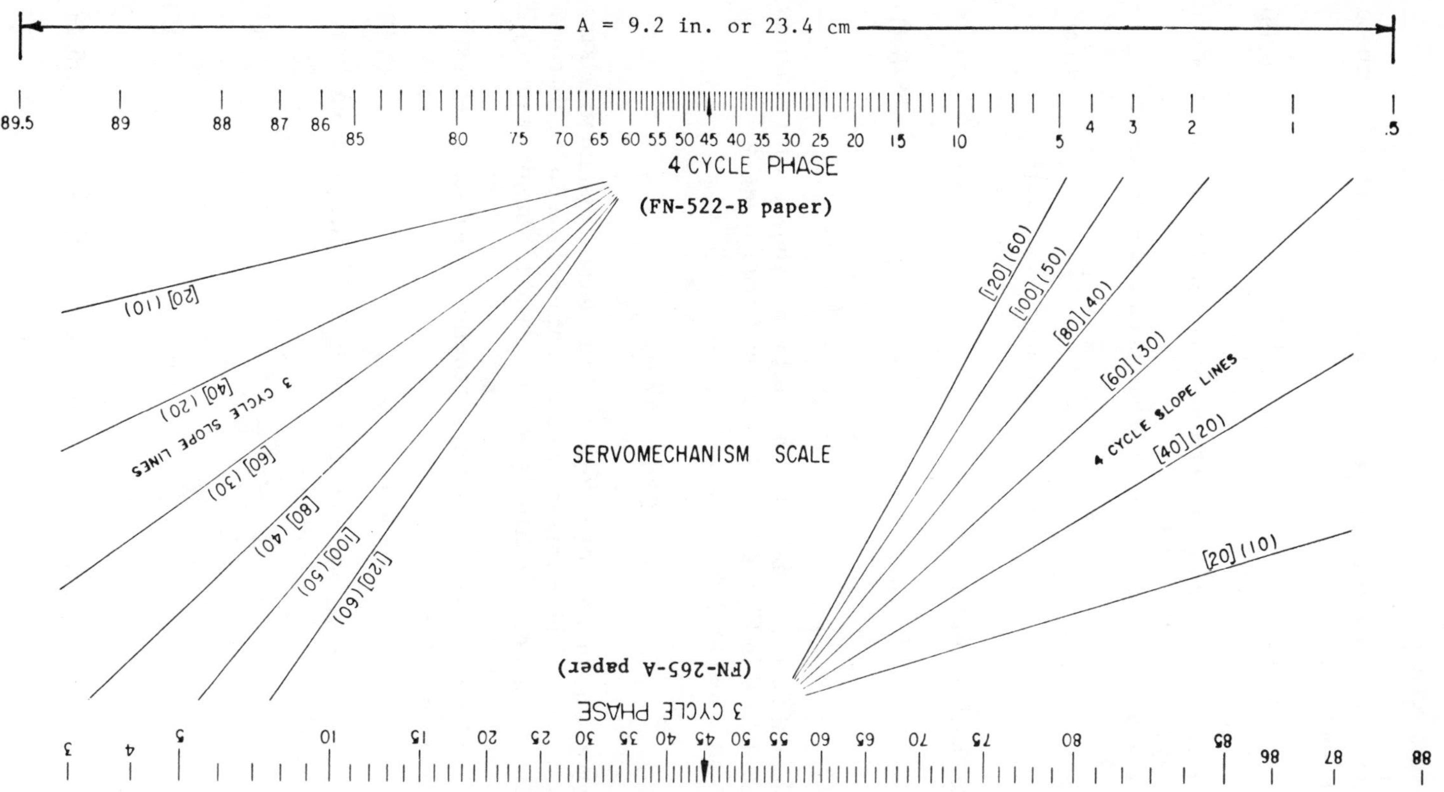

Fig. 5.13. Servomechanism scale.

after the break, and is in error by 6 db at the break frequency. The phase angle of $G(j\omega)$ is

$$\phi = -2 \tan^{-1} \frac{\omega}{\omega_o} . \tag{5.39}$$

The contribution of an mth-order zero or pole of $G(s)H(s)$ to the Bode plots is calculated similarly.

5. *Complex poles or zeros.* If $G(s)H(s)$ has a factor of the form

$$G(s) = \frac{\omega_n^2}{s^2 + 2\zeta\omega_n s + \omega_n^2} = \frac{1}{1 + 2\zeta \dfrac{s}{\omega_n} + \left(\dfrac{s}{\omega_n}\right)^2} , \tag{5.40}$$

then $G(j\omega)H(j\omega)$ has a factor

$$G(j\omega) = \frac{1}{1 + j2\zeta \dfrac{\omega}{\omega_n} - \left(\dfrac{\omega}{\omega_n}\right)^2} . \tag{5.41}$$

The plots of $20 \log|G|$ and ϕ for this factor are shown (with different ordinate labels) in Figs. 4.9 and 4.10. At low frequencies, $20 \log|G| \approx 0$, and at high frequencies

$$20 \log|G| \approx -40 \log \frac{\omega}{\omega_n} , \tag{5.42}$$

which is a straight line with a slope of -40 db/decade, that intersects the ω axis at $\omega = \omega_n$. The asymptotic approximation of the Bode gain curve is easily drawn, and is in error by 6 db or less at the break frequency if $1 \geqslant \zeta \geqslant 0.26$.

6. *Pure Delay.* A linear system might contain a pure delay, defined by its impulse response

$$h(t) = \delta(t - t_1) . \tag{5.43}$$

This pure delay makes no change in the amplitude of a signal, but delays it by the time t_1. Its system function is

$$G(s) = e^{-st_1} \tag{5.44}$$

or

$$G(j\omega) = e^{-j\omega t_1} . \tag{5.45}$$

For this component,

$$20 \log|G| = 0 \qquad \text{and} \qquad \phi = -\omega t_1 . \tag{5.46}$$

The only contribution of a pure delay to the Bode plots is a phase shift that is proportional to frequency ω.

5.7 Determination of Stability

With a little practice, an engineer can quickly add the logarithmic gains and phase angles of the factors to obtain the Bode plots for $G(j\omega)H(j\omega)$. The reader is invited to confirm that the curves for

$$G(j\omega)H(j\omega) = \frac{26.6\left(1 + j\dfrac{\omega}{5.33}\right)}{j\omega\left(1 + j\dfrac{\omega}{2}\right)\left(1 + j\dfrac{\omega}{18.79}\right)} \tag{5.47}$$

are those shown in Fig. 5.14, drawn on FN-265-A semilog paper. To establish the vertical orientation of the approximate gain curve, observe that each factor contributes an approximate gain of one at frequencies lower than its break frequency. At $\omega = 1$, the curve is to the left of every break except the one at the origin. The pole at the origin contributes a gain of one, or zero db, at $\omega = 1$. According to Eq. (5.47), the approximate gain at $\omega = 1$ is

$$20 \log|G(j\omega)H(j\omega)| = 20 \log 26.6 = 28.5 \text{ db} \tag{5.48}$$

as shown in Fig. 5.14. A servomechanism scale reduced by the same amount as Fig. 5.14 will confirm the accuracy of the phase-angle curve at $\omega = 10$ rad/sec. According to the scale, the phase angles contributed by the three downward breaks are $-90°$, $-79°$, and $-27°$. The upward break contributes 62°. Their sum, $-134°$, agrees with the phase-angle curve at $\omega = 10$ rad/sec.

The Bode gain plot of $G(j\omega)H(j\omega)$ has a break to the left of $\omega = 1$ if, for example,

$$G(j\omega)H(j\omega) = \frac{20}{j\omega\left(1 + j\dfrac{\omega}{0.5}\right)}. \tag{5.49}$$

The approximate Bode gain plot is shown in Fig. 5.15. To set the vertical height, either (1) observe that at $\omega = 0.1$, which is to the left of the break, the approximate gain is 200 or 46 db, or (2) observe that without the factor that has the break, the gain at $\omega = 1$ would be 20 or 26 db. Temporarily draw the curve thru this point, and then add the break as in Fig. 5.15.

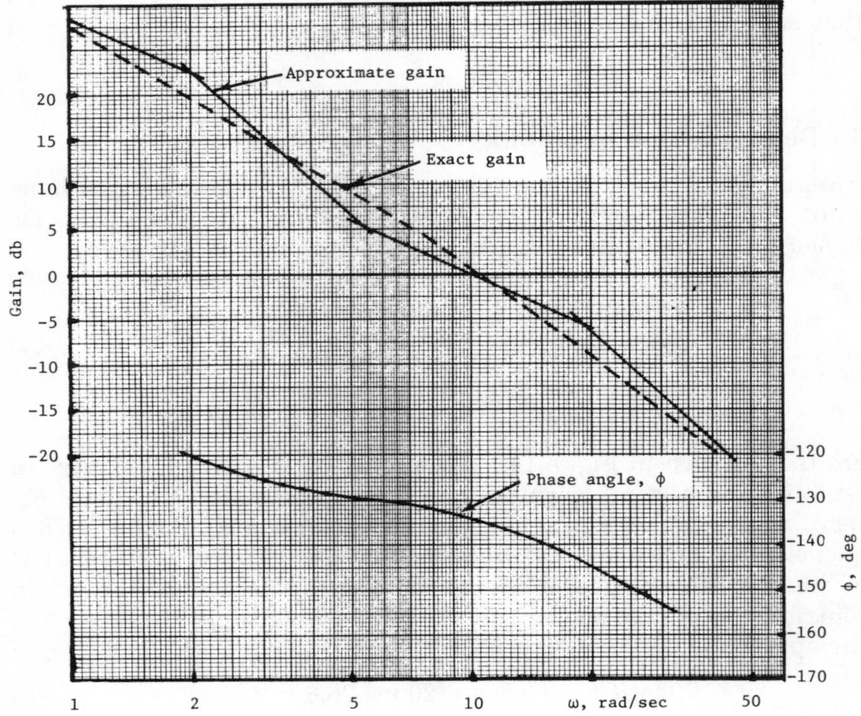

Fig. 5.14. Bode diagrams for Eq. (5.47).

Bode diagrams are in general easier to draw than Nyquist diagrams, and if the system is open-loop stable the Nyquist criterion of stability can be applied to the Bode diagrams. Section 5.4 showed that if all of the poles of $G(s)H(s)$ lie in the left-half plane, the system is closed-loop stable iff the vector $G(j\omega)H(j\omega)$ does not encircle the point $-1 + j0$. According to Fig. 5.10, this is equivalent to saying that the system is stable iff the phase margin is positive. The phase margin can be read on the Bode diagrams. Find the frequency at which the open-loop gain has decreased to 0 db, called the *crossover frequency*. The phase angle at this frequency is ϕ_c, and the phase margin is $180° + \phi_c$. For example, in Fig. 5.14 the crossover frequency is 10.3 rad/sec, $\phi_c = -135°$, and the phase margin is 45°. The system is therefore stable.

If the open-loop transfer function $G(s)H(s)$ has a pole in the right-half plane, the stability of the system is not determined simply by reading the phase margin on the Bode diagrams. The analyst must return to the original Nyquist criterion and determine the number of times the vector

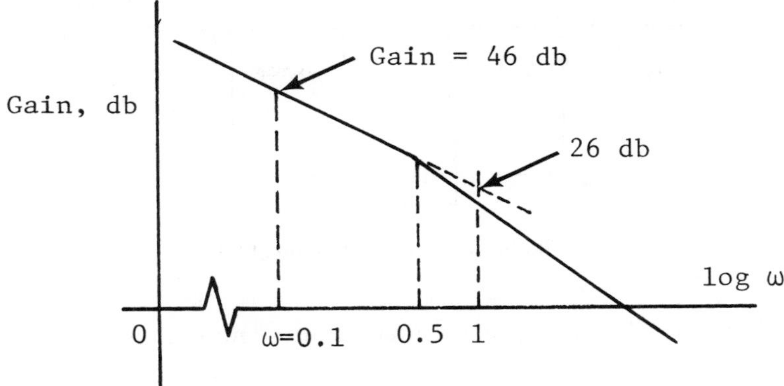

Fig. 5.15. Downward break before $\omega = 1$.

$G(j\omega)H(j\omega)$ encircles the point $-1 + j0$. For systems that are not open-loop stable, a Nyquist diagram is more useful than Bode diagrams for determining closed-loop stability.

The reader is now invited to draw on FN-265-A or FN-522-B semilog paper the Bode gain and phase-angle curves for the system whose open-loop transfer function is

$$G(j\omega)H(j\omega) = \frac{2\left(1 + j\dfrac{\omega}{0.1}\right)}{j\omega\left(1 + j\dfrac{\omega}{0.4}\right)^2}. \tag{5.50}$$

Is this system stable?

5.8 Bode Diagrams of Second-Order Systems

Bode diagrams are popular with control engineers because for many systems the crossover frequency and phase margin allow an accurate prediction of the closed-loop behavior of the system. The reasons for this fortunate fact, briefly stated, are (1) the closed-loop behavior of a second-order system is determined by its crossover frequency and phase margin, and (2) according to the second-order tendency principle explained in Chapter 4, many linear systems behave like second-order systems. To explain these reasons, first draw the Bode diagrams of a second-order system that is in the standard form of Fig. 5.16. The closed-loop transfer function is

$$\frac{G(s)}{1 + G(s)H(s)} = \frac{k}{s^2 + 2\zeta\omega_n s + \omega_n^2}. \tag{5.51}$$

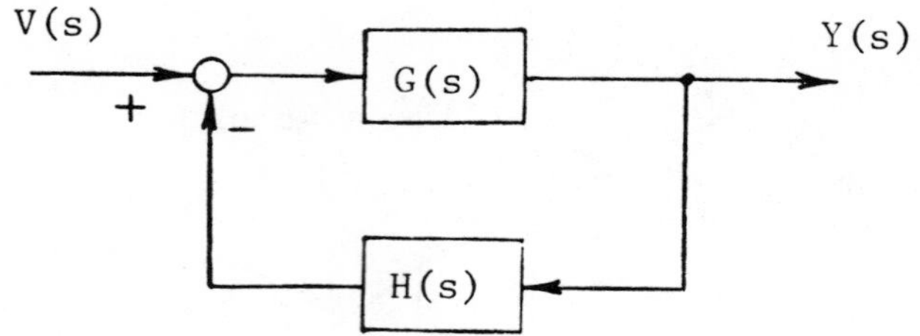

Fig. 5.16. Standard block diagram.

The feedforward and feedback transmittances must therefore be

$$G(s) = \frac{k}{s(s + 2\zeta\omega_n)} \qquad \text{and} \qquad H(s) = \frac{\omega_n^2}{k}. \tag{5.52}$$

The open-loop transfer function is

$$G(s)H(s) = \frac{\omega_n^2}{s(s + 2\zeta\omega_n)} \tag{5.53}$$

whose Bode diagrams are shown in Fig. 5.17. Now calculate the cross-

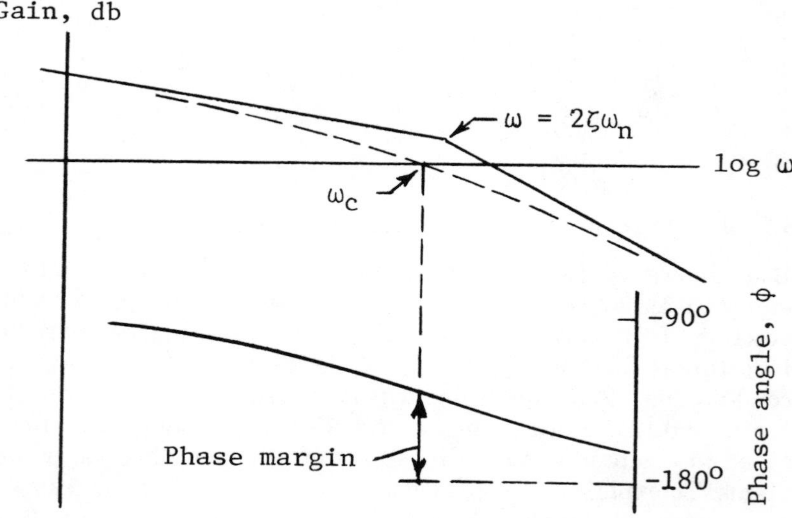

Fig. 5.17. Bode diagrams of a second-order system.

over frequency ω_c and phase margin γ in terms of the damping ration ζ and undamped natural frequency ω_n, since the latter two determine the closed-loop performance of the system. Since the open-loop gain is unity at the crossover frequency,

$$|G(j\omega_c)H(j\omega_c)| = \frac{\omega_n^2}{\omega_c\sqrt{\omega_c^2 + (2\zeta\omega_n)^2}} = 1$$

and

$$\frac{\omega_c}{\omega_n} = \sqrt{\sqrt{4\zeta^4 + 1} - 2\zeta^2}\ . \qquad (5.55)$$

This equation is plotted in Fig. 5.18.

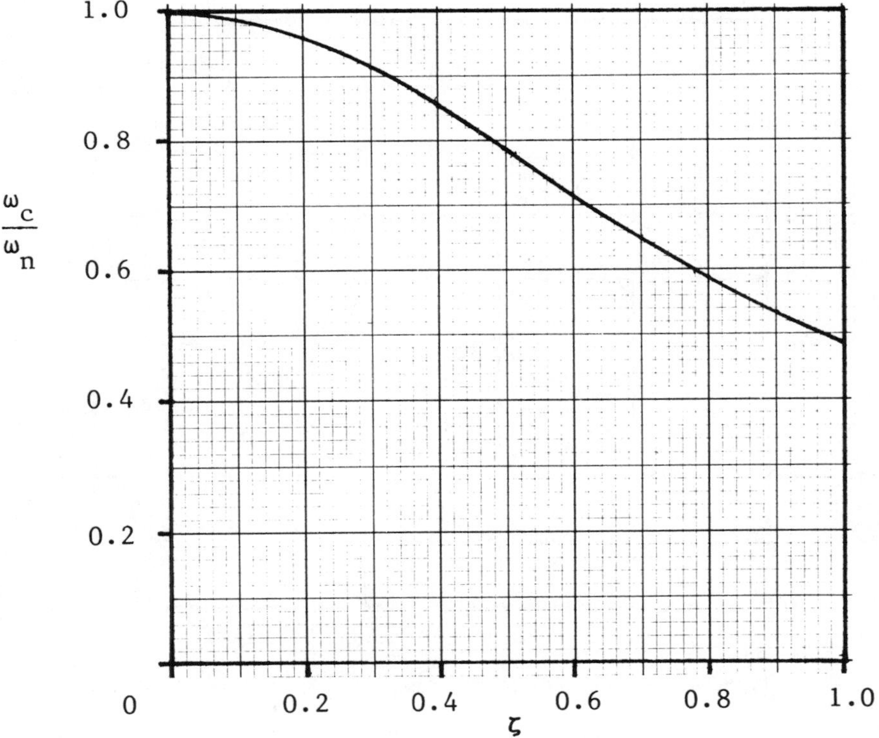

Fig. 5.18. Ratio of crossover frequency to undamped natural frequency of a second-order system.

The phase shift of $G(j\omega)H(j\omega)$ for the second-order system at crossover is

$$\phi_c = -90° - \tan^{-1}\frac{\omega_c}{2\zeta\omega_n}$$

$$= -90° - \tan^{-1}\frac{1}{2\zeta}\sqrt{\sqrt{4\zeta^4+1}-2\zeta^2}\,. \tag{5.56}$$

Therefore the phase margin is

$$\gamma = 180° + \phi_c = \tan^{-1}\frac{2\zeta}{\sqrt{\sqrt{4\zeta^4+1}-2\zeta^2}}\,. \tag{5.57}$$

This equation is plotted in Fig. 5.19. For ζ less than 0.7, the curve can be

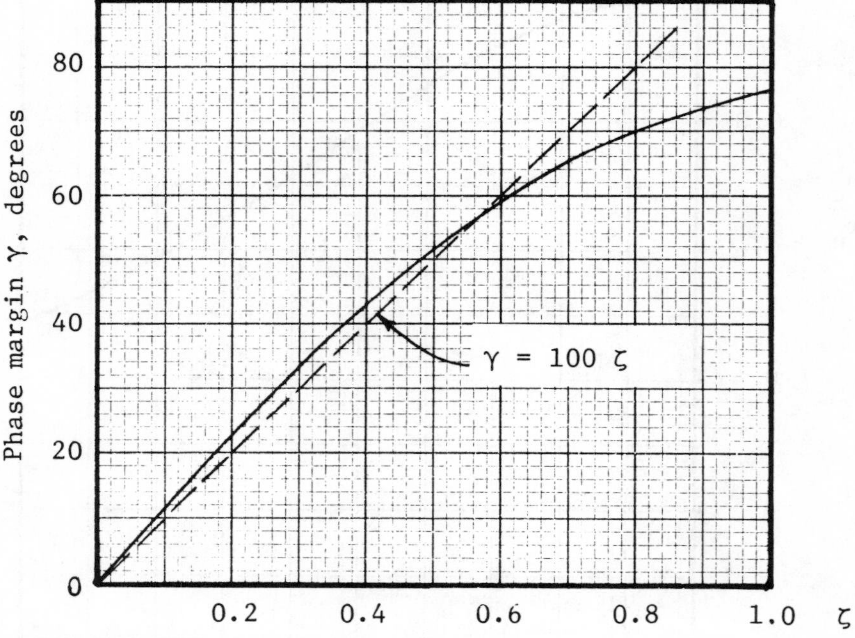

Fig. 5.19. Phase margin as a function of damping ratio for a second-order system.

approximated with reasonable accuracy by the straight line

$$\gamma = 100\zeta\,. \tag{5.58}$$

Figs. 5.19 and 5.18 permit calculation of the closed-loop response of a second-order system when its Bode diagrams have been drawn. They are useful to engineers because many higher-order linear systems behave like second-order systems. As illustrated by Eq. (4.58), typically all but two of the closed-loop poles are either remote from the origin or close to a zero, and therefore contribute little to the transient response or frequency response. The closed-loop transfer function is dominated by a complex pair of poles, and therefore is approximated by Eq. (5.51). Writing the closed-loop transfer function as

$$\frac{G(s)}{1 + G(s)H(s)} = \frac{1}{H(s)} \cdot \frac{G(s)H(s)}{1 + G(s)H(s)} \tag{5.59}$$

shows that if a second-order and a higher-order system have nearly the same closed-loop transfer function and the same feedback transmittance, namely the constant

$$H(s) = \frac{\omega_n^2}{k}, \tag{5.60}$$

then the open-loop transfer functions $G(s)H(s)$ must be nearly the same. The Bode diagrams of the higher-order system therefore look like Fig. 5.17. Figs. 5.18 and 5.19 may be used to determine the closed-loop response of the higher-order system.

A summary of this reasoning is the following: if a linear system has constant feedback and its closed-loop transfer function is dominated by a complex pair of poles, its closed-loop behavior can be determined with reasonable accuracy from its Bode diagrams, with the help of Figs. 5.18 and 5.19. For example, suppose that

$$G(s) = \frac{8000(s+2)}{s(s+1)(s+20)(s+50)} \quad \text{and} \quad H(s) = 2\,. \tag{5.61}$$

The closed-loop transfer function

$$\frac{G(s)}{1 + G(s)H(s)} = \frac{8000(s+2)}{(s+2.13)(s+57.3)[(s+5.77)^2 + (15.13)^2]} \tag{5.62}$$

is dominated by the pair of complex poles. Now

$$\begin{aligned} G(j\omega)H(j\omega) &= \frac{16{,}000(2+j\omega)}{j\omega(1+j\omega)(20+j\omega)(50+j\omega)} \\ &= \frac{32\left(1 + j\dfrac{\omega}{2}\right)}{j\omega(1+j\omega)\left(1 + j\dfrac{\omega}{20}\right)\left(1 + j\dfrac{\omega}{50}\right)}\,. \end{aligned} \tag{5.63}$$

The Bode diagrams are shown in Fig. 5.20. The vertical orientation of

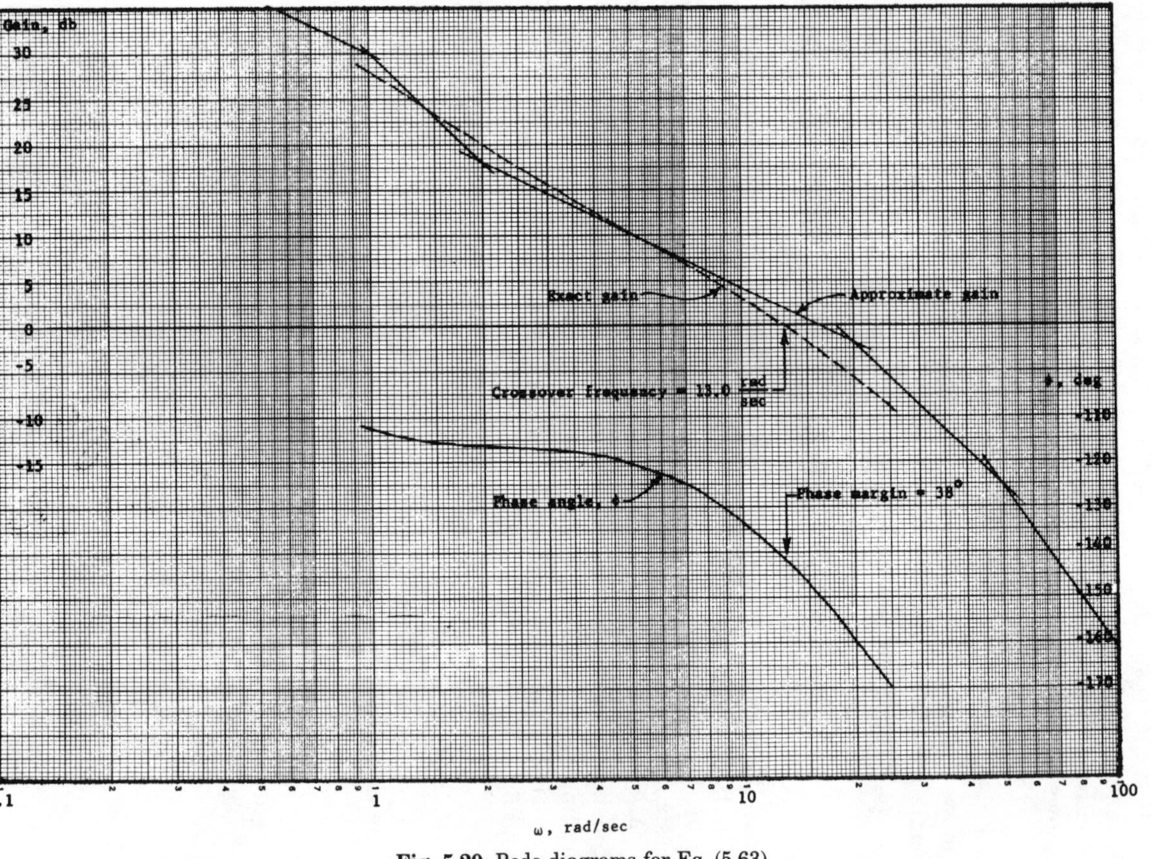

Fig. 5.20. Bode diagrams for Eq. (5.63).

the gain curve is established by observing that at $\omega = 1$, the asymptotic approximation of the gain is

$$20 \log 32 = 30.1 \text{ db}. \tag{5.64}$$

The crossover frequency ω_c is 13.0 rad/sec, and the phase margin γ is 38°. According to Fig. 5.19 the damping ratio ζ is 0.35. Then Fig. 5.18 shows that

$$\frac{\omega_c}{\omega_n} = 0.89 \tag{5.65}$$

and

$$\omega_n = \frac{13.0}{0.89} = 14.6 \text{ rad/sec} . \tag{5.66}$$

The closed-loop transfer function is approximately

$$\frac{G(s)}{1 + G(s)H(s)} = \frac{k}{s^2 + 2\zeta\omega_n s + \omega_n^2} . \tag{5.67}$$

The constant is determined with the help of Eq. (5.60):

$$k = \frac{\omega_n^2}{H(s)} = \frac{(14.6)^2}{2} = 106.6 . \tag{5.68}$$

Now the transfer function of the equivalent second-order system is known:

$$\frac{G(s)}{1 + G(s)H(s)} = \frac{106.6}{s^2 + 10.22s + 213.2} = \frac{106.6}{(s + 5.11)^2 + (13.7)^2} \tag{5.69}$$

and its response to any input can be determined. The amplitude of the frequency response, found by replacing s by $j\omega$ in Eq. (5.69), is shown as the dotted line in Fig. 5.21. The exact frequency response of the system, obtained by replacing s by $j\omega$ in Eq. (5.62), is the solid line. The points for these curves can be obtained either by (1) a computer program that calculates $G(j\omega)/[1 + G(j\omega)H(j\omega)]$ when $G(s)$ and $H(s)$ are specified, or (2) the use of a Nichols chart, which will be described in the next chapter.

This explanation has shown the use of the second-order tendency principle in analyzing higher-order linear systems. The next chapter will show its advantage in designing them. If the damping ratio ζ and undamped natural frequency ω_n of the dominant poles are specified, or may be calculated from the specified overshoot and settling time, the desired phase margin and crossover frequency can be determined from

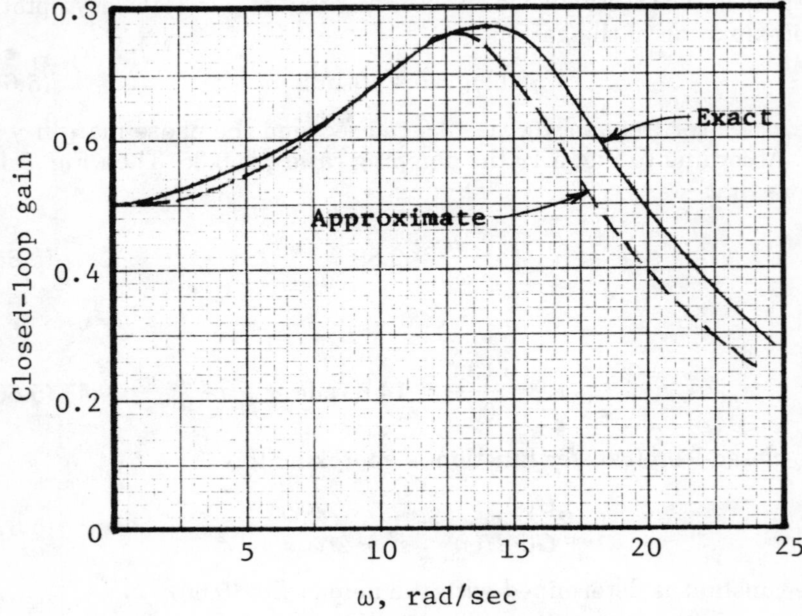

Fig. 5.21. Frequency response of the system represented by Eqs. (3.62).

Figs. 5.19 and 5.18. The compensating networks needed by the system to meet the specifications can be determined readily by manipulating the Bode diagrams to obtain the desired phase margin and crossover frequency.

Chapter 6

COMPENSATION OF FEEDBACK-CONTROL SYSTEMS

6.1 Introduction

The reader who has understood the preceding three chapters now knows how to determine whether a fixed linear system is stable, and knows how to calculate its transient and steady-state response to any input. Now consider the practical problem of improving the system so that it meets the desired specifications. The improvement will be accomplished by compensating networks, designed either on the complex s plane or on the Bode diagrams. Examples will show that the strengths and weaknesses of the two methods complement each other. The chapter begins with a discussion of steady-state error, which like overshoot and settling time is frequently specified for practical control systems.

6.2 Error Constants

The *system error* of the standard feedback-control system in Fig. 6.1 is

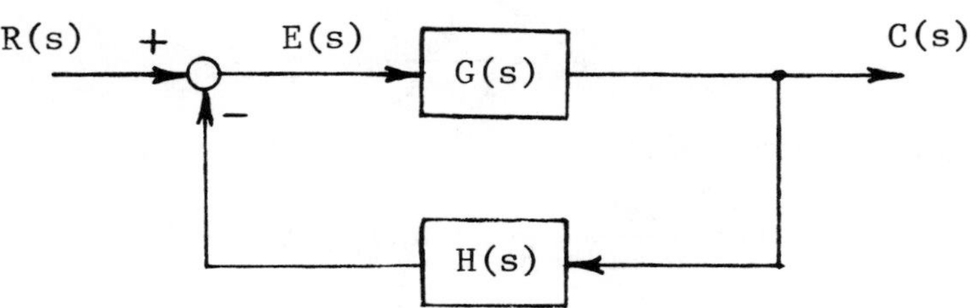

Fig. 6.1. Standard block diagram.

the difference between its input and output, $r(t) - c(t)$. After a change in the input signal, and after the transient in the output has subsided, the difference is called the *steady-state* system error. For many systems such as position controls, the steady-state system error should be small. It can be calculated from the open-loop transfer function. First define the *actuating error* $e(t)$ of the system as the input to the forward block. Then in terms of the Laplace transform of the input, $R(s)$, and of the output, $C(s)$,

$$E(s) = R(s) - H(s)C(s) = R(s) - G(s)H(s)E(s) \tag{6.1}$$

and

$$E(s) = \frac{R(s)}{1 + G(s)H(s)} . \tag{6.2}$$

If the feedback is unity, $H(s) = 1$, and $e(t)$ is also the system error. According to the final-value theorem, the steady-state actuating error is

$$e_{ss} = \lim_{t\to\infty} e(t) = \lim_{s\to 0} sE(s) = \lim_{s\to 0} \frac{s\,R(s)}{1 + G(s)H(s)} . \tag{6.3}$$

If the input to the system is the step

$$r(t) = k_0\, U(t) , \tag{6.4}$$

then

$$R(s) = \frac{k_0}{s} \qquad \text{and} \qquad e_{ss} = \lim_{s\to 0} \frac{k_0}{1 + G(s)H(s)} . \tag{6.5}$$

If the *position error constant* is defined as

$$K_p = \lim_{s\to 0} G(s)H(s) , \tag{6.6}$$

then

$$e_{ss} = \frac{k_0}{1 + K_p} . \tag{6.7}$$

For example, suppose that

$$G(s) = \frac{24(s+1)}{(s+2)(s+3)} \qquad \text{and} \qquad H(s) = 1 . \tag{6.8}$$

This is called a *type* 0 *system*, because the open-loop transfer function $G(s)H(s)$ has no pole at the origin (where $s = 0$). For this system the position error constant K_p is 4, and the steady-state error is

$$e_{ss} = \frac{k_0}{1+4} = \frac{k_0}{5} . \tag{6.9}$$

This system would make a poor position controller, because the output does not equal the input. The steady-state error can be reduced by increasing the gain in the forward block. A better way is to design the forward elements so that $G(s)$ contains a pole at the origin. For example, if

$$G(s)H(s) = \frac{24(s+1)}{s(s+2)(s+3)}, \tag{6.10}$$

the position error constant K_p is infinite. Then according to Eq. (6.7), $e_{ss} = 0$. This is a *type* 1 *system,* since $G(s)H(s)$ has one pole at the origin. Notice that a system of type 1 or higher has no steady-state actuating error if the input is a step.

If the input to a type 1 system is the ramp $r(t) = k_1 t$, then

$$R(s) = k_1/s^2 \tag{6.11}$$

and

$$e_{ss} = \lim_{s\to 0} \frac{s\,R(s)}{1 + G(s)H(s)} = \lim_{s\to 0} \frac{k_1}{s[1 + G(s)H(s)]} = \lim_{s\to 0} \frac{k_1}{sG(s)H(s)} . \tag{6.12}$$

The *velocity error constant* is defined as

$$K_v = \lim_{s\to 0} sG(s)H(s) . \tag{6.13}$$

Then the steady-state error is

$$e_{ss} = k_1/K_v . \tag{6.14}$$

For the system of Eq. (6.10), $K_v = 4$ and therefore $e_{ss} = k_1/4$. If the system is a gun director, and the gunsight is tracking the target at a steady angular velocity of k_1 rad/sec, the gun lags behind the target by k_1/K_v radians. This tracking error can of course be reduced by increasing the gain in $G(s)$. If $G(s)$ is redesigned to have two poles at the origin, the system is type 2. Then $K_v = \infty$ and $e_{ss} = 0$. A type 2 system has a steady-state actuating error if the input is the parabola $r(t) = k_2 t^2$, but not if the input is a step or a ramp.

6.3 Compensating Networks

Frequently the original design of a feedback-control system must be altered because its performance does not meet all the specifications, such as steady-state error, overshoot, and settling time. One effective alteration consists of adding a compensating electrical network in cascade with the amplifiers, motors, and other components in the feedforward block. Two frequently-used compensating networks are the *phase-lead* and *phase-lag networks* (or simply lead and lag networks) shown in Figs. 6.2 and 6.3. They get their names from the shapes of their Bode

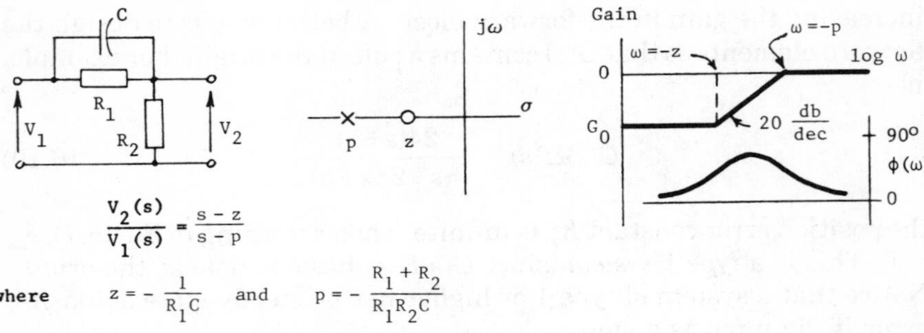

Fig. 6.2. Phase-lead network.

phase-angle curves. The transfer functions and Bode diagrams shown in the figures apply when the networks are open-circuited, i.e., when the input impedance of the component connected to their output terminals is negligibly high. An amplifier with high input impedance connected to the output of one of these networks is called a *buffer amplifier*, since it isolates the network from the low-impedance components that follow. The effect of adding a compensating network to a system can be evaluated either on the *s* plane or on a Bode diagram. The advantages and disadvantages of both methods will be investigated.

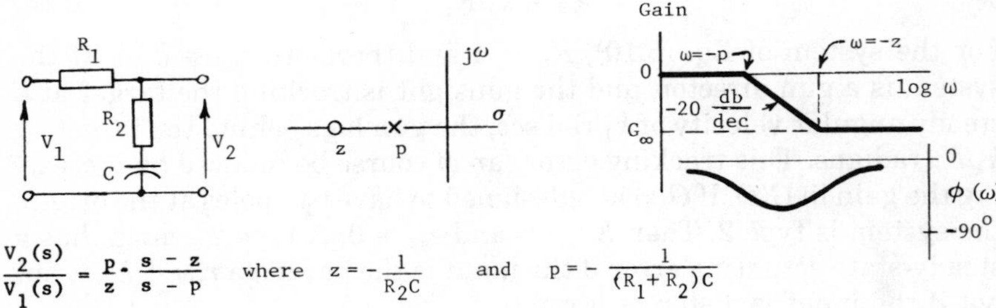

Fig. 6.3. Phase-lag network.

6.4 Design of a Lead Network on the s Plane

An example will show how a lead network can be designed to make a system fulfill its specifications. A system in the standard form of Fig. 6.1 has

$$G(s) = \frac{k}{s(s+2)} \qquad \text{and} \qquad H(s) = 1 \,. \tag{6.15}$$

The gain k can be varied. The system must have (1) an overshoot of 30 percent or less following a step input, (2) a settling time of less than 1 sec, and (3) a steady-state error e_{ss} for a ramp input that is 5 percent or less of the ramp slope k_1. To be safe, design for an overshoot of 20 percent, which according to Fig. 4.6 requires a damping ratio ζ of 0.46 for the dominant pair of poles. According to Eq. (4.26), the product $\zeta\omega_n$ must be greater than 3.91. The loci of the poles of the closed-loop transfer function are shown in Fig. 6.4. The loci coalesce at $\sigma = -1$ on the

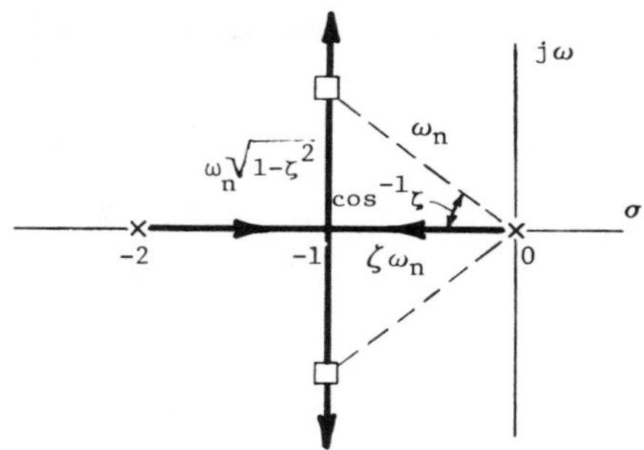

Fig. 6.4. Closed-loop poles before compensation.

real axis when $k = 1$. Clearly the product $\zeta\omega_n$ is 1 for all values of k greater than 1, and a compensating network is needed. A lead network is needed that will force the root loci to pass thru the points for which $\zeta\omega_n = 4$ and $\zeta = 0.46$, namely $s = -4 \pm j7.72$. First, plot the desired complex closed-loop poles in Fig. 6.5, and for convenience put the zero z of the lead network directly between them, so that $z = -4$. The sum of the angles between the real axis and the vectors from all the open-loop poles and zeros to a point on the root loci must be 180°. The angles of the vectors from $s = 0, -2$, and -4 to the upper of the complex closed-loop poles are 117.4, 104.5, and 90 degrees. Then if θ is the angle of the vector from the pole of the lead network,

$$90 - 117.4 - 104.5 - \theta = 180 \tag{6.16}$$

and

$$\theta = 48.1^\circ . \tag{6.17}$$

The dotted line can now be drawn down to the pole of the lead network, which is found to be at $p = -10.93$.

The value of gain k required to put the closed-poles at $-4 \pm j7.72$ can now be calculated. According to the eighth rule for root-locus plots in

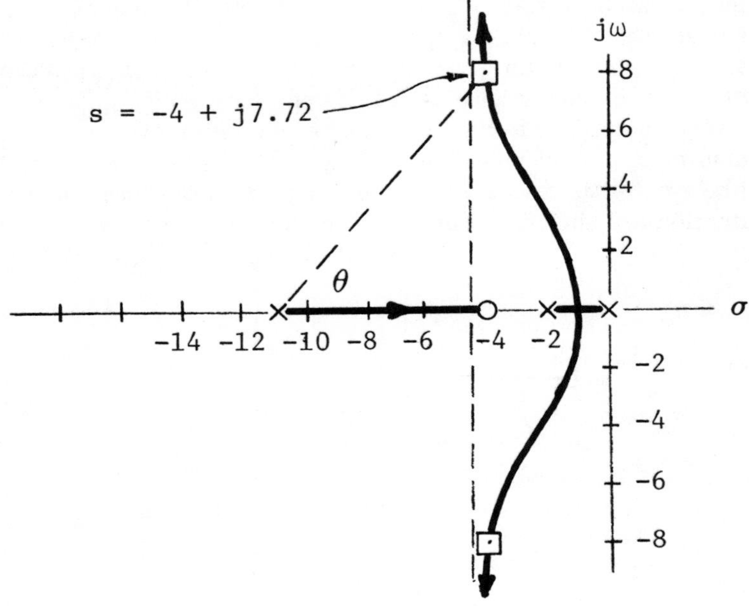

Fig. 6.5. Closed-loop poles after compensation.

Chapter 3, the product and quotient of the lengths of all the vectors from the open-loop poles and zeros to a point on the root loci equals the value of k there. The lengths of the vectors from $s = 0, -2, -4$, and -10.93 to $s = -4 + j7.72$ are 8.69, 7.97, 7.72, and 10.37. Therefore at $s = -4 + j7.72$,

$$k = \frac{(8.69)(7.97)(10.37)}{7.72} = 93.0 \,. \tag{6.18}$$

The open-loop transfer function of the compensated system is

$$G(s)H(s) = \frac{93.0(s+4)}{s(s+2)(s+10.93)} \,. \tag{6.19}$$

The closed-loop transfer function, calculated by a computer, is

$$\frac{C(s)}{R(s)} = \frac{G(s)}{1 + G(s)H(s)} = \frac{93.0(s+4)}{(s + 4.93)[(s + 4.00)^2 + (7.71)^2]} \,. \tag{6.20}$$

The step response $c(t)$, also computer calculated, is shown by the solid line in Fig. 6.6. For comparison, the step response of the ideal second-order system with closed-loop poles at $s = -4 \pm j7.72$ is shown by the dotted line. The closed-loop transfer function of the latter system is

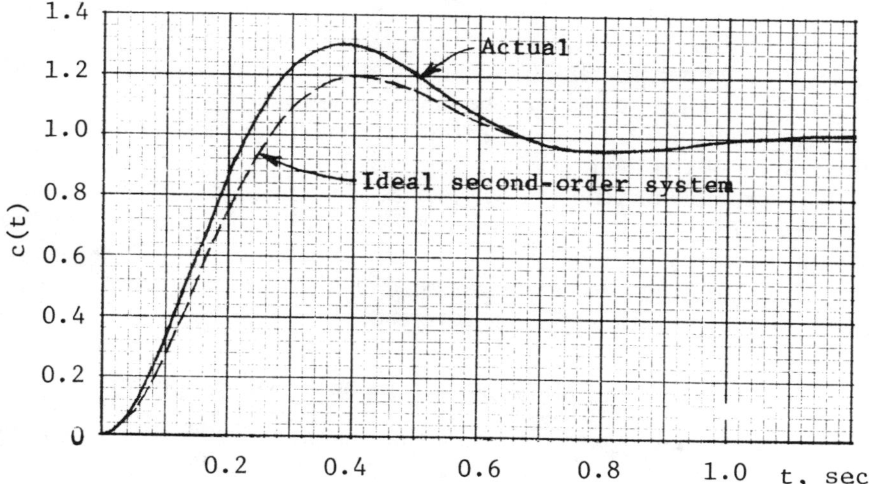

Fig. 6.6. Step response of the system compensated on the s plane.

$$\frac{C(s)}{R(s)} = \frac{75.6}{(s+4)^2 + (7.72)^2} . \tag{6.21}$$

(The numerator is calculated with the help of the final-value theorem, to make the steady-state value of the step response equal to 1.) The curves show that the compensated system does not behave exactly like a second-order system. The closed-loop pole at $s = -4.93$ does not completely cancel the zero at $s = -4$. As a result, the overshoot of the compensated system is 30 percent instead of 20, but does not exceed the specified maximum of 30. The settling time of the compensated system is 0.95 sec, which meets the specification.

The velocity error constant of the compensated system is

$$K_v = \lim_{s \to 0} s\, G(s)H(s) = \frac{(93.0)(4)}{(2)(10.93)} = 17.0 . \tag{6.22}$$

According to the third specification and Eq. (6.14), the required velocity error constant is

$$K_v = \frac{k_1}{e_{ss}} = 20 . \tag{6.23}$$

Unfortunately this goal has not been reached. The steady-state error, namely the difference between the system input and output, is greater than 5 percent of the ramp slope. The complex closed-loop poles must be moved farther out from the origin, to make the vectors from the open-loop poles longer, thereby increasing k and therefore K_v. The damping ratio ζ of the new poles may be made somewhat larger than 0.46, to lower the overshoot. The new settling time will be less than the specified maximum of 1 second.

This example has illustrated the ease of compensating on the s plane to meet step-response requirements, and the difficulty of achieving the required steady-state error. The latter is a cut-and-try process. When the compensating network is designed on the Bode diagram, the easy and difficult requirements are reversed.

6.5 Design of a Lead Network on the Bode Diagram

Again the task is to compensate the system of Fig. 6.1 for which

$$G(s) = \frac{k}{s(s+2)} \qquad \text{and} \qquad H(s) = 1 \tag{6.24}$$

so that the overshoot following a step input is less than 30 percent, the settling time is less than 1 sec, and the steady-state error for a ramp input is 5 percent or less of the ramp slope. Start by plotting the Bode diagrams of an uncompensated system that fulfills the steady-state error requirement. Since the required velocity error constant is

$$K_v = \lim_{s\to 0} sG(s)H(s) = \lim_{s\to 0} \frac{k}{s+2} = \frac{k}{2} = 20\,, \tag{6.25}$$

the required forward gain k is 40. The open-loop transfer function is therefore

$$G(j\omega)H(j\omega) = \frac{40}{j\omega(j\omega+2)} = \frac{20}{j\omega\left(1 + \dfrac{j\omega}{2}\right)}\,. \tag{6.26}$$

Notice that K_v for this or any type 1 system is the height of the Bode approximate gain curve where it passes thru $\omega = 1$ (if any breaks to the left of $\omega = 1$ are ignored). To make this point clear, consider a system for which

$$G(s)H(s) = \frac{k(s+3)}{s(s+4)(s+0.5)}\,. \tag{6.27}$$

The velocity error constant is

$$K_v = \lim_{s\to 0} sG(s)H(s) = \lim_{s\to 0} \frac{k(s+3)}{(s+4)(s+0.5)} = 1.5k\,. \tag{6.28}$$

The sinusoidal open-loop transfer function is

$$G(j\omega)H(j\omega) = \frac{k(j\omega + 3)}{j\omega\,(j\omega + 4)(j\omega + 0.5)} = \frac{3k\left(1 + j\dfrac{\omega}{3}\right)}{(4)(0.5)j\omega\left(1 + j\dfrac{\omega}{4}\right)\left(1 + j\dfrac{\omega}{0.5}\right)} . \tag{6.29}$$

The height of the asymptotic gain curve where it would pass thru $\omega = 1$ without break at $\omega = 0.5$ is

$$G(j1)H(j1) = \frac{3k}{(4)(0.5)} = 1.5\,k\,, \tag{6.30}$$

which is the velocity error constant, K_v.

For the uncompensated system of Eq. (6.26), the Bode gain and phase-angle diagrams are shown in Fig. 6.7. As before, choose a damping ratio ζ of 0.46 for a reasonable overshoot, and choose $\zeta\omega_n = 4$ to satisfy the settling-time requirement. According to Figs. 5.19 and 5.18, the phase margin should be 48 degrees and the crossover frequency on the Bode diagram should be at least

$$\omega_c = 0.82\,\omega_n = \frac{(0.82)(4)}{0.46} = 7.1 \text{ rad/sec}\,. \tag{6.31}$$

To be safe, set the crossover frequency at 10 rad/sec. (This prudent choice will spare the reader a false start, and will be justified later.) Fig. 6.7 shows that at $\omega = 10$ the phase margin is 11 degrees. The extra 37 degrees can be obtained by placing a lead network among the feedforward components. The lead network could be designed by placing the servomechanism scale of Fig. 5.13 along the ω axis of the Bode diagram with the arrow at the crossover frequency, and locating a zero and a pole so that the difference in their phase-angle contributions at $\omega = 10$ is 37 degrees. An infinite number of suitable choices is possible. To be systematic, locate the zero and pole so that the maximum phase shift of the lead network is 37 degrees, and occurs at $\omega = 10$. Then the lead network will not have to produce any more phase shift than is needed at the crossover frequency. The phase-shift curve is shown in Fig. 6.2. A straightforward calculation shows that the phase shift has a peak value of

$$\phi_m = \sin^{-1}\frac{\alpha - 1}{\alpha + 1} \tag{6.32}$$

where $\alpha = p/z$. The frequency at which the peak occurs is

$$\omega_m = \sqrt{zp}\,, \tag{6.33}$$

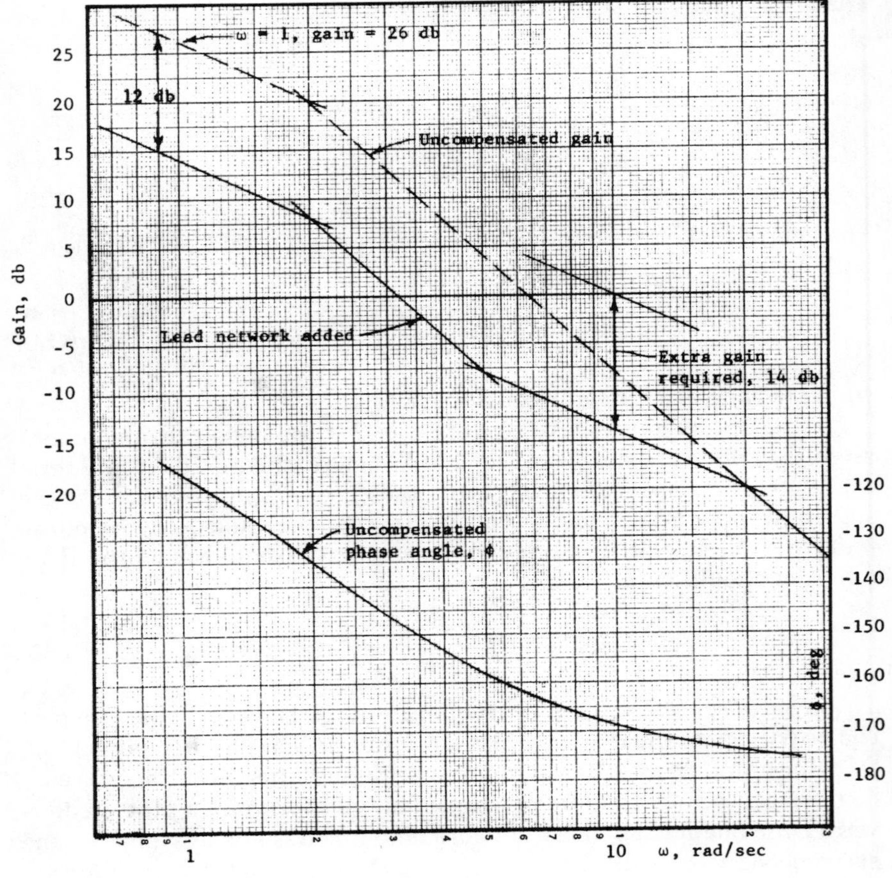

Fig. 6.7. Bode diagrams of the uncompensated system.

which is midway between the zero and pole on the logarithmic frequency scale. In terms of ω_m and α, the locations of the pole and zero are

$$p = -\omega_m \sqrt{\alpha} \qquad \text{and} \qquad z = -\frac{\omega_m}{\sqrt{\alpha}} . \tag{6.34}$$

Let ω_m be the crossover frequency and ϕ_m be the extra phase margin required there. Then α, p, and z can be calculated. In the example,

$$\omega_m = 10, \qquad \phi_m = 37°, \qquad \alpha = 4.025, \qquad p = -20.1, \qquad z = -4.98 . \tag{6.35}$$

The Bode diagram of the system with the lead network added is shown in Fig. 6.7. Notice that the gain of the lead network at low frequencies is

$G_0 = -12$ db. This attenuation must be compensated by 12 db of additional gain in an amplifier in the feedforward block, to restore the velocity error constant K_v to its required value of 20. Notice also that after the lead network is added, the gain curve must be raised 14 db to make it cross over at $\omega = 10$ rad/sec. Therefore the amplifier will be required to add 14 db to the open-loop gain. The Bode diagrams of the system compensated by the lead network and extra amplifier gain are shown in Fig. 6.8. The approximate gain curve, having lost 12 db and

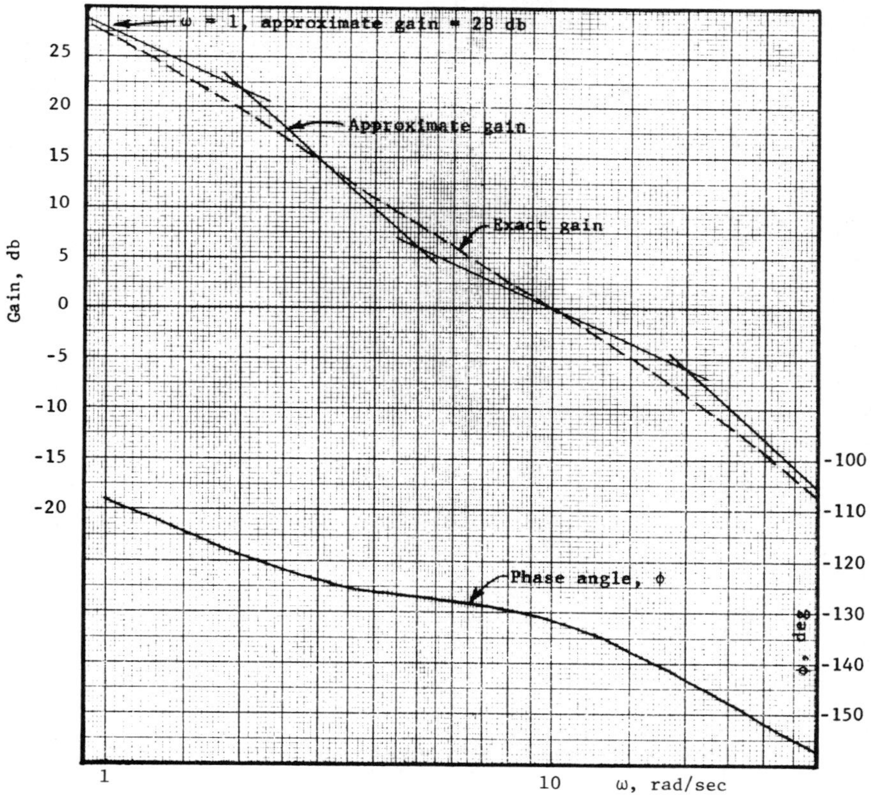

Fig. 6.8. Bode diagrams of the compensated system.

gained 14 db, now passes thru $\omega = 1$ at 28 db, or 2 db higher than before the compensation. The steady-state error will therefore be less than the required 5 percent of the ramp slope. Since the numerical value of 28 db is 25.1, the open-loop transfer function represented by Fig. 6.8 is

$$G(j\omega)H(j\omega) = \frac{25.1\left(1 + j\,\dfrac{\omega}{4.98}\right)}{j\omega\left(1 + j\,\dfrac{\omega}{2}\right)\left(1 + j\,\dfrac{\omega}{20.1}\right)} \tag{6.36}$$

or

$$G(s)H(s) = \frac{202.6(s + 4.98)}{s(s+2)(s+20.1)}\,. \tag{6.37}$$

Clearly the steady-state error specification has been fulfilled. Not so clear are the overshoot and settling time. These can be determined with the help of computer programs that calculate first the closed-loop transfer function

$$\frac{C(s)}{R(s)} = \frac{G(s)}{1 + G(s)H(s)} = \frac{202.6(s+4.98)}{(s+7.61)[(s+7.24)^2 + (8.95)^2]} \tag{6.38}$$

and then the step response. The latter is shown in Fig. 6.9. The over-

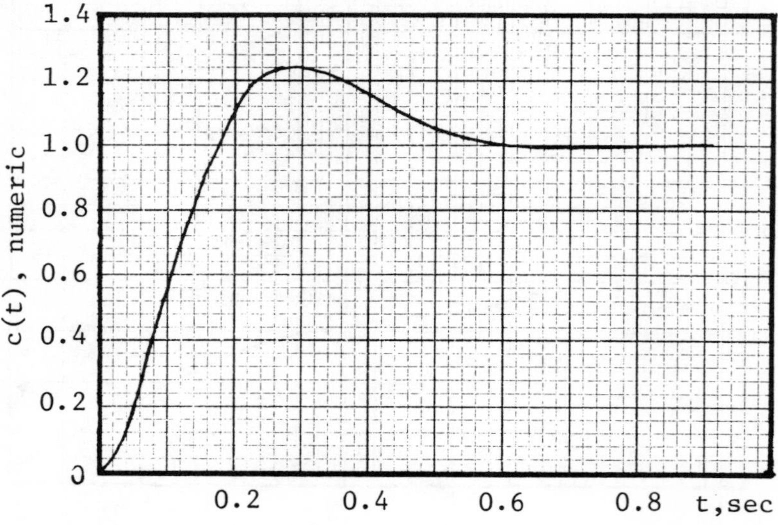

Fig. 6.9. Step response of the system compensated on the Bode diagram.

shoot is 24 percent, and the settling time is about 0.55 sec, both of which are within the specifications. The settling time T_s is less than the specified 1 sec because a crossover frequency ω_c of 10 rad/sec was chosen instead of the 7.1 rad/sec calculated by Eq. (6.31). This choice increased

ω_n and therefore decreased T_s.

Eq. (4.38) does not look very much like the closed-loop transfer function of a second-order system with a damping ratio ζ of 0.46. The pole and zero on the real axis are not close enough to cancel each other, and the damping ratio of the complex pair of poles is 0.63. Fortunately the tendency of the real pole and zero to raise the overshoot was offset by the tendency of the high damping ratio to lower it. As a result the overshoot is within the specified range. This example is typical of the process of choosing a compensating network on the Bode diagram to achieve a desired crossover frequency and phase margin. The process is based on the assumption that the compensated system will act like a second-order system. Experience has shown that this assumption is justified for many "normal" control systems, even when the closed-loop transfer function does not resemble closely that of the ideal second-order system.

The capacitor and resistors of the lead network with $\alpha = 4.025$, $p = -20.1$, and $z = -4.98$ can be chosen according to the equations in Fig. 6.2. One of the components can be chosen arbitrarily. If $C = 1\ \mu\text{F}$, then

$$R_1 = -\frac{1}{zC} = \frac{10^6}{4.98} = 201{,}000 \text{ ohms} . \tag{6.39}$$

Also,

$$\alpha = \frac{p}{z} = \frac{R_1 + R_2}{R_2}$$

and

$$R_2 = \frac{R_1}{\alpha - 1} = \frac{1}{z(\alpha - 1)C} = 66{,}400 \text{ ohms} . \tag{6.40}$$

These components are all of practical size and can be obtained easily. The input impedance of the device following the lead network should be high compared to R_2, say a megohm or higher, so that it will not affect the transfer function of the lead network.

6.6 Comparison of Compensation on the s Plane and on the Bode Diagram

This example has shown the relative merits of the two procedures for choosing compensating networks. On the Bode diagram, the effect of a compensating network on the steady-state error is immediately evident, and any correction in the amplification in $G(s)$ can be made easily. However, the closed-loop step response is known only approximately, and must be checked either by a computer calculation or by operating the system. In the s plane, the designer can put the closed-loop dominant poles exactly where desired to obtain the specified step response. However, a computer calculation is still required to determine the effect of the other closed-loop poles and zeros. Another calculation is needed to determine the steady-state error, after the compensating network is chosen.

6.7 The Nichols Chart

After a system in the form of Fig. 6.1 has been compensated by either method, the open-loop transfer function $G(j\omega)H(j\omega)$ is known. The amplitude and phase angle of the closed-loop frequency response,

$$\frac{G(j\omega)}{1 + G(j\omega)H(j\omega)} = \frac{1}{H(j\omega)} \cdot \frac{G(j\omega)H(j\omega)}{1 + G(j\omega)H(j\omega)}, \tag{6.41}$$

can be calculated by a computer. An interesting pre-computer method for performing this calculation, which also gives a physical picture of the closed-loop frequency response, is the Nichols chart, named for N.B. Nichols. The chart, shown in Fig. 6.10, has a rectangular coordinate system whose coordinates are the phase angle and gain of the open-loop transfer function. Superimposed on it are two families of curves representing the gain and phase angle of

$$\frac{G(j\omega)H(j\omega)}{1 + G(j\omega)H(j\omega)}.$$

If the feedback transmittance $H(j\omega)$ is unity, the closed-loop frequency response at any given frequency is read directly on the chart. If $H(j\omega)$ is any other function, its gain and phase angle at the given frequency must be computed, and combined with the chart reading as in Eq. (6.41). To illustrate the use of the Nichols chart, calculate the closed-loop frequency response of the compensated system whose Bode diagrams are shown in Fig. 6.8. These curves show that at $\omega = 8$ rad/sec, the exact open-loop gain is 2.5 db and the phase angle is -129.6 degrees. According to the Nichols chart the amplitude and phase angle of the closed-loop frequency response at $\omega = 8$ are 1.28 (numeric) and -48 degrees. If points are plotted for various frequencies, the path of the response of the system can be drawn on the Nichols chart. Then a curve of the amplitude of the closed-loop frequency response can be drawn as in Fig. 6.11. This curve shows that the system has a resonant peak of 1.28 and a bandwidth of 16.2 rad/sec. For some systems such as loudspeakers or oscillograph galvanometers the shape of the frequency-response curve is as important as the step response. The customer might

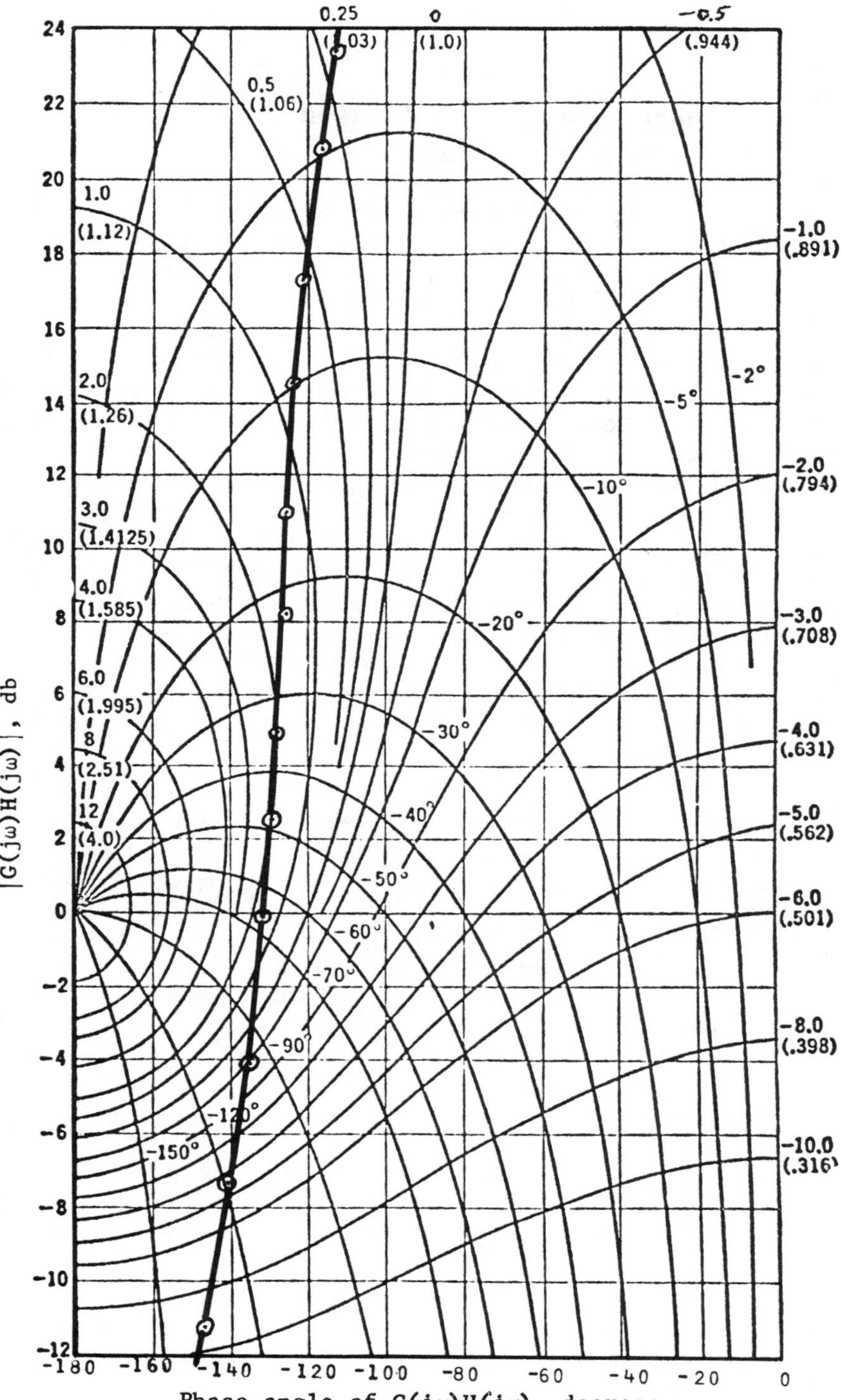

Fig. 6.10. Nichols chart showing the path of the compensated system. Gains in parentheses are numerical values. Those without parentheses are in decibels.

specify the resonant peak and the bandwidth rather than the overshoot and the settling time. The designer would then devote the s-plane or Bode-diagram analysis to approximating a second-order system with the desired closed-loop frequency response.

The Nichols chart enables the designer to visualize Fig. 6.11 without drawing it. Consider the chart to be a contour map on which the horizontal location of a point is given by the open-loop gain and phase angle. The contour lines are the lines of constant closed-loop gain. Ignore the lines of constant closed-loop phase angle. The contour lines show a hill whose peak is at -180 degrees and zero db. The path of the response of the system is a trail along the side of the hill. If the trail is moved to the left, it climbs higher up the hill and the system has a higher resonant peak. The trail in Fig. 6.10 is typical of those of type 1 systems, including the second-order system described by Eq. (5.53). The trail starts at an open-loop gain of infinity and a phase angle of -90 degrees. As ω increases the gain decreases and the phase angle becomes more negative. The trail therefore moves south and west. Where the trail crosses the open-loop gain of 0 db, the open-loop phase angle is -132 degrees. The phase margin is 48°. If the gain k in the forward block of the system is raised, the trail moves to the left, decreasing the phase margin and increasing the resonant peak. If the gain is increased still more, the trail may pass around on the left side of the mountain. There the phase margin is negative, and the system is unstable.

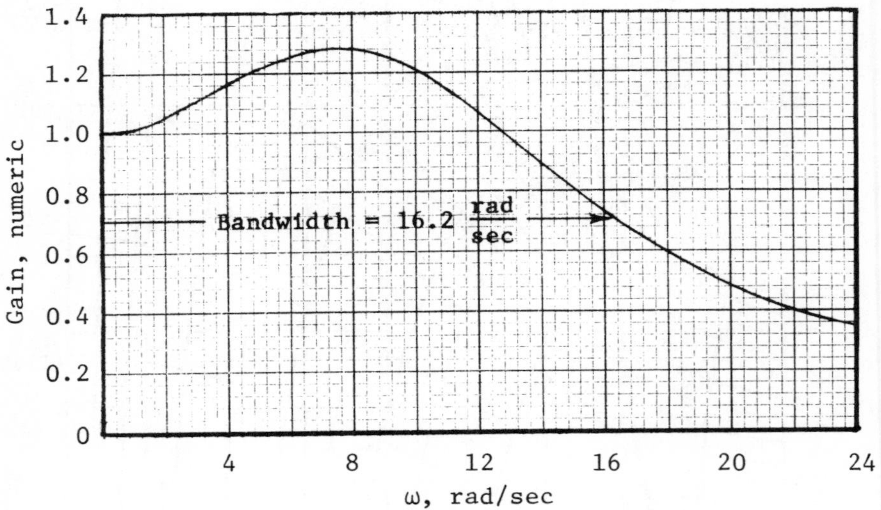

Fig. 6.11. Closed-loop frequency response of the compensated system.

6.8 Compensation with a Lag Network on the Bode Diagram

Some systems such as temperature-measuring devices are not required to respond quickly because the input changes slowly. The settling time can be long, and the undamped natural frequency ω_n can be low. A system with a low ω_n and therefore a narrow bandwidth has the advantage of reduced error due to noise, which normally has high frequencies. Fig. 6.11 shows that a system with a narrow bandwidth does not respond to high-frequency noise in its input. If a low ω_n is permissible, a system can be compensated easily by the phase-lag network of Fig. 6.3. The process can be illustrated by the previous example, for which

$$G(s) = \frac{k}{s(s+2)} \quad \text{and} \quad H(s) = 1 \,, \tag{6.42}$$

without the settling-time specification. Try again for an overshoot of 20 percent, which requires a damping ratio ζ of 0.46 and a phase margin of 48 degrees. The required steady-state error for a ramp input will again be 5 percent or less of the ramp slope. Therefore the straight-line approximation of the gain of $G(j\omega)H(j\omega)$ at $\omega = 1$ must again be 26 db. The Bode diagrams of the uncompensated system are shown in Fig. 6.12.

Introducing a lag network will not change the velocity error constant

$$K_v = \lim_{s \to 0} sG(s)H(s) \tag{6.43}$$

because the transmittance of the lag network according to Fig. 6.3 is

$$\frac{V_2(s)}{V_1(s)} = \frac{1 - \dfrac{s}{z}}{1 - \dfrac{s}{p}} \tag{6.44}$$

and its low-frequency gain is unity. However, the lag network can lower the high-frequency portion of the Bode gain curve any desired amount. To take advantage of this fact, look along the uncompensated phase-angle curve to find where it has the desired phase margin, and then use the lag network to lower the gain curve so that it crosses over at that frequency. The desired phase margin must include a few extra degrees to correct for the phase shift of the lag network. If the zero of the lag network is a decade to the left of the crossover frequency, the lag network will add only about -5 degrees of phase shift.

The system in the example needs a phase margin of 48 degrees or a compensated phase shift of -132 degrees at crossover. The uncompensated phase shift at crossover should therefore be -127 degrees. Fig.

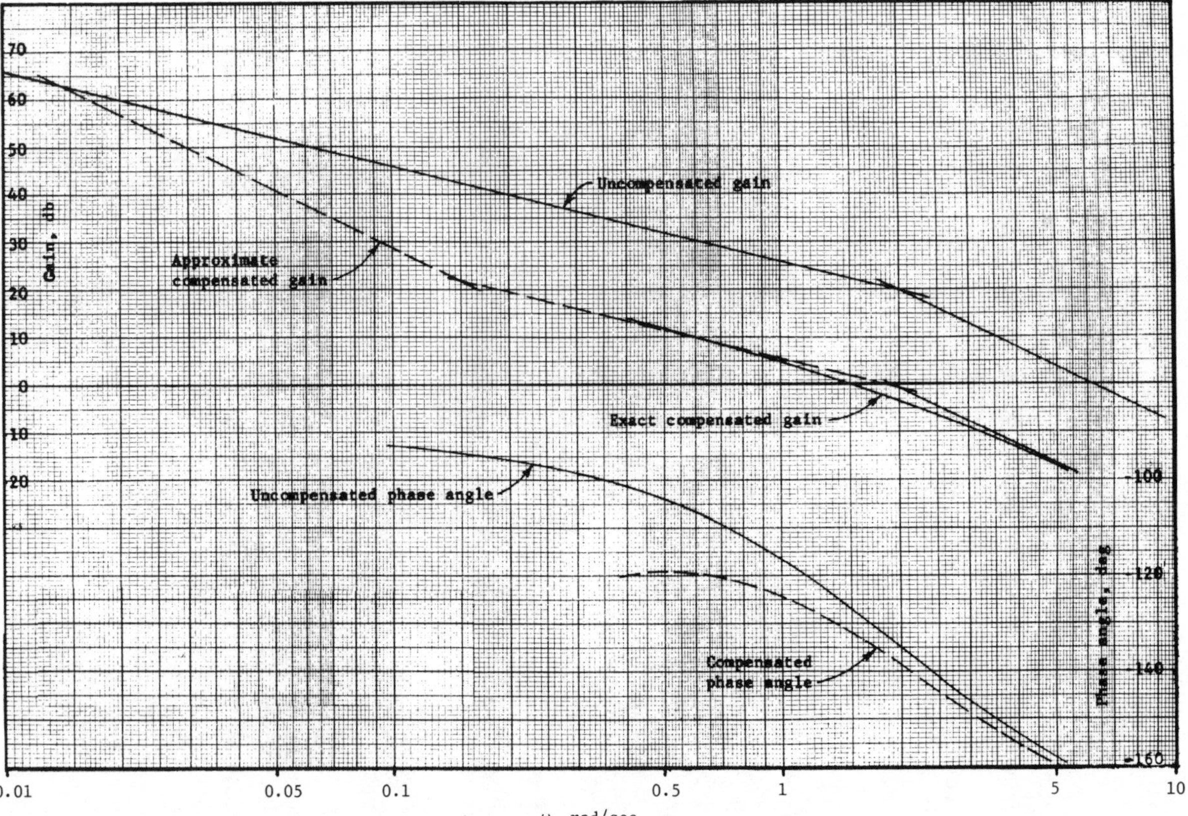

Fig. 6.12. Bode diagrams of a system compensated by a lag network.

6.12 shows that the desired crossover frequency is 1.5 rad/sec. Lower the approximate gain curve almost to zero at this frequency, so that the exact gain curve crosses over at $\omega = 1.5$. Arbitrarily put the zero of the lag network one decade below the crossover frequency, at $\omega = -z = 0.15$ rad/sec. Then draw in the two breaks of the lag network, and find that the pole is at $\omega = -p = 0.0142$ rad/sec. The compensated phase-angle curve can now be drawn. It shows that the lag network adds the anticipated -5 degrees of phase shift at crossover, and that the compensated phase margin is the desired 48 degrees.

This example illustrates the simple purpose of the lag network. It lowers the Bode gain curve to make crossover occur where the phase-angle curve indicates the desired phase margin.

6.9 Compensation with a Lag Network on the s Plane

The choice of a lag network on the *s* plane for the sample system with the same specifications is almost as easy as on the Bode diagram. Fig. 6.13A shows the loci of the closed-loop poles of the uncompensated system, for which

$$G(s)H(s) = \frac{k}{s(s+2)} \,. \tag{6.45}$$

The value of k requires to meet the overshoot specification can be calculated easily. For a 20 percent overshoot, a damping ratio ζ of 0.46 is needed. The two closed-loop poles are shown in squares on Fig. 6.13A at the points where

$$s = -1 \pm j \tan(\cos^{-1} 0.46) = -1 \pm j1.93 \,. \tag{6.46}$$

The length of the vectors from the two open-loop poles to one of these points is

$$\omega_n = \frac{1}{0.46} = 2.173 \,. \tag{6.47}$$

The gain k required to put the closed-loop poles at $-1 \pm j1.93$ is therefore

$$k = (2.173)(2.173) = 4.72 \,. \tag{6.48}$$

The velocity error constant achieved by this gain is

$$K_v = \lim_{s\to 0} sG(s)H(s) = \frac{k}{2} = \frac{4.72}{2} = 2.36 \tag{6.49}$$

which is less than the required 20. (In Bode-diagram terms, the phase margin of the uncompensated system is the desired 48 degrees when $k =$

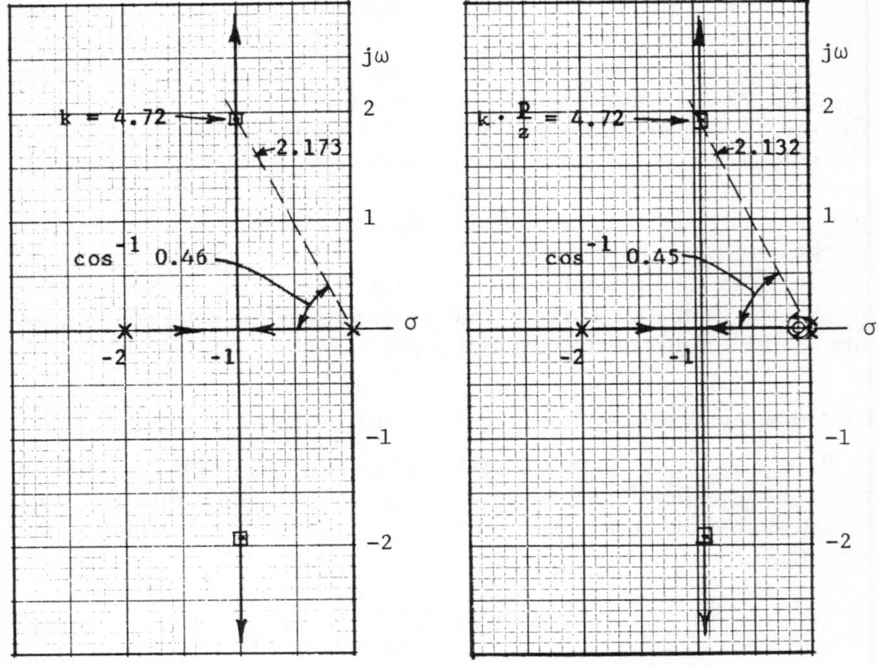

A. Uncompensated system

B. Compensated system

Fig. 6.13. Root loci of a system without and with compensation by a lag network.

4.72, but the gain curve passes thru $\omega = 1$ at too low a gain.) If k is increased to increase K_v, the closed-loop poles will move farther out along the loci, and ζ will be too low.

How can K_v be increased by the factor of $20/2.36 = 8.47$ without decreasing ζ? A simple solution is the addition of a lag network whose high-frequency gain $G_\infty = p/z$ is the reciprocal of this factor, or 0.118. Put the zero and pole close to the origin, say at $z = -0.1$, $p = -0.0118$. Now the open-loop transfer function of the system is

$$G(s)H(s) = \frac{k \cdot \dfrac{p}{z}(s-z)}{s(s+2)(s-p)} = \frac{0.118k(s+0.1)}{s(s+2)(s+0.0118)}. \tag{6.50}$$

The root loci of the system with this compensation are shown in Fig. 6.13B. At the larger values of k, the vectors $s-z$ and $s-p$ of the lag network are almost identical, and therefore have little effect on the shape of the root loci, or on the gain kp/z at any point on the loci. The closed-loop poles of the uncompensated system with $k = 4.72$ are at

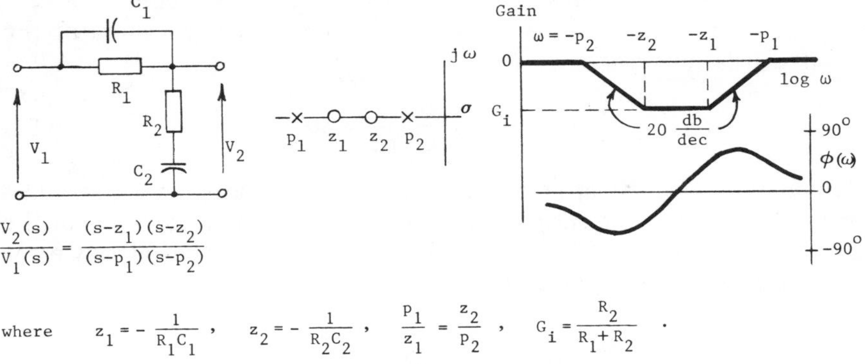

Fig. 6.14. Lag-lead or notch network.

a given frequency is not straightforward, as for a lead network. For comparison, the phase angle of the lead network that produces the right half of the notch, for which

$$\frac{V_2(s)}{V_1(s)} = \frac{s - z_1}{s - p_1} = \frac{s + 30}{s + 300}, \tag{6.54}$$

is plotted in Fig. 6.15. The peak of this curve lies midway between $-z_1$ and $-p_1$, at $\omega = \sqrt{z_1 p_1} = 94.9$ rad/sec. The peak of the notch network's phase-angle curve is lower and slightly to the right, because of the negative phase angle contributed by the left pole and zero, p_2 and z_2. If the two zeros are at least a decade apart, as in Fig. 6.15, the shift of the phase-angle peak to the right is negligible, and the peak is lowered only about two degrees. Therefore p_1 and z_1 can be located with reasonable accuracy by Eqs. (6.32) thru (6.34). If z_1 and z_2 are less than a decade apart, the poles and zeros can be chosen with the help of the servomechanism scale of Fig. 5.13. The right pole and zero should lie at approximately equal distances on opposite sides of the desired crossover frequency, and their phase angle, plus that of the left pair, must add up to the desired extra phase shift.

An example of the usefulness of the notch network is the compensation of the sample system, for which

$$G(s) = \frac{k}{s(s+2)} \qquad \text{and} \qquad H(s) = 1\,, \tag{6.55}$$

to meet the specifications of overshoot, settling time, and steady-state error. In Fig. 6.7 this job was done by a lead network. However, the crossover frequency was set at 10 rad/sec even though the preliminary calculations indicated that 7.1 rad/sec would have been high enough.

nearly the same location as those of the compensated system with $kp/z = 4.72$. To put the closed-loop poles of the compensated system at the desired locations, increase k to

$$k = \frac{4.72}{p/z} = \frac{4.72}{0.118} = 40.0 \, . \tag{6.51}$$

The complex closed-loop poles, shown in Fig. 6.13B, are now at $s = -0.95 \pm j1.91$. The damping ratio is now 0.45, which is satisfactorily near the desired value of 0.46. The increase in k has increased the velocity error constant. Now according to Eq. (6.50),

$$K_v = \lim_{s\to 0} sG(s)H(s) = \frac{k \cdot \dfrac{p}{z} \cdot z}{2p} = \frac{k}{2}\, , \tag{6.52}$$

the same as before the lag network was added. Since k has been increased by the factor $z/p = 8.47 = 20/2.36$, K_v has been increased by the same factor, up to the desired value of 20.

Placing the pole and zero of the lag network near the origin makes this method simple. Since the lag network does not affect the root loci at the higher gains, the compensated root-locus plot does not have to be drawn. The only significant effect of the lag network is to reduce the forward gain from k to kp/z, thereby permitting an increase in k, which in turn increases the velocity error constant K_v. A disadvantage of the method is that since p and z are small, the designer may not be able to implement them with a capacitor and resistors of practical size.

6.10 Notch Networks

The advantages of the lag and the lead network can be combined in the *lag-lead* or *notch network*, whose properties are shown in Fig. 6.14. A lead network alone provides extra positive phase shift at the desired crossover frequency, but increases the steady-state error because its low-frequency gain is less than unity. A lag network has no effect on the steady-state error because its low-frequency gain is unity. A lag-lead network has unity gain at low frequencies, and provides positive phase shift at any frequency in the right half of its Bode diagram, where $\omega > \sqrt{z_1 z_2}$. Fig. 6.15 shows the Bode diagrams of the notch network for which

$$\frac{V_2(s)}{V_1(s)} = \frac{(s+3)(s+30)}{(s+0.3)(s+300)}\, . \tag{6.53}$$

The calculation of pole and zero locations to produce peak phase angle at

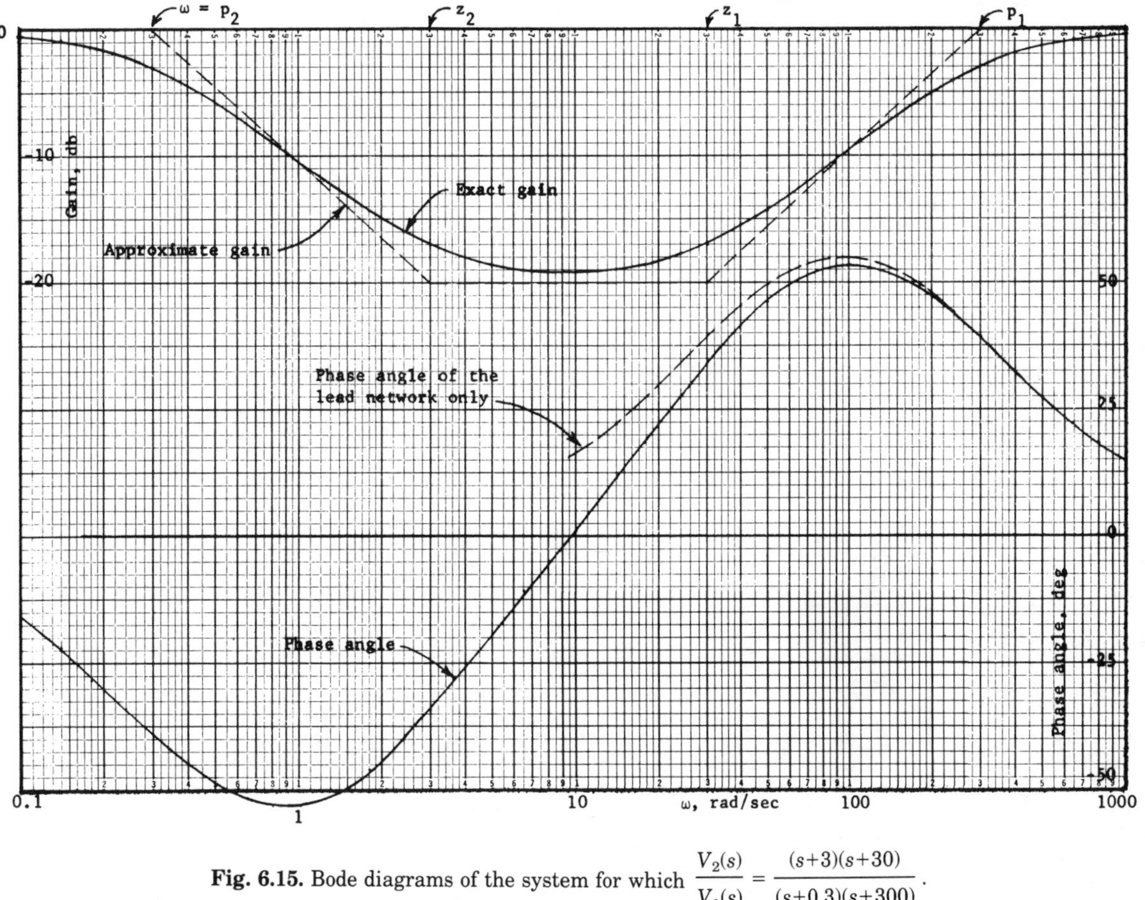

Fig. 6.15. Bode diagrams of the system for which $\dfrac{V_2(s)}{V_1(s)} = \dfrac{(s+3)(s+30)}{(s+0.3)(s+300)}$.

With the higher value, the compensated gain curve was 14 db too low at 10 rad/sec, and 12 db too low at low frequencies. When an extra forward gain of 14 db was added to correct the crossover frequency, the low-frequency gain was 2 db higher than necessary. If the desired crossover frequency were 9 rad/sec or less, the extra gain needed at crossover would be less than the extra gain needed at low frequencies. When the curve was raised to make crossover occur at the desired frequency, the low-frequency gain would be lower than necessary to meet the steady-state error specification. If a crossover frequency of 9 rad/sec or less had been chosen, the system could not have been compensated with a lead network. A notch network, however, would do the job easily. With a notch network, the compensated gain curve would be similar to that of Fig. 6.7 in the region of crossover, but would rise up to meet the uncompensated curve at low frequencies. When extra gain was added to put crossover at the desired frequency, all of this gain would provide a bonus reduction of the steady-state error.

6.11 Compensation with Operational Amplifiers

The compensating networks discussed so far are placed in cascade with the other components of the system, and must be followed by a buffer amplifier. A popular alternative consists of placing the compensating network in the input to, and the feedback around, an operational amplifier. An operational amplifier, represented by the symbol in Fig. 6.16, has a high gain A, typically 100,000 at low frequencies. The input

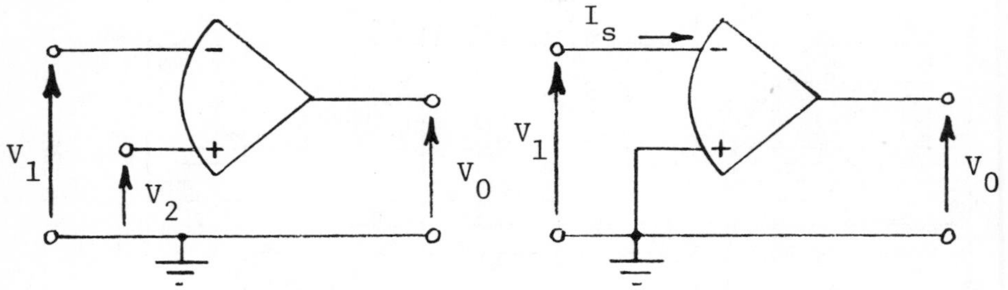

Fig. 6.16. Operational amplifier. **Fig. 6.17.** Single-ended connection.

impedance, measured between the two input terminals, is also high, typically 0.5 megohms. If the voltages applied to the two input terminals are V_1 and V_2, the output voltage is

$$V_0 = A(V_2 - V_1)\,. \tag{6.56}$$

Many applications require the single-ended connection of Fig. 6.17, in which the non-inverting input terminal is connected to ground. Then

$$V_0 = -AV_1 . \tag{6.57}$$

The operational amplifier is useful because it has these two properties:

1. Since the input impedance is high the current I_s flowing into the inverting terminal, called the *summing point*, can be assumed to be zero.
2. Since the gain A is high and the output voltage V_0 is finite, the input voltage V_1 according to Eq. (6.57) is nearly zero. The summing point can therefore be assumed to be at ground potential.

Fig. 6.18 shows an operational amplifier with two impedance networks, one in the input and one in the feedback. Let $Z_1(s)$ be the

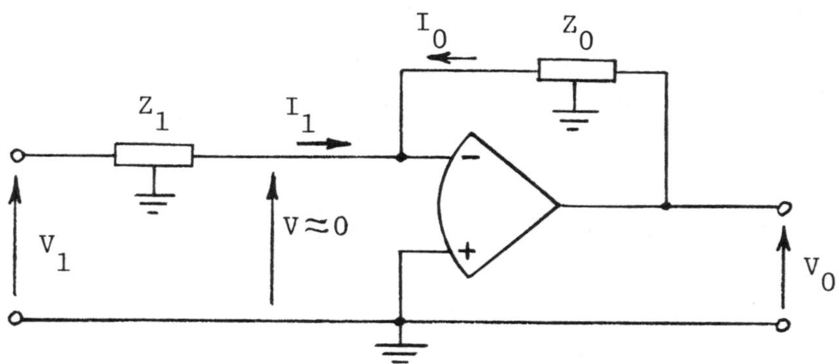

Fig. 6.18. Operational amplifier with feedforward and feedback impedances.

short-circuit transfer impedance of the input network, namely the ratio of the input voltage to the output current when the output is short-circuited to ground. The output of this network is short-circuited because the summing point is at ground potential. Therefore the output current is

$$I_1(s) = \frac{V_1(s)}{Z_1(s)} . \tag{6.58}$$

Similarly, the output current of the feedback network is

$$I_0(s) = \frac{V_0(s)}{Z_0(s)} , \tag{6.59}$$

where $Z_0(s)$ is the short-circuit transfer impedance of that network.

Since these two currents add up to zero at the summing point,

$$\frac{V_1(s)}{Z_1(s)} = -\frac{V_0(s)}{Z_0(s)}$$

and

$$\frac{V_0(s)}{V_1(s)} = -\frac{Z_0(s)}{Z_1(s)}. \tag{6.60}$$

The transfer function of the amplifier is therefore determined by the impedance networks, and not by its open-loop gain A.

The short-circuit transfer impedances of many networks are tabulated in Ref. 126, and can be used to construct the desired transfer function $V_0(s)/V_1(s)$. For example, to make a lead network put the network of Fig. 6.19 in the feedback. Its short-circuit transfer impedance is

$$Z_0(s) = k\,\frac{s-z}{s-p}, \qquad |p| > |z|, \tag{6.61}$$

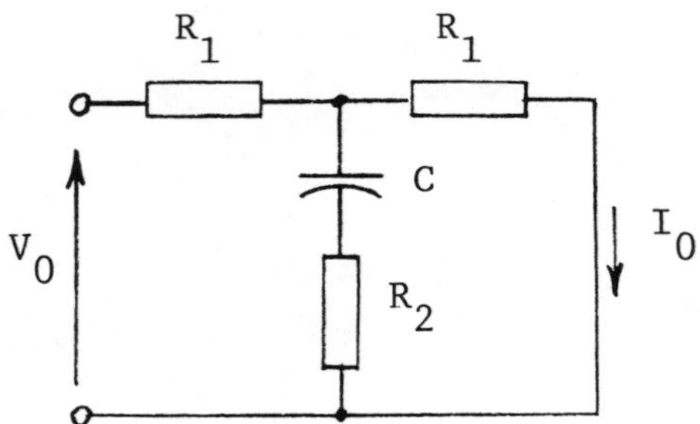

Fig. 6.19. Network for lead compensation.

where

$$k = \frac{R_1(2R_2 + R_1)}{R_2}, \qquad z = -\frac{2}{C(2R_2 + R_1)}, \qquad \text{and} \qquad p = -\frac{1}{CR_2}. \tag{6.62}$$

For the input network choose a resistor with the value

$$Z_1(s) = k = \frac{R_1(2R_2 + R_1)}{R_2}. \tag{6.63}$$

Then the transfer function of the amplifier is

$$\frac{V_0(s)}{V_1(s)} = -\frac{Z_0(s)}{Z_1(s)} = -\frac{s-z}{s-p}. \tag{6.64}$$

This is the same as the transmittance of the cascade lead network shown in Fig. 6.2, except for the polarity reversal. The complete compensating amplifer is shown in Fig. 6.20. The reader is invited to choose feedfor-

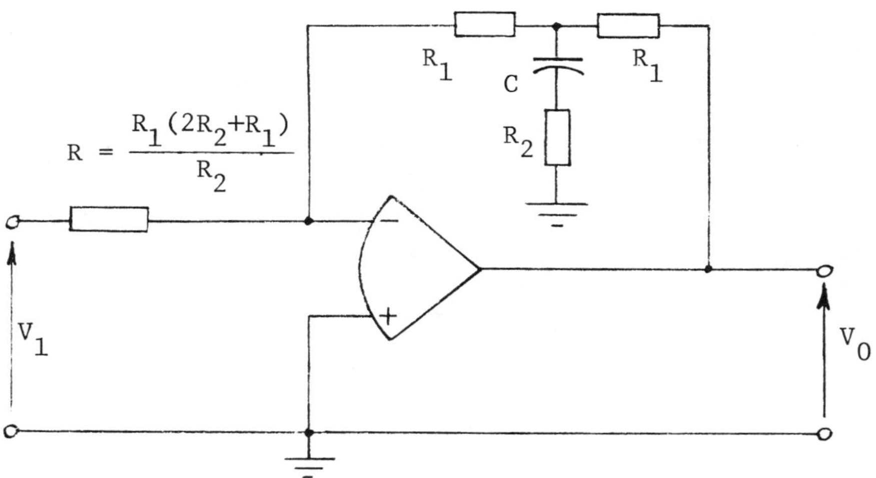

Fig. 6.20. A phase-lead circuit.

ward and feedback networks to provide the notch compensation of Eq. (6.53).

The choice of feedback or cascade compensation depends upon individual applications. Sometimes an operational amplifier is already in the system for some other purpose, such as adding several signals or raising a voltage level. Such an amplifier could not serve as a buffer for a cascade compensating network, because the input impedance of its circuit is not high enough. A buffer requires its own operational amplifier. However, the operational amplifier already in place can fulfill its original function and also provide compensation, if input and feedback networks similar to those in Fig. 6.20 are added. Then feedback compensation is the logical choice, because it saves an operational amplifier. Suppose, for example, that the circuit of Fig. 6.20 needs a gain of 10 as well as lead compensation. The gain can be provided at no cost by reducing the input resistance R by a factor of 10.

Chapter 7

MATRICES AND VECTOR SPACES

7.1 Introduction

A matrix is a simple invention, merely a rectangular array of numbers, that has eliminated much drudgery from the lives of engineers and scientists. For example, matrices and vectors can express a large collection of simultaneous algebraic or differential equations as a single vector equation. The literal solution of the vector equation can be written as simply as that of the corresponding scalar equation. Numerical results can be obtained readily because digital computers can easily handle the large amount of numerical information stored in matrices. Several interesting properties of matrices will be investigated that simplify the mathematics and provide useful information about the physical system they represent, even before numerical results are obtained.

7.2 Matrix Algebra

A simple example will show how matrices appear naturally in engineering. Fig. 7.1 shows a system of five springs with spring constants k_1, k_2, etc., that connect three supporting blocks that are assumed to be massless. The horizontal forces f_1, f_2, and f_3 are applied to the blocks, producing the horizontal deflections x_1, x_2, and x_3. The sums of forces on each block are

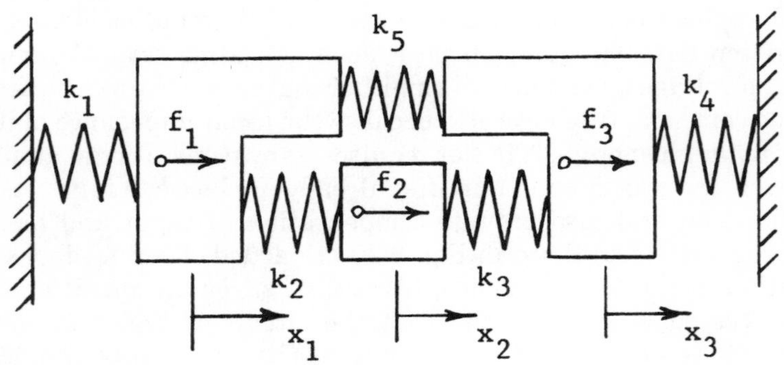

Fig. 7.1. System of five springs and three massless blocks.

$$k_1x_1 + k_2(x_1 - x_2) + k_5(x_1 - x_3) = f_1 \quad (7.1)$$

$$k_2(x_2 - x_1) + k_3(x_2 - x_3) = f_2 \quad (7.2)$$

$$k_3(x_3 - x_2) + k_5(x_3 - x_1) + k_4 x_3 = f_3 . \quad (7.3)$$

Let

$$k_1 = 2 \text{ N/m}, \quad k_2 = 1, \quad k_3 = 3, \quad k_4 = 1, \quad \text{and} \quad k_5 = 1 .$$

Then

$$4x_1 - x_2 - x_3 = f_1 \quad (7.4)$$

$$- x_1 + 4x_2 - 3x_3 = f_2 \quad (7.5)$$

$$- x_1 - 3x_2 + 5x_3 = f_3 . \quad (7.6)$$

These three equations can be written as the single equation

$$\begin{bmatrix} 4 & -1 & -1 \\ -1 & 4 & -3 \\ -1 & -3 & 5 \end{bmatrix} \begin{bmatrix} x_1 \\ x_2 \\ x_3 \end{bmatrix} = \begin{bmatrix} f_1 \\ f_2 \\ f_3 \end{bmatrix} \quad (7.7)$$

in which the array of coefficients is called a *matrix*. A matrix with m rows and n columns is called an $m \times n$ matrix. A square $m \times m$ matrix is said to be of *order* m. Eq. (7.7) can be written more simply as

$$\mathbf{A}\,\mathbf{x} = \mathbf{f} \quad (7.8)$$

in which $\mathbf{A}$ is a 3×3 matrix, and $\mathbf{x}$ and $\mathbf{f}$ are 3×1 matrices. An $m \times 1$ matrix is called a *column vector*, and a $1 \times n$ matrix is called a *row vector*. In general,

$$\begin{bmatrix} a_{11} & a_{12} & \cdot & \cdot & a_{1n} \\ a_{21} & a_{22} & & & \\ \cdot & & \cdot & & \\ \cdot & & & \cdot & \\ a_{m1} & & & & a_{mn} \end{bmatrix} \begin{bmatrix} x_1 \\ x_2 \\ \cdot \\ \cdot \\ \cdot \\ \cdot \\ x_n \end{bmatrix}$$

$$= \begin{bmatrix} a_{11}x_1 + a_{12}x_2 + \cdots + a_{1n}x_n \\ a_{21}x_1 + a_{22}x_2 + \cdots + a_{2n}x_n \\ \cdot \\ \cdot \\ a_{m1}x_1 + a_{m2}x_2 + \cdots + a_{mn}x_n \end{bmatrix} = \begin{bmatrix} f_1 \\ f_2 \\ \cdot \\ \cdot \\ f_m \end{bmatrix} \quad (7.9)$$

or

$$\sum_{k=1}^{n} a_{ik}\, x_k = f_i , \quad i = 1,2, \ldots m . \quad (7.10)$$

Now premultiply both sides of Eq. (7.8) by the matrix **B**:

$$\mathbf{B\,A\,x} = \mathbf{B\,f}\,. \tag{7.11}$$

The operations **A x**, **B**(**A x**), and **B f** are defined by Eq. (7.9). If matrix multiplication is to be associative, i.e., if **B**(**A x**) is to equal (**B A**)**x**, the rule for multiplying **B** and **A** must be

$$\begin{bmatrix} b_{11} & b_{12} & b_{13} \\ b_{21} & b_{22} & b_{23} \\ b_{31} & b_{32} & b_{33} \end{bmatrix} \begin{bmatrix} a_{11} & a_{12} & a_{13} \\ a_{21} & a_{22} & a_{23} \\ a_{31} & a_{32} & a_{33} \end{bmatrix} = \begin{bmatrix} c_{11} & c_{12} & c_{13} \\ c_{21} & c_{22} & c_{23} \\ c_{31} & c_{32} & c_{33} \end{bmatrix} \tag{7.12}$$

where

$$c_{11} = b_{11}\,a_{11} + b_{12}\,a_{21} + b_{13}\,a_{31} \tag{7.13}$$

or in general,

$$c_{ij} = \sum_{k=1}^{n} b_{ik}\,a_{kj}\,. \tag{7.14}$$

This rule applies to nonsquare matrices, if the number of rows of **A** equals the number of columns of **B**, namely n. Matrix multiplication is not commutative. Thus in general, **A B** ≠ **B A**. For example,

$$[2, 1, 2]\begin{bmatrix} 2 \\ 3 \\ 1 \end{bmatrix} = 9\,, \quad \text{but} \quad \begin{bmatrix} 2 \\ 3 \\ 1 \end{bmatrix}[2, 1, 2] = \begin{bmatrix} 4 & 2 & 4 \\ 6 & 3 & 6 \\ 2 & 1 & 2 \end{bmatrix}. \tag{7.15}$$

To multiply a vector by a constant k, multiply each of its components by k. Eq. (7.9) shows that if (k **A**)**x** is to equal k(**A x**), multiplication of a matrix by k must be defined as multiplication of each of its elements by k.

If matrix addition and subtraction are to be distributive, i.e., if **A**(**B** + **C**) = **A B** + **A C**, the rule for adding two matrices must be

$$\mathbf{C} = \mathbf{A} \pm \mathbf{B} \tag{7.16}$$

where

$$c_{ij} = a_{ij} \pm b_{ij}\,. \tag{7.17}$$

The main diagonal of a matrix consists of the elements a_{ii} (the diagonal from upper left to lower right). A *diagonal* matrix is a square matrix, all of whose elements off of the main diagonal are zero. A *unit* or *identity* matrix **I** is a diagonal matrix whose main-diagonal elements are all unity. If **A** is a square matrix of the same order as **I**,

$$\mathbf{I\,A} = \mathbf{A\,I} = \mathbf{A}\,. \tag{7.18}$$

The *transpose* $\mathbf{A}^T$ of a matrix **A** is obtained by interchanging its rows and columns, or rotating it about its main diagonal. If $\mathbf{A} = \mathbf{A}^T$, the matrix is said to be *symmetric*. Many matrices representing linear systems, such as **A** in Eq. (7.8), are symmetric. If **A** and **B** are any two matrices with compatible dimensions,

$$(\mathbf{A}\,\mathbf{B})^T = \mathbf{B}^T\,\mathbf{A}^T\,. \tag{7.19}$$

Some matrices have complex elements. An example is

$$\mathbf{A} = \begin{bmatrix} 2 & 2+j3 \\ 2-j3 & 1 \end{bmatrix}. \tag{7.20}$$

The *complex conjugate* $\mathbf{A}^*$ of a matrix is formed by replacing each element by its complex conjugate. If **A** is given by Eq. (7.20),

$$\mathbf{A}^* = \begin{bmatrix} 2 & 2-j3 \\ 2+j3 & 1 \end{bmatrix}. \tag{7.21}$$

A *hermitian* matrix **A** is a square matrix for which $\mathbf{A}^T = \mathbf{A}^*$. The matrix of Eq. (7.20) is hermitian. A *real* matrix is one whose elements are all real. A real symmetric matrix, like the one in Eq. (7.7), is hermitian.

7.3 Determinants

The determinant of a square nth-order matrix **A** can be written as

$$|\mathbf{A}| = \sum_{i=1}^{n} a_{ij}\,C_{ij} = \sum_{j=1}^{n} a_{ij}\,C_{ij} \tag{7.22}$$

where C_{ij} is the *cofactor* of the element a_{ij}, defined as

$$C_{ij} = (-1)^{i+j}\,|\mathbf{M}_{ij}| \tag{7.23}$$

and $|\mathbf{M}_{ij}|$ is the minor of element a_{ij}, namely the determinant remaining when the ith row and jth column of $|\mathbf{A}|$ are deleted. For example, the determinant of matrix **A** of Eq. (7.8), found by letting $i = 1$, is

$$|\mathbf{A}| = \sum_{j=1}^{3} a_{1j}\,C_{1j} = 4\begin{vmatrix} 4 & -3 \\ -3 & 5 \end{vmatrix} + 1\begin{vmatrix} -1 & -3 \\ -1 & 5 \end{vmatrix} - 1\begin{vmatrix} -1 & 4 \\ -1 & -3 \end{vmatrix} = 29\,. \tag{7.24}$$

7.4 Inverse of a Square Matrix

The forces on the blocks in Fig. 7.1 are expressed in terms of the displacements by Eq. (7.8): $\mathbf{A}\,\mathbf{x} = \mathbf{f}$. How can the displacements be expressed in terms of the forces? Dividing the equation by **A** is not permissible, because mathematicians have chosen not to define the process of division by a matrix. Instead, they define the *inverse* $\mathbf{A}^{-1}$ of a square matrix **A** by the formula

$$\mathbf{A}\,\mathbf{A}^{-1} = \mathbf{I}\,. \tag{7.25}$$

The reader is invited to prove that $\mathbf{A}^{-1}\,\mathbf{A} = \mathbf{I}$. If both sides of Eq. (7.8) are premultiplied by $\mathbf{A}^{-1}$, the result is

$$\mathbf{A}^{-1}\,\mathbf{A}\,\mathbf{x} = \mathbf{I}\,\mathbf{x} = \mathbf{x} = \mathbf{A}^{-1}\,\mathbf{f} \tag{7.26}$$

which is the desired form. The next step is the calculation of $\mathbf{A}^{-1}$. A typical determinant of a square matrix is

$$|\mathbf{A}| = \begin{vmatrix} a_{11} & a_{12} & a_{13} \\ a_{21} & a_{22} & a_{23} \\ a_{31} & a_{32} & a_{33} \end{vmatrix}\,. \tag{7.27}$$

The value of the determinant can be found by expanding it along the first row:

$$|\mathbf{A}| = \sum_{j=1}^{3} a_{1j}\,C_{1j}\,. \tag{7.28}$$

Now expand the determinant along the first row, but use the cofactors for the second row. This is the same as replacing the second row by the first row, expanding along the first row correctly, and changing the sign of the determinant:

$$\sum_{j=1}^{3} a_{1j}\,C_{2j} = -\begin{vmatrix} a_{11} & a_{12} & a_{13} \\ a_{11} & a_{12} & a_{13} \\ a_{31} & a_{32} & a_{33} \end{vmatrix}\,. \tag{7.29}$$

This determinant is zero because the corresponding elements of two rows are equal. In general, the determinant is zero if the kth row is replaced by the ith row. Thus

$$\begin{aligned} \sum_{j=1}^{n} a_{ij}\,C_{kj} &= 0\,, \quad i \neq k \\ &= |\mathbf{A}|\,, \quad i = k\,. \end{aligned} \tag{7.30}$$

This equation shows that

$$\begin{bmatrix} a_{11} & a_{12} & \cdot & \cdot & \cdot \\ a_{21} & a_{22} & & & \\ \cdot & & \cdot & & \\ \cdot & & & \cdot & \\ \cdot & & & & \cdot \end{bmatrix} \begin{bmatrix} C_{11} & C_{21} & \cdot & \cdot & \cdot \\ C_{12} & C_{22} & & & \\ \cdot & & \cdot & & \\ \cdot & & & \cdot & \\ \cdot & & & & \cdot \end{bmatrix}$$

$$= \begin{bmatrix} |\mathbf{A}| & 0 & 0 & \cdot & \cdot \\ 0 & |\mathbf{A}| & 0 & & \\ 0 & 0 & |\mathbf{A}| & & \\ \cdot & & & \cdot & \\ \cdot & & & & \cdot \end{bmatrix} \tag{7.31}$$

or

$$\mathbf{A}\,\mathbf{C}^T = |\mathbf{A}|\,\mathbf{I}\,. \tag{7.32}$$

Thus

$$\frac{\mathbf{A}\,\mathbf{C}^T}{|\mathbf{A}|} = \mathbf{I} \tag{7.33}$$

and

$$\mathbf{A}^{-1} = \frac{\mathbf{C}^T}{|\mathbf{A}|}\,. \tag{7.34}$$

The transpose of the matrix of cofactors, $\mathbf{C}^T$, is called the *adjoint matrix* and is often written Adj **A**. The inverse of matrix **A** is therefore

$$\mathbf{A}^{-1} = \frac{\text{Adj}\,\mathbf{A}}{|\mathbf{A}|}\,. \tag{7.35}$$

A square matrix is said to be *singular* if its determinant is zero. Thus only a nonsingular matrix has an inverse.

For the matrix **A** in Eq. (7.8), the matrix of cofactors is

$$\mathbf{C} = \begin{bmatrix} 11 & 8 & 7 \\ 8 & 19 & 13 \\ 7 & 13 & 15 \end{bmatrix}. \tag{7.36}$$

Accordingly,

$$\mathbf{A}^{-1} = \frac{1}{29}\begin{bmatrix} 11 & 8 & 7 \\ 8 & 19 & 13 \\ 7 & 13 & 15 \end{bmatrix}. \tag{7.37}$$

Now the displacements in Fig. 7.1 can be written as functions of the forces. Since

$$\mathbf{x} = \mathbf{A}^{-1}\,\mathbf{f}\,, \tag{7.38}$$

the displacements are

$$\left.\begin{aligned} x_1 &= \frac{1}{29}(11\,f_1 + 8\,f_2 + 7\,f_3) \\ x_2 &= \frac{1}{29}(8\,f_1 + 19\,f_2 + 13\,f_3) \\ x_3 &= \frac{1}{29}(7\,f_1 + 13\,f_2 + 15\,f_3)\,. \end{aligned}\right\} \tag{7.39}$$

The inversion of a large matrix by Eq. (7.35) requires an excessive amount of calculation. Numerous short-cut methods have been developed for use by computers.

7.5 The Geometric Interpretation of Matrices

The scalar, dot, or *inner product* of two three-dimensional vectors **A** and **B**, written as $\mathbf{A}\cdot\mathbf{B}$ or $<\mathbf{A},\mathbf{B}>$, is defined as the scalar

$$<\mathbf{A},\mathbf{B}> = AB\cos\theta\ , \qquad (7.40)$$

where θ is the angle between the positive directions of the vectors. If the axes x,y, and z of the coordinate system are mutually perpendicular, the inner product can be defined as

$$<\mathbf{A},\mathbf{B}> = A_xB_x + A_yB_y + A_zB_z\ . \qquad (7.41)$$

The definition can be extended to vectors of n dimensions. Thus

$$<\mathbf{x},\mathbf{y}> = x_1\,y_1 + x_2\,y_2 + \cdots + x_n\,y_n = \mathbf{x}^T\,\mathbf{y} = \mathbf{y}^T\,\mathbf{x} \qquad (7.42)$$

where x_i and y_i are the components or elements of **x** and **y** measured along the n mutually-perpendicular coordinate axes. Visualizing such axes is difficult, and fortunately not often necessary. In the solution of problems, vectors such as those in Eq. (7.7) do not have to be drawn as arrows. The analyst can use Eq. (7.42) to calculate inner products without visualizing the coordinate axes.

Vectors **x** and **y** in two or three dimensions are said to be *orthogonal* if they are at right angles to each other, that is, if

$$<\mathbf{x},\mathbf{y}> = 0\ . \qquad (7.43)$$

Similarly, two n-dimensional vectors are orthogonal if their inner product is zero. If the elements x_1, x_2, and x_3 of a three-dimensional vector **x** are distances measured along three orthogonal axes, the length of the vector is

$$\|\mathbf{x}\| = \sqrt{x_1^2 + x_2^2 + x_3^2} = \sqrt{<\mathbf{x},\mathbf{x}>}\ . \qquad (7.44)$$

By extension of this idea, the length or *norm* of a vector of any number of elements is defined as

$$\|\mathbf{x}\| = \sqrt{<\mathbf{x},\mathbf{x}>}\ . \qquad (7.45)$$

Norms frequently have no physical significance, and no thought must be given to the coordinate system in which the vector **x** lies.

The concept of linear independence of functions in Chapter 1 applies also to vectors. The vectors , $\mathbf{x}_1$, $\mathbf{x}_2$, . . . ,$\mathbf{x}_n$ are linearly independent if none of them can be expressed as a linear combination of the others. That is, the equation

$$k_1 \mathbf{x}_1 + k_2 \mathbf{x}_2 + \cdots + k_n \mathbf{x}_n = \mathbf{0} \tag{7.46}$$

can be satisfied only if all the k_i's are zero. For example, in the rectangular coordinate system of Fig. 7.2, the vectors **a, b,** and **c** that lie in the xy plane are linearly dependent, because any of them can be expressed as a linear sum of the other two. But **a, b,** and **d** are linearly independent. Fortunately, the test of linear independence of vectors is simpler than the test required for functions.

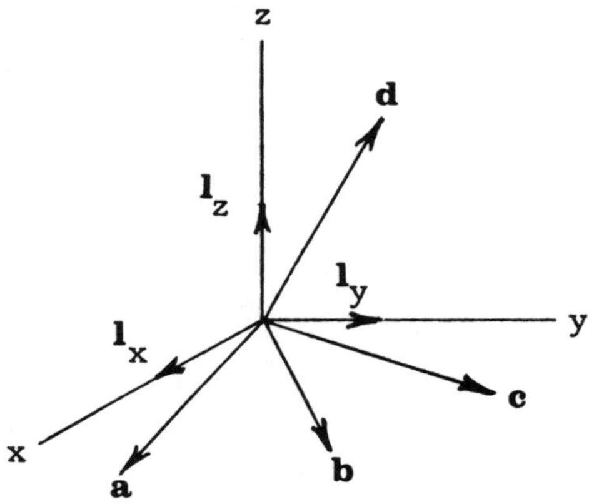

Fig. 7.2. Three-dimensional vectors.

A *basis* is a set of n linearly-independent n-dimensional vectors. They span an n-dimensional *vector space.* Any vector in the n space is a unique linear combination of the basis vectors. For example, if **a, b,** and the unit vector $\mathbf{1}_z$ are chosen as a basis,

$$\mathbf{d} = k_1 \mathbf{a} + k_2 \mathbf{b} + k_3 \mathbf{1}_z \, . \tag{7.47}$$

Thus a basis is a coordinate system. If the basis vectors are all orthogonal to each other, and the length of each basis vector is unity, the basis is said to be *orthonormal.* In Fig. 7.2 the unit vectors $\mathbf{1}_x$, $\mathbf{1}_y$, and $\mathbf{1}_z$ form an orthonormal basis.

Three geometric interpretations of the operation of a square matrix on a vector will be useful. First, the operation

$$\mathbf{y} = \mathbf{A}\,\mathbf{x} \tag{7.48}$$

changes vector **x**, by changing its length and direction, into vector **y**. Viewed this way, a matrix is an example of a general class of operators called *linear transformations*. To obtain the second interpretation, observe that

$$\mathbf{y} = \mathbf{A}\,\mathbf{x} = \begin{bmatrix} a_{11}\,x_1 + a_{12}\,x_2 + \cdots + a_{1n}\,x_n \\ a_{21}\,x_1 + a_{22}\,x_2 + \cdots + a_{2n}\,x_n \\ \cdot \quad\quad \cdot \quad\quad\quad \cdot \\ \cdot \quad\quad \cdot \quad\quad\quad \cdot \\ \cdot \quad\quad \cdot \quad\quad\quad \cdot \\ a_{n1}\,x_1 + a_{n2}\,x_2 + \cdots + a_{nn}\,x_n \end{bmatrix}$$

$$= \begin{bmatrix} a_{11} \\ a_{21} \\ \cdot \\ \cdot \\ \cdot \\ a_{n1} \end{bmatrix} x_1 + \begin{bmatrix} a_{12} \\ a_{22} \\ \cdot \\ \cdot \\ \cdot \\ a_{n2} \end{bmatrix} x_2 + \cdots + \begin{bmatrix} a_{1n} \\ a_{2n} \\ \cdot \\ \cdot \\ \cdot \\ a_{nn} \end{bmatrix} x_n \qquad (7.49)$$

or

$$\mathbf{y} = \mathbf{a}_1\,x_1 + \mathbf{a}_2\,x_2 + \cdots + \mathbf{a}_n\,x_n \qquad (7.50)$$

where $\mathbf{a}_i$ is the column vector consisting of the ith column of $\mathbf{A}$, so that

$$\mathbf{A} = [\mathbf{a}_1, \mathbf{a}_2, \ldots, \mathbf{a}_n]\,. \qquad (7.51)$$

Thus $\mathbf{y}$ is a linear combination of the columns of $\mathbf{A}$, and the coefficients are the components of $\mathbf{x}$. Eq. (7.50) shows that if the columns of $\mathbf{A}$ are linearly independent, so that they form a basis in n space, they serve as a coordinate system for any n-dimensional vector $\mathbf{y}$. If the columns of $\mathbf{A}$ are linearly dependent, they do not span an n-dimensional space, and therefore may not be able to represent $\mathbf{y}$. For example, if

$$\mathbf{A} = [\mathbf{a}_1, \mathbf{a}_2, \mathbf{a}_3] = \begin{bmatrix} 1 & 0 & 1 \\ 0 & 1 & 1 \\ 1 & 1 & 2 \end{bmatrix}, \qquad (7.52)$$

$\mathbf{a}_3$ is a linear combination of $\mathbf{a}_1$ and $\mathbf{a}_2$. In Fig. 7.3 the columns of $\mathbf{A}$ are shown as three-dimensional vectors in a rectangular coordinate system. The columns of $\mathbf{A}$ span only a plane, and coefficients x_i satisfying Eq. (7.50) can be found only if $\mathbf{y}$ happens to lie in that plane.

The third geometric interpretation of Eq. (7.48) is obtained by observing that if $\boldsymbol{\alpha}_i$ is a column vector consisting of the ith row of $\mathbf{A}$, namely

$$\boldsymbol{\alpha}_i = \begin{bmatrix} a_{i1} \\ a_{i2} \\ \cdot \\ \cdot \\ a_{in} \end{bmatrix} \quad \text{or} \quad \boldsymbol{\alpha}_i^T = [a_{i1}, a_{i2}, \ldots a_{in}]\,, \qquad (7.53)$$

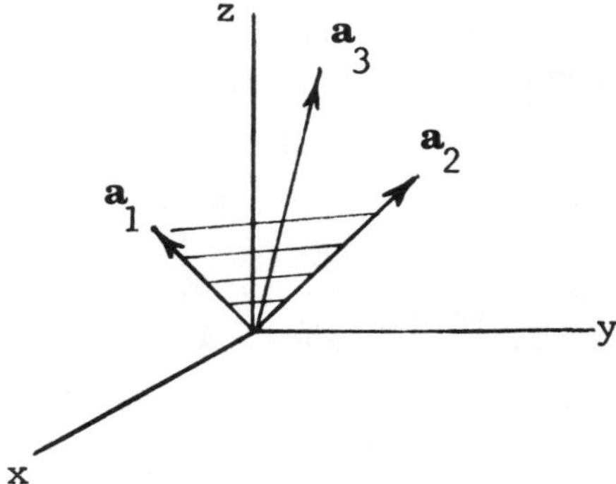

Fig. 7.3. Linearly-dependent vectors.

then

$$\mathbf{A} = \begin{bmatrix} \boldsymbol{\alpha}_1^T \\ \boldsymbol{\alpha}_2^T \\ \cdot \\ \cdot \\ \cdot \\ \boldsymbol{\alpha}_n^T \end{bmatrix} \tag{7.54}$$

and

$$\mathbf{y} = \mathbf{A}\,\mathbf{x} = \begin{bmatrix} \boldsymbol{\alpha}_1^T\,\mathbf{x} \\ \boldsymbol{\alpha}_2^T\,\mathbf{x} \\ \cdot \\ \cdot \\ \boldsymbol{\alpha}_n^T\,\mathbf{x} \end{bmatrix} = \begin{bmatrix} <\boldsymbol{\alpha}_1, \mathbf{x}> \\ <\boldsymbol{\alpha}_2, \mathbf{x}> \\ \cdot \\ \cdot \\ <\boldsymbol{\alpha}_n, \mathbf{x}> \end{bmatrix}. \tag{7.55}$$

Now if $\mathbf{y} = \mathbf{A}\,\mathbf{x} = \mathbf{0}$, each component of $\mathbf{y}$ must be zero, and therefore $\mathbf{x}$ must be orthogonal to each row of $\mathbf{A}$. If for example

$$\mathbf{A} = \begin{bmatrix} \boldsymbol{\alpha}_1^T \\ \boldsymbol{\alpha}_2^T \\ \boldsymbol{\alpha}_3^T \end{bmatrix} = \begin{bmatrix} 1 & 1 & 2 \\ 2 & 4 & 1 \\ 3 & 2 & 1 \end{bmatrix}, \tag{7.56}$$

the rows of $\mathbf{A}$ are linearly independent and therefore form a three-dimensional basis. No nonzero vector $\mathbf{x}$ is orthogonal to all the basis vectors. Therefore $\mathbf{A}\,\mathbf{x}$ cannot be zero. On the other hand if

$$\mathbf{A} = \begin{bmatrix} \boldsymbol{\alpha}_1^T \\ \boldsymbol{\alpha}_2^T \\ \boldsymbol{\alpha}_3^T \end{bmatrix} = \begin{bmatrix} 1 & 0 & 1 \\ 0 & 1 & 1 \\ 1 & 1 & 2 \end{bmatrix} \tag{7.57}$$

as in Eq. (7.52), the three rows of $\mathbf{A}$ span only a two-dimensional space, and any vector $\mathbf{x}$ normal to this plane is orthogonal to all three rows of $\mathbf{A}$, and is therefore a solution of $\mathbf{A}\,\mathbf{x} = \mathbf{0}$. The solution can be obtained by solving two of the three linearly-dependent scalar equations simultaneously. The first two are

$$x_1 + x_3 = 0 \tag{7.58}$$

$$x_2 + x_3 = 0 \,. \tag{7.59}$$

Thus

$$x_1 = x_2 = -\, x_3 \tag{7.60}$$

or

$$\mathbf{x} = \begin{bmatrix} k \\ k \\ -k \end{bmatrix} \tag{7.61}$$

where k is any constant. This vector is orthogonal to all the rows of **A**. Since **A** is symmetric, its rows are the same as its columns. Vector **x** is therefore perpendicular to the plane of columns $\mathbf{a}_1$, $\mathbf{a}_2$, and $\mathbf{a}_3$ shown in Fig. 7.3.

If the rows of an nth-order matrix span only r dimensions, any vector lying in the other $n-r$ dimensions is a solution of $\mathbf{A}\,\mathbf{x} = \mathbf{0}$. The *null space* of the matrix **A** is the $n-r$ dimensional space defined by all solutions of $\mathbf{A}\,\mathbf{x} = \mathbf{0}$. For example, the rows of

$$\mathbf{A} = \begin{bmatrix} 1 & 0 & 0 \\ 2 & 0 & 0 \\ 3 & 0 & 0 \end{bmatrix} \tag{7.62}$$

span only $r = 1$ dimension. If the elements of each row vector $\boldsymbol{\alpha}_i^T$ are the u, v, and w coordinates in the rectangular coordinate system of Fig. 7.4,

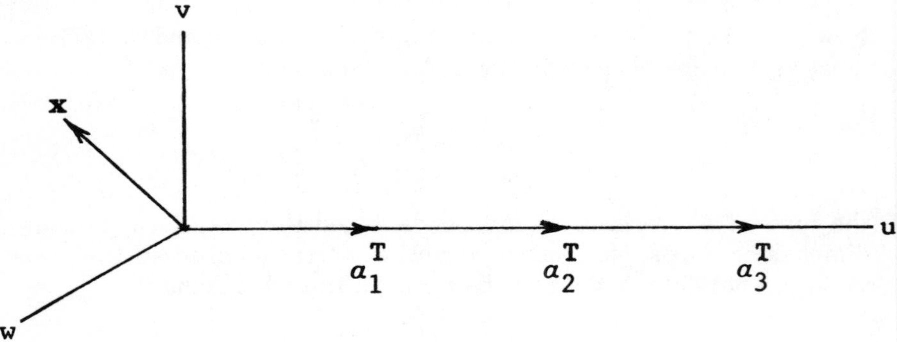

Fig. 7.4. Two-dimensional null space.

each row vector lies along the u axis. The null space is the vw plane. Any vector **x** in this plane, such as

$$\mathbf{x} = \begin{bmatrix} 0 \\ k_1 \\ k_2 \end{bmatrix}, \tag{7.63}$$

satisfies $\mathbf{A}\,\mathbf{x} = \mathbf{0}$. Consider another example. The rows of the matrix

$$\mathbf{A} = \begin{bmatrix} 1 & 1 & 0 & 0 \\ 0 & 0 & 1 & 1 \\ 1 & 1 & 1 & 1 \\ 1 & 1 & 2 & 2 \end{bmatrix} \tag{7.64}$$

span $r = 2$ dimensions. Any vector in the n-$r = 2$ dimensional null space spanned by any two solutions such as

$$\mathbf{x}_1 = \begin{bmatrix} 1 \\ -1 \\ 1 \\ -1 \end{bmatrix} \quad \text{or} \quad \mathbf{x}_2 = \begin{bmatrix} 1 \\ -1 \\ -1 \\ 1 \end{bmatrix} \tag{7.65}$$

is a solution of $\mathbf{A}\,\mathbf{x} = \mathbf{0}$.

7.6 Rank and Degeneracy of a Matrix

Suppose that an nth-order matrix has a determinant

$$|\mathbf{A}| = \begin{vmatrix} \boldsymbol{\alpha}_1^T \\ \boldsymbol{\alpha}_2^T \\ \cdot \\ \cdot \\ \cdot \\ \boldsymbol{\alpha}_n^T \end{vmatrix} \tag{7.66}$$

in which one row is a linear combination of the other rows:

$$\boldsymbol{\alpha}_n^T = k_1\,\boldsymbol{\alpha}_1^T + k_2\,\boldsymbol{\alpha}_2^T + \cdots + k_{n-1}\,\boldsymbol{\alpha}_{n-1}^T\,. \tag{7.67}$$

A determinant is unchanged if k times the elements of one row are added to the corresponding elements of another row. Add

$$-\,(k_1\,\boldsymbol{\alpha}_1^T + k_2\,\boldsymbol{\alpha}_2^T + \cdots + k_{n-1}\,\boldsymbol{\alpha}_{n-1}^T)$$

to $\boldsymbol{\alpha}_n^T$. The determinant is unchanged, but is now obviously zero because the last row is zero. Thus if one of the rows of a determinant is a linear combination of the others, the determinant is zero, and the matrix is singular. Of the remaining $n-1$ rows, one may be a linear combination of the others. If it is, any $n-1 \times n-1$ determinant in the remaining matrix is zero. The dependent row can be removed by repeating the above process. The process can be performed q times until a determinant of order $r = n-q$ is nonzero. Clearly the original n rows of

A spanned only r dimensions, and the remaining r rows constitute an r-dimensional basis. The *rank* r of a matrix is the order of its largest nonzero determinant. The *degeneracy* or *nullity* of a square matrix of order n is $q = n-r$. A square matrix with only r linearly-independent rows has a null space of $n-r$ dimensions. Therefore the number of dimensions of the null space of a square matrix equals its degeneracy.

The rank of a matrix can also be learned by determining which columns are linear combinations of the others. In the matrix of Eq. (7.64), for example, two of the columns are linear combinations of the other two. This observation leads to the conclusion that the rank is $r = 4 - 2 = 2$, the value obtained by looking at the rows.

The test for linear independence of n vectors $\mathbf{a}_1, \mathbf{a}_2, \ldots \mathbf{a}_n$, comparable to the test for linear independence of functions, is now apparent. Instead of a Wronskian determinant, simply form the square matrix

$$\mathbf{A} = [\mathbf{a}_1, \mathbf{a}_2, \ldots \mathbf{a}_n] \tag{7.68}$$

and evaluate its determinant $|\mathbf{A}|$. If $|\mathbf{A}| = 0$, at least one column is a linear combination of the others, i.e., the vectors are linearly dependent. If $|\mathbf{A}| \neq 0$, the vectors are linearly independent. As a simple test of understanding, the reader is invited to answer this question: How would you test the linear independence of three four-dimensional vectors?

7.7 The Reciprocal Basis

In many engineering problems the system being investigated provides a convenient set of basis vectors $\mathbf{x}_1, \mathbf{x}_2, \ldots \mathbf{x}_n$, in which the vector of variables $\mathbf{y}$ can be expressed:

$$\mathbf{y} = k_1 \mathbf{x}_1 + k_2 \mathbf{x}_2 + \cdots + k_n \mathbf{x}_n = \sum_{i=1}^{n} k_i \mathbf{x}_i \,. \tag{7.69}$$

Frequently $\mathbf{y}$ is known and the k_i's are needed. Interpreted geometrically, the problem consists of calculating the components of the vector $\mathbf{y}$ in the coordinate system consisting of the vectors $\mathbf{x}_i$. Eq. (7.69) represents n scalar equations in n unknowns, which can be solved by Cramer's rule. Since it is the same as Eq. (7.50) with different symbols, it can also be written as

$$\mathbf{y} = \mathbf{X}\,\mathbf{k} \tag{7.70}$$

where

$$\mathbf{X} = [\mathbf{x}_1, \mathbf{x}_2, \ldots \mathbf{x}_n] \quad \text{and} \quad \mathbf{k} = \begin{bmatrix} k_1 \\ k_2 \\ \cdot \\ \cdot \\ \cdot \\ k_n \end{bmatrix} . \tag{7.71}$$

Then

$$\mathbf{k} = \mathbf{X}^{-1}\,\mathbf{y}\,. \qquad (7.72)$$

A single component of the vector $\mathbf{k}$ can be written as

$$k_j = <(j\text{th row of } \mathbf{X}^{-1}), \mathbf{y}>\,. \qquad (7.73)$$

This awkward expression can be simplified by the *reciprocal-basis vectors* $\mathbf{r}_j$, defined by the equation

$$<\mathbf{x}_i, \mathbf{r}_j> = \delta_{ij} \qquad (7.74)$$

where

$$\delta_{ij} = 1\,, \quad i = j$$
$$= 0\,, \quad i \neq j\,. \qquad (7.75)$$

Each vector $\mathbf{r}_j$ in the reciprocal basis is orthogonal to every vector in the original basis except $\mathbf{x}_j$. The inner product of $\mathbf{x}_j$ and $\mathbf{r}_j$ is unity. Fig. 7.5 shows a two-dimensional basis $\mathbf{x}_1$, $\mathbf{x}_2$ and its reciprocal basis $\mathbf{r}_1$, $\mathbf{r}_2$.

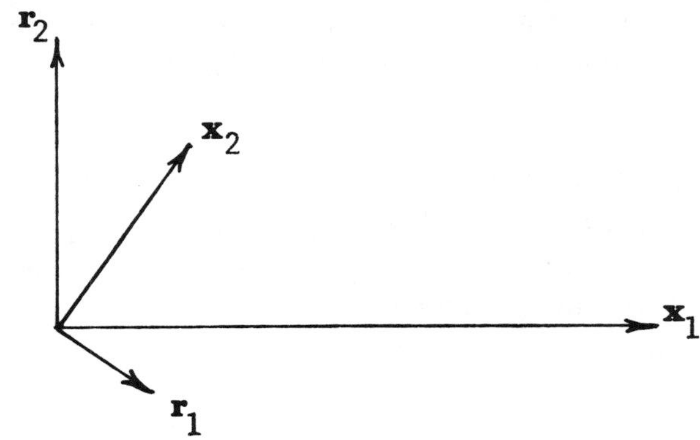

Fig. 7.5. Reciprocal basis.

Forming the inner product of both sides of Eq. (7.69) with $\mathbf{r}_j$ produces the result

$$<\mathbf{y}, \mathbf{r}_j> = k_1 <\mathbf{x}_1, \mathbf{r}_j> + k_2 <\mathbf{x}_2, \mathbf{r}_j> + \cdots + k_n <\mathbf{x}_n, \mathbf{r}_j>$$
$$= k_j <\mathbf{x}_j, \mathbf{r}_j> = k_j\,. \qquad (7.76)$$

Comparing Eqs. (7.76) and (7.73) shows that

$$\mathbf{r}_j = j\text{th row of } \mathbf{X}^{-1}\,. \qquad (7.77)$$

Eq. (7.69) becomes

$$\mathbf{y} = <\mathbf{r}_1, \mathbf{y}>\mathbf{x}_1 + <\mathbf{r}_2, \mathbf{y}>\mathbf{x}_2 + \cdots + <\mathbf{r}_n, \mathbf{y}>\mathbf{x}_n\,. \qquad (7.78)$$

Although the reason is not yet apparent, this form of displaying the coefficients of the basis vectors is useful in engineering problems.

Notice that calculating the components of vector **k**, by either Eq. (7.72) or (7.73), requires the inversion of matrix **X**. This work can be avoided if the basis vectors $\mathbf{x}_j$ happen to be orthogonal. Then

$$< \mathbf{y}, \mathbf{x}_j > = < \sum_{i=1}^{n} k_i \, \mathbf{x}_i, \mathbf{x}_j > = \sum_{i=1}^{n} k_i < \mathbf{x}_i, \mathbf{x}_j >$$
$$= k_j < \mathbf{x}_j, \mathbf{x}_j > . \tag{7.79}$$

Thus

$$k_j = \frac{< \mathbf{y}, \mathbf{x}_j >}{< \mathbf{x}_j, \mathbf{x}_j >} . \tag{7.80}$$

If the basis vectors $\mathbf{x}_j$ are orthonormal, $<\mathbf{x}_j, \mathbf{x}_j> = 1$, and

$$k_j = < \mathbf{y}, \mathbf{x}_j > . \tag{7.81}$$

Thus the components of a vector are calculated most easily in a coordinate system of orthonormal basis vectors, such as the familiar rectangular coordinate system with unit vectors $\mathbf{1}_x$, $\mathbf{1}_y$, and $\mathbf{1}_z$.

7.8 Vector-Space Exercises

The reader is now invited to test his or her understanding by evaluating the x_i's in each of the following four problems, if possible, by the simplest vector or matrix method.

1. $x_1 - x_2 + 2x_3 = 1$

   $4x_2 + x_3 = 2$

   $x_1 + x_2 - 2x_3 = 3$.

2. $4x_1 + 2x_2 - 2x_3 = 1$

   $-5x_1 + 3x_2 + 2x_3 = 2$

   $-2x_1 + 4x_2 + x_3 = 3$.

Just indicate the procedure if a computer is not available.

3. $3x_1 - x_2 + 2x_3 = 1$

   $6x_1 + 4x_2 + x_3 = 2$

   $-3x_1 + x_2 - 2x_3 = 3$.

4. $x_1 + x_2 = 0$

$$x_3 + x_4 = 0$$

$$x_1 + x_2 + x_3 + x_4 = 0$$

$$x_1 + x_2 + 2x_3 + 2x_4 = 0 \, .$$

As a final test, review the explanation of Eq. (1.59) in Chapter 1. It should now be clear that a nonzero vector **c** can be found iff the Wronskian determinant $|\mathbf{W}|$ or W is zero.

Chapter 8

EIGENVECTORS WITH APPLICATIONS TO VIBRATING SYSTEMS

8.1 Introduction

The German word "Eigenwert" means "characteristic value" or "self value." Since "eigen" describes what is meant better than either English prefix, authors use the hybrid word "eigenvalue." Every square matrix has eigenvalues and eigenvectors. These properties provide a convenient method of solving system problems that complements the other methods such as Laplace transforms, state-transition matrices, and classical solution of the simultaneous differential equations. The eigenvector method has two advantages:

1. It gives physical understanding of systems, particularly vibrating systems, that the other methods do not offer.

2. It provides a geometric interpretation of vibrations that mathematically-inclined engineers find irresistible.

8.2 An Example

Eigenvalues and eigenvectors can be introduced conveniently by solving a vibration problem, in which they will appear naturally. Fig. 8.1

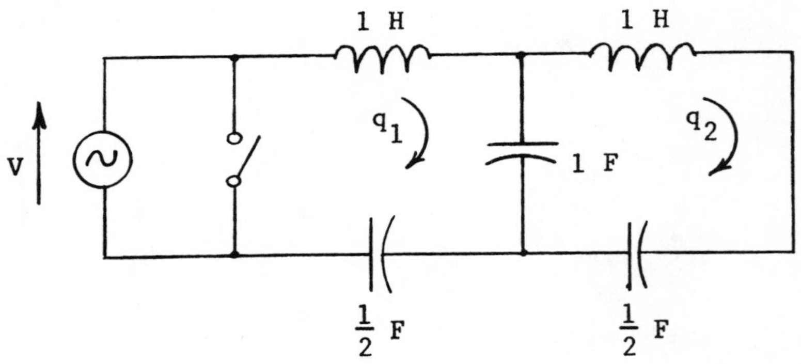

Fig. 8.1. L-C circuit.

shows an L-C circuit whose switch is closed at $t = 0$, so that the voltages around the two loops are

$$\ddot{q}_1 + 3q_1 - q_2 = 0 \tag{8.1}$$

$$-q_1 + \ddot{q}_2 + 3q_2 = 0 \tag{8.2}$$

where q_1 and q_2 are the charges that have flowed in the two loops. What are the charges as functions of time? First solve the problem with Laplace transforms. The transforms of Eqs. (8.1) and (8.2) can be written as

$$(s^2 + 3)Q_1(s) - Q_2(s) = s\, q_1(0) + \dot{q}_1(0) \tag{8.3}$$

$$-Q_1(s) + (s^2 + 3)Q_2(s) = s\, q_2(0) + \dot{q}_2(0)\,. \tag{8.4}$$

Now $Q_1(s)$ can be expressed with the help of Cramer's rule. With the numerator $N(s)$ left in literal form,

$$Q_1(s) = \frac{N(s)}{\begin{vmatrix} s^2 + 3 & -1 \\ -1 & s^2 + 3 \end{vmatrix}} = \frac{N(s)}{s^4 + 6s^2 + 8} = \frac{N(s)}{(s^2 + 2)(s^2 + 4)}\,. \tag{8.5}$$

The inverse of this Laplace transform is

$$q_1(t) = a_1 \sin \sqrt{2}t + b_1 \cos \sqrt{2}t + a_2 \sin 2t + b_2 \cos 2t\,. \tag{8.6}$$

The four constants are of course determined by the four initial conditions in Eqs. (8.3) and (8.4). Substituting Eq. (8.6) into (8.1) reveals that

$$q_2(t) = a_1 \sin \sqrt{2}t + b_1 \cos \sqrt{2}t - a_2 \sin 2t - b_2 \cos 2t\,. \tag{8.7}$$

Notice that very little work produced the information that both charges oscillate at two frequencies. The amplitude and phase of each oscillation is determined by the initial current and charge in each loop.

Now try a matrix solution. Since the circuit contains no resistance, engineering judgment aided by a look at Eqs. (8.6) and (8.7) indicates that each charge oscillates sinusoidally with the form

$$q_i = a \sin \omega t + b \cos \omega t\,. \tag{8.8}$$

Therefore

$$\ddot{q}_i = -\omega^2 q_i\,. \tag{8.9}$$

Although the frequency ω is still unknown, the last equation has reduced the work considerably. The original differential equations (8.1) and (8.2) become

$$(3 - \omega^2)q_1 - q_2 = 0 \tag{8.10}$$

$$-q_1 + (3 - \omega^2)q_2 = 0 \tag{8.11}$$

or

$$\begin{bmatrix} 3 - \omega^2 & -1 \\ -1 & 3 - \omega^2 \end{bmatrix} \begin{bmatrix} q_1 \\ q_2 \end{bmatrix} = \begin{bmatrix} 0 \\ 0 \end{bmatrix} \tag{8.12}$$

or

$$[\mathbf{A} - \omega^2\mathbf{I}]\mathbf{q} = \mathbf{0} \tag{8.13}$$

where

$$\mathbf{A} = \begin{bmatrix} 3 & -1 \\ -1 & 3 \end{bmatrix} \quad \text{and} \quad \mathbf{q} = \begin{bmatrix} q_1 \\ q_2 \end{bmatrix}. \tag{8.14}$$

According to the lesson taught by Eq. (7.55), the vector **q** in Eq. (8.13) is orthogonal to each row of the matrix $[\mathbf{A} - \omega^2\mathbf{I}]$. Vector **q** must lie in the null space of the matrix. Since the rows of the matrix do not span $n = 2$ dimensions, they are linearly dependent, and the determinant of the matrix is zero:

$$|\mathbf{A} - \omega^2\mathbf{I}| = \begin{vmatrix} 3-\omega^2 & -1 \\ -1 & 3-\omega^2 \end{vmatrix} = \omega^4 - 6\omega^2 + 8 = (\omega^2 - 2)(\omega^2 - 4) = 0\,. \tag{8.15}$$

Therefore ω^2 has only the values

$$\omega_1^2 = 2 \quad \text{and} \quad \omega_2^2 = 4\,. \tag{8.16}$$

Eq. (8.15) is called the *characteristic equation* of matrix **A**, and its roots, given by Eqs. (8.16), are the *eigenvalues* of matrix **A**. An nth-order matrix has n eigenvalues. In this example, the square roots of the eigenvalues, $\omega_1 = \sqrt{2}$ and $\omega_2 = 2$, are the natural frequencies of oscillation of charge in the circuit.

8.3 Eigenvectors

The value of the vector **q** for each eigenvalue, called $\mathbf{u}_i$ to avoid confusion in nomenclature, can be found readily. For $\omega_1^2 = 2$, Eq. (8.13) becomes

$$[\mathbf{A} - \omega_1^2\mathbf{I}]\mathbf{u}_1 = \begin{bmatrix} 1 & -1 \\ -1 & 1 \end{bmatrix} \begin{bmatrix} q_{11} \\ q_{21} \end{bmatrix} = \begin{bmatrix} 0 \\ 0 \end{bmatrix}. \tag{8.17}$$

The second subscript on each charge indicates the eigenvalue for which it applies. Since the rows of the matrix $[\mathbf{A} - \omega^2\mathbf{I}]$ are linearly dependent, Eq. (8.17) represents only one scalar equation, namely

$$q_{11} - q_{21} = 0 \quad \text{or} \quad q_{11} = q_{21}\,. \tag{8.18}$$

Therefore the value of vector $\mathbf{u}_1$ for eigenvalue ω_1^2 is either

$$\mathbf{u}_1 = \begin{bmatrix} q_{11} \\ q_{21} \end{bmatrix} = \begin{bmatrix} 1 \\ 1 \end{bmatrix} \tag{8.19}$$

or a vector of any length, in the same direction. That is, $\mathbf{u}_1$ can be any vector that lies in the one-dimensional null space of matrix $[\mathbf{A} - \omega_1^2\mathbf{I}]$. For the first eigenvalue, Eq. (8.8) becomes

$$q_{11} = a_1 \sin \omega_1 t + b_1 \cos \omega_1 t \tag{8.20}$$

and Eqs. (8.18) show that q_{21} equals q_{11}. Thus

$$\mathbf{u}_1 = \begin{bmatrix} q_{11} \\ q_{21} \end{bmatrix} = \begin{bmatrix} 1 \\ 1 \end{bmatrix} (a_1 \sin \omega_1 t + b_1 \cos \omega_1 t) \,. \tag{8.21}$$

Similarly for the second eigenvalue $\omega_2^2 = 4$,

$$[\mathbf{A} - \omega_2^2 \mathbf{I}]\mathbf{u}_2 = \begin{bmatrix} -1 & -1 \\ -1 & -1 \end{bmatrix} \begin{bmatrix} q_{12} \\ q_{22} \end{bmatrix} = \begin{bmatrix} 0 \\ 0 \end{bmatrix} \tag{8.22}$$

and

$$q_{12} = - q_{22} \,. \tag{8.23}$$

According to Eq. (8.8),

$$q_{12} = a_2 \sin \omega_2 t + b_2 \cos \omega_2 t \,. \tag{8.24}$$

Therefore

$$q_{22} = - a_2 \sin \omega_2 t - b_2 \cos \omega_2 t \tag{8.25}$$

and

$$\mathbf{u}_2 = \begin{bmatrix} q_{12} \\ q_{22} \end{bmatrix} = \begin{bmatrix} 1 \\ -1 \end{bmatrix} (a_2 \sin \omega_2 t + b_2 \cos \omega_2 t) \,. \tag{8.26}$$

The vectors $\mathbf{u}_1$ and $\mathbf{u}_2$ are called the *eigenvectors* of matrix $\mathbf{A}$. Usually the eigenvalues are designated by λ. The example has led to these formal definitions:

1. The eigenvalues λ_i of a matrix $\mathbf{A}$ are the solutions of its characteristic equation $|\mathbf{A} - \lambda \mathbf{I}| = 0$.

2. The eigenvectors of matrix $\mathbf{A}$ are the vectors $\mathbf{u}_i$ satisfying the equation

$$[\mathbf{A} - \lambda_i \mathbf{I}]\mathbf{u}_i = \mathbf{0} \qquad \text{or} \qquad \mathbf{A}\,\mathbf{u}_i = \lambda_i \mathbf{u}_i \,. \tag{8.27}$$

The last equation shows that the operation $\mathbf{A}\,\mathbf{u}_i$ changes the length but not the direction of the eigenvector. Do not infer from that equation that $\mathbf{A} = \lambda_i$ or $\mathbf{A} = \lambda_i \mathbf{I}$. These conclusions are reached by dividing by $\mathbf{u}_i$, an operation that is not defined.

8.4 Properties of Eigenvectors

In the example, the eigenvectors $\mathbf{u}_1$ and $\mathbf{u}_2$ are the two *normal modes* of oscillation of the charges. In mode $\mathbf{u}_1$ the charges q_{11} and q_{21} oscillate in phase at frequency ω_1, and in mode $\mathbf{u}_2$ they oscillate out of phase at frequency ω_2. Since the system of Fig. 8.1 is linear, both modes can exist at the same time. In fact, since the charges can oscillate at only frequencies ω_1 and ω_2, any solution $\mathbf{q}$ of the original differential equations (8.1) and (8.2) must be a linear combination of the two modes:

$$\mathbf{q} = \begin{bmatrix} q_1 \\ q_2 \end{bmatrix} = \begin{bmatrix} 1 \\ 1 \end{bmatrix} (a_1 \sin \sqrt{2}t + b_1 \cos \sqrt{2}t) + \begin{bmatrix} 1 \\ -1 \end{bmatrix} (a_2 \sin 2t + b_2 \cos 2t) . \tag{8.28}$$

Geometrically, this means that the solution vector is expressed by its coordinates in the coordinate system (basis) consisting of the eigenvectors. This is the primary usefulness of eigenvectors. In many system problems, the vector of unknown variables can be expressed as a linear combination of the eigenvectors of a matrix derived from the system parameters.

The eigenvectors of a matrix are particularly useful as a coordinate system for three reasons. They are always linearly independent of each other, and for many matrices are orthogonal to each other. In addition, Eq. (8.27) that defines eigenvectors is frequently a help in evaluating the coefficients of the eigenvectors. The following facts can be proved:

1. An nth-order matrix whose eigenvalues are all different (distinct) has n eigenvectors, which therefore constitute a basis.

2. The eigenvectors of a hermitian matrix are mutually orthogonal, and therefore constitute an especially convenient basis.

3. Suppose that a matrix has a repeated eigenvalue λ_i of order p. If the degeneracy of the matrix $[\mathbf{A} - \lambda_i \mathbf{I}]$ is q, there are q eigenvectors for the repeated eigenvalue. An additional $p-q$ linearly-independent vectors can be calculated to complete the basis, but in general these are not eigenvectors. They do not satisfy Eq. (8.27), namely $\mathbf{A}\,\mathbf{u}_i = \lambda_i \mathbf{u}_i$. (See Appendix 2 of Chapter 9.)

4. If a matrix is hermitian, the degeneracy of $[\mathbf{A} - \lambda_i \mathbf{I}]$ for the repeated eigenvalue is $q = p$. Then $q - p = 0$, and there is no shortage of eigenvectors. Therefore a hermitian matrix always has a complete set of eigenvectors. As a bonus, the eigenvectors of a hermitian matrix are orthogonal.

In the example, matrix $\mathbf{A}$, Eq. (8.14), is real and symmetric and therefore hermitian. Eqs. (8.21) and (8.26) confirm that its eigenvectors are orthogonal.

8.5 Evaluation of the Constants

The four arbitrary constants in the eigenvector solution of the example, Eq. (8.28), must be evaluated from the initial conditions, as in the Laplace-transform solution. Assume that when the switch in Fig. 8.1 is closed, $q_1 = 2$ coulombs, $q_2 = 0$, $\dot{q}_1 = 0$, and $\dot{q} = 0$. The left and center capacitors are charged, but the right one is not, and no current is flowing. The vector of charges is given by Eq. (8.28). The derivative of this vector, which is the vector of currents in the two loops, is

$$\dot{\mathbf{q}} = \begin{bmatrix} \dot{q}_1 \\ \dot{q}_2 \end{bmatrix} = \begin{bmatrix} 1 \\ 1 \end{bmatrix} (\sqrt{2}a_1 \cos \sqrt{2}t - \sqrt{2}b_1 \sin \sqrt{2}t) + \begin{bmatrix} 1 \\ -1 \end{bmatrix} (2a_2 \cos 2t - 2b_2 \sin 2t) \,. \tag{8.29}$$

Inserting the initial conditions into these two equations yields

$$\begin{bmatrix} 2 \\ 0 \end{bmatrix} = \begin{bmatrix} 1 \\ 1 \end{bmatrix} b_1 + \begin{bmatrix} 1 \\ -1 \end{bmatrix} b_2 \tag{8.30}$$

and

$$\begin{bmatrix} 0 \\ 0 \end{bmatrix} = \begin{bmatrix} 1 \\ 1 \end{bmatrix} \sqrt{2}a_1 + \begin{bmatrix} 1 \\ -1 \end{bmatrix} 2a_2 \,. \tag{8.31}$$

These two pairs of two scalar equations can be solved easily. To be elegant, let

$$\mathbf{q}(0) = \begin{bmatrix} 2 \\ 0 \end{bmatrix}, \quad \dot{\mathbf{q}}(0) = \begin{bmatrix} 0 \\ 0 \end{bmatrix}, \quad \mathbf{b} = \begin{bmatrix} b_1 \\ b_2 \end{bmatrix}, \quad \mathbf{a} = \begin{bmatrix} \sqrt{2}a_1 \\ 2a_2 \end{bmatrix}. \tag{8.32}$$

Although the definition of an eigenvector, Eq. (8.27), places no restriction on its length, a length must be chosen when the time comes to use it in a calculation. Logical choices for the eigenvectors of $\mathbf{A}$ in this example are

$$\mathbf{u}_1 = \begin{bmatrix} 1 \\ 1 \end{bmatrix} \quad \text{and} \quad \mathbf{u}_2 = \begin{bmatrix} 1 \\ -1 \end{bmatrix}. \tag{8.33}$$

Let $\mathbf{M}$ be a matrix whose columns are the eigenvectors:

$$\mathbf{M} = \begin{bmatrix} 1 & 1 \\ 1 & -1 \end{bmatrix}. \tag{8.34}$$

Then Eqs. (8.30) and (8.31) can be written as

$$\mathbf{q}(0) = \mathbf{M}\,\mathbf{b} \quad \text{and} \quad \dot{\mathbf{q}}(0) = \mathbf{M}\,\mathbf{a} \tag{8.35}$$

and their solutions are

$$\mathbf{b} = \mathbf{M}^{-1}\mathbf{q}(0) = \begin{bmatrix} 1 \\ 1 \end{bmatrix} \quad \text{and} \quad \mathbf{a} = \mathbf{M}^{-1}\dot{\mathbf{q}}(0) = \begin{bmatrix} 0 \\ 0 \end{bmatrix}. \tag{8.36}$$

Since the two eigenvectors are orthogonal, Eqs. (8.30) and (8.31) can also be solved by the method of Eq. (7.80). Now Eq. (8.28) becomes

$$\begin{bmatrix} q_1 \\ q_2 \end{bmatrix} = \begin{bmatrix} 1 \\ 1 \end{bmatrix} \cos \sqrt{2}t + \begin{bmatrix} 1 \\ -1 \end{bmatrix} \cos 2t \,. \tag{8.37}$$

Thus each charge in Fig. 8.1 oscillates at both natural frequencies and exhibits the familiar phenomenon of *beating* shown in Fig. 8.2.

What initial conditions are required to excite only one normal mode? Eqs. (8.28) and (8.29) show that

$$\mathbf{q}(0) = \begin{bmatrix} q_1(0) \\ q_2(0) \end{bmatrix} = \begin{bmatrix} 1 \\ 1 \end{bmatrix} b_1 + \begin{bmatrix} 1 \\ -1 \end{bmatrix} b_2 \tag{8.38}$$

and

$$\dot{\mathbf{q}}(0) = \begin{bmatrix} \dot{q}_1(0) \\ \dot{q}_2(0) \end{bmatrix} = \begin{bmatrix} 1 \\ 1 \end{bmatrix} \sqrt{2}a_1 + \begin{bmatrix} 1 \\ -1 \end{bmatrix} 2a_2 \,. \tag{8.39}$$

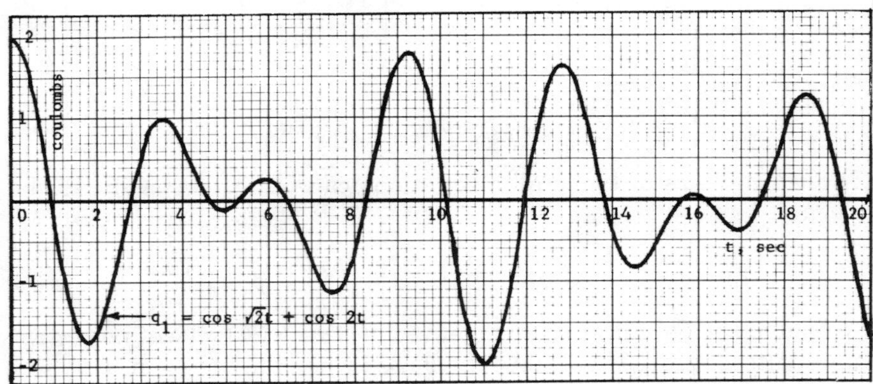

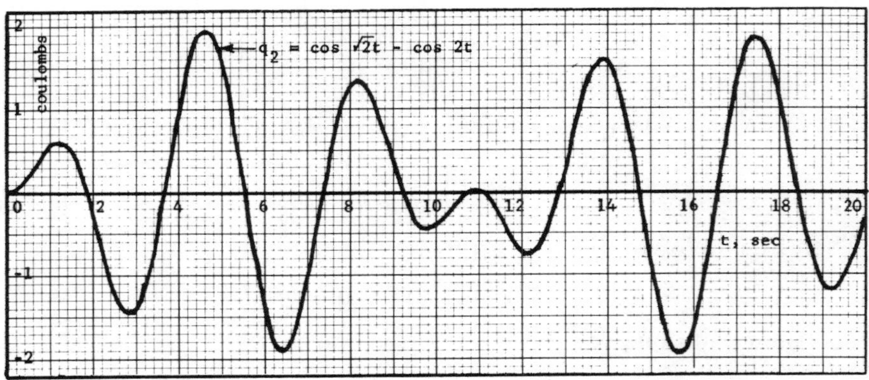

Fig. 8.2. Beating of the circulating charges in the L-C circuit.

To excite only the first normal mode in which the charges oscillate in phase, make $a_2 = b_2 = 0$ by choosing

$$\begin{bmatrix} q_1(0) \\ q_2(0) \end{bmatrix} = b_1 \begin{bmatrix} 1 \\ 1 \end{bmatrix} \quad \text{and} \quad \begin{bmatrix} \dot{q}_1(0) \\ \dot{q}_2(0) \end{bmatrix} = \sqrt{2}a_1 \begin{bmatrix} 1 \\ 1 \end{bmatrix} \tag{8.40}$$

where b_1 and $\sqrt{2}a_1$ are any constants. Eqs. (8.40) show that the vectors $\mathbf{q}(0)$ and $\dot{\mathbf{q}}(0)$ must lie in the same direction as the first eigenvector. Similarly, to excite the second normal mode alone, thereby making the two charges oscillate out of phase, choose

$$\begin{bmatrix} q_1(0) \\ q_2(0) \end{bmatrix} = b_2 \begin{bmatrix} 1 \\ -1 \end{bmatrix} \quad \text{and} \quad \begin{bmatrix} \dot{q}_1(0) \\ \dot{q}_2(0) \end{bmatrix} = 2a_2 \begin{bmatrix} 1 \\ -1 \end{bmatrix} \tag{8.41}$$

so that $\mathbf{q}(0)$ and $\dot{\mathbf{q}}(0)$ point in the same direction as the second eigenvector.

8.6 Torsional Pendulums

A second example of the use of eigenvectors is a mechanical vibration problem in which the oscillations can be seen physically. Fig. 8.3 shows three disks suspended between four wires that constitute torsional springs. The disks oscillate with negligible damping. The torsional moments of inertia J_i are each 3 N·m·s^2/rad, and the torsional spring constants k_i are 1 N·m/rad. Consider these questions:

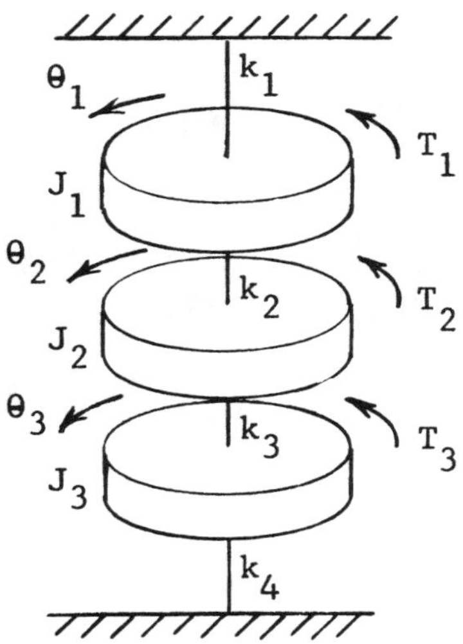

Fig. 8.3. Coupled torsional pendulums.

1. How many natural frequencies does the system have?

2. How are the motions of the three disks related when they are oscillating, undriven, at each natural frequency alone?

3. How should the disks be twisted initially so that when they are released simultaneously, the system will vibrate at one natural frequency only?

To answer them, first write the sum of torques on each of the three disks:

$$\left.\begin{aligned} J_1\ddot{\theta}_1 + k_1\theta_1 + k_2(\theta_1 - \theta_2) &= T_1 \\ J_2\ddot{\theta}_2 + (\theta_2 - \theta_1)k_2 + (\theta_2 - \theta_3)k_3 &= T_2 \\ J_3\ddot{\theta}_3 + (\theta_3 - \theta_2)k_3 + \theta_3 k_4 &= T_3 \end{aligned}\right\} \tag{8.42}$$

where the T_i's are the torques, if any, applied to the disks in the direction of the angular displacements θ_i. As in the first example, the oscillation is undamped so that in each mode,

$$\ddot{\theta}_i = -\omega^2\theta_i\,. \tag{8.43}$$

With the numerical values inserted, the three torque equations are

$$\left.\begin{aligned} (2 - 3\omega^2)\theta_1 \quad - \theta_2 \quad\quad &= T_1 \\ -\theta_1 + (2 - 3\omega^2)\theta_2 \quad - \theta_3 &= T_2 \\ -\theta_2 + (2 - 3\omega^2)\theta_3 &= T_3 \end{aligned}\right\} \tag{8.44}$$

or

$$[\mathbf{A} - \lambda\mathbf{I}]\boldsymbol{\theta} = \mathbf{T} \tag{8.45}$$

where

$$\mathbf{A} = \begin{bmatrix} 2 & -1 & 0 \\ -1 & 2 & -1 \\ 0 & -1 & 2 \end{bmatrix}, \qquad \lambda = 3\omega^2\,, \tag{8.46}$$

$$\boldsymbol{\theta} = \begin{bmatrix} \theta_1 \\ \theta_2 \\ \theta_3 \end{bmatrix}, \quad \text{and} \quad \mathbf{T} = \begin{bmatrix} T_1 \\ T_2 \\ T_3 \end{bmatrix}. \tag{8.47}$$

The eigenvalues are the roots of the characteristic equation

$$|\lambda\mathbf{I} - \mathbf{A}| = \begin{vmatrix} \lambda - 2 & 1 & 0 \\ 1 & \lambda - 2 & 1 \\ 0 & 1 & \lambda - 2 \end{vmatrix} = \lambda^3 - 6\lambda^2 + 10\lambda - 4 = 0\,, \tag{8.48}$$

namely $\lambda_1 = 2$, $\lambda_2 = 2 + \sqrt{2}$, and $\lambda_3 = 2 - \sqrt{2}$. Since $\lambda = 3\omega^2$, the three natural frequencies are

$$\left.\begin{aligned} \omega_1 &= \sqrt{\frac{2}{3}} = 0.817 \text{ rad/s} \\ \omega_2 &= \sqrt{\frac{2+\sqrt{2}}{3}} = 1.067 \text{ rad/s} \\ \omega_3 &= \sqrt{\frac{2-\sqrt{2}}{3}} = 0.442 \text{ rad/s} . \end{aligned}\right\} \tag{8.49}$$

If the system is undriven, Eq. (8.45) is

$$[\mathbf{A} - \lambda \mathbf{I}]\boldsymbol{\theta} = \mathbf{0} . \tag{8.50}$$

The ith eigenvector $\mathbf{u}_i$ is defined by the equation

$$[\mathbf{A} - \lambda_i \mathbf{I}]\mathbf{u}_i = \mathbf{0} . \tag{8.51}$$

Thus for the first eigenvalue, $\lambda_1 = 2$,

$$\begin{bmatrix} 0 & -1 & 0 \\ -1 & 0 & -1 \\ 0 & -1 & 0 \end{bmatrix} \begin{bmatrix} \theta_{11} \\ \theta_{21} \\ \theta_{31} \end{bmatrix} = \begin{bmatrix} 0 \\ 0 \\ 0 \end{bmatrix} \tag{8.52}$$

and the first eigenvector is

$$\mathbf{u}_1 = \begin{bmatrix} \theta_{11} \\ \theta_{21} \\ \theta_{31} \end{bmatrix} = \begin{bmatrix} 1 \\ 0 \\ -1 \end{bmatrix} (a_1 \sin \omega_1 t + b_1 \cos \omega_1 t) . \tag{8.53}$$

For the second eigenvalue, $\lambda_2 = 2 + \sqrt{2}$, Eq. (8.51) becomes

$$\begin{bmatrix} -\sqrt{2} & -1 & 0 \\ -1 & -\sqrt{2} & -1 \\ 0 & -1 & -\sqrt{2} \end{bmatrix} \begin{bmatrix} \theta_{12} \\ \theta_{22} \\ \theta_{32} \end{bmatrix} = \begin{bmatrix} 0 \\ 0 \\ 0 \end{bmatrix} \tag{8.54}$$

and

$$\mathbf{u}_2 = \begin{bmatrix} 1 \\ -\sqrt{2} \\ 1 \end{bmatrix} (a_2 \sin \omega_2 t + b_2 \cos \omega_2 t) . \tag{8.55}$$

For the third eigenvalue, $\lambda_3 = 2 - \sqrt{2}$,

$$\begin{bmatrix} \sqrt{2} & -1 & 0 \\ -1 & \sqrt{2} & -1 \\ 0 & -1 & \sqrt{2} \end{bmatrix} \begin{bmatrix} \theta_{13} \\ \theta_{23} \\ \theta_{33} \end{bmatrix} = \begin{bmatrix} 0 \\ 0 \\ 0 \end{bmatrix} \tag{8.56}$$

and

$$\mathbf{u}_3 = \begin{bmatrix} 1 \\ \sqrt{2} \\ 1 \end{bmatrix} (a_3 \sin \omega_3 t + b_3 \cos \omega_3 t) . \tag{8.57}$$

Notice that since matrix **A** is hermitian, its eigenvectors should be orthogonal to each other. A check of Eqs. (8.53), (8.55), and (8.57) verifies that they are. The second question is answered by these three equations. The first normal mode is easily predictable. The second and third are not. The ambitious reader is invited to visualize the normal modes of *four* coupled pendulums.

The free vibration of the three coupled pendulums is

$$\boldsymbol{\theta} = \mathbf{u}_1 + \mathbf{u}_2 + \mathbf{u}_3 , \tag{8.58}$$

in which the six constants a_i and b_i are determined by the initial conditions. If the disks are to be held in twisted positions before they are released,

$$\dot{\boldsymbol{\theta}}(0) = \dot{\mathbf{u}}_1(0) + \dot{\mathbf{u}}_2(0) + \dot{\mathbf{u}}_3(0) = \mathbf{0} \tag{8.59}$$

or

$$\begin{bmatrix} \dot{\theta}_1(0) \\ \dot{\theta}_2(0) \\ \dot{\theta}_3(0) \end{bmatrix} = \begin{bmatrix} 1 \\ 0 \\ -1 \end{bmatrix} \omega_1 a_1 + \begin{bmatrix} 1 \\ -\sqrt{2} \\ 1 \end{bmatrix} \omega_2 a_2 + \begin{bmatrix} 1 \\ \sqrt{2} \\ 1 \end{bmatrix} \omega_3 a_3 = \begin{bmatrix} 0 \\ 0 \\ 0 \end{bmatrix} \tag{8.60}$$

$$\begin{bmatrix} 1 & 1 & 1 \\ 0 & -\sqrt{2} & \sqrt{2} \\ -1 & 1 & 1 \end{bmatrix} \begin{bmatrix} \omega_1 a_1 \\ \omega_2 a_2 \\ \omega_3 a_3 \end{bmatrix} = \begin{bmatrix} 0 \\ 0 \\ 0 \end{bmatrix} . \tag{8.61}$$

Since the matrix of eigenvectors is not singular and does not have a null space, the vector of $\omega_i a_i$'s must be zero. Therefore

$$a_1 = a_2 = a_3 = 0 . \tag{8.62}$$

The vector of displacements is now

$$\boldsymbol{\theta} = \begin{bmatrix} \theta_1 \\ \theta_2 \\ \theta_3 \end{bmatrix} = \begin{bmatrix} 1 \\ 0 \\ -1 \end{bmatrix} b_1 \cos \omega_1 t + \begin{bmatrix} 1 \\ -\sqrt{2} \\ 1 \end{bmatrix} b_2 \cos \omega_2 t + \begin{bmatrix} 1 \\ \sqrt{2} \\ 1 \end{bmatrix} b_3 \cos \omega_3 t . \tag{8.63}$$

To excite the first normal mode only, make $b_2 = b_3 = 0$. Then

$$\boldsymbol{\theta}(0) = \begin{bmatrix} \theta_1(0) \\ \theta_2(0) \\ \theta_3(0) \end{bmatrix} = \begin{bmatrix} 1 \\ 0 \\ -1 \end{bmatrix} b_1 \tag{8.64}$$

and

$$\boldsymbol{\theta}(t) = \boldsymbol{\theta}(0) \cos \omega_1 t . \tag{8.65}$$

To excite the first mode, twist the disks so that the components of $\boldsymbol{\theta}(0)$ are proportional to the components of the first eignevector. When the disks are released, they vibrate cosinusoidally in the first natural mode. To excite the second or third mode, set the disks at angles proportional to the components of the second or third eigenvector.

8.7 Eigenvalues of Systems

The examples of Figs. 8.1 and 8.3 were chosen so that their equations of undriven motion could be written in the form

$$[\mathbf{A} - \lambda \mathbf{I}]\mathbf{x} = \mathbf{0} \tag{8.66}$$

where $\mathbf{x}$ is the vector of physical coordinates. The values of λ satisfying the characteristic equation

$$|\mathbf{A} - \lambda \mathbf{I}| = 0 \tag{8.67}$$

are the eigenvalues of the matrix $\mathbf{A}$. If the coordinates q_i or θ_i in those examples are chosen differently, the equations of motion are not in the form of Eq. (8.66). An example is provided by the springs and masses of Fig. 8.4, whose vibration is vertical. The coordinates x_1 and x_2 are the changes in spacing of the masses from their rest positions, an increase being positive. The sums of forces on the two masses are

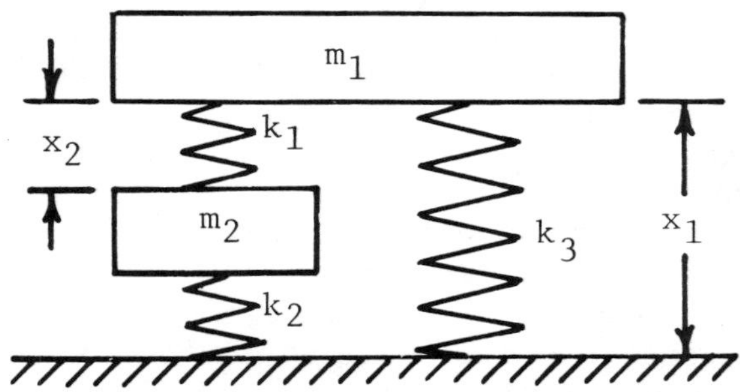

Fig. 8.4. Coupled vibrating masses.

$$m_1\ddot{x}_1 + k_1x_2 + k_3x_1 = 0 \tag{8.68}$$

and

$$m_2(\ddot{x}_1 - \ddot{x}_2) - k_1x_2 + k_2(x_1 - x_2) = 0\,. \tag{8.69}$$

Since $\ddot{x}_i = -\omega^2x_i$ in each mode of vibration,

$$(-\omega^2m_1 + k_3)x_1 + k_1x_2 = 0 \tag{8.70}$$

and

$$(-\omega^2 m_2 + k_2)x_1 + (\omega^2 m_2 - k_1 - k_2)x_2 = 0 \qquad (8.71)$$

or

$$[-\omega^2 \mathbf{M} + \mathbf{K}]\mathbf{x} = \mathbf{0}\,, \qquad (8.72)$$

where

$$\mathbf{M} = \begin{bmatrix} m_1 & 0 \\ m_2 & -m_2 \end{bmatrix}, \quad \mathbf{K} = \begin{bmatrix} k_3 & k_1 \\ k_2 & -(k_1 + k_2) \end{bmatrix}, \quad \text{and} \quad \mathbf{x} = \begin{bmatrix} x_1 \\ x_2 \end{bmatrix}. \qquad (8.73)$$

For this and other systems of vibrating springs and masses, $\mathbf{M}$ is called the *mass matrix* and $\mathbf{K}$ is the *stiffness matrix*. Notice that because of the strange choice of displacement coordinates, the mass matrix is not diagonal, and neither matrix is symmetric. Although Eq. (8.72) is not in the form of Eq. (8.66), it can be used to compute eigenvalues and eigenvectors. Clearly the matrix $[-\omega^2\mathbf{M} + \mathbf{K}]$ is singular, because vector $\mathbf{x}$ is orthogonal to each of its rows. Therefore ω^2 has only the values $\omega_1{}^2$ and $\omega_2{}^2$ that satisfy the characteristic equation

$$|-\omega^2 \mathbf{M} + \mathbf{K}| = 0\,. \qquad (8.74)$$

These roots must be called the eigenvalues of the *system*, since there is no $\mathbf{A}$ matrix as in Eq. (8.67). In the system of Fig. 8.4, ω_1 and ω_2 are the natural frequencies of vibration of the masses. The modes of vibration are the eigenvectors of the system $\mathbf{u}_1$ and $\mathbf{u}_2$ satisfying the equation

$$[-\omega_i{}^2 \mathbf{M} + \mathbf{K}]\mathbf{u}_i = \mathbf{0}\,. \qquad (8.75)$$

As in the first two examples, the free vibration can be expressed conveniently as a sum of the eigenvectors.

For a system of masses and linear springs like that in Fig. 8.4, Eq. (8.72) is simplified by another choice of coordinates. If the choice of the n coordinates is the displacements of the n masses from their rest positions with respect to the fixed ground, the only inertial force present in the equation for the forces on each mass m_i is $m_i\ddot{x}_i$. The mass matrix is therefore diagonal. Because the spring gradients are constant, the superposition principle guarantees that the stiffness matrix is symmetric. If each equation is divided by the mass contained in it, Eq. (8.72) appears as Eq. (8.66). A minor inconvenience is that unless the masses are all equal like the inertias in Fig. 8.3, the resulting $\mathbf{A}$ matrix is not symmetric.

8.8 Normal Coordinates

The three examples have shown that the vector of displacements in a linear system can be expressed conveniently in a basis consisting of the eigenvectors of the system or of a matrix $\mathbf{A}$ that was derived from the parameters of the system. The distances measured along the coordinate axes are called *normal coordinates*. If the n eigenvectors are $\mathbf{u}_i$, the vector of displacements $\boldsymbol{\theta}$ can be written as

$$\boldsymbol{\theta} = x_1\mathbf{u}_1 + x_2\mathbf{u}_2 + \cdots + x_n\mathbf{u}_n \,, \tag{8.76}$$

where the x_i's are the normal coordinates. The matrix whose columns are the eigenvectors of a matrix $\mathbf{A}$ is called its *modal matrix:*

$$\mathbf{M} = [\mathbf{u}_1, \mathbf{u}_2 \,, \cdots \mathbf{u}_n] \,. \tag{8.77}$$

Eq. (8.76) can be written as

$$\boldsymbol{\theta} = \mathbf{M}\,\mathbf{x} \,, \tag{8.78}$$

where

$$\mathbf{x}^T = [x_1, x_2 \,, \cdots x_n] \,. \tag{8.79}$$

The normal coordinates can be found in two ways when $\boldsymbol{\theta}$ is known. If the eigenvectors are orthogonal, Eq. (7.80) can be used:

$$x_i = \frac{< \boldsymbol{\theta}, \mathbf{u}_i >}{< \mathbf{u}_i, \mathbf{u}_i >} \,. \tag{8.80}$$

If the eigenvectors are not orthogonal, the modal matrix must be inverted:

$$\mathbf{x} = \mathbf{M}^{-1}\boldsymbol{\theta} \,. \tag{8.81}$$

This form was used in Eqs. (8.36).

Normal coordinates can be used to uncouple the original equations of motion of the system. To show this, write the three torque equations (8.42) for undriven coupled pendulums as

$$\mathbf{J}\ddot{\boldsymbol{\theta}} + \mathbf{K}\boldsymbol{\theta} = \mathbf{0} \tag{8.82}$$

where

$$\mathbf{J} = \begin{bmatrix} J_1 & 0 & 0 \\ 0 & J_2 & 0 \\ 0 & 0 & J_3 \end{bmatrix} = 3\begin{bmatrix} 1 & 0 & 0 \\ 0 & 1 & 0 \\ 0 & 0 & 1 \end{bmatrix} \tag{8.83}$$

and

$$\mathbf{K} = \begin{bmatrix} k_1 + k_2 & -k_2 & 0 \\ -k_2 & k_2 + k_3 & -k_3 \\ 0 & -k_3 & k_3 + k_4 \end{bmatrix} = \begin{bmatrix} 2 & -1 & 0 \\ -1 & 2 & -1 \\ 0 & -1 & 2 \end{bmatrix} . \tag{8.84}$$

Eqs. (8.82) thru (8.84) are typical of those for a system in which the coordinates are the displacements of the masses from their rest positions. The stiffness matrix $\mathbf{K}$ is symmetric. Because each of the original torque equations (8.42) has only one inertia term, the *inertia matrix* $\mathbf{J}$ is diagonal. If the inertias J_i are not equal, matrix $\mathbf{J}$ can be made into a unit matrix by dividing each of Eqs. (8.42) by the J_i that appears in it.

Then the stiffness matrix is no longer symmetric. The three torque equations are said to be *dynamically uncoupled,* because an angular acceleration $\ddot{\theta}_i$ of the ith disk produces no torque on either of the other disks. The stiffness matrix **K** is not diagonal. The torque equations are coupled *statically*, because an angular displacement θ_i of the ith disk produces a torque on one or both of the other two disks. Each element k_{ij} of the stiffness matrix is called a *stiffness influence coefficient*, because k_{ij} is the torque on disk i due to a one-radian deflection of disk j.

The normal coordinates can remove the static coupling. If the eigenvectors of matrix **K** are $\mathbf{u}_1$, $\mathbf{u}_2$, $\mathbf{u}_3$, form the modal matrix

$$\mathbf{M} = [\mathbf{u}_1, \mathbf{u}_2, \mathbf{u}_3] \tag{8.85}$$

and write the displacements as

$$\boldsymbol{\theta} = x_1\mathbf{u}_1 + x_2\mathbf{u}_2 + x_3\mathbf{u}_3 = \mathbf{M}\,\mathbf{x}\,. \tag{8.86}$$

Substitute this equation into (8.82) to obtain

$$\mathbf{JM}\,\ddot{\mathbf{x}} + \mathbf{KM}\,\mathbf{x} = \mathbf{0} \tag{8.87}$$

and premultiply each term by $\mathbf{M}^{-1}$:

$$\mathbf{M}^{-1}\mathbf{JM}\,\ddot{\mathbf{x}} + \mathbf{M}^{-1}\mathbf{KM}\,\mathbf{x} = \mathbf{0}\,. \tag{8.88}$$

Since **J** is a unit matrix multiplied by the constant 3, the first term reduces to $3\,\mathbf{I}\,\ddot{\mathbf{x}}$. Chapter 9 will show that if **M** is the modal matrix of any square matrix **K,**

$$\mathbf{M}^{-1}\mathbf{KM} = \boldsymbol{\Lambda}\,, \tag{8.89}$$

where $\boldsymbol{\Lambda}$, called the *spectral matrix*, is a diagonal matrix whose diagonal elements are the eigenvalues λ_i of matrix **K**. In passing, note that the derivation of this equation uses the magic property of eigenvectors: $\mathbf{K}\,\mathbf{u}_i = \lambda_i\mathbf{u}_i$. For the example,

$$\boldsymbol{\Lambda} = \begin{bmatrix} \lambda_1 & 0 & 0 \\ 0 & \lambda_2 & 0 \\ 0 & 0 & \lambda_3 \end{bmatrix}. \tag{8.90}$$

Eq. (8.88) becomes

$$3\,\mathbf{I}\,\ddot{\mathbf{x}} + \boldsymbol{\Lambda}\,\mathbf{x} = \mathbf{0} \tag{8.91}$$

which for the example is

$$3\begin{bmatrix} 1 & 0 & 0 \\ 0 & 1 & 0 \\ 0 & 0 & 1 \end{bmatrix}\begin{bmatrix} \ddot{x}_1 \\ \ddot{x}_2 \\ \ddot{x}_3 \end{bmatrix} + \begin{bmatrix} 2 & 0 & 0 \\ 0 & 2+\sqrt{2} & 0 \\ 0 & 0 & 2-\sqrt{2} \end{bmatrix}\begin{bmatrix} x_1 \\ x_2 \\ x_3 \end{bmatrix} = \begin{bmatrix} 0 \\ 0 \\ 0 \end{bmatrix}. \tag{8.92}$$

Now the three equations of motion of the disks are uncoupled statically as well as dynamically. Eq. (8.92) represents three independent scalar equations, like the equations of three independent vibrating systems, that can be solved easily by inspection. The first is

$$3\ddot{x}_1 + 2x_1 = 0 \,, \tag{8.93}$$

whose solution is

$$x_1 = a_1 \sin \sqrt{\frac{2}{3}}\, t + b_1 \cos \sqrt{\frac{2}{3}}\, t \,. \tag{8.94}$$

Notice that when the differential equations are written in terms of the normal coordinates, the sinusoidal form of the oscillation appears in the solutions. It does not have to be guessed, as when the physical coordinates are used. To convert the initial conditions on the physical coordinates θ_i to the initial conditions on the normal coordinates x_i, use the transformation

$$\mathbf{x} = \mathbf{M}^{-1}\boldsymbol{\theta} \tag{8.95}$$

in the forms

$$\mathbf{x}(0) = \mathbf{M}^{-1}\boldsymbol{\theta}(0) \quad \text{and} \quad \dot{\mathbf{x}}(0) = \mathbf{M}^{-1}\dot{\boldsymbol{\theta}}(0) \,. \tag{8.96}$$

If the stiffness matrix **K** is symmetric, as in this example, the work of inverting its modal matrix **M** can of course be avoided. Since the eigenvectors are then orthogonal, Eq. (8.86) shows that

$$x_i = \frac{< \boldsymbol{\theta}, \mathbf{u}_i >}{< \mathbf{u}_i, \mathbf{u}_i >} \,. \tag{8.97}$$

If the eigenvectors are of unit length, they are orthonormal. If eigenvectors of unit length are named $\mathbf{e}_i$, Eq. (8.97) becomes simply

$$x_i = < \boldsymbol{\theta}, \mathbf{e}_i > \,. \tag{8.98}$$

A real square matrix whose columns constitute an orthonormal basis is called an *orthogonal matrix*, and has an interesting property. If, for example,

$$\mathbf{M} = [\mathbf{e}_1, \mathbf{e}_2, \mathbf{e}_3] \,, \tag{8.99}$$

then

$$\mathbf{M}^T\mathbf{M} = \begin{bmatrix} \mathbf{e}_1^T \\ \mathbf{e}_2^T \\ \mathbf{e}_3^T \end{bmatrix} [\mathbf{e}_1, \mathbf{e}_2, \mathbf{e}_3] = \begin{bmatrix} <\mathbf{e}_1, \mathbf{e}_1> & <\mathbf{e}_1, \mathbf{e}_2> & <\mathbf{e}_1, \mathbf{e}_3> \\ <\mathbf{e}_2, \mathbf{e}_1> & <\mathbf{e}_2, \mathbf{e}_2> & <\mathbf{e}_2, \mathbf{e}_3> \\ <\mathbf{e}_3, \mathbf{e}_1> & <\mathbf{e}_3, \mathbf{e}_2> & <\mathbf{e}_3, \mathbf{e}_3> \end{bmatrix}$$

$$= \begin{bmatrix} 1 & 0 & 0 \\ 0 & 1 & 0 \\ 0 & 0 & 1 \end{bmatrix} = \mathbf{I} \,. \tag{8.100}$$

Therefore, for an orthogonal matrix $\mathbf{M}$,

$$\mathbf{M}^T = \mathbf{M}^{-1} . \tag{8.101}$$

The modal matrix in Eq. (8.95) need only be transposed, which is of course less work than inverting. That equation becomes

$$\mathbf{x} = \mathbf{M}^T \boldsymbol{\theta} = \begin{bmatrix} <\mathbf{e}_1, \boldsymbol{\theta}> \\ <\mathbf{e}_2, \boldsymbol{\theta}> \\ <\mathbf{e}_3, \boldsymbol{\theta}> \end{bmatrix} , \tag{8.102}$$

which agrees with Eq. (8.98).

Calculating the free vibration of a lumped system with either the normal coordinates or the actual physical coordinates requires about the same amount of work. For either solution, the eigenvalues and eigenvectors of the stiffness matrix must be calculated, and the modal matrix inverted (or transposed) to apply the initial conditions.

8.9 Driven Response as a Sum of Eigenvectors

The steady-state response of the torsional spring-mass system to sinusoidal driving torques, like its free vibration, also can be expressed conveniently as a sum of the eigenvectors of its stiffness matrix. To illustrate the method, first write Eqs. (8.42) as

$$\mathbf{J}\ddot{\boldsymbol{\theta}} + \mathbf{K}\boldsymbol{\theta} = \mathbf{T} \tag{8.103}$$

where $\mathbf{J}$ and $\mathbf{K}$ are given by Eqs. (8.83) and (8.84). Suppose the upper disk is driven by the torque

$$T_1 = T_0 \sin \omega_0 t . \tag{8.104}$$

Then

$$\mathbf{T} = \begin{bmatrix} T_0 \sin \omega_0 t \\ 0 \\ 0 \end{bmatrix} . \tag{8.105}$$

According to the method of undetermined coefficients, the steady-state displacements are

$$\theta_1 = a_1 \sin \omega_0 t , \quad \theta_2 = a_2 \sin \omega_0 t , \quad \theta_3 = a_3 \sin \omega_0 t . \tag{8.106}$$

Therefore $\ddot{\theta}_i = -\omega_0^2 \theta_i$, and Eq. (8.103) becomes

$$[-\omega_0^2 \mathbf{J} + \mathbf{K}]\boldsymbol{\theta} = \mathbf{T} , \tag{8.107}$$

and

$$\boldsymbol{\theta} = [-\omega_0^2 \mathbf{J} + \mathbf{K}]^{-1}\mathbf{T} . \tag{8.108}$$

The displacements of the disks can be calculated with this equation. If the response to several driving frequencies ω_0 must be determined, the work of inverting the matrix $[-\omega_0^2 \mathbf{J} + \mathbf{K}]$ many times is an inconvenience. This work can be avoided by calculating the eigenvectors $\mathbf{u}_i$ of $\mathbf{K}$, and using them as a coordinate system:

$$\boldsymbol{\theta} = c_1\mathbf{u}_1 + c_2\mathbf{u}_2 + c_3\mathbf{u}_3 = \mathbf{M}\,\mathbf{c}\,, \tag{8.109}$$

where

$$\mathbf{c}^T = [c_1, c_2, c_3]\,. \tag{8.110}$$

Substitute Eq. (8.109) into (8.107) to get

$$[-\omega_0^2\,\mathbf{J} + \mathbf{K}]\mathbf{M}\,\mathbf{c} = \mathbf{T} \tag{8.111}$$

and premultiply the terms by $\mathbf{M}^{-1}$:

$$-\omega_0^2\,\mathbf{M}^{-1}\mathbf{J}\mathbf{M}\,\mathbf{c} + \mathbf{M}^{-1}\mathbf{K}\mathbf{M}\,\mathbf{c} = \mathbf{M}^{-1}\mathbf{T}\,. \tag{8.112}$$

If the inertia matrix $\mathbf{J}$ is a constant k times a unit matrix, as in Eq. (8.83), let

$$\omega_0^2\,\mathbf{J} = \omega_0^2\,k\mathbf{I} = \lambda_0\,\mathbf{I} \tag{8.113}$$

so that

$$\lambda_0 = k\omega_0^2\,. \tag{8.114}$$

Since the spectral matrix is $\boldsymbol{\Lambda} = \mathbf{M}^{-1}\mathbf{K}\mathbf{M}$, Eq. (8.112) becomes

$$[-\lambda_0\,\mathbf{I} + \boldsymbol{\Lambda}]\mathbf{c} = \mathbf{M}^{-1}\mathbf{T}\,. \tag{8.115}$$

The matrix $[-\lambda_0\,\mathbf{I} + \boldsymbol{\Lambda}]$ has the diagonal form

$$[-\lambda_0\,\mathbf{I} + \boldsymbol{\Lambda}] = \begin{bmatrix} \lambda_1 - \lambda_0 & 0 & 0 \\ 0 & \lambda_2 - \lambda_0 & 0 \\ 0 & 0 & \lambda_3 - \lambda_0 \end{bmatrix}. \tag{8.116}$$

The vector of normal coordinates is

$$\mathbf{c} = [-\lambda_0\,\mathbf{I} + \boldsymbol{\Lambda}]^{-1}\mathbf{M}^{-1}\mathbf{T}\,, \tag{8.117}$$

and according to Eq. (8.109),

$$\boldsymbol{\theta} = \mathbf{M}\mathbf{c} = \mathbf{M}[-\lambda_0\,\mathbf{I} + \boldsymbol{\Lambda}]^{-1}\mathbf{M}^{-1}\mathbf{T}\,, \tag{8.118}$$

where

$$[-\lambda_0\mathbf{I} + \boldsymbol{\Lambda}]^{-1} = \begin{bmatrix} \dfrac{1}{\lambda_1 - \lambda_0} & 0 & 0 \\ 0 & \dfrac{1}{\lambda_2 - \lambda_0} & 0 \\ 0 & 0 & \dfrac{1}{\lambda_3 - \lambda_0} \end{bmatrix}. \tag{8.119}$$

Eq. (8.118) is preferable to Eq. (8.108) for calculating the disk displacements at several driving frequencies, because the matrix in brackets in Eq. (8.118) is already inverted.

8.10 Numerical Values of Driven Oscillation

A calculation of the driven response of the coupled pendulums in Fig. 8.3 will illustrate the usefulness of Eq. (8.118). The three eigenvalues are

$$\lambda_1 = 2\,, \quad \lambda_2 = 2 + \sqrt{2}\,, \quad \lambda_3 = 2 - \sqrt{2}\,. \tag{8.120}$$

The modal matrix is

$$\mathbf{M} = \begin{bmatrix} 1 & 1 & 1 \\ 0 & -\sqrt{2} & \sqrt{2} \\ -1 & 1 & 1 \end{bmatrix}, \tag{8.121}$$

and the vector of driving torques is

$$\mathbf{T} = \begin{bmatrix} 0.1 \\ 0 \\ 0 \end{bmatrix} \sin \omega_0 t \tag{8.122}$$

where ω_0 is the driving frequency in rad/s and $\lambda_0 = 3\omega_0^2$. The task of substituting these numbers into Eqs. (8.118) and (8.119) is accomplished by the BASIC computer program in Fig. 8.5. The amplitudes of vibration of the three disks are plotted as functions of the driving frequency in Fig. 8.6. Positive and negative amplitudes indicate vibration in phase and out of phase with the driving torque. The three resonant frequencies are shown as dotted lines. They are the same as the natural frequencies given by Eq. (8.49) because the pendulums are undamped. Notice that until the driving frequency reaches the first resonant frequency, all three disks oscillate in phase with the driving torque. At higher driving frequencies the disks reverse their phases in combinations that could not be guessed in advance. At two frequencies, 0.58 and 1.00 rad/s, the upper disk is stationary while still transmitting torque to the lower two disks. The reader is invited to speculate about how this is possible.

Fig. 8.6 also shows that with one exception, the amplitude of vibration of each disk becomes infinite and the phase reverses as the driving frequency passes thru each resonance. The exception is the vibration of the middle disk, which remains finite at the second resonant frequency. That frequency corresponds to the eigenvalue λ_1 and the normal mode $\mathbf{u}_1$. In this mode of free vibration the upper and lower disks oscillate, but the middle disk is stationary. When the upper disk is driven at the second resonant frequency, it oscillates with infinite amplitude. The

```
100 PRINT "FREQ, RAD/S","DISK 1, RAD","DISK 2, RAD","DISK 3,RAD"
110 PRINT
120 DIM A(3,3),B(3,3),C(3,1),D(3,1),M(3,3),T(3,1)
130 MAT READ M,T
140 DATA 1,1,1,0,-1.414,1.414,-1,1,1,.1,0,0
150 L1=2
160 L2=2+SQR(2)
170 L3=2-SQR(2)
180 MAT A=INV(M)
190 MAT B=A*T
200 MAT A=ZER
210 FOR W= 0 TO 1.5 STEP .05
220 L=3*W*W
230 A(1,1)=1/(L1-L)
240 A(2,2)=1/(L2-L)
250 A(3,3)=1/(L3-L)
260 MAT C=A*B
270 MAT D=M*C
280 PRINT W,D(1,1),D(2,1),D(3,1)
290 NEXT W
300 END
```

FREQ, RAD/S	DISK 1, RAD	DISK 2, RAD	DISK 3,RAD
0	0.075	4.99924E-2	0.025
0.05	7.56637E-2	5.07523E-2	2.54755E-2
0.1	7.77493E-2	0.053158	2.69878E-2
0.15	8.15791E-2	5.76429E-2	2.98327E-2
0.2	8.78575E-2	6.51622E-2	0.034666
0.25	9.81029E-2	7.77998E-2	4.29305E-2
0.3	0.11602	0.1007	5.82168E-2
0.35	0.153362	0.15034	9.21061E-2
0.4	0.27774	0.322116	0.211951
0.45	-1.10654	-1.64061	-1.17836
0.5	-0.102857	-0.228537	-0.182857
0.55	-2.19691E-2	-0.123983	-0.113502
0.6	1.44726E-2	-8.66721E-2	-0.094223
0.65	4.32328E-2	-6.83217E-2	-0.093286
0.7	7.89245E-2	-5.81612E-2	-0.109755
0.75	0.151786	-5.25588E-2	-0.168213
0.8	0.622992	-5.01529E-2	-0.627005
0.85	-0.294261	-5.07037E-2	0.302755
0.9	-0.104434	-5.50851E-2	0.128124
0.95	-4.70793E-2	-6.66813E-2	9.42635E-2
1.	-6.0536E-8	-9.99848E-2	0.1
1.05	0.186845	-0.344248	0.263327
1.1	-0.154743	0.152208	-0.093393
1.15	-7.79903E-2	5.34377E-2	-2.71643E-2
1.2	-5.58469E-2	2.95604E-2	-1.27435E-2
1.25	-4.43339E-2	1.91445E-2	-7.1246E-3
1.3	-3.69603E-2	1.34662E-2	-4.38704E-3
1.35	-3.17164E-2	0.009975	-2.87715E-3
1.4	-2.77475E-2	7.6591E-3	-1.97429E-3
1.45	-2.46177E-2	6.03972E-3	-1.40235E-3
1.5	-2.20765E-2	4.86249E-3	-1.02384E-3

Fig. 8.5. Calculation of driven vibration of the disks.

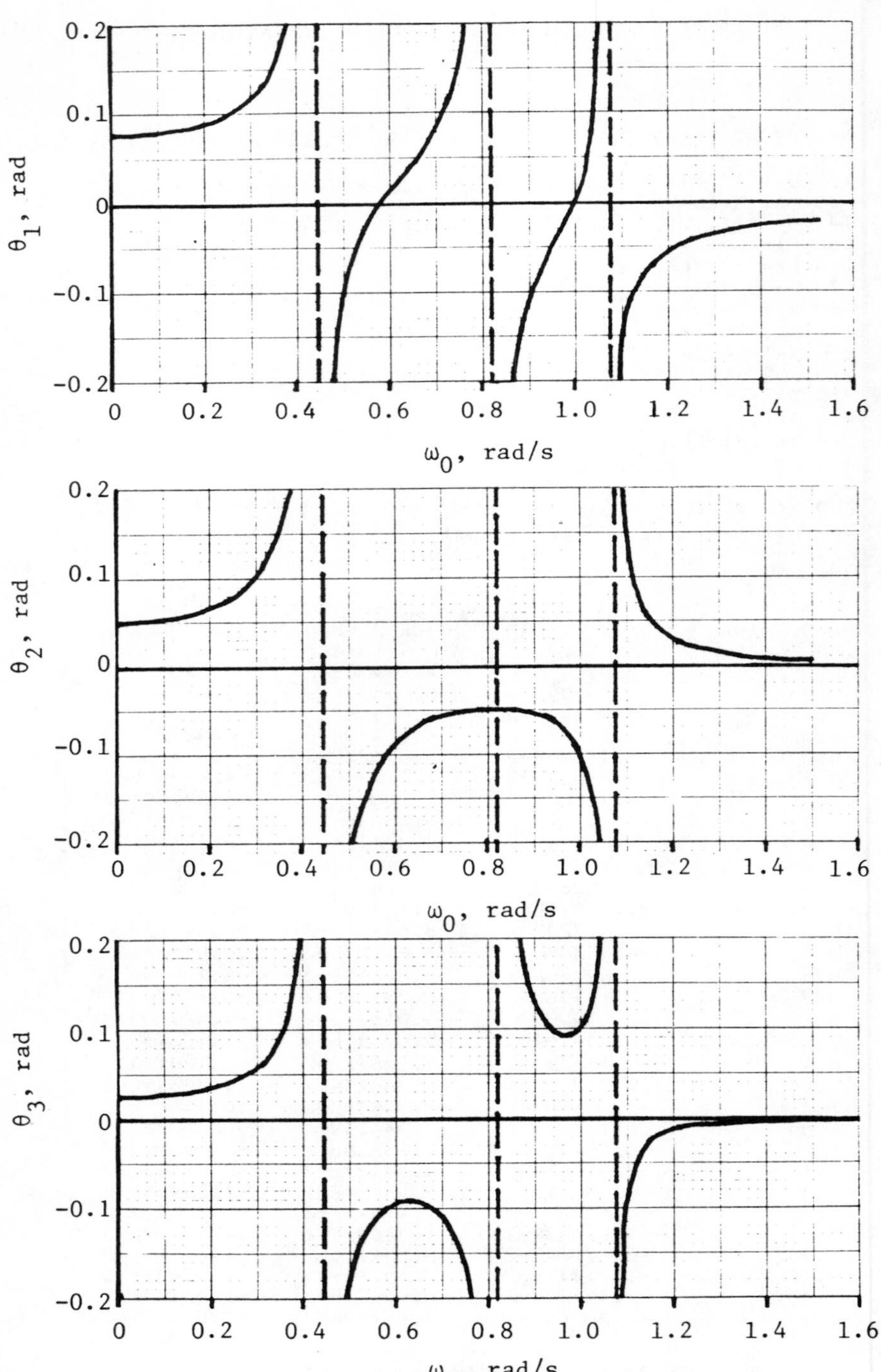

Fig. 8.6. Amplitudes of disk vibration as functions of driving frequency.

middle disk has to oscillate only a small amount to drive the lower disk at infinite amplitude.

An explanation that is more satisfactory mathematically can be obtained by expressing the vector of driven displacements again as a sum of the eigenvectors according to Eq. (8.109):

$$\boldsymbol{\theta} = c_1\mathbf{u}_1 + c_2\mathbf{u}_2 + c_3\mathbf{u}_3 \,. \tag{8.123}$$

To evaluate the normal coordinates c_i, observe that the vector equation (8.115) represents three uncoupled scalar equations, the ith of which is

$$(-\lambda_0 + \lambda_i)c_i = <\mathbf{r}_i, \mathbf{T}> \,, \tag{8.124}$$

where $\mathbf{r}_i$ is a reciprocal-basis vector, namely the ith row of $\mathbf{M}^{-1}$, that was defined by Eq. (7.74) which for this example is

$$<\mathbf{u}_i, \mathbf{r}_j> = \delta_{ij} \,. \tag{8.125}$$

Thus

$$c_i = \frac{<\mathbf{r}_i, \mathbf{T}>}{\lambda_i - \lambda_0} \tag{8.126}$$

and Eq. (8.123) becomes

$$\boldsymbol{\theta} = \frac{<\mathbf{r}_1, \mathbf{T}>}{\lambda_1 - \lambda_0}\mathbf{u}_1 + \frac{<\mathbf{r}_2, \mathbf{T}>}{\lambda_2 - \lambda_0}\mathbf{u}_2 + \frac{<\mathbf{r}_3, \mathbf{T}>}{\lambda_3 - \lambda_0}\mathbf{u}_3 \,. \tag{8.127}$$

This sum of eigenvectors helps to explain the driven oscillation of the disks. When the driving frequency ω_0 coincides with a natural frequency such as ω_2, then $\lambda_0 = \lambda_2$ and one of the normal coordinates is infinite. The amplitudes of oscillation are therefore infinite. The exception occurs because the second component u_{21} of eigenvector $\mathbf{u}_1$ is zero, and the first term of Eq. (8.127) therefore contributes nothing to θ_2. When the driving frequency ω_0 equals ω_1 or 0.817 rad/s, the coefficient of $\mathbf{u}_1$ is infinite and the displacements θ_1 and θ_3 of the upper and lower disks are infinite. The displacement θ_2 of the middle disk, however, has only the finite value given by the sum of the second and third terms of Eq. (8.127).

Eq. (8.127) also illustrates why the length of eigenvectors chosen for numerical calculations is arbitrary. If the length of one of the eigenvectors $\mathbf{u}_i$ is doubled, its reciprocal vector $\mathbf{r}_i$ is halved, and the term for that eigenvector in Eq. (8.127) remains the same.

8.11 Eigenvector Exercises

Now test your understanding of eigenvectors by working these problems.

1. Calculate the modal matrix of the matrix

$$\mathbf{A} = \begin{bmatrix} 4 & 2 & -2 \\ -5 & 3 & 2 \\ -2 & 4 & 1 \end{bmatrix}.$$

Before starting, decide whether the eigenvectors are orthogonal or just linearly independent, and verify the decision after they are calculated. As soon as you calculate the eigenvalues, decide whether or not **A** has a shortage of eigenvectors.

2. Calculate the eigenvectors of the matrix

$$\mathbf{A} = \begin{bmatrix} 7 & 4 & -1 \\ 4 & 7 & -1 \\ -4 & -4 & 4 \end{bmatrix}.$$

Try to explain geometrically why the eigenvectors are not orthogonal.

3. Without doing any calculating, answer these questions about the matrix

$$\mathbf{A} = \begin{bmatrix} 1 & 0 & 0 \\ 0 & 2 & 0 \\ 0 & 0 & 2 \end{bmatrix}:$$

   a. What are its eigenvalues?

   b. Does it have a full set of eigenvectors?

   c. Are the eigenvectors mutually orthogonal?

   d. How is the first eigenvector oriented with respect to the null space of the matrix $[\mathbf{A} - \lambda_2\mathbf{I}]$? Generalize this to $n-p$ eigenvectors of an nth-order hermitian matrix, one of whose eigenvectors is repeated p times.

4. Can a real matrix have complex eigenvalues? Calculate the eigenvalues and eigenvectors of the matrix

$$\mathbf{A} = \begin{bmatrix} 0 & 1 \\ -13 & -4 \end{bmatrix}.$$

Chapter 9

REPRESENTATION OF SYSTEMS IN STATE SPACE

9.1 Introduction

In modern control theory, the variables in a system are put into vector form and the system parameters are combined into matrices. The resulting matrix equations have the advantage of simplicity, and can be handled by the well-developed rules of matrix algebra. This chapter should improve the reader's facility in working with matrix equations. Matrix algebra will be used to develop the fundamental ideas of the state vector of a system, how it can be expressed as a sum of eigenvectors, and how it can be calculated with the state-transition matrix. The latter matrix is so important that four methods of calculating it will be explained. Viewed from a strictly mathematical viewpoint, this chapter explains how to solve simultaneous linear differential equations with matrix algebra.

9.2 The State Equation

Modern control theory is based on the idea of *state*. The *state of a system* is a set of variables that must be known at any time t_0, together with the inputs to the system for $t \geqslant t_0$, in order to determine the behavior of the system from t_0 to t. The state variables at time t_0 are the familiar initial conditions of the differential equations representing the system. The number n of state variables is the same as the order of the differential equation for one of the system variables, or the degree of the characteristic equation of the system, or the number of integrators in the block diagram representing the system. For example, for the system of Fig. 3.4 with dependent variables x and y and the known inputs $v_1(t)$ and $v_2(t)$,

$$\dot{y} - 2x = v_1 \tag{9.1}$$

and

$$\dot{x} + 3y = v_2 \,. \tag{9.2}$$

The differential equation for $x(t)$ is

$$\frac{d^2x}{dt^2} + 6x = \frac{dv_2}{dt} - 3\,v_1 \tag{9.3}$$

and the characteristic equation of the system is

$$s^2 + 6 = 0\,. \tag{9.4}$$

This system has $n = 2$ state variables. They can be x and y, x and $\dot{x}$, or y and $\dot{y}$. The outputs of the integrators in the block diagram always constitute a set of state variables. The vector array of the state variables is called a *state vector*. For this system a suitable state vector is

$$\mathbf{x} = \begin{bmatrix} x \\ y \end{bmatrix}. \tag{9.5}$$

Another example is the R-L-C circuit of Fig. 9.1, in which the voltages around the two loops are

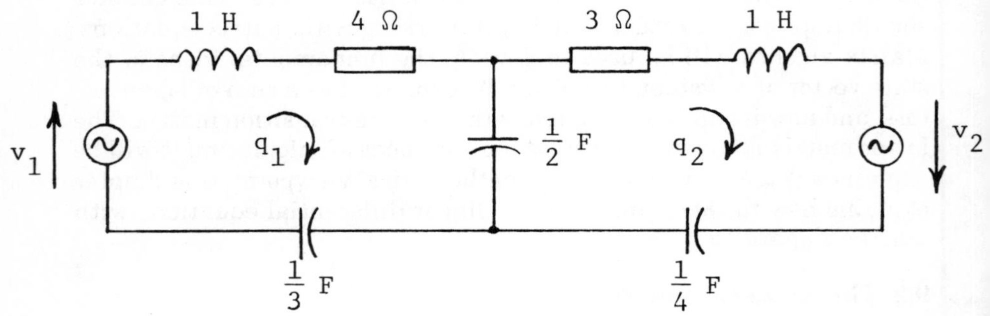

Fig. 9.1. R-L-C circuit with four state variables.

$$\ddot{q}_1 + 4\dot{q}_1 + 5q_1 - 2q_2 = v_1 \tag{9.6}$$

and

$$\ddot{q}_2 + 3\dot{q}_2 + 6q_2 - 2q_1 = v_2\,, \tag{9.7}$$

where q_1 and q_2 are the charges flowing in the loops. Fig. 9.2 is the block diagram representing these equations. A suitable state vector is

$$\mathbf{x} = \begin{bmatrix} q_1 \\ \dot{q}_1 \\ q_2 \\ \dot{q}_2 \end{bmatrix}. \tag{9.8}$$

It lies in an n-dimensional space (here $n = 4$), and its initial length and direction are determined by the initial conditions. Then as the inputs are applied, the tip of the state vector moves around in the n space, and the trajectory of the tip provides a record of the operation of the system.

The differential equations describing a linear system can be expressed concisely as one matrix equation. If the state variables of the R-L-C circuit are called x_1 thru x_4,

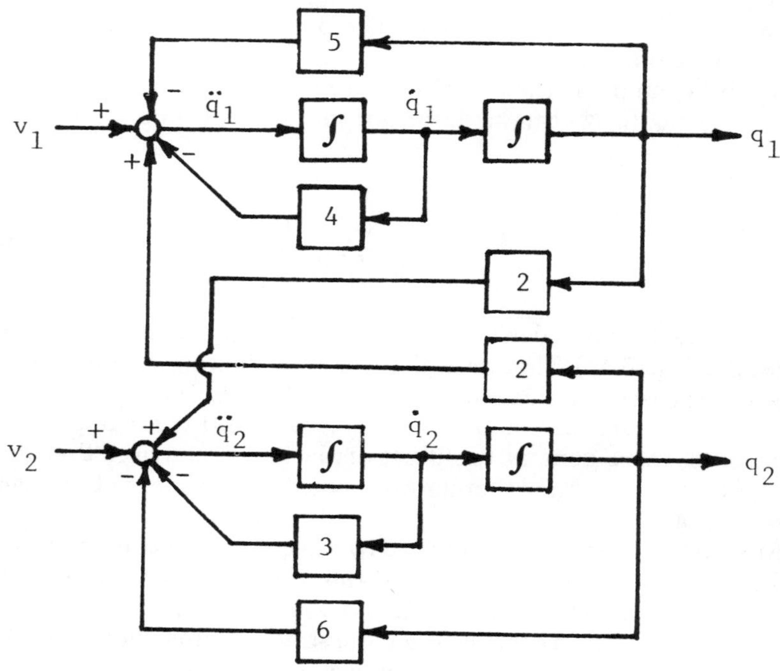

Fig. 9.2. Block diagram of the R-L-C circuit.

$$x_1 = q_1$$
$$x_2 = \dot{q}_1 = \dot{x}_1 \tag{9.9}$$
$$x_3 = q_2$$
$$x_4 = \dot{q}_2 = \dot{x}_3\,. \tag{9.10}$$

Then

$$\dot{x}_2 = \ddot{q}_1 = v_1 - 5q_1 - 4\dot{q}_1 + 2q_2 = v_1 - 5x_1 - 4x_2 + 2x_3 \tag{9.11}$$

and

$$\dot{x}_4 = \ddot{q}_2 = v_2 + 2q_1 - 6q_2 - 3\dot{q}_2 = v_2 + 2x_1 - 6x_3 - 3x_4\,. \tag{9.12}$$

Eqs. (9.9) thru (9.12) can be written as

$$\begin{bmatrix}\dot{x}_1\\ \dot{x}_2\\ \dot{x}_3\\ \dot{x}_4\end{bmatrix} = \begin{bmatrix}0 & 1 & 0 & 0\\ -5 & -4 & 2 & 0\\ 0 & 0 & 0 & 1\\ 2 & 0 & -6 & -3\end{bmatrix}\begin{bmatrix}x_1\\ x_2\\ x_3\\ x_4\end{bmatrix} + \begin{bmatrix}0 & 0\\ 1 & 0\\ 0 & 0\\ 0 & 1\end{bmatrix}\begin{bmatrix}v_1\\ v_2\end{bmatrix} \tag{9.13}$$

or

$$\dot{\mathbf{x}} = \mathbf{A}\mathbf{x} + \mathbf{B}\mathbf{v}\,. \tag{9.14}$$

Notice that the **A** matrix is square. The **B** matrix has as many columns as the system has drivers.

A third example is the L-C circuit of Fig. 8.1, for which an equation similar to Eq. (9.13) can be derived from Eqs. (8.1) and (8.2). This time

$$\mathbf{A} = \begin{bmatrix} 0 & 1 & 0 & 0 \\ -3 & 0 & 1 & 0 \\ 0 & 0 & 0 & 1 \\ 1 & 0 & -3 & 0 \end{bmatrix}. \tag{9.15}$$

Notice that the method of Chapter 8 produced a symmetric **A** matrix of order 2 in Eq. (8.14). The simplicity was a result of the assumption that the charges oscillate sinusoidally because the circuit contains no resistance. The state-space method does not require this assumption. The price of its more general usefulness is larger **A** matrices that are in general asymmetric and therefore do not enjoy the benefit of orthogonal eigenvectors.

Any system that can be described by a set of linear ordinary differential equations can be represented by the simple *state equation* (9.14). If the system is time variant, matrices **A** and **B** are functions of time. A system is said to be in *equilibrium* if the state remains unchanged when no input is applied. Since the state vector is then not changing,

$$\dot{\mathbf{x}} = \mathbf{A}\mathbf{x} = \mathbf{0}. \tag{9.16}$$

If **A** is nonsingular, the only equilibrium state is the origin $\mathbf{x} = \mathbf{0}$. A system having a nonsingular **A** matrix that is in equilibrium is also *initially inert,* according to the definition of the latter term in Section 2.4. If **A** is singular, any state vector in the null space of **A** is an equilibrium state. An example of this pathological case is provided by the system in Fig. 9.3, whose state equation is

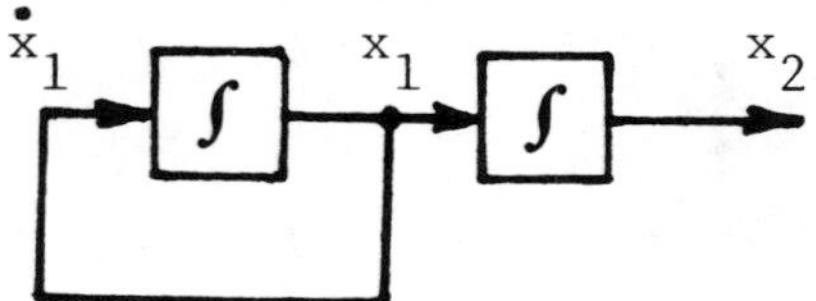

Fig. 9.3. System with a singular **A** matrix.

$$\begin{bmatrix} \dot{x}_1 \\ \dot{x}_2 \end{bmatrix} = \begin{bmatrix} 1 & 0 \\ 1 & 0 \end{bmatrix} \begin{bmatrix} x_1 \\ x_2 \end{bmatrix}. \tag{9.17}$$

Since the **A** matrix is singular, the system remains in equilibrium whenever the state is

$$\mathbf{x} = k \begin{bmatrix} 0 \\ 1 \end{bmatrix}. \tag{9.18}$$

9.3 State of an Undriven System

The state equation (9.14) is a statement, in matrix form, of the differential equations describing a system. The solution of the state equation provides the same information as the solution of the differential equations, namely an expression of the dependent variables as functions of time. The advantages of the matrix representation are

1. It is simple.
2. The analysis and optimization of large systems are performed more easily when the system is represented by matrices.
3. The techniques of matrix algebra are available for solving the state equation.

The first advantage is obvious, and the second will be demonstrated in the next chapter. A solution of the state equation for an undriven system will illustrate the third advantage. The state vector will be expressed as a sum of the eigenvectors of the **A** matrix. Fig. 9.4 shows an undriven linear spring-mass-damper system for which

$$\ddot{y} + 5\dot{y} + 6y = 0 \tag{9.19}$$

and

$$y(0) = 1\,, \quad \dot{y}(0) = 0\,. \tag{9.20}$$

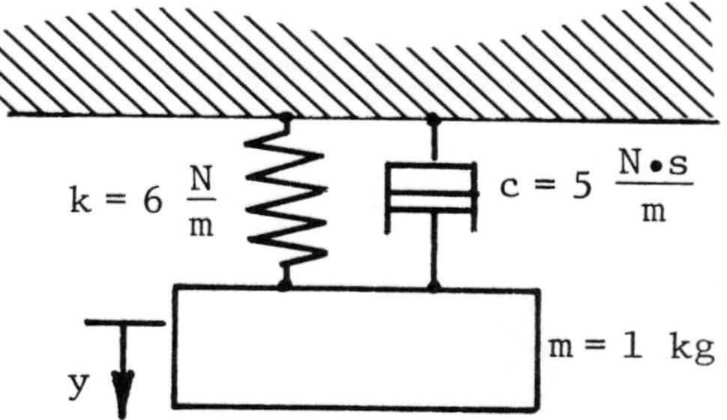

Fig. 9.4. Damped vibrating system.

If the state variables are $x_1 = y$ and $x_2 = \dot{y}$, the state equation is

$$\begin{bmatrix} \dot{x}_1 \\ \dot{x}_2 \end{bmatrix} = \begin{bmatrix} 0 & 1 \\ -6 & -5 \end{bmatrix} \begin{bmatrix} x_1 \\ x_2 \end{bmatrix} \tag{9.21}$$

or

$$\dot{\mathbf{x}} = \mathbf{A}\mathbf{x} \qquad \text{where} \qquad \mathbf{x}(0) = \begin{bmatrix} 1 \\ 0 \end{bmatrix}. \tag{9.22}$$

Matrix **A** has the eigenvalues $\lambda_1 = -2$, $\lambda_2 = -3$, and the eigenvectors

$$\mathbf{u}_1 = \begin{bmatrix} u_{11} \\ u_{21} \end{bmatrix} = \begin{bmatrix} 1 \\ -2 \end{bmatrix} f_1(t) \qquad \text{and} \qquad \mathbf{u}_2 = \begin{bmatrix} u_{12} \\ u_{22} \end{bmatrix} = \begin{bmatrix} 1 \\ -3 \end{bmatrix} f_2(t) \,. \tag{9.23}$$

How do the lengths of the eigenvectors vary with time? Since the eigenvectors are linearly independent, they form a basis in which any state vector can be expressed:

$$\mathbf{x} = k_1\, \mathbf{u}_1(t) + k_2\, \mathbf{u}_2(t) \,. \tag{9.24}$$

Substituting this equation into the state equation (9.22) yields

$$k_1\, \dot{\mathbf{u}}_1 + k_2\, \dot{\mathbf{u}}_2 = k_1\, \mathbf{A}\, \mathbf{u}_1 + k_2\, \mathbf{A}\, \mathbf{u}_2 \,. \tag{9.25}$$

Since the vectors $\mathbf{u}_1$ and $\dot{\mathbf{u}}_1$ point in one direction, and $\mathbf{u}_2$ and $\dot{\mathbf{u}}_2$ point in a different direction,

$$\dot{\mathbf{u}}_1 = \mathbf{A}\, \mathbf{u}_1 \qquad \text{and} \qquad \dot{\mathbf{u}}_2 = \mathbf{A}\, \mathbf{u}_2 \,. \tag{9.26}$$

Thus the eigenvectors satisfy the state equation. Since the ith eigenvector is defined by the relation

$$\mathbf{A}\, \mathbf{u}_i = \lambda_i\, \mathbf{u}_i \,, \tag{9.27}$$

the substitution of Eq. (9.27) into (9.26) gives

$$\dot{\mathbf{u}}_i = \lambda_i\, \mathbf{u}_i \,. \tag{9.28}$$

For

$$\lambda_1 = -2 \,, \quad \dot{\mathbf{u}}_1 = -2\, \mathbf{u}_1 \,. \tag{9.29}$$

The two scalar equations represented by Eq. (9.29) are

$$\dot{u}_{11} = -2\, u_{11} \qquad \text{and} \qquad \dot{u}_{21} = -2\, u_{21} \,. \tag{9.30}$$

Their solutions are

$$u_{11} = e^{-2t}\, u_{11}(0) \qquad \text{and} \qquad u_{21} = e^{-2t}\, u_{21}(0) \,. \tag{9.31}$$

Combining the solutions into a vector equation shows how the first eigenvector varies with time:

$$\mathbf{u}_1(t) = e^{-2t}\, \mathbf{u}_1(0) \,. \tag{9.32}$$

Similarly,

$$\mathbf{u}_2(t) = e^{-3t}\, \mathbf{u}_2(0) \,. \tag{9.33}$$

Therefore according to Eq. (9.24),

$$\mathbf{x} = k_1\, e^{-2t}\, \mathbf{u}_1(0) + k_2\, e^{-3t}\, \mathbf{u}_2(0) \,. \tag{9.34}$$

To evaluate the constants, apply the initial conditions. At $t = 0$,

$$\mathbf{x} = \mathbf{x}(0) = k_1\,\mathbf{u}_1(0) + k_2\,\mathbf{u}_2(0)\,. \tag{9.35}$$

or

$$\mathbf{x}(0) = \mathbf{M}\,\mathbf{k} \tag{9.36}$$

where

$$\mathbf{k} = \begin{bmatrix} k_1 \\ k_2 \end{bmatrix} \tag{9.37}$$

and $\mathbf{M}$ is a matrix whose columns are the eigenvectors:

$$\mathbf{M} = [\mathbf{u}_1(0)\,,\,\mathbf{u}_2(0)]\,. \tag{9.38}$$

Then

$$\mathbf{k} = \mathbf{M}^{-1}\,\mathbf{x}(0)\,. \tag{9.39}$$

As will soon be evident, the lengths of the eigenvectors $\mathbf{u}_1(0)$ and $\mathbf{u}_2(0)$ are arbitrary. If

$$\mathbf{u}_1(0) = \begin{bmatrix} 1 \\ -2 \end{bmatrix} \quad \text{and} \quad \mathbf{u}_2(0) = \begin{bmatrix} 1 \\ -3 \end{bmatrix}, \tag{9.40}$$

then

$$\mathbf{M} = \begin{bmatrix} 1 & 1 \\ -2 & -3 \end{bmatrix}, \quad \mathbf{M}^{-1} = \begin{bmatrix} 3 & 1 \\ -2 & -1 \end{bmatrix}, \tag{9.41}$$

and

$$\mathbf{k} = \begin{bmatrix} 3 & 1 \\ -2 & -1 \end{bmatrix} \begin{bmatrix} 1 \\ 0 \end{bmatrix} = \begin{bmatrix} 3 \\ -2 \end{bmatrix}. \tag{9.42}$$

Finally, according to Eq. (9.34),

$$\mathbf{x} = \begin{bmatrix} y \\ \dot{y} \end{bmatrix} = 3e^{-2t} \begin{bmatrix} 1 \\ -2 \end{bmatrix} - 2e^{-3t} \begin{bmatrix} 1 \\ -3 \end{bmatrix}. \tag{9.43}$$

Notice that if the length of $\mathbf{u}_1(0)$ or $\mathbf{u}_2(0)$ were changed, $\mathbf{M}^{-1}$ and $\mathbf{k}$ would change accordingly, and Eq. (9.43) would remain the same. This equation expresses the state of the undriven system in Fig. 9.4 at any time after $t = 0$, as a sum of the eigenvectors of the $\mathbf{A}$ matrix. It contains the same information as the solution of Eq. (9.19) obtained by the classical method.

9.4 State of a Driven System

Even if a system has inputs, its state can be expressed as a sum of the eigenvectors of the $\mathbf{A}$ matrix. Now it will be convenient to keep the lengths of the eigenvectors constant and let the coefficients k_i be functions of time. Start by expressing each term of the state equation

$$\dot{\mathbf{x}} = \mathbf{A}\mathbf{x} + \mathbf{B}\mathbf{v} \tag{9.44}$$

as a sum of the eigenvectors. If the system has n state variables,

$$\mathbf{x} = \sum_{i=1}^{n} k_i(t)\, \mathbf{u}_i = \mathbf{M}\, \mathbf{k}(t) \tag{9.45}$$

where

$$\mathbf{M} = [\mathbf{u}_1, \mathbf{u}_2, \ldots, \mathbf{u}_n] \tag{9.46}$$

and

$$\mathbf{k}(t) = \begin{bmatrix} k_1(t) \\ k_2(t) \\ \cdot \\ \cdot \\ \cdot \\ k_n(t) \end{bmatrix}. \tag{9.47}$$

Then

$$\dot{\mathbf{x}} = \sum_{i=1}^{n} \dot{k}_i(t)\, \mathbf{u}_i \tag{9.48}$$

and

$$\mathbf{A}\mathbf{x} = \mathbf{A} \sum_{i=1}^{n} k_i(t)\, \mathbf{u}_i = \sum_{i=1}^{n} k_i(t)\, \mathbf{A}\, \mathbf{u}_i\,. \tag{9.49}$$

Again the magic property of eigenvectors is invoked:

$$\mathbf{A}\mathbf{u}_i = \lambda_i \mathbf{u}_i\,, \tag{9.50}$$

to produce the result

$$\mathbf{A}\mathbf{x} = \sum_{i=1}^{n} k_i(t) \lambda_i \mathbf{u}_i\,.$$

The vector $\mathbf{B}\mathbf{v}$ can also be written as a sum of the eigenvectors, weighted by the coefficients $g_i(t)$:

$$\mathbf{B}\mathbf{v} = \sum_{i=1}^{n} g_i(t)\, \mathbf{u}_i = \mathbf{M}\, \mathbf{g}(t) \tag{9.51}$$

where

$$\mathbf{g}(t) = \begin{bmatrix} g_1(t) \\ g_2(t) \\ \cdot \\ \cdot \\ \cdot \\ g_n(t) \end{bmatrix}. \tag{9.52}$$

The state equation (9.44) can now be written as

$$\sum_{i=1}^{n} [\dot{k}_i(t) - \lambda_i \, k_i(t) - g_i(t)]\mathbf{u}_i = 0 \, . \tag{9.53}$$

Since the eigenvectors are linearly independent, this equation is true only if the coefficient of each, the bracketed quantity, is zero. Thus

$$\dot{k}_i(t) - \lambda_i \, k_i(t) = g_i(t) \, . \tag{9.54}$$

This is an ordinary differential equation whose solution is obtained readily by Laplace transforms. Thus

$$s \, K_i(s) - k_i(0) - \lambda_i \, K_i(s) = G_i(s) \tag{9.55}$$

or

$$K_i(s) = \frac{k_i(0)}{s - \lambda_i} + \frac{G_i(s)}{s - \lambda_i} \tag{9.56}$$

and

$$\begin{aligned} k_i(t) &= k_i(0) \, e^{\lambda_i t} + g_i(t) * e^{\lambda_i t} \\ &= k_i(0) \, e^{\lambda_i t} + \int_0^t g_i(x) \, e^{\lambda_i (t-x)} dx \, . \end{aligned} \tag{9.57}$$

The limits of integration can be explained when the coefficients $k_i(0)$ and $g_i(x)$ have been evaluated. According to Eq. (9.45),

$$\mathbf{k}(0) = \mathbf{M}^{-1} \, \mathbf{x}(0) \, . \tag{9.58}$$

If $\mathbf{r}_i$ is the ith row of $\mathbf{M}^{-1}$,

$$k_i(0) = < \mathbf{x}(0) \, , \mathbf{r}_i > . \tag{9.59}$$

Similarly, according to Eq. (9.51),

$$\mathbf{g}(x) = \mathbf{M}^{-1} \, \mathbf{B}\mathbf{v}(x) \tag{9.60}$$

and

$$g_i(x) = < \mathbf{B} \, \mathbf{v}(x) \, , \mathbf{r}_i > . \tag{9.61}$$

The vectors $\mathbf{r}_i$ are called *reciprocal vectors* because of their property

$$\begin{aligned} < \mathbf{r}_i \, , \mathbf{u}_j > &= 1 \, , \quad i = j \\ &= 0 \, , \quad i \neq j \, . \end{aligned} \tag{9.62}$$

Now all the terms in the sum of eigenvectors representing the state of the system, Eq. (9.45), have been evaluated. The equation can be written as

$$\mathbf{x}(t) = \sum_{i=1}^{n} [< \mathbf{x}(0) \, , \mathbf{r}_i > e^{\lambda_i t} + \int_0^t < \mathbf{B} \, \mathbf{v}(x) \, , \mathbf{r}_i > e^{\lambda_i (t-x)} dx]\mathbf{u}_i \, . \tag{9.63}$$

This is the state of the system in terms of its initial state and inputs. The first term within the brackets can be identified as the portion of the transient response due to the initial conditions. The second term is the convolution of the input with the impulse response. Since both are causal functions, the limits of integration are 0 and t. The state vector is measured in a coordinate system whose axes are the eigenvectors. Coordinates measured along the eigenvectors are called *normal coordinates*. In Eq. (9.63) the bracketed terms are normal coordinates.

9.5 The State-Transition Matrix

The two preceding methods for calculating the n-dimensional state vector of a system are based on the assumption that the **A** matrix has n eigenvectors, with which an n-dimensional basis can be constructed. If **A** is not symmetric and has a repeated eigenvalue, it may have fewer than n eigenvectors. The state of a system with any **A** matrix can be calculated with the help of the state-transition matrix, which will now be explained. The state equation of an undriven system is

$$\dot{\mathbf{x}}(t) = \mathbf{A}\,\mathbf{x}(t)\,. \tag{9.64}$$

By analogy to a first-order scalar differential equation, assume the solution

$$\mathbf{x}(t) = e^{\mathbf{A}t}\,\mathbf{x}(0) \tag{9.65}$$

where

$$e^{\mathbf{A}t} = \mathbf{I} + \mathbf{A}t + \frac{(\mathbf{A}t)^2}{2!} + \frac{(\mathbf{A}t)^3}{3!} + \cdots + \frac{(\mathbf{A}t)^k}{k!} + \cdots \tag{9.66}$$

Substitution of the assumed solution back into the differential equation shows that the solution is correct. The matrix

$$\boldsymbol{\phi}(t) = e^{\mathbf{A}t} \tag{9.67}$$

is called the *state-transition matrix* (or transition matrix or fundamental matrix) because it relates the initial state to the state at any later time t.

If a system is driven, its state equation is

$$\dot{\mathbf{x}}(t) = \mathbf{A}\,\mathbf{x}(t) + \mathbf{B}\,\mathbf{v}(t)\,. \tag{9.68}$$

To express the state in terms of the state-transition matrix, solve Eq. (9.68) with Laplace transforms. If $\mathbf{X}(s)$ is the vector of Laplace transforms of the components of $\mathbf{x}(t)$,

$$s\,\mathbf{X}(s) - \mathbf{x}(0) = \mathbf{A}\,\mathbf{X}(s) + \mathbf{B}\,\mathbf{V}(s) \tag{9.69}$$

or

$$\mathbf{X}(s) = [s\mathbf{I} - \mathbf{A}]^{-1}\,\mathbf{x}(0) + [s\mathbf{I} - \mathbf{A}]^{-1}\,\mathbf{B}\,\mathbf{V}(s)\,. \tag{9.70}$$

Comparison of Eq. (9.70) for an undriven system with Eq. (9.65) shows that

$$\mathscr{L}[e^{\mathbf{A}t}] = [s\mathbf{I} - \mathbf{A}]^{-1}\,. \tag{9.71}$$

Thus the inverse transform of Eq. (9.70) is

$$\begin{aligned}\mathbf{x}(t) &= e^{\mathbf{A}t}\,\mathbf{x}(0) + e^{\mathbf{A}t}\,\mathbf{B}{*}v(t)\\ &= e^{\mathbf{A}t}\,\mathbf{x}(0) + \int_0^t e^{\mathbf{A}(t-x)}\,\mathbf{B}\,\mathbf{v}(x)\,dx\,.\end{aligned} \tag{9.72}$$

This form is simpler than Eq. (9.63), and is correct even if **A** has a shortage of eigenvectors. Appendix 1 at the end of this chapter shows that Eq. (9.72) reduces to Eq. (9.63) if **A** has a full set of eigenvectors.

The state equation and its solution in the form of Eq. (9.72) acquire physical meaning when compared to their scalar versions. If a system has only one state variable and one input, the state equation (9.68) reduces to

$$\dot{x}(t) = a\,x(t) + b\,v(t) \tag{9.73}$$

which is represented by the block diagram of Fig. 9.5. The solution of the

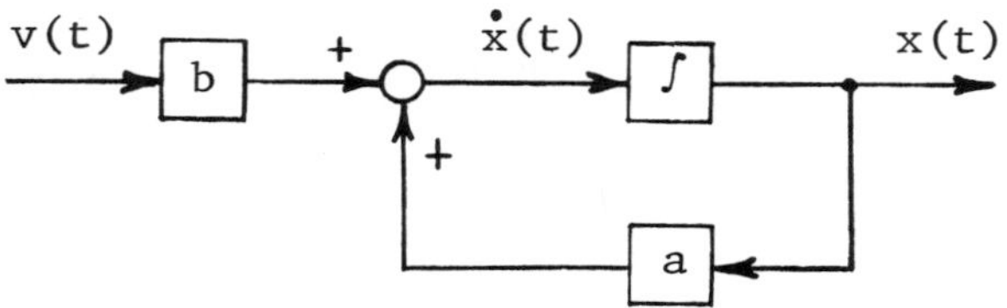

Fig. 9.5. Block diagram representing the state equation with one state variable.

state equation, Eq. (9.72), reduces to

$$x(t) = e^{at}\,x(0) + \int_0^t e^{a(t-x)}\,b\,v(x)\,dx\,. \tag{9.74}$$

The first term on the right is the part of the transient response caused by the initial integrator output. The second term is the convolution of the input $v(t)$ with the impulse response be^{at}, and represents the steady-state response and the remainder of the transient response. Similarly, the vector state equation (9.68) can be represented by the vector block diagram of Fig. 9.6, and the last term of Eq. (9.72) is the convolution of the input vector $\mathbf{v}(t)$ with the *impulse-response matrix* $e^{\mathbf{A}t}\mathbf{B}$. Element *ij* of this matrix is the impulse response of the system between input v_j and state variable x_i.

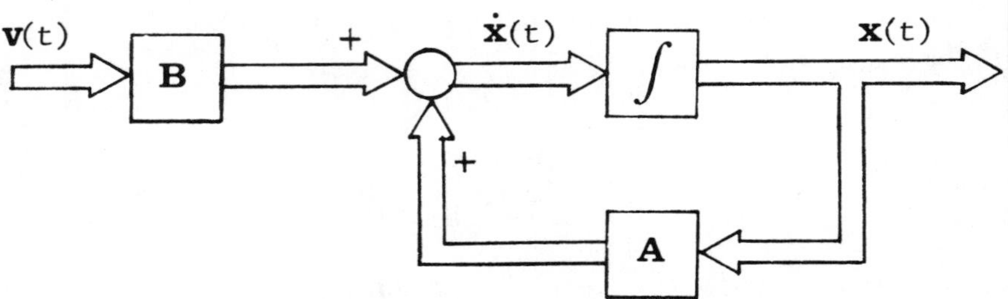

Fig. 9.6. Vector block diagram.

9.6 Evaluation of the Transition Matrix by Laplace Transforms

Now consider various ways of evaluating the state-transition matrix, so that Eq. (9.72) can be used to calculate the state of a system. The easiest method conceptually is given by Eq. (9.71). This equation is easy to remember by analogy with the scalar Laplace transform

$$\mathscr{L}[e^{at}] = (s - a)^{-1} . \tag{9.75}$$

To illustrate the use of Eq. 9.71, calculate $e^{\mathbf{A}t}$ for the system of Fig. 9.4, for which

$$\mathbf{A} = \begin{bmatrix} 0 & 1 \\ -6 & -5 \end{bmatrix} . \tag{9.76}$$

Now

$$s\mathbf{I} - \mathbf{A} = \begin{bmatrix} s & -1 \\ 6 & s+5 \end{bmatrix} \tag{9.77}$$

and

$$[s\mathbf{I} - \mathbf{A}]^{-1} = \frac{1}{s^2 + 5s + 6} \begin{bmatrix} s+5 & 1 \\ -6 & s \end{bmatrix} . \tag{9.78}$$

The inverse Laplace transform, computed term by term, is

$$e^{\mathbf{A}t} = \mathscr{L}^{-1}[s\mathbf{I} - \mathbf{A}]^{-1} = \begin{bmatrix} 3e^{-2t} - 2e^{-3t} & e^{-2t} - e^{-3t} \\ -6e^{-2t} + 6e^{-3t} & -2e^{-2t} + 3e^{-3t} \end{bmatrix} . \tag{9.79}$$

Notice that the four elements of this state-transition matrix contain a total of eight individual terms. If the system has n state variables, the state-transition matrix contains n^3 terms.

9.7 Diagonalized Form of the A Matrix

A second method of computing the transition matrix, that provides an interesting exercise in matrix algebra, requires the diagonalized form of the **A** matrix. First consider an nth-order **A** matrix that has a full set of eigenvectors. For each eigenvector $\mathbf{u}_i$,

$$\lambda_i \mathbf{u}_i = \mathbf{A}\,\mathbf{u}_i \,. \tag{9.80}$$

Construct two matrices whose columns are the two vectors in Eq. (9.80):

$$[\lambda_1 \mathbf{u}_1\,,\, \lambda_2 \mathbf{u}_2\,, \ldots ,\, \lambda_n \mathbf{u}_n] = \mathbf{A}[\mathbf{u}_1\,,\, \mathbf{u}_2\,, \ldots ,\, \mathbf{u}_n]\,. \tag{9.81}$$

The *modal matrix* **M** is defined as the matrix whose columns are the eigenvectors:

$$\mathbf{M} = [\mathbf{u}_1\,,\, \mathbf{u}_2\,, \ldots ,\, \mathbf{u}_n]\,. \tag{9.82}$$

Then Eq. (9.81) can be written as

$$\mathbf{M}\,\mathbf{\Lambda} = \mathbf{A}\,\mathbf{M} \tag{9.83}$$

where

$$\mathbf{\Lambda} = \begin{bmatrix} \lambda_1 & 0 & \cdot & \cdot & \cdot \\ 0 & \lambda_2 & & & \\ \cdot & & \cdot & & \\ \cdot & & & \cdot & \\ \cdot & & & & \lambda_n \end{bmatrix}. \tag{9.84}$$

Therefore

$$\mathbf{\Lambda} = \mathbf{M}^{-1}\,\mathbf{A}\,\mathbf{M} \tag{9.85}$$

and

$$\mathbf{A} = \mathbf{M}\,\mathbf{\Lambda}\,\mathbf{M}^{-1}\,. \tag{9.86}$$

The diagonal matrix $\mathbf{\Lambda}$ has the same eigenvalues as **A**. It is called the *diagonalized form* of **A**, or *spectral matrix.*

Eq. (9.76) shows that

$$\mathbf{A}^2 = (\mathbf{M}\,\mathbf{\Lambda}\,\mathbf{M}^{-1})(\mathbf{M}\,\mathbf{\Lambda}\,\mathbf{M}^{-1}) = \mathbf{M}\,\mathbf{\Lambda}^2\,\mathbf{M}^{-1}\,. \tag{9.87}$$

Repetition of this process shows that

$$\mathbf{A}^n = \mathbf{M}\,\mathbf{\Lambda}^n\,\mathbf{M}^{-1}\,. \tag{9.88}$$

If $f(\mathbf{A})$ is a polynomial or infinite series in **A**,

$$\begin{aligned} f(\mathbf{A}) &= a_0\mathbf{I} + a_1\mathbf{A} + a_2\mathbf{A}^2 + \cdots \\ &= \mathbf{M}(a_0\,\mathbf{I} + a_1\mathbf{\Lambda} + a_2\mathbf{\Lambda}^2 + \cdots)\mathbf{M}^{-1} \\ &= \mathbf{M}\,f(\mathbf{\Lambda})\,\mathbf{M}^{-1}\,. \end{aligned} \tag{9.89}$$

In particular, if

$$f(\mathbf{A}) = e^{\mathbf{A}t} = \mathbf{I} + \mathbf{A}t + \frac{(\mathbf{A}t)^2}{2!} + \cdots \tag{9.90}$$

then

$$e^{\mathbf{A}t} = \mathbf{M}[\mathbf{I} + \Lambda t + \frac{(\Lambda t)^2}{2!} + \cdots]\mathbf{M}^{-1} \tag{9.91}$$

$$= \mathbf{M}\, e^{\Lambda t}\, \mathbf{M}^{-1}\,. \tag{9.92}$$

To see what $e^{\Lambda t}$ looks like, add the terms within the brackets of Eq. (9.91), to obtain

$$e^{\Lambda t} = \begin{bmatrix} 1 + \lambda_1 t + \frac{(\lambda_1 t)^2}{2!} + \cdots & 0 & \cdot\ \cdot \\ 0 & 1 + \lambda_2 t + \frac{(\lambda_2 t)^2}{2!} + \cdots & \\ \cdot & \cdot & \cdot \\ \cdot & \cdot & \cdot \end{bmatrix}$$

$$= \begin{bmatrix} e^{\lambda_1 t} & 0 & \cdot & \cdot \\ 0 & e^{\lambda_2 t} & & \\ \cdot & \cdot & \cdot & \\ \cdot & \cdot & & \cdot \end{bmatrix}. \tag{9.93}$$

To illustrate the use of Eq. (9.92), use it to reevaluate the state-transition matrix of the system in Fig. 9.4, whose eigenvalues are $\lambda_1 = -2$, $\lambda_2 = -3$, and whose eigenvectors are

$$\mathbf{u}_1 = \begin{bmatrix} 1 \\ -2 \end{bmatrix}, \quad \mathbf{u}_2 = \begin{bmatrix} 1 \\ -3 \end{bmatrix}. \tag{9.94}$$

Now

$$\mathbf{M} = \begin{bmatrix} 1 & 1 \\ -2 & -3 \end{bmatrix}, \quad \mathbf{M}^{-1} = \begin{bmatrix} 3 & 1 \\ -2 & -1 \end{bmatrix}, \tag{9.95}$$

and

$$e^{\mathbf{A}t} = \begin{bmatrix} 1 & 1 \\ -2 & -3 \end{bmatrix} \begin{bmatrix} e^{-2t} & 0 \\ 0 & e^{-3t} \end{bmatrix} \begin{bmatrix} 3 & 1 \\ -2 & -1 \end{bmatrix}$$

$$= \begin{bmatrix} 3e^{-2t} - 2e^{-3t} & e^{-2t} - e^{-3t} \\ -6e^{-2t} + 6e^{-3t} & -2e^{-2t} + 3e^{-3t} \end{bmatrix} \tag{9.96}$$

which agrees with Eq. (9.79).

If the **A** matrix of a linear system is not symmetric and has a repeated eigenvalue, it may have a shortage of eigenvectors and therefore not be diagonalizable. Then Eq. (9.92) cannot be used. However, a similar form can be constructed:

$$e^{\mathbf{A}t} = \mathbf{N}\, e^{\mathbf{J}t}\, \mathbf{N}^{-1} \tag{9.97}$$

in which **N** is a square matrix whose columns are the eigenvectors plus as many additional linearly-independent vectors as are needed to complete matrix **N**. These extra vectors are calculated according to a procedure that makes **J** a Jordan canonical matrix. The details of the procedure are explained in Appendix 2 at the end of this chapter.

9.8 The Cayley-Hamilton Technique

The third method of calculating the state-transition matrix is based on the Cayley-Hamilton theorem, which states that *every square matrix satisfies its own characteristic equation.* According to this theorem, if the characteristic equation of an nth-order matrix **A** is

$$P(\lambda_i) = |\lambda_i \mathbf{I} - \mathbf{A}| = \lambda_i^n + a_{n-1}\,\lambda_i^{n-1} + \cdots + a_1\lambda_i + a_0 = 0 \tag{9.98}$$

where λ_i is an eigenvalue, then

$$P(\mathbf{A}) = \mathbf{A}^n + a_{n-1}\,\mathbf{A}^{n-1} + \cdots + a_1\mathbf{A} + a_0\,\mathbf{I} = 0\,. \tag{9.99}$$

The theorem is easily proved if **A** has distinct eigenvalues. Then **A** can be diagonalized, and according to Eq. (9.89)

$$P(\mathbf{A}) = \mathbf{M}\,P(\mathbf{\Lambda})\,\mathbf{M}^{-1} = \mathbf{M}(\mathbf{\Lambda}^n + a_{n-1}\,\mathbf{\Lambda}^{n-1} + \cdots + a_1\mathbf{\Lambda} + a_0\,\mathbf{I})\mathbf{M}^{-1}$$

$$= \mathbf{M}\begin{bmatrix} \lambda_1^n + a_{n-1}\lambda_1^{n-1} + \cdots + a_1\lambda_1 + a_0 & 0 & \cdot\ \cdot \\ 0 & \lambda_2^n + a_{n-1}\lambda_2^{n-1} + \cdots + a_1\lambda_2 + a_0 & \cdot \\ \cdot & \cdot & \\ \cdot & \cdot & \cdot \end{bmatrix}\mathbf{M}^{-1}$$

$$= \mathbf{M}\begin{bmatrix} P(\lambda_1) & 0 & \cdot\ \cdot \\ 0 & P(\lambda_2) & \\ \cdot & \cdot & \cdot \\ \cdot & \cdot & \cdot \end{bmatrix}\mathbf{M}^{-1}\,. \tag{9.100}$$

But

$$P(\lambda_1) = P(\lambda_2) = \cdots = P(\lambda_n) = 0\,. \tag{9.101}$$

Therefore $P(\mathbf{A}) = 0$, and matrix **A** satisfies its own characteristic equation. Reference 38 shows that matrices with repeated eigenvalues also obey the Cayley-Hamilton theorem.

Suppose that $F(\lambda)$ is a polynomial of higher degree than the characteristic polynomial $P(\lambda)$. Long division produces the result

$$\frac{F(\lambda)}{P(\lambda)} = Q(\lambda) + \frac{R(\lambda)}{P(\lambda)} \tag{9.102}$$

or

$$F(\lambda) = P(\lambda)\,Q(\lambda) + R(\lambda) \tag{9.103}$$

where $Q(\lambda)$ is the quotient and $R(\lambda)$ is the remainder, whose degree is lower than that of $P(\lambda)$. Now if λ is an eigenvalue λ_i,

$$F(\lambda_i) = P(\lambda_i)\,Q(\lambda_i) + R(\lambda_i) = R(\lambda_i) \tag{9.104}$$

because $P(\lambda_i) = 0$. (The intermediate variable λ was used to avoid any criticism for dividing by zero.) Now since matrix multiplication like ordinary multiplication is distributive, Eq. (9.103) is valid if the variable is the matrix $\mathbf{A}$:

$$F(\mathbf{A}) = P(\mathbf{A})\,Q(\mathbf{A}) + R(\mathbf{A})\,. \tag{9.105}$$

According to the Cayley-Hamilton theorem, $P(\mathbf{A}) = 0$. Therefore

$$F(\mathbf{A}) = R(\mathbf{A})\,. \tag{9.106}$$

Since this equation is true for any polynomial $F(\mathbf{A})$ no matter how high its degree, it is true if $F(\mathbf{A})$ is an infinite series, if the series converges. The infinite series representing a state-transition matrix is

$$F(\mathbf{A}) = e^{\mathbf{A}t} = \mathbf{I} + \mathbf{A}t + \frac{(\mathbf{A}t)^2}{2!} + \cdots \tag{9.107}$$

It converges if t and all the elements of matrix $\mathbf{A}$ are finite. The coefficients of the powers of $\mathbf{A}$ in this series are functions of time. According to Eq. (9.106), if $\mathbf{A}$ is of order n, then $e^{\mathbf{A}t}$ is a polynomial of degree $n-1$ whose coefficients are also functions of time:

$$e^{\mathbf{A}t} = R(\mathbf{A}) = \alpha_0(t)\mathbf{I} + \alpha_1(t)\mathbf{A} + \alpha_2(t)\mathbf{A}^2 + \cdots + \alpha_{n-1}(t)\mathbf{A}^{n-1}\,. \tag{9.108}$$

Similarly, according to Eq. 9.104,

$$e^{\lambda_i t} = F(\lambda_i) = R(\lambda_i) = \alpha_0(t) + \alpha_1(t)\lambda_i + \alpha_2(t)\lambda_i^2 + \cdots + \alpha_{n-1}(t)\lambda_i^{n-1}\,. \tag{9.109}$$

Now the state-transition matrix can be evaluated. If the eigenvalues of $\mathbf{A}$ are distinct, Eq. (9.109) provides n equations with which the n unknown α_i's can be evaluated. Then Eq. (9.108) gives the state-transition matrix.

If matrix $\mathbf{A}$ has a repeated eigenvalue λ_1 of order p, its characteristic polynomial is of the form

$$P(\lambda) = (\lambda - \lambda_1)^p\,(\lambda - \lambda_2) \cdots (\lambda - \lambda_{n-p+1})\,. \tag{9.110}$$

Then if $F(\lambda) = e^{\lambda t}$, Eq. (9.103) is

$$e^{\lambda t} = R(\lambda) + Q(\lambda)(\lambda - \lambda_1)^p (\lambda - \lambda_2) \cdots \tag{9.111}$$

Thus if $\lambda = \lambda_1$,

$$e^{\lambda_1 t} = R(\lambda_1). \tag{9.112}$$

To obtain another equation, differentiate both sides of Eq. (9.111):

$$\frac{d}{d\lambda} e^{\lambda t} = \frac{dR(\lambda)}{d\lambda} + \text{terms containing } (\lambda - \lambda_1)\,. \tag{9.113}$$

Letting $\lambda = \lambda_1$ again produces the result

$$\left.\frac{d}{d\lambda} e^{\lambda t}\right|_{\lambda=\lambda_1} = te^{\lambda_1 t} = \left.\frac{dR(\lambda)}{d\lambda}\right|_{\lambda=\lambda_1}. \tag{9.114}$$

Similarly,

$$\left.\frac{d^k}{d\lambda^k} e^{\lambda t}\right|_{\lambda=\lambda_1} = t^k e^{\lambda_1 t} = \left.\frac{d^k R(\lambda)}{d\lambda^k}\right|_{\lambda=\lambda_1} \qquad k = 1,2,\ldots,p-1\,. \tag{9.115}$$

Eq. (9.115) provides the remaining $p-1$ equations needed to evaluate the α_i's.

The system of Fig. 9.4 will illustrate the Cayley-Hamilton method of evaluating the state-transition matrix. For the system,

$$\mathbf{A} = \begin{bmatrix} 0 & 1 \\ -6 & -5 \end{bmatrix} \quad \text{and} \quad \lambda_1 = -2, \lambda_2 = -3\,. \tag{9.116}$$

According to Eq. (9.109),

$$e^{-2t} = \alpha_0 - 2\alpha_1 \tag{9.117}$$

and

$$e^{-3t} = \alpha_0 - 3\alpha_1\,. \tag{9.118}$$

Solving for α_0 and α_1 shows that

$$\alpha_0 = 3e^{-2t} - 2e^{-3t}, \qquad \alpha_1 = e^{-2t} - e^{-3t}\,. \tag{9.119}$$

According to Eq. (9.108),

$$\begin{aligned} e^{\mathbf{A}t} &= (3e^{-2t} - 2e^{-3t})\mathbf{I} + (e^{-2t} - e^{-3t})\mathbf{A} \\ &= \begin{bmatrix} 3e^{-2t} - 2e^{-3t} & e^{-2t} - e^{-3t} \\ -6e^{-2t} + 6e^{-3t} & -2e^{-2t} + 3e^{-3t} \end{bmatrix} \end{aligned} \tag{9.120}$$

which of course agrees with Eq. (9.96).

9.9 The Transmittance Method

The fourth method of calculating the state-transition matrix makes use of the fact that each element of this matrix is an impulse response. If the system is simulated on an analog computer, the impulse responses can be observed. If a block diagram of the system is only drawn on paper, the impulse responses can be calculated by a straightforward procedure. The method will be explained by one more calculation of the transition matrix of the system in Fig. 9.4. If a downward force $v(t)$ is applied to the mass,

$$\ddot{y} + 5\dot{y} + 6y = v \ . \tag{9.121}$$

Fig. 9.7 is a block diagram of the system with the additional inputs w_1 and w_2. Notice that the integrator outputs have been chosen to be the state variables x_1 and x_2. The integrator outputs do not *have* to be state variables, but for any system they constitute a satisfactory state vector.

Fig. 9.7 is typical of any linear system whose integrator outputs are the state variables. If the system is simulated on an analog computer, the elements of its state-transition matrix can be observed by applying an impulse at the input of one integrator at a time, and watching an oscilloscope connected to each integrator output. To see why this is so, start the circuit of Fig. 9.7 with no input v or w_2 and no integrator

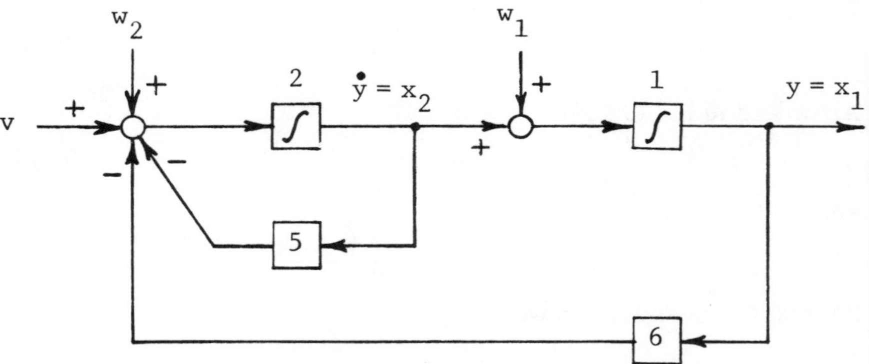

Fig. 9.7. The transmittance method of calculating the state-transition matrix.

output, and apply the impulse $w_1 = \delta(t)$ at the input of integrator 1. This impulse produces the initial output

$$x_1(0) = 1 \ . \tag{9.122}$$

Since the input of integrator 2 is not an impulse, its output increases gradually, and $x_2(0) = 0$. Thus

$$\mathbf{x}(0) = \begin{bmatrix} x_1(0) \\ x_2(0) \end{bmatrix} = \begin{bmatrix} 1 \\ 0 \end{bmatrix}, \tag{9.123}$$

and since

$$\mathbf{x}(t) = \boldsymbol{\phi}(t)\, x(0) \tag{9.124}$$

where $\boldsymbol{\phi}(t)$ is the state-transition matrix,

$$\mathbf{x}(t) = \begin{bmatrix} \phi_{11}(t) & \phi_{12}(t) \\ \phi_{21}(t) & \phi_{22}(t) \end{bmatrix} \begin{bmatrix} 1 \\ 0 \end{bmatrix} = \begin{bmatrix} \phi_{11}(t) \\ \phi_{21}(t) \end{bmatrix}. \tag{9.125}$$

Now start the circuit with $v = w_1 = 0$ and no integrator output, and apply an impulse $w_2 = \delta(t)$ to the input of integrator 2. The impulse establishes the initial integrator outputs

$$x_2(0) = 1 \qquad \text{and} \qquad x_1(0) = 0\,. \tag{9.126}$$

Then

$$\mathbf{x}(0) = \begin{bmatrix} 0 \\ 1 \end{bmatrix} \qquad \text{and} \qquad \mathbf{x}(t) = \begin{bmatrix} \phi_{12}(t) \\ \phi_{22}(t) \end{bmatrix}. \tag{9.127}$$

In an initially-inert linear system of any size whose state variables are the integrator outputs, if an initial impulse is applied to the input of integrator j, the resulting state vector $\mathbf{x}(t)$ is column j of the state-transition matrix. The ith component of the vector, state variable x_i, is element ϕ_{ij} of the matrix. Element ϕ_{ij} is the impulse response of the system between the input of integrator j and the output of integrator i. This impulse response can be observed by connecting an oscilloscope to the output of integrator i.

Eq. (9.72) identifies the matrix $e^{\mathbf{A}t}\mathbf{B}$ as the impulse-response matrix of a system with a vector of inputs $\mathbf{v}(t)$. Matrix $\mathbf{B}$ is needed because the input variables $v_i(t)$ are not in general applied at the integrator inputs. If a system happens to have n integrators and n input variables, one of which is applied at the input of each integrator, $\mathbf{B}$ is a unit matrix and is not needed in Eq. (9.72).

Now instead of observing $\phi_{ij}(t)$ on an analog computer, calculate its Laplace transform $\Phi_{ij}(s)$. Since the Laplace transform of the impulse response of a system is the transfer function of the system, $\Phi_{ij}(s)$ is the transmittance between the input of integrator j and the output of integrator i:

$$\Phi_{ij}(s) = \frac{X_i(s)}{W_j(s)}\,. \tag{9.128}$$

The transmittances can be calculated readily when the block diagram of the system is redrawn as a signal-flow graph. For the system of Fig. 9.7

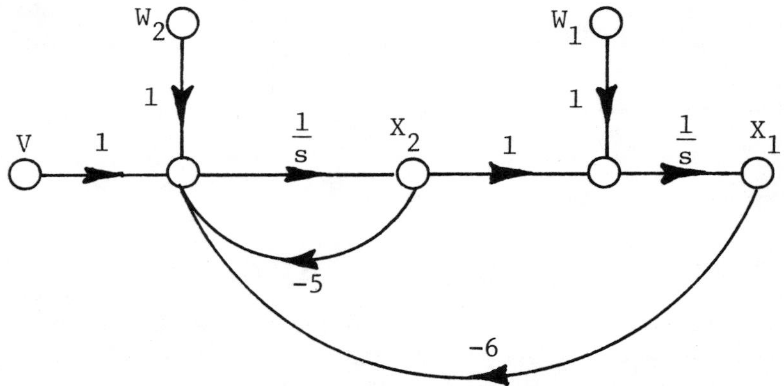

Fig. 9.8. Signal-flow graph for the system of Fig. 9.7.

the signal-flow graph is shown in Fig. 9.8. The transmittances around the two loops are

$$L_1 = -\frac{5}{s}, \qquad L_2 = -\frac{6}{s^2}. \tag{9.129}$$

The graph determinant is

$$\Delta = 1 - L_1 - L_2 = 1 + \frac{5}{s} + \frac{6}{s^2} = \frac{s^2 + 5s + 6}{s^2}. \tag{9.130}$$

The transmittance of the path from W_1 to X_1 is

$$P_1 = \frac{1}{s}. \tag{9.131}$$

The cofactor of this path is

$$\Delta_1 = 1 - L_1 = 1 + \frac{5}{s} = \frac{s+5}{s}. \tag{9.132}$$

The transmittance from W_1 to X_1 is

$$\frac{X_1(s)}{W_1(s)} = \Phi_{11}(s) = \frac{P_1\Delta_1}{\Delta} = \frac{s+5}{s^2 + 5s + 6}. \tag{9.133}$$

Similarly,

$$\frac{X_2(s)}{W_1(s)} = \Phi_{21}(s) = -\frac{6}{s^2 + 5s + 6} \tag{9.134}$$

$$\frac{X_1(s)}{W_2(s)} = \Phi_{12}(s) = \frac{1}{s^2 + 5s + 6} \tag{9.135}$$

and

$$\frac{X_2(s)}{W_2(s)} = \Phi_{22}(s) = \frac{s}{s^2 + 5s + 6} . \tag{9.136}$$

These results agree with Eq. (9.78). The inverses of these Laplace transforms are the elements of the state-transition matrix.

Four methods of calculating the transition matrix of a linear system have been presented. Although these methods will be of use to the reader, probably of greater use are the techniques of matrix algebra that were employed along the way. The ideas of the modal matrix, bases of eigenvectors, null space, normal coordinates, and the Cayley-Hamilton theorem will be encountered in modern control theory. The next chapter will introduce the reader to this field, that is only a few years old and still growing.

9.10 Appendix 1. Reconciliation of Eqs. (9.72) and (9.63)

According to Eq. (9.92), if an nth-order matrix **A** has n eigenvectors, the state-transition matrix is

$$\boldsymbol{\phi}(t) = e^{\mathbf{A}t} = \mathbf{M}\, e^{\Lambda t}\, \mathbf{M}^{-1} . \tag{9.137}$$

The reader can test his ability to manipulate matrices by proving that

$$\mathbf{M}\, e^{\Lambda t}\, \mathbf{M}^{-1} = \sum_{i=1}^{n} e^{\lambda_i t}\, \mathbf{u}_i \mathbf{r}_i^T \tag{9.138}$$

where the $\mathbf{r}_i$'s are the vectors reciprocal to the $\mathbf{u}_i$'s, and are therefore the rows of $\mathbf{M}^{-1}$. Substituting Eq. (9.138) into (9.72) produces

$$\mathbf{x}(t) = \sum_{i=1}^{n} e^{\lambda_i t}\, \mathbf{u}_i \mathbf{r}_i^T \mathbf{x}(0) + \int_0^t \left[\sum_{i=1}^{n} e^{\lambda_i (t-x)}\, \mathbf{u}_i \mathbf{r}_i^T \right] \mathbf{B}\, \mathbf{v}(x) dx . \tag{9.139}$$

Now

$$\mathbf{r}_i^T \mathbf{x}(0) = \langle \mathbf{x}(0) , \mathbf{r}_i \rangle \qquad \text{and} \qquad \mathbf{r}_i^T \mathbf{B}\, \mathbf{v}(x) = \langle \mathbf{B}\, \mathbf{v}(x) , \mathbf{r}_i \rangle . \tag{9.140}$$

The integration and summation in the second term of Eq. (9.139) can be interchanged. This equation becomes

$$\mathbf{x}(t) = \sum_{i=1}^{n} [\langle \mathbf{x}(0) , \mathbf{r}_i \rangle e^{\lambda_i t} + \int_0^t \langle \mathbf{B}\, \mathbf{v}(x) , \mathbf{r}_i \rangle e^{\lambda_i (t-x)} dx] \mathbf{u}_i$$

which is Eq. (9.63).

9.11 Appendix 2. Jordan Form of the A Matrix

If the **A** matrix of a linear system is not real and symmetric and has a repeated eigenvalue, it may have a shortage of eigenvectors and therefore not be diagonalizable. For example, if the system in Fig. 9.4 has m=1 kg, c=2 N·s/m, and k=1 N/m,

$$\ddot{y} + 2\dot{y} + y = 0\,. \tag{9.141}$$

The state equation is

$$\begin{bmatrix} \dot{x}_1 \\ \dot{x}_2 \end{bmatrix} = \begin{bmatrix} 0 & 1 \\ -1 & -2 \end{bmatrix} \begin{bmatrix} x_1 \\ x_2 \end{bmatrix} \quad \text{or} \quad \dot{\mathbf{x}} = \mathbf{A}\mathbf{x}\,. \tag{9.142}$$

The $\mathbf{A}$ matrix has the eigenvalues

$$\lambda_1 = -1\,, \quad \lambda_2 = -1 \tag{9.143}$$

and only one eigenvector,

$$\mathbf{u}_1 = \begin{bmatrix} 1 \\ -1 \end{bmatrix}. \tag{9.144}$$

Therefore a nonsingular nth-order (second-order in this case) matrix $\mathbf{M}$ whose columns are eigenvectors cannot be constructed, and $e^{\mathbf{A}t}$ cannot be calculated by Eq. (9.92). However, vectors $\mathbf{w}_i$ can be chosen that are linearly independent of the eigenvectors $\mathbf{u}_i$ and of each other, to complete the modal matrix. Call this matrix $\mathbf{N}$ now instead of $\mathbf{M}$, because some of its columns are not eigenvectors and therefore do not represent normal modes.

If $\mathbf{A}$ has a repeated eigenvalue λ_1 of order p, and the degeneracy of $[\mathbf{A} - \lambda_1\mathbf{I}]$ is q, there are q eigenvectors for the eigenvalue λ_1, and $p-q$ additional vectors are required. If $p = 4$, $q = 2$, and $\mathbf{u}_1$ and $\mathbf{u}_2$ are the eigenvectors for λ_1, the modal matrix might be either

$$\mathbf{N} = [\mathbf{u}_1\,, \mathbf{w}_1\,, \mathbf{w}_2\,, \mathbf{u}_2\,, \mathbf{u}_3\,, \ldots \mathbf{u}_{n-2}] \tag{9.145}$$

or

$$\mathbf{N} = [\mathbf{u}_1\,, \mathbf{w}_1\,, \mathbf{u}_2\,, \mathbf{w}_2\,, \mathbf{u}_3\,, \ldots \mathbf{u}_{n-2}]\,. \tag{9.146}$$

The locations of the $\mathbf{w}_i$'s in the $\mathbf{N}$ matrix will be chosen so that

$$\mathbf{J} = \mathbf{N}^{-1}\mathbf{A}\,\mathbf{N} \tag{9.147}$$

is a *Jordan canonical matrix*, namely an nth-order matrix whose diagonal elements are the eigenvalues of $\mathbf{A}$, some of the elements just to the right of the main diagonal are 1, and all the other elements are zero. The method of calculating the $\mathbf{w}_i$'s for the example might produce

$$\mathbf{J} = \left[\begin{array}{ccc|cccc} \lambda_1 & 1 & & & & & \\ & \lambda_1 & 1 & & & & \\ & & \lambda_1 & & & & \\ \hline & & & \lambda_1 & & & \\ & & & & \lambda_2 & & \\ & & & & & \cdot & \\ & & & & & & \cdot \end{array}\right] \tag{9.148}$$

if **N** is given by Eq. (9.145), or

$$\mathbf{J} = \begin{bmatrix} \lambda_1 & 1 & & & & \\ & \lambda_1 & & & & \\ & & \lambda_1 & 1 & & \\ & & & \lambda_1 & & \\ & & & & \lambda_2 & \\ & & & & & \cdot \\ & & & & & & \cdot \end{bmatrix} \tag{9.149}$$

if **N** is given by Eq. (9.146). Each dotted section of these matrices, containing the repeated eigenvalue and a full set of 1's, is called a *Jordan block*. The number of 1's in each block is the number of $\mathbf{w}_i$'s following the eigenvector in the **N** matrix. Inspection does not reveal which form of the modal matrix will produce a Jordan form. However, the columns of **N** will be calculated by a method that minimizes fruitless searching. Start by choosing the Jordan form with the largest Jordan block at the top, and calculate the $\mathbf{w}_i$'s by the following method. According to Eq. (9.147),

$$\mathbf{A\,N} = \mathbf{N\,J} \tag{9.150}$$

where **J** is given by Eq. (9.148), and **N** by (9.145). The first columns of the left and right sides of Eq. (9.150) are

$$\mathbf{A}\mathbf{u}_1 = \lambda_1\,\mathbf{u}_1 \qquad \text{or} \qquad [\mathbf{A} - \lambda_1\mathbf{I}]\,\mathbf{u}_1 = \mathbf{0}\,. \tag{9.151}$$

The second columns are

$$\mathbf{A}\mathbf{w}_1 = \mathbf{u}_1 + \lambda_1\,\mathbf{w}_1 \qquad \text{or} \qquad [\mathbf{A} - \lambda_1\mathbf{I}]\mathbf{w}_1 = \mathbf{u}_1\,. \tag{9.152}$$

The third columns are

$$\mathbf{A}\mathbf{w}_2 = \mathbf{w}_1 + \lambda_1\,\mathbf{w}_2 \qquad \text{or} \qquad [\mathbf{A} - \lambda_1\mathbf{I}]\mathbf{w}_2 = \mathbf{w}_1\,. \tag{9.153}$$

A similar equation can be written for each column in the Jordan block. Now $\mathbf{w}_1$ can be calculated by Eq. (9.152), $\mathbf{w}_2$ by Eq. (9.153), and so on. According to Eq. (9.152), $\mathbf{u}_1$ is a linear combination of the columns of $[\mathbf{A} - \lambda_1\mathbf{I}]$. But $[\mathbf{A} - \lambda_1\mathbf{I}]$ is always singular. Thus Eq. (9.152) produces a value of $\mathbf{w}_1$ only if $\mathbf{u}_1$ happens to lie in the space spanned by the columns of $[\mathbf{A} - \lambda_1\mathbf{I}]$. Similarly, Eq. (9.153) has a solution only if $\mathbf{w}_1$ lies in the column space of $[\mathbf{A} - \lambda_1\mathbf{I}]$. If the choice of the Jordan form was wrong, one of the $\mathbf{w}_i$'s, say $\mathbf{w}_r$, will lie outside of this space and cannot be evaluated. However, $\mathbf{w}_1, \mathbf{w}_2, \ldots \mathbf{w}_{r-1}$ already calculated are valid. Switch to another Jordan form whose first block ends at column

$r-1$, and whose second block is the largest of those in the possible Jordan forms remaining. In the example, if $\mathbf{w}_2$ is the first vector that cannot be calculated, switch to the Jordan form of Eq. (9.149) and the modal matrix of Eq. (9.146), and continue the process with

$$[\mathbf{A} - \lambda_1\mathbf{I}]\mathbf{u}_2 = \mathbf{0}\,, \quad [\mathbf{A} - \lambda_1\mathbf{I}]\mathbf{w}_r = \mathbf{u}_2\,, \quad \text{etc.} \tag{9.154}$$

As an example, choose

$$\mathbf{A} = \begin{bmatrix} 0 & 0 & 1 & 0 \\ 0 & 0 & 0 & 1 \\ 0 & 0 & 0 & 0 \\ 0 & 0 & 0 & 0 \end{bmatrix} \tag{9.155}$$

which has a fourth-order eigenvalue, $\lambda = 0$. The degeneracy of $[\mathbf{A} - \lambda\mathbf{I}]$ is $q = 2$. Therefore $p-q = 4-2 = 2$ extra vectors are needed to supplement the two eigenvectors in the modal matrix, and the Jordan matrix will have two 1's. Following the orderly procedure, assume the Jordan form

$$\mathbf{J} = \begin{bmatrix} 0 & 1 & 0 & 0 \\ 0 & 0 & 1 & 0 \\ 0 & 0 & 0 & 0 \\ 0 & 0 & 0 & 0 \end{bmatrix} \tag{9.156}$$

and

$$\mathbf{N} = [\mathbf{u}_1, \mathbf{w}_1, \mathbf{w}_2, \mathbf{u}_2]\,. \tag{9.157}$$

Then according to Eq. (9.151),

$$\begin{bmatrix} 0 & 0 & 1 & 0 \\ 0 & 0 & 0 & 1 \\ 0 & 0 & 0 & 0 \\ 0 & 0 & 0 & 0 \end{bmatrix} \begin{bmatrix} u_{11} \\ u_{21} \\ u_{31} \\ u_{41} \end{bmatrix} = \begin{bmatrix} 0 \\ 0 \\ 0 \\ 0 \end{bmatrix} \quad \text{and} \quad \mathbf{u}_1 = \begin{bmatrix} u_{11} \\ u_{21} \\ u_{31} \\ u_{41} \end{bmatrix} = \begin{bmatrix} a_1 \\ a_2 \\ 0 \\ 0 \end{bmatrix} \tag{9.158}$$

where a_1 and a_2 are arbitrary, except of course that both cannot be zero. According to Eq. (9.152),

$$\begin{bmatrix} 0 & 0 & 1 & 0 \\ 0 & 0 & 0 & 1 \\ 0 & 0 & 0 & 0 \\ 0 & 0 & 0 & 0 \end{bmatrix} \begin{bmatrix} w_{11} \\ w_{21} \\ w_{31} \\ w_{41} \end{bmatrix} = \begin{bmatrix} a_1 \\ a_2 \\ 0 \\ 0 \end{bmatrix} \quad \text{and} \quad \mathbf{w}_1 = \begin{bmatrix} w_{11} \\ w_{21} \\ w_{31} \\ w_{41} \end{bmatrix} = \begin{bmatrix} b_1 \\ b_2 \\ a_1 \\ a_2 \end{bmatrix} \tag{9.159}$$

where b_1 and b_2 are arbitrary. According to Eq. (9.153),

$$\begin{bmatrix} 0 & 0 & 1 & 0 \\ 0 & 0 & 0 & 1 \\ 0 & 0 & 0 & 0 \\ 0 & 0 & 0 & 0 \end{bmatrix} \begin{bmatrix} w_{12} \\ w_{22} \\ w_{32} \\ w_{42} \end{bmatrix} = \begin{bmatrix} b_1 \\ b_2 \\ a_1 \\ a_2 \end{bmatrix}. \tag{9.160}$$

Since $\mathbf{w}_1$ does not lie in the space spanned by the columns of $[\mathbf{A} - \lambda\mathbf{I}]$, $\mathbf{w}_2$ cannot be calculated by Eq. (9.160). Switch to the Jordan form

$$\mathbf{J} = \begin{bmatrix} 0 & 1 & 0 & 0 \\ 0 & 0 & 0 & 0 \\ 0 & 0 & 0 & 1 \\ 0 & 0 & 0 & 0 \end{bmatrix} \tag{9.161}$$

and the modal matrix $\mathbf{N} = [\mathbf{u}_1, \mathbf{w}_1, \mathbf{u}_2, \mathbf{w}_2]$ (9.162)

and continue the process with the second eigenvector

$$\mathbf{u}_2 = \begin{bmatrix} c_1 \\ c_2 \\ 0 \\ 0 \end{bmatrix} \tag{9.163}$$

where c_1 and c_2 are arbitrary except that both cannot be zero, and $\mathbf{u}_2$ cannot point in the same direction as $\mathbf{u}_1$. Then

$$[\mathbf{A} - \lambda\mathbf{I}]\mathbf{w}_2 = \mathbf{u}_2 \tag{9.164}$$

or

$$\begin{bmatrix} 0 & 0 & 1 & 0 \\ 0 & 0 & 0 & 1 \\ 0 & 0 & 0 & 0 \\ 0 & 0 & 0 & 0 \end{bmatrix} \begin{bmatrix} w_{12} \\ w_{22} \\ w_{32} \\ w_{42} \end{bmatrix} = \begin{bmatrix} c_1 \\ c_2 \\ 0 \\ 0 \end{bmatrix} \quad \text{and} \quad \mathbf{w}_2 = \begin{bmatrix} w_{12} \\ w_{22} \\ w_{32} \\ w_{42} \end{bmatrix} = \begin{bmatrix} d_1 \\ d_2 \\ c_1 \\ c_2 \end{bmatrix} \tag{9.165}$$

where d_1 and d_2 are arbitrary. Now according to Eq. (9.162),

$$\mathbf{N} = \begin{bmatrix} a_1 & b_1 & c_1 & d_1 \\ a_2 & b_2 & c_2 & d_2 \\ 0 & a_1 & 0 & c_1 \\ 0 & a_2 & 0 & c_2 \end{bmatrix}. \tag{9.166}$$

This is the modified modal matrix $\mathbf{N}$ for which

$$\mathbf{J} = \mathbf{N}^{-1}\mathbf{A}\,\mathbf{N} \tag{9.167}$$

is a Jordan form. The exact form is given by Eq. (9.161).

To make use of the Jordan form in calculating the state-transition matrix, rewrite Eq. (9.167) as

$$\mathbf{A} = \mathbf{N}\,\mathbf{J}\,\mathbf{N}^{-1}. \tag{9.168}$$

According to the reasoning of Eqs. (9.86) thru (9.92),

$$e^{\mathbf{A}t} = \mathbf{N}\,e^{\mathbf{J}t}\,\mathbf{N}^{-1} \tag{9.97}$$

where

$$e^{\mathbf{J}t} = \mathbf{I} + \mathbf{J}t + \frac{(\mathbf{J}t)^2}{2!} + \cdots \tag{9.169}$$

Now let

$$\mathbf{J} = \mathbf{\Lambda} + \mathbf{H} \tag{9.170}$$

where $\mathbf{\Lambda}$ is a diagonal matrix whose diagonal elements are the diagonal elements of $\mathbf{J}$ (the eigenvalues of $\mathbf{A}$), and $\mathbf{H}$ is a matrix whose only nonzero elements are the off-diagonal 1's of $\mathbf{J}$. Then

$$e^{\mathbf{J}t} = e^{(\mathbf{\Lambda}+\mathbf{H})t} = e^{\mathbf{\Lambda}t}\, e^{\mathbf{H}t} = e^{\mathbf{H}t}\, e^{\mathbf{\Lambda}t}\,. \tag{9.171}$$

Notice that the product of the two matrix exponentials is the product of two infinite series, which consists of terms of the form $\mathbf{H}^m\mathbf{\Lambda}^n t^{m+n}$. In these terms, and therefore in Eq. (9.171), $\mathbf{H}$ and $\mathbf{\Lambda}$ can be interchanged only if $\mathbf{H\Lambda} = \mathbf{\Lambda H}$. Fortunately the special matrices $\mathbf{\Lambda}$ and $\mathbf{H}$ do commute. Now

$$e^{\mathbf{A}t} = \mathbf{N}\, e^{\mathbf{\Lambda}t}\, e^{\mathbf{H}t}\, \mathbf{N}^{-1}\,. \tag{9.172}$$

Eq. (9.93) shows how to write $e^{\mathbf{\Lambda}t}$. To discover the rules for writing $e^{\mathbf{H}t}$ calculate it using the Cayley-Hamilton technique. A typical nth-order $\mathbf{H}$ matrix has the form

$$\mathbf{H} = \begin{bmatrix} 0 & 1 & 0 & 0 & \cdot & \cdot \\ 0 & 0 & 1 & 0 & & \\ \cdot & & 0 & 1 & & \\ \cdot & & & 0 & & \\ & & & & \cdot & \\ & & & & & \cdot \end{bmatrix}. \tag{9.173}$$

The eigenvalues are always an nth-order repeated value of zero. According to Eqs. (9.109) and (9.115),

$$e^0 = 1 = \alpha_0\,, \tag{9.174}$$

$$\left.\frac{de^{\lambda t}}{d\lambda}\right|_{\lambda=0} = t = \alpha_1\,, \tag{9.175}$$

$$\left.\frac{d^2e^{\lambda t}}{d\lambda^2}\right|_{t=0} = t^2 = 2\alpha_2 \qquad \text{or} \qquad \alpha_2 = \frac{t^2}{2}\,. \tag{9.176}$$

Similarly,

$$\alpha_3 = \frac{t^3}{3!}\,, \ldots, \alpha_k = \frac{t^k}{k!}\,. \tag{9.177}$$

Thus according to Eq. (9.108),

$$e^{\mathbf{H}t} = \mathbf{I} + t\mathbf{H} + \frac{t^2}{2!}\mathbf{H}^2 + \cdots + \frac{t^{n-1}}{(n-1)!}\mathbf{H}^{n-1}\,. \tag{9.178}$$

The elements of $\mathbf{H}^2$ are 1 in the locations that are both above and to the right of the 1's in $\mathbf{H}$, and zero otherwise. Likewise, the nonzero elements of $\mathbf{H}^3$ are 1 in the locations that are above and to the right of the 1's in $\mathbf{H}^2$, and so on. Thus for the $\mathbf{H}$ matrix of Eq. (9.173),

$$e^{\mathbf{H}t} = \begin{bmatrix} 1 & t & t^2/2 & t^3/6 & \cdot & \cdot \\ 0 & 1 & t & t^2/2 & & \\ 0 & 0 & 1 & t & & \\ \cdot & & 0 & 1 & & \\ \cdot & & & & \cdot & \\ & & & & & \cdot \end{bmatrix}. \qquad (9.179)$$

The rules for writing $e^{\mathbf{H}t}$ by inspection of $\mathbf{J}$ are now clear:

1. Replace the diagonal elements of $\mathbf{J}$ by 1's.
2. Replace the off-diagonal 1's by t.
3. Complete a pyramid in each Jordan block, by making each of its layers consist of the element $t^k/k!$

To illustrate the use of the Jordan form in calculating the state-transition matrix, continue the example of Eq. (9.142), for which

$$\mathbf{A} = \begin{bmatrix} 0 & 1 \\ -1 & -2 \end{bmatrix}. \qquad (9.180)$$

Arbitrarily double the length of the eigenvector, to make

$$\mathbf{u}_1 = \begin{bmatrix} 2 \\ -2 \end{bmatrix}. \qquad (9.181)$$

Then according to Eq. (9.152),

$$[\mathbf{A} - \lambda_1 \mathbf{I}]\mathbf{w}_1 = \mathbf{u}_1 \quad \text{or} \quad \begin{bmatrix} 1 & 1 \\ -1 & -1 \end{bmatrix} \begin{bmatrix} w_{11} \\ w_{21} \end{bmatrix} = \begin{bmatrix} 2 \\ -2 \end{bmatrix} \qquad (9.182)$$

or

$$\mathbf{w}_1 = \begin{bmatrix} 1 \\ 1 \end{bmatrix}. \qquad (9.183)$$

Thus

$$\mathbf{N} = [\mathbf{u}_1, \mathbf{w}_1] = \begin{bmatrix} 2 & 1 \\ -2 & 1 \end{bmatrix}, \qquad \mathbf{N}^{-1} = \frac{1}{4} \begin{bmatrix} 1 & -1 \\ 2 & 2 \end{bmatrix},$$

$$\mathbf{J} = \begin{bmatrix} -1 & 1 \\ 0 & -1 \end{bmatrix}, \qquad \mathbf{\Lambda} = \begin{bmatrix} -1 & 0 \\ 0 & -1 \end{bmatrix}, \qquad e^{\mathbf{\Lambda}t} = \begin{bmatrix} e^{-t} & 0 \\ 0 & e^{-t} \end{bmatrix},$$

and

$$e^{\mathbf{H}t} = \begin{bmatrix} 1 & t \\ 0 & 1 \end{bmatrix}. \tag{9.184}$$

Now according to Eq. (9.172),

$$\begin{aligned} e^{\mathbf{A}t} = \mathbf{N}e^{\Lambda t}\, e^{\mathbf{H}t}\, \mathbf{N}^{-1} &= \begin{bmatrix} 2 & 1 \\ -2 & 1 \end{bmatrix} \begin{bmatrix} e^{-t} & 0 \\ 0 & e^{-t} \end{bmatrix} \begin{bmatrix} 1 & t \\ 0 & 1 \end{bmatrix} \cdot \frac{1}{4} \begin{bmatrix} 1 & -1 \\ 2 & 2 \end{bmatrix} \\ &= \begin{bmatrix} e^{-t} + te^{-t} & te^{-t} \\ -te^{-t} & e^{-t} - te^{-t} \end{bmatrix}. \end{aligned} \tag{9.185}$$

To verify this result, compute $e^{\mathbf{A}t}$ by the more straightforward Cayley-Hamilton technique. Since the eigenvalue of $\mathbf{A}$ is $\lambda_1 = -1$,

$$e^{\lambda_1 t} = \alpha_0 + \alpha_1 \lambda_1 \qquad \text{or} \qquad e^{-t} = \alpha_0 - \alpha_1 \tag{9.186}$$

and

$$\left. \frac{d}{d\lambda} e^{\lambda t} \right|_{\lambda = \lambda_1} = te^{-t} = \alpha_1 . \tag{9.187}$$

Thus

$$\alpha_0 = e^{-t} + te^{-t} \tag{9.188}$$

and

$$e^{\mathbf{A}t} = \alpha_0 \mathbf{I} + \alpha_1 \mathbf{A} = \begin{bmatrix} e^{-t} + te^{-t} & te^{-t} \\ -te^{-t} & e^{-t} - te^{-t} \end{bmatrix} \tag{9.189}$$

which agrees with Eq. (9.185).

9.12 Appendix 3. Numerical Evaluation of the Transition Matrix

A numerical method of calculating the state-transition matrix that can be used in computer programs was presented in Ref. 83. The method is simple in concept, and is based on the infinite series, Eq. (9.66), that defines the transition matrix:

$$e^{\mathbf{A}t} = \mathbf{I} + \mathbf{A}t + \frac{(\mathbf{A}t)^2}{2!} + \cdots = \sum_{k=0}^{\infty} \frac{\mathbf{A}^k t^k}{k!}. \tag{9.190}$$

The infinite series can be approximated by the sum $\mathbf{M}$ of a few terms, say $K+1$ of them, and the remainder $\mathbf{R}$. Thus

$$e^{\mathbf{A}t} = \mathbf{M} + \mathbf{R} \tag{9.191}$$

where

$$\mathbf{M} = \sum_{k=0}^{K} \frac{\mathbf{A}^k t^k}{k!} \qquad \text{and} \qquad \mathbf{R} = \sum_{k=K+1}^{\infty} \frac{\mathbf{A}^k t^k}{k!}. \tag{9.192}$$

Matrix **M** is easily calculated by a computer. If the elements r_{ij} of matrix **R** are negligibly small compared to the elements m_{ij} of matrix **M**, the calculation is complete. Specify that the elements r_{ij} must be at least d orders of magnitude smaller than the elements m_{ij}:

$$|r_{ij}| \leqslant 10^{-d}\,|m_{ij}| \,. \tag{9.193}$$

This is nearly the same as requiring that $e^{\mathbf{A}t}$ have an accuracy within d significant digits.

To deterimine an upper bound on the size of the elements r_{ij}, start by defining the norm of matrix **A** as the sum of the magnitudes of its elements:

$$\|\mathbf{A}\| = \sum_{i,j=1}^{n} |a_{ij}| \,. \tag{9.194}$$

Applying this definition to the matrix **R**, which is

$$\mathbf{R} = \frac{\mathbf{A}^{K+1}t^{K+1}}{(K+1)!} + \frac{\mathbf{A}^{K+2}t^{K+2}}{(K+2)!} + \cdots \tag{9.195}$$

yields

$$\|\mathbf{R}\| \leqslant \frac{\|\mathbf{A}^{K+1}\|\,t^{K+1}}{(K+1)!} + \frac{\|\mathbf{A}^{K+2}\|\,t^{K+2}}{(K+2)!} + \cdots \tag{9.196}$$

Ref. 60, p. 28, shows that if the norm of matrix **A** is defined by Eq. (9.194),

$$\|\mathbf{A}^{k}\| \leqslant \|\mathbf{A}\|^{k} \,. \tag{9.197}$$

Therefore

$$\|\mathbf{R}\| \leqslant \frac{\|\mathbf{A}\|^{K+1}t^{K+1}}{(K+1)!} + \frac{\|\mathbf{A}\|^{K+2}t^{K+2}}{(K+2)!} + \cdots = \sum_{k=K+1}^{\infty} \frac{\|\mathbf{A}\|^{k}t^{k}}{k!} \,. \tag{9.198}$$

Since the magnitude of each element of **R** is equal to or less than the norm,

$$|r_{ij}| \leqslant \|\mathbf{R}\| \leqslant \sum_{k=K+1}^{\infty} \frac{\|\mathbf{A}\|^{k}t^{k}}{k!} \,. \tag{9.199}$$

An upper limit on the infinite series can be found by letting the ratio of the second term to the first term be ε. Then

$$\varepsilon = \frac{\|\mathbf{A}\|^{K+2}t^{K+2}}{(K+2)!} \cdot \frac{(K+1)!}{\|\mathbf{A}\|^{K+1}t^{K+1}} = \frac{\|\mathbf{A}\|\,t}{K+2} \,. \tag{9.200}$$

The ratio of the nth term to the $n-1$th term is $\|\mathbf{A}\|t/(K+n)$. Thus if $k \geqslant K+2$,

$$\frac{\|\mathbf{A}\|t}{k} \leqslant \varepsilon \,. \tag{9.201}$$

Now Eq. (9.199) can be written as

$$\begin{aligned} |r_{ij}| &\leqslant \sum_{k=K+1}^{\infty} \frac{\|\mathbf{A}\|^k t^k}{k!} \leqslant \frac{\|\mathbf{A}\|^{K+1} t^{K+1}}{(K+1)!} (1 + \varepsilon + \varepsilon^2 + \cdots) \\ &= \frac{\|\mathbf{A}\|^{K+1} t^{K+1}}{(K+1)!} \cdot \frac{1}{1-\varepsilon} \,. \end{aligned} \tag{9.202}$$

The last term is an upper limit on the infinite series representing $\|\mathbf{R}\|$, and is therefore an upper limit on the magnitude of the elements of matrix $\mathbf{R}$.

A procedure is now available for evaluating the state-transition matrix $e^{\mathbf{A}t}$ that can be programmed for a computer. First, arbitrarily choose K, calculate matrix $\mathbf{M}$ by the first of Eqs. (9.192), and select the element m_{ij} having the smallest magnitude. Then calculate the allowable upper limit of $|r_{ij}|$ by (9.193). Finally, calculate the upper limit of $|r_{ij}|$ by (9.202). If it is too high, increase the value of K and repeat the process.

This procedure is conservative, since it compares the smallest element of matrix $\mathbf{M}$ with the largest possible element of matrix $\mathbf{R}$.

9.13 Appendix 4. Use of the Transition Matrix to Invert Laplace Transforms

Ref. 83 also shows an interesting method of inverting Laplace transforms that is suitable for use on a digital computer. This method works for any Laplace transform that is the ratio of two polynomials, the numerator of which is of lower degree, and avoids the usual partial-fraction expansion. Instead, it determines a differential equation represented by the Laplace transform, reduces it to a first-order state equation, and solves it by evaluating the state-transition matrix.

If a linear, homogeneous differential equation with constant coefficients is

$$\dddot{x}(t) + b_2\ddot{x}(t) + b_1\dot{x}(t) + b_0 x(t) = 0 \,, \tag{9.203}$$

its Laplace transform is

$$X(s) = \frac{x(0)s^2 + [\dot{x}(0) + b_2 x(0)]s + [\ddot{x}(0) + b_2\dot{x}(0) + b_1 x(0)]}{s^3 + b_2 s^2 + b_1 s + b_0} \,. \tag{9.204}$$

In general, if

$$X(s) = \frac{a_{n-1}s^{n-1} + a_{n-2}s^{n-2} + \cdots + a_1 s + a_0}{s^n + b_{n-1}s^{n-1} + \cdots + b_1 s + b_0}, \tag{9.205}$$

a corresponding differential equation is

$$x^{(n)}(t) + b_{n-1}x^{(n-1)}(t) + \cdots + b_1\dot{x}(t) + b_0 x(t) = 0 \tag{9.206}$$

with the initial conditions

$$\left.\begin{aligned}
x(0) &= a_{n-1} \\
\dot{x}(0) &= a_{n-2} - b_{n-1}x(0) \\
\ddot{x}(0) &= a_{n-3} - b_{n-1}\dot{x}(0) - b_{n-2}x(0) \\
&\ \ \vdots \\
x^{(n-1)}(0) &= a_0 - b_{n-1}x^{(n-2)}(0) - b_{n-2}x^{(n-3)}(0) - \cdots - b_1 x(0)\,.
\end{aligned}\right\} \tag{9.207}$$

Now solve this differential equation, thereby calculating the inverse of the Laplace transform. This is not the only differential equation whose Laplace transform is Eq. (9.205). However, one-sided Laplace transforms have only one inverse. All the differential equations whose Laplace transform is Eq. (9.205) have the same solution, which is found by solving Eq. (9.206).

If the state vector is defined as

$$\mathbf{x}(t) = \begin{bmatrix} x(t) \\ \dot{x}(t) \\ \cdot \\ \cdot \\ \cdot \\ x^{(n-1)}(t) \end{bmatrix}, \tag{9.208}$$

the state equation of the system represented by Eq. (9.206) is

$$\dot{\mathbf{x}} = \mathbf{A}\,\mathbf{x} \tag{9.209}$$

where

$$\mathbf{A} = \begin{bmatrix} 0 & 1 & 0 & \cdots & 0 & 0 \\ 0 & 0 & 1 & \cdots & 0 & 0 \\ \cdot & & & & & \cdot \\ \cdot & & & & & \cdot \\ \cdot & & & & & \cdot \\ 0 & 0 & 0 & \cdots & 0 & 1 \\ -b_0 & -b_1 & -b_2 & \cdots & -b_{n-2} & -b_{n-1} \end{bmatrix}. \tag{9.210}$$

The solution of the state equation (9.209) is given by Eq. (9.65):

$$\mathbf{x}(t) = e^{\mathbf{A}t}\mathbf{x}(0)\,. \tag{9.65}$$

The components of $\mathbf{x}(0)$ are given by Eqs. (9.207).

A computer program can be written to compute $\mathbf{x}(t)$ at intervals T. A curve of its first component $x(t)$ vs. time is a plot of the inverse of the Laplace transform. The calculation is simplified by the fact that

$$\begin{aligned}\mathbf{x}[(n+1)T] &= e^{\mathbf{A}(n+1)T}\mathbf{x}(0) = e^{\mathbf{A}T}\,e^{\mathbf{A}nT}\,\mathbf{x}(0)\\ &= e^{\mathbf{A}T}\mathbf{x}(nT)\,.\end{aligned} \tag{9.211}$$

The matrix $e^{\mathbf{A}T}$ must be calculated only once. If the error accumulated by the recursion formula (9.211) is significant, the more accurate formula (9.65) can be used occasionally for comparison, say whenever n is a multiple of 10. If the difference is too great, the values of $\mathbf{x}(nT)$ calculated by Eq. (9.211) for the preceding ten values of n are discarded, and recalculated starting from the previous vector calculated by Eq. (9.65).

This method of inverting Laplace transforms has the advantage of avoiding the calculation of roots of the denominator and partial fractions. It has the disadvantage of not providing a display of the inverse transform as a function of time.

Chapter 10

AN INTRODUCTION TO MODERN CONTROL THEORY

10.1 Introduction

The preceding chapter introduced a new concept of the state of a system, and showed how the state can be determined. Any competent mathematician, however, would recognize that the essence of Chapter 9 was an explanation of how to solve simultaneous ordinary differential equations using matrix algebra. Now the mathematics will be extended to develop some modern ideas that are useful in the design of practical hardware systems. One of these ideas is optimal control, the design of the system that is best according to a predetermined criterion of excellence. Two others are controllability and observability, fundamental properties to be considered in the design of complex systems.

10.2 Performance Indices

A *performance index* is a quantitative measure of the performance of a system during a prescribed mission, that emphasizes the quantities that are important to the user. An *optimal control system* is the system that produces the best value of the performance index, usually the minimum value. For the simple spring-mass-damper system of Fig. 10.1, for which

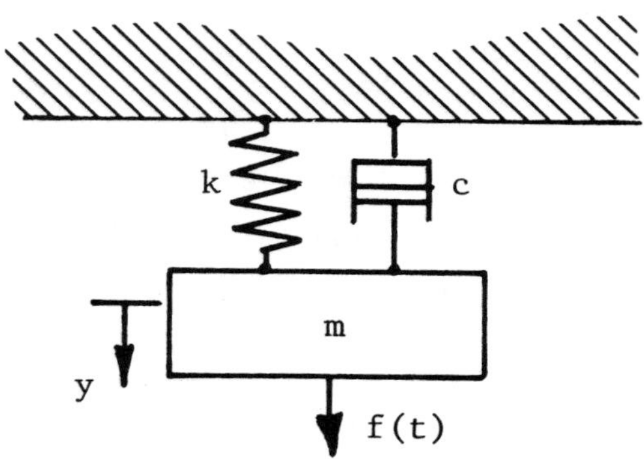

Fig. 10.1. System whose performance is to be optimized.

$$m\ddot{y} + c\dot{y} + ky = f(t)\,, \tag{10.1}$$

the important quantity might be settling time. Then the optimal system is the one with shortest settling time. Many performance indices J are time integrals. One important one is

$$J = \int_0^\infty |f(t)|dt \tag{10.2}$$

which minimizes the integral of the controlling force $f(t)$ over the duration of the mission. In a spaceship, for example, $f(t)$ might be provided by rockets. If this force is proportional to the rate of burning of rocket fuel, then J is proportional to the total fuel used. For the simple system of Fig. 10.1 the mission might be to return from the state $y = 1$, $\dot{y} = 0$ after the constant force f is removed, to the state of rest $y = \dot{y} = 0$, with as little displacement from the rest position as possible, and as little velocity as possible during the mission. These requirements can reasonably be expressed by the performance index

$$J = \int_0^\infty [ay^2(t) + b\dot{y}^2(t)]dt\,, \tag{10.3}$$

in which the relative magnitudes of the constants a and b depend on the relative importance to the user of minimizing the displacement and the velocity.

10.3 The Plant and the Controller

In order to design a system to minimize its performance index, first arrange it into the block diagram of Fig. 10.2. The *plant* is the portion of the system containing the parameters and connections that are already in place, and cannot be varied. The *controller* is the negotiable portion of the system that can be designed to minimize the performance index J. Since the input to the plant is $\mathbf{u}(t)$ instead of $\mathbf{v}(t)$ as in the preceding chapter, the state equation representing the plant is

$$\dot{\mathbf{x}} = \mathbf{A}\mathbf{x} + \mathbf{B}\mathbf{u}\,. \tag{10.4}$$

If all of the system is in the plant, $\mathbf{u} = \mathbf{v}$, and the state equation is (9.14). In Fig. 10.2, $\mathbf{x}(t)$ is the state vector and $\mathbf{u}(t)$ is the *control vector*, whose purpose is to drive the plant so that it minimizes J while fulfilling its mission. The controller receives as inputs the state of the system $\mathbf{x}(t)$ and the vector of external inputs or *input vector* $\mathbf{v}(t)$, and generates the control vector according to the *control law*

$$\mathbf{u}(t) = f(\mathbf{x},\mathbf{v})\,. \tag{10.5}$$

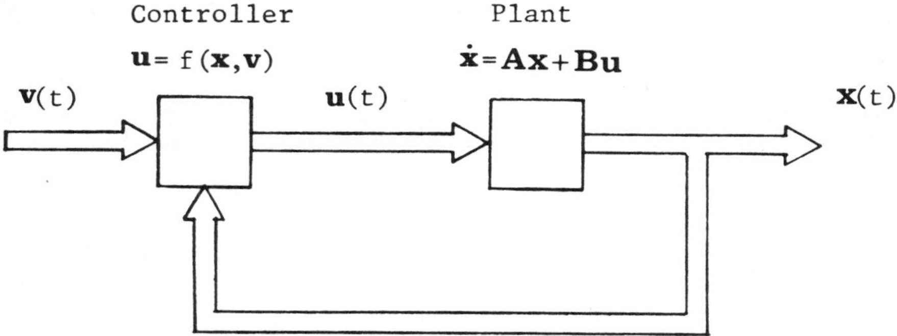

Fig. 10.2. Block diagram showing controller and plant.

If the controller is designed correctly, it generates the optimal control vector $\mathbf{u}(t)$ that produces a minimum performance index. This introductory discussion will let the input vector $\mathbf{v}(t)$ be zero, and will consider only linear, time-invariant controllers, namely those that produce control variables that are linear combinations of the state variables:

$$\mathbf{u} = \mathbf{H}\,\mathbf{x} \tag{10.6}$$

where $\mathbf{H}$ is a constant matrix. Fig. 10.2 might then represent the system for landing a spacecraft on the moon, in which the control effort $\mathbf{u}(t)$ exerted by the rockets is determined only by the state of the spacecraft $\mathbf{x}(t)$, namely its altitude, velocity, attitude, etc.

Consider a simple optimization problem. The state of the system in Fig. 10.1 is

$$\mathbf{x}(t) = \begin{bmatrix} x_1(t) \\ x_2(t) \end{bmatrix} = \begin{bmatrix} y(t) \\ \dot{y}(t) \end{bmatrix}. \tag{10.7}$$

Choose the spring and damper so that the performance index

$$J = \int_0^\infty (x_1^2 + x_2^2)dt = \int_0^\infty \mathbf{x}^T\mathbf{x}\;dt \tag{10.8}$$

is minimized when the system moves with no applied force $f(t)$ from the initial state

$$\mathbf{x}(0) = \begin{bmatrix} 1 \\ 0 \end{bmatrix} \tag{10.9}$$

to the final state

$$\mathbf{x}(\infty) = \begin{bmatrix} 0 \\ 0 \end{bmatrix}. \tag{10.10}$$

The sum of forces on the mass, Eq. (10.1), can be written as

$$\ddot{y} + a_2\dot{y} + a_1 y = \frac{f}{m} = 0\,, \tag{10.11}$$

where $a_1 = k/m$ and $a_2 = c/m$. Since the parameters a_1 and a_2 are negotiable, put them in the controller. The block diagram of the system is shown in Fig. 10.3. The controller is represented by the equation

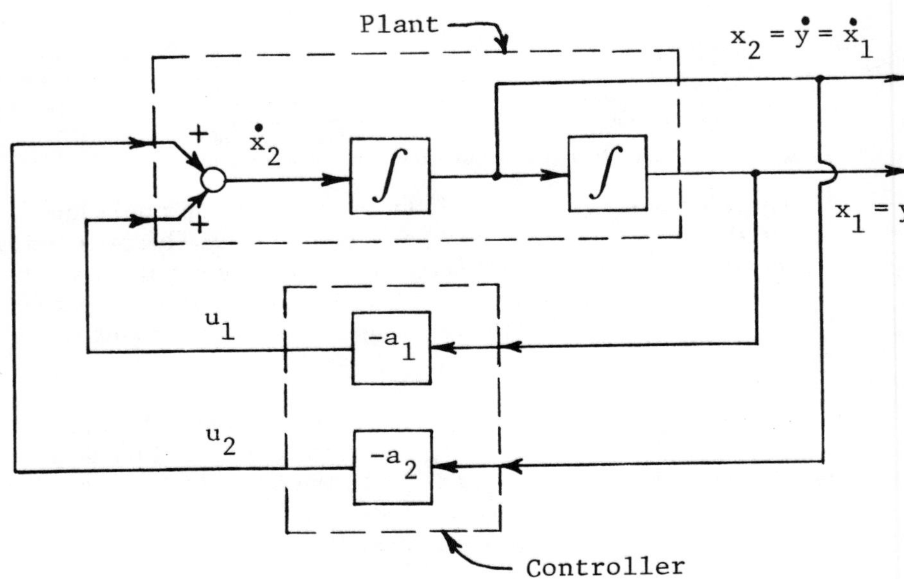

Fig. 10.3. Details of the controller and plant.

$$\begin{bmatrix} u_1 \\ u_2 \end{bmatrix} = \begin{bmatrix} -a_1 & 0 \\ 0 & -a_2 \end{bmatrix} \begin{bmatrix} x_1 \\ x_2 \end{bmatrix} \quad \text{or} \quad \mathbf{u} = \mathbf{H}\,\mathbf{x} \tag{10.12}$$

where

$$\mathbf{H} = \begin{bmatrix} -a_1 & 0 \\ 0 & -a_2 \end{bmatrix}. \tag{10.13}$$

The plant is represented by the equation

$$\begin{bmatrix} \dot{x}_1 \\ \dot{x}_2 \end{bmatrix} = \begin{bmatrix} 0 & 1 \\ 0 & 0 \end{bmatrix} \begin{bmatrix} x_1 \\ x_2 \end{bmatrix} + \begin{bmatrix} 0 & 0 \\ 1 & 1 \end{bmatrix} \begin{bmatrix} u_1 \\ u_2 \end{bmatrix}. \tag{10.14}$$

Thus

$$\mathbf{A} = \begin{bmatrix} 0 & 1 \\ 0 & 0 \end{bmatrix} \quad \text{and} \quad \mathbf{B} = \begin{bmatrix} 0 & 0 \\ 1 & 1 \end{bmatrix}. \tag{10.15}$$

Now the controller can be designed to optimize the control law.

10.4 A Method of Optimizing the Control Law

The system in Fig. 10.3 has a controller of fixed structure. Only the parameters are negotiable. Other systems do not have a controller initially, and the engineer's job is to design one. Methods of optimization are available that produce the design of the structure as well as the parameters of the optimal controller. One of these methods is illustrated in the next chapter. The control law of the system in Fig. 10.3 will be optimized by a method that requires (1) a linear, time-invariant controller of fixed structure, (2) a system that is undriven ($\mathbf{v} = \mathbf{0}$) and stable so that $\mathbf{x}(\infty) = \mathbf{0}$, and (3) a performance index that can be written in the form

$$J = \int_0^\infty \mathbf{x}^T \mathbf{Q} \mathbf{x} \, dt \tag{10.16}$$

where $\mathbf{Q}$ is an $n \times n$ square matrix. This form reduces to Eq. (10.8) if

$$\mathbf{Q} = \begin{bmatrix} 1 & 0 \\ 0 & 1 \end{bmatrix} . \tag{10.17}$$

The optimizing method is based on the invention of a new constant matrix $\mathbf{P}$ for which

$$\frac{d}{dt}(\mathbf{x}^T \mathbf{P} \mathbf{x}) = -\mathbf{x}^T \mathbf{Q} \mathbf{x} . \tag{10.18}$$

Then the performance index can be written as

$$J = -\int_0^\infty \frac{d}{dt}(\mathbf{x}^T \mathbf{P} \mathbf{x}) dt = -\mathbf{x}^T(t) \mathbf{P} \mathbf{x}(t) \Big|_0^\infty . \tag{10.19}$$

Since the system is undriven and stable, $\mathbf{x}(\infty) = \mathbf{0}$. Therefore

$$J = \mathbf{x}^T(0) \mathbf{P} \mathbf{x}(0) . \tag{10.20}$$

The analysis will show that the matrix $\mathbf{P}$ is a function of the parameters in the controller. When it is evaluated, J can be calculated and minimized by differentiating it by the parameter that is to be optimized. To evaluate $\mathbf{P}$ expand Eq. (10.18):

$$\frac{d}{dt}[\mathbf{x}^T(t) \mathbf{P} \mathbf{x}(t)] = \dot{\mathbf{x}}^T \mathbf{P} \mathbf{x} + \mathbf{x}^T \mathbf{P} \dot{\mathbf{x}} . \tag{10.21}$$

Combine Eqs. (10.4) and (10.12) to get

$$\dot{\mathbf{x}} = \mathbf{A}\mathbf{x} + \mathbf{B}\mathbf{u} = \mathbf{A}\mathbf{x} + \mathbf{B}\mathbf{H}\mathbf{x} = (\mathbf{A} + \mathbf{B}\mathbf{H})\mathbf{x} . \tag{10.22}$$

Let

$$\mathbf{A} + \mathbf{B}\,\mathbf{H} = \mathbf{D} . \tag{10.23}$$

Then

$$\dot{\mathbf{x}} = \mathbf{D}\,\mathbf{x}\,. \tag{10.24}$$

Now **D** is the same as matrix **A** of Eq. (9.14). Eq. (10.21) becomes

$$\frac{d}{dt}[\mathbf{x}^T\,\mathbf{P}\,\mathbf{x}] = (\mathbf{D}\,\mathbf{x})^T\,\mathbf{P}\,\mathbf{x} + \mathbf{x}^T\,\mathbf{P}\,(\mathbf{D}\,\mathbf{x})$$

$$= \mathbf{x}^T\,\mathbf{D}^T\,\mathbf{P}\,\mathbf{x} + \mathbf{x}^T\,\mathbf{P}\,\mathbf{D}\,\mathbf{x} = \mathbf{x}^T(\mathbf{D}^T\,\mathbf{P} + \mathbf{P}\,\mathbf{D})\mathbf{x}\,. \tag{10.25}$$

Now according to Eq. (10.18) that defines **P**,

$$\mathbf{D}^T\,\mathbf{P} + \mathbf{P}\,\mathbf{D} = -\,\mathbf{Q}\,. \tag{10.26}$$

This equation produces the value of **P** for use in Eq. (10.20).

For example, calculate **P** and J for the spring-mass-damper system. First,

$$\mathbf{D} = \mathbf{A} + \mathbf{B}\,\mathbf{H} = \begin{bmatrix} 0 & 1 \\ 0 & 0 \end{bmatrix} + \begin{bmatrix} 0 & 0 \\ 1 & 1 \end{bmatrix} \begin{bmatrix} -a_1 & 0 \\ 0 & -a_2 \end{bmatrix} = \begin{bmatrix} 0 & 1 \\ -a_1 & -a_2 \end{bmatrix}. \tag{10.27}$$

Eq. (10.26) becomes

$$\begin{bmatrix} 0 & -a_1 \\ 1 & -a_2 \end{bmatrix} \begin{bmatrix} p_{11} & p_{12} \\ p_{21} & p_{22} \end{bmatrix} + \begin{bmatrix} p_{11} & p_{12} \\ p_{21} & p_{22} \end{bmatrix} \begin{bmatrix} 0 & 1 \\ -a_1 & -a_2 \end{bmatrix} = \begin{bmatrix} -1 & 0 \\ 0 & -1 \end{bmatrix}. \tag{10.28}$$

Performing the matrix multiplication and addition yields four scalar equations that can be expressed in the form

$$\begin{bmatrix} 0 & -a_1 & -a_1 & 0 \\ 1 & -a_2 & 0 & -a_1 \\ 1 & 0 & -a_2 & -a_1 \\ 0 & 1 & 1 & -2a_2 \end{bmatrix} \begin{bmatrix} p_{11} \\ p_{12} \\ p_{21} \\ p_{22} \end{bmatrix} = \begin{bmatrix} -1 \\ 0 \\ 0 \\ -1 \end{bmatrix}. \tag{10.29}$$

The solution is

$$p_{11} = \frac{a_1 + a_1^2 + a_2^2}{2a_1a_2}, \quad p_{21} = p_{12} = \frac{1}{2a_1}, \quad p_{22} = \frac{1 + a_1}{2a_1a_2}\,. \tag{10.30}$$

Now J can be evaluated according to Eq. (10.20):

$$J = \mathbf{x}^T(0)\,\mathbf{P}\,\mathbf{x}(0) = [1 \quad 0] \begin{bmatrix} p_{11} & p_{12} \\ p_{21} & p_{22} \end{bmatrix} \begin{bmatrix} 1 \\ 0 \end{bmatrix} = p_{11}$$

$$= \frac{a_1 + a_1^2 + a_2^2}{2a_1a_2}\,. \tag{10.31}$$

The performance index J can be minimized by varying either a_1 or a_2. The relationships are made clearer by Fig. 10.4, which is a map of the

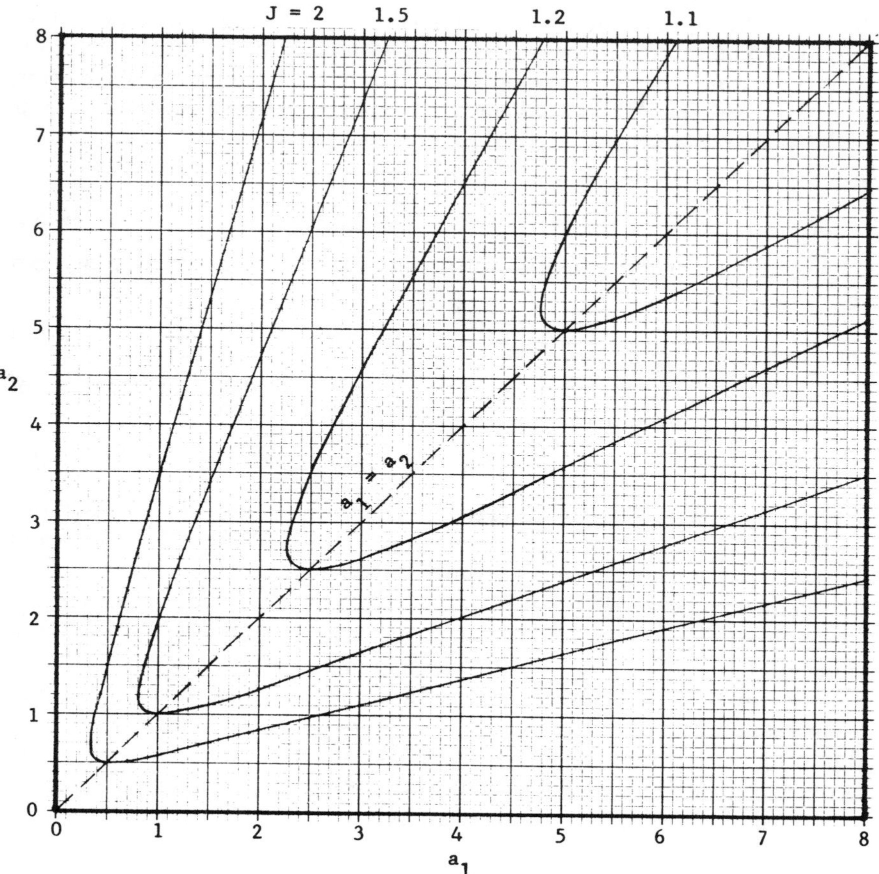

Fig. 10.4. Contours of constant performance index J.

contours of constant J, with the coordinates a_1 and a_2. The map shows that if a_2 is specified, the performance index is minimized by making $a_1 = a_2$, or $k = c$. This fact is verified by differentiating Eq. (10.31) with respect to a_1 and setting the derivative equal to zero. If a_1 is specified, the optimal value of a_2 if found by differentiating with respect to a_2:

$$\frac{dJ}{da_2} = \frac{(2a_1a_2)(2a_2) - (a_1 + a_1^2 + a_2^2)(2a_1)}{(2a_1a_2)^2} = 0 \ . \tag{10.32}$$

The result is

$$a_2 = \sqrt{a_1 + a_1^2} \ . \tag{10.33}$$

This equation indicates, and the contour map verifies, that the optimal value of a_2 lies above the line $a_1 = a_2$. If neither a_1 nor a_2 is specified but both have practical upper limits, the map will show which parameter should be set at its upper limit, and which one below its upper limit.

The parameters chosen by optimal control theory do not always seem correct according to classical control-theory standards. For example, if a_2 of the sample system is fixed at 0.04, the optimal value of a_1 is 0.04. Eq. (10.11) becomes

$$\ddot{y} + 0.04\,\dot{y} + 0.04\,y = 0\,. \tag{10.34}$$

The standard form of the differential equation of a second-order system is

$$\ddot{y} + 2\zeta\omega_n\,\dot{y} + \omega_n^2\,y = 0\,. \tag{10.35}$$

Therefore the undamped natural frequency ω_n and damping ratio ζ of the optimal system are

$$\omega_n = 0.2\,, \quad \zeta = 0.1\,. \tag{10.36}$$

According to Fig. 4.4 the step response of this system has a 73-percent overshoot. A system whose step response rings this badly does not seem like the best choice to minimize the displacement and velocity during its prescribed mission. If a_1 is increased, however, the damping ratio ζ becomes even smaller and the overshoot becomes worse. If a_1 is decreased, ζ increases, but ω_n decreases. Then the transient response is slower, and the performance index increases because it is an integral with respect to time. If a_2 is fixed at some value greater than 4, the damping ratio ζ of the optimal system is greater than 1, and the system is overdamped. An overdamped system seems too sluggish by classical standards to minimize the displacement and velocity during the mission.

Eq. (10.20) shows that the performance index is a function not only of the parameters in the controller, but also of the initial state. A controller that is designed to be the best for one mission may not be the best for another.

10.5 Controllability

A fundamental of modern control theory is the concept of *controllability*, introduced by R.E. Kalman in 1961. *A linear, fixed system is controllable iff a control vector* $\mathbf{u}(t)$ *can be found that will change the state from any initial value* $\mathbf{x}(0)$ *to any final value* $\mathbf{x}(T)$ *in a specified finite time* T. Inspection of the block diagram or equations does not always reveal whether a system is controllable. The usefulness of the concept is evident in the design of spaceships. A spaceship should be able to land, starting from wherever it is and whatever it is doing. It should be able to reach state $\mathbf{x}(T) = \mathbf{0}$ from any state $\mathbf{x}(0)$.

A method will now be derived, with which the designer can determine whether the system is controllable. The designer can make the final state $\mathbf{x}(T)$ zero without losing the generality of the definition of controllability. To show this, observe that the state equation of any linear, fixed plant is

$$\dot{\mathbf{x}} = \mathbf{A}\mathbf{x} + \mathbf{B}\mathbf{u} . \tag{10.4}$$

According to Eq. (9.72) the state of the system at any time T is

$$\mathbf{x}(T) = e^{\mathbf{A}T}\,\mathbf{x}(0) + \int_0^T e^{\mathbf{A}(T-x)}\,\mathbf{B}\,\mathbf{u}(x)\,dx . \tag{10.37}$$

Define a new initial state as

$$\mathbf{x}_1(0) = \mathbf{x}(0) - e^{-\mathbf{A}T}\,\mathbf{x}(T) \tag{10.38}$$

where $e^{-\mathbf{A}T}$ is the inverse of $e^{\mathbf{A}T}$. Now $\mathbf{x}_1(0)$ is as general as $\mathbf{x}(0)$. Eq. (10.37) can be written as

$$\mathbf{x}(T) = e^{\mathbf{A}T}\,[\mathbf{x}_1(0) + e^{-\mathbf{A}T}\,\mathbf{x}(T)] + \int_0^T e^{\mathbf{A}(T-x)}\,\mathbf{B}\,\mathbf{u}(x)\,dx \tag{10.39}$$

or

$$\mathbf{0} = e^{\mathbf{A}T}\,\mathbf{x}_1(0) + \int_0^T e^{\mathbf{A}(T-x)}\,\mathbf{B}\,\mathbf{u}(x)\,dx . \tag{10.40}$$

This equation shows that the same input that drives the system from the arbitrary state $\mathbf{x}_1(0)$ to the origin also drives the system between the two arbitrary states $\mathbf{x}(0)$ and $\mathbf{x}(T)$. Therefore the definition of controllability can be amended: a linear, fixed system is controllable iff a control vector $\mathbf{u}(t)$ can be found that will change the state from any initial value $\mathbf{x}_1(0)$ to the final value $\mathbf{x}(T) = \mathbf{0}$ in a specified finite time T. Now drop the subscript 1 in Eq. (10.40), and write

$$\mathbf{0} = e^{\mathbf{A}T}\,\mathbf{x}(0) + \int_0^T e^{\mathbf{A}(T-x)}\,\mathbf{B}\,\mathbf{u}(x)\,dx \tag{10.41}$$

or

$$\mathbf{x}(0) = -\int_0^T e^{-\mathbf{A}x}\,B\,\mathbf{u}(x)\,dx . \tag{10.42}$$

The next step makes use of the Cayley-Hamilton technique explained in Chapter 9. If the $\mathbf{A}$ matrix is of order n, the state-transition matrix is also of order n, and so is its inverse $e^{-\mathbf{A}x}$. According to the Cayley-Hamilton technique, the latter can be expressed as a polynomial of degree $n - 1$:

$$e^{-\mathbf{A}x} = \alpha_0(x)\mathbf{I} + \alpha_1(x)\mathbf{A} + \cdots + \alpha_{n-1}(x)\mathbf{A}^{n-1} . \tag{10.43}$$

Then

$$e^{-\mathbf{A}x}\,\mathbf{B} = \alpha_0\mathbf{B} + \alpha_1\mathbf{AB} + \cdots + \alpha_{n-1}\mathbf{A}^{n-1}\mathbf{B}$$
$$= \mathbf{B}\,\alpha_0\,\mathbf{I} + \mathbf{AB}\,\alpha_1\,\mathbf{I} + \cdots + \mathbf{A}^{n-1}\mathbf{B}\,\alpha_{n-1}\,\mathbf{I}\,. \tag{10.44}$$

If r is the number of control variables, $\mathbf{B}$ is an $n \times r$ matrix, and $\mathbf{I}$ in Eq. (10.44) is $r \times r$. This equation can be written like an inner product:

$$e^{-\mathbf{A}x}\,\mathbf{B} = [\mathbf{B}, \mathbf{AB}, \ldots, \mathbf{A}^{n-1}\mathbf{B}]\begin{bmatrix}\alpha_0\,\mathbf{I}\\ \alpha_1\,\mathbf{I}\\ \cdot\\ \cdot\\ \cdot\\ \alpha_{n-1}\,\mathbf{I}\end{bmatrix}. \tag{10.45}$$

The last step is possible because the first bracketed matrix on the right side of Eq. (10.45) can be partitioned into n submatrices, each $n \times r$, forming a $1 \times n$ row. In the second bracketed matrix, each $\alpha_i\mathbf{I}$ is an $r \times r$ matrix. This second matrix can be partitioned into n submatrices, each $r \times r$, forming an $n \times 1$ column. Since the submatrices of the two matrices are conformable, producing products that are $n \times r$, they can be multiplied as if they were scalar vector components. This multiplication converts Eq. (10.45) to Eq. (10.44).

If $\mathbf{C}(x)$ is the $nr \times r$ matrix

$$\mathbf{C}(x) = \begin{bmatrix}\alpha_0(x)\,\mathbf{I}\\ \alpha_1(x)\,\mathbf{I}\\ \cdot\\ \cdot\\ \cdot\\ \alpha_{n-1}(x)\,\mathbf{I}\end{bmatrix},$$

then

$$e^{-\mathbf{A}x}\,\mathbf{B} = [\mathbf{B}, \mathbf{AB}, \ldots, \mathbf{A}^{n-1}\,\mathbf{B}]\,\mathbf{C}(x) \tag{10.47}$$

and Eq. (10.42) becomes

$$\mathbf{x}(0) = -\int_0^T [\mathbf{B}, \mathbf{AB}, \ldots, \mathbf{A}^{n-1}\,\mathbf{B}]\,\mathbf{C}(x)\,\mathbf{u}(x)\,dx$$
$$= -\,[\mathbf{B}, \mathbf{AB}, \ldots, \mathbf{A}^{n-1}\,\mathbf{B}]\int_0^T \mathbf{C}(x)\,\mathbf{u}(x)\,dx\,. \tag{10.48}$$

The quantity

$$-\int_0^T \mathbf{C}(x)\,\mathbf{u}(x)\,dx$$

is an $nr \times 1$ column vector. The columns of

$$[\mathbf{B}, \mathbf{AB}, \ldots, \mathbf{A}^{n-1}\mathbf{B}]$$

constitute nr vectors, each $n \times 1$. If they span an n-dimensional space, they constitute a coordinate system in which the n-dimensional vector $\mathbf{x}(0)$ can be written, by the proper choice of components of the vector

$$-\int_0^T \mathbf{C}(x)\, \mathbf{u}(x)\, dx\,. \qquad (10.49)$$

If the nr vectors do not span an n-dimensional space, the vector $\mathbf{x}(0)$ might have a component in one of the dimensions not spanned. Then no value of vector (10.49) can be found that satisfies Eq. (10.48). Working backward thru the analysis shows that then no function $\mathbf{u}(x)$ can be found that satisfies Eq. (10.41). This means that the system cannot be driven from state $\mathbf{x}(0)$ to state $\mathbf{x}(T) = \mathbf{0}$. This reasoning has produced a criterion for controllability, in terms of the parameters of the system, that is useful to the designer: *a linear, fixed system is controllable iff the rank of the $n \times nr$ matrix* $[\mathbf{B}, \mathbf{AB}, \ldots, \mathbf{A}^{n-1}\mathbf{B}]$ *is n.*

10.6 Two Examples

To illustrate the usefulness of the criterion, determine whether the system in Fig. 10.5 is controllable. The equations describing the system are

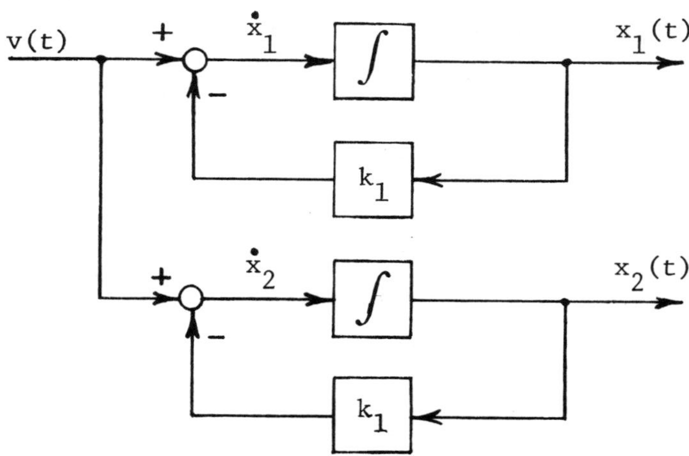

Fig. 10.5. An uncontrollable system.

$$\dot{x}_1 = v - k_1 x_1 \tag{10.50}$$

$$\dot{x}_2 = v - k_1 x_2 \,. \tag{10.51}$$

The state equation is

$$\begin{bmatrix} \dot{x}_1 \\ \dot{x}_2 \end{bmatrix} = \begin{bmatrix} -k_1 & 0 \\ 0 & -k_1 \end{bmatrix} \begin{bmatrix} x_1 \\ x_2 \end{bmatrix} + \begin{bmatrix} 1 \\ 1 \end{bmatrix} v \tag{10.52}$$

or

$$\dot{\mathbf{x}} = \mathbf{A}\mathbf{x} + \mathbf{B}\mathbf{v} \,, \tag{10.53}$$

and

$$[\mathbf{B}, \mathbf{AB}] = \begin{bmatrix} 1 & -k_1 \\ 1 & -k_1 \end{bmatrix} . \tag{10.54}$$

This matrix must have rank $n = 2$ if the system is controllable. However, the rank is only 1 and the system is not controllable. The reason can be seen physically by observing that the system consists of two identical subsystems driven by the same input. Their outputs at time T are

$$x_1(T) = e^{-k_1 T} x_1(0) + \int_0^T e^{-k_1(T-x)} v(x)\, dx \tag{10.55}$$

$$x_2(T) = e^{-k_1 T} x_2(0) + \int_0^T e^{-k_1(T-x)} v(x)\, dx \,. \tag{10.56}$$

The driven components of the two outputs are equal. Subtracting the second equation from the first shows that if the system is to reach the state $x_1(T)$, $x_2(T)$, the difference between the initial state variables must be

$$x_1(0) - x_2(0) = [x_1(T) - x_2(T)]e^{k_1 T} \,. \tag{10.57}$$

If the initial difference is anything else, the system cannot reach the desired destination.

Another example of the use of the controllability criterion is provided by the system in Fig. 10.6. The equations describing the system are

$$\dot{x}_1 = v_1 + k_2 v_2 - k_1 x_1 \tag{10.58}$$

$$\dot{x}_2 = v_2 - k_1 x_2 \,. \tag{10.59}$$

Therefore

$$\begin{bmatrix} \dot{x}_1 \\ \dot{x}_2 \end{bmatrix} = \begin{bmatrix} -k_1 & 0 \\ 0 & -k_1 \end{bmatrix} \begin{bmatrix} x_1 \\ x_2 \end{bmatrix} + \begin{bmatrix} 1 & k_2 \\ 0 & 1 \end{bmatrix} \begin{bmatrix} v_1 \\ v_2 \end{bmatrix} \tag{10.60}$$

or

$$\dot{\mathbf{x}} = \mathbf{A}\mathbf{x} + \mathbf{B}\mathbf{v} \,, \tag{10.61}$$

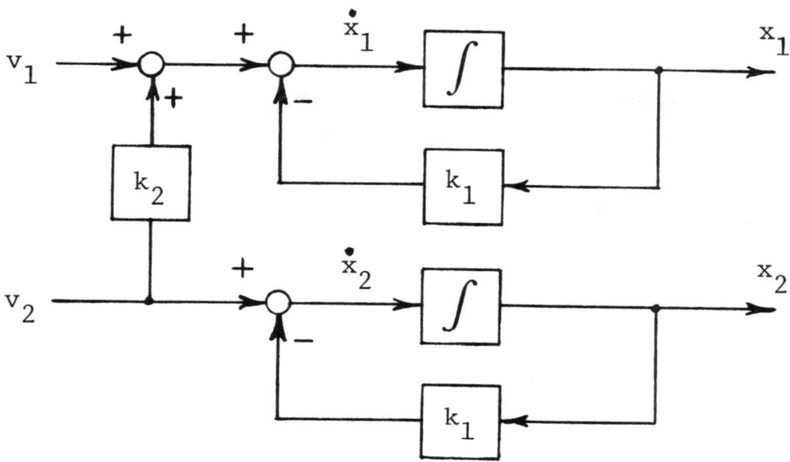

Fig. 10.6. A controllable system.

and

$$[\mathbf{B}, \mathbf{AB}] = \begin{bmatrix} 1 & k_2 & -k_1 & -k_1k_2 \\ 0 & 1 & 0 & -k_1 \end{bmatrix}, \tag{10.62}$$

whose columns span a two-dimensional space. This system is therefore controllable. The two drivers v_1 and v_2 can get the system from any state to any other. This chapter will avoid the general problem of choosing the input function $\mathbf{v}(t)$. For the example $v_2(t)$ could be any function such as a step that would move x_2 from $x_2(0)$ to the desired $x_2(T)$. The step required to change x_1 from $x_1(0)$ to $x_1(T)$ could then be calculated, and the step in k_2v_2 subtracted off to determine the required step of v_1.

10.7 Another View of Controllability

The requirement for controllability can be stated another convenient way, if the **A** matrix of the system has distinct eigenvalues. It then has a full set of eigenvectors $\mathbf{u}_i$ and a modal matrix

$$\mathbf{M} = [\mathbf{u}_1, \mathbf{u}_2, \ldots, \mathbf{u}_n]. \tag{10.63}$$

The eigenvectors constitute an n-dimensional coordinate system in which the state vector $\mathbf{x}$ can be expressed:

$$\mathbf{x} = \mathbf{u}_1q_1 + \mathbf{u}_2q_2 + \cdots + \mathbf{u}_nq_n = \mathbf{M}\,\mathbf{q}. \tag{10.64}$$

The distances q_i measured along the coordinate axes are the normal coordinates. Eq. (9.63) shows that the normal coordinates are functions of the initial state $\mathbf{x}(0)$ and the input vector $\mathbf{v}(t)$. The state equation is

$$\dot{\mathbf{x}} = \mathbf{A}\mathbf{x} + \mathbf{B}\mathbf{v}\,. \tag{10.65}$$

(If the controller is separate from the plant, $\mathbf{v}$ is replaced by the control vector $\mathbf{u}$, which should not be confused with the eigenvectors $\mathbf{u}_i$.) Substituting Eq. (10.64) into Eq. (10.65) produces

$$\mathbf{M}\,\dot{\mathbf{q}} = \mathbf{A}\,\mathbf{M}\,\mathbf{q} + \mathbf{B}\,\mathbf{v}\,. \tag{10.66}$$

Premultiplying by $\mathbf{M}^{-1}$ yields

$$\mathbf{M}^{-1}\,\mathbf{M}\,\dot{\mathbf{q}} = \mathbf{M}^{-1}\,\mathbf{A}\,\mathbf{M}\,\mathbf{q} + \mathbf{M}^{-1}\,\mathbf{B}\,\mathbf{v}\,. \tag{10.67}$$

Therefore

$$\dot{\mathbf{q}} = \mathbf{\Lambda}\,\mathbf{q} + \mathbf{M}^{-1}\,\mathbf{B}\,\mathbf{v} \tag{10.68}$$

or

$$\begin{bmatrix} \dot{q}_1 \\ \dot{q}_2 \\ \cdot \\ \cdot \\ \cdot \\ \dot{q}_n \end{bmatrix} = \begin{bmatrix} \lambda_1 & & & & \\ & \lambda_2 & & & \\ & & \cdot & & \\ & & & \cdot & \\ & & & & \cdot \\ & & & & & \lambda_n \end{bmatrix} \begin{bmatrix} q_1 \\ q_2 \\ \cdot \\ \cdot \\ \cdot \\ q_n \end{bmatrix} + [\mathbf{M}^{-1}\,\mathbf{B}] \begin{bmatrix} v_1 \\ v_2 \\ \cdot \\ \cdot \\ v_r \end{bmatrix} \tag{10.69}$$

where $\mathbf{\Lambda}$ is a diagonal $n \times n$ matrix, and $\mathbf{M}^{-1}\,\mathbf{B}$ is an $n \times r$ matrix. This matrix equation represents n scalar equations of the form

$$\dot{q}_i = \lambda_i\, q_i + < \mathbf{s}_i, \mathbf{v} > \tag{10.70}$$

where $\mathbf{s}_i$ is the ith row of $\mathbf{M}^{-1}\,\mathbf{B}$. The solution of this first-order ordinary differential equation is

$$q_i = e^{\lambda_i t}\, q_i(0) + < \mathbf{s}_i, \mathbf{v}(t) > * \, e^{\lambda_i t}\,. \tag{10.71}$$

The initial value $q_i(0)$, determined from Eq. (10.64), is

$$q_i(0) = < \mathbf{r}_i, \mathbf{x}(0) > \tag{10.72}$$

where $\mathbf{r}_i$ is the ith row of $\mathbf{M}^{-1}$. Eq. (10.71) is an alternate form of the bracketed term of Eq. (9.63). According to Eq. (10.64) the state $\mathbf{x}(t)$ is a vector sum of normal coordinates, each of which contains a driven and an undriven term. Now if the ith row of $\mathbf{M}^{-1}\mathbf{B}$ consists of zeros, Eq. (10.71) reduces to

$$q_i = e^{\lambda_i t}\, q_i(0) \tag{10.73}$$

and $\mathbf{x}(t)$ contains the term

$$\mathbf{u}_i\, e^{\lambda_i t}\, q_i(0) \tag{10.74}$$

which is called a *mode*, because it represents one of the n kinds of undriven response of the system. A mode does not die out to zero in a finite time. Since this mode is not accompanied by a driven term, it cannot be driven to zero. Furthermore, it cannot be canceled by the other terms in Eq. (10.64), to get the system to the state $\mathbf{x}(T) = \mathbf{0}$, because the eigenvectors are linearly independent.

An alternate criterion of controllability is now available for a linear, fixed system whose $\mathbf{A}$ matrix has distinct eigenvalues: *the system is controllable iff each row of* $\mathbf{M}^{-1}\mathbf{B}$ *has at least one non-zero element*. Ref. 21 (p. 350) states that if $\mathbf{A}$ has a repeated eigenvalue but is diagonalizable, this criterion is necessary but not sufficient.

10.8 The Output Vector

Related to *controllability* is *observability*. In general terms, an observable system is one whose state variables can either be measured, or calculated from other variables that can be measured. The concept is important because the designer needs to know whether all the state variables of a plant are available, before he can design the controller. In some systems such as the rotating kiln in a cement mill, not all of the state variables can be determined, and control is consequently more difficult. A simple example of a system whose state variables are not all measurable is shown in Fig. 10.1. A continuous record of the displacement $y(t)$ of the vibrating mass could be obtained by connecting a linear potentiometer between the mass and a stationary surface. The acceleration $\ddot{y}(t)$ could also be measured by mounting an accelerometer on the mass. The velocity $\dot{y}(t)$, however, could not be measured easily. The vector of the variables that are measured is called the *output vector* $\mathbf{y}(t)$. The analysis is restricted to linear, fixed plants whose output variables are linear combinations of the state and control variables. Then

$$\dot{\mathbf{x}} = \mathbf{A}\mathbf{x} + \mathbf{B}\mathbf{u} \tag{10.75}$$

and

$$\mathbf{y} = \mathbf{C}\mathbf{x} + \mathbf{D}\mathbf{u} \tag{10.76}$$

where $\mathbf{x}$ is $n \times 1$, $\mathbf{u}$ is $r \times 1$, $\mathbf{y}$ is $m \times 1$, $\mathbf{A}$ is $n \times n$, $\mathbf{B}$ is $n \times r$, $\mathbf{C}$ is $m \times n$, and $\mathbf{D}$ is $m \times r$. For example, for the system of Fig. 10.7,

$$\begin{bmatrix} \dot{x}_1 \\ \dot{x}_2 \\ \dot{x}_3 \end{bmatrix} = \begin{bmatrix} 0 & 1 & 0 \\ -5 & 1 & 4 \\ 1 & 0 & 0 \end{bmatrix} \begin{bmatrix} x_1 \\ x_2 \\ x_3 \end{bmatrix} + \begin{bmatrix} 0 & 0 \\ 2 & 0 \\ 0 & 3 \end{bmatrix} \begin{bmatrix} v_1 \\ v_2 \end{bmatrix} \tag{10.77}$$

and

$$\begin{bmatrix} y_1 \\ y_2 \end{bmatrix} = \begin{bmatrix} 0 & 1 & 0 \\ 1 & 0 & 0 \end{bmatrix} \begin{bmatrix} x_1 \\ x_2 \\ x_3 \end{bmatrix} + \begin{bmatrix} 6 & 0 \\ 0 & 1 \end{bmatrix} \begin{bmatrix} v_1 \\ v_2 \end{bmatrix}. \tag{10.78}$$

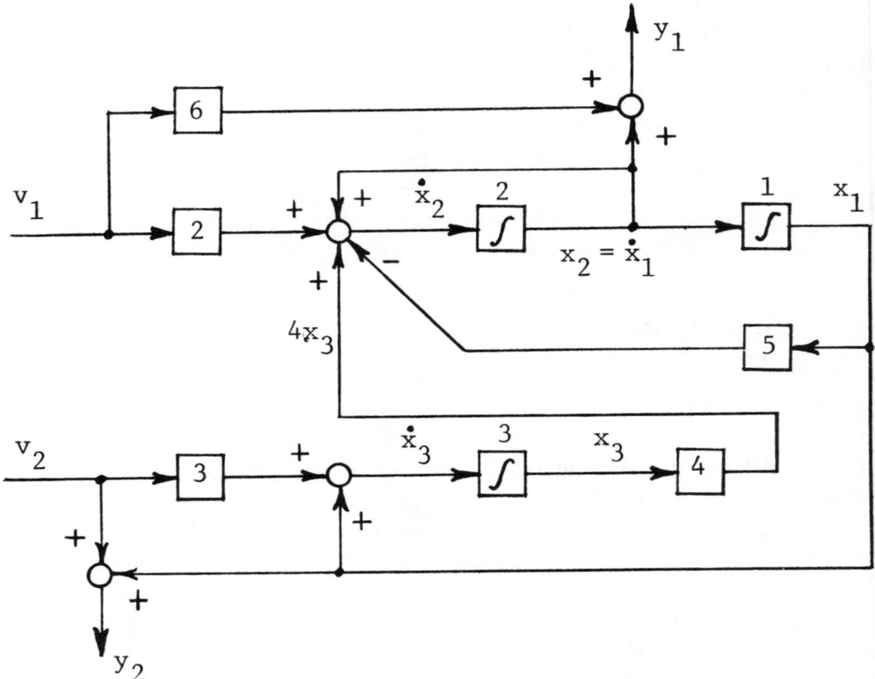

Fig. 10.7. An observable system.

Since all of this system is in the plant, the control vector **u** is the input vector **v**.

10.9 Observability

Specifically, *a system is said to be observable iff the initial state* $\mathbf{x}(0)$ *can be determined by measurement of the output vector* $\mathbf{y}(t)$ *and knowledge of the control vector* $\mathbf{u}(t)$ *during a finite interval* $0 \leqslant t \leqslant T$. If the only measured variable in Fig. 10.1 is the displacement y, and the system is observable (it is), the initial values $y(0)$ and $\dot{y}(0)$ of the state variables can both be determined by measuring $y(t)$ for a finite time. A criterion for observability in terms of the parameters of the system will be developed, starting with the state of a linear, fixed plant:

$$\mathbf{x}(t) = e^{\mathbf{A}t}\,\mathbf{x}(0) + \int_0^t e^{\mathbf{A}(t-x)}\,\mathbf{B}\,\mathbf{u}(x)\,dx\,. \tag{10.79}$$

According to Eq. (10.76),

$$\mathbf{y}(t) = \mathbf{C}\,e^{\mathbf{A}t}\,\mathbf{x}(0) + \mathbf{C}\int_0^t e^{\mathbf{A}(t-x)}\,\mathbf{B}\,\mathbf{u}(x)\,dx + \mathbf{D}\,\mathbf{u}(t)\,. \tag{10.80}$$

The second and third terms on the right are known, and can be subtracted from $\mathbf{y}(t)$ to produce

$$\mathbf{y}_1(t) = \mathbf{C}\, e^{\mathbf{A}t}\, \mathbf{x}(0)\,. \tag{10.81}$$

What are the conditions under which $\mathbf{x}(0)$ can be calculated from the known $\mathbf{y}_1(t)$? According to the Cayley-Hamilton technique,

$$e^{\mathbf{A}t} = \alpha_0(t)\,\mathbf{I} + \alpha_1(t)\,\mathbf{A} + \cdots + \alpha_{n-1}(t)\,\mathbf{A}^{n-1}\,. \tag{10.82}$$

Therefore

$$\begin{aligned}\mathbf{y}_1(t) &= \mathbf{C}[\alpha_0\,\mathbf{I} + \alpha_1\,\mathbf{A} + \cdots + \alpha_{n-1}\,\mathbf{A}^{n-1}]\mathbf{x}(0)\\ &= [\alpha_0\,\mathbf{I}\,\mathbf{C} + \alpha_1\,\mathbf{I}\,\mathbf{C}\,\mathbf{A} + \cdots + \alpha_{n-1}\mathbf{I}\,\mathbf{C}\,\mathbf{A}^{n-1}]\mathbf{x}(0)\end{aligned} \tag{10.83}$$

where $\mathbf{I}$ is an $m \times m$ unit matrix. The terms in the brackets constitute the inner product of two partitioned matrices:

$$\alpha_0\,\mathbf{I}\,\mathbf{C} + \alpha_1\,\mathbf{I}\,\mathbf{C}\,\mathbf{A} + \cdots + \alpha_{n-1}\,\mathbf{I}\,\mathbf{C}\,\mathbf{A}^{n-1}$$

$$= \Bigg[\underbrace{\begin{matrix}\alpha_0 & & & \\ & \alpha_0 & & \\ & & \ddots & \\ & & & \alpha_0\end{matrix}}_{m}\;\Bigg|\;\begin{matrix}\alpha_1 & & & \\ & \alpha_1 & & \\ & & \ddots & \\ & & & \alpha_1\end{matrix}\;\Bigg|\;\begin{matrix}\alpha_2 & & \\ & \ddots & \\ & & \ddots\end{matrix}\Bigg]\begin{bmatrix}\mathbf{C}\\ \hline \mathbf{CA}\\ \hline \vdots\\ \hline \mathbf{CA}^{n-1}\end{bmatrix} \tag{10.84}$$

in which each submatrix of the first matrix is $m \times m$, and each submatrix of the second matrix is $m \times n$. Therefore

$$\mathbf{y}_1(t) = [\alpha_0(t)\,\mathbf{I}, \alpha_1(t)\,\mathbf{I}, \ldots, \alpha_{n-1}(t)\,\mathbf{I}]\mathbf{E}\,\mathbf{x}(0)\,, \tag{10.85}$$

where

$$\mathbf{E} = \begin{bmatrix}\mathbf{C}\\ \mathbf{CA}\\ \vdots\\ \mathbf{CA}^{n-1}\end{bmatrix} \tag{10.86}$$

is an $mn \times n$ matrix. If the rows of $\mathbf{E}$ do not span an n-dimensional space, $\mathbf{x}(0)$ might lie in their null space and be orthogonal to all of them. An infinite number of state $\mathbf{x}(0)$ can lie in the null space, any of which produces

$$\mathbf{E}\,\mathbf{x}(0) = \mathbf{0} \tag{10.87}$$

and therefore

$$\mathbf{y}_1(t) = \mathbf{0} \tag{10.88}$$

for all subsequent values of t. This output vector does not allow identification of the initial state $\mathbf{x}(0)$, and the system is not observable.

If the rows of $\mathbf{E}$ *do* span n space, Eq. (10.85) represents m equations in the n elements $x_i(0)$:

$$\begin{aligned} y_1(t) &= a_{11}\,x_1(0) + a_{12}\,x_2(0) + \cdots + a_{1n}\,x_n(0) \\ y_2(t) &= a_{21}\,x_1(0) + a_{22}\,x_2(0) + \cdots + a_{2n}\,x_n(0) \\ &\vdots \\ y_m(t) &= a_{m1}\,x_1(0) + a_{m2}\,x_2(0) + \cdots + a_{mn}\,x_n(0)\,. \end{aligned} \tag{10.89}$$

The coefficients a_{ij} can be calculated. The $y_i(t)$'s are obtained by measuring $\mathbf{y}_1(t)$ at a given time. If $m < n$, the $n - m$ extra equations needed to solve for the $x_i(0)$'s can be obtained by calculating $\mathbf{y}_1(t)$ at a different time.

A workable criterion of observability is now apparent: *a fixed, linear system is observable iff the rank of the $mn \times n$ matrix*

$$\begin{bmatrix} \mathbf{C} \\ \mathbf{CA} \\ \cdot \\ \cdot \\ \cdot \\ \mathbf{CA}^{n-1} \end{bmatrix}$$

is n.

10.10 An Example

To illustrate the use of the criterion, find out if the system of Fig. 10.7 is observable. According to Eqs. (10.78) and (10.77),

$$\mathbf{C} = \begin{bmatrix} 0 & 1 & 0 \\ 1 & 0 & 0 \end{bmatrix}, \qquad \mathbf{A} = \begin{bmatrix} 0 & 1 & 0 \\ -5 & 1 & 4 \\ 1 & 0 & 0 \end{bmatrix}, \tag{10.90}$$

$$\mathbf{CA} = \begin{bmatrix} 0 & 1 & 0 \\ 1 & 0 & 0 \end{bmatrix} \begin{bmatrix} 0 & 1 & 0 \\ -5 & 1 & 4 \\ 1 & 0 & 0 \end{bmatrix} = \begin{bmatrix} -5 & 1 & 4 \\ 0 & 1 & 4 \end{bmatrix}, \tag{10.91}$$

and

$$\mathbf{CA}^2 = \begin{bmatrix} -5 & 1 & 4 \\ 0 & 1 & 0 \end{bmatrix} \begin{bmatrix} 0 & 1 & 0 \\ -5 & 1 & 4 \\ 1 & 0 & 0 \end{bmatrix} = \begin{bmatrix} -1 & -4 & 4 \\ -5 & 1 & 4 \end{bmatrix}. \tag{10.92}$$

Then

$$\begin{bmatrix} \mathbf{C} \\ \mathbf{CA} \\ \mathbf{CA}^2 \end{bmatrix} = \begin{bmatrix} 0 & 1 & 0 \\ 1 & 0 & 0 \\ -5 & 1 & 4 \\ 0 & 1 & 0 \\ -1 & -4 & 4 \\ -5 & 1 & 4 \end{bmatrix}, \tag{10.93}$$

whose rank is 3. The system is therefore observable. Any state $\mathbf{x}(0)$ can be determined by measuring $y_1(t)$ and $y_2(t)$, together with the inputs $v_1(t)$ and $v_2(t)$.

If the wire carrying the signal $4x_3$ in Fig. 10.7 is cut, the $\mathbf{A}$ matrix becomes

$$\mathbf{A} = \begin{bmatrix} 0 & 1 & 0 \\ -5 & 1 & 0 \\ 1 & 0 & 0 \end{bmatrix}. \tag{10.94}$$

Then

$$\mathbf{CA} = \begin{bmatrix} 0 & 1 & 0 \\ 1 & 0 & 0 \end{bmatrix} \begin{bmatrix} 0 & 1 & 0 \\ -5 & 1 & 0 \\ 1 & 0 & 0 \end{bmatrix} = \begin{bmatrix} -5 & 1 & 0 \\ 0 & 1 & 0 \end{bmatrix}, \tag{10.95}$$

$$\mathbf{CA}^2 = \begin{bmatrix} -5 & 1 & 0 \\ 0 & 1 & 0 \end{bmatrix} \begin{bmatrix} 0 & 1 & 0 \\ -5 & 1 & 0 \\ 1 & 0 & 0 \end{bmatrix} = \begin{bmatrix} -5 & -4 & 0 \\ -5 & 1 & 0 \end{bmatrix}, \tag{10.96}$$

and

$$\begin{bmatrix} \mathbf{C} \\ \mathbf{CA} \\ \mathbf{CA}^2 \end{bmatrix} = \begin{bmatrix} 0 & 1 & 0 \\ 1 & 0 & 0 \\ -5 & 1 & 0 \\ 0 & 1 & 0 \\ -5 & -4 & 0 \\ -5 & 1 & 0 \end{bmatrix}, \tag{10.97}$$

whose rank is 2. The system is now unobservable. Physically, the reason is that $x_3(t)$ does not appear in either measured variable, $y_1(t)$ or $y_2(t)$.

10.11 Another View of Observability

If the $\mathbf{A}$ matrix of a linear, fixed system has distinct eigenvalues and therefore a full set of eigenvectors $\mathbf{u}_i$, the criterion for observability can be stated in another convenient form. The normal coordinates q_i are defined by Eq. (10.64):

$$\mathbf{x} = \mathbf{M}\,\mathbf{q} = \mathbf{u}_1\, q_1(t) + \mathbf{u}_2\, q_2(t) + \cdots + \mathbf{u}_n\, q_n(t)\,. \tag{10.64}$$

Substitute this form into Eq. (10.76) to express the output vector $\mathbf{y}$ in terms of the normal coordinates:

$$\mathbf{y} = \mathbf{C}\,\mathbf{M}\,\mathbf{q} + \mathbf{D}\,\mathbf{u}\,. \tag{10.98}$$

If the columns of $\mathbf{C}\ \mathbf{M}$ are called $\mathbf{b}_i$, then

$$\begin{aligned}\mathbf{y}(t) &= [\mathbf{b}_1, \mathbf{b}_2, \ldots, \mathbf{b}_n]\mathbf{q} + \mathbf{D}\,\mathbf{u} \\ &= \mathbf{b}_1\, q_1(t) + \mathbf{b}_2\, q_2(t) + \cdots + \mathbf{b}_n\, q_n(t) + \mathbf{D}\,\mathbf{u}\,.\end{aligned} \tag{10.99}$$

If a column of $\mathbf{C}\ \mathbf{M}$ consists of zeros, say the ith column, the normal coordinate $q_i(t)$ does not appear in any component of $\mathbf{y}$. Since $q_i(t)$, which is also a component of $\mathbf{x}(t)$, cannot be observed, the state vector cannot be determined. *For a fixed, linear system whose* $\mathbf{A}$ *matrix has distinct eigenvalues, a necessary and sufficient condition for observability is that each column of the* $m \times n$ *matrix* $\mathbf{C}\ \mathbf{M}$ *contain at least one non-zero element.* A shrewd reader will observe that the analysis has proved the necessity of this condition, but not its sufficiency.

This chapter has discussed controllability, observability, and one method for minimizing the performance index of a system. The method requires that the system have a controller of fixed structure, and that the mission be of infinite duration. The next chapter will explain a method that does not have these limitations. Instead, the method produces an optimal control law whose form suggests the design of the controller, and the mission can be of any duration.

Chapter 11

THE USE OF VARIATIONAL CALCULUS IN OPTIMAL CONTROL

11.1 Introduction

The field of optimal control offers splendid opportunities for the mathematical techniques of optimization developed in the past, and has inspired the development of new techniques such as the maximum principle of Pontryagin, and dynamic programming by Richard Bellman. In recent years the literature has exploded with analyses of optimization with various performance indices, random inputs, noise in the system, limits on the variables, nonlinear components, unobservable state variables, etc. The theory is ahead of practice. Still to be completed is the educators' job of sifting thru this vast pile of ideas to find the significant ones, and fitting them together into an organized package of knowledge for use by the designers of control-system hardware. The following chapter is offered to give the engineer a better understanding of the concepts of optimal control, and to show how one of the old optimization techniques, the calculus of variations, is used to solve modern control problems.

11.2 Performance Indices Are Functionals

The application of the calculus of variations to optimal control is natural because the problem of minimizing an integral performance index is the same as the problem for which variational calculus was invented by Leonhard Euler over 200 years ago. Consider the task of driving the system in Fig. 11.1 with the control variable u from a given

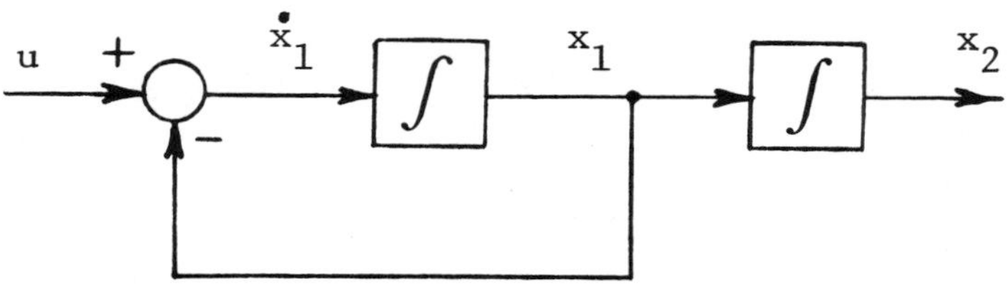

Fig. 11.1. System to be controlled.

state $\mathbf{x}(0)$ to a final state $\mathbf{x}(\infty) = \mathbf{0}$ while minimizing the performance index

$$J = \int_0^\infty (x_2^2 + 0.1\, u^2)dt\,. \tag{11.1}$$

The equations describing the systems are

$$\dot{x}_2 = x_1 \tag{11.2}$$

$$\dot{x}_1 = u - x_1\,. \tag{11.3}$$

This is a typical optimal-control problem. The performance index is an example of the very general form

$$J = \int_{t_1}^{t_2} F(\mathbf{x}, \dot{\mathbf{x}}, \mathbf{u}, \dot{\mathbf{u}}, \mathbf{v}, \dot{\mathbf{v}}, t)dt \tag{11.4}$$

where $\mathbf{x}$, $\mathbf{u}$, and $\mathbf{v}$ are the vectors of state variables, control variables, and external inputs, and F is a scalar function of the elements of the vectors. The need for the derivatives of the vectors will become apparent later. Time t may or may not appear explicitly in Eq. (11.4) which might, for example, be

$$J = \int_{t_1}^{t_2} (x_1^2 + x_2^2 + u^2)dt\,. \tag{11.5}$$

For simplicity, lump $\mathbf{x}$, $\mathbf{u}$, and $\mathbf{v}$ into one $n \times 1$ vector $\mathbf{y}$. Then

$$J = \int_{t_1}^{t_2} F(\mathbf{y}, \dot{\mathbf{y}}, t)dt\,. \tag{11.6}$$

The scalar version of this equation is

$$J = \int_{t_1}^{t_2} F(y, \dot{y}, t)dt\,. \tag{11.7}$$

The problem of finding the extreme value, maximum or minimum, of this integral between the known boundaries $y(t_1) = y_1$ and $y(t_2) = y_2$ is called the fundamental problem of the calculus of variations.

Notice that the integral J in Eq. (11.7) is not a function of time. If a function $y(t)$ is inserted into the integral, a numerical value of J can be calculated. The integral is called a *functional*, namely a process that assigns numbers to functions. The purpose of variational calculus is to determine the function that produces the extreme value of a functional. Proving that the extreme value is a maximum or a minimum is difficult, and fortunately is frequently unnecessary because the physical picture is clear. The following analysis will show how to find the optimal function $y(t)$ that minimizes J in Eq. (11.7), and then the functions $y_1(t)$, $y_2(t), \ldots, y_n(t)$ that constitute the optimal vector $\mathbf{y}$ in Eq. (11.6). The method of calculating these functions will even produce the design of the optimal controller for some systems, that generates the optimal functions and minimizes the performance index.

11.3 The Euler-Lagrange Equation

First find the function $y(t)$ that minimizes the integral of Eq. (11.7) and satisfies the known boundary conditions $y(t_1) = y_1$ and $y(t_2) = y_2$. Suppose that the optimal function $y_o(t)$ has the curve shown in Fig. 11.2. Choose any smooth function $n(t)$ that is zero at t_1 and t_2, and plot $y_o(t) + \varepsilon\, n(t)$, where ε is a constant. The increment $\varepsilon\, n(t)$ is called a *variation* of $y_o(t)$. The function $y_o(t) + \varepsilon\, n(t)$, represented by the dotted line, is not the optimal, and the integral

$$J = \int_{t_1}^{t_2} F(y_o + \varepsilon n, \dot{y}_o + \varepsilon \dot{n}, t)dt \tag{11.8}$$

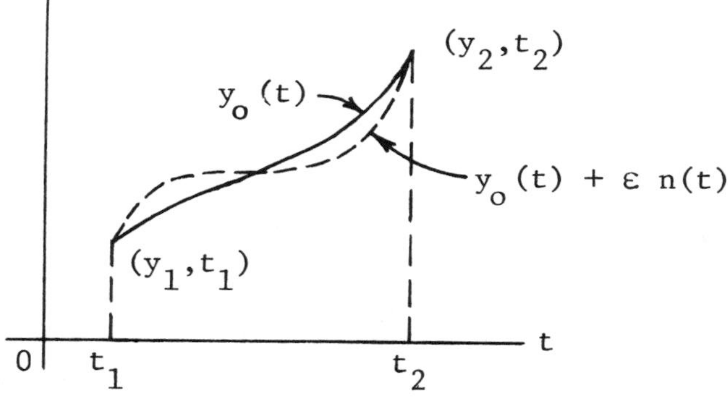

Fig. 11.2. Derivation of the Euler-Lagrange Equation.

is not the minimum unless $\varepsilon = 0$. Thus when $\varepsilon = 0$,

$$\frac{dJ}{d\varepsilon} = 0\,. \tag{11.9}$$

Since in general

$$y = y_o + \varepsilon n \qquad \text{and} \qquad \dot{y} = \dot{y}_o + \varepsilon \dot{n}\,, \tag{11.10}$$

$$\begin{aligned} \frac{dF}{d\varepsilon} &= \frac{\partial F}{\partial y}\frac{dy}{d\varepsilon} + \frac{\partial F}{\partial \dot{y}}\frac{d\dot{y}}{d\varepsilon} + \frac{\partial F}{\partial t}\frac{dt}{d\varepsilon} \\ &= \frac{\partial F}{\partial y} n + \frac{\partial F}{\partial \dot{y}} \dot{n}\,. \end{aligned} \tag{11.11}$$

The derivative of Eq. (11.7) is therefore

$$\frac{dJ}{d\varepsilon} = \frac{d}{d\varepsilon}\int_{t_1}^{t_2} F\,dt = \int_{t_1}^{t_2} \frac{dF}{d\varepsilon}\,dt$$

$$= \int_{t_1}^{t_2} \left(\frac{\partial F}{\partial y}\,n + \frac{\partial F}{\partial \dot{y}}\,\dot{n}\right) dt\,. \tag{11.12}$$

According to Eqs. (11.12) and (11.9), the condition for minimizing J is

$$\int_{t_1}^{t_2} \left(\frac{\partial F}{\partial y}\,n + \frac{\partial F}{\partial \dot{y}}\,\dot{n}\right) dt = 0\,. \tag{11.13}$$

The function $y(t)$ that minimizes J satisfies this condition. To eliminate the function n, first integrate the second term by parts:

$$\int_{t_1}^{t_2} \frac{\partial F}{\partial \dot{y}}\,\dot{n}\,dt = n\,\frac{\partial F}{\partial \dot{y}}\bigg|_{t_1}^{t_2} - \int_{t_1}^{t_2} n\,\frac{d}{dt}\left(\frac{\partial F}{\partial \dot{y}}\right) dt\,. \tag{11.14}$$

The function $n(t)$ was chosen so that $n(t_1) = n(t_2) = 0$. Therefore the first term on the right side of Eq. (11.14) is zero. Eq. (11.13) can now be written as

$$\int_{t_1}^{t_2} \left[\frac{\partial F}{\partial y} - \frac{d}{dt}\left(\frac{\partial F}{\partial \dot{y}}\right)\right] n\,dt = 0\,. \tag{11.15}$$

Since n is an arbitrary function, the quantity in brackets must be zero:

$$\frac{\partial F}{\partial y} - \frac{d}{dt}\left(\frac{\partial F}{\partial \dot{y}}\right) = 0\,. \tag{11.16}$$

This is the *Euler-Lagrange equation*, another statement of the condition that must be fulfilled by the function $y(t)$ that minimizes the functional J. To put the condition into still another useful form, observe that according to Eq. (11.7), F is a function of y, $\dot{y}$, and t. Therefore in general $\partial F/\partial \dot{y}$ is also a function of y, $\dot{y}$, and t, and

$$\frac{d}{dt}\left(\frac{\partial F}{\partial \dot{y}}\right) = \frac{\partial}{\partial y}\left(\frac{\partial F}{\partial \dot{y}}\right)\frac{dy}{dt} + \frac{\partial}{\partial \dot{y}}\left(\frac{\partial F}{\partial \dot{y}}\right)\frac{d\dot{y}}{dt} + \frac{\partial}{\partial t}\left(\frac{\partial F}{\partial \dot{y}}\right). \tag{11.17}$$

If $\partial F/\partial y$ is written as F_y, etc., Eq. (11.16) becomes

$$F_{\dot{y}\dot{y}}\frac{d^2y}{dt^2} + F_{y\dot{y}}\frac{dy}{dt} + (F_{\dot{y}t} - F_y) = 0\,. \tag{11.18}$$

In this form, the condition on $y(t)$ is seen to be a second-order differential equation whose coefficients are known. The optimal function $y(t)$ is the solution of the differential equation whose two arbitrary constants are chosen to satisfy the two boundary conditions $y(t_1) = y_1$ and $y(t_2) = y_2$.

The differential equation (11.18) derived by variational calculus has two properties of great importance to the design of optimal controllers. First, suppose that the functional J is a quadratic function of y and $\dot{y}$:

$$J = \int_{t_1}^{t_2} F\,dt = \int_{t_1}^{t_2} [k_1 y + k_2 y^2 + k_3 \dot{y} + k_4 \dot{y}^2 + f(t]dt \qquad (11.19)$$

where $f(t)$ is any function of time. Then

$$F_y = k_1 + 2k_2 y \qquad (11.20)$$

$$F_{\dot{y}\dot{y}} = 2k_4 \qquad (11.21)$$

$$F_{\dot{y}t} = F_{y\dot{y}} = 0 \qquad (11.22)$$

and Eq. (11.18) is linear with constant coefficients. This fact is a strong argument for quadratic performance indices. The linear Euler-Lagrange equations are not only easier to solve, but also permit the design of simple controllers.

The second important property of Eq. (11.18) is the fact that its boundary conditions $y(t_1)$ and $y(t_2)$ are at opposite ends of the path of $y(t)$. This is called a *two-point boundary-value problem.* Even if the differential equation is linear with constant coefficients, the two constants of integration cannot be evaluated by Laplace transforms. Analytical solutions of two-point boundary-value problems are possible only in special cases, and trial-and-error solutions must frequently be used.

11.4 The Vector Euler-Lagrange Equation

Now the analysis can go a step farther and find the functions $y_1(t)$, $y_2(t), \ldots, y_n(t)$ that minimize the more general functional of Eq. (11.6), namely

$$J = \int_{t_1}^{t_2} F(\mathbf{y}, \dot{\mathbf{y}}, t)dt$$

$$= \int_{t_1}^{t_2} F(y_1, \dot{y}_1, y_2, \dot{y}_2, \ldots, y_n, \dot{y}_n, t)dt\,. \qquad (11.23)$$

If J is the performance index of a system, the functions $y_i(t)$ are interrelated by the equations describing the system. For the present, assume that the $y_i(t)$'s are independent of each other. Introduce n smooth, arbitrary functions $n_1(t), n_2(t), \ldots, n_n(t)$, all of which are zero at t_1 and t_2. Because the $y_i(t)$'s can be varied independently, write

$$y_i(t) = y_{oi}(t) + \varepsilon\, n_i(t) \qquad (11.24)$$

where $y_{oi}(t)$ is the optimal form of the function $y_i(t)$, and the independence of $y_i(t)$ is represented by the arbitrary $n_i(t)$. When $\varepsilon = 0$, J has its minimum value and $dJ/d\varepsilon = 0$. Extending the previous analysis, write

$$\frac{dF}{d\varepsilon} = \frac{\partial F}{\partial y_1}\frac{dy_1}{d\varepsilon} + \frac{\partial F}{\partial \dot{y}_1}\frac{d\dot{y}_1}{d\varepsilon} + \frac{\partial F}{\partial y_2}\frac{dy_2}{d\varepsilon} + \frac{\partial F}{\partial \dot{y}_2}\frac{d\dot{y}_2}{d\varepsilon} + \cdots$$

$$= \left(\frac{\partial F}{\partial y_1} n_1 + \frac{\partial F}{\partial \dot{y}_1}\dot{n}_1\right) + \left(\frac{\partial F}{\partial y_2} n_2 + \frac{\partial F}{\partial \dot{y}_2}\dot{n}_2\right) + \cdots \tag{11.25}$$

Follow the previous steps to arrive at the equation

$$\int_{t_1}^{t_2} \left[\left\{\frac{\partial F}{\partial y_1} - \frac{d}{dt}\left(\frac{\partial F}{\partial \dot{y}_1}\right)\right\} n_1 + \left\{\frac{\partial F}{\partial y_2} - \frac{d}{dt}\left(\frac{\partial F}{\partial \dot{y}_2}\right)\right\} n_2 + \cdots\right] dt = 0 \,. \tag{11.26}$$

Since the functions $n_i(t)$ are arbitrary, each bracketed term must be zero:

$$\frac{\partial F}{\partial y_i} - \frac{d}{dt}\left(\frac{\partial F}{\partial \dot{y}_i}\right) = 0 \,, \qquad i = 1, 2, \ldots, n \,. \tag{11.27}$$

Thus the performance index of Eq. (11.6) is minimized when each of the n state, control, and external variables in it satisfies an Euler-Lagrange equation. The n equations (11.27) can be written as one with the help of the gradient operators ∇_y and $\nabla_{\dot{y}}$ defined by

$$\nabla_y F = \begin{bmatrix} \dfrac{\partial F}{\partial y_1} \\ \dfrac{\partial F}{\partial y_2} \\ \cdot \\ \cdot \\ \cdot \\ \dfrac{\partial F}{\partial y_n} \end{bmatrix} \qquad \nabla_{\dot{y}} F = \begin{bmatrix} \dfrac{\partial F}{\partial \dot{y}_1} \\ \dfrac{\partial F}{\partial \dot{y}_2} \\ \cdot \\ \cdot \\ \cdot \\ \dfrac{\partial F}{\partial \dot{y}_n} \end{bmatrix} . \tag{11.28}$$

The n scalar equations are all included in the vector form of the Euler-Lagrange equation

$$\nabla_y F - \frac{d}{dt}(\nabla_{\dot{y}} F) = \mathbf{0} \,. \tag{11.29}$$

11.5 Lagrange Multipliers

The analysis has shown how to calculate the functions $y_i(t)$ that minimize the performance index of a system, but has not yet recognized that these functions are interrelated by the equations describing the system, summarized in the state equation

$$\dot{\mathbf{x}} = \mathbf{A}\mathbf{x} + \mathbf{B}\mathbf{u} . \tag{11.30}$$

When these constraints on the functions are included, the performance index can still be minimized, but the minimum will in general be larger than it was. A straightforward way of accounting for the constraints is provided by the method of Lagrange multipliers. To investigate the method, solve a simple problem that is unrelated to control systems.

The height of a surface above the y_1y_2 plane in Fig. 11.3 is

$$f = (y_1 - 3)^2 + (y_2 - 2)^2 . \tag{11.31}$$

Where is the lowest point on the surface? When f is at its extreme value, which is obviously a minimum,

$$df = \frac{\partial f}{\partial y_1} dy_1 + \frac{\partial f}{\partial y_2} dy_2 = 0 . \tag{11.32}$$

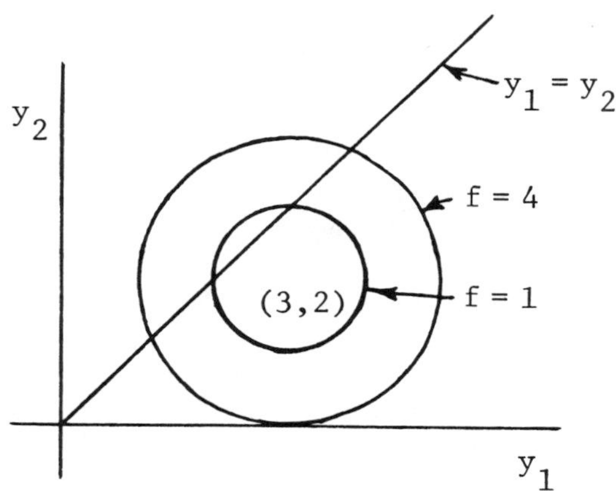

Fig. 11.3. Example of minimizing a function subject to a constraint.

Since dy_1 and dy_2 can be varied independently,

$$\frac{\partial f}{\partial y_1} = 0 \qquad \text{and} \qquad \frac{\partial f}{\partial y_2} = 0 . \tag{11.33}$$

Therefore

$$2(y_1 - 3) = 0 \qquad \text{and} \qquad 2(y_2 - 2) = 0 \tag{11.34}$$

and the minimum height is $f = 0$, occurring at $y_1 = 3$, $y_2 = 2$.

Now find the lowest point on the path $y_2 = y_1$. In other words, find the minimum of f, subject to the constraint

$$\phi = y_1 - y_2 = 0 \,. \tag{11.35}$$

The constraint could be used to eliminate one of the variables in Eq. (11.31), say y_2, and the resulting equation differentiated to solve for y_1. This method is awkward if there are several variables and several constraint equations. A simpler procedure consists of first calculating the total differential of ϕ:

$$d\phi = \frac{\partial \phi}{\partial y_1}\, dy_1 + \frac{\partial \phi}{\partial y_2}\, dy_2 = 0 \,. \tag{11.36}$$

Then multiply each term by a new variable λ, called a *Lagrange multiplier*, and write

$$df + \lambda\, d\phi = \left(\frac{\partial f}{\partial y_1} + \lambda \frac{\partial \phi}{\partial y_1}\right) dy_1 + \left(\frac{\partial f}{\partial y_2} + \lambda \frac{\partial \phi}{\partial y_2}\right) dy_2 = 0 \,. \tag{11.37}$$

Now arbitrarily choose λ to be the function that makes one of the quantities in parentheses vanish. Then

$$\frac{\partial f}{\partial y_1} + \lambda \frac{\partial \phi}{\partial y_1} = 0 \,. \tag{11.38}$$

Since dy_2 can be chosen arbitrarily,

$$\frac{\partial f}{\partial y_2} + \lambda \frac{\partial \phi}{\partial y_2} = 0 \,. \tag{11.39}$$

These two equations plus the constraint, Eq. (11.35), constitute three equations in the three unknowns y_1, y_2, and λ. The solution satisfies Eq. (11.37), and because $d\phi$ is zero, it also satisfies the condition for a minimum, namely $df = 0$. It also satisfies the constraint, and is therefore the desired solution, namely the location of the lowest point on the path $y_2 = y_1$.

Notice that the three equations (11.38), (11.39), and (11.35) are also obtained by calculating the minimum of $f + \lambda\phi$ with y_1, y_2, and λ treated as independent variables. That is,

$$\frac{\partial (f + \lambda\phi)}{\partial y_1} = \frac{\partial f}{\partial y_1} + \lambda \frac{\partial \phi}{\partial y_1} = 0 \tag{11.40}$$

$$\frac{\partial (f + \lambda\phi)}{\partial y_2} = \frac{\partial f}{\partial y_2} + \lambda \frac{\partial \phi}{\partial y_2} = 0 \tag{11.41}$$

$$\frac{\partial (f + \lambda\phi)}{\partial \lambda} = \phi = 0 \,. \tag{11.42}$$

For the example,

$$f + \lambda\phi = (y_1 - 3)^2 + (y_2 - 2)^2 + \lambda(y_1 - y_2)\,. \tag{11.43}$$

Then

$$\frac{\partial(f + \lambda\phi)}{\partial y_1} = 2(y_1 - 3) + \lambda = 0 \tag{11.44}$$

$$\frac{\partial(f + \lambda\phi)}{\partial y_2} = 2(y_2 - 2) - \lambda = 0 \tag{11.45}$$

$$\frac{\partial(f + \lambda\phi)}{\partial \lambda} = y_1 - y_2 = 0\,, \tag{11.46}$$

which yield

$$y_1 = \frac{5}{2}\,, \quad y_2 = \frac{5}{2}\,, \quad \lambda = 1\,. \tag{11.47}$$

These values locate the bottom of the path, whose height is

$$f = \left(\frac{5}{2} - 3\right)^2 + \left(\frac{5}{2} - 2\right)^2 = \frac{1}{2}\,. \tag{11.48}$$

The numerical value of the Lagrange multiplier has no physical significance in this problem.

The method of Lagrange multipliers works equally well for finding the minimum of a function $f(y_1, y_2, \ldots, y_n)$ of n variables, subject to m constraints, where $m < n$:

$$\phi_i(y_1, y_2, \ldots, y_n) = 0\,, \qquad i = 1, 2, \ldots, m\,. \tag{11.49}$$

Now

$$df = \frac{\partial f}{\partial y_1}\,dy_1 + \frac{\partial f}{\partial y_2}\,dy_2 + \cdots + \frac{\partial f}{\partial y_n}\,dy_n \tag{11.50}$$

and

$$d\phi_i = \frac{\partial \phi_i}{\partial y_1}\,dy_1 + \frac{\partial \phi_i}{\partial y_2}\,dy_2 + \cdots + \frac{\partial \phi_i}{\partial y_n}\,dy_n = 0\,, \qquad i = 1, 2, \ldots, m\,. \tag{11.51}$$

Multiply each constraint by its own Lagrange multiplier λ_i. Then when f is at its minimum, $df = 0$ and

$$df + \lambda_1\,d\phi_1 + \lambda_2\,d\phi_2 + \cdots + \lambda_m\,d\phi_m = 0 \tag{11.52}$$

or

$$\left(\frac{\partial f}{\partial y_1} + \lambda_1\,\frac{\partial \phi_1}{\partial y_1} + \lambda_2\,\frac{\partial \phi_2}{\partial y_1} + \cdots + \lambda_m\,\frac{\partial \phi_m}{\partial y_1}\right) dy_1$$

$$+\left(\frac{\partial f}{\partial y_2}+\lambda_1\frac{\partial \phi_1}{\partial y_2}+\lambda_2\frac{\partial \phi_2}{\partial y_2}+\cdots+\lambda_m\frac{\partial \phi_m}{\partial y_2}\right)dy_2$$

$$+\cdots$$

$$+\left(\frac{\partial f}{\partial y_n}+\lambda_1\frac{\partial \phi_1}{\partial y_n}+\lambda_2\frac{\partial \phi_2}{\partial y_n}+\cdots+\lambda_m\frac{\partial \phi_m}{\partial y_n}\right)dy_n=0\,. \qquad (11.53)$$

Now choose the functions λ_1 thru λ_m to make the first m of the quantities in parentheses zero. The remaining $n - m$ terms of Eq. (11.53) are

$$(\quad)\,dy_{m+1}+(\quad)\,dy_{m+2}+\cdots+(\quad)\,dy_n=0\,. \qquad (11.54)$$

As Eq. (11.49) shows, the constraints consist of m equations in n variables. Therefore $n - m$ variables can be chosen independently. Choose $dy_{m+1}, dy_{m+2}, \ldots, dy_n$ to be independent. Accordingly each of the last $n - m$ quantities in parentheses, namely those in Eq. (11.54), is zero. There are now n equations

$$\frac{\partial}{\partial y_i}\left(f+\sum_{j=1}^{m}\lambda_j\,\phi_j\right)=0\,, \qquad i=1,2,\ldots,n \qquad (11.55)$$

and m constraints, which can be solved simultaneously to evaluate the n variables y_i and the m Lagrange multipliers λ_j. The solution satisfies the constraint equations and Eq. (11.52). Since each $d\phi_i$ is zero, the solution also satisfies the condition for a minimum, namely $df = 0$. It therefore includes the desired solution, namely the values of the y_i's that minimize f subject to the constraints.

Notice that the $n + m$ simultaneous equations (11.55) and (11.49) are also obtained by calculating the minimum of

$$f+\sum_{j=1}^{m}\lambda_j\,\phi_j$$

with all the y_i's and λ_j's treated as independent variables.

11.6 Application of Variational Calculus to Control Systems

Lagrange multipliers can be used to account for the relationships between the variables that appear in the performance index of a control system. In the preceding section Lagrange multipliers were used to find the numerical values of variables that minimized the function f. Now use Lagrange multipliers to find the functions that minimize a functional J. The performance index of a system has the form

$$J=\int_{t_1}^{t_2}F(\mathbf{y},\dot{\mathbf{y}},t)dt=\int_{t_1}^{t_2}F(y_1,\dot{y}_1,y_2,\dot{y}_2,\ldots,y_n,\dot{y}_n,t)dt\,. \qquad (11.56)$$

It could be minimized by solving n scalar Euler-Lagrange equations like Eq. (11.27), but the solution would in general be incorrect because it would not satisfy the equations describing the system. These equations can be written as

$$\phi_j(\mathbf{y}, \dot{\mathbf{y}}, t) = 0\,, \qquad j = 1, 2, \ldots, m\,. \tag{11.57}$$

The functions $y_i(t)$ that satisfy these constraints also satisfy the more convenient integral form

$$\int_{t_1}^{t_2} \phi_j\,(\mathbf{y}, \dot{\mathbf{y}}, t)dt = 0\,, \qquad j = 1, 2, \ldots, m\,. \tag{11.58}$$

Now let

$$F_1 = F + \sum_{j=1}^{m} \lambda_j\,\phi_j \tag{11.59}$$

and form the integral

$$\begin{aligned} J_1 &= \int_{t_1}^{t_2} F_1\,(\mathbf{y}, \dot{\mathbf{y}}, t)dt \\ &= \int_{t_1}^{t_2} [F\,(\mathbf{y}, \dot{\mathbf{y}}, t) + \sum_{j=1}^{m} \lambda_j\,\phi_j\,(\mathbf{y}, \dot{\mathbf{y}}, t)]dt\,. \end{aligned} \tag{11.60}$$

The procedure is now nearly the same as in the preceding section. Calculate the minimum of J_1 by treating the n variables y_i and the m variables λ_j as independent. Since the integrand of Eq. (11.60) is a function of $\mathbf{y}$, $\dot{\mathbf{y}}$, and t, the functions $y_i(t)$ that minimize J_1 are found by writing n Euler-Lagrange equations and solving them simultaneously with the m constraint equations (11.57). Since each ϕ_j is zero, the functions $y_i(t)$ that minimize J_1 also minimize the performance index J given by Eq. (11.56).

To illustrate the method, optimize the system of Fig. 11.1. According to Eqs. (11.1) thru (11.3),

$$F = x_2^2 + 0.1\,u^2 \tag{11.61}$$

$$\phi_1 = x_1 - \dot{x}_2 = 0 \tag{11.62}$$

$$\phi_2 = u - x_1 - \dot{x}_1 = 0 \tag{11.63}$$

and

$$F_1 = x_2^2 + 0.1\,u^2 + \lambda_1(x_1 - \dot{x}_2) + \lambda_2(u - x_1 - \dot{x}_1)\,. \tag{11.64}$$

The vector $\mathbf{y}$ in Eq. (11.60) now has the three elements x_1, x_2, and u. The three Euler-Lagrange equations are

$$\frac{\partial F_1}{\partial x_1} - \frac{d}{dt}\left(\frac{\partial F_1}{\partial \dot{x}_1}\right) = \lambda_1 - \lambda_2 + \dot{\lambda}_2 = 0 \tag{11.65}$$

$$\frac{\partial F_1}{\partial x_2} - \frac{d}{dt}\left(\frac{\partial F_1}{\partial \dot{x}_2}\right) = 2x_2 + \dot{\lambda}_1 = 0 \tag{11.66}$$

$$\frac{\partial F_1}{\partial u} - \frac{d}{dt}\left(\frac{\partial F_1}{\partial \dot{u}}\right) = 0.2u + \lambda_2 = 0\,. \tag{11.67}$$

Eqs. (11.65) thru (11.67) and the two constraints (11.62) and (11.63) constitute four simultaneous, first-order, linear differential equations and one algebraic equation in the five variables x_1, x_2, u, λ_1, and λ_2. They cannot be solved by Laplace transforms because the necessary four initial conditions $x_1(0)$, $x_2(0)$, $\lambda_1(0)$, and $\lambda_2(0)$ are not all known. Instead, the initial conditions $x_1(0)$ and $x_2(0)$, and the final conditions $x_1(\infty) = x_2(\infty) = 0$ are known. A systematic procedure consists of solving each of the equations for its highest derivative:

$$\begin{aligned} \dot{x}_2 &= x_1 \\ \dot{x}_1 &= u - x_1 \\ \dot{\lambda}_2 &= \lambda_2 - \lambda_1 \\ \dot{\lambda}_1 &= -2x_2 \\ u &= -5\lambda_2 \end{aligned} \tag{11.68}$$

and drawing the signal-flow graph of the system represented by these equations, in Fig. 11.4. The determinant of the graph is

$$\Delta = 1 - \left(\frac{1}{s} - \frac{1}{s} - \frac{10}{s^4}\right) + \left(-\frac{1}{s^2}\right) = \frac{s^4 - s^2 + 10}{s^4}\,. \tag{11.69}$$

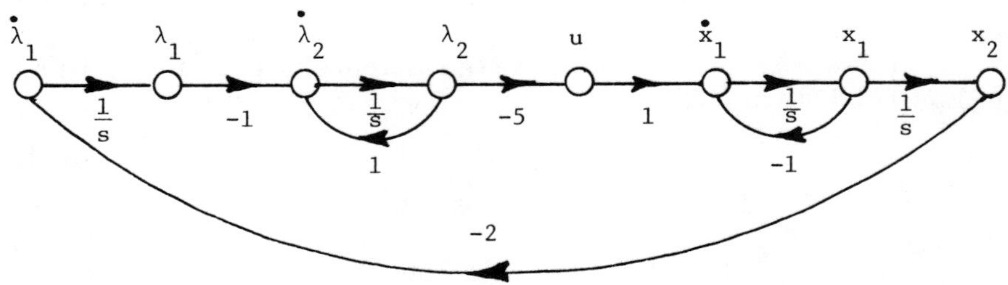

Fig. 11.4. Signal-flow graph used to solve the differential equations.

Apply a fictitious input $v(t)$ anywhere in the system. According to Mason's loop rule explained in Chapter 3, the transmittance between $v(t)$ and any of the variables, say $x_i(t)$, is

$$\frac{X_i(s)}{V(s)} = \frac{\sum_k P_k \Delta_k}{\Delta} . \tag{11.70}$$

In any transmittance in the system the denominator of this fraction is the numerator of Δ. Since the system has no input $v(t)$,

$$(s^4 - s^2 + 10)X_i(s) = 0 , \tag{11.71}$$

and $x_i(t)$ is governed by the differential equation

$$\left(\frac{d^4}{dt^4} - \frac{d^2}{dt^2} + 10\right) x_i(t) = 0 . \tag{11.72}$$

The initial and final values of x_1 and x_2 are known. The four constants in the solution for x_2 can be evaluated because fortunately x_1 and x_2 are related simply by the equation $x_1 = \dot{x}_2$. The roots of the characteristic polynomial are

$$s = \pm(1.35 \pm j1.15) . \tag{11.73}$$

Therefore

$$\begin{aligned} x_2 &= e^{-1.35\,t}(A_1 \sin 1.15\,t + A_2 \cos 1.15\,t) \\ &\quad + e^{1.35\,t}(A_3 \sin 1.15\,t + A_4 \cos 1.15\,t) . \end{aligned} \tag{11.74}$$

Since

$$x_2(\infty) = 0, \qquad A_3 = A_4 = 0 , \qquad \text{and}$$

$$x_2 = e^{-1.35\,t}(A_1 \sin 1.15\,t + A_2 \cos 1.15\,t) . \tag{11.75}$$

Now

$$\begin{aligned} x_1 &= \dot{x}_2 \\ &= -1.35\,e^{-1.35\,t}(A_1 \sin 1.15\,t + A_2 \cos 1.15\,t) \\ &\quad + 1.15\,e^{-1.35\,t}(A_1 \cos 1.15\,t - A_2 \sin 1.15\,t) . \end{aligned} \tag{11.76}$$

The remaining two constants are evaluated by applying the initial conditions to the last two equations:

$$x_2(0) = A_2 \tag{11.77}$$

$$x_1(0) = -1.35\,A_2 + 1.15\,A_1 . \tag{11.78}$$

Therefore

$$A_1 = 0.870\,x_1(0) + 1.173\,x_2(0) \tag{11.79}$$

and

$$A_2 = x_2(0) . \tag{11.80}$$

The Euler-Lagrange equations and the system constraint equations have been successfully solved to determine the functions that represent the state variables when the system is optimally controlled. These functions are given by Eqs. (11.75) and (11.76). The optimal control variable is obtained from Eqs. (11.68):

$$\begin{aligned} u &= x_1 + \dot{x}_1 \\ &= e^{-1.35\,t}[(-0.850\,A_1 + 1.955\,A_2)\sin 1.15\,t \\ &\quad - (1.955\,A_1 + 0.850\,A_2)\cos 1.15\,t]\,. \end{aligned} \tag{11.81}$$

This control can be applied externally as in Fig. 11.1. Then the control law is said to be *open loop*, since it is pre-programmed for a given initial state of the system, and is not responsive to any disturbance of the system. Since u is of the same form as x_1 and x_2, namely

$$e^{-1.35\,t}(A_5 \sin 1.15\,t + A_6 \cos 1.15\,t)\,,$$

a controller can be designed that will generate u as a linear sum of x_1 and x_2:

$$u = ax_1 + bx_2\,. \tag{11.82}$$

This is the same type as the controller designed in Chapter 10, for which in general

$$\mathbf{u} = \mathbf{H}\,\mathbf{x}\,. \tag{11.83}$$

The coefficients a and b could be evaluated by the brute-force method of substituting the formulas for x_1, x_2, and u into Eq. (11.82). An easier way is discovered by noting that if Eq. (11.82) is true,

$$u(0) = a\,x_1(0) + b\,x_2(0) \tag{11.84}$$

for any initial values $x_1(0)$ and $x_2(0)$. Eq. (11.81) can be put into this form by substituting Eqs. (11.79) and (11.80) into it:

$$\begin{aligned} u(0) &= -\,1.955[0.870\,x_1(0) + 1.173\,x_2(0)] - 0.850\,x_2(0) \\ &= -\,1.702\,x_1(0) - 3.145\,x_2(0)\,. \end{aligned} \tag{11.85}$$

The system with this optimal control law is shown in Fig. 11.5. Now the control law is said to be *closed loop* because the state variables are fed back to provide input to the controller. Even if one of the state variables is disturbed, the controller continues to generate the optimal control variable, based on the present values of the state variables.

The optimal controller has the simple linear form given by Eq. (11.83) for three reasons:

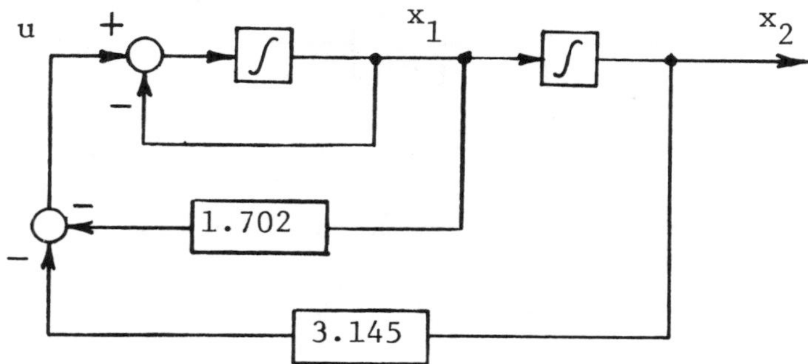

Fig. 11.5. Optimized system.

1. An unconstrained performance index of quadratic form, such as Eq. (11.19), produces linear Euler-Lagrange equations.

2. If the system is linear, the functional produced by adding the system equations into the performance index, as in Eq. (11.60), still produces linear Euler-Lagrange equations.

3. The E-L equations and system equations constitute a linear system, represented for the example by Fig. 11.4. Since in a linear system all of the variables are of the same functional form, the control variables can be expressed as a linear combination of the state and input variables. The input variables are zero in the example.

Thus if a linear system has a quadratic performance index, a solution of the Euler-Lagrange equations produces the design of the optimal closed-loop controller. Unfortunately, for a system more complex than that of Fig. 11.1, the solution of the E-L equations may be prohibitively difficult.

Notice the absence of worry about the stability of the system in the example. If the performance index of a linear system can be minimized over an infinite time interval, the state variables appearing in the performance index must be bounded, and the system is therefore stable.

11.7 Design of an Open-Loop Controller

The optimization of another simple system will show that the final time of an optimal mission need not be infinite. The mission is to drive the system of Fig. 11.6 with the control variable u for a time $T = 1$, between states $x(0) = 1$ and $x(1) = 0$, while minimizing the control effort:

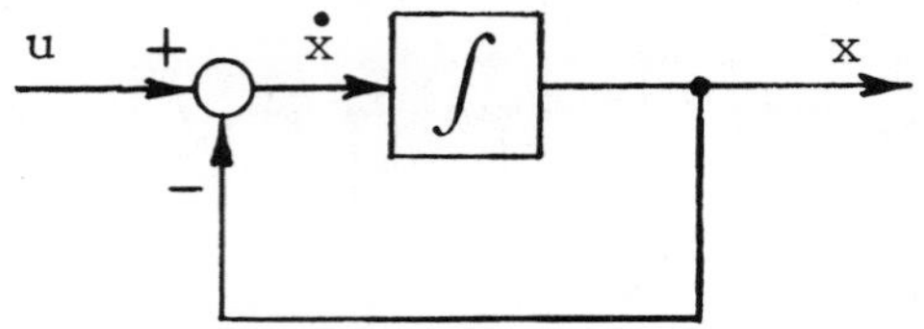

Fig. 11.6. System to be controlled in a finite time.

$$J = \int_0^1 F\,dt = \int_0^1 u^2\,dt\,. \tag{11.86}$$

The equation describing the system, which is the constraint on u, is

$$\dot{x} = u - x \tag{11.87}$$

or

$$\phi = \dot{x} + x - u = 0\,. \tag{11.88}$$

With this constraint the performance index becomes

$$J_1 = \int_0^1 F_1\,dt = \int_0^1 (F + \lambda\phi)dt = \int_0^1 [u^2 + \lambda(\dot{x} + x - u)]dt\,. \tag{11.89}$$

The Euler-Lagrange equations that specify the optimal functions u and x are

$$\frac{\partial F_1}{\partial u} - \frac{d}{dt}\left(\frac{\partial F_1}{\partial \dot{u}}\right) = 2u - \lambda = 0 \tag{11.90}$$

$$\frac{\partial F_1}{\partial x} - \frac{d}{dt}\left(\frac{\partial F_1}{\partial \dot{x}}\right) = \lambda - \dot{\lambda} = 0\,. \tag{11.91}$$

The signal-flow graph of the system represented by the E-L and system equations is shown in Fig. 11.7. The graph determinant is

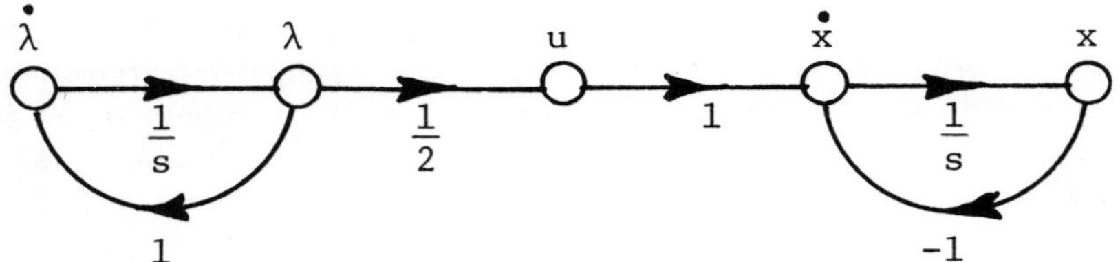

Fig. 11.7. Signal-flow graph of the differential equations.

$$\Delta = 1 - \left(\frac{1}{s} - \frac{1}{s}\right) + \left(-\frac{1}{s^2}\right) = \frac{s^2 - 1}{s^2}\,. \tag{11.92}$$

Therefore

$$\left(\frac{d^2}{dt^2} - 1\right) x(t) = 0 \tag{11.93}$$

and

$$x(t) = Ae^t + Be^{-t} . \tag{11.94}$$

Substituting in the initial and final condition produces the two relations

$$A + B = 1 \tag{11.95}$$

$$Ae + Be^{-1} = 0 \tag{11.96}$$

which yield

$$A = -\ 0.1565 , \quad B = 1.1565 , \tag{11.97}$$

and

$$x = -\ 0.1565\ e^t + 1.1565\ e^{-t} . \tag{11.98}$$

Then according to Eq. (11.87),

$$\begin{aligned} u = \dot{x} + x &= -\ 0.1565\ e^t - 1.1565\ e^{-t} - 0.1565\ e^t + 1.1565e^{-t} \\ &= -\ 0.313\ e^t . \end{aligned} \tag{11.99}$$

This is the control variable that requires the least effort as measured by Eq. (11.86), while reducing $x(t)$ from 1 at $t = 0$ to zero at $t = 1$. Unlike the control variable in the first example, it cannot be obtained as a linear sum of the state variables, there being only one state variable, x.

This example belongs to a class of optimization problems that can be solved by a straightforward general procedure that avoids the tedious evaluation of constants in the Euler-Lagrange equations. The procedure will be developed now, and then the example will be reworked.

11.8 A General Procedure

Consider the more general problem of calculating the optimal control vector $\mathbf{u}$ for a linear plant whose state is to be driven from $\mathbf{x}(0)$ to a final value of $\mathbf{x}(T) = \mathbf{0}$, and whose performance index is a quadratic function of only the control variables:

$$J = \int_0^T F\, dt = \int_0^T \mathbf{u}^T\, \mathbf{W}\, \mathbf{u}\, dt \tag{11.100}$$

where $\mathbf{W}$ is a symmetric matrix. Even with this restriction on $\mathbf{W}$, the integrand can be any linear sum of the squares of the control variables and their cross products. The constraints on $\mathbf{u}$ are given by the state equation

$$\dot{\mathbf{x}} = \mathbf{A}\mathbf{x} + \mathbf{B}\mathbf{u} . \tag{11.101}$$

To put the constraints into a more convenient form, first write the solution:

$$\mathbf{x} = e^{\mathbf{A}t}\,\mathbf{x}(0) + \int_0^t e^{\mathbf{A}(t-\tau)}\mathbf{B}\,\mathbf{u}(\tau)\,d\tau . \tag{11.102}$$

Since $\mathbf{x}(T) = \mathbf{0}$,

$$\mathbf{0} = e^{\mathbf{A}T}\,\mathbf{x}(0) + \int_0^T e^{\mathbf{A}(T-\tau)}\mathbf{B}\,\mathbf{u}(\tau)\,d\tau . \tag{11.103}$$

Premultiplying each term by the inverse of $e^{\mathbf{A}T}$ yields

$$\mathbf{x}(0) + \int_0^T e^{-\mathbf{A}\tau}\,\mathbf{B}\,\mathbf{u}(\tau)\,d\tau = \mathbf{0} . \tag{11.104}$$

The dummy variable τ can be replaced by t. Thus

$$\mathbf{x}(0) = -\int_0^T e^{-\mathbf{A}t}\,\mathbf{B}\,\mathbf{u}(t)\,dt . \tag{11.105}$$

This is a convenient expression of the constraints on the control variables. To fit the form of Eq. (11.60), let

$$\boldsymbol{\phi} = e^{-\mathbf{A}t}\,\mathbf{B}\,\mathbf{u}(t)\,dt . \tag{11.106}$$

Then the constrained performance index is

$$\begin{aligned} J_1 &= \int_0^T (F + \boldsymbol{\lambda}^T\boldsymbol{\phi})dt + \boldsymbol{\lambda}^T\mathbf{x}(0) \\ &= \int_0^T F_1\,dt + \boldsymbol{\lambda}^T\,\mathbf{x}(0) \\ &= \int_0^T [\mathbf{u}^T\,\mathbf{W}\mathbf{u} + \boldsymbol{\lambda}^T\,e^{-\mathbf{A}t}\,\mathbf{B}\,\mathbf{u}]dt + \boldsymbol{\lambda}^T\,\mathbf{x}(0) . \end{aligned} \tag{11.107}$$

As before, terms have been added to J that total zero. Therefore minimizing J_1 also minimizes the system performance index J. Also as before, the integral is minimized by writing n scalar Euler-Lagrange equations, one for each control variable, and solving them simultaneously with the m constraint equations represented by Eq. (11.105). The extra term $\boldsymbol{\lambda}^T\mathbf{x}(0)$ in Eq. (11.107) does not enter the E-L equations because it is not a function of $\mathbf{u}$ or $\dot{\mathbf{u}}$. Note that the equations $\partial J_1/\partial\lambda_i = 0$ reproduce the constraint equation (11.105), as expected.

Now write the E-L equations for Eq. (11.107) in the vector form of Eq. (11.29), namely

$$\nabla_u F_1 - \frac{d}{dt}(\nabla_{\dot{u}} F_1) = \mathbf{0}\,. \tag{11.108}$$

The reader can confirm that

$$\nabla_u (\mathbf{u}^T \mathbf{W} \mathbf{u}) = (\mathbf{W} + \mathbf{W}^T)\mathbf{u} \tag{11.109}$$

by writing **u** and **W**, for example, as

$$\mathbf{u} = \begin{bmatrix} u_1 \\ u_2 \end{bmatrix}, \quad \mathbf{W} = \begin{bmatrix} w_{11} & w_{12} \\ w_{21} & w_{22} \end{bmatrix} \tag{11.110}$$

and performing the differentiation and matrix arithmetic. Since **W** is symmetric, $\mathbf{W} = \mathbf{W}^T$, and

$$\nabla_u (\mathbf{u}^T \mathbf{W} \mathbf{u}) = 2\,\mathbf{W}\,\mathbf{u}\,. \tag{11.111}$$

Now

$$\nabla_u (\boldsymbol{\lambda}^T e^{-\mathbf{A}t} \mathbf{B}\, \mathbf{u})$$

is an $n \times 1$ column vector whose ith element is

$$\frac{d}{du_i}[\boldsymbol{\lambda}^T e^{\mathbf{A}t} \mathbf{B}] \begin{bmatrix} u_1 \\ u_2 \\ \cdot \\ \cdot \\ \cdot \\ u_n \end{bmatrix}, \tag{11.112}$$

namely the ith element of the $1 \times n$ row vector $\boldsymbol{\lambda}^T e^{-\mathbf{A}t}\mathbf{B}$. The column vector is the transpose of the row vector:

$$\nabla_u (\boldsymbol{\lambda}^T e^{-\mathbf{A}t} \mathbf{B}\, \mathbf{u}) = \mathbf{B}^T (e^{-\mathbf{A}t})^T \boldsymbol{\lambda}\,. \tag{11.113}$$

In the second term of the E-L equation (11.108),

$$\nabla_{\dot{u}} F_1 = \nabla_{\dot{u}}[\mathbf{u}^T \mathbf{W}\,\mathbf{u} + \boldsymbol{\lambda}^T e^{-\mathbf{A}t} \mathbf{B}\,\mathbf{u}] = \mathbf{0}\,. \tag{11.114}$$

The E-L equation becomes

$$\nabla_u F_1 = 2\mathbf{W}\,\mathbf{u} + \mathbf{B}^T (e^{-\mathbf{A}t})^T \boldsymbol{\lambda} = \mathbf{0}\,. \tag{11.115}$$

Unlike most of the E-L equations encountered earlier in this chapter, this one is not a differential equation, but just an algebraic equation that can be solved directly:

$$\mathbf{u} = -\frac{1}{2}\mathbf{W}^{-1} \mathbf{B}^T (e^{-\mathbf{A}t})^T \boldsymbol{\lambda}\,. \tag{11.116}$$

To eliminate the Lagrange multipliers, substitute this equation into the vector constraint equation (11.105):

$$\mathbf{x}(0) = \mathbf{V}\boldsymbol{\lambda}\,, \tag{11.117}$$

where

$$\mathbf{V} = \frac{1}{2}\int_0^T e^{-\mathbf{A}t}\,\mathbf{B}\,\mathbf{W}^{-1}\,\mathbf{B}^T\,(e^{-\mathbf{A}t})^T\,dt \tag{11.118}$$

and

$$\boldsymbol{\lambda} = \mathbf{V}^{-1}\,\mathbf{x}(0)\,. \tag{11.119}$$

Finally,

$$\mathbf{u} = -\,\frac{1}{2}\,\mathbf{W}^{-1}\,\mathbf{B}^T\,(e^{-\mathbf{A}t})^T\mathbf{V}^{-1}\,\mathbf{x}(0)\,. \tag{11.120}$$

This is the desired optimal control vector. The matrices **W**, **B**, **A**, and **V** are all obtainable from the performance index and the parameters of the system. Notice that the control law is open loop, since it is preset for a given initial state of the system.

11.9 The Second Example Reworked

To illustrate the use of Eq. (11.120), rework the example of Fig. 11.6, calculating the control vector (the scalar u in this case) that will drive the system from state $x(0) = 1$ to $x(1) = 0$ in the time $T = 1$, while minimizing the performance index

$$J = \int_0^1 u^2\,dt\,. \tag{11.121}$$

For this system the state equation

$$\dot{\mathbf{x}} = \mathbf{A}\mathbf{x} + \mathbf{B}\mathbf{u} \tag{11.122}$$

is

$$\dot{x} = -\,x + u\,. \tag{11.123}$$

Therefore

$$A = -\,1, \quad B = 1, \quad W = 1, \quad \text{and}$$

$$V = \frac{1}{2}\int_0^1 e^{2t}\,dt = \frac{e^2 - 1}{4}\,. \tag{11.124}$$

Then

$$u = -\,\frac{1}{2}\,e^t\,\frac{4}{e^2 - 1} = \frac{2e^t}{1 - e^2} = -\,0.313\,e^t \tag{11.125}$$

which agrees with Eq. (11.99).

This chapter has developed a straightforward "cookbook" procedure for calculating the optimal open-loop control law for driving to rest a linear plant with a performance index that is a quadratic function of the control variables. This procedure avoids the difficulty of solving two-point boundary-value problems. For other cases the method of variational calculus becomes cumbersome. Other optimization techniques are available, and more are being developed. Until the subject of optimal control becomes better organized, the interested engineer must read the voluminous literature, and try to sift out the facts that are important.

Chapter 12

DIFFERENCE EQUATIONS AND z TRANSFORMS

12.1 A Party Game

Start a series with any two numbers, and make each subsequent term the sum of the preceding two. For example, the series might be −2,7,5, 12,17,29,46,75,121,196, . . . These are called Fibonacci numbers. No matter which two initial numbers you choose, the ratio of two successive numbers quickly converges toward 1.618. You can learn why, by reading this chapter.

12.2 Where Difference Equations Arise

Difference equations are functions of a variable that has only discrete, uniformly-spaced values. Fig. 12.1 shows an example, in which the variable k is the sequence number of a repeated resistive network. Define $v(k)$ as the voltage on the kth node. The sum of the currents flowing into the kth node is

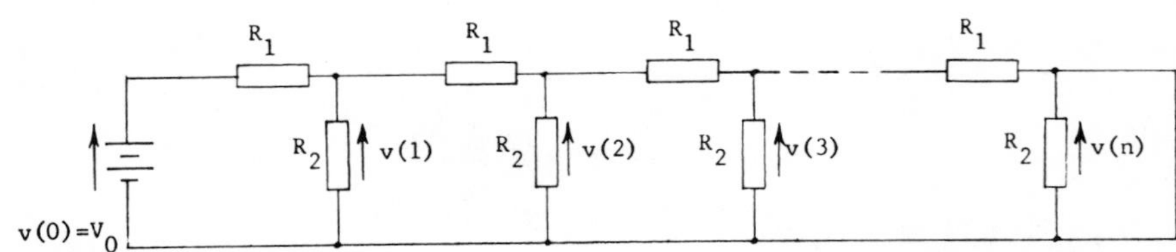

Fig. 12.1. Repeated network.

$$\frac{v(k-1)-v(k)}{R_1}+\frac{v(k+1)-v(k)}{R_1}-\frac{v(k)}{R_2}=0 \qquad (12.1)$$

or

$$v(k+1)-\left(2+\frac{R_1}{R_2}\right)v(k)+v(k-1)=0\,. \qquad (12.2)$$

Advancing the independent variable by one produces

$$v(k+2) - \left(2 + \frac{R_1}{R_2}\right) v(k+1) + v(k) = 0 \,. \tag{12.3}$$

This is a second-order, linear difference equation with constant coefficients. It is also homogeneous, of course, because its right side is zero.

Difference equations also arise in systems that sample a continuous function at periodic intervals. Examples are (1) a radar, whose receiver gets an echo from the target once per second, and (2) communication by pulse modulation, in which a voice signal is sampled periodically, and each sample is converted to a pulse whose height or duration is proportional to the amplitude of the sample. These are called *discrete-time* systems. The independent variable in their difference equations is a sequence of uniformly-spaced instants of time.

12.3 Difference Equations and Differential Equations

Engineering students study differential equations because R-L-C circuits and spring-mass-damper systems appear frequently in engineering. In the past, difference equations were neglected because they had little practical application. The digital computer, radar, and communication theory have changed that, and now it is time to study difference equations. The theory parallels that of differential equations. Difference equations are linear or nonlinear. The linear equations have complementary and particular solutions. The latter are obtained by the method of undetermined coefficients or by variation of parameters. A system of simultaneous linear difference equations has a characteristic equation whose roots determine whether the system is stable or not. The system can be represented by a state equation, and has a state-transition matrix. It has system functions, and can be displayed as a block diagram. The difference equations of the system can be solved by one-sided or two-sided transforms, depending on whether or not the input is causal. A remarkable and pleasant fact about difference equations is that at every step the theory is easier than the corresponding theory for differential equations. The numerical solution of difference equations on a computer is almost trivial. And with the exception of inverting transforms, the theory of difference equations has no need for calculus. It would make an excellent introduction to calculus, differential equations, and continuous systems. Perhaps in a few years students will study difference equations before differential equations.

12.4 Classical Solution of Difference Equations

An nth-order homogeneous linear difference equation with constant coefficients is

$$a_n y(k+n) + a_{n-1} y(k+n-1) + \cdots + a_1 y(k+1) + a_0 y(k) = 0\,. \quad (12.4)$$

To solve it, assume solutions of the form

$$y(k) = \beta^k \quad (12.5)$$

where β is a constant. Then

$$y(k+n) = \beta^{k+n} = \beta^k \beta^n\,, \quad (12.6)$$

and the difference equation becomes

$$a_n \beta^k \beta^n + a_{n-1}\beta^k \beta^{n-1} + \cdots + a_1 \beta^k \beta + a_0 \beta^k = 0 \quad (12.7)$$

or

$$a_n \beta^n + a_{n-1}\beta^{n-1} + \cdots + a_1 \beta + a_0 = 0\,. \quad (12.8)$$

This is the *characteristic equation*, which of course can be written by inspection of the difference equation (12.4). If the roots $\beta_1, \beta_2, \ldots, \beta_n$ of this polynomial are distinct, the general solution of the homogeneous difference equation is

$$y_c(k) = b_1 \beta_1^k + b_2 \beta_2^k + \cdots + b_n \beta_n^k\,. \quad (12.9)$$

The subscript c indicates that this is the complementary solution of the difference equation if its right side is not zero. If a root, say β_1, is repeated m times, the general solution is

$$y_c(k) = (b_1 + b_2 k + b_3 k^2 + \cdots + b_m k^{m-1})\beta_1^k + b_{m+1}\beta_2^k + \cdots + b_n \beta_{n-m+1}^k\,. \quad (12.10)$$

If the coefficients a_i in the difference equation are real, two of the roots of the characteristic equation might be a complex conjugate pair,

$$\beta_1 = re^{j\theta} \quad \text{and} \quad \beta_2 = re^{-j\theta}\,, \quad (12.11)$$

whose coefficients b_1 are b_2 are also a complex conjugate pair. Their contribution to the solution can be written in a more convenient form:

$$\begin{aligned} b_1\beta_1^k + b_2\beta_2^k &= b_1(re^{j\theta})^k + b_2(re^{-j\theta})^k \\ &= r^k(b_1 e^{jk\theta} + b_2 e^{-jk\theta}) \\ &= r^k(c_1 \sin k\theta + c_2 \cos k\theta) \quad (12.12) \\ &= c_3 r^k \sin(k\theta + \phi) \quad (12.13) \end{aligned}$$

where $c_1 = j(b_1 - b_2)$ and $c_2 = b_1 + b_2$, and c_1, c_2, c_3, and ϕ are real constants.

Evaluation of the n constants in the solution of the homogeneous difference equation requires the value of $y_c(k)$ at n values of k. It seems reasonable to call these *initial conditions* if they are the first n values of $y_c(k)$, and *boundary conditions* if some other values are included. For the system in Fig. 12.1 what are the two known boundary conditions that will allow evaluation of the two constants in the solution of Eq. (12.3)?

12.5 The Particular Solution

The procedure for finding the particular solution of the nonhomogeneous difference equation

$$a_n y(k + n) + a_{n-1} y(k + n - 1) + \cdots + a_1 y(k + 1) + a_0 y(k) = f(k) \tag{12.14}$$

is almost exactly the same as for a differential equation. The method of undetermined coefficients can be used if the coefficients a_i are constant and if repeated increases of k in $f(k)$ (which is the analog of differentiation of a continuous function) produce a finite number of linearly-independent terms. The latter requirement limits $f(k)$ to a polynomial, exponential, sinusoidal, or hyperbolic function of k such as $b_1 k$ or $\cosh \theta k$, or a sum or product of these functions. The particular solution is assumed to be a linear combination of the terms in $f(k)$ and its recursions $f(k + 1)$, $f(k + 2)$, etc. If one of the terms in the assumed solution duplicates a term in the complementary solution, each term in its family must be multiplied by k enough times to eliminate the duplication. To illustrate the method of undetermined coefficients, solve the equation

$$y(k + 2) + 2y(k + 1) + y(k) = k(-1)^k \tag{12.15}$$

with the initial conditions

$$y(0) = 1\,, \quad y(1) = 0\,. \tag{12.16}$$

The characteristic equation is

$$\beta^2 + 2\beta + 1 = 0\,. \tag{12.17}$$

Its solutions are $\beta_1 = \beta_2 = -1$. The complementary solution is therefore

$$y_c(k) = b_1(-1)^k + b_2 k(-1)^k\,. \tag{12.18}$$

The right side of the difference equation is

$$f(k) = k(-1)^k\,. \tag{12.19}$$

Thus

$$f(k + 1) = (k + 1)(-1)^{k+1} = (k + 1)(-1)(-1)^k$$
$$= - k(-1)^k - (-1)^k . \qquad (12.20)$$

Clearly $f(k)$ and its recursions can be written as the linear combination

$$Ak(-1)^k + B(-1)^k . \qquad (12.21)$$

To eliminate the duplication of the complementary solution, write the particular solution as

$$y_p(k) = Ak^3(-1)^k + Bk^2(-1)^k . \qquad (12.22)$$

Substitute it into the difference equation (12.15) to get

$$A(k + 2)^3(-1)^{k+2} + B(k + 2)^2(-1)^{k+2} + 2A(k + 1)^3(-1)^{k+1}$$
$$+ 2B(k + 1)^2(-1)^{k+1} + Ak^3(-1)^k + Bk^2(-1)^k = k(-1)^k . \qquad (12.23)$$

Now equate coefficients of like powers of k. The result is

$$A = \frac{1}{6} \quad \text{and} \quad B = -\frac{1}{2} . \qquad (12.24)$$

The complete solution is

$$y(k) = y_c(k) + y_p(k) = (b_1 + b_2 k - \frac{1}{2} k^2 + \frac{1}{6} k^3)(-1)^k . \quad (12.25)$$

The first of the initial conditions (12.16) shows that $b_1 = 1$, and the second yields

$$0 = \left(1 + b_2 - \frac{1}{2} + \frac{1}{6}\right)(-1) \quad \text{or} \quad b_2 = -\frac{2}{3} . \qquad (12.26)$$

Finally, the complete solution for the given initial conditions is

$$y(k) = \left(1 - \frac{2}{3} k - \frac{1}{2} k^2 + \frac{1}{6} k^3\right)(-1)^k . \qquad (12.27)$$

The method of variation of parameters can be used to find the particular solution of any linear difference equation (12.14) for any $f(k)$, even if the coefficients a_i are functions of k. The method is nearly the same as that for differential equations, with integration replaced by summation and differentiation by recursion. It is explained in Ref. 21, pages 88–92.

12.6 z Transforms

Linear difference equations with constant coefficients can be solved conveniently by *z transforms*, which serve the same purpose as Laplace transforms for differential equations. z transforms reduce difference equations to algebraic equations and include the initial conditions automatically. The two-sided z transform of the discrete function $f(k)$ is defined as

$$\mathscr{Z}[f(k)] = F(z) = \sum_{k=-\infty}^{\infty} f(k)z^{-k} \tag{12.28}$$

where z is the complex variable $z = x + jy$. Until near the end, this chapter considers only causal functions, for which

$$f(k) = 0\,, \quad k < 0\,, \tag{12.29}$$

and therefore requires only one-sided z transforms:

$$F(z) = \sum_{k=0}^{\infty} f(k)z^{-k}\,. \tag{12.30}$$

To illustrate the use of one-sided z transforms, solve the difference equation

$$y(k+2) + 5y(k+1) + 6y(k) = (-4)^k \tag{12.31}$$

with the initial conditions

$$y(0) = 0\,, \quad y(1) = 1\,. \tag{12.32}$$

First form the z transform of both sides:

$$\mathscr{Z}[y(k+2)] + 5\mathscr{Z}[y(k+1)] + 6Y(z) = \mathscr{Z}[(-4)^k]\,. \tag{12.33}$$

To evaluate the second term, observe that

$$\mathscr{Z}[y(k+1)] = \sum_{k=0}^{\infty} y(k+1)z^{-k} = z\sum_{k=0}^{\infty} y(k+1)z^{-(k+1)}\,. \tag{12.34}$$

Let $m = k + 1$. Then

$$\begin{aligned}\mathscr{Z}[y(k+1)] &= z\sum_{m=1}^{\infty} y(m)z^{-m} = z\sum_{m=0}^{\infty} y(m)z^{-m} - zy(0)\\ &= zY(z) - zy(0)\,.\end{aligned} \tag{12.35}$$

Advancing k by one shows that

$$\begin{aligned}\mathscr{Z}[y(k+2)] &= z\,\mathscr{Z}[y(k+1)] - zy(1)\\ &= z^2Y(z) - z^2y(0) - zy(1)\,.\end{aligned} \tag{12.36}$$

Notice that the initial conditions are not included in exactly the same way as in Laplace transforms.

To evaluate the last term of Eq. (12.33), observe that if a is any constant, real or complex,

$$\mathfrak{Z}[a^k] = \sum_{k=0}^{\infty} a^k z^{-k} = \sum_{k=0}^{\infty} \left(\frac{a}{z}\right)^k . \tag{12.37}$$

In general,

$$\frac{1}{1-z} = 1 + z + z^2 + \cdots = \sum_{k=0}^{\infty} z^k . \tag{12.38}$$

The right side is a Taylor series that converges only for $|z| < 1$. Similarly,

$$\frac{1}{1-\frac{a}{z}} = \frac{z}{z-a} = \sum_{k=0}^{\infty} \left(\frac{a}{z}\right)^k , \quad \text{if} \quad \left|\frac{a}{z}\right| < 1 \quad \text{or} \quad |z| > |a| . \tag{12.39}$$

Therefore

$$\mathfrak{Z}[a^k] = \frac{z}{z-a} , \quad |z| > |a| , \tag{12.40}$$

and for the special case,

$$\mathfrak{Z}[(-4)^k] = \frac{z}{z+4} . \tag{12.41}$$

When one-sided z transforms are being used, the values of z for which a transform exists is not a concern. Eq. (12.33) can now be written as the algebraic equation

$$z^2Y(z) - z + 5zY(z) + 6Y(z) = \frac{z}{z+4} \tag{12.42}$$

or

$$(z^2 + 5z + 6)Y(z) = \frac{z}{z+4} + z = \frac{z^2+5z}{z+4} . \tag{12.43}$$

Thus

$$Y(z) = \frac{z^2+5z}{(z+2)(z+3)(z+4)} . \tag{12.44}$$

This quotient is not quite ready for expansion into partial fractions. Although partial fractions are of the form $k/(z+2)$, Eq. (12.40) requires the form $kz/(z+2)$. Divide both sides of Eq. (12.44) by z:

$$\frac{Y(z)}{z} = \frac{z+5}{(z+2)(z+3)(z+4)} = \frac{3/2}{z+2} - \frac{2}{z+3} + \frac{1/2}{z+4} . \qquad (12.45)$$

Now restore z to each numerator:

$$Y(z) = \frac{\frac{3}{2}z}{z+2} - \frac{2z}{z+3} + \frac{\frac{1}{2}z}{z+4} . \qquad (12.46)$$

The transform is inverted with the help of Eq. (12.40):

$$y(k) = \frac{3}{2}(-2)^k - 2(-3)^k + \frac{1}{2}(-4)^k . \qquad (12.47)$$

The reader is invited to verify that this solution satisfies the difference equation (12.31) and the initial conditions (12.32).

12.7 A Few Other Useful Transforms

Several discrete functions and their z transforms are listed in Table 12.1. A few transforms deserving special mention will be derived here.

1. *Delta Function.* A delta function occurring at $k = n$ is defined as

$$\delta(k-n) = \begin{cases} 1, & k = n \\ 0, & k \neq n \end{cases} \qquad (12.48)$$

as shown in Fig. 12.2. Note that it has the same symbol as a unit impulse. The difference is indicated by the argument. Its z transform is

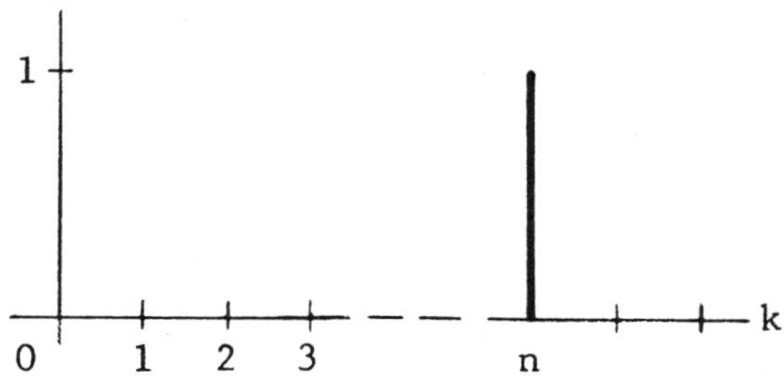

Fig. 12.2. Delta function.

$$\mathcal{Z}[\delta(k-n)] = \sum_{k=0}^{\infty} \delta(k-n)z^{-k} = z^{-n} . \qquad (12.49)$$

If the delta function occurs at the origin, $n = 0$, and

$$\mathcal{Z}[\delta(k)] = 1, \qquad (12.50)$$

TABLE 12.1. ONE-SIZED z TRANSFORMS

No.	$f(k)$	$F(z)$
1	$\delta(k)$	1
2	$U(k) = \begin{cases} 1, & k \geq 0 \\ 0, & k < 0 \end{cases}$	$\dfrac{z}{z-1}$
3	a^k	$\dfrac{z}{z-a}$
4	$\cos k\theta$	$\dfrac{z(z-\cos\theta)}{z^2 - 2z\cos\theta + 1}$
5	$\sin k\theta$	$\dfrac{z\sin\theta}{z^2 - 2z\cos\theta + 1}$
6	$f(k-n)U(k-n)$	$z^{-n}F(z)$
7	$f(k+1)$	$zF(z) - zf(0)$
8	$f(k+2)$	$z^2F(z) - z^2f(0) - zf(1)$
9	$\sum_{n=0}^{k} f_1(n)f_2(k-n)$	$F_1(z)F_2(z)$

which is the same as the Laplace transform of a unit impulse at the origin.

The reader is invited to derive the z transform of the unit step, defined as

$$U(k-n) = \begin{cases} 1, & k \geq n \\ 0, & k < n \end{cases} \tag{12.51}$$

2. *Cosine*. To find the z transform of $\cos k\theta$, first calculate

$$\mathcal{Z}[e^{jk\theta}] = \frac{z}{z - e^{j\theta}} \quad \text{and} \quad \mathcal{Z}[e^{-jk\theta}] = \frac{z}{z - e^{-j\theta}} . \tag{12.52}$$

Then if

$$f(k) = \cos k\theta = \frac{1}{2}(e^{jk\theta} + e^{-jk\theta}),$$

$$F(z) = \frac{z}{2}\left[\frac{1}{z - e^{j\theta}} + \frac{1}{z - e^{-j\theta}}\right] = \frac{z}{2}\left[\frac{z - e^{-j\theta} + z - e^{j\theta}}{z^2 - z(e^{j\theta} + e^{-j\theta}) + 1}\right]$$

$$= \frac{z(z - \cos\theta)}{z^2 - 2z\cos\theta + 1}, \quad |z| > |e^{j\theta}| = 1 . \tag{12.53}$$

The poles of $F(z)$ are at $z = \cos\theta \pm j\sin\theta$, on the circle of unit radius centered at the origin of the z plane in Fig. 12.3. This is called the *unit circle.*

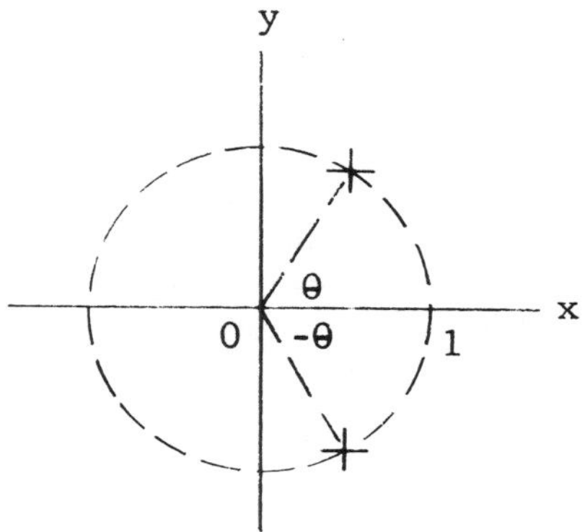

Fig. 12.3. Poles of $\mathfrak{Z}[\cos k\theta]$.

3. *k Shift.* Fig. 12.4 shows a typical causal discrete function $f(k)$, and Fig. 12.5 shows the same function shifted n steps to the right, to make it

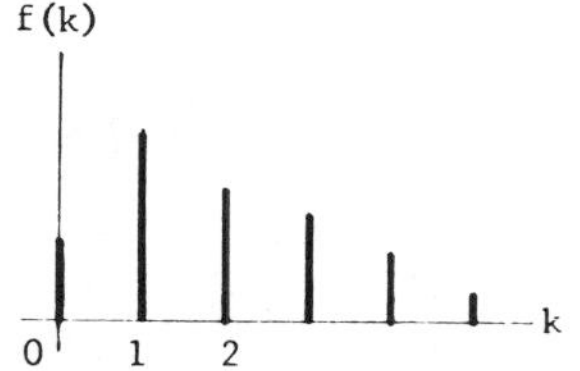

Fig. 12.4. Causal function.

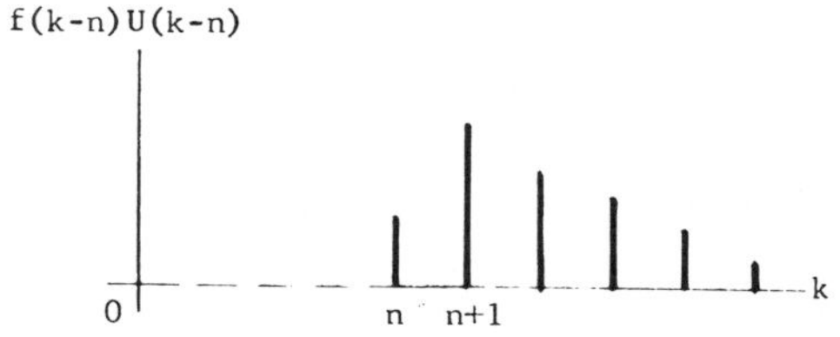

Fig. 12.5. Same function shifted.

$f(k-n)U(k-n)$. The unit step $U(k-n)$ is a reminder that the new function is zero for $k < n$. The z transform of the shifted function is

$$\mathfrak{Z}[f(k-n)U(k-n)] = \sum_{k=0}^{\infty} f(k-n)U(k-n)z^{-k}$$

$$= \sum_{k=n}^{\infty} f(k-n)z^{-k}. \tag{12.54}$$

If $k - n = j$,

$$\mathfrak{Z}[f(k-n)U(k-n)] = \sum_{j=0}^{\infty} f(j)z^{-(n+j)} = z^{-n}\sum_{j=0}^{\infty} f(j)z^{-j}$$

$$= z^{-n}F(z). \tag{12.55}$$

Thus if a discrete function is shifted by n steps (or *delayed*, if k is time), its z transform is multiplied by z^{-n}.

4. *Convolution.* The numerical convolution of two discrete functions of k, $f_1(k)$ and $f_2(k)$, is

$$f(k) = \sum_{n=-\infty}^{\infty} f_1(n) f_2(k-n) . \tag{12.56}$$

If f_1 is causal, the lower limit of summation is zero. If f_2 is causal, the upper limit is k. No harm is done by leaving the upper limit at infinity, because when $n > k$, $f_2(k - n) = 0$. Rewrite the convolution as

$$f(k) = \sum_{n=0}^{\infty} f_1(n) f_2(k-n) . \tag{12.57}$$

Its z transform is

$$\begin{aligned} F(z) &= \sum_{k=0}^{\infty} \sum_{n=0}^{\infty} f_1(n) f_2(k-n) z^{-k} \\ &= \sum_{n=0}^{\infty} f_1(n) \sum_{k=0}^{\infty} f_2(k-n) z^{-k} . \end{aligned} \tag{12.58}$$

According to Eq. (12.55),

$$\mathscr{Z}[f_2(k-n)] = z^{-n} F_2(z) . \tag{12.59}$$

Therefore

$$F(z) = \sum_{n=0}^{\infty} f_1(n) z^{-n} F_2(z) = F_1(z) F_2(z) , \tag{12.60}$$

which is certainly what you expected.

12.8 System Function and Delta Response

A difference equation can be regarded as the description of a discrete system that can also be described by its *system function* or its *delta response*. To understand these terms, consider the equation

$$y(k+2) + 5y(k+1) + 6y(k) = v(k) . \tag{12.61}$$

This equation is the description of a system with input $v(k)$ and output $y(k)$. Assume that the system is initially inert, i.e., the values of $y(k)$ required by the z transforms ($y(0)$ and $y(1)$ in this case) are zero. The z transform of the equation is

$$(z^2 + 5z + 6) Y(z) = V(z) \tag{12.62}$$

or

$$\frac{Y(z)}{V(z)} = \frac{1}{z^2 + 5z + 6} . \tag{12.63}$$

The ratio of the z transforms of the output and input of an initially-inert, linear, discrete system with constant coefficients (a fixed system) is called the *system function, transfer function,* or *transmittance:*

$$H(z) = \frac{Y(z)}{V(z)} . \tag{12.64}$$

It is sometimes called the *pulsed* or *sampled transfer function,* to avoid confusion with $H(s)$, which is a quotient of Laplace transforms. If the input to a fixed, linear, initially-inert discrete system is the delta function

$$v(k) = \delta(k) , \qquad \text{for which} \qquad V(z) = 1 , \tag{12.65}$$

the output is

$$Y(z) = H(z) \tag{12.66}$$

whose inverse transform is

$$y(k) = \hbar(k) . \tag{12.67}$$

The function $\hbar(k)$ is appropriately called the *delta response.* Thus the system function is the z transform of the delta response. A discrete system can be represented by either of the ways shown in Fig. 12.6. To

Fig. 12.6. Two ways to represent a discrete system.

find the delta response of the system represented by Eq. (12.63), write

$$\frac{H(z)}{z} = \frac{1}{z(z+2)(z+3)} = \frac{1/6}{z} - \frac{1/2}{z+2} + \frac{1/3}{z+3}$$

and

$$H(z) = \frac{1}{6} - \frac{\frac{1}{2}z}{z+2} + \frac{\frac{1}{3}z}{z+3} . \tag{12.68}$$

The delta response is therefore

$$\hbar(k) = \frac{1}{6}\,\delta(k) - \frac{1}{2}(-2)^k + \frac{1}{3}(-3)^k . \tag{12.69}$$

12.9 Block Diagrams

A system described by simultaneous difference equations can be displayed pictorially as a block diagram. An example is the system of Fig. 12.7, represented by the two difference equations

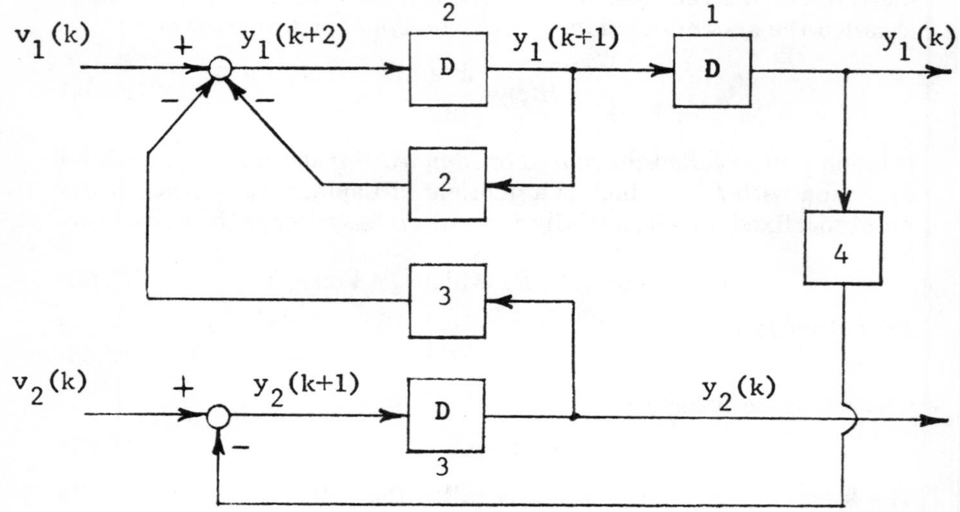

Fig. 12.7. Block diagram with discrete variables.

$$y_1(k+2) + 2y_1(k+1) + 3y_2(k) = v_1(k) \tag{12.70}$$

$$4y_1(k) + y_2(k+1) = v_2(k)\ . \tag{12.71}$$

Each block labeled D is a unit delay, whose output is the input delayed by one increment of k. A unit delay is also called a *delayor*, to suggest the analogy with the integrators in a continuous system. The storage registers of a digital computer are unit delays when they are used in an iterative calculation. They hold the values of the variables during each step. For example, the FORTRAN or BASIC instruction $Y = Y + 4$ means

$$y(k+1) = y(k) + 4\ . \tag{12.72}$$

The value of y at step k is delayed one step, and then 4 is added to it to make the value at step $k + 1$. If the output of a unit delay is $y(k)$, its input is $y(k + 1)$. Its transfer function, calculated with $y(0) = 0$, is

$$H(z) = \frac{\mathscr{Z}[y(k)]}{\mathscr{Z}[y(k+1)]} = \frac{Y(z)}{zY(z)} = \frac{1}{z}\ . \tag{12.73}$$

The block diagram can be relabeled as in Fig. 12.8 with each variable replaced by its z transform. Either block diagram conveys exactly the same information as the difference equations, and has the advantage of showing the relationships between the variables. The concept of initial inertness now has physical significance. The system is initially inert if the initial output of each unit delay is zero.

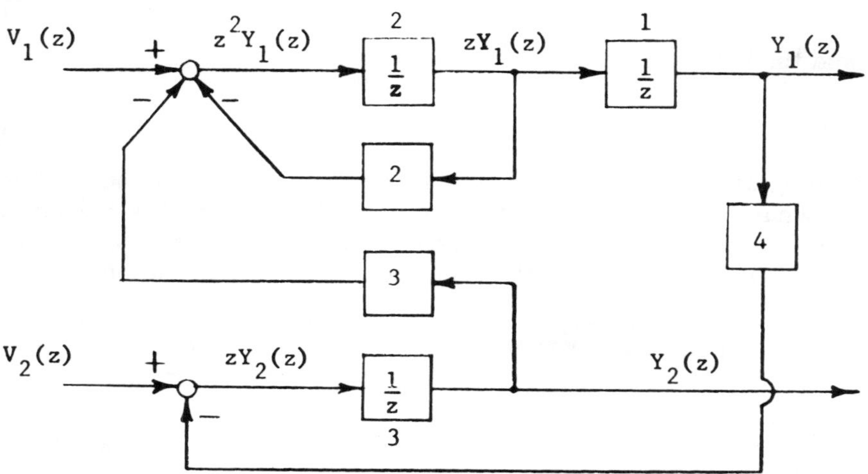

Fig. 12.8. Block diagram with z transforms.

12.10 Numerical Solution of Difference Equations

Anyone familiar with the problems of numerical integration of differential equations may relax now. For difference equations no elaborate approximate integration procedure such as the Runge-Kutta method is needed. The analyst need not worry about the truncation error, the varying cost of computing time, and possible instability caused by the choice of computing interval, because that interval is fixed. The procedure of numerical solution can be illustrated by setting up a BASIC program with a format like that of a Runge-Kutta program, that operates the system of Fig. 12.7. Choose

$$v_1(k) = \cos k \qquad \text{and} \qquad v_2(k) = (-0.5)^k \tag{12.74}$$

and let the initial outputs of the delays (for $k = 0$) be

$$y_1(0) = 0\ , \quad y_1(1) = 1\ , \quad y_2(0) = 0\ . \tag{12.75}$$

The three delay outputs will be called

$$y_1(k) = X1$$

$$y_1(k + 1) = X2$$

$$y_2(k) = X3\ . \tag{12.76}$$

The three delay inputs will be called

$$y_1(k+1) = I1$$

$$y_1(k+2) = I2$$

$$y_2(k+1) = I3 \tag{12.77}$$

and the inputs are

$$v_1(k) = V1$$

$$v_2(k) = V2\,. \tag{12.78}$$

A program that calculates and prints 11 values of $y_1(k)$ and $y_2(k)$ is shown in Table 12.2. Notice that at each step the output of each delay is simply replaced by the input. The numerical solution of difference equations is exact, and is the same as the analytical solution.

TABLE 12.2. OPERATION OF A DISCRETE SYSTEM WITH A FORMAT BASED ON EXPERIENCE WITH NUMERICAL INTEGRATION

```
A                16:33EDT              06/03/75

10 PRINT "K", "Y1(K)", "Y2(K)"
20 X2=1                           <---- The only nonzero initial delay output
30 FOR K=0 TO 10
40 PRINT K,X1,X3
50 V1=COS(K)                      } Auxiliary variables
60 V2=(-.5)↑K
70 I1=X2                          }
80 I2=V1-2*X2-3*X3                } Delay inputs
90 I3=V2-4*X1                     }
100 X1=I1                         }
110 X2=I2                         } Delay outputs
120 X3=I3                         }
130 NEXT K
140 END

READY
RUN
A                16:34EDT              06/03/75

K               Y1(K)                       Y2(K)
 0               0                           0
 1               1                           1
 2              -1                          -4.5
 3              -0.459698                    4.25
 4               14.0032                     1.71379
 5              -41.7465                    -55.9505
 6               77.698                      166.955
 7               12.7392                    -310.776
 8              -525.382                    -50.9647
 9               1983.85                     2101.53
10              -3814.95                    -7935.39

USED             .69 NEW UNITS
```

A little reflection leads to the conclusion that a program for solving difference equations need not be laid out like a program for Runge-

Kutta integration. The difference equations (12.70) and (12.71) can be solved directly when they are written in the form

$$y_1(k+2) = v_1(k) - 2y_1(k+1) - 3y_2(k)$$

$$y_2(k+1) = v_2(k) - 4y_1(k)\,, \tag{12.79}$$

since the preceding values of each variable and the inputs are known. These equations are solved by the BASIC program in Table 12.3, in which $y_1(k)$ and $y_2(k)$ are represented by the dimensioned variables $X(K)$ and $Y(K)$. Notice that the times required by the two programs are nearly the same.

TABLE 12.3. OPERATION OF A DISCRETE SYSTEM BY DIRECT SOLUTION OF THE DIFFERENCE EQUATIONS

```
B             16:35EDT             06/03/75

10 PRINT "K","Y1(K)","Y2(K)"
20 DIM X(12),Y(11)
30 X(1)=1
40 FOR K=0 TO 10
50 V1=COS(K)
60 V2=(-.5)↑K
70 X(K+2)=V1-2*X(K+1)-3*Y(K)
80 Y(K+1)=V2-4*X(K)
90 PRINT K,X(K),Y(K)
100 NEXT K
110 END

READY
RUN
B             16:36EDT             06/03/75

K                  Y1(K)                   Y2(K)
 0                  0                       0
 1                  1                       1
 2                 -1                      -4.5
 3                 -0.459698                4.25
 4                  14.0032                 1.71379
 5                 -41.7465               -55.9505
 6                  77.698                 166.955
 7                  12.7392               -310.776
 8                 -525.382                -50.9647
 9                  1983.85                2101.53
 10                -3814.95               -7935.39

USED            .70 NEW UNITS
```

12.11 Stability

To demonstrate the meaning of stability of a discrete system, calculate the output $y_1(k)$ of the system in Fig. 12.7. Let the system be initially inert, and give it the inputs $v_1(k) = 0$ and $v_2(k) = (-0.5)^k$. The transmittance between $v_2(k)$ and $y_1(k)$ could be calculated with the help of Mason's loop rule. Probably it will be easier to write the z transforms of Eqs. (12.70) and (12.71):

$$(z^2 + 2z)Y_1(z) + 3Y_2(z) = 0$$
$$4Y_1(z) + zY_2(z) = V_2(z) \tag{12.80}$$

and solve for $Y_1(z)$:

$$Y_1(z) = \frac{\begin{vmatrix} 0 & 3 \\ V_2(z) & z \end{vmatrix}}{\begin{vmatrix} z^2 + 2z & 3 \\ 4 & z \end{vmatrix}} = \frac{-3V_2(z)}{z^3 + 2z^2 - 12} . \tag{12.81}$$

The transmittance is

$$H(z) = \frac{Y_1(z)}{V_2(z)} = \frac{-3}{z^3 + 2z^2 - 12} . \tag{12.82}$$

The characteristic equation is the equation formed by setting the denominator of the transmittance equal to zero:

$$z^3 + 2z^2 - 12 = (z - 1.78)[(z + 1.89)^2 + (1.78)^2] = 0 . \tag{12.83}$$

Since the input is

$$V_2(z) = \frac{z}{z + 0.5} , \tag{12.84}$$

the output is

$$Y_1(z) = \frac{-3z}{(z + 0.5)(z^3 + 2z^2 - 12)} . \tag{12.85}$$

Then

$$\frac{Y_1(z)}{z} = -\frac{3}{(z + 0.5)(z - 1.78)[(z + 1.89)^2 + (1.78)^2]}$$
$$= \frac{K_1}{z + 0.5} + \frac{K_2}{z - 1.78} + \frac{K_3 + jK_4}{z + 2.60e^{j0.754}} + \frac{K_3 - jK_4}{z + 2.60e^{-j0.754}} \tag{12.86}$$

and

$$y_1(k) = K_1(-0.5)^k + K_2(1.78)^k + (K_3 + jK_4)(-2.60e^{j0.754})^k$$
$$+ (K_3 - jK_4)(-2.60e^{-j0.754})^k . \tag{12.87}$$

This is the desired output of the system. Its first term is the steady-state response, whose form is that of the input. The remaining three terms are the transient response, whose form is determined by the roots of the characteristic equation. For any input the transient response consists of the same three terms. Only the literal coefficients vary. This system is unstable because the transient terms increase without bound as k increases. The rule for stability of a fixed, linear, discrete system is easily deduced: the system is stable iff all the roots of the characteristic equation lie within the unit circle. The locations of the roots of Eq. (12.83) are shown in Fig. 12.9.

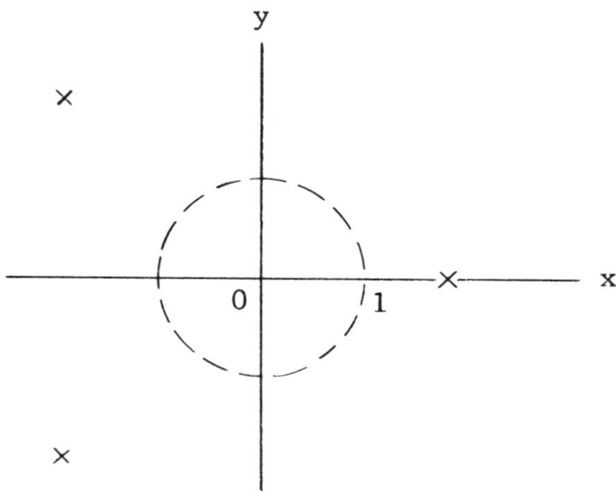

Fig. 12.9. Roots of the characteristic equation in the z plane.

The last two terms of Eq. (12.87) can be written in the more convenient form

$$K_5(2.60)^k \sin(2.386k + K_6)$$

where K_5 and K_6 are real constants. This form is derived in the appendix to this chapter, Section 12.14.

12.12 State Space

The concept of state space can be used to bring the power and majesty of matrices to bear on the solution of difference equations. The state of a system of difference equations is a set of variables that must be known at any initial value of k, say k_0, together with the inputs to the system for $k \geqslant k_0$, in order to determine the behavior of the system from k_0 to k. The number n of state variables is the number of initial or boundary conditions that must be known in order to solve the difference equations, or the degree of the characteristic equation of the transmittances. The vector array of the state variables is the state vector $\mathbf{x}(k)$. The outputs of the unit delays in a discrete system always constitute a satisfactory state vector. For the system in Fig. 12.7 a suitable state vector is

$$\mathbf{x}(k) = \begin{bmatrix} x_1(k) \\ x_2(k) \\ x_3(k) \end{bmatrix} = \begin{bmatrix} y_1(k) \\ y_1(k+1) \\ y_2(k) \end{bmatrix}. \qquad (12.88)$$

The difference equations representing a fixed, linear, discrete system can always be written as a first-order vector *state equation*:

$$\mathbf{x}(k+1) = \mathbf{A}\mathbf{x}(k) + \mathbf{B}\mathbf{v}(k)\,, \tag{12.89}$$

where $\mathbf{v}(k)$ is a vector of the inputs. For the system of Fig. 12.7,

$$\mathbf{v}(k) = \begin{bmatrix} v_1(k) \\ v_2(k) \end{bmatrix} \tag{12.90}$$

and the state equation is

$$\begin{bmatrix} y_1(k+1) \\ y_1(k+2) \\ y_2(k+1) \end{bmatrix} = \begin{bmatrix} 0 & 1 & 0 \\ 0 & -2 & -3 \\ -4 & 0 & 0 \end{bmatrix} \begin{bmatrix} y_1(k) \\ y_1(k+1) \\ y_2(k) \end{bmatrix} + \begin{bmatrix} 0 & 0 \\ 1 & 0 \\ 0 & 1 \end{bmatrix} \begin{bmatrix} v_1(k) \\ v_2(k) \end{bmatrix}. \tag{12.91}$$

The solution of the difference state equation parallels that of the differential state equation for a continuous system. First observe that for an undriven system, it is

$$\mathbf{x}(k+1) = \mathbf{A}\mathbf{x}(k)\,, \tag{12.92}$$

and assume the solution

$$\mathbf{x}(k) = \mathbf{A}^k\mathbf{x}(0)\,. \tag{12.93}$$

Since this solution satisfies the difference equation and contains n constants determined by the initial conditions, it is the correct solution. The matrix $\mathbf{A}^k$ is called the *state-transition* matrix. Now form the z transform of both sides of Eq. (12.89):

$$z\mathbf{X}(z) - z\mathbf{x}(0) = \mathbf{A}\mathbf{X}(z) + \mathbf{B}\mathbf{V}(z)\,, \tag{12.94}$$

where $\mathbf{X}(z)$ and $\mathbf{V}(z)$ are vectors of the z transforms of the elements of $\mathbf{x}(k)$ and $\mathbf{v}(k)$. Then

$$(z\mathbf{I} - \mathbf{A})\mathbf{X}(z) = z\mathbf{x}(0) + \mathbf{B}\mathbf{V}(z) \tag{12.95}$$

and

$$\begin{aligned} \mathbf{X}(z) &= z(z\mathbf{I} - \mathbf{A})^{-1}\mathbf{x}(0) + (z\mathbf{I} - \mathbf{A})^{-1}\mathbf{B}\mathbf{V}(z) \\ &= z(z\mathbf{I} - \mathbf{A})^{-1}\mathbf{x}(0) + z^{-1}[z(z\mathbf{I} - \mathbf{A})^{-1}\mathbf{B}\mathbf{V}(z)]\,. \end{aligned} \tag{12.96}$$

Comparing Eq. (12.96) for an undriven system with Eq. (12.93) shows that

$$\mathscr{Z}[\mathbf{A}^k] = z(z\mathbf{I} - \mathbf{A})^{-1}\,. \tag{12.97}$$

The bracketed term in Eq. (12.96) is the product of two z transforms:

$$z(z\mathbf{I} - \mathbf{A})^{-1}\mathbf{B} = \mathscr{Z}[\mathbf{A}^k\mathbf{B}] \tag{12.98}$$

and

$$\mathbf{V}(z) = \mathscr{Z}[\mathbf{v}(k)]\,. \tag{12.99}$$

The inverse transform is the convolution of the two functions of k:

$$\sum_{i=0}^{k} \mathbf{A}^{k-i}\mathbf{B}\mathbf{v}(i)\,, \quad k = 0,1,2,\ldots \tag{12.100}$$

which is a function of k. According to Eq. (12.55),

$$\mathcal{Z}[f(k-1)] = z^{-1}F(z)\,. \tag{12.101}$$

Therefore the last term of Eq. (12.96) is

$$z^{-1}[z(z\mathbf{I}-\mathbf{A})^{-1}\mathbf{B}\mathbf{V}(z)] = \mathcal{Z}\left[\sum_{i=0}^{k-1} \mathbf{A}^{k-1-i}\mathbf{B}\mathbf{v}(i)\right], \quad k = 1,2,3,\ldots \tag{12.102}$$

and the inverse transform of Eq. (12.96) is

$$\mathbf{x}(k) = \mathbf{A}^{k}\mathbf{x}(0) + \sum_{i=0}^{k-1} \mathbf{A}^{k-1-i}\mathbf{B}\mathbf{v}(i)\,, \quad k = 1,2,3,\ldots \tag{12.103}$$

This is the solution of the state equation (12.89). It gives the state of the system at any step k in terms of the inputs and the initial state. The calculation of numerical values of $\mathbf{x}(k)$ is a straightforward job for a computer, if the state-transition matrix $\mathbf{A}^k$ is known. This matrix can be evaluated by multiplying $\mathbf{A}$ by itself $k-1$ times, or by any of the methods used to evaluate the state-transition matrix of a continuous system, namely transforms, diagonalizing the $\mathbf{A}$ matrix, the Cayley-Hamilton remainder technique, and the transmittance method.

If once again an effort is made to escape from the notions formed by years of working with continuous systems, another simplification becomes apparent. The difference state equation (12.89) can be used directly to calculate numerical values of the state at each step, since the inputs and preceding states are known. Even if only a final value of the state is wanted, not intermediate values, or if the system is undriven, Eq. (12.89) probably requires less calculation than Eq. (12.103).

12.13 Sampled-Data Systems

Radars and pulse-modulation communication systems make use of z transforms in a way that has not been considered yet. These are called *discrete-time* or *sampled-data systems* because their inputs are periodic samples of a continuous signal. Fig. 12.10 shows an example, namely a continuous controller on a satellite, whose impulse response (a continuous function of time) is $h(t)$. The position of a commuter rocket coming up to dock at the satellite is $v(t)$. The radar on the satellite samples $v(t)$ at intervals of T seconds. The sampling process is represented by the

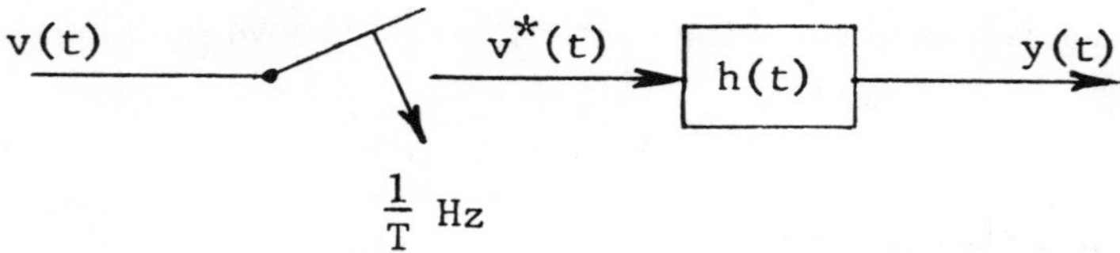

Fig. 12.10. Sampled-data system.

switch in Fig. 12.10. The input to the controller is the train of pulses shown hatched in Fig. 12.11. If the width ΔT of each pulse is narrow

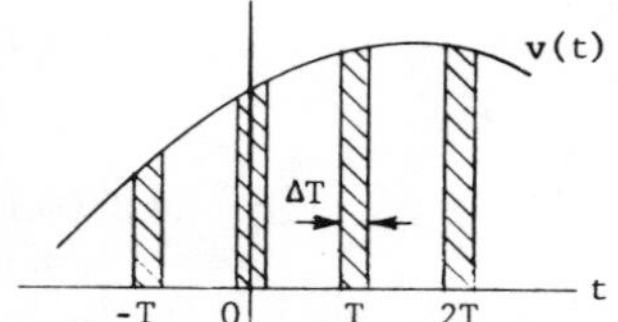

Fig. 12.11. Sampled input.

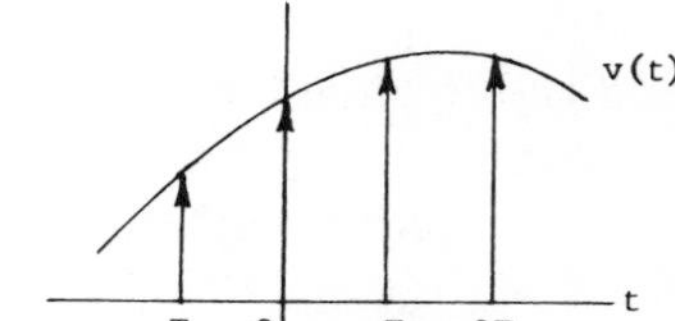

Fig. 12.12. Representation by impulses.

compared to the sampling interval T, the controller input can be represented as a train of impulses:

$$v^*(t) = \sum_{n=-\infty}^{\infty} [v(nT)\Delta T]\delta(t - nT) \tag{12.104}$$

where $\delta(t - nT)$ is a unit impulse, defined by the functional

$$f(nT) = \int_{-\infty}^{\infty} \delta(t - nT)f(t)dt\,. \tag{12.105}$$

If the constant ΔT is incorporated in the gain of the controller, its input becomes

$$\begin{aligned} v^*(t) &= \sum_{n=-\infty}^{\infty} v(nT)\delta(t - nT) \\ &= \cdots + v(-T)\delta(t + T) + v(0)\delta(t) + v(T)\delta(t - T) \\ &\quad + v(2T)\delta(t - 2T) + \cdots + v(mT)\delta(t - mT) + \cdots \end{aligned} \tag{12.106}$$

This is the train of impulses shown in Fig. 12.12.

Now calculate the Laplace transform of the impulse train. The two-sided Laplace transform of a function $f(t)$ is

$$\mathcal{L}[f(t)] = \int_{-\infty}^{\infty} f(t)e^{-st}dt\,. \tag{12.107}$$

The two-sided Laplace transform of Eq. (12.106) is

$$\mathscr{L}[v^*(t)] = V^*(s) = \cdots + v(-T)e^{sT} + v(0) + v(T)e^{-sT} + v(2T)e^{-2sT} + \cdots + v(mT)e^{-msT} + \cdots \tag{12.108}$$

The definition $z = e^{sT}$ converts this equation to the form

$$\begin{aligned}\mathscr{L}[v^*(t)]_{z=e^{sT}} &= \cdots + v(-T)z + v(0) + v(T)z^{-1} + v(2T)z^{-2} \\ &\quad + \cdots + v(mT)z^{-m} + \cdots \\ &= \sum_{n=-\infty}^{\infty} v(nT)z^{-n} .\end{aligned} \tag{12.109}$$

This is an alternate form of Eq. (12.28), and is a two-sided z transform. It is called the z transform of the *continuous* function $v(t)$. If the history of the system prior to $t = 0$ is summarized by initial conditions, $v(t)$ can be considered to be causal. It has the one-sided z transform

$$\begin{aligned}\mathscr{Z}[v(t)] = V(z) = \mathscr{Z}[v(nT)] &= \sum_{n=0}^{\infty} v(nT)z^{-n} \\ &= \mathscr{L}[v^*(t)]_{z=e^{sT}} ,\end{aligned} \tag{12.110}$$

where the Laplace transform is also one sided. The z transforms in tables constructed from Eq. (12.110) look different from those calculated previously from Eq. (12.30) because they contain T. For example, according to Eq. (12.110)

$$\begin{aligned}\mathscr{Z}[a^t] = \sum_{n=0}^{\infty} (a^{nT})z^{-n} &= \sum_{n=0}^{\infty} \left(\frac{a^T}{z}\right)^n \\ &= \frac{z}{z - a^T}, \quad |z| > |a^T| .\end{aligned} \tag{12.111}$$

Letting $T = 1$ in those tables converts the transforms to those in Table 12.1. Alternatively, if the transforms in a table have been constructed from Eq. (12.30), they can be converted to the form of Eq. (12.110). The latter yields

$$\mathscr{Z}\left[v\left(\frac{t}{T}\right)\right] = \sum_{n=0}^{\infty} v(n)z^{-n} , \tag{12.112}$$

whose right side has the form of Eq. (12.30). For example, Eq. (12.30) produced the transform

$$\mathscr{Z}[a^k] = \frac{z}{z - a}, \quad |z| > |a| . \tag{12.113}$$

Then according to Eq. (12.112),

$$\mathscr{Z}[a^{t/T}] = \frac{z}{z - a} \tag{12.114}$$

and

$$\mathscr{Z}[a^t] = \mathscr{Z}[(a^T)^{t/T}] = \frac{z}{z - a^T} \,. \tag{12.115}$$

The z transform of the output of the sampled-data system in Fig. 12.10 is found in an expected way. Since the impulse response $h(t)$ of the controller is a continuous function, the Laplace transform of the output is

$$\mathscr{L}[y(t)] = \mathscr{L}[v^*(t)]\mathscr{L}[h(t)] \,. \tag{12.116}$$

A theorem proved in Ref. 21, pages 168–169, states that if

$$\mathscr{L}[f(t)] = \mathscr{L}[f_1^*(t)]\mathscr{L}[f_2(t)] \,,$$

then

$$F^*(s) = F_1^*(s)F_2^*(s) \,. \tag{12.117}$$

In this equation each term with an asterisk is the Laplace transform of the *sampled* version of the time function. Replacing e^{sT} by z produces the form

$$F(z) = F_1(z)F_2(z) \,, \tag{12.118}$$

where $F_1(z)$ and $F_2(z)$ are the z transforms of $f_1(t)$ and $f_2(t)$. The z transform of $y(t)$ is therefore

$$Y(z) = V(z)H(z) \,, \tag{12.119}$$

where $H(z)$ is the z transform of $h(t)$. It is not a pulsed transfer function given by Eq. (12.64). Eq. (12.119) is the expression for the output of a fixed, linear, sampled-data system that might be expected. It is similar to the formula for the Laplace transform of the output of a continuous linear system. The inverse transform of Eq. (12.119) of course gives the output $y(nT)$ only at the sampling instants.

12.14 Appendix. z Transforms with Complex Poles

If a z transform $F(z)$ is a ratio of two polynomials, it is inverted by dividing both sides by z, expanding the result into partial fractions, restoring the z to the partial fractions, and inverting them individually. If $F(z)$ has a pair of complex conjugate poles, such as those in Eq. (12.86), the inverse transform of their partial fractions can be obtained conveniently by a simple trick. First the transform is written as

$$\frac{F(z)}{z} = \frac{N(z)}{D_1(z)[(z+\alpha)^2+\beta^2]} = \frac{Az+B}{[(z+\alpha)^2+\beta^2]} + \text{partial fractions for } D_1(z)\,. \tag{12.120}$$

Make the definitions

$$Me^{j\theta} = \frac{N(-\alpha+j\beta)}{D_1(-\alpha+j\beta)} \tag{12.121}$$

and

$$re^{j\omega} = -\alpha + j\beta\,. \tag{12.122}$$

The inverse transform of $F(z)$ is then

$$f(k) = \frac{M}{\beta}\,r^k \sin(\omega k+\theta) + \text{terms from } D_1(z)\,. \tag{12.123}$$

To prove this formula, write Eq. (12.120) as

$$\frac{F(z)}{z} = \frac{N(z)}{D_1(z)(z+\alpha-j\beta)(z+\alpha+j\beta)}\,. \tag{12.124}$$

Expanding the right side into partial fractions produces

$$\begin{aligned}\frac{F(z)}{z} &= \frac{N(-\alpha+j\beta)}{D_1(-\alpha+j\beta)(j2\beta)}\cdot\frac{1}{z+\alpha-j\beta}\\ &\quad+\frac{N(-\alpha-j\beta)}{D_1(-\alpha-j\beta)(-j2\beta)}\cdot\frac{1}{z+\alpha+j\beta}\\ &\quad+\text{partial fractions for } D_1(z)\,.\end{aligned} \tag{12.125}$$

If the first two terms on the right side are called $F_1(z)/z$, this equation can be written as

$$\frac{F(z)}{z} = \frac{F_1(z)}{z} + \text{partial fractions for } D_1(z) \tag{12.126}$$

where

$$\frac{F_1(z)}{z} = \frac{Me^{j\theta}}{j2\beta}\cdot\frac{1}{z-re^{j\omega}} - \frac{Me^{-j\theta}}{j2\beta}\cdot\frac{1}{z-re^{-j\omega}} \tag{12.127}$$

or

$$F_1(z) = \frac{M}{j2\beta}\left[\frac{ze^{j\theta}}{z-re^{j\omega}} - \frac{ze^{-j\theta}}{z-re^{-j\omega}}\right]. \tag{12.128}$$

The inverse transform of this equation is

$$f_1(k) = \frac{M}{\beta}\left[\frac{e^{j\theta}(re^{j\omega})^k - e^{-j\theta}(re^{-j\omega})^k}{j2}\right]$$

$$= \frac{M}{\beta} r^k \sin(\omega k + \theta) \,. \tag{12.129}$$

Finally, the inverse transform of Eq. (12.128) is

$$f(k) = f_1(k) + \text{terms from } D_1(z) \,, \tag{12.130}$$

which is Eq. (12.123). This labor-saving device is a discrete version of the Trick of Papoulis, explained in Section 2.9.

Chapter 13

NUMERICAL SOLUTION OF DIFFERENTIAL EQUATIONS

13.1 Introduction

Fixed, linear systems such as R-L-C circuits and spring-mass-damper assemblies can be represented by simultaneous linear differential equations with constant coefficients. The outputs of these systems can be found by classical solutions, Laplace transforms, solution of the standard eigenvalue problem, and state-space methods. Unfortunately, most real systems are nonlinear, and their outputs cannot be found by these elegant methods. Unless a nonlinear system is simple, calculation is practical only if the differential equations representing it are either (1) patched on an analog computer, or (2) approximated by difference equations and solved numerically. Methods of solving differential equations numerically, which have interested mathematicians ever since calculus began, are still being developed. The interest increased greatly when the digital computer arrived, with its ability to perform the tedious, repetitive arithmetic of numerical integration. No single method has emerged as the best way to solve differential equations on a digital computer. This chapter will explain three popular methods: (1) the Euler method which is the simplest, (2) the Runge-Kutta method which is easy to program, self starting, and cooperative, and (3) the Adams-Moulton method which is considered by some authorities to be faster than Runge-Kutta.

13.2 The Euler Method

The numerical solution of differential equations begins with the display of the system they represent. A block diagram is drawn with individual integrators. For example, the nonlinear differential equation

$$\frac{d^2y}{dt^2} + y\,\frac{dy}{dt} + 3\,y = w(t) \tag{13.1}$$

can be solved for its highest derivative,

$$\ddot{y} = w(t) - y\,\dot{y} - 3y \tag{13.2}$$

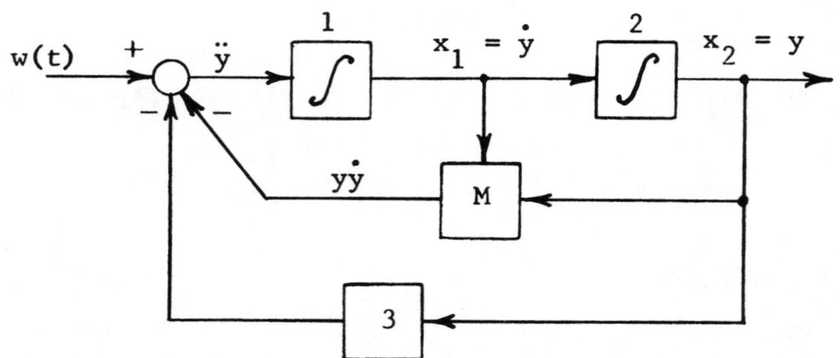

Fig. 13.1. Block diagram of a nonlinear differential equation.

and displayed by the block diagram of Fig. 13.1. In the block marked M, the two variables y and $\dot{y}$ are multiplied. Another nonlinear system is represented by the block diagram of Fig. 13.2. The diagram contains

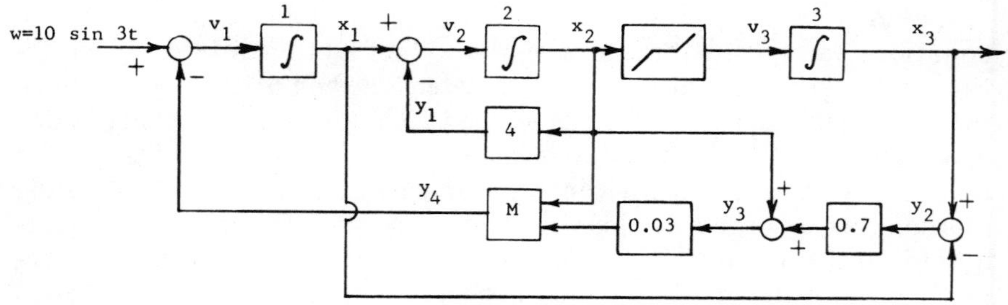

Fig. 13.2. Block diagram of a larger system.

three integrators, a multiplier, and a deadband shown in detail in Fig. 13.3. The deadband might represent the play in a steering wheel.

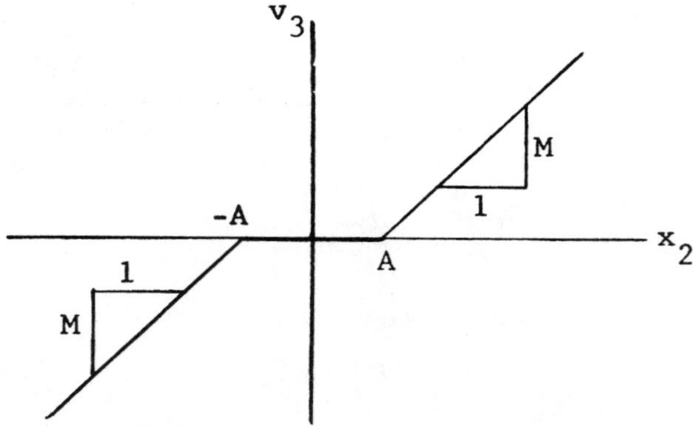

Fig. 13.3. Details of the deadband.

The variables in a system like the one in Fig. 13.2 can be calculated if the input w is known, and the integrator outputs x_1, x_2, and x_3 are known at an initial time t_0. The output of each integrator can be computed numerically at time intervals h by the *Euler method*, illustrated in Fig. 13.4. At time t_0 the output of the integrator, a continuous function of time, is $x(t_0)$ and the input is $v(t_0)$. The output is assumed to change at the rate $v(t_0)$ during the interval h, so that at the end of the interval the output is

$$x(t_0 + h) = x(t_0) + h\,v(t_0)\,. \tag{13.3}$$

This operation is performed on all of the integrators in the system. Then time is advanced to $t_0 + h$. The new values of the system inputs and the new integrator outputs $x(t_0 + h)$ are used to calculate new values of all

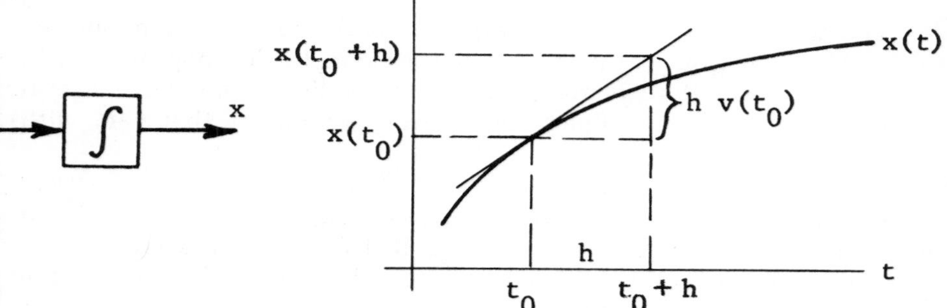

Fig. 13.4. Euler method of numerical integration.

the other variables in the system, including the integrator inputs. For the system of Fig. 13.2, the new values are

$$w = 10 \sin 3(t_0 + h) \tag{13.4}$$

$$y_2 = x_3 - x_1 \tag{13.5}$$

$$y_3 = 0.7\,y_2 + x_2 \tag{13.6}$$

$$y_4 = x_2 \cdot 0.03\,y_3 \tag{13.7}$$

$$y_1 = 4\,x_2 \tag{13.8}$$

$$v_1 = w - y_4 \tag{13.9}$$

$$v_2 = x_1 - y_1 \tag{13.10}$$

$$v_3 = \frac{M}{2}\,(x_2 - A + |x_2 - A|) + \frac{M}{2}\,(x_2 + A - |x_2 + A|)\,. \tag{13.11}$$

The equations must be ordered so that new values are used to calculate other new values. For example, Eq. (13.5) must precede Eq. (13.6) because the new value of y_2 is needed before the new y_3 can be calculated. Eq. (13.8) can appear anywhere before Eq. (13.10), because y_1 is a function of only an integrator output. The process of calculating new integrator inputs v_i, illustrated by Eqs. (13.4) thru (13.11), can be generalized by the equations

$$v_1 = f_1(t, x_1, x_2, x_3)$$
$$v_2 = f_2(t, x_1, x_2, x_3)$$
$$v_3 = f_3(t, x_1, x_2, x_3) \tag{13.12}$$

which can be consolidated elegantly into the vector form

$$\mathbf{v} = \mathbf{f}(t, \mathbf{x}) . \tag{13.13}$$

The new integrator inputs are functions of the new integrator outputs and the new value of time $t_0 + h$. In the example, time appears only in the formula for the driver, Eq. (13.4). Other systems might have several time-varying driving functions, or even parameters that vary with time.

Eqs. (13.3) and (13.13) constitute the Euler method of numerical integration. Each use of these equations advances all of the variables in the system by one time interval h. Fig. 13.4 shows that the new value of the integrator output $x(t_0 + h)$ produced by Eq. (13.3) is exact only if the actual integrator output x is a first-degree polynomial or ramp. The degree of the highest polynomial for which the numerical integration produces no error is called the *order* of the method. The Euler method is only of first order. In general, an error is committed in the calculation of each integrator output at each step. The errors accumulated when the derivative of the slope of x is negative (as in Fig. 13.4) tend to cancel those accumulated when the derivative is positive. In addition, the errors can be made small by decreasing the computing interval h. The Euler method is used in the DYNAMO program developed at the MIT Sloan School of Management for models of business and social systems.

Table 13.1 is a program in BASIC that operates the system of Fig. 13.2 by the Euler method. The initial integrator outputs are all zero, and the computing interval h is 0.0025 seconds.

13.3 The Runge-Kutta Method for a System with One Integrator

Methods of numerical integration have been developed that can achieve the same accuracy as the Euler method with a longer computing interval. Although more computation is required at each step, the net

TABLE 13.1. OPERATION OF THE SYSTEM OF FIG. 13.2 BY THE EULER METHOD

```
A               10:53EST            02/12/80

10 PRINT "T","X1","X2","X3"
20 H=.0025
30 A=.1
40 M=.5
50 GO TO 200
60 T=T+H
70 W=10*SIN(3*T)
80 Y2=X3-X1
90 Y3=.7*Y2+X2
100 Y4=X2*.03*Y3
110 Y1=4*X2
120 V1=W-Y4
130 V2=X1-Y1
140 V3=(X2-A+ABS(X2-A)+X2+A-ABS(X2+A))*M/2
150 X1=X1+H*V1
160 X2=X2+H*V2
170 X3=X3+H*V3
180 N=N+1
190 IF N<1/H THEN 230
200 PRINT T,X1,X2,X3
210 IF T>5.9 THEN 240
220 N=0
230 GO TO 60
240 END

READY
RUN

A               10:54EST            02/12/80
```

T	X1	X2	X3
0	0	0	0
1.	6.67374	1.30617	0.195881
2.	0.221983	0.453607	0.737696
3.	6.4897	1.18163	0.92919
4.	0.675621	0.636382	1.51484
5.	6.04069	1.02025	1.68848
5.99999	1.3271	0.831339	2.29814

USED 7.63 UNITS

result is a shorter total computer time. One of the most popular of these methods is the Runge-Kutta, which is practical in second, third, or fourth-order form. The derivation of this method consists of first writing an integrator output at the end of a computing interval h as a Taylor series in h:

$$x(t_0 + h) = x(t_0) + \frac{h}{1!}\dot{x}(t_0) + \frac{h^2}{2!}\ddot{x}(t_0) + \cdots \tag{13.14}$$

Then the same variable is written in a form that will be useful for calculations. For convenience, let $x(t_0) = x_0$. For the fourth-order Runge-Kutta method the form is

$$x(t_0 + h) = x_0 + \mu_1 k_1 + \mu_2 k_2 + \mu_3 k_3 + \mu_4 k_4 \tag{13.15}$$

where the μ_i's are constants, and the k_i's are functions of time and the integrator outputs. The k_i's are also expressed as Taylor series, and the terms in Eq. (13.15) are collected as a power series in h. The 13 constants in the latter equation are chosen so that the two series agree up thru the fourth power of h. The details of the derivation are shown in Section 13.9. For a system with only one integrator, Eq. (13.15) becomes

$$x(t_0 + h) = x_0 + \frac{1}{6}(k_1 + 2\,k_2 + 2\,k_3 + k_4) \tag{13.16}$$

where

$$k_1 = h\,f(t_0, x_0) \tag{13.17}$$

$$k_2 = h\,f\left(t_0 + \frac{h}{2}, x_0 + \frac{k_1}{2}\right) \tag{13.18}$$

$$k_3 = h\,f\left(t_0 + \frac{h}{2}, x_0 + \frac{k_2}{2}\right) \tag{13.19}$$

$$k_4 = h\,f(t_0 + h, x_0 + k_3)\,. \tag{13.20}$$

The last five equations constitute the fourth-order Runge-Kutta method for a system with only one integrator. They replace the simple Eq. (13.3) of the Euler method. Since the approximate Eq. (13.16) agrees with the exact Eq. (13.14) up thru the fourth power of h, the method gives exact values of integrator output $x(t)$ if this function happens to be a polynomial of any degree up to four. In general, the integrator outputs are calculated more accurately for any step size by the Runge-Kutta method than by the Euler method.

While the Euler method was explained graphically with Fig. 13.4, Eqs. (13.16) thru (13.20) defy graphical interpretation. For the purpose of computing numbers, they are more convenient if arranged in the four steps shown in Table 13.2. They start with the integrator input v_0 and output x_0 at time t_0, and compute x_4, which is $x(t_0 + h)$. Variables v_1, v_2, v_3 and x_1, x_2, x_3 are intermediate values of integrator input and output without physical significance. The auxiliary variables y_1, y_2, and y_3 are introduced to collect the values of the k_i's as they are calculated. Notice that the integrator input and output must be calculated four times in each computing interval.

13.4 The Runge-Kutta Method for a System with Several Integrators

The method can be extended to handle a system with any number of integrators. When a system contains several integrators, as in Fig. 13.2, each integrator input is a function of time and several integrator outputs, as indicated by Eqs. (13.12) and (13.13). As in the Euler method,

TABLE 13.2. THE FOURTH-ORDER RUNGE-KUTTA PROCESS

Step 1	$v_0 = f(t_0, x_0)$
	$x_1 = x_0 + \frac{h}{2} v_0$
2	$v_1 = f(t_0 + \frac{h}{2}, x_1)$
	$y_1 = v_0 + 2v_1$
	$x_2 = x_0 + \frac{h}{2} v_1$
3	$v_2 = f(t_0 + \frac{h}{2}, x_2)$
	$y_2 = y_1 + 2\, v_2$
	$x_3 = x_0 + h\, v_2$
4	$v_3 = f(t_0 + h, x_3)$
	$y_3 = y_2 + v_3$
	$x_4 = x_0 + \frac{h}{6} y_3$

these equations are used to calculate the new integrator inputs at each step. Each integrator output at the end of the next computing interval is found by formulas similar to Eqs. (13.16) thru (13.20). Each k_i is now a function of time and several integrator outputs. A repeat of the analysis in Section 13.9 for a system with two integrators is a formidable task. The result is provided by Ref. 52. A set of k_i's is needed for each integrator output, and the formula for each k_i must be modified to include both integrator outputs. The first subscript in the resulting formulas designates the integrator number:

$$x_1(t_0 + h) = x_{10} + \frac{1}{6}(k_{11} + 2\, k_{12} + 2\, k_{13} + k_{14}) \tag{13.21}$$

$$x_2(t_0 + h) = x_{20} + \frac{1}{6}(k_{21} + 2\, k_{22} + 2\, k_{23} + k_{24}) \tag{13.22}$$

where

$$k_{11} = h\, f_1(t_0, x_{10}, x_{20})$$

$$k_{12} = h\, f_1\left(t_0 + \frac{h}{2}, x_{10} + \frac{k_{11}}{2}, x_{20} + \frac{k_{21}}{2}\right)$$

$$k_{13} = h\, f_1\left(t_0 + \frac{h}{2}, x_{10} + \frac{k_{12}}{2}, x_{20} + \frac{k_{22}}{2}\right)$$

$$k_{14} = h\, f_1(t_0 + h, x_{10} + k_{13}, x_{20} + k_{23}) \tag{13.23}$$

and

$$k_{21} = h\, f_2(t_0, x_{10}, x_{20})$$

$$k_{22} = h\, f_2\left(t_0 + \frac{h}{2}, x_{10} + \frac{k_{11}}{2}, x_{20} + \frac{k_{21}}{2}\right)$$

$$k_{23} = h\, f_2\left(t_0 + \frac{h}{2}, x_{10} + \frac{k_{12}}{2}, x_{20} + \frac{k_{22}}{2}\right)$$

$$k_{24} = h\, f_2(t_0 + h, x_{10} + k_{13}, x_{20} + k_{23})\,. \qquad (13.24)$$

Similar formulas can be written for a system with any number of integrators, and summarized in the vector form

$$\mathbf{x}(t_0 + h) = \mathbf{x}_0 + \frac{1}{6}(\mathbf{k}_1 + 2\,\mathbf{k}_2 + 2\,\mathbf{k}_3 + \mathbf{k}_4)$$

where

$$\mathbf{k}_1 = h\,\mathbf{f}(t_0, \mathbf{x}_0)$$

$$\mathbf{k}_2 = h\,\mathbf{f}\left(t_0 + \frac{h}{2}, \mathbf{x}_0 + \frac{\mathbf{k}_1}{2}\right)$$

$$\mathbf{k}_3 = h\,\mathbf{f}\left(t_0 + \frac{h}{2}, \mathbf{x}_0 + \frac{\mathbf{k}_2}{2}\right)$$

$$\mathbf{k}_4 = h\,\mathbf{f}(t_0 + h, \mathbf{x}_0 + \mathbf{k}_3)\,. \qquad (13.25)$$

These five equations constitute the fourth-order Runge-Kutta method for a system with any number integrators. Their vector notation means that at each step in the calculation, the integrator outputs are all computed in parallel. Each integrator has its own function f and its own set of four k_i's.

An efficient computer program for performing the calculations in BASIC is shown in Table 13.3. The four steps of Table 13.2 are included in lines 320 thru 470. The MAT instructions permit the calculation of all the integrator inputs and outputs in parallel. Since MAT instructions require dimensioned variables, the integrator inputs are $V(1)$, $V(2)$, etc., and the integrator outputs are $X(1)$, $X(2)$, etc. The user must

1. Choose the computing interval $K1$, the printing interval $K2$, and the total time $K3$. The ratio $K2/K1$ must be an integer.

2. Set the dimensions of the vectors V, E, X, and Y in line 150 equal to the number of integrators.

3. Write the equations for the auxiliary variables that connect the integrator outputs to the integrator inputs, in correct order, in lines 230 to 260.

TABLE 13.3. A PROGRAM IN BASIC FOR SOLVING DIFFERENTIAL EQUATIONS BY THE FOURTH-ORDER RUNGE-KUTTA METHOD

```
RUNGE            17:33EDT          05/20/76

100 REM K1=COMPUTING INTERVAL, K2=PRINTING INTERVAL, K3=TOTAL TIME
110 READ K1,K2,K3
120 DATA .1,1,10
130 PRINT "T,SEC","X(1),VOLTS"
140 REM THE DIMENSION OF VECTORS V,E,X,Y IS THE NO. OF INTEGRATORS.
150 DIM B(4),V(7),E(7),X(7),Y(7)
160 MAT READ B
170  DATA .5,.5,1,2
180 ┐
190 │
200 │ Initial integrator outputs (if other than zero) and constants
210 ┘
220 FOR P=1 TO 4
230 ┐
240 │
250 │ Auxiliary variables
260 ┘
270 IF U=0 THEN 500
280 ┐
290 │
300 │ Integrator inputs V(1), V(2), etc.
310 ┘
320 ON P GO TO 330,360,360,390
330 MAT E=V
340 MAT Y=X
350 GO TO 430
360 MAT X=(2)*V
370 MAT E=E+X
380 GO TO 430
390 MAT X=E+V
400 MAT X=(K1/6)*X
410 MAT X=Y+X
420 GO TO 470
430 MAT X=(K1*B(P))*V
440 MAT X=Y+X
450 IF P=2 THEN 470
460 T=T+K1/2
470 NEXT P
480 N=N+1
490 IF N<K2/K1-.5 THEN 220
500 ┐
510 │
520 │ PRINT statements
530 ┘
540 U=U+1
550 IF T>K3-K1/2 THEN 580
560 N=0
570 GO TO 220
580 END
```

4. Write formulas for the integrator inputs in lines 280 to 310.

5. List any initial integrator outputs that are not zero, and any constants that are needed, in lines 180 to 210.

6. Write captions in line 130, and PRINT statements in lines 500 to 530.

The system in Fig. 13.2 is operated by this program in Table 13.4. The results are tabulated in Table 13.5. Notice that they agree closely with those obtained in Table 13.1 by the Euler method, but required less computer time. Notice also that the computing interval $K1$ used in Table 13.4 for the Runge-Kutta method is 50 times the step size H required for comparable accuracy by the Euler method in Table 13.1.

TABLE 13.4. OPERATION OF THE SYSTEM OF FIG. 12.2 BY THE RUNGE-KUTTA METHOD

```
B              13:55EDT              05/28/76

100 REM K1=COMPUTING INTERVAL, K2=PRINTING INTERVAL, K3=TOTAL TIME
110 READ K1,K2,K3
120 DATA .125,1,6
130 PRINT "T","X(1)","X(2)","X(3)"
140 REM THE DIMENSION OF VECTORS V,E,X,Y IS THE NO. OF INTEGRATORS.
150 DIM B(4),V(3),E(3),X(3),Y(3)
160 MAT READ B
170 DATA .5,.5,1,2
180 A=.1
190 M=.5
220 FOR P=1 TO 4
230 W=10*SIN(3*T)
240 Y2=X(3)-X(1)
250 Y3=.7*Y2+X(2)
260 Y4=X(2)*.03*Y3
265 Y1=4*X(2)
270 IF U=0 THEN 500
280 V(1)=W-Y4
290 V(2)=X(1)-Y1
300 V(3)=(X(2)-A+ABS(X(2)-A)+X(2)+A-ABS(X(2)+A))*M/2
320 ON P GO TO 330,360,360,390
330 MAT E=V
340 MAT Y=X
350 GO TO 430
360 MAT X=(2)*V
370 MAT E=E+X
380 GO TO 430
390 MAT X=E+V
400 MAT X=(K1/6)*X
410 MAT X=Y+X
420 GO TO 470
430 MAT X=(K1*B(P))*V
440 MAT X=Y+X
450 IF P=2 THEN 470
460 T=T+K1/2
470 NEXT P
480 N=N+1
490 IF N<K2/K1-.5 THEN 220
500 PRINT T,X(1),X(2),X(3)
540 U=U+1
550 IF T>K3-K1/2 THEN 580
560 N=0
570 GO TO 220
580 END
```

TABLE 13.5. RUN OF THE PROGRAM IN TABLE 13.4

T	X(1)	X(2)	X(3)
0	0	0	0
1	6.67207	1.30422	0.195945
2	0.225485	0.455429	0.737302
3	6.48465	1.17985	0.92926
4	0.682341	0.638131	1.51448
5	6.03268	1.01862	1.68856
6	1.33649	0.832868	2.29782
USED	2.98 UNITS		

13.5 Stability of Numerical Integration

If the computing interval h is too large, numerical operation of a system (i.e., numerical solution of the differential equations that represent the system) produces unbounded variables, even though the system is stable. To see why, consider the simple feedback circuit of Fig. 13.5 that has a time constant k. If k is positive, the system is stable. Now

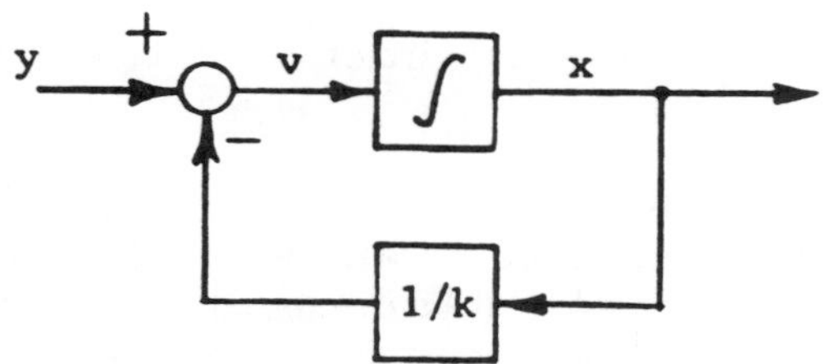

Fig. 13.5. Simple feedback circuit.

the notation of difference equations will be adopted, in which $x(n)$ and $x(n + 1)$ are the integrator outputs at times nh and $(n + 1)h$. In this circuit the driver y is a function of time, and Eq. (13.13) can be written as

$$v(n) = f[t(n), x(n)] = y(n) - \frac{1}{k} x(n) . \tag{13.26}$$

The system will be operated by the Euler method. In the new notation the new integrator output according to Eq. (13.3) is

$$x(n + 1) = x(n) + h\, v(n) . \tag{13.27}$$

Combination of these two equations produces the result

$$x(n + 1) + \left(\frac{h}{k} - 1\right) x(n) = h\, y(n) . \tag{13.28}$$

This is a first-order linear difference equation, whose transient or complementary solution is

$$x_c(n) = b\left(1 - \frac{h}{k}\right)^n , \tag{13.29}$$

where b is an arbitrary constant. If h/k is greater than 2, the transient component of the integrator output appears to increase without bound. The Euler method cannot be used to operate the circuit of Fig. 13.5 if $h/k \geqslant 2$.

If the initial integrator output $x(0)$ is zero and the input y is the unit step

$$y(n) = \begin{cases} 0, & n < 0 \\ 1, & n \geqslant 0 , \end{cases} \tag{13.30}$$

the complete solution for the integrator output is

$$x(n) = k\left[1 - \left(1 - \frac{h}{k}\right)^n\right]. \tag{13.31}$$

The step response of the actual circuit is

$$x = k(1 - e^{-t/k}) . \tag{13.32}$$

Although $x(n)$ is bounded if $h/k < 2$, it does not represent accurately the true value of x at $t = nh$ unless h/k is made considerably smaller than 2. The problem of choosing h will be discussed in the next section.

A similar analysis shows the range of h for which the fourth-order Runge-Kutta method produces bounded values of integrator output in Fig. 13.5. If Eqs. (13.16) thru (13.20) are written in difference-equation notation and combined with Eq. (13.26), the result is the difference equation

$$x(n + 2) - A\, x(n) = B\, y(n + 2) + C\, y(n + 1) + D\, y(n) \tag{13.33}$$

where

$$A = 1 - \frac{h}{k} + \frac{1}{2}\left(\frac{h}{k}\right)^2 - \frac{1}{6}\left(\frac{h}{k}\right)^3 + \frac{1}{24}\left(\frac{h}{k}\right)^4 . \tag{13.34}$$

The transient solution is

$$x_c(n) = [b_1 + (-1)^n\, b_2]A^{n/2} , \tag{13.35}$$

which is stable only if $|A| < 1$. The range of real, positive values of h/k that satisfy this requirement is

$$0 < \frac{h}{k} < 2.78529 . \tag{13.36}$$

The fourth-order Runge-Kutta method is therefore stable for the simple feedback circuit of Figs. 13.5 until h/k is almost 2.8.

13.6 The Choice of Computing Interval

To illustrate the effect of the computing step size on the accuracy of numerical integration, consider the system of Fig. 13.6, consisting of three simple feedbacks in cascade, with time constants 1/2.7, 1/0.27, and

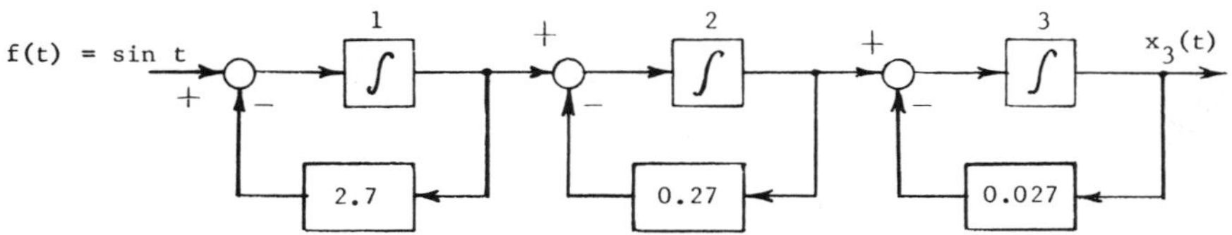

Fig. 13.6. Illustration of the effect of changing step size.

1/0.027 *s*. If the initial conditions are zero and the input is $f(t) = \sin t$, the output of the system is

$$x_3(t) = 0.0185712\, e^{-2.7t} - 1.57844\, e^{-0.27t} + 1.53843\, e^{-0.027t} + 0.335185 \sin(t + 3.07759)\,, \qquad (13.37)$$

which is plotted in Figs. 13.7. The first 10 seconds of operation of the system are calculated by the Euler method in the program of Table 13.6.

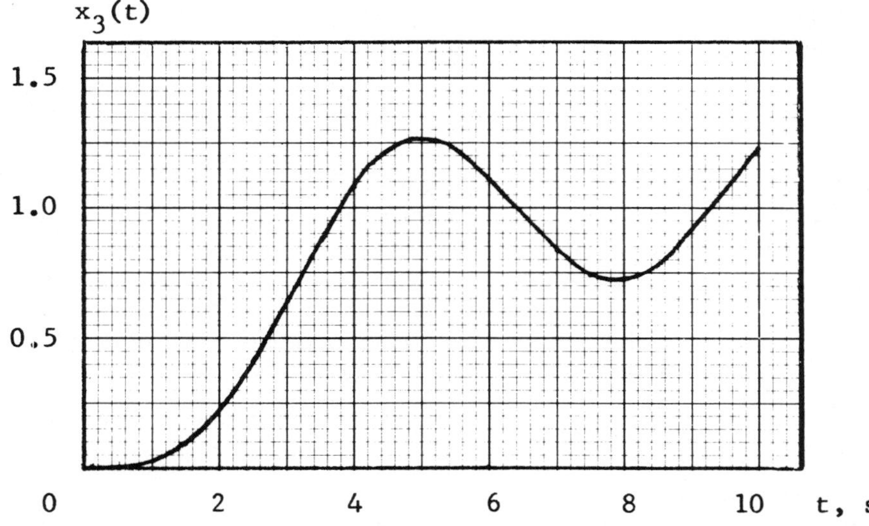

Fig. 13.7. Output of the system in Fig. 13.6.

TABLE 13.6. OPERATION OF THE SYSTEM OF FIG. 13.6 BY THE EULER METHOD

```
EULER              15:23EDT              05/24/76

100 REM K1=COMPUTING INTERVAL, K2=PRINTING INTERVAL, K3=TOTAL TIME
110 READ K1,K2,K3
120 DATA 1,1,10
130 PRINT "T","X3","ERROR"
270 GO TO 491
274 T=T+K1
280 V1=SIN(T)-2.7*X1
290 V2=X1-.27*X2
300 V3=X2-.027*X3
320 X1=X1+K1*V1
330 X2=X2+K1*V2
340 X3=X3+K*V3
360 N=N+1
490 IF N<K2/K1-.5 THEN 274
491 A=.0185712*EXP(-2.7*T)
492 B=1.57844*EXP(-.27*T)
493 C=1.53843*EXP(-.027*T)
494 D=.335185*SIN(T+3.07759)
495 E=A-B+C+D
496 F=X3-E
500 PRINT T,X3,F
550 IF T>K3-K1/2 THEN 580
560 N=0
570 GO TO 274
580 END
```

The numerical calculation of each integrator output is unstable if $h/k > 2$, where $1/k$ is the feedback gain or k is the time constant. The largest h for which the calculation is stable is therefore determined by the shortest time constant (the largest feedback gain), and is

$$h = 2\,k = \frac{2}{2.7} = 0.74 \text{ s}\,. \tag{13.38}$$

Table 13.7, the run of the Euler program, verifies this fact. The columns are time in seconds, the output of the third integrator, and the difference between the output calculated numerically and the exact output. In the first run the computing interval h is 1 s. Clearly the numerical integration is unstable. In the second run h is 0.5 s. Although the largest error of 0.0877 is substantial, the process of numerical integration is now stable. The same program was run with eight step sizes $K1$ from 0.5 down to 0.005. In each run the printing interval $K2$ was near 1 s and a multiple of $K1$, and the total time $K3$ was 10 seconds if 10 was a multiple of $K2$, or nearly 10 seconds if not. The magnitudes of the largest errors observed are plotted as a function of step size in Fig. 13.8. Notice that the largest error in the run is very nearly proportional to the step size. When the step size is halved, the largest error is halved.

TABLE 13.7. OUTPUT OF THE SYSTEM OF FIG. 13.6 CALCULATED BY THE EULER METHOD

```
120 DATA 1,1,10
RUN
EULER          15:26EDT          05/24/76

T              X3                ERROR
 0              0                  7.0408E-7
 1              0                 -2.38596E-2
 2              0                 -0.224728
 3              0.841471           0.193345
 4              0.911822          -0.172221
 5              1.98231            0.720514
 6              0.225232          -0.88479
 7              2.2717             1.44027
 8             -2.17414           -2.89761
 9              5.34174            4.43154
 10            -6.48776           -7.72007

USED           1.32 UNITS

120 DATA .5,1,10
RUN
EULER          15:28EDT          05/24/76

T              X3                ERROR
 0              0                  7.0408E-7
 1              0                 -2.38596E-2
 2              0.195166          -2.95624E-2
 3              0.664443           0.016317
 4              1.15797            7.39226E-2
 5              1.3495             8.77018E-2 <—— Largest error
 6              1.15059            4.05673E-2
 7              0.802186          -2.92492E-2
 8              0.660759          -6.27159E-2
 9              0.876283          -3.39174E-2
 10             1.25862            2.63037E-2

USED           1.38 UNITS
```

The system of Figs. 13.6 was also run for 10 seconds by the Runge-Kutta method with the help of the program RUNGE in Table 13.3. When the equations representing the system were added, the program became Table 13.8. Again the largest errors were plotted as a function of step size in Fig. 13.8. This curve illustrates the *cooperative* nature of the fourth-order Runge-Kutta method. According to inequality (13.36), the largest step size for which numerical operation of the system of Fig. 13.6 will be stable is

$$h = 2.78529\,k = \frac{2.78529}{2.7} = 1.03\,. \qquad (13.39)$$

Fig. 13.8 shows that when $h = 1$, the calculation is not only stable, but produces a maximum error of only 0.0161. If the step size is halved to 0.5, the largest error is reduced to only 0.0004. References 58 and 112

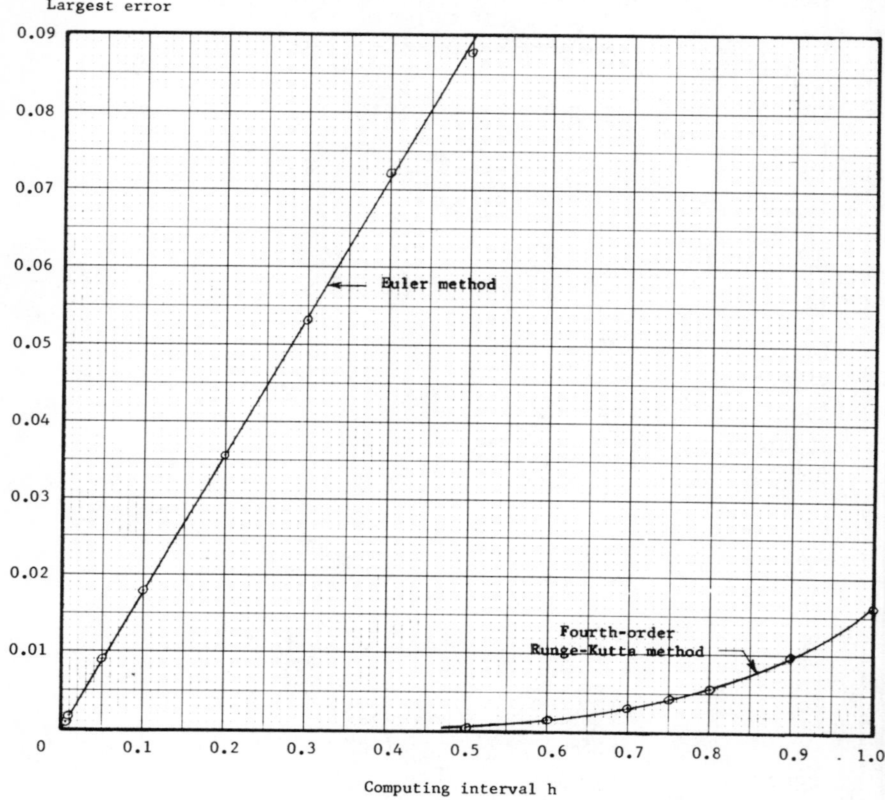

Fig. 13.8. The effect on accuracy of reducing the computing interval.

give a formula for estimating the error of an integrator output when the true value is unknown. Let X be a true integrator output at a given time in the calculation, x_{2h} be the calculated value when the step size is $2h$, x_h be the calculated value when the step size is h, and r be the order of the Runge-Kutta process. The error with the smaller step size is approximately

$$x_h - X \approx \frac{x_{2h} - x_h}{2^r - 1}. \tag{13.40}$$

In the example the true integrator output is known. The errors for two different step sizes can be compared by rearranging Eq. (13.40) to the form

$$x_h - X \approx \frac{x_{2h} - X}{2^r}. \tag{13.41}$$

TABLE 13.8. OPERATION OF THE SYSTEM OF FIG. 13.6 BY THE RUNGE-KUTTA METHOD

```
C               14:07EDT                05/28/76

100 REM K1=COMPUTING INTERVAL, K2=PRINTING INTERVAL, K3=TOTAL TIME
110 READ K1,K2,K3
120 DATA 1,1,10
130 PRINT "T","X(3)","ERROR"
140 REM THE DIMENSION OF VECTORS V,E,X,Y IS THE NO. OF INTEGRATORS.
150 DIM B(4),V(3),E(3),X(3),Y(3)
160 MAT READ B
170 DATA .5,.5,1,2
220 FOR P=1 TO 4
270 IF U=0 THEN 491
280 V(1)=SIN(T)-2.7*X(1)
290 V(2)=X(1)-.27*X(2)
300 V(3)=X(2)-.027*X(3)
320 ON P GO TO 330,360,360,390
330 MAT E=V
340 MAT Y=X
350 GO TO 430
360 MAT X=(2)*V
370 MAT E=E+X
380 GO TO 430
390 MAT X=E+V
400 MAT X=(K1/6)*X
410 MAT X=Y+X
420 GO TO 470
430 MAT X=(K1*B(P))*V
440 MAT X=Y+X
450 IF P=2 THEN 470
460 T=T+K1/2
470 NEXT P
480 N=N+1
490 IF N<K2/K1-.5 THEN 220
491 A=.0185712*EXP(-2.7*T)
492 B=1.57844*EXP(-.27*T)
493 C=1.53843*EXP(-.027*T)
494 D=.335185*SIN(T+3.07759)
495 E=A-B+C+D
496 F=X(3)-E
500 PRINT T,X(3),F
540 U=U+1
550 IF T>K3-K1/2 THEN 580
560 N=0
570 GO TO 220
580 END
```

For the fourth-order process, the error with the smaller step size is approximately

$$x_h - X \approx \frac{x_{2h} - X}{16}. \tag{13.42}$$

When the step size is halved, the error is reduced by a factor of about 16. The accuracy of the approximation increases as the step size h decreases. The curve in Fig. 13.8 shows a similar sharp reduction in the greatest error in the 10-second span, although it is not a curve of the error at a given time in the calculation, and does not extend to very small values of h. A better test of Eq. (13.42) is provided by trying $h = 0.25$ and $2h = 0.5$ in the program of Table 13.8. At $t = 2$ s, for example,

$$X = 0.224728, \qquad x_h = 0.224714, \qquad \text{and} \qquad x_{2h} = 0.224403\,. \tag{13.43}$$

Then

$$\frac{x_{2h} - X}{16} = -\ 0.0000203 \tag{13.44}$$

is approximately equal to

$$x_h - X = -\ 0.000014\,. \tag{13.45}$$

The appendix in Section 13.9 shows that the *first-order* Runge-Kutta method is the Euler method. For this method Eq. (13.41) becomes

$$x_h - X \approx \frac{x_{2h} - X}{2}\,. \tag{13.46}$$

If the step size is halved, the error is halved, and the curve of error as a function of step size is approximately a straight line. Fig. 13.8 verifies this conclusion, although its ordinate is the greatest error in a 10-second span, not the error at a given time.

The cost of computing by the two methods is shown in Fig. 13.9. In the General Electric time-sharing computer service, computer units are a combination of time and various functions performed by the computer. The user is charged a fixed rate for computer units, which are therefore a measure of the relative cost of the various numerical-integration calculations. Fig. 13.9 shows that

1. To achieve a given small maximum error, the fourth-order Runge-Kutta method (hereafter called RK4) costs less than the Euler method.

2. The curve for the Euler method has a knee beyond which the cost increases rapidly.

3. The cost of RK4 does not increase much when the step size is decreased to achieve the usual engineering accuracies. The Runge-Kutta curve in Fig. 13.9 has a knee, not shown, in the range of very low errors.

Although Figs. 13.8 and 13.9 apply only for the system in Fig. 13.6, they illustrate the usual behavior of the two methods. Unlike the Euler method, RK4 cooperates with the user in three respects:

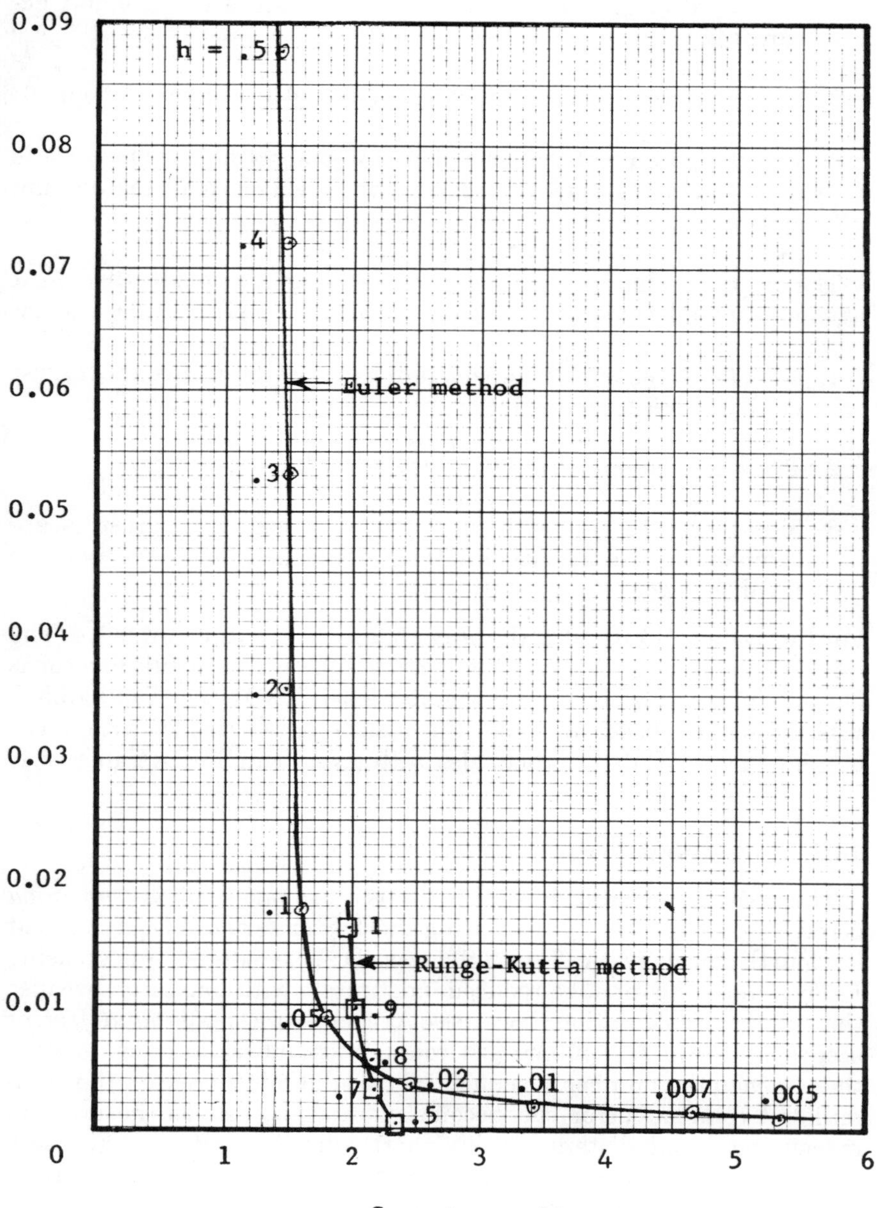

Fig. 13.9. The cost in computer units of accuracy for the Euler and fourth-order Runge-Kutta methods. The computing interval h is listed beside each datum.

1. If the computing interval h is just small enough to make the numerical integration stable, the calculations are reasonably accurate.

2. If the step size is halved, the error is reduced by a factor of about 16.

3. The computer cost does not increase sharply as the step size is reduced, in the range of values that yield normal engineering accuracies.

The choice of computing interval for operating a system by RK4 must be made by trial and error. A logical procedure consists of these steps:

1. Look for the shortest time constant k in the system, i.e., the largest gain $1/k$ in a feedback loop.

2. Try a convenient step size h just below 2.8 k.

3. Make another run with half that step size. If the results are comparable, use the larger h. If not, continue to halve the step size until the accuracy is satisfactory.

For the system of Fig. 13.2, the only apparent time constant is 1/4. The limiting step size is therefore about $2.8/4 = 0.7$ s. The calculation turns out to be unstable when h is 1 and stable when h is 0.5. For Table 13.5, h was reduced to 0.125 to make the results agree closely with those obtained by the Euler method, also with a very small h, in Table 13.1.

13.7 More about Errors

The error $x_h - X$ that has been discussed so far is called *truncation* error. It is committed by truncating the Taylor series of Eq. (13.14) at the fourth power of h. As Fig. 13.8 shows, it can be reduced by decreasing h. The step size cannot be reduced indefinitely with impunity, because the number of calculations increases. At each step a small *roundoff error* occurs, since the computer must round off numbers in order to store them. When the number of sequential calculations increases, the accumulated roundoff error can become significant, just as the error in measuring a long distance with a short ruler is significant. Fig. 13.8 shows that the roundoff error was not noticeable for the step sizes used in running the sample system.

Numerical integration is also vulnerable to error when a nonlinear parameter in the system contains a discontinuity. An example is shown in Fig. 13.10, that contains a sgn function:

$$\operatorname{sgn} x = \begin{cases} 1, & x > 0 \\ -1, & x < 0 \\ 0, & x = 0\,. \end{cases} \tag{13.47}$$

If the driving function $w(t)$ is always between 10 and -10, the integrator input $v(t)$ is negative whenever the output $x(t)$ is positive, and vice versa. If the initial integrator output x_0 is zero, the output is therefore always zero. This result is not obtained by operating the system with RK4. The details of the calculation can be shown by following the steps of Table 13.2. When $x_0 = 0+$, and the driver is the unit step $w(t) = U(t)$, and the computing interval h has the value 0.1 that seems small enough to make the numerical integration stable, the numbers appear as in Table 13.9. Several irregularities are apparent. The integrator input has only the values -9 and 11, and alternates between them. At $t = 0.1$ the integrator output is $x_4 = 0.1$, not zero. Repeating the four-step process for the

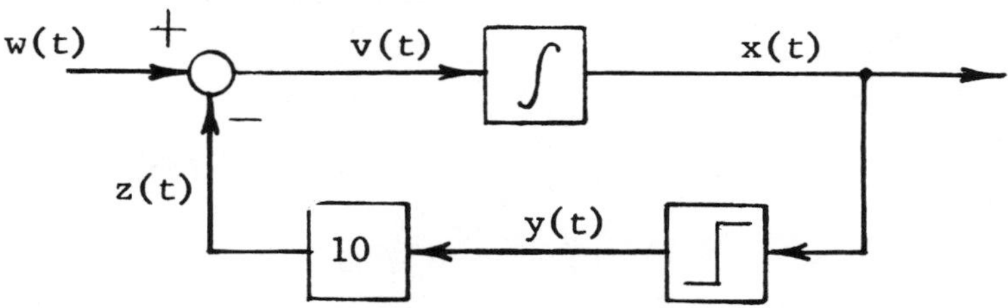

Fig. 13.10. Parameter containing a discontinuity.

TABLE 13.9. OPERATION OF THE SYSTEM IN FIG. 13.10 WITH RK4

Step 1	$v_0 = 1 - 10 = -9$
	$x_1 = x_0 + \frac{h}{2} v_0 = -0.45$
2	$v_1 = 1 + 10 = 11$
	$y_1 = v_0 + 2\,v_1 = -9 + 22 = 13$
	$x_2 = x_0 + \frac{h}{2} v_1 = 0.55$
3	$v_2 = 1 - 10 = -9$
	$y_2 = y_1 + 2\,v_2 = 13 - 18 = -5$
	$x_3 = x_0 + h\,v_2 = -0.9$
4	$v_3 = 1 + 10 = 11$
	$y_3 = y_2 + v_3 = -5 + 11 = 6$
	$x_4 = x_0 + \frac{h}{6} y_3 = 0.1$

next four computing intervals produces values of x_4 that are 0.2, 0.3, 0.4, and 0.5 instead of zero. Clearly RK4 cannot integrate accurately when the integrator input must alternate between a large positive and a large negative value. One solution of the problem consists of giving the vertical part of the sgn function a finite slope, as in Fig. 13.11. The new function can be represented by the expression

$$y = \frac{x}{A} + \frac{1}{2}[1 + \mathrm{sgn}(x - A)]\left(1 - \frac{x}{A}\right) + \frac{1}{2}[1 + \mathrm{sgn}(-x - A)]\left(-1 - \frac{x}{A}\right) \tag{13.48}$$

When the step size h is reduced to 0.01 and $A = 0.04$, RK4 produces accurate results. The modified sgn function acts as a gain of 25, and the integrator output rises to its steady value of 0.004 with a time constant

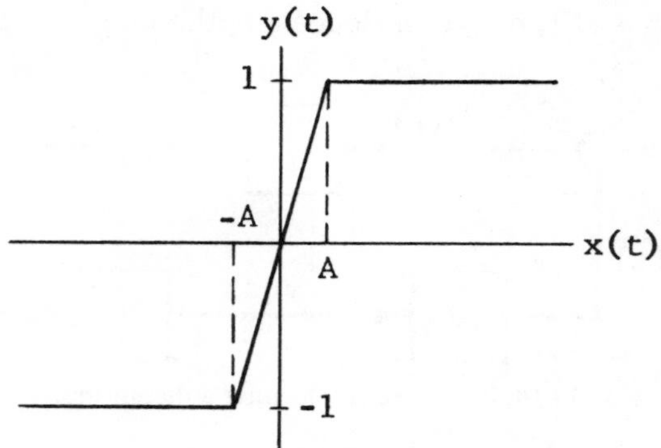

Fig. 13.11. Modified sgn function.

of 1/250. Since now $h/k = (0.01)(250) = 2.5$, the numerical integration is stable. When A is reduced to 0.03, the calculation is erratic and inaccurate. The maximum slope that can be tolerated by RK4 is just above 25, namely, 27.8529. Even if a slope is chosen that makes the numerical integration accurate, the modified sgn function may no longer represent the discontinuity in the real system accurately. One way to tell is to try various smaller slopes, and see if changing the slope has a significant effect on the variables in the system. If it does not, the effect of reducing the slope from infinity to 25 is probably not significant either.

This method of modifying a discontinuity, and the brute-force method of estimating the effect of the modification on the system variables, is applicable for any discontinuity in any system.

13.8 Predictor-Corrector Methods

Many methods of numerical integration can be classified as either single-step or predictor-corrector. The single-step methods, of which

Runge-Kutta is an example, are self starting. If the initial state vector (consisting of the initial values of all of the integrator outputs) is known, the calculation can begin. No previous value of integrator input v or output x is required. As the calculation proceeds, old values of v and x are discarded because only the present values of x are needed at the start of each computing interval. This feature of the method, which is an advantage in starting, has been criticized because old information is thrown away which might help in the calculation of new integrator outputs. Two other disadvantages of Runge-Kutta are the difficulty of determining the truncation error at each step, and the fixed step size h. If the integrator outputs are changing rapidly and the errors are large, the step size is the same as if the variables are changing slowly and the errors are small.

These three criticisms are overcome by the *predictor-corrector* methods, illustrated by the fourth-order Adams-Moulton method. Let v_n and x_n be an integrator input and output at step n. Starting with x_n, this method calculates *predicted* values of v_{n+1} and x_{n+1}:

$$x_{n+1}^p = x_n + \frac{h}{24}(55\, v_n - 59\, v_{n-1} + 37\, v_{n-2} - 9\, v_{n-3}) \tag{13.49}$$

and

$$v_{n+1}^p = f(t_{n+1}, x_{n+1}^p)\,. \tag{13.50}$$

Then *corrected* values are calculated:

$$x_{n+1} = x_n + \frac{h}{24}(9\, v_{n+1}^p + 19\, v_n - 5\, v_{n-1} + v_{n-2}) \tag{13.51}$$

and

$$v_{n+1} = f(t_{n+1}, x_{n+1})\,. \tag{13.52}$$

Notice that the method is not self starting. Before the calculation can begin, three previous values of the integrator input must be calculated. Several methods can be used to obtain these previous values, the most common of which is the Runge-Kutta method. At each step in the calculation, the difference between x_{n+1}^p and x_{n+1} provides an estimate of the truncation error. The program can therefore include an automatic increase or decrease of step size to keep the error within a chosen limit, thereby minimizing the computing time. Notice also that the fourth-order Adams-Moulton method requires only two calculations of the integrator inputs $f(t, x)$ during each computing interval, while RK4 requires four. For these reasons, some authorities such as Hamming (Ref. 52, page 212) and Ralston (Ref. 108, page 203) consider predictor-corrector methods to be generally faster than Runge-Kutta. Because the step-size adjustment and auxiliary starting procedure add to the length of predictor-corrector programs, they are usually used in the batch mode on computers in which storage is not a serious limitation. One such program is ADA (Automated Dynamic Analyzer), developed at the General Electric Corporate Research and Development Center. On time-shared computers, program length is limited, and the shorter Runge-Kutta procedures are more attractive. On the General Electric time-sharing system the analyst may use the canned, user-oriented Runge-Kutta program DYSIM***, or may construct his or her own by filling in the blanks in Table 13.3.

Runge-Kutta is not necessarily the second-best method. At least one reputable analyst, P.R. Benyon (Ref. 4) has tried various methods on a representative problem and found that (1) RK4 is faster than either of two fourth-order predictor-corrector methods (Adams-Bashforth and Adams-Moulton), and (2) the *second-order* Runge-Kutta method, RK2, is faster than either RK1, RK3, or RK4. The development of numerical-integration methods continues, but is not likely to produce a single method whose speed for a given accuracy is superior to that of all other methods in the solution of all differential equations.

13.9 Appendix. Derivation of the Runge-Kutta Method

The Integrator Output as a Taylor Series. In a typical system containing n integrators, like that in Fig. 13.2, each integrator input v_i is a function of time t and all of the integrator outputs x_i. Thus

$$v_i = \frac{dx_i}{dt} = f_i(t, x_1, x_2, x_3 , \ldots x_n) . \tag{13.53}$$

If the system has only one integrator, this equation can be written as

$$\frac{dx}{dt} = \dot{x} = f(t, x) . \tag{13.54}$$

For the example in Fig. 13.12,

$$\dot{x} = \sin 3\, t - e^x . \tag{13.55}$$

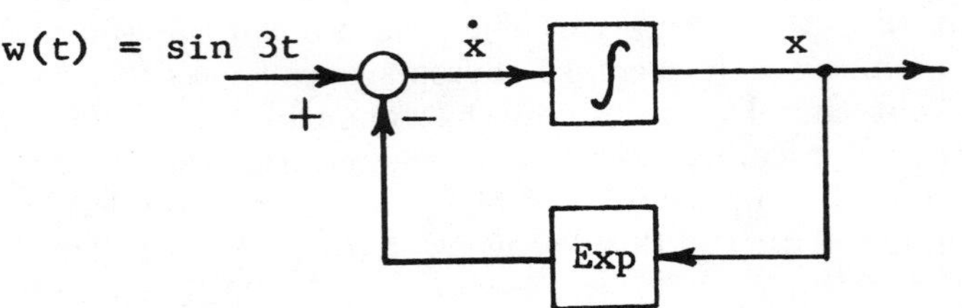

Fig. 13.12. A system with one integrator.

The derivation of the Runge-Kutta method begins with a one-integrator system, whose integrator output at time t_0 is $x(t_0)$. If $x(t)$ has a continuous derivative during the subsequent time interval h, its value at $t_0 + h$ can be written as a Taylor series:

$$x(t_0 + h) = x(t_0) + \frac{h}{1!}\dot{x}(t_0) + \frac{h^2}{2!}\ddot{x}(t_0) + \cdots \tag{13.56}$$

Let the initial integrator output be $x(t_0) = x_0$. Then

$$x(t_0 + h) = x_0 + \frac{h}{1!}\dot{x}_0 + \frac{h^2}{2!}\ddot{x}_0 + \cdots \tag{13.57}$$

Next express the series in terms of $f(t, x)$ and its derivatives evaluated at (t_0, x_0). The first two derivatives are

$$\frac{df(t, x)}{dt} = \ddot{x} = \frac{\partial f}{\partial t} + \frac{\partial f}{\partial x}\frac{dx}{dt} = \frac{\partial f}{\partial t} + \frac{\partial f}{\partial x} f \tag{13.58}$$

and

$$\begin{aligned}
\frac{d}{dt}\left(\frac{df}{dt}\right) = \dddot{x} &= \frac{\partial}{\partial t}\left(\frac{df}{dt}\right) + \frac{\partial}{\partial x}\left(\frac{df}{dt}\right)\frac{dx}{dt} \\
&= \frac{\partial}{\partial t}\left(\frac{\partial f}{\partial t} + \frac{\partial f}{\partial x} f\right) + f\frac{\partial}{\partial x}\left(\frac{\partial f}{\partial t} + \frac{\partial f}{\partial x} f\right) \\
&= \frac{\partial^2 f}{\partial t^2} + f\frac{\partial^2 f}{\partial t \partial x} + \frac{\partial f}{\partial t}\frac{\partial f}{\partial x} + f\frac{\partial^2 f}{\partial t \partial x} + f^2\frac{\partial^2 f}{\partial x^2} + f\left(\frac{\partial f}{\partial x}\right)^2 \\
&= \frac{\partial^2 f}{\partial t^2} + 2f\frac{\partial^2 f}{\partial t \partial x} + f^2\frac{\partial^2 f}{\partial x^2} + \frac{\partial f}{\partial t}\frac{\partial f}{\partial x} + f\left(\frac{\partial f}{\partial x}\right)^2 .
\end{aligned} \tag{13.59}$$

For convenience, let the initial integrator input be

$$\dot{x}(t_0) = \dot{x}_0 = f(t_0, x_0) = f_0 . \tag{13.60}$$

The series of Eq. (13.57) becomes

$$\begin{aligned}
x(t_0 + h) &= x_0 + h\, f_0 + \frac{h^2}{2}\left(\frac{\partial f_0}{\partial t} + f_0\frac{\partial f_0}{\partial x}\right) \\
&+ \frac{h^3}{6}\left[\frac{\partial^2 f_0}{\partial t^2} + 2\, f_0\frac{\partial^2 f_0}{\partial t \partial x} + f_0^2\frac{\partial^2 f_0}{\partial x^2} + \frac{\partial f_0}{\partial t}\frac{\partial f_0}{\partial x} + f_0\left(\frac{\partial f_0}{\partial x}\right)^2\right] + \cdots
\end{aligned} \tag{13.61}$$

Now the integrator output at the end of the time interval h has been expressed as a Taylor series, in terms of the initial integrator input f_0 and its derivatives.

A Form for Use in Calculations. The integrator output at time $t_0 + h$ can be expressed approximately by a formula that will be useful for calculations:

$$x(t_0 + h) = x_0 + \mu_1 k_1 + \mu_2 k_2 + \mu_3 k_3 + \cdots \tag{13.62}$$

where

$$\begin{aligned} k_1 &= h f(t_0, x_0) \\ k_2 &= h f(t_0 + \alpha_1 h, x_0 + \beta_1 k_1) \\ k_3 &= h f(t_0 + \alpha_2 h, x_0 + \beta_2 k_1 + \gamma_1 k_2) \\ k_4 &= h f(t_0 + \alpha_3 h, x_0 + \beta_3 k_1 + \gamma_2 k_2 + \delta_1 k_3) \\ &\text{etc.} \end{aligned} \tag{13.63}$$

All of the Greek letters are constants that will be evaluated. Notice that if $\mu_1 = 1$ and $\mu_2 = \mu_3 = \cdots = 0$,

$$x(t_0 + h) = x_0 + h f(t_0, x_0) , \tag{13.64}$$

which is the same as Eq. (13.3). Then the Runge-Kutta method is first-order, and becomes the Euler method. To obtain a process of higher order, write each k_i as a Taylor series with two independent variables. With the understanding that $f_0 = f(t_0, x_0)$, this series is

$$\begin{aligned} f[(t_0 + a), (x_0 + b)] = f_0 &+ \left(a \frac{\partial f_0}{\partial t} + b \frac{\partial f_0}{\partial x} \right) \\ &+ \frac{1}{2!}\left(a^2 \frac{\partial^2 f_0}{\partial t^2} + 2\, a\, b \frac{\partial^2 f_0}{\partial t \partial x} + b^2 \frac{\partial^2 f_0}{\partial x^2} \right) \\ &+ \cdots \\ &+ \frac{1}{n!} \sum_{r=0}^{n} \binom{n}{r} a^{n-r} b^r \frac{\partial^n f_0}{\partial t^{n-r} \partial x^r} \\ &+ \cdots \end{aligned} \tag{13.65}$$

where $\binom{n}{r}$ is the number of combinations of n things taken r at a time. Applying this formula to Eqs. (13.63) yields the series

$$k_1 = h f_0 \tag{13.66}$$

$$\begin{aligned} k_2 &= h f_0 + h^2 \left(\alpha_1 \frac{\partial f_0}{\partial t} + \beta_1 f_0 \frac{\partial f_0}{\partial x} \right) \\ &+ \frac{h^3}{2}\left(\alpha_1^2 \frac{\partial^2 f_0}{\partial t^2} + 2\, \alpha_1 \beta_1 f_0 \frac{\partial^2 f_0}{\partial t \partial x} + \beta_1^2 f_0^2 \frac{\partial^2 f_0}{\partial x^2} \right) + h^4(\quad) + \cdots \end{aligned} \tag{13.67}$$

$$k_3 = h\, f_0 + h^2 \left[\alpha_2 \frac{\partial f_0}{\partial t} + (\beta_2 + \gamma_1)\, f_0 \frac{\partial f_0}{\partial x} \right] + h^3 \left[\gamma_1 \left(\alpha_1 \frac{\partial f_0}{\partial t} + \beta_1 f_0 \frac{\partial f_0}{\partial x} \right) \frac{\partial f_0}{\partial x} \right.$$

$$\left. + \frac{1}{2} \left\{ \alpha_2^2 \frac{\partial^2 f_0}{\partial t^2} + 2\, \alpha_2 (\beta_2 + \gamma_1)\, f_0 \frac{\partial^2 f_0}{\partial t \partial x} + (\beta_2 + \gamma_1)^2 f_0^2 \frac{\partial^2 f_0}{\partial x^2} \right\} \right]$$

$$+ h^4(\quad) + \cdots \tag{13.68}$$

Can the Greek letters be chosen so that Eq. 13.62 agrees exactly with the true integrator output given by Eq. (13.61)? Unfortunately, an infinite number of terms would be needed in Eq. (13.62). The method can be made third-order if only the first three k_i's in Eq. (13.62) are retained. All of the remaining Greek letters can be evaluated by equating the coefficients of like powers of h in Eqs. (13.61) and (13.62) up to the third power. The powers of h in Eq. (13.62) are shown in Eqs. (13.66) thru (13.68). The first terms of Eqs. (13.61) and (13.62) are identical. Equating the coefficients of the first, second, and third powers of h, respectively, yields

$$f_0 = \mu_1 f_0 + \mu_2 f_0 + \mu_3 f_0\,, \tag{13.69}$$

$$\frac{1}{2}\left(\frac{\partial f_0}{\partial t} + f_0 \frac{\partial f_0}{\partial x} \right) = \mu_2 \left(\alpha_1 \frac{\partial f_0}{\partial t} + \beta_1 f_0 \frac{\partial f_0}{\partial x} \right)$$

$$+ \mu_3 \left[\alpha_2 \frac{\partial f_0}{\partial t} + (\beta_2 + \gamma_1)\, f_0 \frac{\partial f_0}{\partial x} \right], \tag{13.70}$$

and

$$\frac{1}{6}\left[\frac{\partial^2 f_0}{\partial t^2} + 2\, f_0 \frac{\partial^2 f_0}{\partial t \partial x} + f_0^2 \frac{\partial^2 f_0}{\partial x^2} + \frac{\partial f_0}{\partial t} \frac{\partial f_0}{\partial x} + f_0 \left(\frac{\partial f_0}{\partial x} \right)^2 \right]$$

$$= \frac{\mu_2}{2} \left(\alpha_1^2 \frac{\partial^2 f_0}{\partial t^2} + 2\, \alpha_1 \beta_1 f_0 \frac{\partial^2 f_0}{\partial t \partial x} + \beta_1^2 f_0^2 \frac{\partial^2 f_0}{\partial x^2} \right)$$

$$+ \mu_3 \left[\gamma_1 \left(\alpha_1 \frac{\partial f_0}{\partial t} + \beta_1 f_0 \frac{\partial f_0}{\partial x} \right) \frac{\partial f_0}{\partial x} + \frac{1}{2} \left\{ \alpha_2^2 \frac{\partial^2 f_0}{\partial t^2} + 2\, \alpha_2 (\beta_2 + \gamma_1)\, f_0 \frac{\partial^2 f_0}{\partial t \partial x} \right. \right.$$

$$\left. \left. + (\beta_2 + \gamma_1)^2 f_0^2 \frac{\partial^2 f_0}{\partial x^2} \right\} \right]. \tag{13.71}$$

If these three equations are satisfied, Eqs. (13.61) and (13.62) agree thru the first three powers of h. To satisfy the three equations, equate coefficients of the various derivatives of $f(t, x)$. Eq. (13.69) shows that

$$\mu_1 + \mu_2 + \mu_3 = 1\,. \tag{13.72}$$

According to Eq. (13.70),

$$\alpha_1 \mu_2 + \alpha_2 \mu_3 = \frac{1}{2} \tag{13.73}$$

and

$$\beta_1 \mu_2 + (\beta_2 + \gamma_1) \mu_3 = \frac{1}{2}. \tag{13.74}$$

According to Eq. (13.71),

$$\frac{1}{2} \alpha_1^2 \mu_2 + \frac{1}{2} a_2^2 \mu_3 = \frac{1}{6} \tag{13.75}$$

$$\alpha_1 \beta_1 \mu_2 + \alpha_2(\beta_2 + \gamma_1) \mu_3 = \frac{1}{3} \tag{13.76}$$

$$\frac{1}{2} \beta_1^2 \mu_2 + \frac{1}{2} (\beta_2 + \gamma_1)^2 \mu_3 = \frac{1}{6} \tag{13.77}$$

$$\alpha_1 \gamma_1 \mu_3 = \frac{1}{6} \tag{13.78}$$

$$\beta_1 \gamma_1 \mu_3 = \frac{1}{6}. \tag{13.79}$$

Of the last eight equations, only six are independent. To show this, observe that according to Eqs. (13.78) and (13.79), $\alpha_1 = \beta_1$. Substituting this fact into Eq. (13.73) and comparing it to Eq. (13.74) shows that $\alpha_2 = \beta_2 + \gamma_1$. Now Eqs. (13.75), (13.76), and (13.77) are identical. If the last two are eliminated, the six independent equations in the eight variables α_1, α_2, β_1, β_2, γ_1, μ_1, μ_2, and μ_3 can be written as

$$\mu_1 + \mu_2 + \mu_3 = 1 \tag{13.80}$$

$$\alpha_1 \mu_2 + \alpha_2 \mu_3 = \frac{1}{2} \tag{13.81}$$

$$\alpha_2 = \beta_2 + \gamma_1 \tag{13.82}$$

$$\alpha_1^2 \mu_2 + \alpha_2^2 \mu_3 = \frac{1}{3} \tag{13.83}$$

$$\alpha_1 \gamma_1 \mu_3 = \frac{1}{6} \tag{13.84}$$

$$\alpha_1 = \beta_1 . \tag{13.85}$$

Two of the variables can be chosen arbitrarily. With the choices

$$\alpha_1 = \frac{1}{2}, \quad \alpha_2 = 1, \tag{13.86}$$

the other variables are

$$\beta_1 = \frac{1}{2}, \quad \beta_2 = -1, \quad \gamma_1 = 2, \quad \mu_1 = \frac{1}{6}, \quad \mu_2 = \frac{2}{3}, \quad \mu_3 = \frac{1}{6}. \tag{13.87}$$

Notice that if only the first two k_i's in Eq. (13.62) had been retained, the μ_3 term in Eq. (13.71) would not be present, and this equation could not be satisfied. If the first four k_i's in Eq. (13.62) had been retained, the eight equations (13.72) thru (13.79) would contain five more unnecessary Greek letters. The analysis continues with the correct number of k_i's, namely three. Eq. (13.62) becomes

$$x(t_0 + h) \approx x_0 + \frac{1}{6}(k_1 + 4\,k_2 + k_3) \tag{13.88}$$

and according to Eqs. (13.63),

$$k_1 = h\,f(t_0, x_0) \tag{13.89}$$

$$k_2 = h\,f\left(t_0 + \frac{h}{2}, x_0 + \frac{k_1}{2}\right) \tag{13.90}$$

$$k_3 = h\,f(t_0 + h, x_0 - k_1 + 2\,k_2)\,. \tag{13.91}$$

Eqs. (13.88) thru (13.91) constitute the third-order Runge-Kutta method for calculating $x(t_0 + h)$, the approximate value of the integrator output x at time $t_0 + h$. If x is a third-degree polynomial in t, the Taylor-series expansion of $x(t_0 + h)$ given by Eq. (13.61) terminates at the h^3 term, and the third-order Runge-Kutta method gives exact results.

The Fourth-Order Runge-Kutta Method. If the first four k_i's are retained in Eq. (13.62), and Eqs. (13.61) and (13.62) are made to agree thru the fourth power of h, two of the 13 Greek letters are arbitrary. Runge made the choice $\alpha_1 = 1/2$, $\delta_1 = 1$. Eqs. (13.62) and (13.63) then became

$$x(t_0 + h) = x_0 + \frac{1}{6}(k_1 + 2\,k_2 + 2\,k_3 + k_4) \tag{13.92}$$

where

$$k_1 = h\,f(t_0, x_0) \tag{13.93}$$

$$k_2 = h\, f\left(t_0 + \frac{h}{2}, x_0 + \frac{k_1}{2}\right) \tag{13.94}$$

$$k_3 = h\, f\left(t_0 + \frac{h}{2}, x_0 + \frac{k_2}{2}\right) \tag{13.95}$$

$$k_4 = h\, f(t_0 + h, x_0 + k_3)\,. \tag{13.96}$$

These are the equations of the fourth-order Runge-Kutta method. They integrate Eq. (13.54) exactly if $x(t)$ is a polynomial of degree four or less.

Chapter 14

SYSTEM DYNAMICS: THE APPLICATION OF CONTROL THEORY TO BUSINESS AND SOCIAL PROBLEMS

14.1 The Controversy

The idea of applying feedback-control theory to the relationships between people instead of electrical components is relatively new. This application, called *system dynamics*, was introduced to the world by Jay W. Forrester in 1961 in his book *Industrial Dynamics* (Ref. 35). Since then he has published *Urban Dynamics* (Ref. 36) and *World Dynamics* (Ref. 37), and other people have applied the technique to a variety of social problems. A few examples are narcotics addiction in a section of New York City, the use and conservation of natural gas, and the rise and fall of popular magazines. The method has two big advantages:

1. It requires the human mind to investigate each portion of the system in detail, and the computer to calculate the many interrelated variables. This arrangement allows each partner to do the job it does better.

2. It replaces arguments about political or economic theories with discussions about how the model might be changed.

The disadvantage of system dynamics is that in reducing human relations to equations, the analyst must make dozens of assumptions, any of which might be challenged. Some system-dynamics studies produce controversial, counter-intuitive results. For example, Forrester's study of the world ecology (Ref. 37) showed that humanity can avoid an intolerable future by, among other things, reducing the production of food by 20 percent, and reducing the money spent on capital investment (including the industrialization of underdeveloped nations) by 40 percent. The less thoughtful opponents of such results attack the results or their author. The more thoughtful investigate the model, and suggest reasonable changes. The latter people share with the author the greatest benefit of system dynamics, namely *insight* into how the system being studied actually works.

14.2 Control Theory Applied to Business Systems

One of the reasons for the development of system dynamics was the unexplained cyclic nature of many businesses. Clearly the skiing or toy industry has an unavoidable cycle of one year. But why did the manufacturers of power-generating machinery experience fluctuations in their business before 1974, when the annual peak demand for electric power increased smoothly along an exponentially-increasing curve? These fluctuations caused cycles of layoffs and price cutting, followed by periods of rapid hiring and factory expansion (Ref. 87). In attempting to make a mathematical model of a business, Forrester decided that the important variables in a business system include rates of flow and levels of materials, orders, money, personnel, capital equipment, and information. A control engineer can easily visualize a rate of flow and a level as the input and output of an integrator. Other operations in a business consist of the delay of a variable, the summation of several variables, or the generation of one variable as a nonlinear function of another. Quite logically then, Forrester's models can be displayed as continuous-system block diagrams that look like the analog-computer model of an electromechanical system. For the benefit of non-technical readers, Forrester adopted novel symbols for use in his block diagrams, and a specialized way of writing the equations relating the variables, that are used by many others in the field. A special-purpose computer compiler, DYNAMO, (Ref. 107) has been developed for generating computer programs using the specialized equations. Although these conventions are useful, they are not necessary. Showing the block diagram of a business system with integrators, summing junctions, and gain coefficients is a convenience for the engineer who is already familiar with analog computers. This form of the block diagram is also more convenient for the analyst who writes the program in BASIC or FORTRAN rather than DYNAMO. Because of the large number of nonlinear blocks in the model of a typical business or social system, and the greater availability of digital computers, the model is usually operated by numerical integration on a digital computer rather than on an analog computer.

Forrester's early models explained the oscillatory nature of business cycles. Since the models contained integrators and feedback loops, they had natural frequencies. If the damping was low, the variables in the model suffered large periodic swings when the input or a system parameter was perturbed. Although the managers of such a business are tempted to blame the cycles on outside influences, the business is responsible for its own cycles. The model is a help in devising ways of smoothing the oscillations. If the analyst is familiar enough with the business to know which changes are feasible, he can make changes in the parameters and structure of the model that look promising, and then operate the model on the computer again to evaluate the effect of the changes. The techniques of optimal control theory have not been applied to system-dynamics models to any significant extent. Their precision is not justified because the models are only approximations of the real systems.

Construction of an analog-computer model of a business or social system is more difficult than for a physical system, because wiring diagrams and component specifications are not available. The structure of the model and the results of operating it must be determined simultaneously by trial and error. The time required for this process has been called the "period of despair." It ends when each of the equations that constitute the model is a reasonable description of the relationship it represents, and the results of operating the model appear reasonable to the operator and agree with what he knows about the operation of the actual system.

14.3 Delays

The basic concepts of Forrester that breathed life into system dynamics are (1) the idea of levels and rates of flow of business variables, which has been mentioned already, and (2) the concept of representing business operations by delays. In the model of a business, delays simulate backlogs, the time required to manufacture products, the delay of management in making decisions, and the time required for information to percolate thru an organization to the people who need it. Delays also represent the vital function of smoothing information. In order to operate a business, management must know rates of flow of materials and information such as orders received, raw materials received, and products shipped. These rates are usually not smooth functions, but are irregular and may even contain impulses. For example, the arrival of a single large order constitutes an impulse in the rate of orders received. The rates must be smoothed before management can use them in the formulation of plans for the future. The smoothing is accomplished by either simple averaging of the rates of flow, or by a more sophisticated process such as exponential averaging. Both processes are represented by delays.

14.4 First-Order Delays

The simplest and most common delay is illustrated by Fig. 14.1, which shows a water tank in which the volume of water is $x(t)$, mea-

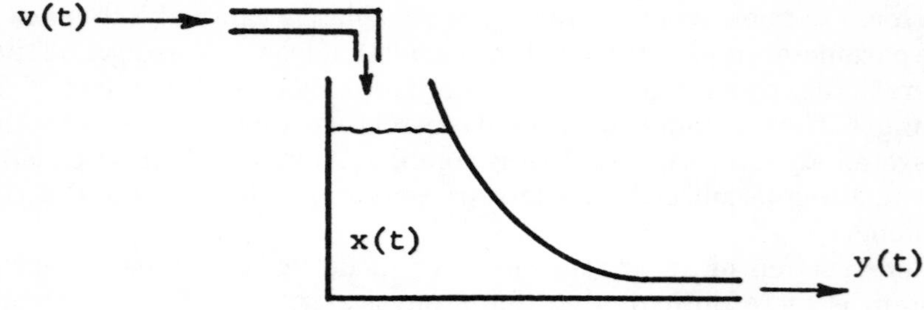

Fig. 14.1. A tapered water tank.

sured, for example, in liters. The rates of flow into and out of the tank are $v(t)$ and $y(t)$ liters/sec. Then

$$\frac{dx}{dt} = v - y \,. \tag{14.1}$$

If the tank is tapered so that $y = kx$ where k is a constant, then

$$\frac{dx}{dt} = v - kx \,. \tag{14.2}$$

These two equations are represented by the block diagram of Fig. 14.2.

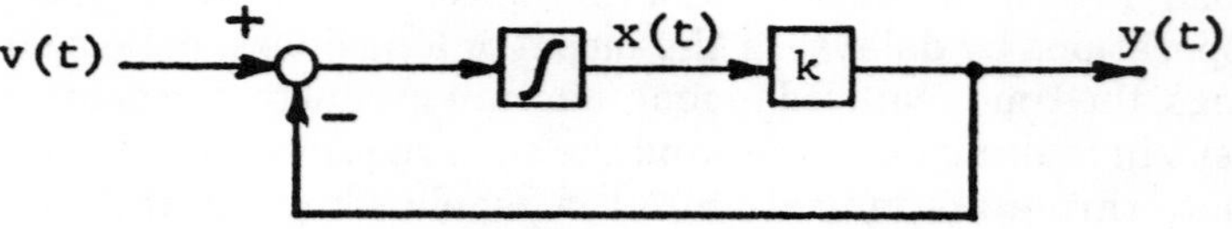

Fig. 14.2. First-order delay.

The subsystem is called by Forrester a *first-order delay*. Notice that the statement that $y = kx$ requires the tacit assumption that the rate of flow of water out of the tank is as smooth as the volume of water in the tank. From a microscopic viewpoint the water consists of discrete atoms. As water flows out of the tank, $x(t)$ decreases in small discrete steps, and $y(t)$ is a train of small impulses. A macroscopic viewpoint requires the assumption that x and y are continuously averaged or smoothed over some short period, so that $y = kx$. This assumption permits the representation of many business operations as first-order delays. For example, let $x(t)$ be the number of shoppers in a department store, and $v(t)$ and $y(t)$ be the rate of flow of customers entering and leaving. Then

$$\frac{dx}{dt} = v - y \,. \tag{14.1}$$

It seems reasonable to assume that except for the hour after opening and the hour before closing, the rate of customers leaving the store is proportional to the number of people in the store. As before, both variables are tacitly averaged over some short interval. Then $y = kx$, and

$$\frac{dx}{dt} = v - kx\,. \tag{14.2}$$

First-order delays also represent many business operations in which the effort to reduce a backlog is proportional to the backlog. For example, the rate of shipment $y(t)$ of products from a mail-order company can reasonably be expected to be proportional to the level $x(t)$ of unfilled orders that have reached the shipping department. If the rate of receipt of orders by the shipping department is $v(t)$, that department of the company is represented by Fig. 14.2.

The transfer function of this subsystem is

$$H(s) = \frac{k}{s + k}\,, \tag{14.3}$$

and its impulse response is

$$h(t) = ke^{-kt}\,. \tag{14.4}$$

A plot of $h(t)$, with k equal to 0.5, is shown in Fig. 14.3. The choice of Eq. (14.4) as the impulse response might be challenged because $h(0)$ is not zero. A pile of orders delivered to the shipping supervisor constitutes an

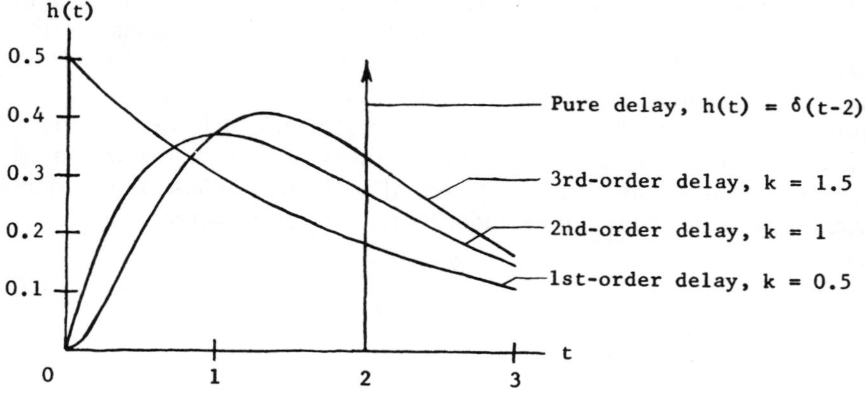

Fig. 14.3. Impulse responses of delays.

impulse of input $v(t)$. However, he is not able to produce the step increase in shipping rate $y(t)$ required by Eq. (14.4). This criticism can be answered in two ways:

1. Indeed, the subsystem cannot produce the response of Eq. (14.4) to an impulse input, but can *approximate* it. The approximation may be accurate enough for the purpose of the system model, particularly if the parameter k is not known precisely.

2. The subsystem can be represented by a delay of higher order.

14.5 Higher-Order Delays

Two first-order delays in cascade as in Fig. 14.4 constitute a second-order delay, whose transfer function is

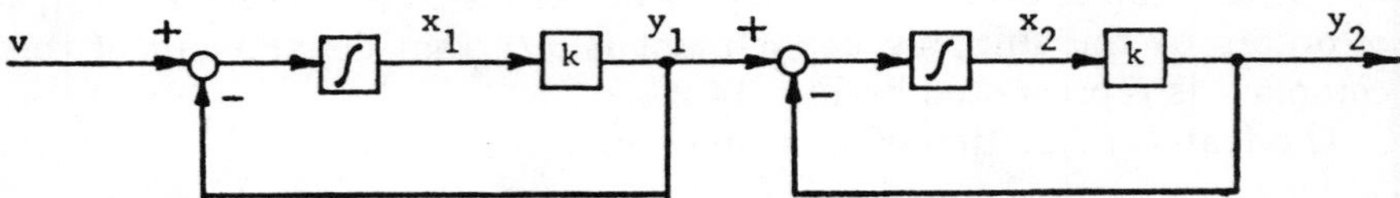

Fig. 14.4. Second-order delay.

$$H(s) = \left(\frac{k}{s+k}\right)^2 . \tag{14.5}$$

The impulse response of this subsystem,

$$h(t) = k^2 t e^{-kt} , \tag{14.6}$$

is shown with $k = 1$ in Fig. 14.3. Section 14.7 will show that this choice of k makes the average abscissa or "average delay" of the first- and second-order delays in Fig. 14.3 equal. The impulse response of the second-order delay is initially zero. This delay might be considered to be more reasonable than a first-order delay as a representation of a shipping department. The choice of representations, which must be made several times in the modeling of a business system, is a compromise between accuracy and simplicity. An nth-order delay consists of n identical first-order delays in cascade. Its transfer function is

$$H(s) = \left(\frac{k}{s+k}\right)^n \tag{14.7}$$

and its impulse response is

$$h(t) = \frac{k^n}{(n-1)!} t^{n-1} e^{-kt} . \tag{14.8}$$

If the parameter k of each stage is increased as the number n of stages increases so that their ratio is the constant

$$\frac{n}{k} = t_1 , \tag{14.9}$$

the impulse-response pulse becomes narrower. Fig. 14.3 shows the impulse response of delays of order $n = 1$, 2, and 3, for which $t_1 = 2$. Appendix 1 of Ref. 87 shows that

1. as n increases, the peak of the pulse moves from $t = 0$ toward $t = t_1$.

2. the first $n - 2$ derivatives of $h(t)$ are initially zero.

3. as n approaches infinity, the impulse response approaches that of a pure delay:

$$h(t) = \delta(t - t_1) , \tag{14.10}$$

where $\delta(t)$ is a unit impulse. The transfer function of the pure delay is

$$H(s) = e^{-t_1 s} . \tag{14.11}$$

The shape of the impulse response can therefore be adjusted by the choice of n. The logical choice of n is either 1, 2, 3, or infinity, because (1) the true nature of a system is normally not known well enough to justify the complication of more than three first-order sections in cascade and (2) a pure delay, as will be seen, can be simulated on a digital computer by a simple model. A pure delay, called "pipeline" delay by Forrester, represents a flow of information or material in which no mixing occurs and whose transit time is constant. For example, if $v(t)$ is the rate of receipt of orders by a factory and $y(t)$ is the rate of shipment of completed products, and all orders are filled in the same elapsed time t_1 in the order of their receipt, then

$$h(t) = \delta(t - t_1) \tag{14.12}$$

and

$$y(t) = \int_0^t v(t - x)h(x)dx = v(t - t_1) . \tag{14.13}$$

14.6 Return-Mail Delays

Some business delays cannot be represented by an nth-order delay of any order. An example is the U.S. mail, whose input and output are the rates at which mail is sent and received. Suppose that a congressman applies an impulse at the input of this system by mailing a question-

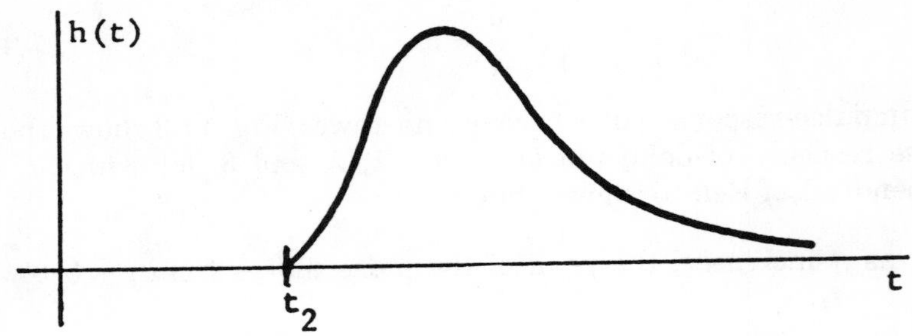

Fig. 14.5. Impulse response of a return-mail delay.

naire to 10,000 addressees in one batch. The output, which is the rate of return of the questionnaires, is zero for a few days. Then it rises, peaks, and tails off as in Fig. 14.5. If all the addressees return the questionnaire, the area under the output pulse equals the magnitude of the input impulse. This system can be simulated by an *n*th-order delay whose transfer function is

$$H_1(s) = \left(\frac{k}{s+k}\right)^n \tag{14.14}$$

in series with a pure delay whose transfer function is

$$H_2(s) = e^{-t_2 s} , \tag{14.15}$$

as shown in Fig. 14.6. The transfer function of the system is

$$H(s) = H_1(s)H_2(s) = e^{-t_2 s}\left(\frac{k}{s+k}\right)^n \tag{14.16}$$

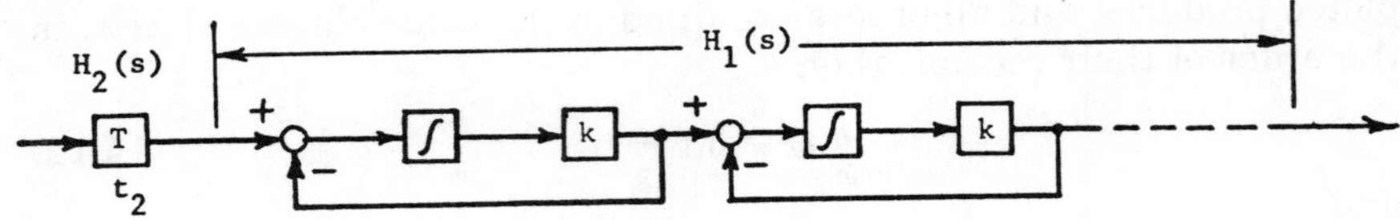

Fig. 14.6. Return-mail delay.

and its impulse response is

$$h(t) = \frac{k^n}{(n-1)!}(t-t_2)^{n-1}e^{-k(t-t_2)}U(t-t_2) , \tag{14.17}$$

where $U(t)$ is a unit step function. The system represented by Eq. (14.17) can reasonably be called a *return-mail delay*. It has three parameters k, t_2, and n that can be chosen to fit the physical system. A choice of n greater than three is seldom justified by the depth of understanding of the physical system.

14.7 Average Delay of a Delay

The delays discussed so far represent a flow of physical items such as cans or dollars. All of the items entering the input eventually leave at the output. The area under the impulse-response curve, which must equal the magnitude of an input unit impulse, is therefore unity:

$$\int_0^\infty h(t)dt = 1\,. \tag{14.18}$$

The impulse response of either an nth-order delay (Eq. 14.8) or a return-mail delay (Eq. 14.17) fulfills this requirement. If the input to a delay is a rate in *items per unit time*, an impulse of input is measured in *items*. The impulse-response curve, such as those in Fig. 14.3 or Fig. 14.5, shows the distribution of delays of the items in passing thru the delay. The average delay μ of the items contained in a unit impulse of input is the mean abscissa:

$$\mu = \int_0^\infty t\, h(t)\, dt\,. \tag{14.19}$$

(Notice that the mean abscissa is the first moment of the area under the impulse-response curve about the $h(t)$ axis.) If the input to the delay is an impulse of magnitude k instead of unity, namely

$$v(t) = k\,\delta(t)\,, \tag{14.20}$$

and the delay is a linear system, its output is

$$y(t) = k\,h(t)\,. \tag{14.21}$$

A plot of this output is the impulse response, scaled up or down by the factor k. The average delay or mean abscissa is now

$$\frac{\displaystyle\int_0^\infty t\,k\,h(t)\,dt}{\displaystyle\int_0^\infty k\,h(t)\,dt} = \frac{k\mu}{k} = \mu\,. \tag{14.22}$$

Thus μ is the average delay of the items in an input impulse of any magnitude. Any input $v(t)$ can be represented by a train of impulses of area $v(x)dx$, as shown in Fig. 14.7. The output at any time t is the sum of the responses to all of these impulses. If the delay is a *fixed* linear system its output is

$$y(t) = \int_0^t v(x)h(t - x)dx\,. \tag{14.23}$$

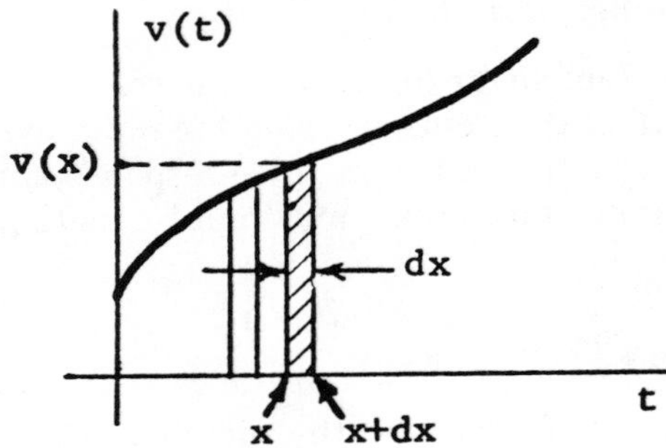

Fig. 14.7. Representation of a function by a train of impulses.

Since the average delay of the items in each of the impulses is μ, the average delay of the items in the input $v(t)$, or in any input to the delay, is μ. The average delay of a delay represented by a fixed linear system is therefore given by Eq. (14.19). All of the delays in this chapter are fixed and linear.

According to Eq. (14.8), the average delay of an nth-order delay is

$$\mu = \frac{k^n}{(n-1)!}\int_0^\infty t^n e^{-kt} dt = \frac{n}{k} . \tag{14.24}$$

In Eq. (14.9) this ratio n/k was called t_1. Thus cascades of any number of first-order sections have the same average delay t_1 if the parameter k of each section is proportional to the number of sections n:

$$\mu = \frac{n}{k} = t_1 . \tag{14.25}$$

To test his or her understanding, the reader is invited to answer this question: if the average delay of the first-order delay in Fig. 14.2 is 4 minutes, what is the value of the parameter k? The average delay of a return-mail delay, obtained either by substituting Eq. (14.17) into Eq. (14.19) or by inspection of Fig. 14.5, is

$$\mu = \frac{n}{k} + t_2 = t_1 + t_2 . \tag{14.26}$$

According to Eq. (14.18) the area under the impulse response of a delay representing a rate of flow of physical items is unity. An impulse-response pulse, such as the one in Fig. 14.5, can therefore be interpreted as a probability density. It shows the probability

$$\int_{t_a}^{t_b} h(t) dt$$

that an item will come out of the delay during the time $t_a \leqslant t \leqslant t_b$.

14.8 Inventories and Backlogs

Some delays occur in business whose input and output are not directly related. An example is a manufacturer's inventory of finished goods $x(t)$. The rate of input $v(t)$ to the inventory is the rate of completion of goods, and the rate of output $y(t)$ is the rate of delivery to customers. Until the rest of the business is studied, the analyst knows only that

$$\frac{dx}{dt} = v - y , \tag{14.27}$$

which is represented by the block diagram of Fig. 14.8. Since y is not in general proportional to x, the first-order delay of Fig. 14.9 does not

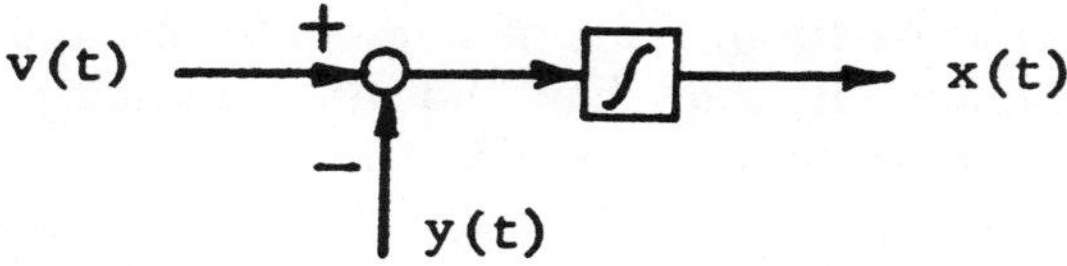

Fig. 14.8. Representation of an inventory.

represent the inventory, and the average stay of an item in the inventory cannot be calculated easily. Define a quantity

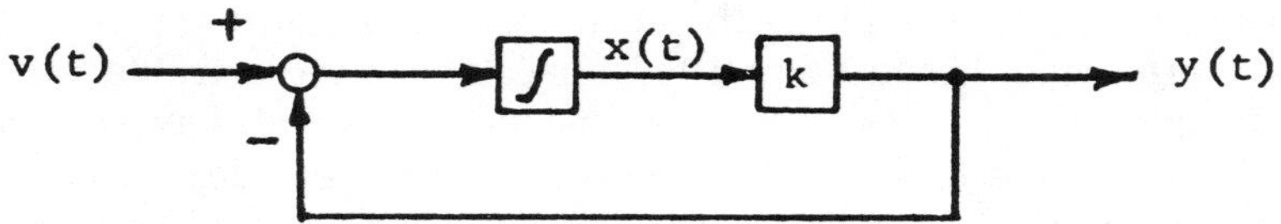

Fig. 14.9. First-order delay.

$$\mu_1 = \frac{x(t)}{y(t)} , \tag{14.28}$$

which is the time required to deplete the present inventory $x(t)$ if no more is added to it and the present rate of depletion $y(t)$ is maintained. In business, μ_1 is called *months or years of inventory*. If $v(t)$ is the rate of receipt of orders and $y(t)$ is the rate at which orders are filled, $x(t)$ is the amount of orders in the backlog, and μ_1 is the *months or years of backlog*. The quantity μ_1 is the average delay of some delays, but not all. Appendix 2 of Ref. 87 shows that μ_1 is always the average delay of a first-order delay, but is the average delay of a pure delay only for some inputs.

Many business managers attempt to keep the number of months of inventory μ_1 constant. When an increased sales rate $y(t)$ makes μ_1 fall below the desired value, they take steps to restore it by increasing the completion rate of goods. The purpose of an inventory is to allow the factory production rate to vary in a smooth, orderly way even though the rate of sales fluctuates widely. If the manager attempts to correct μ_1 to its desired value too quickly, he defeats the purpose of the inventory. A good analogy is a flywheel on an engine with a speed governor. If the governor is set correctly, the torque on the engine remains relatively smooth even when the load torque on the flywheel fluctuates. If the governor is too sensitive, it may call for throttle adjustments that make the engine torque vary as much as the load torque. If the flywheel is to be useful, it must be allowed to speed up and slow down. Similarly, if an inventory is to be useful, it must be allowed to rise and fall.

A later example will show how the input and output rates of an inventory are related in a typical business.

14.9 Calculation of Rates

First-order delays are used in a system-dynamics model to represent the calculation of rates of flow of things or information. To see why, refer to the water tank in Fig. 14.1. The rate of flow of water $y(t)$ out of the tank could be measured by either (1) catching the flow in buckets for a measured time and weighing the buckets, or (2) installing a flowmeter in the outlet pipe. The latter method is of course more desirable, because it gives continuous rates with little time delay, instead of average rates with a long time delay. Unfortunately, flowmeters do not exist for measuring rates of flow of orders and goods in business systems, and the equivalent of buckets must be used. Only average rates can be calculated, by accumulating the flow for a period to establish a level, and then dividing by the period. Consider the rate of receipt of orders $v(t)$ shown in Fig. 14.10. If the simple average of $v(t)$ is calculated at intervals T for the period T just preceding, the measured rate is the stepped curve, whose formula is

$$y_a[(n+1)T] = \frac{1}{T}\int_{(n-1)T}^{nT} v(t)dt \tag{14.29}$$

where $y_a[(n+1)T]$ is the value of $y_a(t)$ in the interval

$$nT < t < (n+1)T\,.$$

The stepped curve $y_a(t)$ lags behind the true rate of ordering $v(t)$ by about one averaging interval T, and does not have as high a peak. The

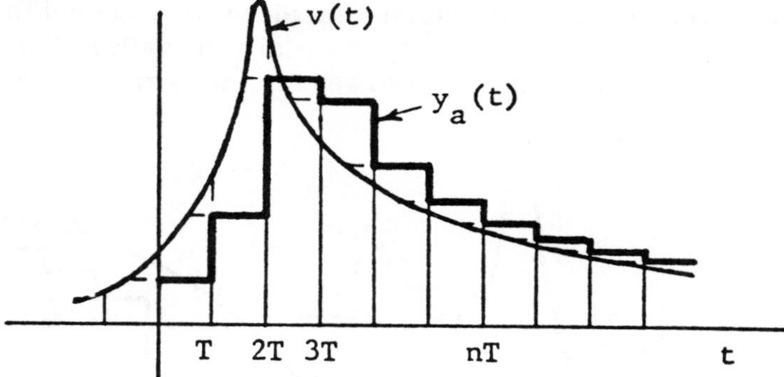

Fig. 14.10. Simple averaging.

delay and smoothing suggest that a continuous approximation of $y_a(t)$ might be the output $y(t)$ of the first-order delay in Fig. 14.11, whose average delay is T. Appendix 3 of Ref. 87 shows that the approximation

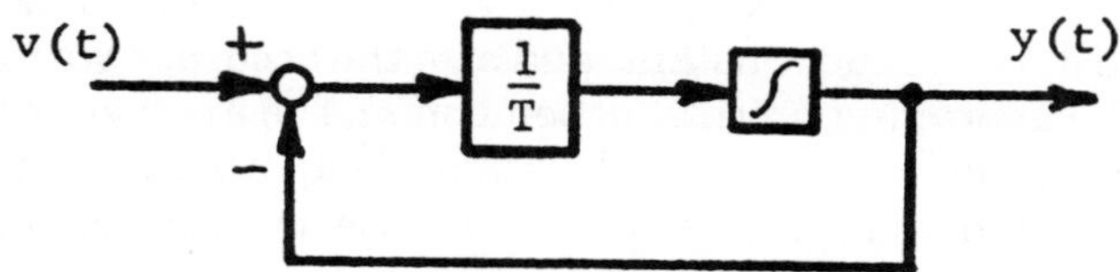

Fig. 14.11. Delay that approximates simple averaging.

is good if $v(t)$ is the ramp $v = kt$ or the exponential $v = \exp(at)$, and fair if $v(t)$ is the sinusoid $v(t) = \sin \omega_0 t$. A process of simple averaging of a rate in a real business is therefore represented in the system-dynamics model by a first-order delay. The internal level of this delay, namely

$$x(t) = \int_{-\infty}^{t} [v(x) - y(x)]dx \, , \tag{14.30}$$

has no physical significance. For this reason the positions of the integrator and the gain coefficient can be interchanged, as in Fig. 14.11. The exchange is worthwhile because it simplifies the computer program.

An average rate can also be calculated at intervals T by accumulating the flow for several time intervals, say m intervals of length T, and then dividing by mT. This is a *moving average*. For this process, Eq. (14.29) becomes

$$y_a[(n + 1)T] = \frac{1}{mT}\int_{(n-m)T}^{nT} v(t)dt \, . \tag{14.31}$$

A moving average lags farther than a simple average behind the true rate, and provides more smoothing of the peaks and valleys. For example, Fig. 14.12 shows a moving average of $v(t)$ with $m = 3$. A moving

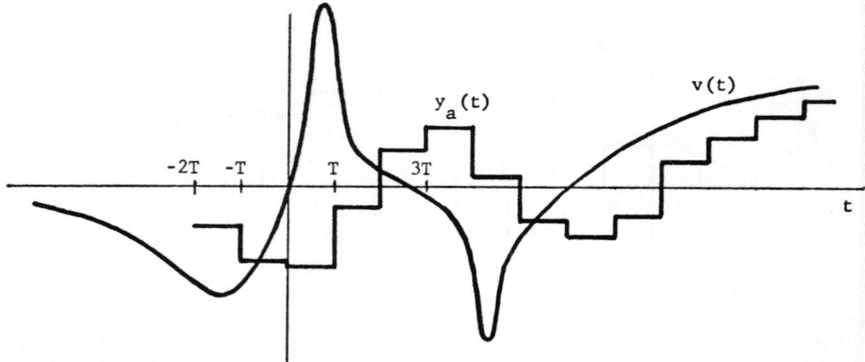

Fig. 14.12. Greater smoothing produced by a moving average.

average can also be represented by a first-order delay. The optimal choice of the delay's time constant, and also the accuracy with which it simulates the averaging process, depend on m, the average interval T, and the form of the input rate $v(t)$. Fortunately another form of averaging, more commonly used, is easier to simulate accurately, and will be discussed next.

14.10 Exponential Averaging

The averaging required to calculate a rate of flow produces a delay, so that the known rate is always a delayed and smoothed version of the actual rate. Although the time lapse is often a disadvantage, the smoothing is often necessary. For example, the orders for large steam turbines are few, but each order is large. The ordering rate $v(t)$ consists of a train of impulses of varying magnitudes, occurring at irregular intervals. The manufacturer must know a smoothed ordering rate in order to determine the need for more employees and factory additions. A simple average of the ordering rate consists of a stepped curve as in Fig. 14.10, and each step occupies an interval T during which no new information is obtained. If T is long enough to provide enough smoothing, each step may be intolerably wide. This difficulty can be overcome by a two-part process. Suppose the true ordering rate $v(t)$ is the train of impulses in Fig. 14.13. First, simple periodic averages $x(t)$ are calculated over short intervals T, say one month:

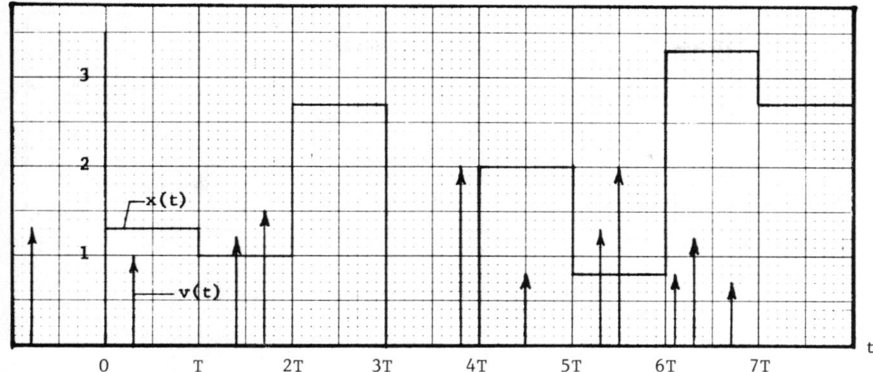

Fig. 14.13. The first step of exponential averaging.

$$x[(n + 1)T] = \frac{1}{T}\int_{(n-1)T}^{nT} v(t)dt \tag{14.32}$$

to produce a train of known levels. Because the steps are short, the train of these averages is too irregular to show any trend in the ordering rate. Next, a weighted average of $x(nT)$ is calculated for all past values of n:

$$y[(n + 1)T] = kT[x(nT) + (1 - kT)\, x\{(n - 1)T\} + (1 - kT)^2\, x\{(n - 2)T\} + \cdots + (1 - kT)^m\, x\{(n - m)T\} + \cdots] \,. \tag{14.33}$$

This is called an *exponential average*. For example, if $kT = 0.2$,

$$y[(n + 1)T] = 0.2\, x(nT) + 0.16\, x[(n - 1)T] + 0.128\, x[(n - 2)T] + 0.1024\, x[(n - 3)T] + \cdots \tag{14.34}$$

Each coefficient is a constant fraction, 0.8 in this example, of the preceding coefficient. Exponential averaging has intuitive appeal, because it assigns the heaviest weights to the most recent information. Eq. (14.33) can be generated by the difference equation

$$y[(n + 1)T] = (1 - kT)\, y(nT) + kT\, x(nT) \,. \tag{14.35}$$

The next value of the exponential average $y(t)$ is a weighted sum of the present value of $y(t)$ and the present value of the level being averaged, $x(t)$. This formula was used to calculate the exponential averages of the levels $x(t)$ in Fig. 14.13, with $kT = 0.2$ and $y(T) = 1$. The result is the solid line in Fig. 14.14. The train of exponential averages is smoother than the simple averages in Fig. 14.13.

The astute reader may wonder why an exponential average can be called an "average". The number $y(nT)$ is an average of the preceding values of $x(nT)$ if

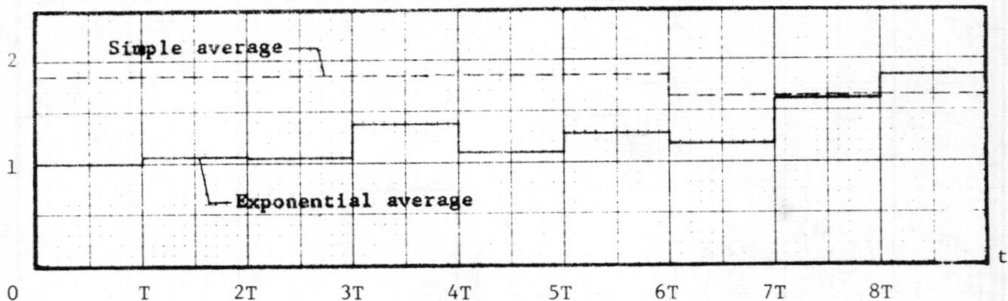

Fig. 14.14. Exponential and simple averages.

1. the long-time totals of $y(nT)$ and $x(nT)$ are equal:

$$\sum_{n=0}^{\infty} x(nT) = \sum_{n=0}^{\infty} y(nT) , \qquad \text{and} \tag{14.36}$$

2. the train of values of $y(nT)$ is smoother than that of $x(nT)$.

Appendix 4 of Ref. 87 shows that the exponential average $y(nT)$ fulfills the first criterion if $0 < kT < 2$, and fulfills the second criterion if $0 < kT < 1$.

The two-part process consists of calculating simple averages over short intervals T to produce a train of levels, and then calculating the exponential averages of the levels. To see why this process avoids the disadvantages of simple averaging, construct the delay circuit that represents the two-part process in a block diagram. Eq. (14.35) can be written as

$$\frac{y[(n+1)T] - y(nT)}{T} = k[x(nT) - y(nT)] . \tag{14.37}$$

As the averaging interval T approaches zero, nT becomes t, and

$$\lim_{T \to 0} \frac{y[(n+1)T] - y(nT)}{T} = \frac{dy}{dt} = k[x(t) - y(t)] . \tag{14.38}$$

Therefore if the averaging interval is short, exponential averaging is simulated by the first-order delay of Fig. 14.15. Appendix 4 of Ref. 87 shows that the difference between

$$\frac{y[(n+1)T] - y(nT)}{T} \qquad \text{and} \qquad \frac{dy}{dt}$$

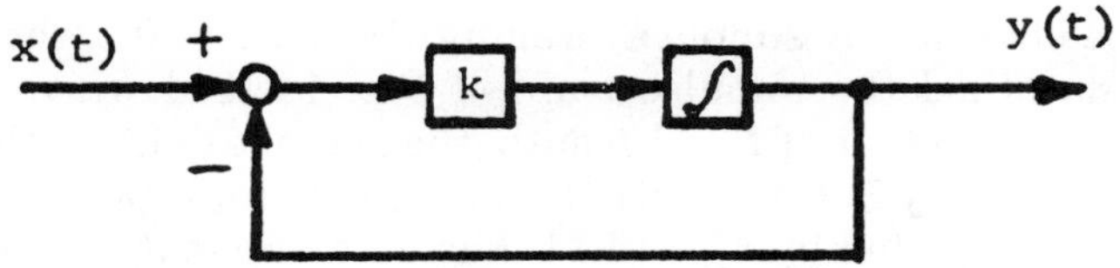

Fig. 14.15. Delay that approximates exponential averaging.

$$\text{at} \qquad t = nT \qquad \text{is} \qquad \frac{T}{2}\ddot{y}(\theta T)\,,$$

where θ is some number between n and $n + 1$. If T is a short interval and $y(t)$ does not have sharp bends so that its second derivative is small, a first-order delay is a good simulation of periodic exponential averaging.

Now the two-part process can be simulated. The calculation of simple averages $x(t)$ at short intervals T is represented by Fig. 14.11, with output $x(t)$ instead of $y(t)$. Combining this delay with the delay representing exponential averaging produces Fig. 14.16. The average delay

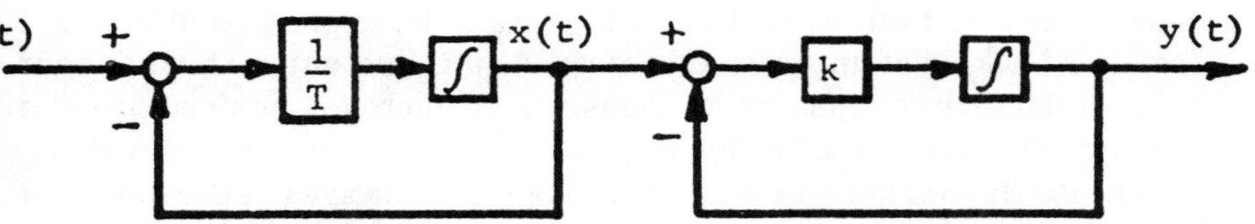

Fig. 14.16. Delay that approximates simple averaging followed by exponential averaging.

of the two stages is $T + 1/k$. The simulation can be simplified if T is small compared to $1/k$. As T approaches zero, the impulse response of the first stage approaches an impulse, and that stage can be neglected. Concurrently, the second stage becomes an exact simulation of the exponential averaging process. The two-part process used to smooth the rate $v(t)$ is then represented by the single first-order delay of Fig. 14.15. The output $y(t)$ of this delay is a close approximation of the solid line in Fig. 14.14. Since the purpose of the two-part process is to smooth the rate $v(t)$, the delay used to represent it is called a *smoother*. The amount of smoothing can be adjusted arbitrarily in the two-part process by the choice of kT. Since T is known, the parameter k in the simulation can be chosen accordingly. If kT is small, $y(t)$ is very smooth, but responds sluggishly to changes in $v(t)$. The choice of kT is a compromise between the desires for (1) a smoothly-varying measure of the rate $v(t)$, and (2) up-to-date information about $v(t)$.

How can smoothing comparable to that obtained by the two-part process be obtained by simple averaging? With $kT = 0.2$, the two-part process smoothed the impulse train of Fig. 14.13 down to the solid staircase of Fig. 14.14. If $T = 1$ month, the average delay of the process was approximately $T + 1/k = 6$ months. A comparable process of simple averaging, simulated by Fig. 14.11, has an average delay of approximately 6 months if the parameter T in that figure is 6 months. The latter process produces a staircase of simple averages over 6-month intervals, two of whose steps are the dotted line in Fig. 14.14. The advantages of exponential averaging, that make it preferable to simple averaging over longer intervals that produce the same average delay, are now clear. First, the width of the flat steps during which no new information is obtained is $T + 1/k$ for simple averaging, but only T for the two-part method. And second, the two-part process is simulated more accurately than the simple-averaging process by a first-order delay if T is small compared to $1/k$.

14.11 Decision-Making Delays

The natural wait-and-see attitudes of circumspect managers can be represented by first-order delays. For example, suppose that $v(t)$ is a factory's backlog of unprocessed orders. As $v(t)$ fluctuates, the manager of manufacturing must make decisions to increase or decrease the amount of overtime worked by his people. Being cautious and unwilling to confuse the workers, he will not make rapid changes in the length of the work week in response to rapid changes in the backlog. His intuitive smoothing of the changes can be represented approximately by Fig. 14.17, in which $v(t)$ is the backlog in months or years of unprocessed

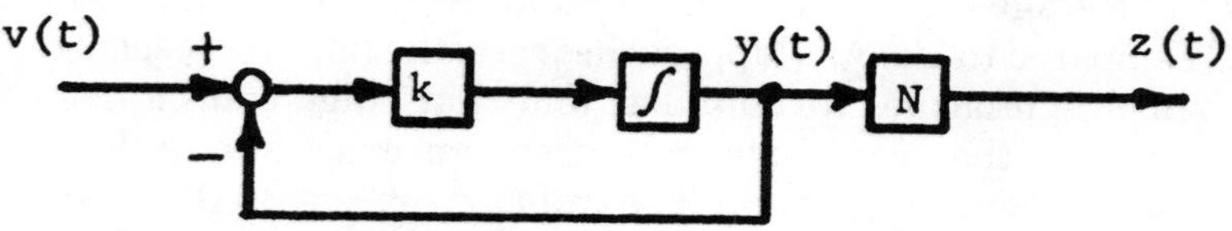

Fig. 14.17. A decision-making delay.

orders, $y(t)$ is the smoothed value of backlog in the manager's mind, N is the overtime policy, and $z(t)$ is the fraction of the 40-hour work week being worked. There is of course no rule for calculating the average delay $1/k$ exactly. The choice requires judgment and familiarity with the situation. After the model of the system is completed, runs can be made with various values of k. The amount of additional attention that should be given to the choice of k depends on the sensitivity of the variables in the system to changes in k.

14.12 Use of Delays in Forecasting

Business forecasts require the extrapolation of monthly or annual data that do not lie on smooth curves. For example, Fig. 14.18 shows a

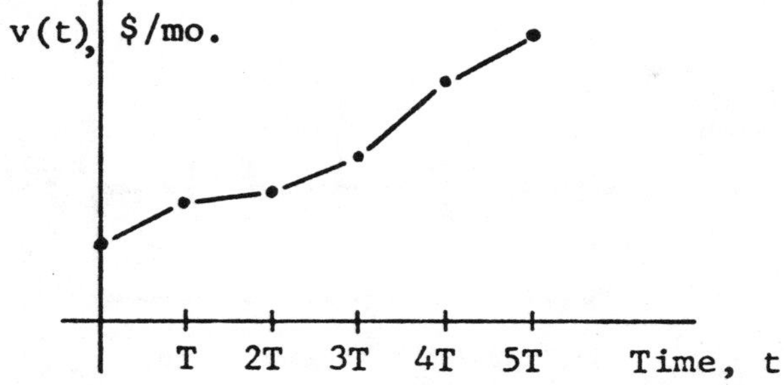

Fig. 14.18. Average sales rate v(t) during the past periods T.

typical curve of the average sales rate $v(t)$ dollars per month during the past one-month periods T. How can this curve be extrapolated to forecast future sales rates? If the curve has approximated a straight line in the past, a reasonable procedure is as follows:

1. Calculate the average rate of increase $x(nT)$ of sales rate over each of the past periods T:

$$x(nT) = \frac{v(nT) - v[(n-1)T]}{T}. \tag{14.39}$$

   This is the slope of the curve over each interval.

2. Use Eq. (14.33) or (14.35) to calculate the exponential average of the train of slopes, $y[(n+1)T]$. This is the smoothed present value of the slope. The calculation makes good business sense, because it weighs the most recent information more heavily than the old information.

3. Assume that in the near future, the curve will continue to rise with the slope $y[(n+1)T]$. To extrapolate the curve ahead by m periods, multiply $y[(n+1)T]$ by mT, and add the result to the present value of $v(nT)$. The result is the forecasted sales rate m periods (months or years) from now.

Steps 1 and 2 can be represented simply in a system-dynamics model of the business. As the averaging interval T approaches zero, $x(nT)$ in Eq. (14.39) becomes

$$x(t) = \frac{dv}{dt} \,. \tag{14.40}$$

This differentiation is represented by Fig. 14.19 if k_1 is very large. To see why, observe that the transfer function of the first-order delay is

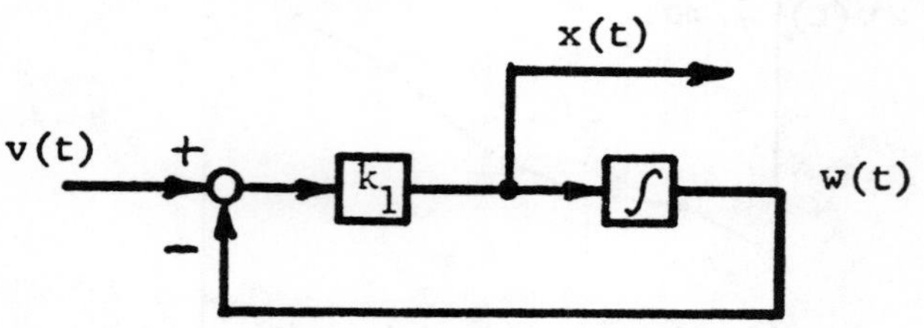

Fig. 14.19. A differentiating circuit.

$$\frac{W(s)}{V(s)} = \frac{k_1}{s + k_1} = \frac{1}{\frac{s}{k_1} + 1} \,. \tag{14.41}$$

Then

$$\lim_{k_1 \to \infty} \frac{W(s)}{V(s)} = 1 \,, \tag{14.42}$$

and

$$\lim_{k_1 \to \infty} w(t) = v(t) \,. \tag{14.43}$$

Therefore

$$\lim_{k_1 \to \infty} x(t) = \frac{dv}{dt} \,. \tag{14.44}$$

Fig. 14.19 therefore produces a continuous approximation of step 1. According to Eq. (14.38), as T approaches zero the exponential averaging process in step 2 becomes

$$\frac{dy}{dt} = k(x - y) \,, \tag{14.45}$$

which is represented by a first-order delay with the parameter k. The continuous approximation of steps 1 and 2 together, which produces the smoothed rate of increase in sales rate, $y(t)$, is represented by Fig. 14.20. This circuit is not practical in a system-dynamics model operated by numerical integration on a digital computer. The short time constant

$1/k_1$ requires a prohibitively short computing interval to keep the numerical integration stable. Fortunately the circuit can be simplified. It has the transfer functions

$$\frac{X(s)}{V(s)} = \frac{k_1 s}{s + k_1} \quad \text{and} \quad \frac{Y(s)}{X(s)} = \frac{k}{s + k}. \tag{14.46}$$

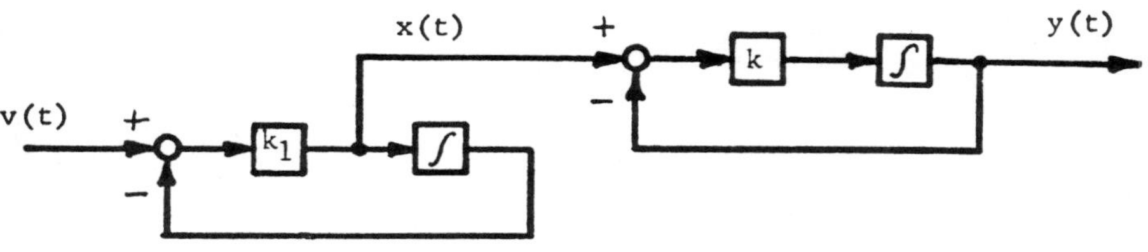

Fig. 14.20. Differentiation and smoothing by delays.

Thus

$$\frac{Y(s)}{V(s)} = \frac{k\, k_1\, s}{(s + k_1)(s + k)}, \tag{14.47}$$

and

$$\lim_{k_1 \to \infty} \frac{Y(s)}{V(s)} = \frac{ks}{s + k}. \tag{14.48}$$

Nature has been kind. When the parameter k_1 becomes very large, as required for accurate differentiation, it disappears from the circuit's overall transfer function! The combined process of differentiation and smoothing, consisting of steps 1 and 2 in the forecasting process, can be simulated by the single first-order delay in Fig. 14.21. This continuous

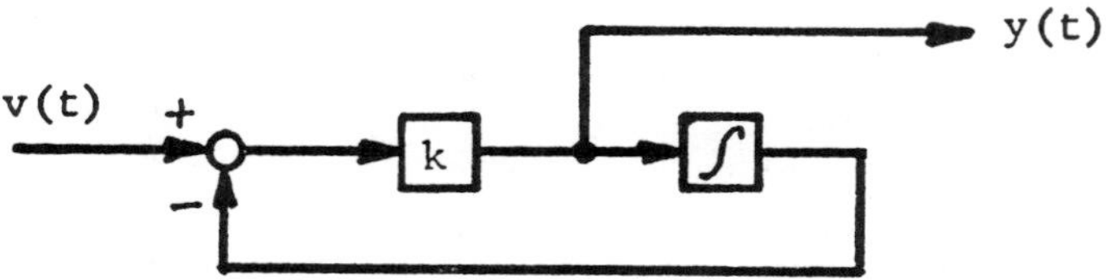

Fig. 14.21. Differentiation and smoothing by one first-order delay.

model represents the actual process of calculating periodic slopes and their exponential average. The accuracy of the representation increases as the calculating interval T decreases.

The implementation of step 3 of the forecasting process is straightforward. For example, suppose that the average sales rate $v(t)$ in Fig.

14.18 is plotted monthly, and the manager of marketing wants a monthly forecast of $v(t)$ three months in the future. The smoothed present value of the slope of Fig. 14.18 is $y(t)$, calculated by the circuit in Fig. 14.21. The forecasted sales rate is

$$z(t) = v(t) + 3y(t) . \tag{14.49}$$

Fig. 14.22 shows how this calculation is performed by the model.

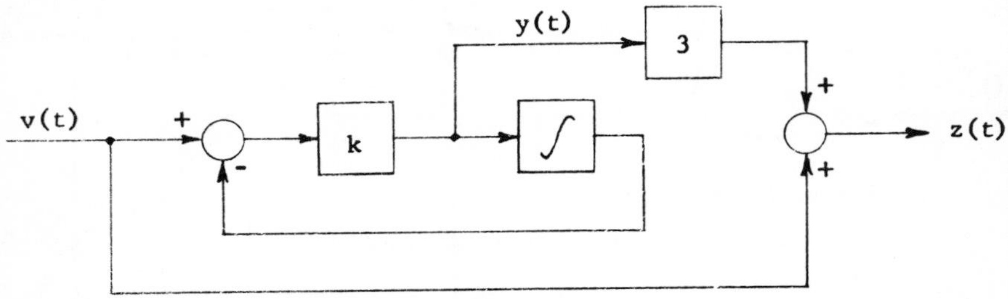

Fig. 14.22. Calculation of forecasted sales rate.

14.13 Pure Delays

A pure or pipeline delay of t_1 months is an nth-order delay consisting of an infinite number of first-order stages in cascade. According to Eq. (14.25), the parameter k of each stage is infinite. Two facts about this delay are clear:

1. It cannot be implemented on an analog or digital computer in this form, because it requires an infinite number of integrators and an infinite number of infinite gains.

2. It has an infinite number of state variables, namely the integrator outputs, and therefore contains an infinite number of discrete pieces of information.

Fig. 14.23 shows a pure delay of t_1 months, whose input is $v(t)$ and whose

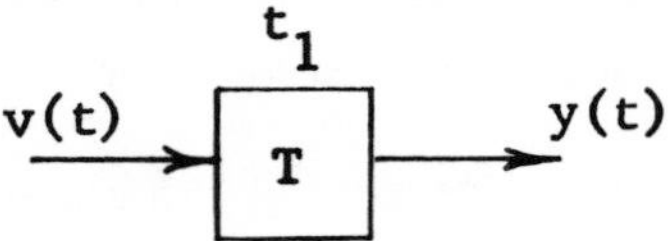

Fig. 14.23. A pure delay.

output is $y(t)$. At time $t = t_2$ the content of the delay is all the values of the function $y(t)$ in the interval

$$t_2 \leqslant t \leqslant t_2 + t_1 ,$$

or all the values of the function $v(t)$ in the interval

$$t_2 - t_1 \leqslant t \leqslant t_2 .$$

These values constitute an infinite number of pieces of information. If the function $v(t)$ entering the delay represents a stepped function generated by averaging a rate, such as $y_a(t)$ in Fig. 14.10, one might think that the delay contains only a discrete number of items of information. The stepped curve, however, is represented in the system-dynamics model by a smooth curve generated by a first-order delay.

An approximation of a pure delay that avoids the requirement of an infinite number of first-order sections, and is admirably suited to a digital computer, is a *boxcar train*, shown in Fig. 14.24. It consists of m

Fig. 14.24. A boxcar train.

of the computer's storage registers, that contain m previous values of $v(t)$, chosen at regular intervals. During the operation of the model by the Euler method of numerical integration, the value of $v(t)$ at the start of each computing interval is stored in a register, saved for m intervals, and then read out as $y(t)$. If the computing interval is h, the number of storage registers required for a delay of t_1 is

$$m = t_1/h . \tag{14.50}$$

The fourth-order Runge-Kutta method requires four values of $v(t)$ during each computing interval. The number of registers in the boxcar train is then

$$m = 4t_1/h . \tag{14.51}$$

Before a run of the model begins, the registers must be loaded with the m preceding values of $v(t)$. This is accomplished in BASIC by a FOR-NEXT loop. For example, if the initial value of $y(t)$ in Fig. 14.23 is 10 and the initial value of $v(t)$ is 30, and $v(t)$ has been increasing with constant slope during the preceding time t_1, the initial content $R(I)$ of each Ith register is computed and stored by these lines:

```
170 M = 4*T1/H
175 FOR I = 1 TO M
180 R(I) = 10 + 20*(I - 1)/M
185 NEXT I
```
(14.52)

During operation of the model, the oldest number in the boxcar train is removed at each step and assigned to $y(t)$, and the present value of $v(t)$

is inserted into the train. The shifting can be accomplished in two ways:

1. Remove the content of register 1, shift the content of each register I to the register $I - 1$ on its right, and put the present value of $v(t)$ into register m.

2. Instead of reloading each car in the train, walk along the train. At each step remove the content of register J, call it $y(t)$, and insert the present value of $v(t)$ into that register. At the next step, move to register $J + 1$ and repeat the transfer. After reloading register m at the left end of the train, return to register 1 and start the walk again.

The second method is much faster and is the obvious choice, because at each step only one register must be reloaded, instead of all m. The second method is implemented in BASIC by these lines:

```
220 J = J + 1
225 IF J < = M THEN 235
230 J = 1
235 Y = R(J)
240 R(J) = V                                  (14.53)
```

14.14 Elimination of Starting Transients

Frequently a model of a business or social system is constructed to show the effects of changes in policy, but not to reproduce historical data or predict the future. The runs of such a model can be started most conveniently in steady state. Then after a short period the input or the system parameters can be perturbed to display the transient behavior of the system. How can the first-order delay shown in Fig. 14.25 be started without a transient? Since

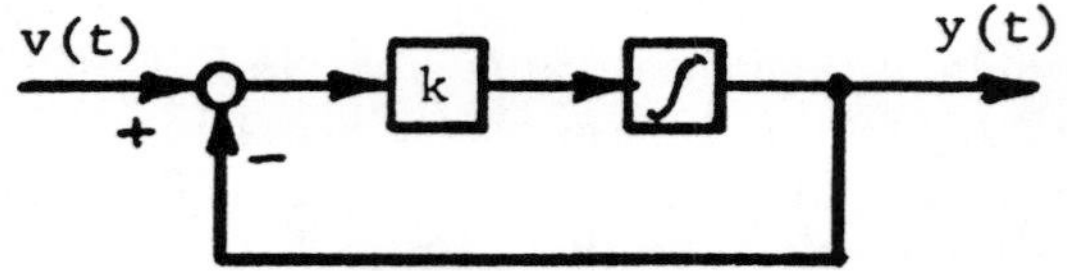

Fig. 14.25. First-order delay.

$$\dot{y} + ky = kv\,, \tag{14.54}$$

then

$$Y(s) = \frac{y(0)}{s + k} + \frac{k\,V(s)}{s + k}\,. \tag{14.55}$$

If the input is the ramp

$$v(t) = a + bt\,, \tag{14.56}$$

then

$$Y(s) = \frac{y(0)}{s+k} + \frac{k(as+b)}{s^2(s+k)} \tag{14.57}$$

and

$$y(t) = a - \frac{b}{k} + bt + \left[\frac{b}{k} - a + y(0)\right] e^{-kt}\,. \tag{14.58}$$

The starting transient is eliminated if the initial integrator output is

$$y(0) = a - \frac{b}{k}\,. \tag{14.59}$$

The reader can easily verify that if the input is the constant

$$v(t) = A\;U(t)\,,$$

the starting transient is eliminated if the initial integrator output is $y(0) = A$. If the input is the rising exponential

$$v(t) = a_0 e^{a_1 t}\,, \tag{14.60}$$

the starting transient is eliminated by making the initial integrator output

$$y(0) = \frac{k}{k+a_1}\,a_0 = \frac{k}{k+a_1}\,v(0)\,. \tag{14.61}$$

To see how to start the pure delay in Fig. 14.26 without a transient,

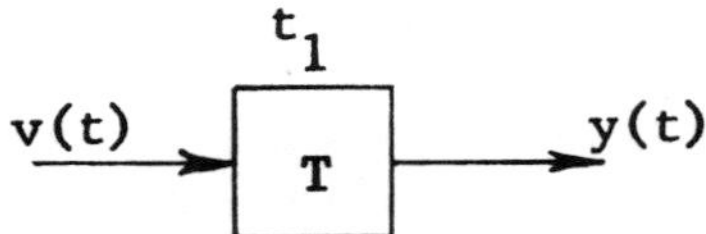

Fig. 14.26. A pure delay.

observe that if the delay is initially inert (unloaded) and $v(t)$ is causal ($v(t) = 0$ for $t < 0$), then

$$y(t) = v(t - t_1)U(t - t_1)\,. \tag{14.62}$$

If the input is the ramp

$$v(t) = (a + bt)U(t)\,, \tag{14.63}$$

then

$$y(t) = [a + b(t - t_1)]U(t - t_1) = [v(t) - bt_1]U(t - t_1)\,, \tag{14.64}$$

as shown in Fig. 14.27. Until time t_1 the output $y(t)$ has the transient value of zero. To eliminate this transient the analyst must provide the dotted extension of the steady-state value of $y(t)$, so that

$$y(t) = [v(t) - bt_1]U(t) \tag{14.65}$$

and

$$y(0) = v(0) - bt_1 \,. \tag{14.66}$$

If $y(0) = 10$ and $v(0) = 30$, Eqs. (14.52) add the dotted extension in the computer program representing the model.

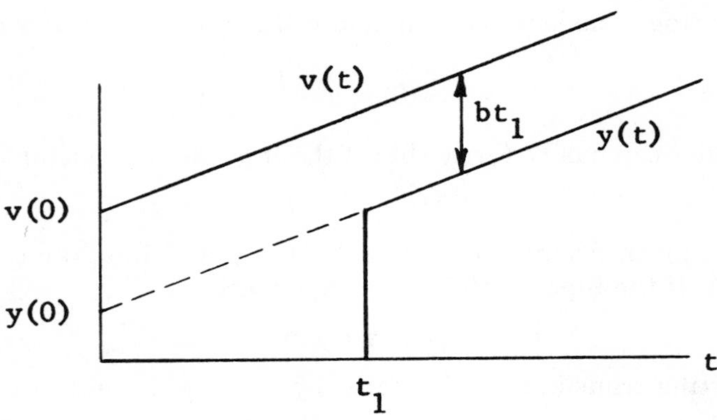

Fig. 14.27. Response of a pure delay.

14.15 An Example

To apply some of the techniques of system dynamics, consider the trouble of an electrical-appliance dealer whose business suffers large oscillations even though the rate of ordering by customers does not oscillate. A block diagram of the business, shown in Fig. 14.28, will be explained step by step. Each week the dealer calculates the rate of ordering by his customers during the preceding week, as in Fig. 14.10. This known rate of ordering, which will be called $X(1)$, is the actual rate of ordering by customers A delayed by one week. The first-order delay of one week representing the process is shown in Fig. 14.28. The input to integrator 1 is

$$V(1) = A - X(1) \,. \tag{14.67}$$

Large appliances cannot be delivered when ordered, because the installations must be scheduled when the service men are available and the customers are at home. On the average, the dealer delivers appliances two weeks after they are ordered. A first-order delay of two weeks between the rate of ordering A and the rate of delivery to customers C is shown in Fig. 14.28. The input to integrator 3 is

$$V(3) = A - C \quad \$/\text{wk}. \tag{14.68}$$

The integrator output $X(3)$ is the dealer's backlog of orders, and

$$C = 0.5\, X(3) \quad \$/\text{wk}. \tag{14.69}$$

The dealer receives appliances from the distributor at the rate of B \$/wk. The accumulated difference $X(2)$ between B and C is the dealer's inventory. The input to integrator 2 is therefore

$$V(2) = B - C \quad \$/\text{wk}. \tag{14.70}$$

The dealer tries to keep two weeks of inventory on hand. His desired inventory, based on the known rate of ordering by customers, is

$$E = 2\, X(1) \quad \text{dollars}. \tag{14.71}$$

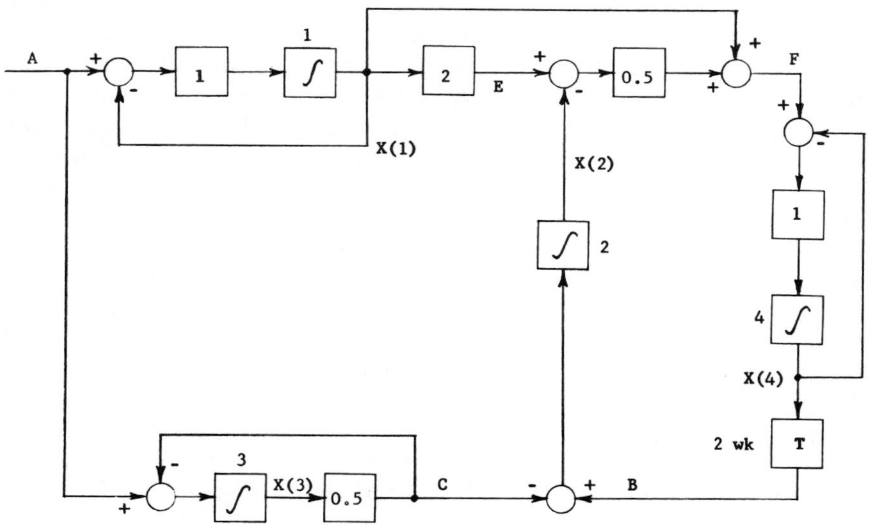

A rate of ordering by customers, \$/wk
B rate of delivery to dealer from distributor, \$/wk
C rate of delivery to customers, \$/wk
E dealer's desired inventory, \$
F rate of ordering by dealer, \$/wk
t time, wk
X(1) known rate of ordering by customers, \$/wk
X(2) dealer's inventory, \$
X(3) dealer's backlog of orders, \$
X(4) auxiliary variable without physical significance

Fig. 14.28. Block diagram of the retail appliance business.

Each week the dealer orders appliances from the distributor. His order includes all of the orders received from customers in the preceding week, plus an amount for correcting his inventory. The latter amount is half the difference between his desired and actual inventories. The dealer's rate of ordering is therefore

$$F = X(1) + 0.5\,[E - X(2)] \quad \$/\text{wk}. \tag{14.72}$$

The delay in getting deliveries from the distributor is simulated in Fig. 14.28 by a 3-week return-mail delay, consisting of a first-order delay of one week in series with a pure delay of two weeks. This 3-week delay is described by the equations

$$V(4) = F - X(4) \tag{14.73}$$

and

$$B \text{ at time } t = X(4) \text{ at time } t - 2\,. \tag{14.74}$$

The system is represented by Eqs. (14.67) thru (14.74), which are included in the BASIC computer program in Table 14.1. The model will start in steady state, with the rate of ordering by customers A set at 4000 \$/wk. A starting transient is eliminated by setting the initial values of $X(1)$ and C at 4000 \$/wk. Then E and F are initially \$8000 and 4000 \$/wk, respectively. In steady state, the actual dealer's inventory $X(2)$ equals the desired inventory E. The initial value of $X(2)$ is therefore \$8000. The initial values of $X(3)$ and $X(4)$ are easily seen to be \$8000 and 4000 \$/wk. These four initial integrator outputs are included in the computer program. When a run of the model is started, the program calculates the integrator outputs using the fourth-order Runge-Kutta method. After one week of steady-state operation, the rate of ordering by customers A is increased by 25 percent to 5000 \$/wk. The effect on two of the variables in the business is shown in Fig. 14.30. The dealer's inventory $X(2)$ and the rate of delivery to the dealer B experience large fluctuations with a period of 12.5 weeks. These fluctuations mean trouble for the dealer. His need for storage space varies with his inventory, and his need for warehouse workers varies with the rate of delivery of appliances to his back door.

14.16 An Improvement

What is causing the fluctuations? When the rate of ordering by customers increases as in the test run, the dealer's inventory is reduced. He increases his rate of ordering new inventory, but ignores the orders already in the pipeline to and from the distributor. When the increased orders in the pipeline start appearing after a 3-week delay as deliveries to his warehouse, his inventory quickly rises and overflows. He calls for a large reduction in inventory, and now orders too little. After a 3-week delay, the shortage of orders in the pipeline appears as reduced deliveries, and the inventory drops below the desired level. He increases his rate of ordering again, and the cycle repeats.

The fluctuations can be reduced by recognizing that for the purpose of planning, the orders in the distributor pipeline are a part of the dealer's inventory. Fig. 14.29 shows the modified block diagram. The accumulated difference $X(5)$ between F and B is the level of unfilled orders from the distributor. The input to integrator 5 is therefore

$$V(5) = F - B\,. \tag{14.75}$$

The level $X(5)$ and the inventory on hand, $X(2)$, constitute the total inventory. The dealer still tries to keep 2 weeks of inventory on hand, namely $2X(1)$. He now also tries to control the level of orders in the distributor pipeline. Since the average delay in the pipeline is 3 weeks, the desired level of orders in the pipeline is $3\,X(1)$. The total desired inventory, no longer given by Eq. (14.71), is now

$$E = 5\,X(1) \quad \text{dollars.} \tag{14.76}$$

The difference between the desired and actual total inventories is $E - X\,(2) - X(5)$. The dealer's rate of ordering, formerly given by Eq. (14.72), becomes

$$F = X(1) + 0.5[E - X(2) - X(5)] \quad \$/\text{wk}. \tag{14.77}$$

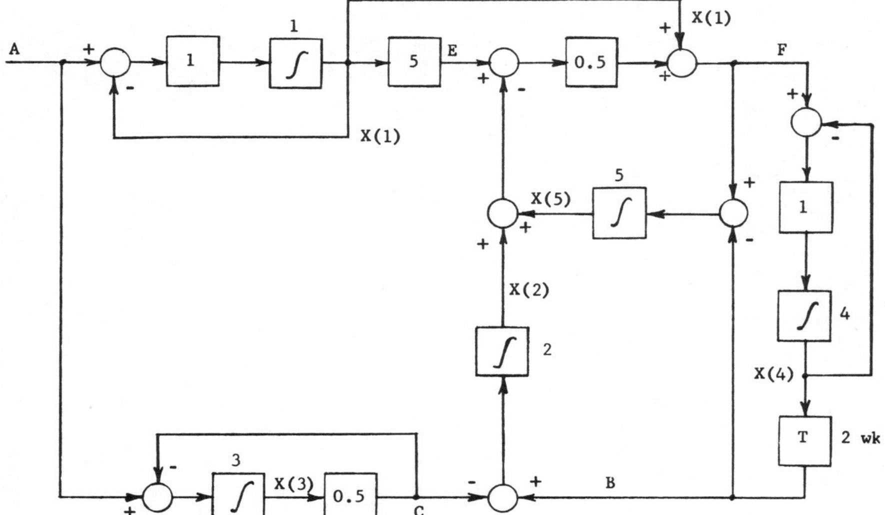

Fig. 14.29. Block diagram of the business with improved inventory correction.

In the initial steady state, the distributor pipeline contains 3 weeks of orders at 4000 \$/wk. The initial value of $X(5)$ is therefore \$12,000.

To test the changes in the operation of the business, include these lines in the computer program:

```
150 DIM B(4), V(5), E(5), X(5), Y(5), Z(16)
195 X(5) = 12000
270 E = 5*X(1)
280 F = X(1) + .5*(E-X(2)-X(5))
395 V(5) = F - B
```

The new behavior of the dealer's inventory on hand and the rate of delivery to the dealer are shown in Fig. 14.31. The improvement is dramatic. The 12.5-week fluctuations have been eliminated and the initial transients have been reduced. The reader is invited to consider other feasible changes in the dealer's procedures that might reduce the initial transients even more.

TABLE 14.1. LIST OF THE BASIC PROGRAM REPRESENTING THE APPLIANCE DEALER'S BUSINESS

```
100 REM K1=COMPUTING INTERVAL, K2=PRINTING INTERVAL, K3=TOTAL WEEKS
110 READ K1,K2,K3
120 DATA .5,1,40
130 PRINT "T","X(2)","X(3)","F","B"
140 PRINT
150 DIM B(4),V(4),E(4),X(4),Y(4),Z(16)
160 MAT READ B
170 DATA .5,.5,1,2
180 X(1)=X(4)=4000
190 X(2)=X(3)=8000
200 M=4*2/K1
210 FOR I=1 TO M
220 Z(I)=4000
230 NEXT I
240 I=0
250 A=4000
260 FOR P=1 TO 4
270 E=2*X(1)
280 F=X(1)+.5*(E-X(2))
290 I=I+1
300 IF I<=M THEN 320
310 I=1
320 B=Z(I)
330 Z(I)=X(4)
340 C=.5*X(3)
350 IF U=0 THEN 580
360 V(1)=A-X(1)
370 V(2)=B-C
380 V(3)=A-C
390 V(4)=F-X(4)
400 ON P GO TO 410,440,440,470
410 MAT E=(1)*V
420 MAT Y=(1)*X
430 GO TO 510
440 MAT X=(2)*V
450 MAT E=E+X
460 GO TO 510
470 MAT X=E+V
480 MAT X=(K1/6)*X
490 MAT X=Y+X
500 GO TO 550
510 MAT X=(K1*B(P))*V
520 MAT X=Y+X
530 IF P=2 THEN 550
540 T=T+K1/2
550 NEXT P
560 N=N+1
570 IF N<K2/K1-.5 THEN 600
580 PRINT T,X(2),X(3),F,B
590 N=0
600 U=U+1
610 IF T>K3-K1/2 THEN 650
620 IF T<1-K1/2 THEN 260
630 A=5000
640 GO TO 260
650 END
```

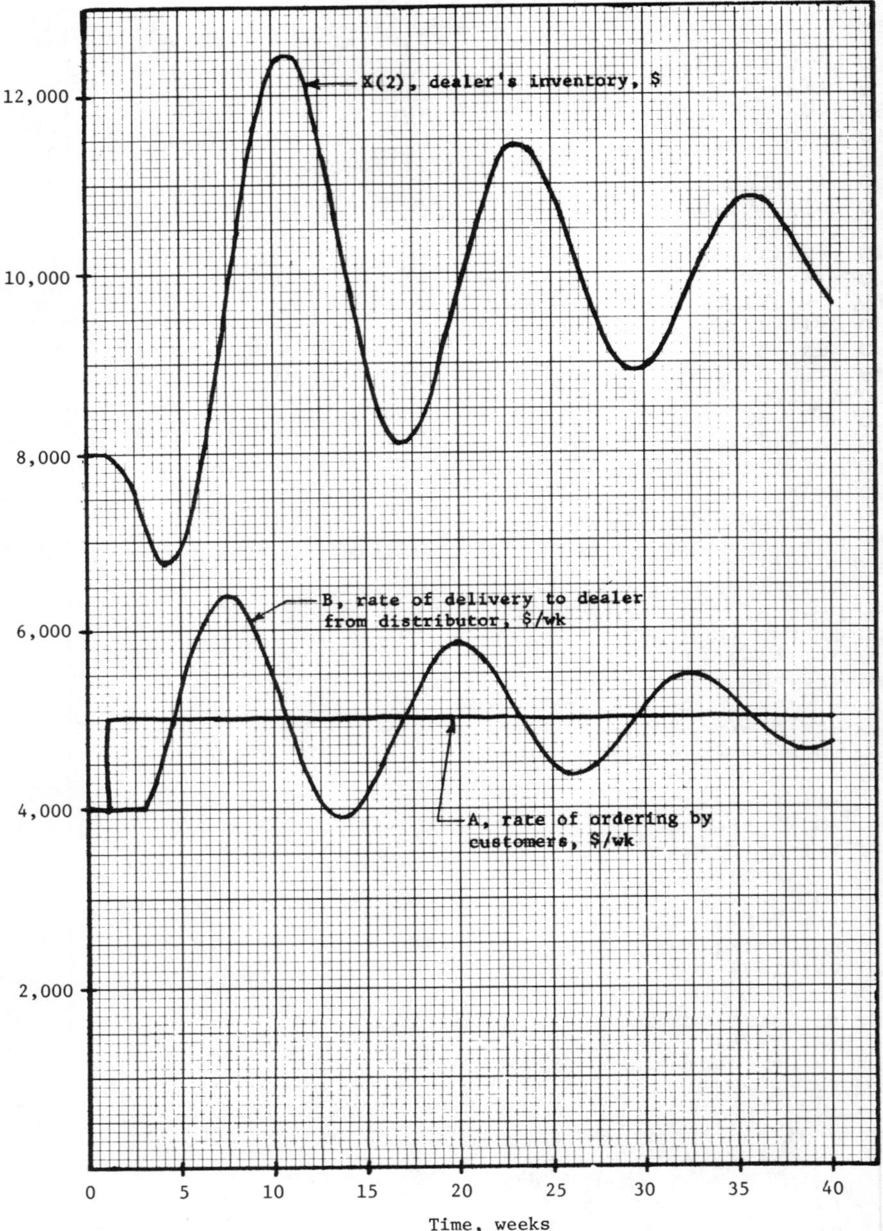

Fig. 14.30. Response of two variables to a step increase in the rate of ordering by customers.

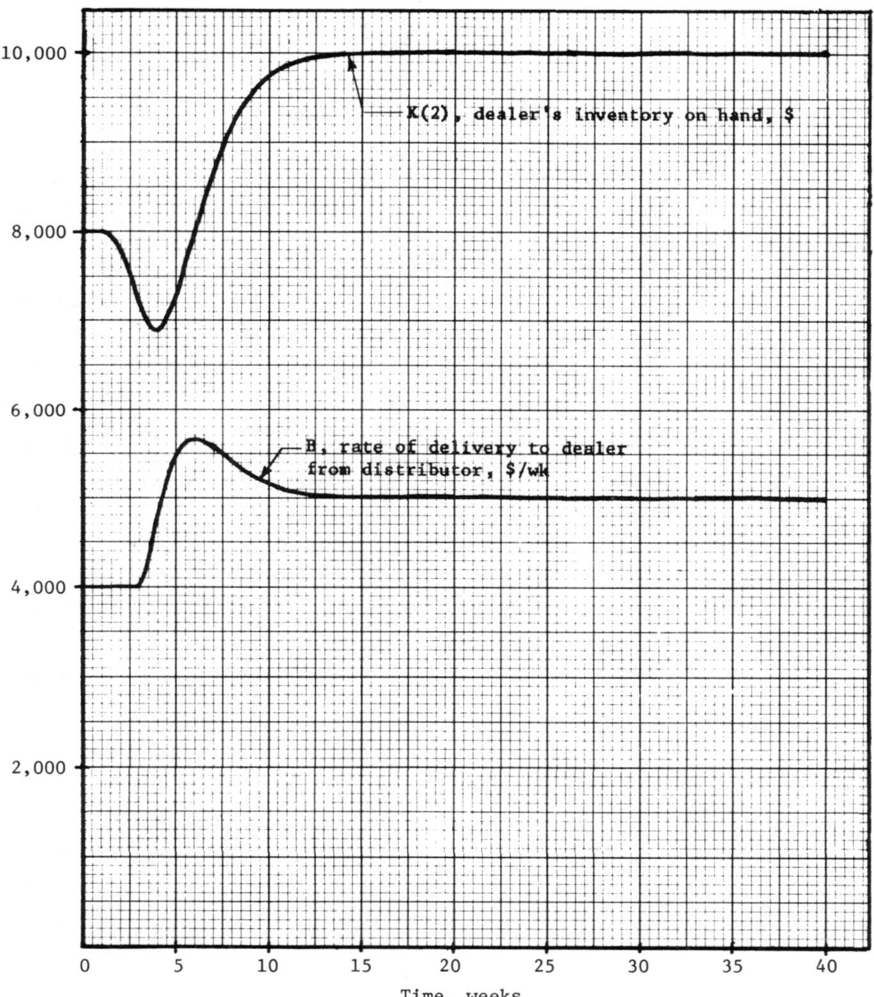

Fig. 14.31. Improved operation by the appliance dealer.

Chapter 15

FUNCTION SPACES AND FOURIER SERIES

15.1 Introduction

The idea of function space can be approached conveniently starting with vector space, which has physical meaning. Vectors can be visualized in a three-dimensional space, and the concept can be extended to n dimensions. An n-dimensional vector is the vector sum of its components in the directions of the n orthogonal basis vectors. The inner product of two vectors is the sum of products of corresponding components of the two vectors. In this chapter these concepts will be extended to *functions*. Let n go to infinity, and express functions as a sum of an infinite number of "basis" functions. One of these sums is the well-known Fourier series. The inner product of two functions becomes, as might be expected, not a product but an integral. The formulas for the coefficients in a Fourier series are inner products. Because the Fourier series is so important in engineering calculations, it will receive special attention. Methods are presented for (a) taking advantage of waveform symmetry to determine the Fourier coefficients efficiently, and (b) calculating the output of a linear system as a Fourier series when the input is periodic.

15.2 Inner Products of Vectors

Mathematicians agree that any operation on two vectors **x** and **y** that is called an inner product must satisfy these three requirements (Ref. 60, p. 6):

1. $$<\mathbf{x}, \mathbf{y}> = <\mathbf{y}, \mathbf{x}>^* \qquad (15.1)$$

   where the asterisk denotes the complex conjugate,

2. $$<a\mathbf{x} + b\mathbf{z}, \mathbf{y}> = a<\mathbf{x}, \mathbf{y}> + b<\mathbf{z}, \mathbf{y}> , \qquad (15.2)$$

   where a and b are constants and **z** is another vector, and

3. $$<\mathbf{x}, \mathbf{x}> \text{ is greater than zero iff } \mathbf{x} \neq 0 . \qquad (15.3)$$

The following definition of the inner product of two n-dimensional vectors fulfills the requirements, and is the one generally used:

$$<\mathbf{x}, \mathbf{y}> = \sum_{i=1}^{n} x_i y_i^* . \tag{15.4}$$

The reason for including the complex conjugate will be apparent soon.

When a vector is represented by a sum of orthogonal vectors, inner products are used to evaluate the coefficients. Any n linearly-independent n-dimensional vectors $\mathbf{x}_i$ constitute an n-dimensional coordinate system, or basis, or *vector space*. Any n-dimensional vector $\mathbf{y}$ can be expressed in this coordinate system:

$$\mathbf{y} = c_1\mathbf{x}_1 + c_2\mathbf{x}_2 + \cdots + c_n\mathbf{x}_n . \tag{15.5}$$

If the basis vectors are orthogonal,

$$<\mathbf{x}_i, \mathbf{x}_j> = 0 , \quad i \neq j , \tag{15.6}$$

and forming the inner product of both sides of Eq. (15.5) with $\mathbf{x}_i$ produces

$$\begin{aligned} <\mathbf{y}, \mathbf{x}_i> &= c_1<\mathbf{x}_1, \mathbf{x}_i> + c_2<\mathbf{x}_2, \mathbf{x}_i> + \cdots + c_n<\mathbf{x}_n, \mathbf{x}_i> \\ &= c_i<\mathbf{x}_i, \mathbf{x}_i> \end{aligned} \tag{15.7}$$

and

$$c_i = \frac{<\mathbf{y}, \mathbf{x}_i>}{<\mathbf{x}_i, \mathbf{x}_i>} . \tag{15.8}$$

If the $\mathbf{x}_i$'s are of unit length, the basis is orthonormal and

$$<\mathbf{x}_i, \mathbf{x}_j> = \delta_{ij} \tag{15.9}$$

and

$$c_i = <\mathbf{y}, \mathbf{x}_i> . \tag{15.10}$$

A vector can be expressed conveniently in an orthogonal basis because the coordinates c_i can be calculated easily by Eq. (15.8). If the basis is orthonormal, the calculation is even easier, by Eq. (15.10).

Why does the definition of the inner product, Eq. (15.4), require the complex conjugate of one of the vectors? If the elements x_i of a vector $\mathbf{x}$ are real numbers, the length or *norm* of the vector is defined as

$$\|\mathbf{x}\| = \sqrt{x_1^2 + x_2^2 + \cdots + x_n^2} = \sqrt{<\mathbf{x}, \mathbf{x}>} . \tag{15.11}$$

If the elements x_i are complex numbers, a logical extension of the definition of the norm is

$$\|\mathbf{x}\| = \sqrt{|x_1|^2 + |x_2|^2 + \cdots + |x_n|^2} . \tag{15.12}$$

Now for any complex number x_i,

$$|x_i|^2 = x_i x_i^* .$$

Therefore, according to Eq. (15.12),

$$\|\mathbf{x}\|^2 = x_1 x_1^* + x_2 x_2^* + \cdots + x_n x_n^* \,. \tag{15.13}$$

If Eq. (15.4) is the definition of the inner product, Eq. (15.13) becomes

$$\|\mathbf{x}\|^2 = <\mathbf{x}, \mathbf{x}> \,. \tag{15.14}$$

The complex conjugate is used in the definition of the inner product so that the norm of a vector with complex elements, defined by Eq. (15.12), will also satisfy Eq. (15.14). For example, consider the vector

$$\mathbf{x} = \begin{bmatrix} 1 + j2 \\ 1 - j3 \end{bmatrix} . \tag{15.15}$$

Its length calculated by Eq. (15.12) is

$$\|\mathbf{x}\| = \sqrt{(\sqrt{5})^2 + (\sqrt{10})^2} = \sqrt{15} \,, \tag{15.16}$$

and its length calculated by Eq. (15.14) is

$$\|\mathbf{x}\|^2 = (1 + j2)(1 - j2) + (1 - j3)(1 + j3) = 5 + 10 \,,$$

or

$$\|\mathbf{x}\| = \sqrt{15} \,. \tag{15.17}$$

15.3 Function Space

The idea of the inner product can be extended from vectors to functions. Define the inner product of two functions as

$$<g_i(t), g_j(t)> = \int_{t_1}^{t_2} g_i(t) g_j^*(t) dt \,, \tag{15.18}$$

which is similar to Eq. (15.4). The functions are *orthogonal* if

$$<g_i(t), g_j(t)> = 0 \,, \quad i \neq j \,. \tag{15.19}$$

For example, choose

$$g_m(t) = e^{jm\omega_o t} \qquad \text{and} \qquad g_n(t) = e^{jn\omega_o t} \tag{15.20}$$

where m and n are integers, and the interval

$$-\frac{T}{2} \leq t \leq \frac{T}{2} \,, \qquad \text{where} \qquad T = \frac{2\pi}{\omega_o} \,. \tag{15.21}$$

Then

$$<g_m(t), g_n(t)> = \int_{-T/2}^{T/2} e^{jm\omega_o t} e^{-jn\omega_o t} dt$$

or

$$<g_m(t), g_n(t)> = \frac{2\sin(m-n)\pi}{(m-n)\omega_o} = \frac{T\sin(m-n)\pi}{(m-n)\pi} = T\delta_{mn} . \quad (15.22)$$

Therefore the functions $e^{jm\omega_o t}$ and $e^{jn\omega_o t}$ are orthogonal over the interval $-\pi/\omega_o \leq t \leq \pi/\omega_o$. The norm of a function is of course defined as

$$\|f(t)\| = \sqrt{<f(t), f(t)>} = \sqrt{\int_{t_1}^{t_2} f(t)f^*(t)dt} . \quad (15.23)$$

The functions

$$\frac{1}{\sqrt{T}} e^{jm\omega_o t} \quad \text{and} \quad \frac{1}{\sqrt{T}} e^{jn\omega_o t} \quad (15.24)$$

are *orthonormal*, because they are orthogonal and the norm of each is unity.

By analogy with vectors, a function can be expressed as a sum of orthogonal functions over the interval (t_1, t_2):

$$f(t) \approx c_1 g_1(t) + c_2 g_2(t) + \cdots + c_n g_n(t) + \cdots \quad (15.25)$$

If this were a true equation like Eq. (15.5), then as for vectors

$$\begin{aligned} <f(t), g_i(t)> &= c_1<g_1(t), g_i(t)> + c_2<g_2(t), g_i(t)> + \cdots \\ &= c_i<g_i(t), g_i(t)> , \end{aligned} \quad (15.26)$$

so that

$$c_i = \frac{<f(t), g_i(t)>}{<g_i(t), g_i(t)>} = \frac{\int_{t_1}^{t_2} f(t)g_i^*(t)dt}{\int_{t_1}^{t_2} g_i(t)g_i^*(t)dt} . \quad (15.27)$$

15.4 A Complete Set of Orthogonal Functions

In Eq. (15.25) how many orthogonal functions $g_i(t)$ are needed to form a basis in which $f(t)$ can be expressed exactly? To answer this question, first define a partial sum

$$\begin{aligned} s_n(t) &= d_1 g_1(t) + d_2 g_2(t) + \cdots + d_n g_n(t) \\ &= \sum_{i=1}^{n} d_i g_i(t) . \end{aligned} \quad (15.28)$$

A useful measure of the error of the partial-sum representation of $f(t)$ is

$$\frac{1}{t_2 - t_1} \|f(t) - s_n(t)\|^2 = \frac{1}{t_2 - t_1} <f(t) - s_n(t), f(t) - s_n(t)>$$

$$= \frac{1}{t_2 - t_1} \int_{t_1}^{t_2} [f(t) - s_n(t)][f^*(t) - s_n^*(t)]dt . \tag{15.29}$$

This is called the *mean-square error*, because if $f(t)$ and $s_n(t)$ are real functions, Eq. (15.29) gives the average of the square of the difference between $f(t)$ and $s_n(t)$ over the interval (t_1, t_2). The analysis will show that the mean-square error is minimized by making $d_i = c_i$, the c_i's being chosen according to Eq. (15.27).

If d_i and c_i are different, let their difference be

$$e_i = d_i - c_i . \tag{15.30}$$

Since

$$s_n(t) = \sum_{i=1}^{n} d_i g_i(t) = \sum_{i=1}^{n} (e_i + c_i) g_i(t) , \tag{15.31}$$

$$\begin{aligned} \|f(t) - s_n(t)\|^2 &= \int_{t_1}^{t_2} [f(t)f^*(t) - s_n(t)f^*(t) - f(t)s_n^*(t) + s_n(t)s_n^*(t)]dt \\ &= \int_{t_1}^{t_2} [f(t)f^*(t) - \sum_{i=1}^{n} (e_i + c_i)g_i(t)f^*(t) \\ &\quad - \sum_{i=1}^{n} (e_i^* + c_i^*)f(t)g_i^*(t) \\ &\quad + \sum_{i=1}^{n} (e_i + c_i)g_i(t) \sum_{i=1}^{n} (e_i^* + c_i^*)g_i^*(t)]dt . \end{aligned} \tag{15.32}$$

To simplify this expression, note first that the inner product of $g_i(t)$ (or any function) with itself is a real, positive constant K_i. This can be seen by writing $g_i(t)$ in terms of its real and imaginary components:

$$g_i(t) = u(t) + jv(t) . \tag{15.33}$$

Then

$$g_i^*(t) = u(t) - jv(t) \tag{15.34}$$

and

$$g_i(t)g_i^*(t) = u^2(t) + v^2(t) . \tag{15.35}$$

Then

$$<g_i(t), g_i(t)> = \int_{t_1}^{t_2} [u^2(t) + v^2(t)]dt . \tag{15.36}$$

Since the integrand is never negative, the integral is positive, and

$$<g_i(t), g_i(t)> = \int_{t_1}^{t_2} g_i(t)g_i^*(t)dt = K_i \,. \qquad (15.37)$$

Next, note that if the c_i's are chosen according to Eq. (15.27),

$$<f(t), g_i(t)> = \int_{t_1}^{t_2} f(t)g_i^*(t)dt = c_i \int_{t_1}^{t_2} g_i(t)g_i^*(t)dt = c_iK_i \qquad (15.38)$$

where c_i is in general a complex constant. And finally, note that forming the conjugate of both sides of Eq. (15.27) produces

$$c_i^* = \frac{\int_{t_1}^{t_2} f^*(t)g_i(t)dt}{\int_{t_1}^{t_2} g_i^*(t)g_i(t)dt} \qquad (15.39)$$

or

$$\int_{t_1}^{t_2} g_i(t)f^*(t)dt = c_i^* \int_{t_1}^{t_2} g_i(t)g_i^*(t)dt = c_i^*K_i \qquad (15.40)$$

or

$$<g_i(t), f(t)> = c_i^*<g_i(t), g_i(t)> = c_i^*K_i \,. \qquad (15.41)$$

Eqs. (15.41) and (15.38) show that $<f(t), g(t)> = <g(t), f(t)>^*$, which is the first requirement of an inner product, given by Eq. (15.1).

Now Eq. (15.32) can be simplified. Applying Eqs. (15.37), (15.38), and (15.40) in Eq. (15.32) where appropriate produces the expression

$$\begin{aligned}\|f(t) - s_n(t)\|^2 &= \int_{t_1}^{t_2} f(t)f^*(t)dt - \sum_{i=1}^{n} (e_i + c_i)c_i^*K_i \\ &\quad - \sum_{i=1}^{n} (e_i^* + c_i^*)c_iK_i + \sum_{i=1}^{n} (e_i + c_i)(e_i^* + c_i^*)K_i \\ &= \int_{t_1}^{t_2} f(t)f^*(t)dt + \sum_{i=1}^{n} (-e_ic_i^* - c_ic_i^* - e_i^*c_i - c_i^*c_i \\ &\quad + e_ie_i^* + e_ic_i^* + c_ie_i^* + c_ic_i^*)K_i \\ &= \int_{t_1}^{t_2} f(t)f^*(t)dt + \sum_{i=1}^{n} (e_ie_i^* - c_ic_i^*)K_i \,. \qquad (15.42)\end{aligned}$$

The left side of this equation is never negative, nor is any of the terms $e_ie_i^*K_i$ or $c_ic_i^*K_i$ on the right. Thus the mean-square error between the function $f(t)$ and its partial-sum approximation $s_n(t)$ is minimized by making each e_i zero. Then $d_i = c_i$. Now it is clear that the partial sum of Eq. (15.28) represents $f(t)$ with the least mean-square error if the coefficients are chosen according to Eq. (15.27). Since the left side of Eq. (15.42) is non-negative and $e_i = 0$,

$$\int_{t_1}^{t_2} f(t)f^*(t)dt \geqslant \sum_{i=1}^{n} c_i c_i^* K_i \,. \tag{15.43}$$

This is a form of *Bessel's inequality*.

If the number n of orthogonal functions $g_i(t)$ in the basis of Eq. (15.28) increases, the number of terms on the right side of Bessel's inequality increases. Since these terms are all positive, the right side keeps increasing, approaching the value of the left side, and the mean-square error decreases. Reducing the mean-square error to zero requires a *complete* or *closed set* of orthogonal functions, namely all of the functions $g_i(t)$ that are orthogonal to each other. To test whether a function $x(t)$ belongs in the set, calculate

$$\int_{t_1}^{t_2} x(t)g_i^*(t)dt \,,$$

using each of the functions $g_i(t)$ already known to be in the set. If the integral is zero for every $g_i(t)$, $x(t)$ belongs in the set. An example of a complete set of orthogonal functions for the interval $(-\pi/\omega_o, \pi/\omega_o)$ is

$$e^{jn\omega_o t}, \quad n = 0, \pm 1, \pm 2, \ldots, \pm\infty \,. \tag{15.44}$$

The number of orthogonal functions in a complete set is infinite. If the orthogonal functions in Eq. (15.28) constitute a complete set, then Bessel's inequality becomes an equality,

$$\int_{t_1}^{t_2} f(t)f^*(t)dt = \sum_{i=1}^{\infty} c_i c_i^* K_i \,, \tag{15.45}$$

and the mean-square error is zero. Eq. (15.42) becomes

$$\|f(t) - \sum_{i=1}^{\infty} c_i g_i(t)\|^2 = 0 \,. \tag{15.46}$$

The series representation of $f(t)$ in the interval (t_1, t_2) is said to *converge in the mean* to $f(t)$ as $n \to \infty$ because the mean-square error converges to zero. This analysis has not proved that

$$f(t) - \sum_{i=1}^{\infty} c_i g_i(t) = 0 \,, \tag{15.47}$$

namely that the infinite series represents the function at every point in the interval (t_1, t_2). Actually, the value given by the series is the value of $f(t)$ anywhere in the interval except at discontinuities in $f(t)$. There the number given by the series is the average of the limits of $f(t)$ obtained by approaching the discontinuity from the left and from the right.

The useful conclusion of this lengthy analysis is that a function $f(t)$ can be represented over an arbitrary interval as an infinite sum of orthogonal functions. The latter constitute an infinite-dimensional orthogonal basis. The components in this coordinate system, namely the coefficients of the infinite series, are calculated like the coordinates of a vector in a basis of orthogonal vectors. The infinite series is called a *generalized Fourier Series.*

15.5 Real Form of the Fourier Series

One complete set of orthogonal functions that is of great value in engineering calculations is

$$\sin\frac{2\pi nt}{T} \quad \text{and} \quad \cos\frac{2\pi nt}{T}, \qquad n = 0,1,2,\ldots \tag{15.48}$$

They are orthogonal over the interval t_o to $t_o + T$, where t_o is any starting time, because

$$\int_{t_o}^{t_o+T} \sin\frac{2\pi mt}{T}\sin\frac{2\pi nt}{T}\,dt = \frac{T}{2}\,\delta_{mn}, \tag{15.49}$$

$$\int_{t_o}^{t_o+T} \cos\frac{2\pi mt}{T}\cos\frac{2\pi nt}{T}\,dt = \frac{T}{2}\,\delta_{mn}, \tag{15.50}$$

and

$$\int_{t_o}^{t_o+T} \sin\frac{2\pi mt}{T}\cos\frac{2\pi nt}{T}\,dt = 0 \tag{15.51}$$

for all integral values of m and n. A function $f(t)$ can therefore be represented over the interval $(t_o, t_o + T)$ by the infinite series

$$f(t) = a_0 + \sum_{n=1}^{\infty}\left(a_n\cos\frac{2\pi nt}{T} + b_n\sin\frac{2\pi nt}{T}\right). \tag{15.52}$$

This is the real or sinusoidal form of the *Fourier series*. Notice that the right side is unchanged if t is replaced by $t + mT$, where m is any integer. Therefore the series is periodic with period T. If $f(t)$ happens to be periodic with the same period, the series represents $f(t)$ over every interval of width T, and therefore represents it over all time.

According to Eq. (15.27) the coefficients in the Fourier series are

$$a_n = \frac{<f(t), \cos \frac{2\pi nt}{T}>}{<\cos \frac{2\pi nt}{T}, \cos \frac{2\pi nt}{T}>} = \frac{2}{T}\int_{t_o}^{t_o+T} f(t) \cos \frac{2\pi nt}{T}\, dt\,, \tag{15.53}$$

$$b_n = \frac{<f(t), \sin \frac{2\pi nt}{T}>}{<\sin \frac{2\pi nt}{T}, \sin \frac{2\pi nt}{T}>} = \frac{2}{T}\int_{t_o}^{t_o+T} f(t) \sin \frac{2\pi nt}{T}\, dt\,. \tag{15.54}$$

If $f(t)$ is a real function, these coefficients are real numbers. The constant or "DC" term of the series is a special case of Eq. (15.53):

$$a_0 = \frac{<f(t), 1>}{<1, 1>} = \frac{\int_{t_o}^{t_o+T} f(t)dt}{\int_{t_o}^{t_o+T} dt} = \frac{1}{T}\int_{t_o}^{t_o+T} f(t)dt\,. \tag{15.55}$$

Clearly a_0 is the average value of $f(t)$ over the interval. Notice that if $f(t)$ is periodic, t_o is arbitrary and can be set at any convenient value such as 0 or $-T/2$.

As an example, represent the sawtooth wave of Fig. 15.1 by a Fourier series. Over the interval $(0, T)$, $f(t)$ has the formula

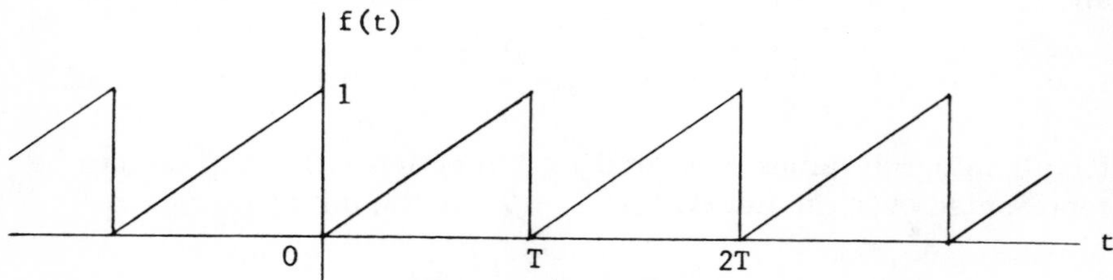

Fig. 15.1. A sawtooth wave.

$$f(t) = \frac{t}{T}, \quad 0 < t < T\,. \tag{15.56}$$

According to Eqs. (15.53) thru (15.55),

$$a_0 = \frac{1}{T}\int_0^T \frac{t}{T}\, dt = \frac{1}{2}, \tag{15.57}$$

$$a_n = \frac{2}{T^2}\int_0^T t \cos \frac{2\pi nt}{T}\, dt = 0 , \tag{15.58}$$

and

$$b_n = \frac{2}{T^2}\int_0^T t \sin \frac{2\pi nt}{T}\, dt = -\frac{1}{n\pi} . \tag{15.59}$$

Therefore

$$f(t) = \frac{1}{2} - \frac{1}{\pi} \sum_{n=1}^{\infty} \frac{1}{n} \sin \frac{2\pi nt}{T} . \tag{15.60}$$

The sawtooth waveform can therefore be represented by an infinite series of sine waves whose frequencies are harmonics or integral multiples of the fundamental frequency $2\pi/T$. Notice that the series includes no cosine term. The next section will show why.

If $f(t)$ is a real function, Eq. (15.52) can also be written in the form

$$f(t) = a_0 + \sum_{n=1}^{\infty} A_n \cos(n\omega_o t + \theta_n) , \tag{15.61}$$

where

$$\omega_o = \frac{2\pi}{T} , \tag{15.62}$$

$$A_n = \sqrt{a_n^2 + b_n^2} , \tag{15.63}$$

and

$$\theta_n = -\tan^{-1} \frac{b_n}{a_n} . \tag{15.64}$$

This form shows the amplitude A_n and the frequency $n\omega_o$ of the nth harmonic of the waveform. If $f(t)$ is applied as a voltage to the input terminals of an electronic wave analyzer, a bar graph of the amplitudes of the harmonics is displayed on a cathode-ray tube as in Fig. 15.2. This display is called the *frequency spectrum*. A Fourier series can be written for any periodic function that satisfies the *Dirichlet conditions*, namely that it has a finite number of maxima, minima, and discontinuities in one period, and the area under one cycle of the curve is finite. Thus any waveform that is not off-scale or "hashy" when displayed on an oscilloscope can be expressed by a Fourier series.

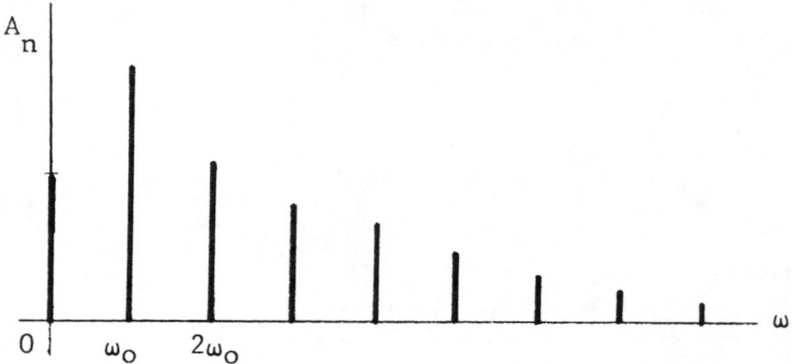

Fig. 15.2. A frequency spectrum.

15.6 Taking Advantage of Symmetry in the Waveform

For many periodic waveforms that are commonly encountered in engineering, the Fourier coefficients can be found more easily than by Eqs. (15.53), (15.54), and (15.55). To show how the formulas are simplified, start by observing that a function $f(t)$ is said to be *even* if $f(t) = f(-t)$ as in Fig. 15.3, and *odd* if $f(t) = -f(-t)$ as in Fig. 15.4. The product of two functions

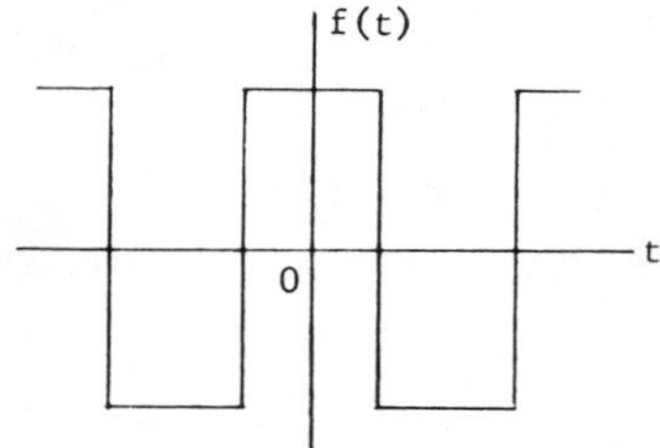

Fig. 15.3. An even function.

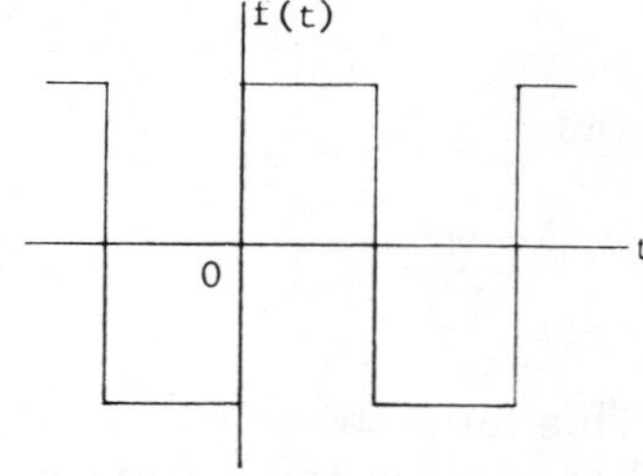

Fig. 15.4. An odd function.

$$h(t) = f(t)g(t) \tag{15.65}$$

is even if $f(t)$ and $g(t)$ are both even or both odd, but is odd if one is even and one is odd. For an odd function,

$$\int_{-a}^{a} f(t)dt = 0 \tag{15.66}$$

where a is any value of t. The Fourier coefficients, Eqs. (15.53) and (15.54), can be written as

$$a_n = \frac{2}{T}\int_{-T/2}^{T/2} f(t)\cos\frac{2\pi nt}{T}\,dt \tag{15.67}$$

$$b_n = \frac{2}{T}\int_{-T/2}^{T/2} f(t)\sin\frac{2\pi nt}{T}\,dt\,. \tag{15.68}$$

Now $\cos(2\pi nt/T)$ is even and $\sin(2\pi nt/T)$ is odd. Therefore if $f(t)$ is odd, $f(t)\cos(2\pi nt/T)$ is odd and $a_n = 0$. If $f(t)$ is even, $f(t)\sin(2\pi nt/T)$ is odd, and $b_n = 0$. Furthermore, an odd function has an average value of zero. Thus if $f(t)$ is even, the Fourier series has the simplified form

$$f(t) = a_0 + \sum_{n=1}^{\infty} a_n \cos\frac{2\pi nt}{T} \tag{15.69}$$

and if $f(t)$ is odd,

$$f(t) = \sum_{n=1}^{\infty} b_n \sin\frac{2\pi nt}{T}\,. \tag{15.70}$$

Periodic functions with quarter-wave symmetry can be either even or odd, depending on the location of the vertical axis. Each half of a cycle must be symmetrical about its center, the quarter-wave point, and the second half must be the mirror image of the first half, on the other side of the horizontal axis. The square wave of Figs. 15.3 and 15.4 is an example.

The evaluation of a_n and b_n in Eqs. (15.69) and (15.70) is simplified by the fact that if $f(t)$ is even or odd, the integrand of Eq. (15.67) or (15.68) is even. For any even function $f(t)$,

$$\int_{-a}^{a} f(t)dt = 2\int_{0}^{a} f(t)dt\,, \tag{15.71}$$

where a is any value of t. Thus if $f(t)$ is even, instead of Eq. (15.67) write

$$a_n = \frac{4}{T}\int_{0}^{T/2} f(t)\cos\frac{2\pi nt}{T}\,dt \tag{15.72}$$

and if $f(t)$ is odd, instead of Eq. (15.68),

$$b_n = \frac{4}{T}\int_{0}^{T/2} f(t)\sin\frac{2\pi nt}{T}\,dt\,, \tag{15.73}$$

and then integrate over only half a period. Fig. 15.5 shows a typical odd function $f(t)$, and explains graphically why for $n = 1$ the integral of Eq.

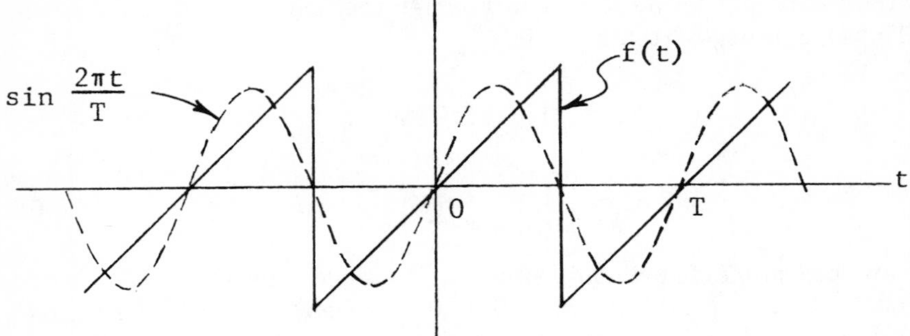

Fig. 15.5. Typical odd function.

(15.73) from 0 to $T/2$ is the same as that from $-T/2$ to 0. Similarly, the integral from 0 to $T/2$ is the same as that from $T/2$ to T. Thus Eq. (15.73) gives the same result as Eq. (15.54) with $t_o = 0$. The latter equation would be a poor choice, because $f(t)$ has two different formulas in the interval from 0 to T.

If a waveform has quarter-wave symmetry as in Fig. 15.6, the calcula-

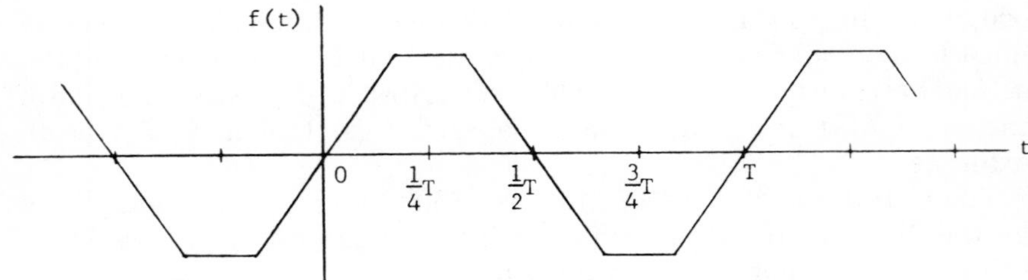

Fig. 15.6. A waveform that can be either even or odd.

tion of the Fourier coefficients is simplified even further. If the ordinate axis is located to make this waveform odd, as in Fig. 15.6, the Fourier series contains neither cosine terms nor even-numbered sine terms. A quick sketch of a few harmonic sine waves on the waveform shows why this is true. Furthermore, for odd-numbered sine terms the integral (15.68) is the same over each quarter cycle. Although $f(t)$ has five different formulas in one cycle, the only calculation needed is

$$b_n = \frac{8}{T}\int_0^{T/4} f(t) \sin \frac{2\pi nt}{T}\, dt\,, \quad n = 1,3,5,\ldots \tag{15.74}$$

In this interval $f(t)$ has only two different formulas. Eq. (15.74) is valid only for odd values of n, and will not give the correct value $b_n = 0$ for even n.

15.7 Exponential Form of the Fourier Series

A function $f(t)$ can be represented over the interval $(-T/2, T/2)$ by the complete set of orthogonal functions

$$e^{jn\omega_o t}, \quad n = 0, \pm 1, \pm 2, \ldots$$

where $\omega_o = 2\pi/T$. The series representation is

$$f(t) = \sum_{n=-\infty}^{\infty} c_n e^{jn\omega_o t} . \tag{15.75}$$

This is the exponential form of the Fourier series. According to Eq. (15.27) the coefficients are

$$c_n = \frac{\displaystyle\int_{-T/2}^{T/2} f(t) e^{-jn\omega_o t} dt}{\displaystyle\int_{-T/2}^{T/2} e^{jn\omega_o t} e^{-jn\omega_o t} dt} = \frac{1}{T}\int_{-T/2}^{T/2} f(t) e^{-jn\omega_o t} dt . \tag{15.76}$$

They are related to the parameters a_0, A_n, and θ_n in the form of Eq. (15.61) by the formulas

$$c_0 = a_0 \qquad \text{and} \qquad c_{\pm n} = \frac{A_n}{2} e^{\pm j\theta_n}, \quad n = 1,2, \ldots \tag{15.77}$$

For the exponential form the frequency spectrum includes negative as well as positive frequencies, and each component in the spectrum is a complex number. The magnitude of each c_n and c_{-n} is half of the value A_n that a wave analyzer displays.

An example will show an advantage of the exponential form of the Fourier series in analyzing linear systems. Suppose the input $v(t)$ to the fixed linear system of Fig. 15.7 is the square wave shown in Fig. 15.8.

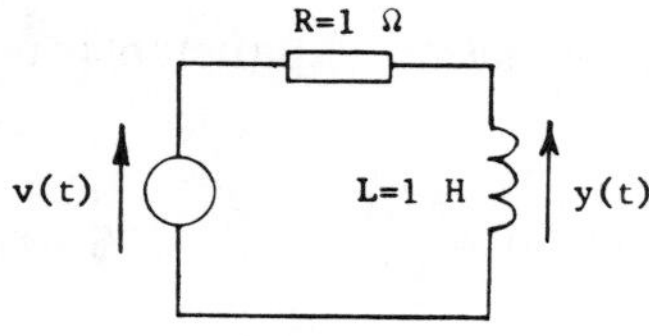

Fig. 15.7. Linear system.

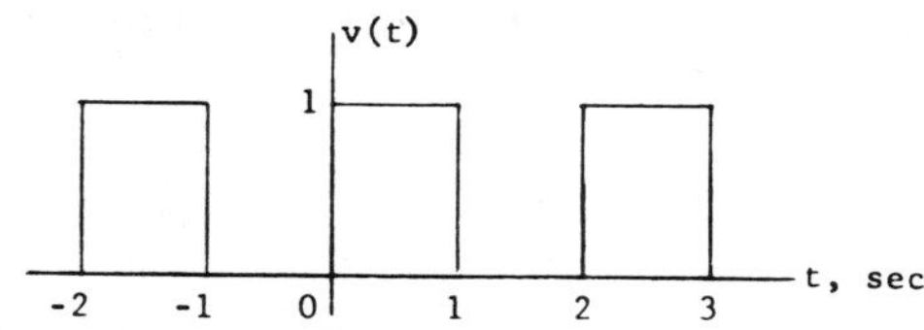

Fig. 15.8. Input waveform.

What is the steady-state output voltage $y(t)$? To find out, first write the input as an exponential Fourier series. The period T is 2 sec. Therefore

$$\omega_o = \frac{2\pi}{T} = \pi \qquad \text{rad/sec}\,, \tag{15.78}$$

and Eq. (15.76) becomes

$$c_n = \frac{1}{2}\int_0^1 e^{-jn\pi t}dt = \frac{j}{2n\pi}\,(e^{-jn\pi}-1)$$
$$= \begin{cases} -\dfrac{j}{n\pi}, & n \text{ odd} \\ 0\,, & n \text{ even} \end{cases} \tag{15.79}$$

and

$$c_0 = \frac{1}{2}\,. \tag{15.80}$$

Then

$$v(t) = \sum_{n=-\infty}^{\infty} c_n e^{jn\omega_o t} = \frac{1}{2} - \frac{j}{\pi}\sum_{n=-\infty}^{\infty}\frac{e^{jn\pi t}}{n}\,, \qquad n \text{ odd}\,. \tag{15.81}$$

The input to the system can therefore be represented as the sum of a series of complex numbers or phasors of the form $\exp(j\omega t)$. To calculate the steady-state response of the system to this input, observe first that if the input to any fixed, linear system is

$$v(t) = e^{at} \qquad \text{or} \qquad V(s) = \frac{1}{s-a}\,, \tag{15.82}$$

its output is

$$Y(s) = V(s)H(s) = \frac{H(s)}{s-a}\,, \tag{15.83}$$

where $H(s)$ is the system function. A partial-fraction expansion produces

$$Y(s) = \frac{H(s)}{s-a} = H_1(s) + \frac{K}{s-a} = H_1(s) + \frac{H(a)}{s-a}\,. \tag{15.84}$$

The two terms on the right are the Laplace transforms of the transient and steady-state components of the output. The steady-state output is therefore

$$y_s(t) = H(a)e^{at}\,. \tag{15.85}$$

If the input to the system is the phasor $v(t) = e^{j\omega t}$, the steady-state output is

$$y_s(t) = H(j\omega)e^{j\omega t} . \tag{15.86}$$

Electrical engineers are experienced in writing $H(j\omega)$ for a passive R-L-C circuit by replacing R, L, and C by the impedances $R, j\omega L$, and $-j/\omega C$. Mechanical engineers may have to calculate the transfer function for the circuit of Fig. 15.7 by writing the differential equation relating $v(t)$ to $y(t)$, and taking its Laplace transform. Either way, the result is

$$H(s) = \frac{Y(s)}{V(s)} = \frac{Ls}{R + Ls} = \frac{s}{1 + s} \tag{15.87}$$

and

$$H(j\omega) = \frac{j\omega}{1 + j\omega} . \tag{15.88}$$

Therefore the steady-state response of the system to the input

$$v(t) = e^{j\omega t} \tag{15.89}$$

is

$$y_s(t) = \frac{j\omega}{1 + j\omega} e^{j\omega t} . \tag{15.90}$$

The input to the system, given by Eq. (15.81), contains a spectrum of phasors. The response to the harmonic

$$-\frac{j}{\pi n} e^{jn\pi t} \quad \text{is} \quad -\frac{j}{n\pi} \cdot \frac{jn\pi}{1 + jn\pi} e^{jn\pi t} . \tag{15.91}$$

The response to the DC component of 1/2 is zero. This can be seen either by letting $\omega = 0$ in Eq. (15.90), or by observing that the DC component of $v(t)$ appears across the resistor, not the inductor. Since the system is linear, the steady-state output is the sum of the responses to each of the harmonics:

$$y_s(t) = \sum_{n=-\infty}^{\infty} \frac{1}{1 + jn\pi} e^{jn\pi t} , \quad n \text{ odd} . \tag{15.92}$$

With the help of Eqs. (15.77) and (15.61), the sum becomes

$$y_s(t) = \sum_{n=1}^{\infty} \frac{2}{\sqrt{1 + (n\pi)^2}} \cos(n\pi t - \tan^{-1} n\pi) , \quad n \text{ odd} . \tag{15.93}$$

Notice that the response to the real input is real, as it must be for any realizable system. The waveform of $y_s(t)$ is shown in Fig. 15.9.

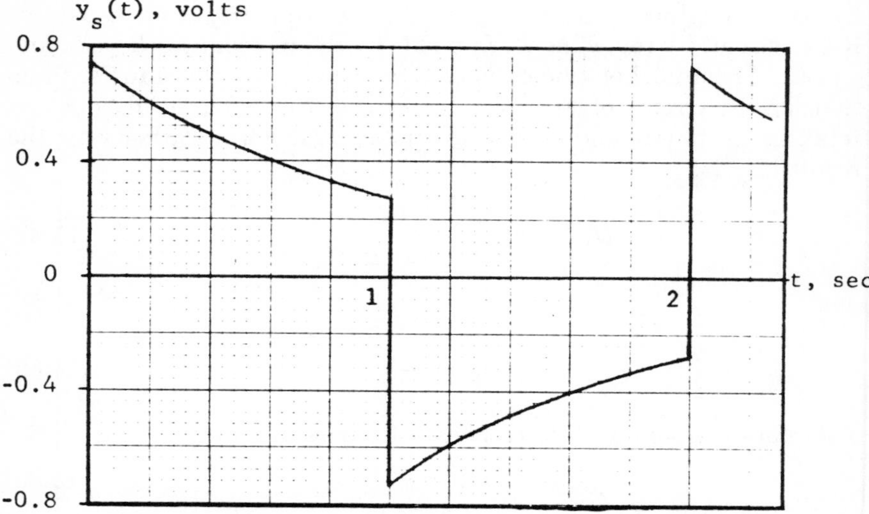

Fig. 15.9. Waveform of the steady-state output voltage.

This method of calculating the output of a linear system, whose input is a periodic wave, is useful for obtaining the amplitude of the harmonics in the spectrum of the output. It is not the best way of calculating $y_s(t)$, because the latter appears as an infinite series. The example was presented in anticipation of the Fourier transform. The process of calculating $y_s(t)$ can be interpreted like this:

1. Calculate the amplitude of each harmonic in the spectrum of the input:

$$c_n = \frac{1}{T}\int_{-T/2}^{T/2} v(t)e^{-jn\omega_o t}dt \ . \tag{15.94}$$

   In anticipation of the next chapter, call this quantity $V(n\omega_o)$.

2. Multiply each harmonic of the frequency spectrum by the system function to obtain $Y(n\omega_o)$, the corresponding harmonic in the spectrum of the output:

$$Y(n\omega_o) = V(n\omega_o)H(jn\omega_o) \ . \tag{15.95}$$

3. Calculate the output from its frequency spectrum:

$$y_s(t) = \sum_{n=-\infty}^{\infty} Y(n\omega_o)e^{jn\omega_o t}. \tag{15.96}$$

The three steps consist of (1) performing a transformation on the input function of time, (2) multiplying the transform by the system function to obtain the transform of the output, and (3) inverting the latter to obtain the output function of time. These are the same three steps used with Laplace transforms. The next chapter will make the transition from the exponential Fourier series to the Fourier integral or transform, and will use the same three steps to analyze linear systems. The Fourier transform produces the output in closed form, and handles aperiodic as well as periodic inputs.

Chapter 16

THE FOURIER TRANSFORM

16.1 Introduction

The preceding chapter prepared the way for converting the Fourier series to the Fourier integral or transform. The method that will be used is not rigorous mathematically, and requires the act of faith always needed to pass from a summation to an integral. Some authors avoid the transition, and start by defining the Fourier transform. That approach, however, deprives the student of a useful physical picture. Once achieved, the Fourier transform is of enormous advantage in system engineering. It is sometimes more helpful than the Laplace transform in analyzing linear systems. It is the primary tool for the analysis of frequency spectra required in radar, communication systems, and noise identification. At the present state of the art, computers used to filter the noise out of digital signals compute the Fourier transform of the signal, process the transform, and compute the inverse, all *on line*, because the transform technique is faster than processing the signal in the time domain.

16.2 Conversion to the Fourier Integral

According to the preceding chapter, if a function is periodic with period T it can be expressed by the Fourier series

$$f(t) = \sum_{n=-\infty}^{\infty} c_n e^{jn\omega_o t}, \tag{16.1}$$

where

$$\omega_o = \frac{2\pi}{T} \tag{16.2}$$

and

$$c_n = \frac{1}{T}\int_{-T/2}^{T/2} f(t)e^{-jn\omega_o t}dt\,. \tag{16.3}$$

Fig. 16.1 shows a typical periodic function, and Fig. 16.2 shows the amplitude of its frequency spectrum. Does an aperiodic function have a frequency spectrum, and if so, what does it look like? An aperiodic function such as a pulse can be considered as a periodic function with an

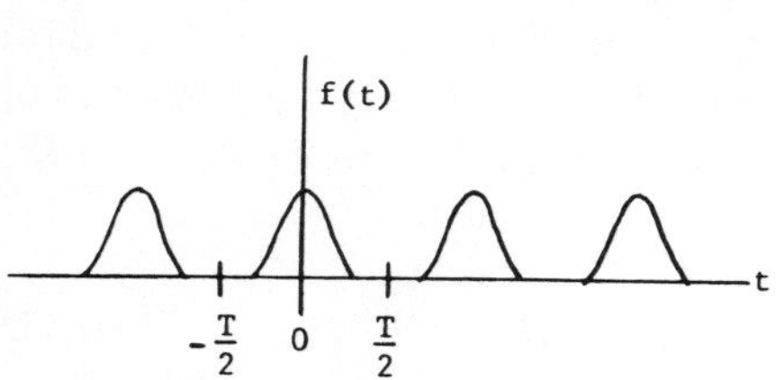

Fig. 16.1. A periodic function.

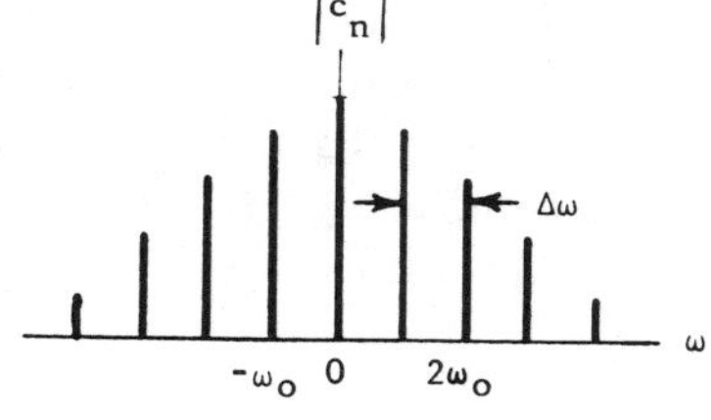

Fig. 16.2. Spectrum of a periodic function.

infinite period. To find the spectrum of the latter, combine Eqs. (16.1) and (16.3) into the form

$$f(t) = \frac{1}{T} \sum_{n=-\infty}^{\infty} \left[\int_{-T/2}^{T/2} f(x) e^{-jn\omega_o x} dx \right] e^{jn\omega_o t} . \tag{16.4}$$

Letting

$$\Delta\omega = \omega_o = \frac{2\pi}{T} \qquad \text{and} \qquad \omega_n = n\omega_o \tag{16.5}$$

converts the function to the form

$$f(t) = \frac{1}{2\pi} \sum_{n=-\infty}^{\infty} \left[\int_{-T/2}^{T/2} f(x) e^{-j\omega_n x} dx \right] e^{j\omega_n t} \Delta\omega . \tag{16.6}$$

Now make the definition

$$F(\omega_n) = Tc_n = \int_{-T/2}^{T/2} f(t) e^{-j\omega_n t} dt . \tag{16.7}$$

Eq. (16.6) becomes

$$f(t) = \frac{1}{2\pi} \sum_{n=-\infty}^{\infty} F(\omega_n) e^{j\omega_n t} \Delta\omega . \tag{16.8}$$

If the pulse width in Fig. 16.1 remains constant and the period T approaches infinity, the function becomes an aperiodic pulse centered at the origin. Then $\Delta\omega$ approaches zero, the discrete spectrum of Fig. 16.2 becomes a continuous band of frequencies, and the summation in Eq. (16.8) becomes the integral

$$f(t) = \frac{1}{2\pi} \int_{-\infty}^{\infty} F(\omega) e^{j\omega t} d\omega . \tag{16.9}$$

Eq. (16.7) becomes

$$F(\omega) = \int_{-\infty}^{\infty} f(t) e^{-j\omega t} dt . \tag{16.10}$$

$F(\omega)$ is called the *Fourier integral* or *Fourier transform* of $f(t)$. Notice the symmetry of the operations of calculating the Fourier transform and its inverse. Some authors (such as Ref. 147) put the $1/2\pi$ in $F(\omega)$ instead of $f(t)$, and some assign $1/\sqrt{2\pi}$ to each. Others (such as Refs. 39 and 145) let $f = \omega/2\pi$, and write

$$F(f) = \int_{-\infty}^{\infty} f(t)e^{-j2\pi ft}dt \tag{16.11}$$

and

$$\begin{aligned} f(t) &= \frac{1}{2\pi}\int_{-\infty}^{\infty} F(f)e^{j2\pi ft}d(2\pi f) \\ &= \int_{-\infty}^{\infty} F(f)e^{j2\pi ft}df \ , \end{aligned} \tag{16.12}$$

thereby avoiding the multiplier of $1/2\pi$. The choice in this book is Eqs. (16.9) and (16.10), because the latter looks like the Laplace transform of $f(t)$ with s replaced by $j\omega$. These two formulas ease the transition from Laplace to Fourier transforms and vice versa. The Fourier transform of the impulse response $h(t)$ of a fixed linear system is called $H(\omega)$ according to Eq. (16.10), not $H(j\omega)$. If $v(t)$ is the input to such a system and $y(t)$ is its output, what is the relationship between $V(\omega)$ and $Y(\omega)$? Experience with Laplace transforms would indicate that

$$Y(\omega) = V(\omega)H(\omega) \ . \tag{16.13}$$

The next section will show that this is a fact, and a very useful one.

The preceding chapter shows that the output of a linear system can be computed by the use of Fourier series when the input is periodic. Only the steady-state output is obtained, and in the form of an infinite series. If Fourier transforms are used with a single-pulse input, the output is still the steady-state response to a pulse train of infinite period. Mathematically, the response to each pulse in the train dies out before the next pulse occurs. The calculated output is therefore the *complete* response to the actual single pulse. The calculation does not account for initial conditions in the system, because it assumes that all initial conditions are zero. Fourier transforms, unlike Laplace transforms, give correct outputs only for initially-inert systems.

Eq. (16.13) is not limited to pulse inputs. Although this vigorous analysis does not offer proof, it works for any input $v(t)$ and any system impulse response $h(t)$ whose Fourier transforms exist. The input might be periodic like $\sin \omega_o t$, causal like $U(t) \sin \omega_o t$, or exist for all time like $v(t) = 1$. Because the inverse Fourier transform Eq. (16.9) is an integral instead of an infinite series, it has the advantage of producing the output in closed form.

16.3 Some Fourier Transforms

The Fourier transforms of several commonly-encountered time functions will be derived here, and summarized in Table 16.1 at the end of the chapter.

Exponential. According to Eq. (16.10), the Fourier transform of the causal exponential function

$$f(t) = e^{-at}U(t)\,, \quad a > 0 \tag{16.14}$$

is

$$F(\omega) = \int_{-\infty}^{\infty} e^{-at}U(t)e^{-j\omega t}dt = \int_{0}^{\infty} e^{-(a+j\omega)t}dt$$

or

$$F(\omega) = \frac{1}{a + j\omega} = \frac{1}{\sqrt{a^2 + \omega^2}}\, e^{-j\tan^{-1}(\omega/a)}\,. \tag{16.15}$$

The transform pair can be expressed in the form

$$e^{-at}U(t) \leftrightarrow \frac{1}{a + j\omega}\,. \tag{16.16}$$

They are plotted in Fig. 16.3. Notice that the frequency spectrum is

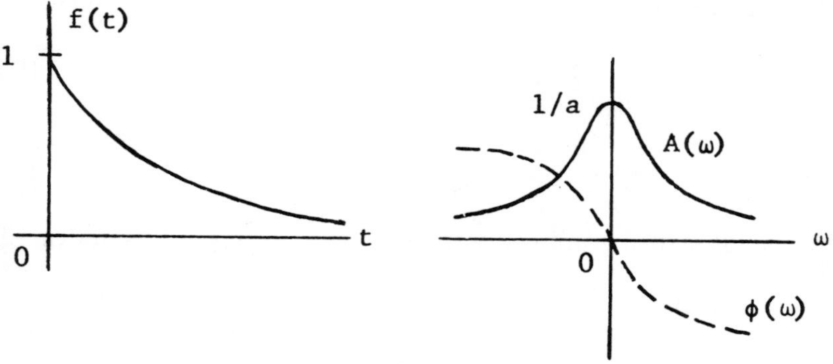

Fig. 16.3. Fourier transform of a causal exponential.

continuous. If the Fourier transform is written in the form

$$F(\omega) = A(\omega)e^{j\phi(\omega)}\,, \tag{16.17}$$

$A(\omega)$ is the magnitude of $F(\omega)$, also called the *Fourier spectrum* of $f(t)$, and $\phi(\omega)$ is the phase angle of $F(\omega)$.

Notice the symmetry of $F(\omega)$. If $f(t)$ is any real function, its Fourier transform has the same kind of symmetry. To show this, let $R(\omega)$ and $X(\omega)$ be the real and imaginary parts of $F(\omega)$:

$$F(\omega) = R(\omega) + jX(\omega) \,. \tag{16.18}$$

Since

$$F(\omega) = \int_{-\infty}^{\infty} f(t)e^{-j\omega t}dt = \int_{-\infty}^{\infty} f(t)(\cos \omega t - j \sin \omega t)dt \,, \tag{16.19}$$

$$R(\omega) = \int_{-\infty}^{\infty} f(t) \cos \omega t \, dt \qquad \text{and} \qquad X(\omega) = -\int_{-\infty}^{\infty} f(t) \sin \omega t \, dt \,. \tag{16.20}$$

Since $\cos \omega t$ is an even function and $\sin \omega t$ is odd,

$$R(-\omega) = R(\omega) \qquad \text{and} \qquad X(-\omega) = -X(\omega) \,. \tag{16.21}$$

Therefore

$$F(-\omega) = R(\omega) - jX(\omega) = F^*(\omega) \,, \tag{16.22}$$

as illustrated by Fig. 16.3. The reader is invited to show that the function

$$f(t) = e^{at}U(t) \,, \quad a > 0$$

does not have a Fourier transform.

Unit Impulse. The Fourier transform of a unit impulse $\delta(t)$ is

$$F(\omega) = \int_{-\infty}^{\infty} \delta(t)e^{-j\omega t}dt = 1 \,. \tag{16.23}$$

Thus

$$\delta(t) \leftrightarrow 1 \,. \tag{16.24}$$

This pair is shown graphically in Fig. 16.4. The impulse is indicated by

Fig. 16.4. Fourier transform of an impulse.

an arrow, and the number beside it is its area. The frequency spectrum of an impulse contains all frequencies with equal amplitude. Similarly, if $F(\omega)$ is a unit impulse $\delta(\omega)$, its inverse transform is

$$f(t) = \frac{1}{2\pi}\int_{-\infty}^{\infty} \delta(\omega)e^{j\omega t}d\omega = \frac{1}{2\pi} . \tag{16.25}$$

Thus

$$1 \leftrightarrow 2\pi\delta(\omega) . \tag{16.26}$$

This is a statement of the obvious fact that a DC signal of 1 volt contains only one frequency, namely zero.

Symmetry Theorem. Transform pairs (16.24) and (16.26) indicate a symmetry between $f(t)$ and $F(\omega)$. To obtain the general rule, write Eq. (16.9) with t replaced by $-t$:

$$f(-t) = \frac{1}{2\pi}\int_{-\infty}^{\infty} F(\omega)e^{-j\omega t}d\omega , \tag{16.27}$$

and then change the name of t to ω and vice versa, to get

$$2\pi f(-\omega) = \int_{-\infty}^{\infty} F(t)e^{-j\omega t}dt . \tag{16.28}$$

The right side of this equation is the Fourier transform of $F(t)$. Thus

$$F(t) \leftrightarrow 2\pi f(-\omega) . \tag{16.29}$$

This is the *symmetry theorem*, that will save work in the derivation of other transform pairs.

Rectangular Pulse. Fig. 16.5 shows a rectangular pulse called $p_T(t)$,

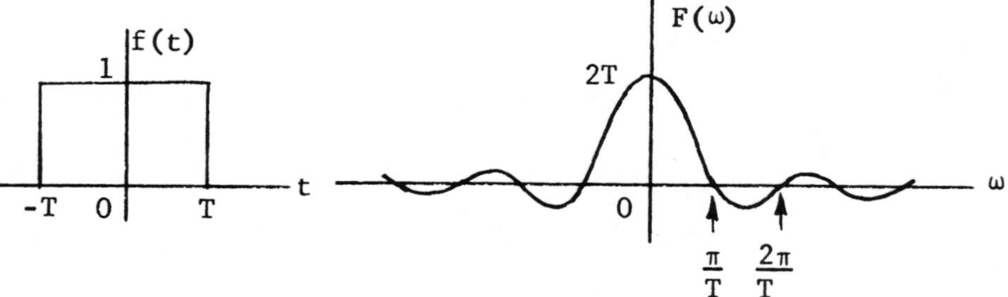

Fig. 16.5. Fourier transform of a rectangular pulse.

for which $f(t) = 1$, $-T < t < T$. Its Fourier transform is

$$F(\omega) = \int_{-T}^{T} e^{-j\omega t}dt = -\frac{2}{j2\omega}(e^{-j\omega T} - e^{j\omega T}) = \frac{2}{\omega}\sin \omega T . \tag{16.30}$$

Thus

$$p_T(t) \leftrightarrow \frac{2}{\omega} \sin \omega T \,. \tag{16.31}$$

If $F(\omega)$ is a rectangular pulse $p_T(\omega)$, transform pair (16.31) and the symmetry theorem (16.29) show that

$$\frac{2}{t} \sin tT \leftrightarrow 2\pi p_T(-\omega) \,. \tag{16.32}$$

Since the rectangular pulse is an even function,

$$p_T(-\omega) = p_T(\omega) \,. \tag{16.33}$$

Changing the name of T to a produces the transform pair

$$\frac{\sin at}{\pi t} \leftrightarrow p_a(\omega) \,. \tag{16.34}$$

Ref. 39 defines the *sinc function* as

$$\operatorname{sinc} t = \frac{\sin \pi t}{\pi t} \,. \tag{16.35}$$

Although sinc functions are not often generated physically, they are frequently used in system calculations.

Time and Frequency Shift. If a time function $f(t)$ whose Fourier transform is $F(\omega)$ is delayed by the time t_o and thereby shifted to the right as in Fig. 16.6, it becomes $f(t - t_o)$. Letting $x = t - t_o$ shows that

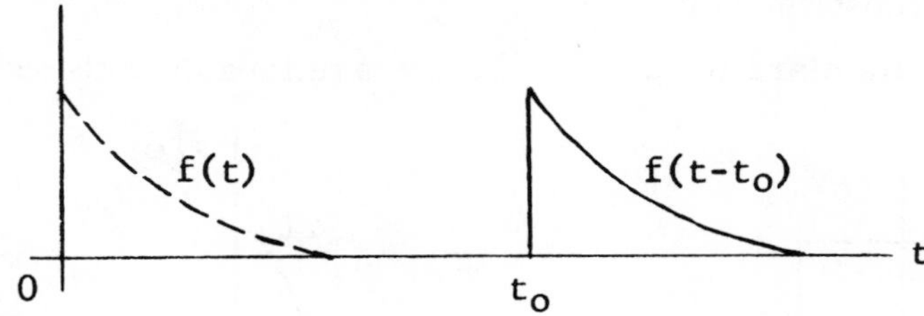

Fig. 16.6. Time-delayed function.

the Fourier transform of the shifted function is

$$\int_{-\infty}^{\infty} f(t - t_o)e^{-j\omega t}dt = \int_{-\infty}^{\infty} f(x)e^{-j\omega(x+t_o)}dx$$

$$= e^{-j\omega t_o}\int_{-\infty}^{\infty} f(x)e^{-j\omega x}dx = e^{-j\omega t_o}F(\omega) \,. \tag{16.36}$$

Therefore

$$f(t - t_o) \leftrightarrow e^{-j\omega t_o} F(\omega) \,. \tag{16.37}$$

The Fourier spectrum is unchanged by the time shift, and the phase angle is decreased by the amount ωt_o. Similarly, if the Fourier transform of $f(t)$ is $F(\omega)$, the transform of $e^{j\omega_o t} f(t)$ is

$$\int_{-\infty}^{\infty} f(t) e^{j\omega_o t} e^{-j\omega t} dt = \int_{-\infty}^{\infty} f(t) e^{-j(\omega-\omega_o)t} dt = F(\omega - \omega_o) \,. \tag{16.38}$$

Thus a frequency-shifted Fourier transform and its inverse are

$$e^{j\omega_o t} f(t) \leftrightarrow F(\omega - \omega_o) \,. \tag{16.39}$$

Unit Step. Some texts, such as Refs. 21 and 147, state that in order for a function to have a Fourier transform, it must satisfy the Dirichlet conditions and be absolutely integrable:

$$\int_{-\infty}^{\infty} |f(t)| dt < \infty \,. \tag{16.40}$$

Although these two conditions are sufficient, the latter is not necessary. The function $f(t) = 1$ does not fulfill condition (16.40), but has a Fourier transform given by pair (16.26). Another function that does not fulfill this condition is the unit step $U(t)$ shown in Fig. 16.7. An attempt to

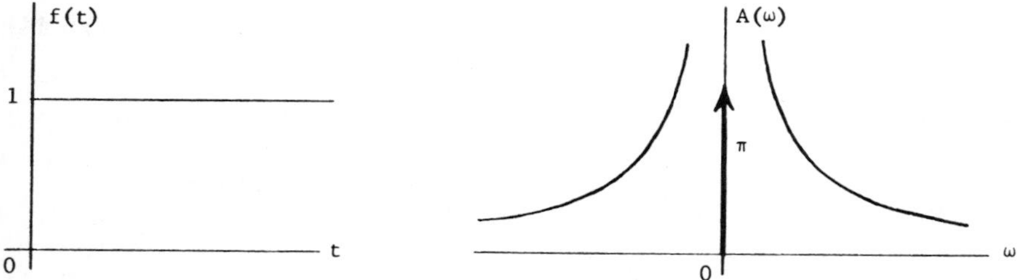

Fig. 16.7. Fourier transform of a unit step function.

evaluate its Fourier transform with the definition of Eq. (16.10) leads to the expression

$$F(\omega) = \int_{0}^{\infty} e^{-j\omega t} dt \tag{16.41}$$

which cannot be evaluated. Instead, write the unit step as

$$U(t) = \frac{1}{2} + \frac{1}{2}\,\text{sgn}\, t\,, \tag{16.42}$$

where

$$\text{sgn}\, t = \frac{t}{|t|}\,, \tag{16.43}$$

shown in Fig. 16.8. The Fourier transform of sgn t can be evaluated by

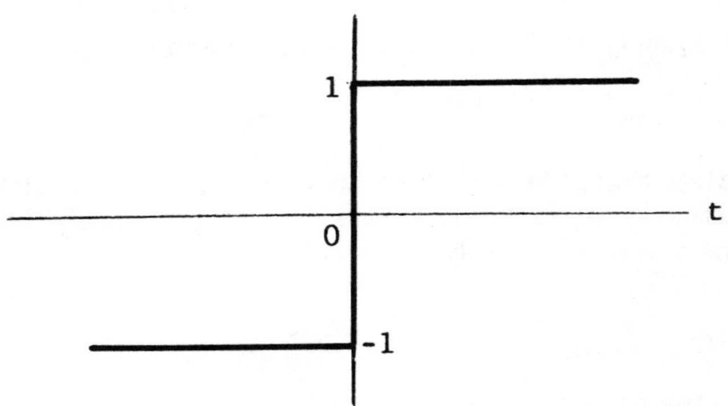

Fig. 16.8. The sgn function.

guessing its transform and working backward. The guess, aided by hindsight, is

$$F(\omega) = \frac{2}{j\omega}\,. \tag{16.44}$$

Its inverse is

$$f(t) = \frac{1}{2\pi}\int_{-\infty}^{\infty} \frac{2}{j\omega}\, e^{j\omega t} d\omega = \frac{1}{\pi}\int_{-\infty}^{\infty} \frac{1}{j\omega}\,(\cos\omega t + j\sin\omega t) d\omega$$

$$= \frac{1}{\pi}\int_{-\infty}^{\infty} \frac{\cos\omega t}{j\omega}\, d\omega + \frac{1}{\pi}\int_{-\infty}^{\infty} \frac{\sin\omega t}{\omega}\, d\omega\,. \tag{16.45}$$

Since the integrand of the first integral is an odd function, that integral is zero. A table of integrals shows that the value of the second integral is π if $t > 0$ and $-\pi$ if $t < 0$. Thus

$$\text{sgn}\, t \leftrightarrow \frac{2}{j\omega}\,. \tag{16.46}$$

Transform pair (16.26) shows that

$$\frac{1}{2} \leftrightarrow \pi\delta(\omega)\,. \tag{16.47}$$

Thus

$$\frac{1}{2} + \frac{1}{2}\,\text{sgn}\, t = U(t) \leftrightarrow \pi\delta(\omega) + \frac{1}{j\omega}\,. \tag{16.48}$$

This useful transform pair, presented by Papoulis in Ref. 100 and shown graphically in Fig. 16.7, is strangely absent from much of the literature on linear systems.

Sine Waves. The non-causal function $\sin \omega_o t$ can be written as

$$\sin \omega_o t = -\frac{j}{2}\,(e^{j\omega_o t} - e^{-j\omega_o t})\,. \tag{16.49}$$

According to transform pairs (16.39) and (16.26),

$$e^{\pm j\omega_o t} \leftrightarrow 2\pi\delta(\omega \mp \omega_o)\,. \tag{16.50}$$

Therefore

$$\sin \omega_o t \leftrightarrow -\frac{j}{2}\,[2\pi\delta(\omega - \omega_o) - 2\pi\delta(\omega + \omega_o)]$$

$$= j\pi[\delta(\omega + \omega_o) - \delta(\omega - \omega_o)]\,. \tag{16.51}$$

This pair is shown in Fig. 16.9. The frequency spectrum of the sine wave consists of course of the single frequency ω_o.

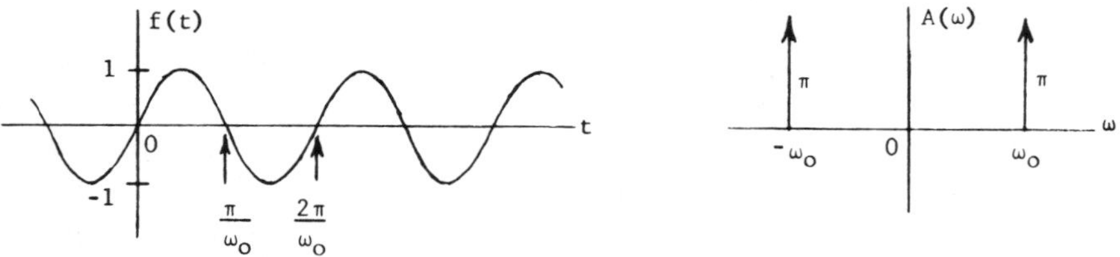

Fig. 16.9. Fourier transform of a non-causal sine wave.

Finding the transform of a step-modulated sine wave $U(t)\sin\omega_o t$ requires an intermediate transform, namely that of $f(t)\sin \omega_o t$. Since

$$f(t)\sin \omega_o t = \frac{1}{2j}\,f(t)(e^{j\omega_o t} - e^{-j\omega_o t})\,, \tag{16.52}$$

transform pair (16.39) can be applied to produce

$$f(t)\sin \omega_o t \leftrightarrow \frac{j}{2}\,[F(\omega + \omega_o) - F(\omega - \omega_o)]\,. \tag{16.53}$$

Now combine pairs (16.53) and (16.48) to get

$$U(t)\sin\omega_o t \leftrightarrow \frac{j}{2}\left[\pi\{\delta(\omega+\omega_o)-\delta(\omega-\omega_o)\} + \frac{1}{j(\omega+\omega_o)} - \frac{1}{j(\omega-\omega_o)}\right]$$

$$= \frac{j\pi}{2}\,[\delta(\omega+\omega_o)-\delta(\omega-\omega_o)] + \frac{\omega_o}{\omega_o^2-\omega^2}\,. \qquad (16.54)$$

This function and transform are plotted in Fig. 16.10. Notice that

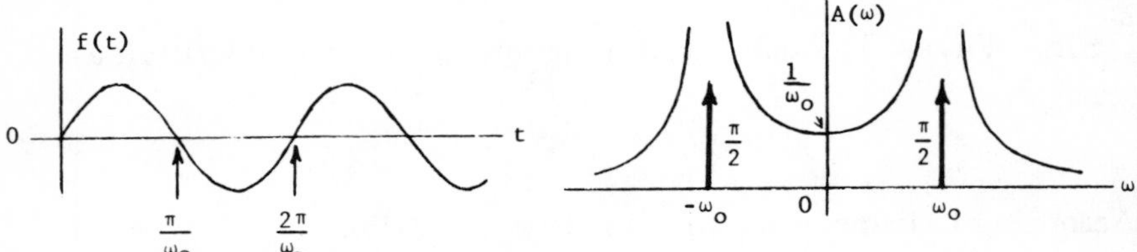

Fig. 16.10. Fourier transform of a step-modulated sine wave.

because the sine wave now starts at $t = 0$ instead of $t = -\infty$, its spectrum contains a continuous band of frequencies in addition to the expected impulses at $\pm\omega_o$.

Convolution. The convolution of two functions $f_1(t)$ and $f_2(t)$ is

$$f(t) = \int_{-\infty}^{\infty} f_1(x)f_2(t-x)dx = \int_{-\infty}^{\infty} f_1(t-x)f_2(x)dx\,. \qquad (16.55)$$

Its Fourier transform is

$$F(\omega) = \int_{t=-\infty}^{\infty}\left[\int_{x=-\infty}^{\infty} f_1(t-x)f_2(x)dx\right] e^{-j\omega t}dt$$

or

$$F(\omega) = \int_{x=-\infty}^{\infty} f_2(x)\left[\int_{t=-\infty}^{\infty} f_1(t-x)e^{-j\omega t}dt\right] dx\,. \qquad (16.56)$$

The quantity in brackets is the Fourier transform of $f_1(t-x)$, which according to transform pair (16.37) is

$$e^{-j\omega x}F_1(\omega)\,.$$

Eq. (16.56) becomes

$$F(\omega) = F_1(\omega)\int_{-\infty}^{\infty} f_2(x)e^{-j\omega x}dx = F_1(\omega)F_2(\omega)\,, \qquad (16.57)$$

revealing the transform pair

$$\int_{-\infty}^{\infty} f_1(x)f_2(t-x)dx \leftrightarrow F_1(\omega)F_2(\omega)\,. \qquad (16.58)$$

Linear Systems. If the input to the fixed linear system of Fig. 16.11 is the unit impulse

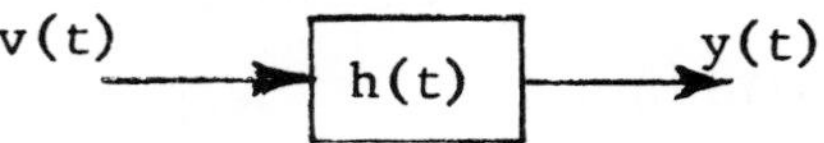

Fig. 16.11. A fixed linear system.

$$v(t) = \delta(t)\ , \tag{16.59}$$

the output is the impulse response $h(t)$:

$$y(t) = h(t)\ . \tag{16.60}$$

If the input is a unit impulse at time $t = x$, namely

$$v(t) = \delta(t - x)\ , \tag{16.61}$$

the output is

$$y(t) = h(t - x)\ . \tag{16.62}$$

As Fig. 16.12 shows, any input can be considered to be a train of

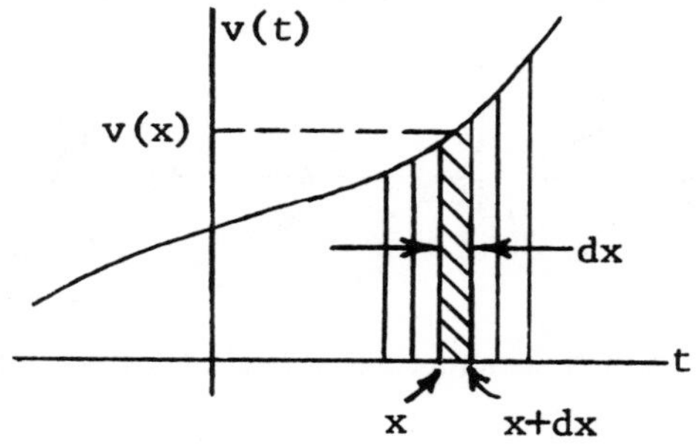

Fig. 16.12. A function represented by a train of impulses.

impulses, each of area $v(x)dx$. The hatched area is the impulse

$$v(x)dx\ \delta(t - x)\ .$$

The sum of all these impulses is

$$v(t) = \int_{-\infty}^{\infty} v(x)\delta(t - x)dx\ . \tag{16.63}$$

The response of the system to this input is the sum of the responses to each of the impulses:

$$y(t) = \int_{-\infty}^{\infty} v(x)h(t - x)dx\ . \tag{16.64}$$

According to transform pair (16.58), the Fourier transform of this convolution is

$$Y(\omega) = V(\omega)H(\omega) , \tag{16.65}$$

as predicted by Eq. (16.13).

16.4 Output of a Linear System

An example will show how Eq. (16.65) can be used to determine the output of a fixed linear system. An advantage of Fourier transforms over Laplace transforms will become apparent. The system is an ideal low-pass filter whose system function

$$H(\omega) = A_o p_{\omega_c}(\omega) e^{-j\omega t_o} \tag{16.66}$$

is shown in Fig. 16.13. The input to the filter is the non-causal sine wave

$$v(t) = A_1 \sin \omega_o t \tag{16.67}$$

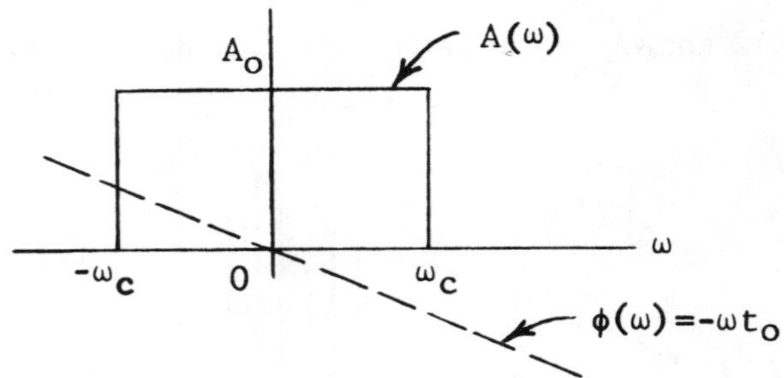

Fig. 16.13. System function of an ideal low-pass filter.

shown in Fig. 16.14. The frequency ω_o of the sine wave is less than the

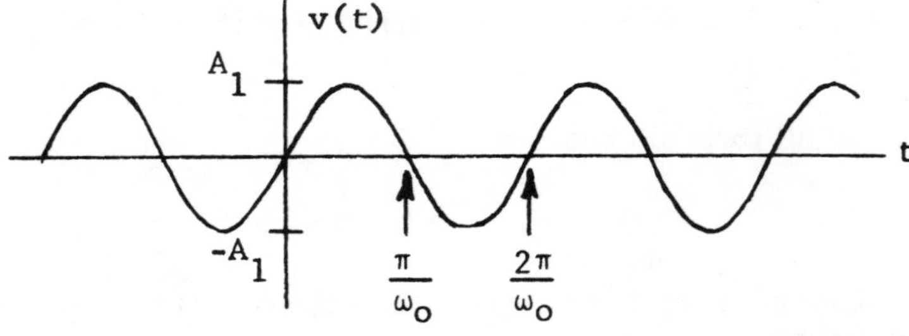

Fig. 16.14. Non-causal sine wave.

cutoff frequency ω_c of the filter. The Fourier transform of the input,

$$V(\omega) = j\pi A_1[\delta(\omega + \omega_o) - \delta(\omega - \omega_o)] , \tag{16.68}$$

consists of two impulses. Their amplitude and the amplitude of the system function are shown in Fig. 16.15. The Fourier transform of the filter output is

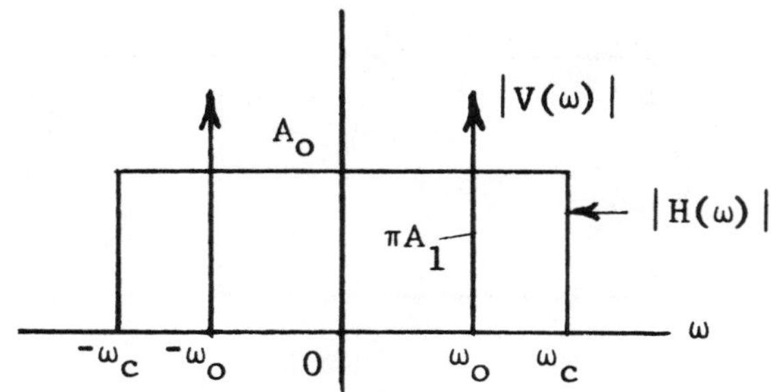

Fig. 16.15. System function and input spectrum.

$$Y(\omega) = V(\omega)H(\omega) = j\pi A_1[\delta(\omega + \omega_o) - \delta(\omega - \omega_o)]A_o p_{\omega_c}(\omega)e^{-j\omega t_o} . \tag{16.69}$$

According to Eq. (16.9), the filter output is

$$y(t) = \frac{j\pi A_1 A_o}{2\pi}\int_{-\omega_c}^{\omega_c} [\delta(\omega + \omega_o) - \delta(\omega - \omega_o)]e^{j\omega(t-t_o)}d\omega . \tag{16.70}$$

The limits of integration have been reduced from $(-\infty, \infty)$ to $(-\omega_c, \omega_c)$ because the amplitude of $p_{\omega_c}(\omega)$ is zero beyond the interval $(-\omega_c, \omega_c)$. Since the two impulses turn on only at $\omega = -\omega_o$ and $\omega = \omega_o$, Eq. (16.70) becomes

$$\begin{aligned} y(t) &= \frac{jA_o A_1}{2}[e^{-j\omega_o(t-t_o)} - e^{j\omega_o(t-t_o)}] \\ &= A_o A_1 \sin[\omega_o(t - t_o)] . \end{aligned} \tag{16.71}$$

The filter has increased the signal by the factor A_o, and has delayed it by the time t_o. This simple example illustrates an advantage of Fourier transforms over Laplace transforms or time-domain analysis in the study of linear systems. The system function $H(\omega)$ can frequently be measured or calculated easily, and displayed as in Fig. 16.13. When the spectrum of the input is superimposed as in Fig. 16.15, information about the output is available by inspection. For example, if the input frequency ω_o is made larger than the filter cutoff frequency ω_c, the output of the filter is obviously zero.

16.5 A Disadvantage of Fourier Transforms

Another example illustrates a disadvantage of Fourier transforms in analyzing linear systems. Calculate the output $v_2(t)$ of the R-C circuit in Fig. 16.16, whose input is

$$v_1(t) = e^{-t}U(t) . \tag{16.72}$$

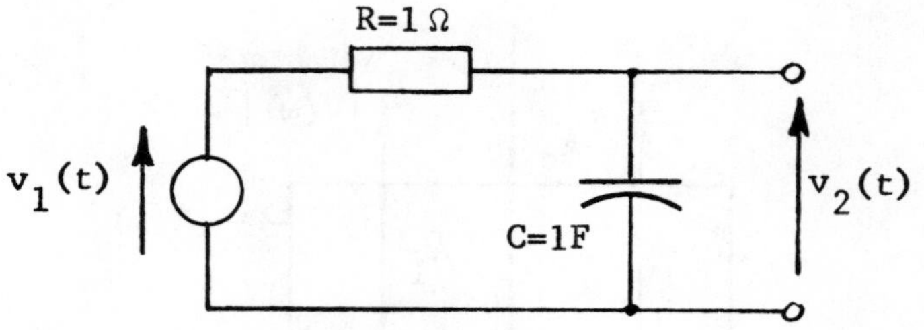

Fig. 16.16. An R-C circuit.

Since

$$V_1(\omega) = \frac{1}{1 + j\omega} \tag{16.73}$$

and

$$H(\omega) = \frac{\dfrac{1}{j\omega}}{1 + \dfrac{1}{j\omega}} = \frac{1}{1 + j\omega}, \tag{16.74}$$

then

$$V_2(\omega) = V_1(\omega)H(\omega) = \frac{1}{(1 + j\omega)^2} \tag{16.75}$$

and

$$v_2(t) = \frac{1}{2\pi}\int_{-\infty}^{\infty} \frac{e^{j\omega t}}{(1 + j\omega)^2}\, d\omega . \tag{16.76}$$

This is the desired output, but in the form of an integral that must be evaluated by complex-plane integration. The calculation of $v_2(t)$ by Laplace transforms is simple. In general, if the input to a linear system is causal, a formula for the output can be determined more easily by Laplace transforms.

16.6 Periodic Time Function

In the preceding chapter a periodic function $f(t) = f(t - nT)$ was represented by the Fourier series

$$f(t) = \sum_{n=-\infty}^{\infty} c_n e^{jn\omega_o t} , \tag{16.77}$$

where

$$\omega_o = 2\pi/T \tag{16.78}$$

and

$$c_n = \frac{1}{T}\int_{-T/2}^{T/2} f(t)e^{-jn\omega_o t}dt . \tag{16.79}$$

Eq. (16.77) represents the function as a sum of phasors, each with the frequency $n\omega_o$ and magnitude $|c_n|$. What does the frequency spectrum look like when calculated as a Fourier transform? According to transform pair (16.50),

$$e^{jn\omega_o t} \leftrightarrow 2\pi\delta(\omega - n\omega_o) . \tag{16.80}$$

The sum of the Fourier transforms of the terms of Eq. (16.77) is

$$F(\omega) = 2\pi \sum_{n=-\infty}^{\infty} c_n\delta(\omega - n\omega_o) . \tag{16.81}$$

This gives almost the same information as Eq. (16.77). It says that the frequency spectrum of the periodic function $f(t)$ contains discrete components with frequency $n\omega_o$ and magnitude $2\pi|c_n|$. The spectrum is now a train of impulses of magnitude $2\pi|c_n|$ instead of phasors with amplitudes $|c_n|$ as in Fig. 16.2. The inverse Fourier transform of $F(\omega)$ is of course $f(t)$:

$$\begin{aligned} &\frac{1}{2\pi}\int_{\omega=-\infty}^{\infty} [2\pi \sum_{n=-\infty}^{\infty} c_n\delta(\omega - n\omega_o)]e^{j\omega t}d\omega \\ &= \sum_{n=-\infty}^{\infty} [c_n \int_{\omega=-\infty}^{\infty} \delta(\omega - n\omega_o)e^{j\omega t}d\omega] \\ &= \sum_{n=-\infty}^{\infty} c_n e^{jn\omega_o t} = f(t) . \end{aligned} \tag{16.82}$$

The constants c_n can be expressed in a more convenient form. Since

$$F(\omega) = \int_{-\infty}^{\infty} f(t)e^{-j\omega t}dt , \tag{16.83}$$

the Fourier transform of *one cycle* of the periodic function $f(t)$ is

$$F_o(\omega) = \int_{-T/2}^{T/2} f(t)e^{-j\omega t}dt \,. \tag{16.84}$$

Then

$$F_o(n\omega_o) = \int_{-T/2}^{T/2} f(t)e^{-jn\omega_o t}dt \,. \tag{16.85}$$

Eq. (16.79) can now be written as

$$c_n = \frac{F_o(n\omega_o)}{T} \,. \tag{16.86}$$

The Fourier transform of the periodic function $f(t) = f(t - nT)$ becomes

$$F(\omega) = \frac{2\pi}{T} \sum_{n=-\infty}^{\infty} F_o(n\omega_o)\delta(\omega - n\omega_o) \,, \tag{16.87}$$

where $F_o(\omega)$ is the Fourier transform of one cycle of $f(t)$.

16.7 The Sampling Theorem

Of great importance in control and communication engineering are *discrete-time* or *sampled-data systems*, so named because their inputs are periodic samples of a continuous signal $f(t)$. Examples of sampled signals are the return echo of a radar or sonar, or the output of a rotary selector switch that scans the outputs of many transducers repetitively. The sampling process is represented by the switch in Fig. 16.17. The

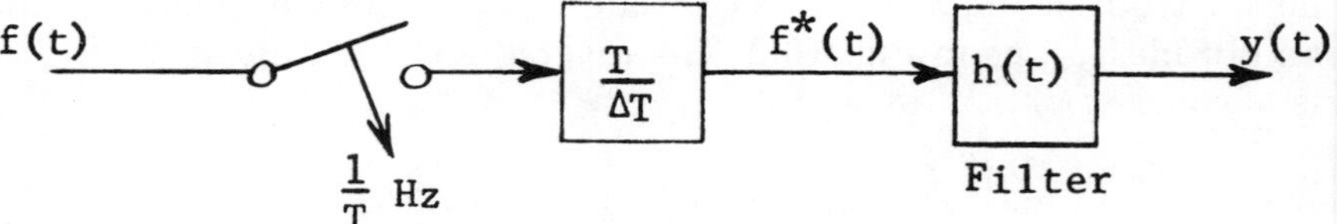

Fig. 16.17. Sampled-data system.

output of the switch is the train of pulses shown in Fig. 16.18. If the width ΔT of each pulse of height $f(nT)$ is narrow compared to the sampling interval T, the pulse can be represented by an impulse of area $\Delta T f(nT)$. If the filter is preceded by an amplifier with a gain of $T/\Delta T$, the filter input can be represented by a train of impulses:

$$f^*(t) = T \sum_{n=-\infty}^{\infty} f(nT)\delta(t - nT) \,, \tag{16.88}$$

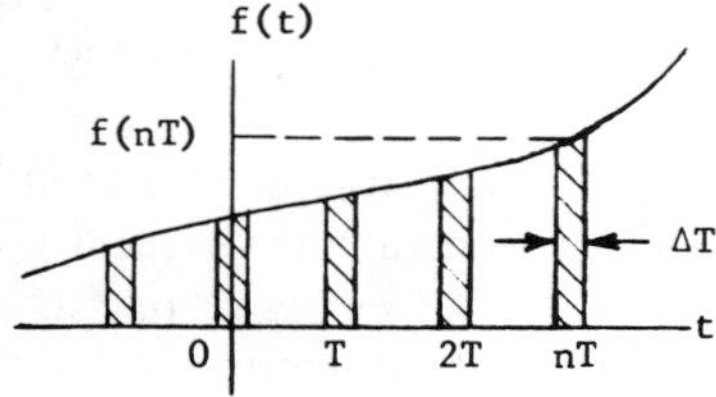

Fig. 16.18. Sampled input.

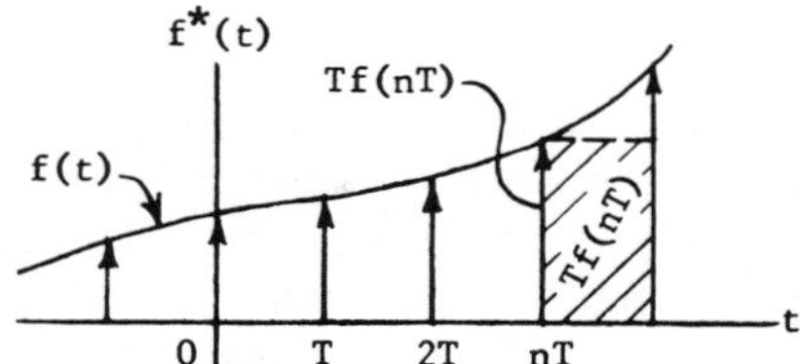

Fig. 16.19. Representation by impulses.

as shown in Fig. 16.19. Each impulse, occurring at time nT, has an area $Tf(nT)$. Notice that this is also the area of the inscribed rectangle of height $f(nT)$ and width T. As T approaches zero, the area under the train of impulses approaches the area under the curve of $f(t)$.

The Fourier transform of the impulse train is

$$F^*(\omega) = T\int_{t=-\infty}^{\infty}\left[\sum_{n=-\infty}^{\infty} f(nT)\delta(t-nT)\right]e^{-j\omega t}dt$$

$$= T\sum_{n=-\infty}^{\infty} f(nT)e^{-jnT\omega}\,. \tag{16.89}$$

This is a Fourier series in ω. An investigation of its appearance will lead to Shannon's remarkable sampling theorem.

If the Fourier spectrum $A(\omega)$ or $|F(\omega)|$ of a signal is zero beyond some cutoff frequency ω_c as in Fig. 16.20, the signal is said to be *band limited.*

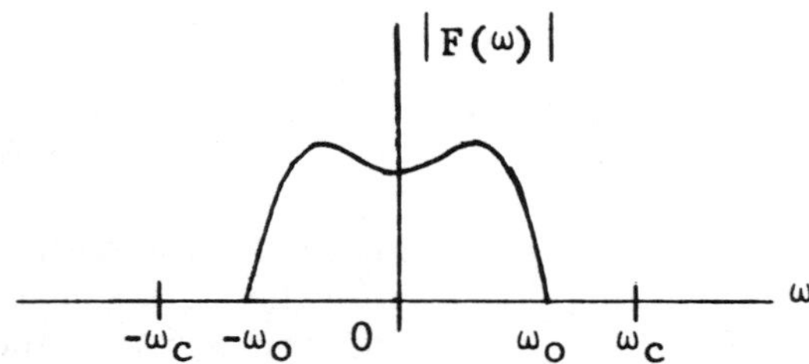

Fig. 16.20. Spectrum of a band-limited signal.

An example is the audio signal of a radio transmission, whose bandwidth is limited by low-pass filtering to prevent interference with the adjacent channels. Assume that the signal $f(t)$ in Fig. 16.17 is band limited, with a highest frequency of ω_o as in Fig. 16.20. The inverse of its Fourier transform can be written with reduced limits of integration:

$$f(t) = \frac{1}{2\pi}\int_{-\omega_c}^{\omega_c} F(\omega)e^{j\omega t}d\omega\,. \tag{16.90}$$

For $t = nT$, this equation becomes

$$f(nT) = \frac{1}{2\pi}\int_{-\omega_c}^{\omega_c} F(\omega)e^{jnT\omega}d\omega \ . \tag{16.91}$$

Now write the Fourier transform $F(\omega)$ of the original continuous signal $f(t)$ as an exponential Fourier series in the interval $(-\omega_c, \omega_c)$, remembering that the independent variable is ω, not t. Let the sampling frequency $1/T$ Hz or $2\pi/T$ rad/sec be twice the cutoff frequency ω_c rad/sec. The period of this new series is

$$2\omega_c = 2\pi/T \tag{16.92}$$

and the fundamental "frequency" of the series is $2\pi/2\omega_c = T$. The series can be written as

$$F(\omega) = \sum_{n=-\infty}^{\infty} c_n e^{-jnT\omega} \ , \quad -\omega_c < \omega < \omega_c \tag{16.93}$$

where

$$c_n = \frac{T}{2\pi}\int_{-\omega_c}^{\omega_c} F(\omega)e^{jnT\omega}d\omega \ . \tag{16.94}$$

Notice that the signs of the exponents in these two equations have been reversed. No harm is done, because the infinite series of Eq. (16.93) is unchanged, and each term has the same value of c_n that it had before the signs were reversed. Comparing Eqs. (16.94) and (16.91) shows that

$$c_n = Tf(nT) \ , \tag{16.95}$$

and according to Eq. (16.93),

$$F(\omega) = T \sum_{n=-\infty}^{\infty} f(nT)e^{-jnT\omega} \ , \quad -\omega_c < \omega < \omega_c \ . \tag{16.96}$$

This is the Fourier-series representation of the band-limited spectrum of Fig. 16.20, in the interval $(-\omega_c, \omega_c)$. The right side of Eq. (16.96) is periodic with period $2\omega_c$. It represents the periodic repetition of $F(\omega)$ shown in Fig. 16.21, which according to Eq. (16.89) is $F^*(\omega)$, the Fourier

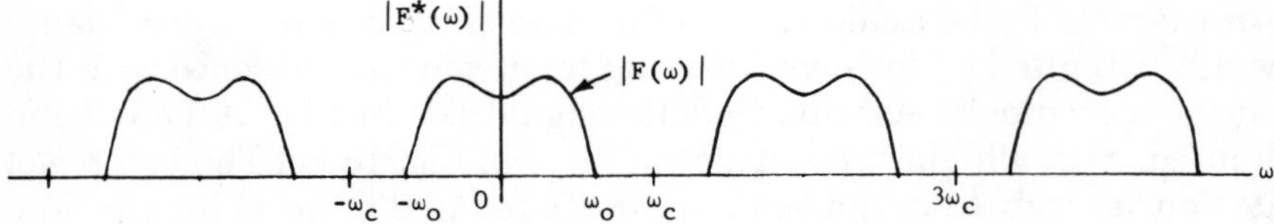

Fig. 16.21. Periodic spectrum.

transform of the train of samples of $f(t)$. The conclusion is that the frequency spectrum of uniformly-spaced samples of a band-limited signal is the periodic repetition of the spectrum of the band-limited signal.

If $\omega_c > \omega_o$, i.e., if the sampling frequency $1/T = 2\omega_c/2\pi$ Hz is higher than twice the highest frequency $\omega_o/2\pi$ Hz in the spectrum of the continuous signal, the cycles of $F^*(\omega)$ do not overlap.

Now pass the sampled signal $f^*(t)$ thru an ideal low-pass filter whose system function is

$$H(\omega) = A_o p_{\omega_c}(\omega) e^{-j\omega t_o} , \tag{16.97}$$

shown in Fig. 16.13. The output of the filter is

$$\begin{aligned} Y(\omega) = H(\omega)F^*(\omega) &= A_o p_{\omega_c}(\omega) e^{-j\omega t_o} T \sum_{n=-\infty}^{\infty} f(nT) e^{-jnT\omega} \\ &= A_o T e^{-j\omega t_o} \sum_{n=-\infty}^{\infty} f(nT) e^{-jnT\omega} , \quad -\omega_c < \omega < \omega_c \\ &= A_o e^{-j\omega t_o} F(\omega) . \end{aligned} \tag{16.98}$$

The filter rejects every cycle of $F^*(\omega)$ except the one straddling the origin, which is the Fourier transform of $f(t)$. The filter output is

$$y(t) = A_o f(t - t_o) . \tag{16.99}$$

A remarkable thing has happened. The discrete-time system has sampled the original signal $f(t)$ at discrete instants, passed the train of samples thru an ideal low-pass filter, and recovered the original signal! The amplification and time delay constitute distortionless transmission.

Eq. (16.92) shows that if the sampling frequency $2\pi/T$ is lowered, ω_c decreases. The spacing $2(\omega_c - \omega_o)$ between the cycles of $F^*(\omega)$ decreases until $\omega_c = \omega_o$. Then the cycles touch each other, $T = \pi/\omega_o$, and the sampling frequency is $2\pi/T = 2\omega_o$ rad/sec. If the sampling frequency is made still lower, the cycles of $F^*(\omega)$ overlap and look like Fig. 16.22. The

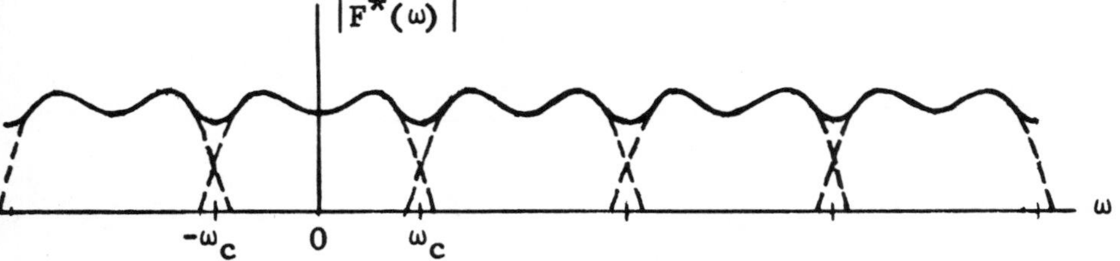

Fig. 16.22. Periodic spectrum with the sampling frequency too low.

cycle passed by the filter is missing its higher frequencies and includes the lower frequencies of the next cycle. It is not the Fourier transform of $f(t)$. The resulting distortion in the filter output $y(t)$ is called *aliasing*. The conclusion is *Shannon's sampling theorem*:

If a signal contains no frequency above ω_o in its spectrum, it is completely defined by impulse samples taken at instants spaced uniformly π/ω_o seconds or less apart (i.e., at a frequency of at least $2\omega_o$ rad/sec. The original signal can be restored by passing the impulse train thru an ideal low-pass filter having a cutoff frequency of ω_o rad/sec.

The frequency $2\omega_o$ is called the *Nyquist rate*. In practice, signals are not often truly band limited, and the pass band of a low-pass filter is not ideal as in Fig. 16.13, but is shaped more nearly as shown in Fig. 16.23.

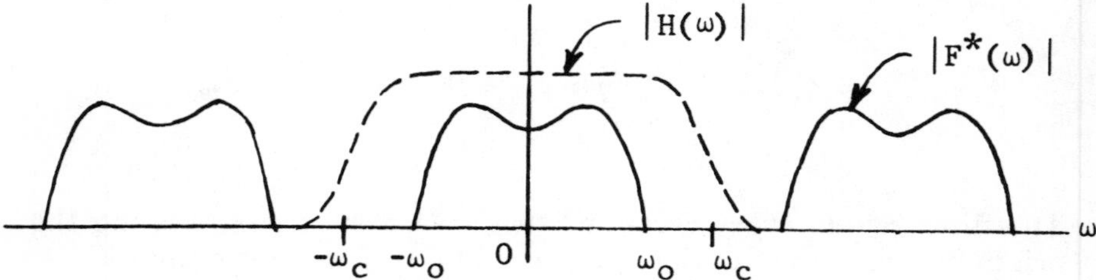

Fig. 16.23. System function of a practical low-pass filter.

The input $f(t)$ can be made very nearly band limited by low-pass filtering *before* sampling. If the sampling rate $2\omega_c$ is made higher than twice the signal bandwidth ω_o as shown in Fig. 16.23, aliasing can be made negligible in real circuits.

The sampling theorem, which was not presented until 1949 (Ref. 121), is the basis of the rapidly-expanding field of digital signal processing. It assures the designer that the advantages of digital processing, such as noise-free amplification and recording, are available for analog signals such as music and speech.

TABLE 16.1. FOURIER TRANSFORMS

No.	$f(t)$	$F(\omega)$
1	$e^{-at}U(t)\,,\quad a > 0$	$\dfrac{1}{a + j\omega}$
2	$\delta(t)$	1
3	1	$2\pi\delta(\omega)$
4	$F(t)$	$2\pi f(-\omega)$
5	$p_T(t)$	$\dfrac{2}{\omega}\sin\omega T$
6	$\dfrac{\sin at}{\pi t}$	$p_a(\omega)$
7	$f(t - t_o)$	$e^{-j\omega t_o}F(\omega)$
8	$e^{j\omega_o t}f(t)$	$F(\omega - \omega_o)$
9	$U(t)$	$\pi\delta(\omega) + \dfrac{1}{j\omega}$
10	$\sin\omega_o t$	$j\pi[\delta(\omega + \omega_o) - \delta(\omega - \omega_o)]$
11	$f(t)\sin\omega_o t$	$\dfrac{j}{2}[F(\omega + \omega_o) - F(\omega - \omega_o)]$
12	$U(t)\sin\omega_o t$	$\dfrac{j\pi}{2}[\delta(\omega + \omega_o) - \delta(\omega - \omega_o)] + \dfrac{\omega_o}{\omega_o^2 - \omega^2}$
13	$\int_{-\infty}^{\infty} f_1(x)f_2(t - x)dx$	$F_1(\omega)F_2(\omega)$
14	$f(t) = f(t - nT)$	$\dfrac{2\pi}{T}\sum_{n=-\infty}^{\infty} F_o(n\omega_o)\delta(\omega - n\omega_o)\,,\quad \omega_o = \dfrac{2\pi}{T}$
15	$T\sum_{n=-\infty}^{\infty} f(nT)\delta(t - nT)$	$F(\omega) = F(\omega - n\omega_o)$

Chapter 17

VECTORS AND PARTIAL DIFFERENTIAL EQUATIONS

17.1 Introduction

A three-dimensional vector can be regarded as a line segment having both length or magnitude, and direction. It can represent any physical quantity having these properties, such as force, torque, surface area, velocity, or field intensity. This chapter will explain the calculus of three-dimensional vectors, which is admirably suited for expressing natural laws of field quantities, and for deriving the partial differential equations encountered in engineering and science. One of these, Laplace's equation, is chosen to illustrate two useful methods of solving partial differential equations, namely the method of separation of variables and the method of iteration.

17.2 Vector Algebra

In hand-written or typed work, the symbol for a vector is a letter with a bar or an arrow over or under it. In this book as in most typeset work, the symbol is a bold-face letter. If a vector **A** lies in three-dimensional space as in Fig. 17.1, it can be expressed as the vector sum of its

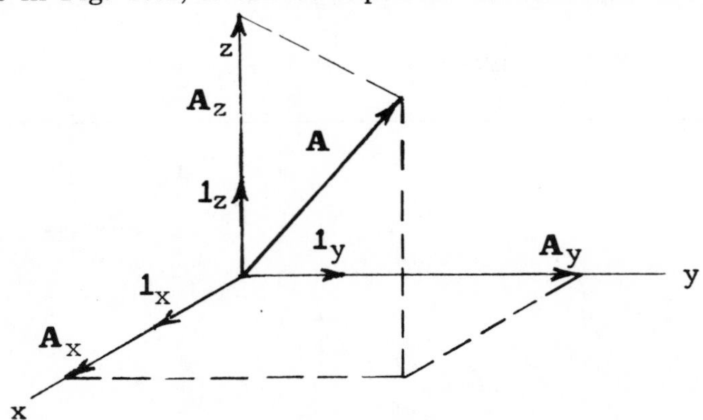

Fig. 17.1. Three-dimensional vector.

components parallel to three mutually-perpendicular coordinate axes:

$$\mathbf{A} = \mathbf{A}_x + \mathbf{A}_y + \mathbf{A}_z \tag{17.1}$$

or in terms of unit vectors parallel to the coordinate axes:

$$\mathbf{A} = \mathbf{1}_x A_x + \mathbf{1}_y A_y + \mathbf{1}_z A_z \tag{17.2}$$

where A_x, A_y, and A_z are the magnitudes of the vectors $\mathbf{A}_x$, $\mathbf{A}_y$, and $\mathbf{A}_z$. Eq. (17.1) or (17.2) may also be written as

$$\mathbf{A} = \begin{bmatrix} A_x \\ A_y \\ A_z \end{bmatrix} . \tag{17.3}$$

This form is more useful if **A** lies in a space with more than three dimensions, but will not be used for the three-dimensional vectors considered in this chapter.

The *scalar, dot*, or *inner product* of two vectors **A** and **B**, written as $\mathbf{A} \cdot \mathbf{B}$ or $(\mathbf{A}, \mathbf{B})$ or $<\mathbf{A}, \mathbf{B}>$ is defined as the scalar

$$\mathbf{A} \cdot \mathbf{B} = AB \cos \theta \tag{17.4}$$

where θ is the angle between the positive directions of the vectors. Clearly

$$\begin{aligned} \mathbf{A} \cdot \mathbf{B} &= (\mathbf{1}_x A_x + \mathbf{1}_y A_y + \mathbf{1}_z A_z) \cdot (\mathbf{1}_x B_x + \mathbf{1}_y B_y + \mathbf{1}_z B_z) \\ &= A_x B_x + A_y B_y + A_z B_z . \end{aligned} \tag{17.5}$$

This form can also be used as the definition of the scalar product, in a coordinate system whose axes are mutually perpendicular. The *vector* or *cross product* is defined as the vector

$$\mathbf{A} \times \mathbf{B} = \mathbf{1}_e AB \sin \theta \tag{17.6}$$

where $\mathbf{1}_e$ is a unit vector normal to the plane of **A** and **B**, whose sense is that of the thumb of the right hand, when the fingers are moved from the positive direction of **A** to the positive direction of **B** thru the smaller angle between them. This relationship is shown in Fig. 17.2. Note that

$$\mathbf{A} \times \mathbf{B} = -\,\mathbf{B} \times \mathbf{A} \tag{17.7}$$

and

$$\begin{aligned} \mathbf{A} \times \mathbf{B} &= (\mathbf{1}_x A_x + \mathbf{1}_y A_y + \mathbf{1}_z A_z) \times (\mathbf{1}_x B_x + \mathbf{1}_y B_y + \mathbf{1}_z B_z) \\ &= \begin{vmatrix} \mathbf{1}_x & \mathbf{1}_y & \mathbf{1}_z \\ A_x & A_y & A_z \\ B_x & B_y & B_z \end{vmatrix} . \end{aligned} \tag{17.8}$$

A coordinate system *xyz* is said to be right-handed if

$$\mathbf{1}_x \times \mathbf{1}_y = \mathbf{1}_z . \tag{17.9}$$

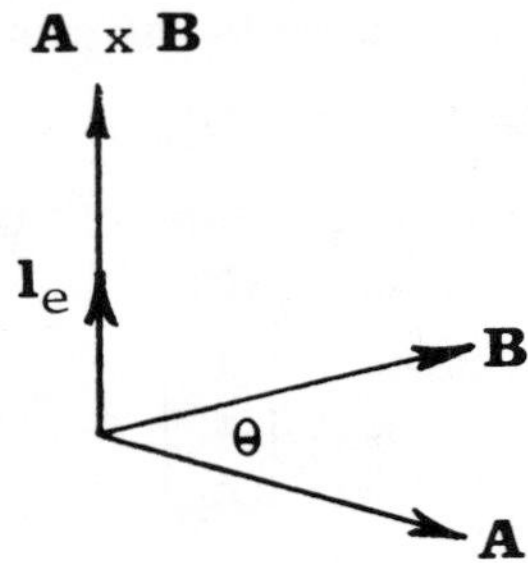

Fig. 17.2. Cross product of two vectors.

17.3 Vector Representation of Physical Quantities

Work. If a force **F** moves a body from a to b as in Fig. 17.3, the work

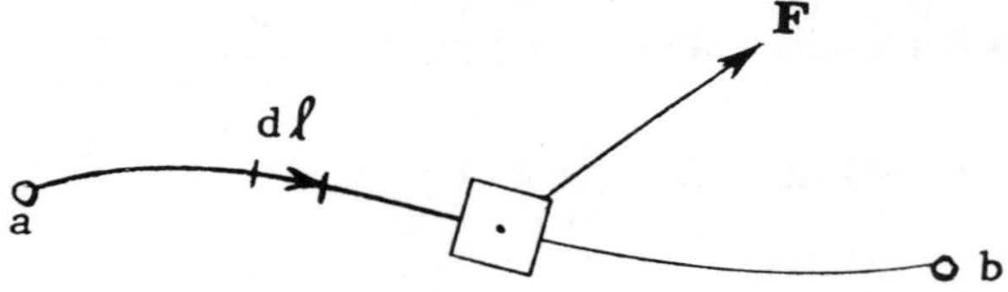

Fig. 17.3. Force acting on a body.

done by the force is

$$W = \int_a^b \mathbf{F} \cdot d\ell \qquad (17.10)$$

where $d\ell$ is an element of the path of the body. The force **F** can of course vary along the path.

Surface. A plane surface is represented by a vector whose magnitude is the area of the surface, and whose direction is normal to the plane. If the plane is part of a closed surface, the sense of the vector is outward. If the surface is not closed, the sense of the vector must be defined ad hoc. If $d\mathbf{s}$ is the vector representing a differential area of a curve surface, the vector representing the entire surface is the surface integral of $d\mathbf{s}$. The vector representing a closed surface, such as a ball, can be shown to be

$$\oint_s d\mathbf{s} = 0 \,. \qquad (17.11)$$

The amount of a flux flowing thru an open surface as in Fig. 17.4 is the

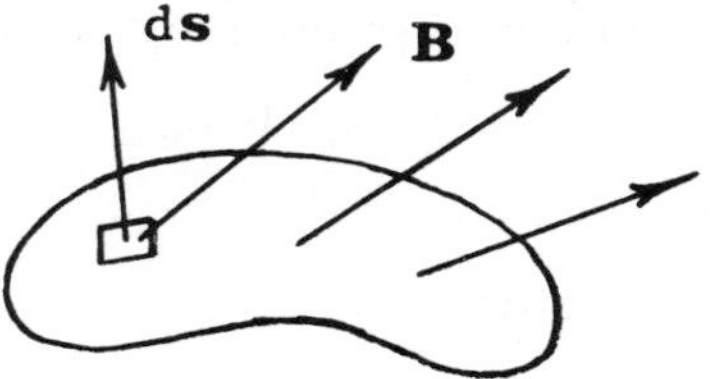

Fig. 17.4. Flux thru an open surface.

surface integral of the flux density **B**. If **B** is magnetic flux density in teslas or Wb/m^2, the flux crossing the surface is

$$\phi = \int_s \mathbf{B} \cdot d\mathbf{s} \qquad \text{webers} \,. \tag{17.12}$$

If the density of heat flux in a heated body is $\mathbf{q}''$ W/m^2, the rate of heat flow across an open surface is

$$q = \int_s \mathbf{q}'' \cdot d\mathbf{s} \qquad \text{watts} \,. \tag{17.13}$$

If the flux density is the density of flow of water $\rho\mathbf{u}$ kg/s·m^2, where ρ is the density of the water in kg/m^3 and $\mathbf{u}$ is its velocity in m/s, the flux or rate of flow of water thru an open surface is

$$Q = \int_s \rho\mathbf{u} \cdot d\mathbf{s} \qquad \text{kg/s} \,. \tag{17.14}$$

Torque. If a force **F** is applied to a wheel of radius **R** as in Fig. 17.5,

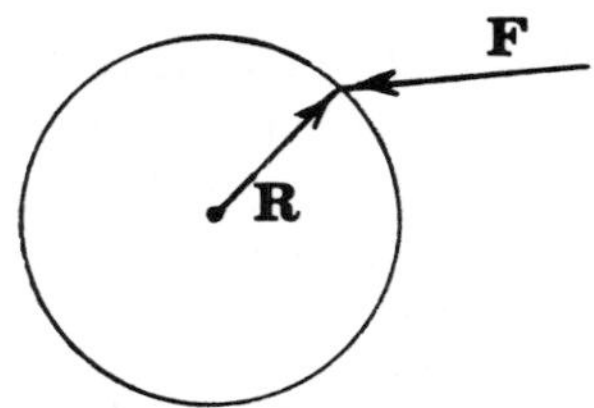

Fig. 17.5. Torque applied to a wheel.

the torque applied to the wheel is

$$\mathbf{T} = \mathbf{R} \times \mathbf{F} \,. \tag{17.15}$$

The direction of this torque is that of the resulting angular velocity $\boldsymbol{\omega}$, namely up if the rotation is counterclockwise. Thus if the moment of inertia is I,

$$\mathbf{T} = I \frac{d\boldsymbol{\omega}}{dt} \tag{17.16}$$

and the velocity of a point on the periphery of the wheel is

$$\mathbf{v} = \boldsymbol{\omega} \times \mathbf{R}\,. \tag{17.17}$$

17.4 Derivative of a Vector

Fig. 17.6 shows a vector

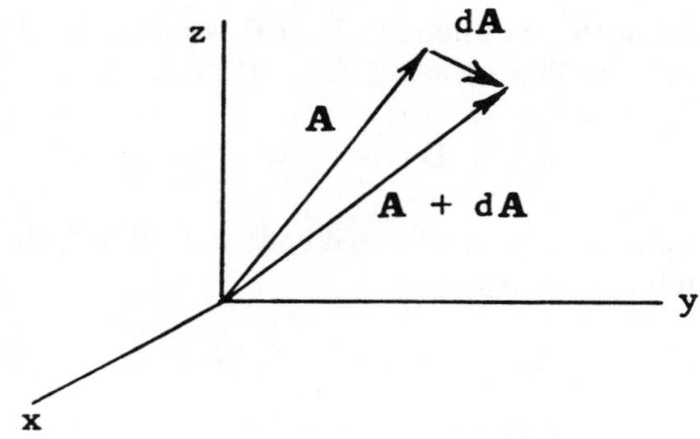

Fig. 17.6. Vector in a rectangular coordinate system.

$$\mathbf{A} = \mathbf{1}_x A_x + \mathbf{1}_y A_y + \mathbf{1}_z A_z \tag{17.18}$$

in a fixed rectangular coordinate system at time t, and also at time $t + dt$ when it has changed to $\mathbf{A} + d\mathbf{A}$. The derivative

$$\frac{d\mathbf{A}}{dt} = \mathbf{1}_x \frac{dA_x}{dt} + \mathbf{1}_y \frac{dA_y}{dt} + \mathbf{1}_z \frac{dA_z}{dt} \tag{17.19}$$

is tangent to the curve described by the tip of **A**. This derivative is the velocity of an object being tracked by the vector.

In some problems the coordinate system is allowed to rotate with an angular velocity $\boldsymbol{\omega}$. Now the derivative of a vector **A** is somewhat more complicated, because the unit vectors rotate and have derivatives. Instead of Eq. (17.19), the derivative is now

$$\frac{d\mathbf{A}}{dt} = \mathbf{1}_x \frac{dA_x}{dt} + \mathbf{1}_y \frac{dA_y}{dt} + \mathbf{1}_z \frac{dA_z}{dt} + A_x \frac{d\mathbf{1}_x}{dt} + A_y \frac{d\mathbf{1}_y}{dt} + A_z \frac{d\mathbf{1}_z}{dt}\,. \tag{17.20}$$

To calculate the derivatives of the unit vectors, first resolve the angular velocity of the coordinate system $\boldsymbol{\omega}$ into three components ω_x, ω_y and ω_z along the three axes. Fig. 17.7 shows the unit vectors $\mathbf{1}_x$ and $\mathbf{1}_y$ in the xy plane. The component of angular velocity ω_z rotates the unit vectors, and in the time dt causes $\mathbf{1}_x$ to change by the amount

$$d\mathbf{1}_x = \mathbf{1}_y \omega_z dt\,. \tag{17.21}$$

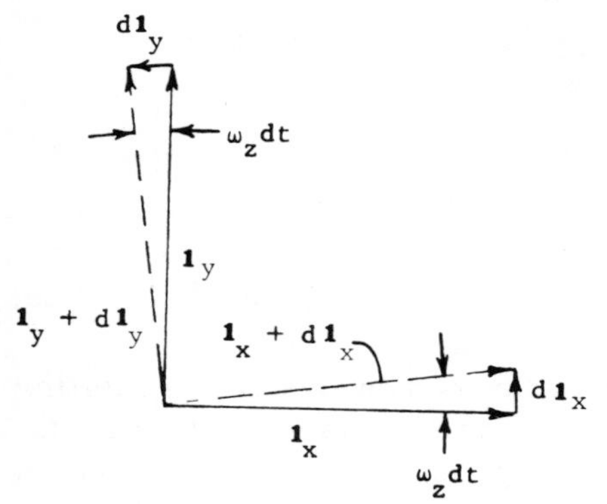

Fig. 17.7. Unit vectors in the xy plane.

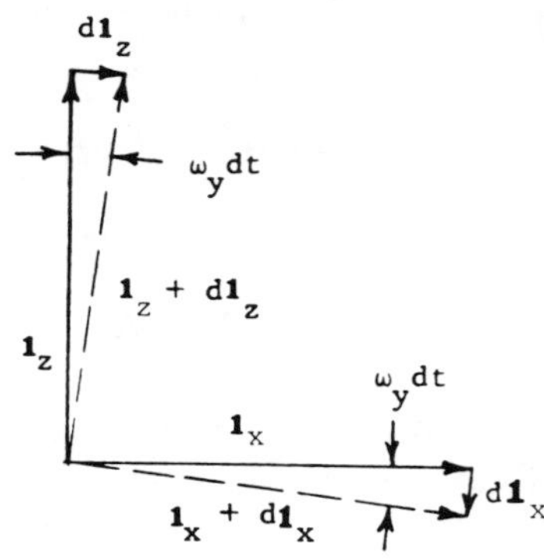

Fig. 17.8. Unit vectors in the xz plane.

Similarly,

$$d\mathbf{1}_y = -\,\mathbf{1}_x\omega_z dt\,. \tag{17.22}$$

Fig. 17.8 is a view of the unit vectors $\mathbf{1}_x$ and $\mathbf{1}_z$ in the xz plane. The component of angular displacement $\omega_y\,dt$ causes $\mathbf{1}_x$ and $\mathbf{1}_z$ to change by the amounts

$$d\mathbf{1}_x = -\,\mathbf{1}_z\omega_y dt \qquad \text{and} \qquad d\mathbf{1}_z = \mathbf{1}_x\omega_y dt\,. \tag{17.23}$$

Similarly, a view of the yz plane shows that $\mathbf{1}_y$ and $\mathbf{1}_z$ change by the additional amounts

$$d\mathbf{1}_y = \mathbf{1}_z\omega_x dt \qquad \text{and} \qquad d\mathbf{1}_z = -\,\mathbf{1}_y\omega_x dt\,. \tag{17.24}$$

The total change in $\mathbf{1}_x$ is

$$d\mathbf{1}_x = \mathbf{1}_y\omega_z dt - \mathbf{1}_z\omega_y dt \tag{17.25}$$

and therefore

$$\frac{d\mathbf{1}_x}{dt} = \mathbf{1}_y\omega_z - \mathbf{1}_z\omega_y\,. \tag{17.26}$$

Likewise, the derivatives of the other two unit vectors are

$$\frac{d\mathbf{1}_y}{dt} = \mathbf{1}_z\omega_x - \mathbf{1}_x\omega_z \tag{17.27}$$

$$\frac{d\mathbf{1}_z}{dt} = \mathbf{1}_x\omega_y - \mathbf{1}_y\omega_x\,. \tag{17.28}$$

Eq. (17.20) can now be written as

$$\frac{d\mathbf{A}}{dt} = \mathbf{1}_x \frac{dA_x}{dt} + \mathbf{1}_y \frac{dA_y}{dt} + \mathbf{1}_z \frac{dA_z}{dt}$$

$$+ A_x(\mathbf{1}_y\omega_z - \mathbf{1}_z\omega_y) + A_y(\mathbf{1}_z\omega_x - \mathbf{1}_x\omega_z) + A_z(\mathbf{1}_x\omega_y - \mathbf{1}_y\omega_x)$$

$$= \frac{\delta\mathbf{A}}{\delta t} + \boldsymbol{\omega} \times \mathbf{A}\,, \tag{17.29}$$

where $\delta\mathbf{A}/\delta t$ is the derivative of the vector seen by an observer rotating with the coordinate system. For example, a radar mounted at the center of a merry-go-round could measure the location **A** and velocity $\delta\mathbf{A}/\delta t$ of a passing automobile. The actual velocity of the automobile (relative to a fixed coordinate system) includes the correction term $\boldsymbol{\omega} \times \mathbf{A}$, where $\boldsymbol{\omega}$ is the angular velocity of the merry-go-round.

17.5 Fields

A *field* or *potential* is a physical quantity that is distributed in space, and has a single value at each point. The quantity can be a scalar like temperature or electric potential, or a vector like electric current density or air velocity. The equations defining fields are most conveniently derived with vector calculus, which will now be explained.

17.6 Gradient

The *gradient* of a scalar field is a vector whose direction and magnitude at a point are the direction and magnitude of the maximum rate of change with respect to distance of the field at that point. An example of a scalar field is the potential energy W of a one-kg mass in the vicinity of the earth. At the surface of the earth the gradient is

$$\text{Grad } W = \mathbf{1}_r g \tag{17.30}$$

where $\mathbf{1}_r$ is directed upward, and g is 9.81 N/kg or m/s^2. To obtain a mathematical expression for the gradient, draw two surfaces on which a potential such as temperature T is constant, as in Fig. 17.9. The surfaces

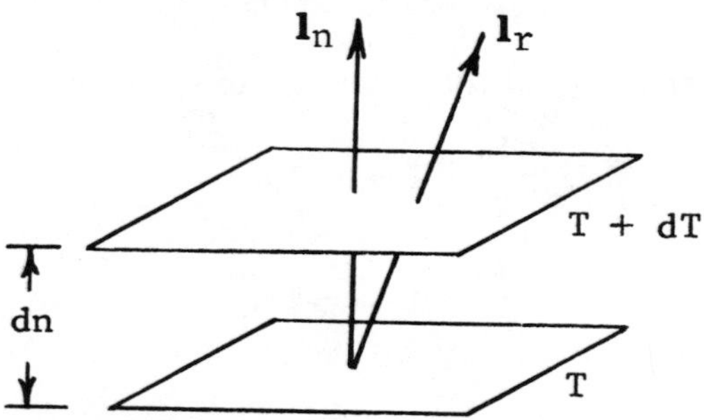

Fig. 17.9. Two plane, parallel surfaces.

are close enough together to be parallel, and the portions shown are small enough to be plane. If $\mathbf{1}_n$ is a unit vector normal to the equipotential surfaces, and the distance between them is dn,

$$\text{Grad } T = \mathbf{1}_n \frac{dT}{dn} . \tag{17.31}$$

Fig. 17.10 shows that the component of the vector Grad T in any other

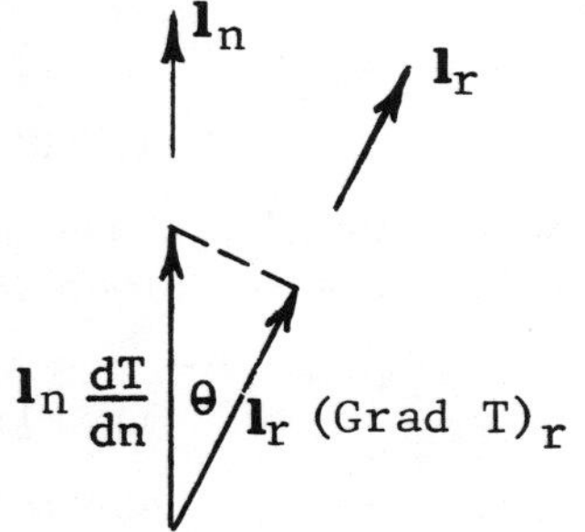

Fig. 17.10. Component of gradient.

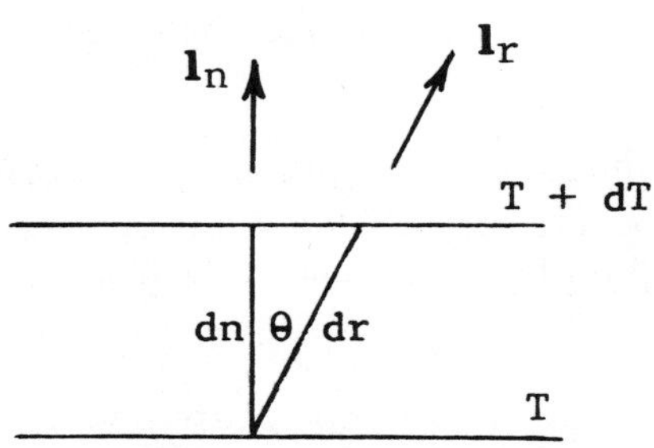

Fig. 17.11. Distances between the surfaces.

direction r at an angle θ from $\mathbf{1}_n$ is

$$(\text{Grad } T)_r = \frac{dT}{dn} \cos \theta . \tag{17.32}$$

Fig. 17.11 shows that if the distance between the surfaces in the r direction is dr,

$$\cos \theta = \frac{dn}{dr} . \tag{17.33}$$

Thus the directional derivative of T in the r direction is

$$(\text{Grad } T)_r = \frac{dT}{dr} . \tag{17.34}$$

If T is expressed as a function of the rectangular coordinates x, y, and z, the components of Grad T in these three directions are

$$(\text{Grad } T)_x = \frac{\partial T}{\partial x} \tag{17.35}$$

$$(\text{Grad } T)_y = \frac{\partial T}{\partial y} \tag{17.36}$$

$$(\text{Grad } T)_z = \frac{\partial T}{\partial z} . \tag{17.37}$$

Thus

$$\text{Grad } T = \mathbf{1}_x \frac{\partial T}{\partial x} + \mathbf{1}_y \frac{\partial T}{\partial y} + \mathbf{1}_z \frac{\partial T}{\partial z} . \tag{17.38}$$

Defining the operator

$$\nabla = \mathbf{1}_x \frac{\partial}{\partial x} + \mathbf{1}_y \frac{\partial}{\partial y} + \mathbf{1}_z \frac{\partial}{\partial z} , \tag{17.39}$$

called *del*, produces the useful abbreviation

$$\text{Grad } T = \nabla T . \tag{17.40}$$

Thermal gradients cause heat to flow. According to Fourier's law of heat conduction, the heat flux density vector (rate of heat flow per unit area) in a body conducting heat is

$$\mathbf{q}'' = -\,k\,\nabla T \tag{17.41}$$

where T is temperature and k is thermal conductivity. In an electrostatic field such as that between the plates of a capacitor, if V is the potential at any point in the field, ∇V is the force on a unit negative charge.

17.7 Divergence

Imagine a stationary porous box immersed in a fluid that is moving with a velocity $\mathbf{u}$ that varies from place to place. The velocity is measured in m/s or $m^3/s{\cdot}m^2$, and can be regarded as a flux density. If more or less fluid flows out of the box than flows in, the velocity is said to *diverge*. Water velocity does not diverge, but heat and electric flux densities sometimes do. *Divergence* is defined as the net amount of fluid or flux coming out of a volume v, per unit volume, as the volume approaches zero, i.e., at a point:

$$\text{Div } \mathbf{u} = \lim_{v \to 0} \frac{1}{v} \oint_s \mathbf{u} \cdot d\mathbf{s} . \tag{17.42}$$

To convert this definition to a useful form, calculate the flow out of each face of the differential rectangular box of Fig. 17.12, to find that the net flow out of the box is

$$\oint_s \mathbf{u} \cdot d\mathbf{s} = \left(\frac{\partial u_x}{\partial x} dx \right) dy\,dz + \left(\frac{\partial u_y}{\partial y} dy \right) dx\,dz + \left(\frac{\partial u_z}{\partial z} dz \right) dx\,dy . \tag{17.43}$$

Since the volume of the box is $v = dx\,dy\,dz$,

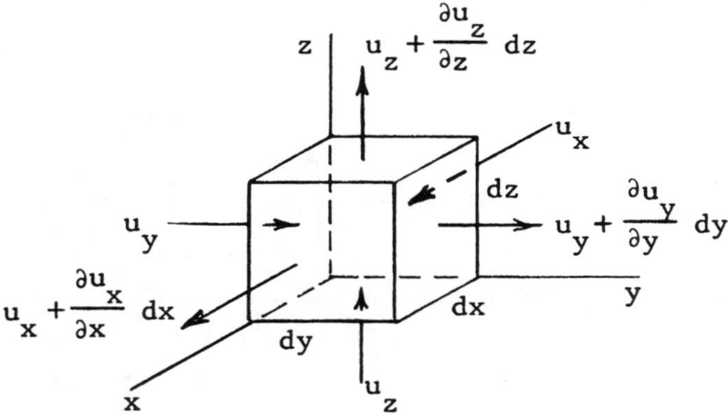

Fig. 17.12. Differential box for calculating divergence.

$$
\begin{aligned}
\text{Div}\,\mathbf{u} &= \lim_{v\to 0}\frac{1}{v}\oint_s \mathbf{u}\cdot d\mathbf{s} = \frac{\partial u_x}{\partial x} + \frac{\partial u_y}{\partial y} + \frac{\partial u_z}{\partial z} \\
&= \left(\mathbf{1}_x\frac{\partial}{\partial x} + \mathbf{1}_y\frac{\partial}{\partial y} + \mathbf{1}_z\frac{\partial}{\partial z}\right)\cdot\left(\mathbf{1}_x u_x + \mathbf{1}_y u_y + \mathbf{1}_z u_z\right) \\
&= \nabla\cdot\mathbf{u}\,. \qquad (17.44)
\end{aligned}
$$

For incompressible fluids, $\nabla\cdot\mathbf{u} = 0$. Magnetic flux density $\mathbf{B}$ has no divergence, but electric flux density $\mathbf{D}$ has divergence at any point at which electric charge density ρ is present. Thus

$$\nabla\cdot\mathbf{B} = 0 \quad \text{and} \quad \nabla\cdot\mathbf{D} = \rho\,. \qquad (17.45)$$

17.8 Divergence in Cylindrical Coordinates

The calculation of divergence is a little more complicated in cylindrical coordinates. The differential rectangular box now appears as in Fig. 17.13. The flow of fluid into the back of the box is $u_r\, rd\theta\, dz$. The flow out of the front is

$$u_r\, rd\theta\, dz + \frac{\partial}{\partial r}(u_r\, rd\theta\, dz)\, dr\,.$$

The surface area $rd\theta\, dz$ must be included in the derivative because it is a function of r. The flows into the bottom and out of the top of the box are

$$u_z\, dr\, rd\theta \quad \text{and} \quad u_z\, dr\, rd\theta + \frac{\partial}{\partial z}(u_z\, dr\, rd\theta)\, dz\,.$$

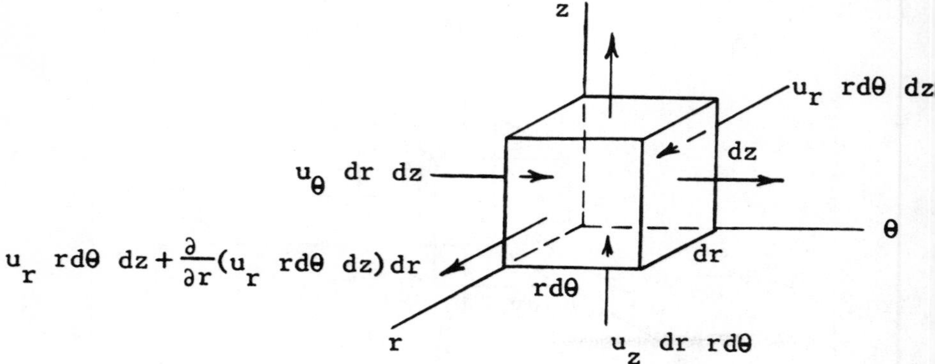

Fig. 17.13. Differential box in cylindrical coordinates.

The flows into the left side and out of the right side are

$$u_\theta \, dr \, dz \qquad \text{and} \qquad u_\theta \, dr \, dz + \frac{\partial}{\partial \theta}(u_\theta \, dr \, dz) d\theta \, .$$

The net flow out of the box is

$$\oint_s \mathbf{u} \cdot d\mathbf{s} = \frac{\partial (r u_r)}{\partial r} dr \, d\theta \, dz + \frac{\partial u_z}{\partial z} dr \, r d\theta \, dz + \frac{\partial u_\theta}{\partial \theta} dr \, d\theta \, dz \, . \tag{17.46}$$

Since the volume v of the box is $dr \, rd\theta \, dz$,

$$\text{Div } \mathbf{u} = \lim_{v \to 0} \frac{1}{v} \oint_s \mathbf{u} \cdot d\mathbf{s} = \frac{1}{r} \frac{\partial (r u_r)}{\partial r} + \frac{1}{r} \frac{\partial u_\theta}{\partial \theta} + \frac{\partial u_z}{\partial z} . \tag{17.47}$$

To confirm that this is the same as $\nabla \cdot \mathbf{u}$, form the scalar product of the operator ∇ and the vector $\mathbf{u}$ in cylindrical coordinates, namely

$$\nabla \cdot \mathbf{u} = \left(\mathbf{1}_r \frac{\partial}{\partial r} + \mathbf{1}_\theta \frac{1}{r} \frac{\partial}{\partial \theta} + \mathbf{1}_z \frac{\partial}{\partial z} \right) \cdot \left(\mathbf{1}_r \, u_r + \mathbf{1}_\theta \, u_\theta + \mathbf{1}_z \, u_z \right) . \tag{17.48}$$

Notice that the expansion of this expression will contain terms like

$$\left(\mathbf{1}_r \frac{\partial}{\partial r} \right) \cdot \left(\mathbf{1}_r \, u_r \right) .$$

The meaning of this term, not proved here, is

$$\left(\mathbf{1}_r \frac{\partial}{\partial r} \right) \cdot (\mathbf{1}_r \, u_r) = \mathbf{1}_r \cdot \frac{\partial}{\partial r} (\mathbf{1}_r \, u_r) = \mathbf{1}_r \cdot \left(\mathbf{1}_r \frac{\partial u_r}{\partial r} + \frac{\partial \mathbf{1}_r}{\partial r} u_r \right) = \frac{\partial u_r}{\partial r} . \tag{17.49}$$

Similarly,

$$\left(\mathbf{1}_\theta \frac{1}{r}\frac{\partial}{\partial\theta}\right)\cdot(\mathbf{1}_r u_r) = \mathbf{1}_\theta \cdot \frac{1}{r}\frac{\partial}{\partial\theta}(\mathbf{1}_r u_r) = \mathbf{1}_\theta \cdot \frac{1}{r}\left(\mathbf{1}_r \frac{\partial u_r}{\partial\theta} + \frac{\partial \mathbf{1}_r}{d\theta} u_r\right). \quad (17.50)$$

In a cylindrical coordinate system, the unit vector $\mathbf{1}_z$ is fixed, and $\mathbf{1}_r$ and $\mathbf{1}_\theta$ can rotate. Thus

$$\frac{d\mathbf{1}_r}{d\theta} = \mathbf{1}_\theta\,, \qquad \frac{d\mathbf{1}_\theta}{d\theta} = -\,\mathbf{1}_r\,, \qquad \text{and} \qquad \frac{d\mathbf{1}_z}{d\theta} = 0\,. \quad (17.51)$$

The unit vectors do not vary with r and z. Eq. (17.50) becomes

$$\mathbf{1}_\theta \cdot \frac{1}{r}\frac{\partial}{\partial\theta}(\mathbf{1}_r u_r) = \mathbf{1}_\theta \cdot \frac{1}{r}\left(\mathbf{1}_r \frac{\partial u_r}{\partial\theta} + \mathbf{1}_\theta u_r\right) = \frac{u_r}{r}\,. \quad (17.52)$$

Now Eq. (17.48) can be expanded:

$$\begin{aligned}
\nabla \cdot \mathbf{u} = {} & \mathbf{1}_r \cdot \frac{\partial}{\partial r}(\mathbf{1}_r u_r) + \mathbf{1}_r \cdot \frac{\partial}{\partial r}(\mathbf{1}_\theta u_\theta) + \mathbf{1}_r \cdot \frac{\partial}{\partial r}(\mathbf{1}_z u_z) \\
& + \mathbf{1}_\theta \cdot \frac{1}{r}\frac{\partial}{\partial\theta}(\mathbf{1}_r u_r) + \mathbf{1}_\theta \cdot \frac{1}{r}\frac{\partial}{\partial\theta}(\mathbf{1}_\theta u_\theta) + \mathbf{1}_\theta \cdot \frac{1}{r}\frac{\partial}{\partial\theta}(\mathbf{1}_z u_z) \\
& + \mathbf{1}_z \cdot \frac{\partial}{\partial z}(\mathbf{1}_r u_r) + \mathbf{1}_z \cdot \frac{\partial}{\partial z}(\mathbf{1}_\theta u_\theta) + \mathbf{1}_z \cdot \frac{\partial}{\partial z}(\mathbf{1}_z u_z) \\
= {} & \frac{\partial u_r}{\partial r} + 0 + 0 \\
& + \frac{u_r}{r} + \frac{1}{r}\frac{\partial u_\theta}{\partial\theta} + 0 \\
& + 0 + 0 + \frac{\partial u_z}{\partial z}
\end{aligned} \quad (17.53)$$

or

$$\nabla \cdot \mathbf{u} = \frac{\partial u_r}{\partial r} + \frac{u_r}{r} + \frac{1}{r}\frac{\partial u_\theta}{\partial\theta} + \frac{\partial u_z}{\partial z}\,. \quad (17.54)$$

Comparing this result with Eq. (17.47) shows that in cylindrical as well as rectangular coordinates,

$$\text{Div}\,\mathbf{u} = \nabla \cdot \mathbf{u}\,. \quad (17.55)$$

17.9 Gauss's Divergence Theorem

Gauss's divergence theorem is the statement that the net flow of flux out of a volume v enclosed by the surface s is the integral of the net outward flow from every point within:

$$\oint_s \mathbf{u} \cdot d\mathbf{s} = \int_v (\nabla \cdot \mathbf{u})\, dv \,. \tag{17.56}$$

The proof is intuitive. According to Eq. (17.42) the net flow out of a differential volume dv having surface area s_1 is

$$\nabla \cdot \mathbf{u}\, dv = \oint_{s_1} \mathbf{u} \cdot d\mathbf{s} \,. \tag{17.57}$$

When the contributions of all of the differential volumes in the volume v are added, the left side becomes

$$\int_v \nabla \cdot \mathbf{u}\, dv \,.$$

The right side becomes the sum of the surface integrals over all of the differential volumes. The contributions of the surface integrals on faces common to two differential volumes cancel, leaving only the integral over the surface s:

$$\oint_s \mathbf{u} \cdot d\mathbf{s} \,.$$

Gauss's theorem is useful for converting equations from integral to differential form. For example, the net electric flux emanating from a closed surface s is equal to the charge Q enclosed by the surface:

$$\oint_s \mathbf{D} \cdot d\mathbf{s} = \int_v \rho\, dv = Q \tag{17.58}$$

where ρ is charge density and v is the volume enclosed by the surface. This is the integral form of Gauss's flux law (not to be confused with Gauss's divergence theorem). Applying Gauss's theorem to Eq. (17.58) converts it to the form

$$\oint_s \mathbf{D} \cdot d\mathbf{s} = \int_v (\nabla \cdot \mathbf{D})\, dv = \int_v \rho\, dv \,. \tag{17.59}$$

Since this equation is valid over any volume v, the integrands must be equal:

$$\nabla \cdot \mathbf{D} = \rho \,. \tag{17.60}$$

This is the differential form of Gauss's flux law.

17.10 Curl

The *circulation* of a vector field **A** is the line integral

$$\oint \mathbf{A} \cdot d\ell \tag{17.61}$$

counterclockwise around a closed path enclosing a surface **s**, as in Fig. 17.14. The *curl* of **A** is defined as a vector whose component in the **s** direction is

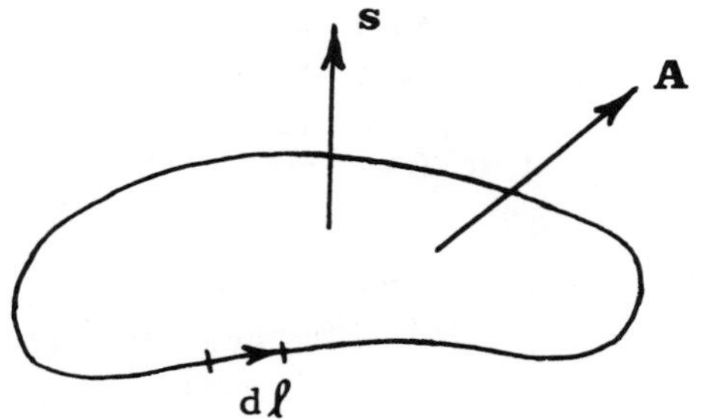

Fig. 17.14. Circulation of a vector field.

$$(\text{Curl }\mathbf{A})_s = \lim_{s \to 0} \frac{1}{s} \oint \mathbf{A} \cdot d\ell\,. \tag{17.62}$$

To put this definition into a usable form, construct three sides of a differential rectangular box as in Fig. 17.15 and label the components of

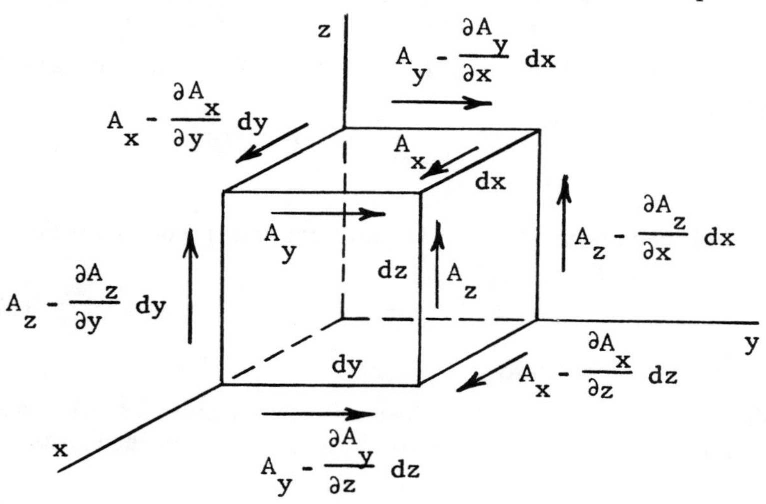

Fig. 17.15. Differential box for calculating curl.

the vector field **A** parallel to each side. Integrating around the front side produces one component of the curl:

$$(\text{Curl }\mathbf{A})_x = \frac{1}{dy\,dz}\left[A_z dz - A_y dy - \left(A_z - \frac{\partial A_z}{\partial y}dy\right)dz + \left(A_y - \frac{\partial A_y}{\partial z}dz\right)dy\right] = \frac{\partial A_z}{\partial y} - \frac{\partial A_y}{\partial z}. \quad (17.63)$$

Integrating around the right and top sides produces the other two components:

$$(\text{Curl }\mathbf{A})_y = \frac{\partial A_x}{\partial z} - \frac{\partial A_z}{\partial x} \quad (17.64)$$

$$(\text{Curl }\mathbf{A})_z = \frac{\partial A_y}{\partial x} - \frac{\partial A_x}{\partial y}. \quad (17.65)$$

Thus

$$\text{Curl }\mathbf{A} = \mathbf{1}_x\left(\frac{\partial A_z}{\partial y} - \frac{\partial A_y}{\partial z}\right) + \mathbf{1}_y\left(\frac{\partial A_x}{\partial z} - \frac{\partial A_z}{\partial x}\right) + \mathbf{1}_z\left(\frac{\partial A_y}{\partial x} - \frac{\partial A_x}{\partial y}\right) = \begin{vmatrix} \mathbf{1}_x & \mathbf{1}_y & \mathbf{1}_z \\ \dfrac{\partial}{\partial x} & \dfrac{\partial}{\partial y} & \dfrac{\partial}{\partial z} \\ A_x & A_y & A_z \end{vmatrix} \quad (17.66)$$

or

$$\text{Curl }\mathbf{A} = \left(\mathbf{1}_x\frac{\partial}{\partial x} + \mathbf{1}_y\frac{\partial}{\partial y} + \mathbf{1}_z\frac{\partial}{\partial z}\right) \times (\mathbf{1}_x A_x + \mathbf{1}_y A_y + \mathbf{1}_z A_z) = \nabla \times \mathbf{A}. \quad (17.67)$$

According to Faraday's law, if $\mathbf{E}$ is electric field intensity and $\mathbf{B}$ is magnetic flux density,

$$\nabla \times \mathbf{E} = -\frac{\partial \mathbf{B}}{\partial t}. \quad (17.68)$$

In a fluid such as water, if $\boldsymbol{\omega}$ is the angular velocity of a particle whose linear velocity is $\mathbf{v}$,

$$\nabla \times \mathbf{v} = 2\boldsymbol{\omega}. \quad (17.69)$$

17.11 Stokes' Theorem

Stokes' theorem states that the circulation around a surface $\mathbf{s}$ as in Fig. 17.16 is the integral of the circulations around all the points on the surface:

$$\oint \mathbf{A} \cdot d\ell = \int_s (\nabla \times \mathbf{A}) \cdot d\mathbf{s}. \quad (17.70)$$

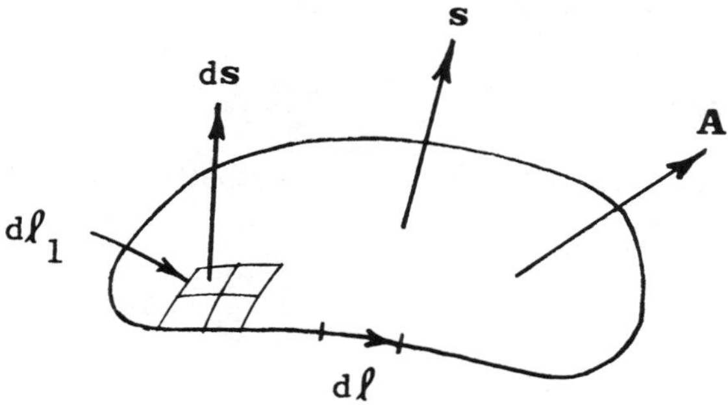

Fig. 17.16. Summation of line integrals.

The proof is simple. Since $\nabla \times \mathbf{A} = \text{Curl } \mathbf{A}$,

$$(\nabla \times \mathbf{A}) \cdot d\mathbf{s} = (\text{Curl } \mathbf{A})_s \, ds \,. \tag{17.71}$$

In Fig. 17.16, $d\ell_1$ is a differential length of the path around the differential area $d\mathbf{s}$. According to Eq. (17.62), the component of curl normal to $d\mathbf{s}$ is

$$(\text{Curl } \mathbf{A})_s = \frac{1}{ds} \oint \mathbf{A} \cdot d\ell_1 \,. \tag{17.72}$$

A combination of the last two equations is

$$\oint \mathbf{A} \cdot d\ell_1 = (\nabla \times \mathbf{A}) \cdot d\mathbf{s} \,. \tag{17.73}$$

When the contributions of all the differential areas in the surface **s** are added, the right side becomes

$$\int_s (\nabla \times \mathbf{A}) \cdot d\mathbf{s} \,.$$

The contributions of the line integrals along adjacent sides of two differential areas cancel each other, leaving only the line integral around the periphery of the surface **s**, as shown by Eq. (17.70).

Stokes' theorem, like Gauss's theorem, is useful for converting equations from integral to differential form. For example, the integral form of Faraday's law is

$$\oint \mathbf{E} \cdot d\ell = -\frac{d\phi}{dt} \tag{17.74}$$

where ϕ is the magnetic flux linking the path of the line integral, and

$$\phi = \int_s \mathbf{B} \cdot d\mathbf{s} \,. \tag{17.75}$$

The application of Stokes' theorem shows that

$$\oint \mathbf{E} \cdot d\ell = \int_s (\nabla \times \mathbf{E}) \cdot d\mathbf{s} = -\frac{d}{dt}\int_s \mathbf{B} \cdot d\mathbf{s}\,. \tag{17.76}$$

If the path of the line integral is fixed so that s is not a function of t, $d(d\mathbf{s})/dt = 0$, and

$$\int_s (\nabla \times \mathbf{E}) \cdot d\mathbf{s} = -\int_s \frac{\partial \mathbf{B}}{\partial t} \cdot d\mathbf{s}\,. \tag{17.77}$$

Since this equation is valid over any open surface,

$$\nabla \times \mathbf{E} = -\frac{\partial \mathbf{B}}{\partial t}\,. \tag{17.78}$$

This is the differential form of Faraday's law.

17.12 Partial Differential Equations

The *Laplacian operator* ∇^2 is defined as the divergence of the gradient. Thus if A is a scalar potential,

$$\nabla^2 A = \nabla \cdot \nabla A\,. \tag{17.79}$$

In rectangular coordinates,

$$\nabla^2 A = \frac{\partial^2 A}{\partial x^2} + \frac{\partial^2 A}{\partial y^2} + \frac{\partial^2 A}{\partial z^2}\,. \tag{17.80}$$

The Laplacian of a vector has the same symbol but a more complicated meaning:

$$\nabla^2 \mathbf{A} = \nabla(\nabla \cdot \mathbf{A}) - \nabla \times (\nabla \times \mathbf{A})\,. \tag{17.81}$$

For rectangular coordinates this formula reduces to the simple expression

$$\nabla^2 \mathbf{A} = \mathbf{1}_x\, \nabla^2 A_x + \mathbf{1}_y\, \nabla^2 A_y + \mathbf{1}_z\, \nabla^2 A_z\,. \tag{17.82}$$

The Laplacian operator appears in all of the common partial differential equations, because it describes the spatial variation of a field such as temperature or magnetic field intensity. These equations are

Laplace $\quad \nabla^2 A = 0$

Poisson $\quad \nabla^2 A = f(x,y,z)$

Diffusion $\quad \nabla^2 \mathbf{A} = k\,\dfrac{\partial \mathbf{A}}{\partial t}$

Wave $\nabla^2 \mathbf{A} = k \dfrac{\partial^2 \mathbf{A}}{\partial t^2}$

Schroedinger $k_1 \nabla^2 \psi - f(x,y,z)\psi = k_2 \dfrac{\partial \psi}{\partial t}$.

General solutions of these equations can be obtained by the method of separation of variables. The application of a general solution to a specific field is called a boundary-value problem. Although boundary-value problems can theoretically be solved if the value of the field and/or its normal derivative on all the boundaries are known (the requirements vary with the type of equation), the computation is practicable only if the field has a simple shape. An example will show how a boundary-value problem using Laplace's equation is solved by separation of variables.

17.13 A Solution by Separation of Variables

For a given potential that obeys Laplace's equation, a unique solution can be obtained if the potential is specified along all of the boundaries. The problem consists of finding a solution of Laplace's equation that fulfills all of the boundary conditions. Such a "well-posed" problem is provided in Fig. 17.17, which shows a section of a long copper cylinder

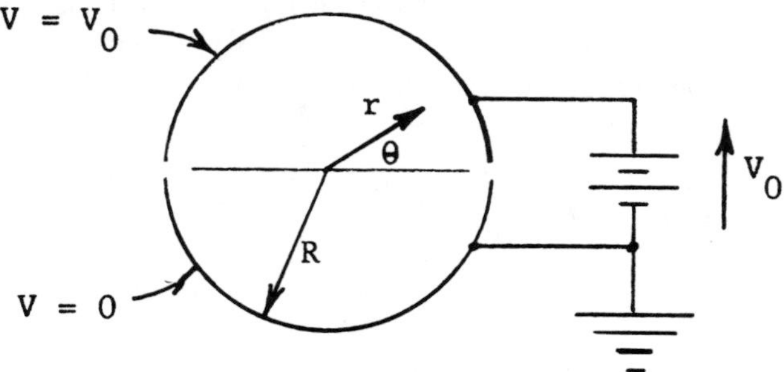

Fig. 17.17. Cylinder in two halves.

cut into two halves that are at electric potentials 0 and V_0. Calculate the electric potential V at any point (r, θ) inside the cylinder. Since the cylinder is long, ignore its ends and assume that the potential does not vary in the z direction (perpendicular to the paper). The potential obeys Laplace's equation, which in polar coordinates is

$$\frac{\partial^2 V}{\partial r^2} + \frac{1}{r}\frac{\partial V}{\partial r} + \frac{1}{r^2}\frac{\partial^2 V}{\partial \theta^2} = 0 . \qquad (17.83)$$

Assume a product solution of the form

$$V = R(r)\,T(\theta) \tag{17.84}$$

in which the independent variables r and θ are separated in the two functions R and T. Substituting the solution back into Laplace's equation produces

$$T\frac{\partial^2 R}{\partial r^2} + \frac{1}{r}T\frac{\partial R}{\partial r} + \frac{1}{r^2}R\frac{\partial^2 T}{\partial \theta^2} = 0 \tag{17.85}$$

or

$$\frac{1}{R}\left(r^2\frac{\partial^2 R}{\partial r^2} + r\frac{\partial R}{\partial r}\right) = -\frac{1}{T}\frac{\partial^2 T}{\partial \theta^2}\,. \tag{17.86}$$

The right side of this equation is not a function of r, and therefore does not vary when r is varied. Therefore the left side does not vary either. Since the left side is a function of r only, it must equal a constant. The right side equals the same constant, called the *separation constant*, which will be called k^2. Thus

$$\frac{1}{R}\left(r^2\frac{\partial^2 R}{\partial r^2} + r\frac{\partial R}{\partial r}\right) = -\frac{1}{T}\frac{\partial^2 T}{\partial \theta^2} = k^2\,. \tag{17.87}$$

The sign and exponent of the separation constant are chosen, usually with the wisdom of hindsight, to simplify the solution. Since R is a function of r only and T is a function of θ only, the partial derivatives become total derivatives, and Eq. (17.87) produces the two ordinary differential equations

$$r^2\frac{d^2 R}{dr^2} + r\frac{dR}{dr} - k^2 R = 0 \tag{17.88}$$

and

$$\frac{d^2 T}{d\theta^2} + k^2 T = 0\,. \tag{17.89}$$

The first of these is an Euler equation whose solution is

$$R = Ar^k + Br^{-k}\,, \quad k \neq 0\,. \tag{17.90}$$

The solution of the second ordinary differential equation is

$$T = C\sin k\theta + D\cos k\theta\,, \quad k \neq 0\,. \tag{17.91}$$

If $k = 0$, the solutions are

$$R = A_0 + B_0 \ln r \tag{17.92}$$

and

$$T = C_0 + D_0\theta \, . \tag{17.93}$$

A look at Laplace's equation (17.83) shows that if $V(k_1)$ and $V(k_2)$ are solutions with any two values of the separation constant k^2, then $V(k_1) + V(k_2)$ is also a solution. Therefore the most general solution of Eq. (17.83) is

$$V = \sum_k (A_k r^k + B_k r^{-k})(C_k \sin k\theta + D_k \cos k\theta)$$

$$+ (A_0 + B_0 \ln r)(C_0 + D_0\theta) \tag{17.94}$$

where k can have any value except zero. Now since the potential V has a single value at each point (r, θ),

$$V(r, \theta) = V(r, \theta + 2\pi n) \tag{17.95}$$

when n is any integer. Therefore $D_0 = 0$ and

$$\sin k\theta = \sin k(\theta + 2\pi n) = \sin k\theta \cos 2\pi kn + \cos k\theta \sin 2\pi kn \tag{17.96}$$

which is true only if k is also an integer. Eq. (17.94) therefore reduces to

$$V = \sum_{k=1}^{\infty} (A_k r^k + B_k r^{-k})(C_k \sin k\theta + D_k \cos k\theta) + A_0 + B_0 \ln r \, . \tag{17.97}$$

The negative values of k are not needed because the coefficients of their terms can be lumped with those for the terms with positive k. For example,

$$C_k \sin k\theta + C_{-k} \sin(-k\theta) = (C_k - C_{-k}) \sin k\theta \, . \tag{17.98}$$

Thus the coefficient of $\sin k\theta$ includes those for both $\sin k\theta$ and $\sin(-k\theta)$. Eq. (17.97) is the general solution of Laplace's equation in polar coordinates. The solution of a particular boundary-value problem is obtained by applying the boundary conditions to evaluate the constants. Since the solution is specified uniquely if the potentials on all of the boundaries are specified, all of the constants can be evaluated (in principle) with no boundary condition left over. In many problems one or both of the terms in Eq. (17.97) for $k = 0$ are not needed. A justification for setting A_0 or B_0 equal to zero, although helpful to the reader, is not necessary if the solution fulfills all of the boundary conditions when all of the remaining constants have been evaluated.

In the field of Fig. 17.17, A_0 is needed because it is the average potential in the cylinder. Clearly B_0 is zero because the potential V is not infinite at $r = 0$. For the same reason, all of the B_k's are zero. With renamed coefficients, Eq. (17.97) is now

$$V = \sum_{k=1}^{\infty} r^k (C_k \sin k\theta + D_k \cos k\theta) + A_0 . \qquad (17.99)$$

The potential on the boundary at $r = R$ is

$$V(R, \theta) = \sum_{k=1}^{\infty} R^k (C_k \sin k\theta + D_k \cos k\theta) + A_0 \qquad (17.100)$$

and is distributed as in Fig. 17.18. The Fourier series representing this wave is

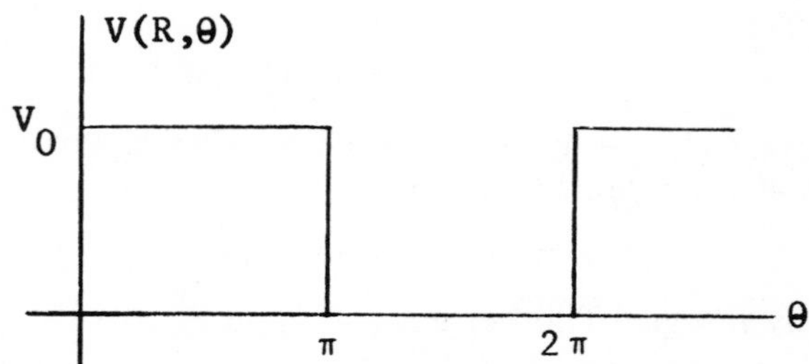

Fig. 17.18. Potential distribution along r = R.

$$V(R, \theta) = \frac{2V_0}{\pi} \sum_{k=1}^{\infty} \frac{\sin k\theta}{k} + \frac{V_0}{2}, \quad k \text{ odd} . \qquad (17.101)$$

Comparison of Eqs. (17.100) and (17.101) shows that

$$C_k = \frac{2V_0}{\pi k R^k}, \qquad D_k = 0 , \qquad A_0 = \frac{V_0}{2} . \qquad (17.102)$$

Thus according to Eq. (17.99), the potential anywhere inside the cylinder of Fig. 17.17 is

$$V = \frac{2V_0}{\pi} \sum_{k=1}^{\infty} \frac{1}{k}\left(\frac{r}{R}\right)^k \sin k\theta + \frac{V_0}{2}, \quad k = 1, 3, 5, \ldots \qquad (17.103)$$

Frequently the Fourier series representing a boundary condition like that in Fig. 17.18 is not known. Rather than deriving it and then matching terms with the product solution, evaluate the remaining constants by taking advantage of the orthogonality of the sine and cosine functions in the product solution. To evaluate C_k in this example, multiply both sides of Eq. (17.100) by $\sin m\theta$ and integrate along the boundary from $\theta = 0$ to 2π:

$$\int_0^{2\pi} V(R,\theta) \sin m\theta \, d\theta = \int_0^{2\pi} \sin m\theta \sum_{k=1}^{\infty} R^k (C_k \sin k\theta + D_k \cos k\theta) d\theta + \int_0^{2\pi} A_0 \sin m\theta \, d\theta . \qquad (17.104)$$

Allow m to have only integral values. Since

$$\begin{aligned} V(R, \theta) &= V_0 , \quad 0 < \theta < \pi \\ &= 0 , \quad \pi < \theta < 2\pi , \end{aligned} \tag{17.105}$$

the first term of Eq. (17.104) is

$$\begin{aligned} V_0 \int_0^{\pi} \sin m\theta \, d\theta &= - \frac{V_0 \cos m\theta}{m} \bigg|_0^{\pi} \\ &= \frac{2V_0}{m} , \quad m \text{ odd} \\ &= 0 , \quad m \text{ even} . \end{aligned} \tag{17.106}$$

To evaluate the second term of Eq. (17.104), observe the orthogonality of sine functions:

$$\int_0^{2\pi} \sin k\theta \sin m\theta \, d\theta = \pi \, \delta_{km} \tag{17.107}$$

$$\int_0^{2\pi} \cos k\theta \sin m\theta \, d\theta = 0 . \tag{17.108}$$

The second term of Eq. (17.104) becomes

$$\int_0^{2\pi} \sin m\theta \sum_{k=1}^{\infty} R^k (C_k \sin k\theta + D_k \cos k\theta) d\theta = \pi \, R^m C_m \, . \tag{17.109}$$

The third term of Eq. (17.104) is

$$\int_0^{2\pi} A_0 \sin m\theta \, d\theta = 0 . \tag{17.110}$$

Combining the three terms produces the result

$$\begin{aligned} \pi \, R^m C_m &= \frac{2V_0}{m} , \quad m \text{ odd} \\ &= 0 , \quad m \text{ even} \end{aligned} \tag{17.111}$$

or

$$\begin{aligned} C_k &= \frac{2V_0}{\pi \, k \, R^k} , \quad k \text{ odd} \\ &= 0 , \quad k \text{ even} . \end{aligned} \tag{17.112}$$

The values of D_k in Eq. (17.100) could be determined by multiplying both sides of the equation by cos $m\theta$ and integrating from $\theta = 0$ to 2π. This work can be avoided, however, by observing the waveform of $V(R, \theta)$ in Fig. 17.18. If the average value is subtracted, the waveform is odd. Therefore $V(R,\theta)$ contains no cosine term and $D_k = 0$. The average value is

$$A_0 = \frac{1}{2\pi}\int_0^{2\pi} V(R, \theta)d\theta = \frac{V_0}{2}. \tag{17.113}$$

These values of C_k, D_k, and A_0 of course agree with those given by Eqs. (17.102).

17.14 The Method of Iteration

If the boundaries of a field are irregular, the coefficients in a product solution of the partial differential equation cannot be evaluated easily. Several methods of obtaining approximate numerical solutions are available, one of which is the *method of iteration*. The partial differential equation is converted to a difference equation for which the numerical solution is tedious but simple, and well suited to a digital computer. The procedure will be illustrated for Laplace's equation.

Fig. 17.19 shows part of a two-dimensional Laplacian field near an irregular equipotential boundary. Establish a square grid system on the field with line spacing h. Now derive a formula for the potential V_0 at any node in terms of the potentials V_1 thru V_4 of its four neighboring nodes or points of known potential, whichever are closer. Start by locating the origin of coordinates x and y in Fig. 17.19 at node 0. Express

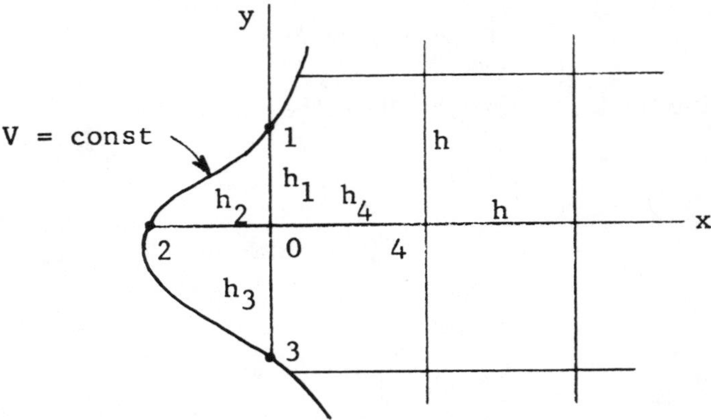

Fig. 17.19. Grid network for solving Laplace's equation.

the potential in the vicinity of node 0 as the power series

$$V = V_0 + a_1 x + a_2 y + a_3 x^2 + a_4 y^2 + a_5 xy + a_6 x^2 y + a_7 xy^2 + \cdots \tag{17.114}$$

Since the coordinates of point 1 are $(0, h_1)$, its potential is

$$V_1 = V_0 + a_2 h_1 + a_4 h_1^2 . \tag{17.115}$$

Similarly, the potentials of points 2, 3, and 4 are

$$V_2 = V_0 - a_1 h_2 + a_3 h_2^2 \tag{17.116}$$

$$V_3 = V_0 - a_2 h_3 + a_4 h_3^2 \tag{17.117}$$

$$V_4 = V_0 + a_1 h_4 + a_3 h_4^2 . \tag{17.118}$$

The simultaneous solution of these four equations is

$$a_3 = \frac{h_4(V_2 - V_0) + h_2(V_4 - V_0)}{h_2 h_4^2 + h_4 h_2^2} \tag{17.119}$$

$$a_4 = \frac{h_1(V_3 - V_0) + h_3(V_1 - V_0)}{h_1 h_3^2 + h_3 h_1^2} . \tag{17.120}$$

The coefficients a_1 and a_2 will not be needed. Near the origin where x and y are small, the higher terms of the power series (17.114) are negligible, and

$$\frac{\partial^2 V}{\partial x^2} = 2a_3 , \qquad \frac{\partial^2 V}{\partial y^2} = 2a_4 . \tag{17.121}$$

Substituting Eqs. (17.119) thru (17.121) into Laplace's equation

$$\frac{\partial^2 V}{\partial x^2} + \frac{\partial^2 V}{\partial y^2} = 0 \tag{17.122}$$

and introducing the dimensionless ratios

$$s_i = \frac{h_i}{h} , \quad i = 1, 2, 3, 4 \tag{17.123}$$

produces

$$V_0 = \frac{1}{\dfrac{1}{s_1 s_3} + \dfrac{1}{s_2 s_4}} \left[\frac{V_1}{s_1(s_1 + s_3)} + \frac{V_2}{s_2(s_2 + s_4)} + \frac{V_3}{s_3(s_1 + s_3)} + \frac{V_4}{s_4(s_2 + s_4)} \right] . \tag{17.124}$$

For nodes away from the boundary, where the nearest neighbors are grid nodes, this equation reduces to

$$V_0 = \frac{1}{4}(V_1 + V_2 + V_3 + V_4)\,. \tag{17.125}$$

Eqs. (17.124) and (17.125) are difference equations for computing the potential at any node in terms of the potentials of its four neighbors. The accuracy of these equations increases as the grid size decreases. To calculate the potential at all the nodes, start by writing the known potential at each boundary point, and the best guess at each node. Then traverse across the grid, calculating a new value of potential at each node, using Eq. (17.125) or (17.124). Use the new value immediately in calculating the new value of potential at the next node. For the nodes with equidistant neighbors, the traverse is accomplished in BASIC by putting the statement

$$V(I, J) = (V(I + 1, J) + V(I - 1, J) + V(I, J + 1) + V(I, J - 1))/4 \tag{17.126}$$

within nested FOR-NEXT loops for I and J. After the traverse is completed, the process is repeated until the potentials do not change significantly, i.e., until the difference between the right and left side of Eq. (17.124) or (17.125) at each node, called the *residual*, has been "relaxed" to almost zero. Computer time can be saved by starting with a coarse grid, relaxing its residuals, and then using the potentials at its nodes to guess at the potentials at the nodes of a finer grid. The method of iteration is also called the *relaxation method* for its early application in stress analysis, in which the residuals were unwanted forces to be relaxed to zero.

Chapter 18

BESSEL FUNCTIONS AND SERIES SOLUTIONS OF DIFFERENTIAL EQUATIONS

18.1 Linear, Ordinary Differential Equations

Some linear, ordinary differential equations (LODE's) can be solved by straightforward methods that produce solutions in closed form. For example, any first-order LODE can be written as

$$\frac{dy}{dx} + a(x)y = f(x) ,$$

and can be solved with the help of an integrating factor, or by the method of adjoints. The Euler differential equation

$$a_n x^n \frac{d^n y}{dx^n} + a_{n-1} x^{n-1} \frac{d^{n-1} y}{dx^{n-1}} + \cdots + a_1 x \frac{dy}{dx} + a_0 y = f(t)$$

is converted into a form with constant coefficients by the substitution

$$x = e^z .$$

Any LODE with constant coefficients can be solved by (1) solving its characteristic equation to determine the complementary solution, and (2) applying either the method of undetermined coefficients or the method of variation of parameters to evaluate the particular solution.

Unfortunately many LODE's, including some that arise in the product solutions of partial differential equations, cannot be solved by these methods. An example is Bessel's equation. To show how it appears, solve Laplace's equation in cylindrical coordinates:

$$\frac{\partial^2 T}{\partial r^2} + \frac{1}{r}\frac{\partial T}{\partial r} + \frac{1}{r^2}\frac{\partial^2 T}{\partial \theta^2} + \frac{\partial^2 T}{\partial z^2} = 0 , \tag{18.1}$$

where T might be the temperature in a cylindrical oven. Assume the product solution

$$T = R(r)\Phi(\theta)Y(z) . \tag{18.2}$$

Substituting this solution into Laplace's equation produces

$$\Phi Y \frac{\partial^2 R}{\partial r^2} + \frac{\Phi Y}{r}\frac{\partial R}{\partial r} + \frac{RY}{r^2}\frac{\partial^2 \Phi}{\partial \theta^2} + R\Phi \frac{\partial^2 Y}{\partial z^2} = 0 . \tag{18.3}$$

To separate the variables in all but one term, divide by $R\Phi Y$:

$$\frac{1}{R}\frac{\partial^2 R}{\partial r^2}+\frac{1}{rR}\frac{\partial R}{\partial r}+\frac{1}{r^2\Phi}\frac{\partial^2\Phi}{\partial\theta^2}+\frac{1}{Y}\frac{\partial^2 Y}{\partial z^2}=0\,, \tag{18.4}$$

or

$$\frac{1}{R}\frac{\partial^2 R}{\partial r^2}+\frac{1}{rR}\frac{\partial R}{\partial r}+\frac{1}{r^2\Phi}\frac{\partial^2\Phi}{\partial\theta^2}=-\frac{1}{Y}\frac{\partial^2 Y}{\partial z^2}\,. \tag{18.5}$$

Since the left side is independent of z, the right side must be also. The right side must be constant. Therefore

$$\frac{1}{R}\frac{\partial^2 R}{\partial r^2}+\frac{1}{rR}\frac{\partial R}{\partial r}+\frac{1}{r^2\Phi}\frac{\partial^2\Phi}{\partial\theta^2}=-\frac{1}{Y}\frac{\partial^2 Y}{\partial z^2}=-k^2\,. \tag{18.6}$$

The ordinary differential equation in z is

$$\frac{d^2Y}{dz^2}-k^2Y=0\,. \tag{18.7}$$

Its solution is

$$Y=Ae^{kz}+Be^{-kz}\,. \tag{18.8}$$

Now rearrange Eq. (18.4) again. Replace the term in z by k^2, and multiply thru by r^2 to separate the remaining variables:

$$\frac{r^2}{R}\frac{\partial^2 R}{\partial r^2}+\frac{r}{R}\frac{\partial R}{\partial r}+k^2r^2=-\frac{1}{\Phi}\frac{\partial^2\Phi}{\partial\theta^2}\,. \tag{18.9}$$

Each side of this equation must equal another constant, which will be called n^2:

$$\frac{r^2}{R}\frac{\partial^2 R}{\partial r^2}+\frac{r}{R}\frac{\partial R}{\partial r}+k^2r^2=-\frac{1}{\Phi}\frac{\partial^2\Phi}{\partial\theta^2}=n^2\,. \tag{18.10}$$

The ordinary differential equation in θ is

$$\frac{d^2\Phi}{d\theta^2}+n^2\Phi=0\,. \tag{18.11}$$

Its solution is

$$\Phi=C\sin n\theta+D\cos n\theta\,. \tag{18.12}$$

The ordinary differential equation in r is

$$r^2\frac{d^2R}{dr^2}+r\frac{dR}{dr}+(k^2r^2-n^2)R=0\,. \tag{18.13}$$

To simplify this equation, let $kr = x$. Then

$$\frac{dR}{dr} = \frac{dR}{dx}\,\frac{dx}{dr} = k\,\frac{dR}{dx} \tag{18.14}$$

and

$$\begin{aligned}\frac{d^2R}{dr^2} &= \frac{d}{dr}\left(\frac{dR}{dr}\right) = \frac{d}{dx}\left(\frac{dR}{dr}\right)\frac{dx}{dr} = \left(k\,\frac{d^2R}{dx^2}\right)(k)\\ &= k^2\,\frac{d^2R}{dx^2}\,.\end{aligned} \tag{18.15}$$

Eq. (18.13) becomes

$$r^2k^2\,\frac{d^2R}{dx^2} + rk\,\frac{dR}{dx} + (k^2r^2 - n^2)R = 0 \tag{18.16}$$

or

$$x^2\,\frac{d^2R}{dx^2} + x\,\frac{dR}{dx} + (x^2 - n^2)R = 0\,. \tag{18.17}$$

This is *Bessel's equation*. It also arises in the product solution of the wave equation in polar coordinates, and of the diffusion equation in cylindrical coordinates.

Another ordinary, linear, second-order differential equation, that appears in the solution of Laplace's equation in *spherical* coordinates, is *Legendre's equation*:

$$(1 - \theta^2)\,\frac{d^2T}{d\theta^2} - 2\theta\,\frac{dT}{d\theta} + n(n + 1)\theta = 0 \tag{18.18}$$

where n is a constant.

18.2 The Power-Series Method

The equations of Bessel, Legendre, and Euler are examples of the general linear differential equation

$$\frac{d^ny}{dx^n} + b_{n-1}(x)\,\frac{d^{n-1}y}{dx^{n-1}} + \cdots + b_1(x)\,\frac{dy}{dx} + b_0(x)y = f(x)\,, \tag{18.19}$$

in which each coefficient $b_i(x)$ can be any function of x. There is no standard method of solution of this equation (for orders higher than the first) that always works. A method that *frequently* works consists of expressing the solution as a power series in x:

$$y = a_0x^m + a_1x^{m+1} + \cdots + a_kx^{m+k} + \cdots\,, \tag{18.20}$$

substituting it into the differential equation, and equating the coefficients of like powers of x. If the differential equation is not homogeneous, its right side can be written as a Maclaurin series:

$$f(x) = f(0) + \frac{f'(0)}{1!}x + \frac{f''(0)}{2!}x^2 + \cdots + \frac{f^{(k)}(0)}{k!}x^k + \cdots, \quad (18.21)$$

and its terms collected with the others with like powers of x. When this procedure is followed, m and the coefficients a_i can frequently be evaluated, so that the final form of Eq. (18.20) consists of n linearly-independent series. To learn how the power-series method works, solve the differential equation

$$\frac{d^2y}{dx^2} - x\frac{dy}{dx} = 0\,. \quad (18.22)$$

According to Eq. (18.20),

$$\frac{dy}{dx} = ma_0x^{m-1} + (m + 1)a_1x^m + (m + 2)a_2x^{m+1} + \cdots, \quad (18.23)$$

$$x\frac{dy}{dx} = ma_0x^m + (m + 1)a_1x^{m+1} + (m + 2)a_2x^{m+2} + \cdots, \quad (18.24)$$

and

$$\frac{d^2y}{dx^2} = m(m - 1)a_0x^{m-2} + (m + 1)(m)a_1x^{m-1} + (m + 2)(m + 1)a_2x^m + \cdots \quad (18.25)$$

Substitute these into the differential equation (18.22) to get

$$m(m - 1)a_0x^{m-2} + (m + 1)(m)a_1x^{m-1} + (m + 2)(m + 1)a_2x^m + \cdots - ma_0x^m - (m + 1)a_1x^{m+1} - (m + 2)a_2x^{m+2} - \cdots = 0\,. \quad (18.26)$$

The coefficients of like powers of x are equated in Table 18.1. The first

TABLE 18.1. COEFFICIENTS OF LIKE POWERS OF X

Power of x	*Coefficient*	
$m - 2$	$m(m - 1)a_0 = 0$	(18.27)
$m - 1$	$(m + 1)(m)a_1 = 0$	(18.28)
m	$(m + 2)(m + 1)a_2 - ma_0 = 0$	(18.29)
$m + 1$	$(m + 3)(m + 2)a_3 - (m + 1)a_1 = 0$	(18.30)
.	.	
.	.	
.	.	
$m + k$	$(m + k + 2)(m + k + 1)a_{k+2} - (m + k)a_k = 0$	(18.31)

equation in the table, Eq. (18.27), is called the *indicial equation.* It permits two values of m, 0 or 1. Choosing $m = 0$ and inserting it into Eq. (18.31) produces the difference equation

$$(k + 2)(k + 1)a_{k+2} - ka_k = 0 \tag{18.32}$$

or

$$a_{k+2} = \frac{k}{(k + 1)(k + 2)} a_k \; . \tag{18.33}$$

The latter is called a *recursion formula.* It generates each coefficient in the series of Eq. (18.20) from is grandparent. Since $m = 0$, Eqs. (18.27) and (18.28) are satisfied with any values of a_0 and a_1. According to the recursion formula, a_2 must be zero, and therefore all even-numbered coefficients a_4, a_6, etc. are zero. Also

$$a_3 = \frac{1}{(2)(3)} a_1 = \frac{1}{3!} a_1 \tag{18.34}$$

$$a_5 = \frac{3}{(4)(5)} a_3 = \frac{3}{5!} a_1 \tag{18.35}$$

$$a_7 = \frac{5}{(6)(7)} a_5 = \frac{3 \cdot 5}{7!} a_1 \tag{18.36}$$

$$a_9 = \frac{7}{(8)(9)} a_7 = \frac{3 \cdot 5 \cdot 7}{9!} a_1 \; . \tag{18.37}$$

The solution of the differential equation (18.22) is therefore

$$y = a_0 + a_1\left(x + \frac{1}{3!} x^3 + \frac{3}{5!} x^5 + \frac{3 \cdot 5}{7!} x^7 + \frac{3 \cdot 5 \cdot 7}{9!} x^9 + \cdots\right) . \tag{18.38}$$

This is the complete solution, because it contains two linearly-independent solutions and two arbitrary constants. To determine whether the series converges, apply the ratio test. The ratio of two successive terms is

$$\frac{a_{k+2}}{a_k} x^2 = \frac{kx^2}{(k + 1)(k + 2)} \; . \tag{18.39}$$

Since

$$\lim_{k \to \infty} \left| \frac{kx^2}{(k + 1)(k + 2)} \right| = 0 < 1 \; , \tag{18.40}$$

the series converges. A prize is offered to anyone who can express the series in closed form.

What happens if $m = 1$ is chosen instead of $m = 0$ to satisfy the indicial equation? In this case a_0 is still arbitrary, but Eq. (18.28) requires that a_1 be zero. According to Eq. (18.31) the recursion formula is now

$$a_{k+2} = \frac{k+1}{(k+2)(k+3)} a_k . \tag{18.41}$$

All odd-numbered coefficients are zero, and

$$a_2 = \frac{1}{(2)(3)} a_0 = \frac{1}{3!} a_0 \tag{18.42}$$

$$a_4 = \frac{3}{(4)(5)} a_2 = \frac{3}{5!} a_0 \tag{18.43}$$

$$a_6 = \frac{5}{(6)(7)} a_4 = \frac{3\cdot5}{7!} a_0 . \tag{18.44}$$

According to Eq. (18.20) the series solution of the differential equation is

$$y = a_0\left(x + \frac{1}{3!}x^3 + \frac{3}{5!}x^5 + \frac{3\cdot5}{7!}x^7 + \cdots\right) \tag{18.45}$$

which is only one of the two linearly-independent solutions. In general, an indicial equation like (18.27) does not reveal which value of m will produce the complete solution. For some differential equations, no one value of m produces the complete solution, and more than one must be used.

18.3 Bessel's Equation

Now make a series solution of Bessel's equation

$$x^2 \frac{d^2y}{dx^2} + x\frac{dy}{dx} + (x^2 - n^2)y = 0 , \tag{18.46}$$

again using the series of Eq. (18.20) as the assumed solution. The terms $x\, dy/dx$ and d^2y/dx^2 have already been written out in Eqs. (18.24) and (18.25). In addition,

$$x^2 \frac{d^2y}{dx^2} = m(m-1)a_0x^m + (m+1)ma_1x^{m+1}$$
$$+ (m+2)(m+1)a_2x^{m+2} + \cdots \tag{18.47}$$

and

$$(x^2 - n^2)y = a_0x^{m+2} + a_1x^{m+3} + a_2x^{m+4} + \cdots$$
$$- n^2a_0x^m - n^2a_1x^{m+1} - n^2a_2x^{m+2} - \cdots \qquad (18.48)$$

Substitute these equations into Bessel's equation and equate like powers of x to construct Table 18.2. The recursion formula is

TABLE 18.2. COEFFICIENTS OF POWERS OF X IN THE SERIES SOLUTION OF BESSEL'S EQUATION

Power of x	*Coefficient*	
m	$m(m-1)a_0 + ma_0 - n^2a_0 = (m^2 - n^2)a_0 = 0$	(18.49)
$m+1$	$(m+1)ma_1 + (m+1)a_1 - n^2a_1 = [(m+1)^2 - n^2]a_1 = 0$	(18.50)
$m+2$	$(m+2)(m+1)a_2 + (m+2)a_2 + a_0 - n^2a_2 = [(m+2)^2 - n^2]a_2 + a_0 = 0$	
$m+3$	$(m+3)(m+2)a_3 + (m+3)a_3 + a_1 - n^2a_3 = [(m+3)^2 - n^2]a_3 + a_1 = 0$	(18.51)
·	·	
·	·	
·	·	
$m+k$	$[(m+k)^2 - n^2]a_k + a_{k-2} = 0$	(18.52)

$$a_k = -\frac{1}{(m+k)^2 - n^2}\,a_{k-2}\,. \qquad (18.53)$$

According to the indicial equation (18.49), $m = n$ or $m = -n$. If the choice is $m = n$, the recursion formula becomes

$$a_k = -\frac{a_{k-2}}{(n+k)^2 - n^2} = -\frac{a_{k-2}}{k(2n+k)}\,. \qquad (18.54)$$

Eq. (18.49) shows that a_0 can be chosen arbitrarily, but according to Eq. (18.50), a_1 must be zero. The recursion formula shows that all odd-numbered coefficients a_3, a_5, etc. are zero, and

$$a_2 = -\frac{a_0}{2(2n+2)} = -\frac{a_0}{2^2(n+1)} \qquad (18.55)$$

$$a_4 = -\frac{a_2}{4(2n+4)} = \frac{a_0}{2^2(n+1)(4)(2n+4)} = \frac{a_0}{2^4{\cdot}2!(n+1)(n+2)} \qquad (18.56)$$

$$a_6 = -\frac{a_4}{6(2n+6)} = -\frac{a_0}{2^4{\cdot}2!(n+1)(n+2)(6)(2n+6)}$$

$$= -\frac{a_0}{2^6{\cdot}3!(n+1)(n+2)(n+3)}\,. \qquad (18.57)$$

The assumed solution, Eq. (18.20), becomes

$$y_1(x) = a_0 x^n \left[1 - \frac{x^2}{2^2(n+1)} + \frac{x^4}{2^4 \cdot 2!(n+1)(n+2)} - \frac{x^6}{2^6 \cdot 3!(n+1)(n+2)(n+3)} + \cdots\right]. \tag{18.58}$$

If the choice is $m = -n$, the solution of Bessel's equation is just Eq. (18.58) with n replaced by $-n$:

$$y_2(x) = a_0 x^{-n} \left[1 + \frac{x^2}{2^2(n-1)} + \frac{x^4}{2^4 \cdot 2!(n-1)(n-2)} + \frac{x^6}{2^6 \cdot 3!(n-1)(n-2)(n-3)} + \cdots\right]. \tag{18.59}$$

Both of these series solutions pass the convergence test if n is not an integer. They are linearly independent unless $n = 0$, in which case they are identical. Thus if n is neither zero nor an integer, the complete solution of Bessel's equation is

$$y(x) = k_1 y_1(x) + k_2 y_2(x) . \tag{18.60}$$

The two convergent infinite series might be given names such as Smith and Jones functions. Then the solution is

$$y(x) = k_1 \, \mathrm{Smi}_n(x) + k_2 \, \mathrm{Jon}_n(x) . \tag{18.61}$$

18.4 Bessel Functions of the First Kind

The two solutions can be put in a more convenient form that will not blow up when n is an integer. In Eq. (18.58) let a_0 be the constant

$$a_0 = \frac{1}{2^n \Gamma(n+1)} . \tag{18.62}$$

The gamma function is defined as

$$\Gamma(n) = \int_0^\infty x^{n-1} e^{-x} dx , \quad n > 0 , \tag{18.63}$$

and has the property

$$\Gamma(n+1) = n\Gamma(n) . \tag{18.64}$$

Thus

$$\Gamma(1) = \int_0^\infty e^{-x} dx = 1 , \tag{18.65}$$

$$\Gamma(2) = (1)\Gamma(1) = 1\,, \quad \Gamma(3) = 2\Gamma(2) = 2\,, \quad \Gamma(4) = 3\Gamma(3) = 3!\,, \quad \text{etc.}$$

If n is a positive integer,

$$\Gamma(n + 1) = n! \tag{18.66}$$

The integral in Eq. (18.63) exists only when n is positive. However, the property of Eq. (18.64) can be used to extend the definition to negative values of n. In particular, since

$$\Gamma(1) = 1 = (0)\Gamma(0)\,, \tag{18.67}$$

$\Gamma(0)$ is infinite. Similarly,

$$\Gamma(0) = (-1)\Gamma(-1) \tag{18.68}$$

and $\Gamma(-1)$ is infinite. The gamma function of zero and every negative integer is infinite. Fig. 18.1 shows a plot of the gamma function.

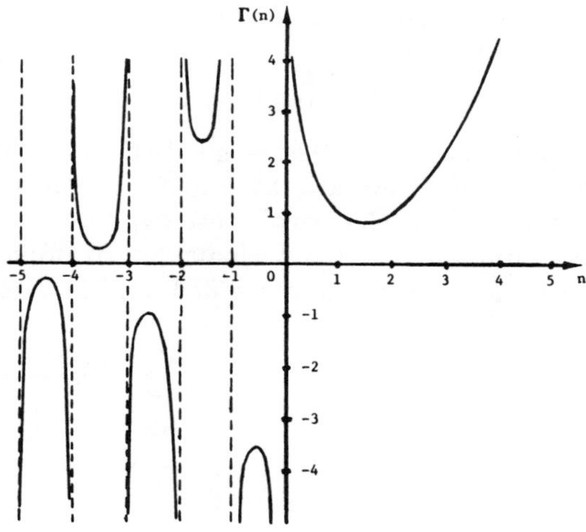

Fig. 18.1. The gamma function.

With a_0 replaced by the new constant given in Eq. (18.62), the first solution of Bessel's equation, Eq. (18.58), becomes

$$J_n(x) = x^n \left[\frac{1}{2^n\Gamma(n+1)} - \frac{x^2}{2^{n+2}(n+1)\Gamma(n+1)} + \frac{x^4}{2^{n+4}\cdot 2!(n+1)(n+2)\Gamma(n+1)} - \frac{x^6}{2^{n+6}\cdot 3!(n+1)(n+2)(n+3)\Gamma(n+1)} + \cdots \right]$$

or

$$J_n(x) = x^n \sum_{m=0}^{\infty} \frac{(-1)^m x^{2m}}{2^{2m+n} m! \Gamma(m + n + 1)} . \tag{18.69}$$

The function defined by this series is called the *Bessel function of the first kind of order n*. The second solution of Bessel's equation, Eq. (18.59), is the first solution with n replaced by $-n$. Now if Eq. (18.62) is applied with n replaced by $-n$, Eq. (18.59) becomes Eq. (18.69) with n replaced by $-n$:

$$J_{-n}(x) = x^{-n} \sum_{m=0}^{\infty} \frac{(-1)^m x^{2m}}{2^{2m-n} m! \Gamma(m - n + 1)} . \tag{18.70}$$

Both of the last two equations pass the ratio test of convergence. And unlike Eqs. (18.58) and (18.59) they exist even when n is an integer, because the gamma function is never zero. If n is not zero or an integer the two solutions are linearly independent, and the general solution of Bessel's equation (18.46) is

$$y(x) = A_1 J_n(x) + A_2 J_{-n}(x) . \tag{18.71}$$

The Bessel functions of the first kind $J_0(x)$ and $J_1(x)$ appear frequently in engineering. They are tabulated like sines and cosines in handbooks such as Ref. 69. Curves of these two functions are shown in Fig. 18.2. Bessel functions are not periodic. For example, the first four zeros of $J_0(x)$ are at $x = 2.405$, 5.520, 8.654, and 11.792.

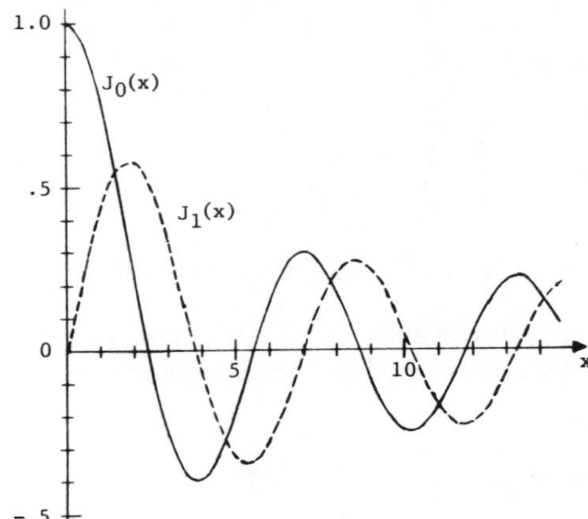

Fig. 18.2. Two Bessel functions of the first kind.

Unfortunately, the two solutions $J_n(x)$ and $J_{-n}(x)$ are linearly dependent if n is zero or a positive integer. (Negative integers are of no concern because n appears squared in Bessel's equation.) The reason can be seen by looking at Eq. (18.70). For $m = 0,1,2, \ldots, n - 1$, the value of $m - n + 1$ is zero or a negative integer, and $\Gamma(m - n + 1)$ is infinite. The first n terms of the series are therefore zero, and the series can be written as

$$J_{-n}(x) = x^{-n} \sum_{m=n}^{\infty} \frac{(-1)^m x^{2m}}{2^{2m-n} m! \Gamma(m - n + 1)} . \tag{18.72}$$

Let $s = m - n$. Then

$$J_{-n}(x) = x^{-n} \sum_{s=0}^{\infty} \frac{(-1)^{s+n} x^{2(s+n)}}{2^{2s+n} (s + n)! \Gamma(s + 1)} . \tag{18.73}$$

Now

$$\begin{aligned} (s + n)!\Gamma(s + 1) &= s!(s + 1)\Gamma(s + 1)(s + 2)(s + 3) \cdots (s + n) \\ &= s!(s + 2)\Gamma(s + 2)(s + 3) \cdots (s + n) \\ &= \cdots \\ &= s!\Gamma(s + n + 1) . \end{aligned} \tag{18.74}$$

Therefore

$$J_{-n}(x) = (-1)^n x^n \sum_{s=0}^{\infty} \frac{(-1)^s x^{2s}}{2^{2s+n} s! \Gamma(s + n + 1)} . \tag{18.75}$$

Comparison of this equation to (18.69) shows that if n is zero or a positive integer,

$$J_{-n}(x) = (-1)^n J_n(x) , \quad n = 0,1,2, \ldots \tag{18.76}$$

The two solutions are certainly not independent.

18.5 Bessel Functions of the Second Kind

How can a second solution of Bessel's equation be found that is linearly independent of the first solution for integral values of n? One way is the method of variation of parameters. Assume a solution

$$Y_n(x) = U(x) J_n(x) \tag{18.77}$$

and then determine the function $U(x)$ so that $Y_n(x)$ satisfies Bessel's equation. The derivatives of the assumed solution are

$$Y_n' = \frac{dY_n(x)}{dx} = UJ_n' + U'J_n \tag{18.78}$$

and

$$Y_n'' = UJ_n'' + 2U'J_n' + U''J_n . \tag{18.79}$$

Substituting these into Bessel's differential equation (18.46) yields

$$x^2(UJ_n'' + 2U'J_n' + U''J_n) + x(UJ_n' + U'J_n) + (x^2 - n^2)UJ_n = 0 \quad (18.80)$$

or

$$x^2J_nU'' + (2x^2J_n' + xJ_n)U' + [x^2J_n'' + xJ_n' + (x^2 - n^2)J_n]U = 0\,. \quad (18.81)$$

Since $J_n(x)$ is a solution of Bessel's equation, the coefficient of U is zero, and this equation reduces to

$$x^2J_n\frac{dU'}{dx} + (2x^2J_n' + xJ_n)U' = 0\,. \quad (18.82)$$

Multiplying thru by $dx/(x^2J_nU')$ produces

$$\frac{dU'}{U'} + \left[\frac{2J_n'(x)}{J_n(x)} + \frac{1}{x}\right]dx = 0\,. \quad (18.83)$$

The integral of this equation is

$$\ln U' + 2\ln J_n(x) + \ln x = \ln k_1 \quad (18.84)$$

or

$$U'(x) = \frac{k_1}{xJ_n^2(x)}\,. \quad (18.85)$$

Then

$$U(x) = k_1\int\frac{dx}{xJ_n^2(x)} + k_2\,. \quad (18.86)$$

Now the assumed solution of Bessel's equation, Eq. (18.77), becomes

$$Y_n(x) = k_1\,J_n(x)\int\frac{dx}{xJ_n^2(x)} + k_2\,J_n(x)\,. \quad (18.87)$$

For the commonly-accepted values of k_1 and k_2, this equation becomes

$$Y_n(x) = \frac{J_n(x)\cos n\pi - J_{-n}(x)}{\sin n\pi}\,. \quad (18.88)$$

This is the *Bessel function of the second kind of order n*. It is also called the *Neumann function*, $N_n(x)$. It is linearly independent of $J_n(x)$ for all values of n. The general solution of Bessel's equation is therefore

$$y(x) = c_1\,J_n(x) + c_2\,Y_n(x)\,. \quad (18.89)$$

The more frequently-used functions $Y_0(x)$ and $Y_1(x)$ are tabulated in handbooks. Fig. 18.3 shows the curves of these functions. The functions

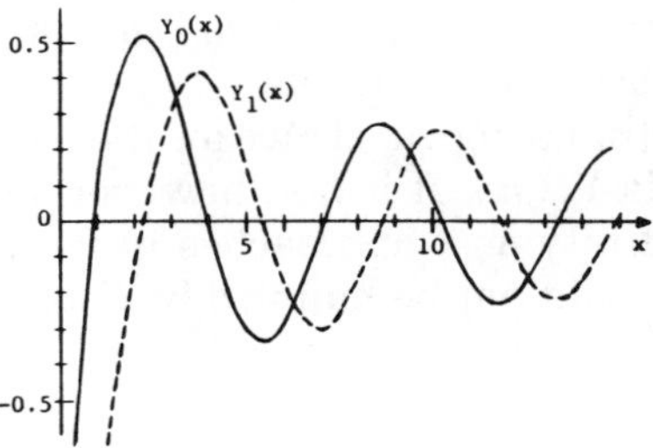

Fig. 18.3. Two Bessel functions of the second kind.

$Y_n(x)$ frequently disappear from the solutions of boundary-value problems, because they all approach plus or minus infinity as x approaches zero.

18.6 Other Bessel Functions

Numerous variations of Bessel functions have been developed to handle particular problems. One such variation is the *Hankel functions*, or *Bessel functions of the third kind of order n*, defined as

$$H_n^{(1)}(x) = J_n(x) + jY_n(x) \tag{18.90}$$

$$H_n^{(2)}(x) = J_n(x) - jY_n(x)\ . \tag{18.91}$$

They arise in the solution of the wave equation in cylindrical coordinates. The solution of the ordinary differential equation in r is

$$A_1H_n^{(1)}(kr) + A_2H_n^{(2)}(kr)\ , \tag{18.92}$$

where A_1 and A_2 are real constants.

If Bessel's equation is in the form

$$x^2\frac{d^2y}{dx^2} + x\frac{dy}{dx} - (x^2 + n^2)y = 0\ , \tag{18.93}$$

the solution is

$$y = A_1J_n(jx) + A_2Y_n(jx)\ . \tag{18.94}$$

Then the *modified Bessel function of the first kind of order n* is useful:

$$I_n(x) = j^{-n}J_n(jx)\ . \tag{18.95}$$

When jx is imaginary, $I_n(x)$ is real. The relationship between these two functions is something like that between $\cos jx$ and $\cosh x$, namely

$$\cosh x = \cos jx\ . \tag{18.96}$$

Fig. 18.2 shows that $J_n(x)$ is oscillatory or "cos-like." On the other hand, $I_n(x)$ is non-oscillatory and "cosh-like."

One might think that a logical choice for the modified Bessel function of the second kind is $Y_n(jx)$. It is not, however, because both $I_n(x)$ and $Y_n(jx)$ approach infinity as x approaches infinity. Problems in which $y(\infty)$ is not infinite could not be handled by this combination. Instead, use

$$K_n(x) = \frac{\pi}{2} j^{n+1} H_n^{(1)}(jx) \tag{18.97}$$

and write the solution of the Eq. (18.93) version of Bessel's equation as

$$y = c_1\, I_n(x) + c_2\, K_n(x)\,. \tag{18.98}$$

In the calculation of the current density in round conductors carrying alternating current, Bessel's equation appears in the form

$$x^2 \frac{d^2y}{dx^2} + x\,\frac{dy}{dx} - jx^2 y = 0\,. \tag{18.99}$$

Its solution is

$$y = A_1\, J_0(j^{3/2}x) + A_2\, K_0(j^{1/2}x)\,. \tag{18.100}$$

To handle the complex functions $J_0(j^{3/2}x)$ and $K_0(j^{1/2}x)$, define the *ber, bei, ker,* and *kei functions:*

$$\mathrm{ber}_n x + j\,\mathrm{bei}_n x = J_n(j^{3/2}x) \tag{18.101}$$

$$\mathrm{ker}_n x + j\,\mathrm{kei}_n x = j^{-n}\, K_n(j^{1/2}x)\,. \tag{18.102}$$

All four of the new functions are real.

18.7 Derivatives of Bessel Functions

Differentiating the formula for $J_n(x)$, Eq. (18.69), produces two useful derivatives:

$$\frac{d}{dx}\,[x^n J_n(kx)] = kx^n J_{n-1}(kx) \tag{18.103}$$

$$\frac{d}{dx}\,[x^{-n} J_n(kx)] = -\,kx^{-n} J_{n+1}(kx)\,. \tag{18.104}$$

The reader is invited to verify Eq. (18.103) by substituting Eq. (18.69) into its left side, and performing the differentiation.

18.8 Orthogonality of Bessel Functions

Bessel functions have the useful property of orthogonality, much like that of sines and cosines. In a product solution of a partial differential equation such as Laplace's equation, the function sin kx frequently appears, k being a separation constant. A boundary condition may make sin $kx = 0$ when $x = a$. Then

$$\sin ka = 0 \,, \qquad \text{or} \qquad ka = m\pi$$

and

$$k = \frac{m\pi}{a} \,, \qquad m = 0,1,2, \ldots \tag{18.105}$$

The application of another boundary condition might take advantage of the orthogonality of sine functions:

$$\int_0^a \sin\frac{m\pi x}{a} \sin\frac{n\pi x}{a}\, dx = \delta_{mn}\frac{a}{2} \tag{18.106}$$

where

$$\begin{aligned} \delta_{mn} &= 0 \,, \qquad m \neq n \\ &= 1 \,, \qquad m = n \,. \end{aligned}$$

Similarly, a product solution may contain the term $J_n(kr)$. A boundary condition may require that $J_n(kr) = 0$ when $r = R$. Then

$$J_n(kR) = 0 \,, \qquad \text{and} \qquad k = k_1, k_2, \ldots k_r, \ldots \tag{18.107}$$

where $k_r R$ is the rth zero of $J_n(kR)$. Now the values of the separation constant k are known. Application of a second boundary condition might make use of the orthogonality of Bessel functions. Two forms are available. If $k_r R$ and $k_s R$ are zeros number r and s of $J_n(kR)$,

$$\int_0^R x J_n(k_r x) J_n(k_s x) dx = \delta_{rs}\frac{R^2}{2} J_{n+1}^2(k_r R) \,. \tag{18.108}$$

Alternatively, if k_r and k_s are roots of the equation

$$\frac{d}{dx} J_n(kx)\big|_{x=R} = J_n'(kR) = 0 \,, \tag{18.109}$$

then

$$\int_0^R x J_n(k_r x) J_n(k_s x) dx = \delta_{rs}\frac{(k_r R)^2 - n^2}{2k_r^2} J_n^2(k_r R) \,. \tag{18.110}$$

Notice that the Bessel functions, unlike sines and cosines, are orthogonal with respect to a weighting function x.

Bessel functions, sines, cosines, and the solutions of many second-order linear differential equations have similar properties. They are explained in a neat package of mathematics called Sturm-Liouville theory.

18.9 An Example

An example will illustrate the utility of Bessel functions. Compute the steady-state temperature distribution throughout the interior of the right circular cylinder of radius R and height L shown in Fig. 18.4. The

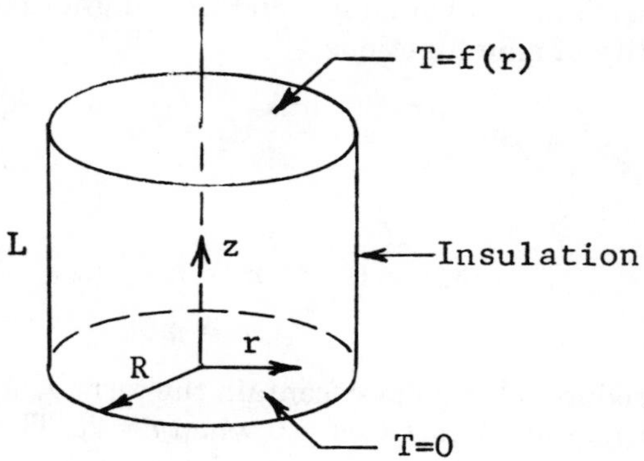

Fig. 18.4. A heated cylinder.

bottom is at zero temperature, the side is insulated, and the temperature across the top has a known distribution $f(r)$. The temperature in the cylinder is governed by Laplace's equation

$$\nabla^2 T(r,z) = 0 , \qquad 0 \leqslant r \leqslant R , \qquad 0 \leqslant z \leqslant L . \tag{18.111}$$

Since the cylinder has a circular cross section, the temperature is not a function of θ. According to Fourier's law of heat conduction, the rate of flow of heat flux density in any given direction, say the r direction, is

$$q_r'' = -\, k \frac{\partial T}{\partial r} \qquad W/m^2 , \tag{18.112}$$

where k is thermal conductivity. Since no heat flows thru the side of the cylinder, $q_r''(R,z) = 0$. With the abbreviation $T_r = \partial T/\partial r$, this boundary condition is

$$T_r(R,z) = 0 , \qquad 0 \leqslant z \leqslant L . \tag{18.113}$$

The other boundary conditions are

$$T(r,0) = 0\,, \qquad 0 \leqslant r \leqslant R \tag{18.114}$$

and

$$T(r,L) = f(r)\,, \qquad 0 \leqslant r \leqslant R\,. \tag{18.115}$$

With no θ variation, Laplace's equation in cylindrical coordinates is

$$\frac{\partial^2 T}{\partial r^2} + \frac{1}{r}\,\frac{\partial T}{\partial r} + \frac{\partial^2 T}{\partial z^2} = 0\,. \tag{18.116}$$

Assume the product solution

$$T(r,z) = R(r)Y(z)\,, \tag{18.117}$$

substitute it into Laplace's equation, and separate the variables to get

$$\frac{1}{R}\,\frac{\partial^2 R}{\partial r^2} + \frac{1}{rR}\,\frac{\partial R}{\partial r} = -\,\frac{1}{Y}\,\frac{\partial^2 Y}{\partial z^2} = -\,k^2\,. \tag{18.118}$$

The solution of the ordinary differential equation in z is

$$Y = A \sinh kz + B \cosh kz\,. \tag{18.119}$$

The ordinary differential equation in r is

$$r^2\,\frac{d^2R}{dr^2} + r\,\frac{dR}{dr} + k^2r^2R = 0\,. \tag{18.120}$$

This is Bessel's equation in the form of Eq. (18.13) with $n = 0$. Its solution, according to Eq. (18.89), is

$$R = C\,J_0(kr) + DY_0(kr)\,. \tag{18.121}$$

The solutions for $k = 0$ are special cases, but will not be needed in this problem. The product solution of Laplace's equation is therefore

$$T(r,z) = \sum_k (A_k \sinh kz + B_k \cosh kz)[C_kJ_0(kr) + D_kY_0(kr)]\,. \tag{18.122}$$

Fig. 18.3 shows that $Y_0(kr)$ is infinite at $r = 0$. Since the temperature is not infinite along the axis of the cylinder, each D_k is zero, and

$$T(r,z) = \sum_k J_0(kr)(A_k \sinh kz + B_k \cosh kz)\,. \tag{18.123}$$

According to the second boundary condition (18.114),

$$T(r,0) = \sum_k J_0(kr)B_k = 0\,, \tag{18.124}$$

and each B_k is therefore zero. Eq. (18.123) reduces to

$$T(r,z) = \sum_k A_k J_0(kr) \sinh kz . \tag{18.125}$$

To apply the first boundary condition (18.113), observe that

$$T_r(r,z) = \sum_k A_k \left[\frac{d}{dr} J_0(kr)\right] \sinh kz . \tag{18.126}$$

Then

$$T_r(R,z) = \sum_k A_k J_0'(kR) \sinh kz = 0 , \tag{18.127}$$

and therefore

$$J_0'(kR) = 0 . \tag{18.128}$$

According to Eq. (18.104),

$$J_1(kR) = 0 . \tag{18.129}$$

If k_1R, k_2R, . . . are the successive roots of this equation, that can be found in Ref. 69, page 166,

$$k = k_n , \qquad n = 1,2, \ldots \tag{18.130}$$

and according to Eq. (18.125),

$$T(r,z) = \sum_{n=1}^{\infty} A_n J_0(k_n r) \sinh k_n z . \tag{18.131}$$

Application of the third boundary condition (18.115) produces

$$T(r,L) = \sum_{n=1}^{\infty} A_n J_0(k_n r) \sinh k_n L = f(r) . \tag{18.132}$$

Now the orthogonality of Bessel functions is useful. Multiply both sides of this equation by $rJ_0(k_m r)$, where m is an integer, and integrate:

$$\int_0^R r J_0(k_m r) \sum_{n=1}^{\infty} A_n J_0(k_n r) \sinh k_n L \, dr = \int_0^R r f(r) J_0(k_m r) dr . \tag{18.133}$$

According to Eqs. (18.109) and (18.110), if $J_0'(k_n R) = 0$,

$$\int_0^R r J_0(k_n r) J_0(k_m r) dr = \delta_{mn} \frac{R^2}{2} J_0^2(k_n R) . \tag{18.134}$$

Eq. (18.133) becomes

$$A_m \frac{R^2}{2} J_0^2(k_m R) \sinh k_m L = \int_0^R r f(r) J_0(k_m r) dr \qquad (18.135)$$

and

$$A_m = \frac{2}{R^2 J_0^2(k_m R) \sinh k_m L} \int_0^R r f(r) J_0(k_m r) dr . \qquad (18.136)$$

Each coefficient A_m can be evaluated by this formula. The integration can be performed numerically if necessary. The temperature anywhere in the cylinder is then found from Eq. (18.131).

Chapter 19

LINEAR PROGRAMMING

19.1 Introduction

Mathematical programming is the name given to the techniques for finding the optimal value (maximum or minimum) of a function of several variables, subject to constraints on the variables. The function to be optimized is called the *objective function*. One of the techniques, *linear programming*, is the process of minimizing an objective function that is a linear combination of the variables, subject to constraints that are also linear combinations of the variables. Although the technique is limited to a narrow class of problems, it deserves study for two reasons:

1. Many real programming problems in engineering, manufacturing, and commerce are linear, or can be made linear with a few judicious assumptions.

2. A straightforward and efficient technique for solving linear-programming problems, called the *simplex method*, was developed by George B. Dantzig in 1947.

The simplex method has been refined, modified, and thoroughly investigated mathematically. The work up to 1963 is reported in Dantzig's *Linear Programming and Extensions* (Ref. 19). This chapter will explain the simplex method, a modification called the *revised simplex method*, and a computer program of the revised simplex method that is available in the General Electric time-sharing library.

19.2 A Typical Problem

This study of linear programming begins with a simple but typical problem. The manager of an aircraft-engine testing laboratory is preparing an appropriation request for oscillographs. His study of requirements for the next few years has produced these facts:

1. Oscillographs are available with one or six channels. They cost \$1500 and \$7000, respectively.

2. One large measurement project is anticipated that will require 100 channels.

3. Many 8-channel jobs are anticipated, so that at least two single-channel machines should be available for each 6-channel machine.

4. The budget allows \$200,000 for oscillographs.

How many of each size should the manager request to minimize the investment?

To put the problem in mathematical form, let x_1 and x_2 be the number of 1 and 6-channel oscillographs, respectively. The manager wants to minimize the total cost z, which according to fact 1 is $1500\,x_1 + 7000\,x_2$. The problem is

$$\text{minimize} \quad z = 1500\,x_1 + 7000\,x_2 \tag{19.1}$$

$$\text{subject to} \quad x_1 + 6\,x_2 \geqslant 100\,, \tag{19.2}$$

$$x_1 \geqslant 2\,x_2 \quad \text{or} \quad x_1 - 2\,x_2 \geqslant 0\,, \tag{19.3}$$

$$1500\,x_1 + 7000\,x_2 \leqslant 200{,}000\,, \tag{19.4}$$

$$\text{and} \quad x_1, x_2 \geqslant 0\,. \tag{19.5}$$

This simple problem is solved graphically in Fig. 19.1. The lines repre-

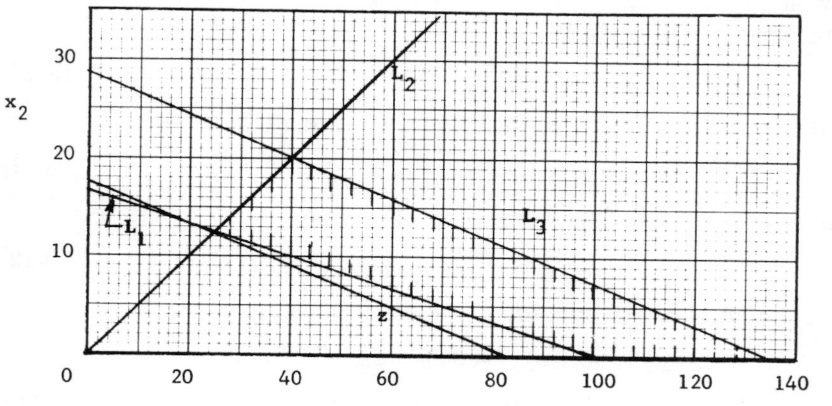

Fig. 19.1. Graphical solution of a two-variable problem.

senting the limits of the constraints are

$$L_1\colon \quad x_1 + 6\,x_2 = 100 \tag{19.6}$$

$$L_2\colon \quad x_1 - 2\,x_2 = 0 \tag{19.7}$$

$$L_3\colon \quad 1500\,x_1 + 7000\,x_2 = 200{,}000\,. \tag{19.8}$$

The variables x_1 and x_2 are constrained to lie within the area outlined with hatch marks. The objective function z is represented by the line shown in Fig. 19.1 or any line parallel to it. Clearly z has its minimum allowable value when its line intersects the left corner of the constraint region. This is the intersection of L_1 and L_1, where $x_1 = 25$, $x_2 = 12.5$. Since the variables in this problem are integers, round x_2 down to 12. The minimum value of the objective function is then

$$z = (1500)(25) + (7000)(12) = \$121{,}500 \,. \tag{19.9}$$

The problem of rounding off fractional assignments of integral variables is sometimes not simple, and is the subject of *integer programming*. Notice that the minimum value of the objective function z was found at one of the vertices of the polygon-shaped constraint region. In any such two-dimensional problem the solution is at a vertex, unless the line representing the minimum z coincides with one of the constraint lines. The same idea will apply in problems with more than two variables.

19.3 The Standard Form

If a linear-programming problem has more than two variables, the graphical method is difficult and a mathematical solution is preferable. To begin, first write the constraints as *equalities* whose variables are all non-negative. This is accomplished by adding *slack variables*. The "greater-than" constraint

$$x_1 + 6\,x_2 \geqslant 100 \tag{19.10}$$

is made an equality by subtracting the slack variable x_3:

$$x_1 + 6\,x_2 - x_3 = 100 \,. \tag{19.11}$$

Notice that $x_3 \geqslant 0$. The "less-than" constraint

$$1500\,x_1 + 7000\,x_2 \leqslant 200{,}000 \tag{19.12}$$

is made an equality by *adding* the slack variable x_5:

$$1500\,x_1 + 7000\,x_2 + x_5 = 200{,}000 \,. \tag{19.13}$$

The oscillograph problem is put into standard form by the addition of the slack variables x_3, x_4, and x_5, and becomes

$$\text{minimize} \quad z = 1500\,x_1 + 7000\,x_2 \tag{19.14}$$

$$\text{subject to} \quad x_1 + 6\,x_2 - x_3 = 100 \tag{19.15}$$

$$x_1 - 2\,x_2 - x_4 = 0 \tag{19.16}$$

$$1500\,x_1 + 7000\,x_2 + x_5 = 200{,}000 \,. \tag{19.17}$$

The standard form of a linear-programming problem is

$$\text{minimize} \quad z = \mathbf{c}^T\mathbf{x} \tag{19.18}$$

$$\text{subject to} \quad \mathbf{Ax} = \mathbf{b} \tag{19.19}$$

$$\text{and} \quad x_i \geqslant 0, \quad i = 1,2, \ldots n\,. \tag{19.20}$$

where $\mathbf{x}$ is a vector whose elements are the n variables, $\mathbf{c}$ is an n-dimensional vector of the coefficients in the objective function, and Eq. (19.19) is the constraint equations written in matrix form. If there are m constraints, $\mathbf{A}$ is an $m \times n$ matrix, and $\mathbf{b}$ is an m-dimensional vector. For the oscillograph problem,

$$\mathbf{c} = \begin{bmatrix} 1500 \\ 7000 \\ 0 \\ 0 \\ 0 \end{bmatrix}, \quad \mathbf{A} = \begin{bmatrix} 1 & 6 & -1 & 0 & 0 \\ 1 & -2 & 0 & -1 & 0 \\ 1500 & 7000 & 0 & 0 & 1 \end{bmatrix}, \quad \mathbf{b} = \begin{bmatrix} 100 \\ 0 \\ 200{,}000 \end{bmatrix}. \tag{19.21}$$

After the slack variables are added, linear programming is the process of solving m simultaneous linear algebraic equations with n (more than m) unknowns. Of the infinity of solutions, choose the one that minimizes the objective function z. If the physical problem at hand is to *maximize* the linear sum of the variables $\mathbf{c}^T\mathbf{x}$, this sum is put into standard form by reversing its sign. The problem is solved by minimizing $\mathbf{z} = -\,\mathbf{c}^T\mathbf{x}$.

19.4 The Canonical Form

The various solutions of the linear-programming problem have special names. Any n-dimensional vector $\mathbf{x}$ that satisfies the constraints in standard form, Eq. (19.19), is said to be a *solution.* If in addition all the variables x_i are non-negative, it is called a *feasible solution.* If at least n-m of the variables are zero, it is a *basic solution.* If the non-zero variables are all positive, it is a *basic feasible* solution.The optimal solution is always a basic feasible solution. An example is given by the oscillograph problem, for which $m = 3$ and $n = 5$. The graphical solution showed that $x_1 = 25$ and $x_2 = 12.5$. According to Eqs. (19.15), (19.16), and (19.17), $x_3 = 0$, $x_4 = 0$, and $x_5 = 75{,}000$. The optimal solution is the basic feasible solution

$$\mathbf{x} = \begin{bmatrix} x_1 \\ x_2 \\ x_3 \\ x_4 \\ x_5 \end{bmatrix} = \begin{bmatrix} 25 \\ 12.5 \\ 0 \\ 0 \\ 75{,}000 \end{bmatrix}. \tag{19.22}$$

The *n-m* variables at zero are called *non-basic variables*, and the remaining m are called *basic variables*. The basic solution for any choice of basic variables is easily found from the constraints. For example, suppose that the problem is

$$\text{minimize} \quad z = -2x_1 - 3x_2 \tag{19.23}$$

$$\text{subject to} \quad 2x_1 - 3x_2 - x_3 = -6 \tag{19.24}$$

$$3x_1 + 2x_2 + x_4 = 6 \tag{19.25}$$

$$x_1 + x_2 - x_5 = 1 \tag{19.26}$$

$$\text{and} \quad x_i \geqslant 0, \quad i = 1,2,3,4,5\,. \tag{19.27}$$

To find the basic solution for the basic variables x_1, x_2, x_5, set the non-basic variables at zero to obtain m equations and m unknowns. Here $m = 3$, and

$$\begin{bmatrix} 2 & -3 & 0 \\ 3 & 2 & 0 \\ 1 & 1 & -1 \end{bmatrix} \begin{bmatrix} x_1 \\ x_2 \\ x_5 \end{bmatrix} = \begin{bmatrix} -6 \\ 6 \\ 1 \end{bmatrix}. \tag{19.28}$$

The square $m \times m$ matrix of the remaining coefficients is called the **B** *matrix*. The columns of the **B** matrix constitute a basis if the matrix is non-singular. In linear programming the word "basis" is used to denote specifically the columns of the **B** matrix. Eq. (19.28) can be written as

$$\mathbf{B}\,\mathbf{x} = \mathbf{b}\,. \tag{19.29}$$

Then

$$\mathbf{x} = \mathbf{B}^{-1}\,\mathbf{b} = \begin{bmatrix} 6/13 \\ 30/13 \\ 23/13 \end{bmatrix} \tag{19.30}$$

and the basic solution is the 5-dimensional vector

$$\mathbf{x}^T = \left[\frac{6}{13}, \frac{30}{13}, 0, 0, \frac{23}{13}\right]. \tag{19.31}$$

The solution of a linear program by the simplex method starts with a display of the standard form in a special arrangement called the *canonical form*. First a basis is chosen. Then the equations are written so that each basic variable appears in only one constraint equation with a coefficient of unity, each constraint equation contains only one basic variable, and none of the basic variables is in the objective function. For example, the canonical form of the problem of Eqs. (19.23) thru (19.27), for the basic variables x_1, x_2, x_5, is

$$\text{minimize} \qquad z = -\frac{102}{13} + \frac{5}{13}x_3 + \frac{12}{13}x_4 \tag{19.32}$$

$$\text{subject to} \qquad \begin{bmatrix} 1 & 0 & -\frac{2}{13} & \frac{3}{13} & 0 \\ 0 & 1 & \frac{3}{13} & \frac{2}{13} & 0 \\ 0 & 0 & \frac{1}{13} & \frac{5}{13} & 1 \end{bmatrix} \begin{bmatrix} x_1 \\ x_2 \\ x_3 \\ x_4 \\ x_5 \end{bmatrix} = \begin{bmatrix} \frac{6}{13} \\ \frac{30}{13} \\ \frac{23}{13} \end{bmatrix} . \tag{19.33}$$

Notice that the **B** matrix is now a unit matrix, and the basic solution (19.31) can be written by inspection. Notice also that the value of the objective function (19.32) for this basis is the constant term, because the non-basic variables are zero. The shrewd reader will see that this is the optimal solution. For any other feasible solution, x_3 or x_4 will be greater than zero, and z will rise from its minimum value of $-102/13$.

19.5 Hyperplanes and Vertices

Is there a systematic way to search for the optimal solution of a linear program? Consider the simple problem

$$\text{minimize} \qquad z = x_1 + x_2 \tag{19.34}$$

$$\text{subject to} \qquad x_1 + x_2 + x_3 = 1, \tag{19.35}$$

$$\text{and} \qquad x_i \geqslant 0, \quad i = 1,2,3 . \tag{19.36}$$

The single constraint equation forms the triangular plane shown in Fig. 19.2. Any point on the plane is a solution. Notice that $m = 1, n = 3$, and

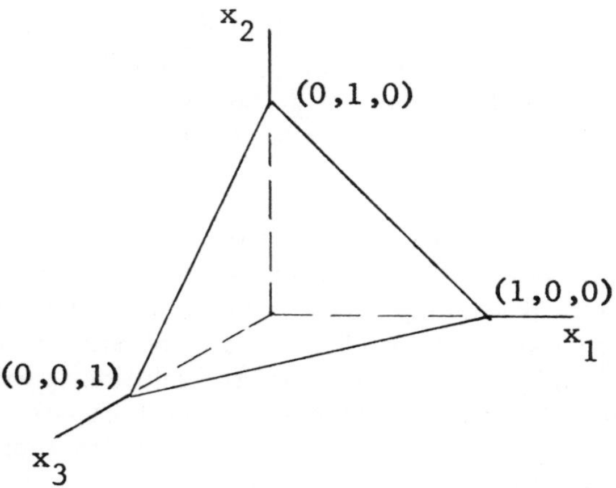

Fig. 19.2. Single constraint plane.

there are 3 basic solutions, all 3 of which are feasible. The optimal solution is $\mathbf{x}^T = [0,0,1]$, for which $z = 0$.

Another simple problem is

$$\text{minimize} \quad z = x_2 + x_3 \tag{19.37}$$

$$\text{subject to} \quad x_1 + x_3 = 2 \tag{19.38}$$

$$2\,x_2 + x_3 = 4 \tag{19.39}$$

$$\text{and} \quad x_i \geqslant 0, \quad i = 1,2,3\ . \tag{19.40}$$

Now $m = 2$ and $n = 3$. The two constraint planes are shown in Fig. 19.3.

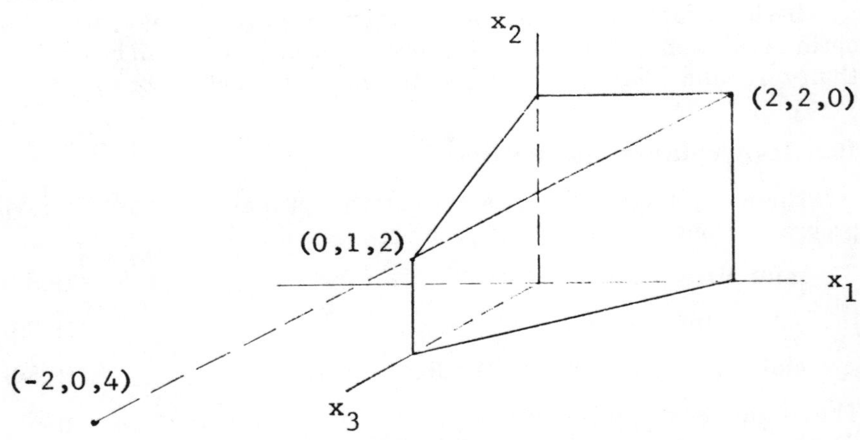

Fig. 19.3. Two constraint planes.

The solutions must lie on the intersection of the two planes. There are 3 basic solutions, 2 of which are feasible. One of the latter, $\mathbf{x}^T = [2,2,0]$, is the optimal solution, for which $z = 2$. Suppose a third constraint equation is included with (19.38) and (19.39), namely

$$x_1 + x_2 = 2\ . \tag{19.41}$$

Now $m = 3$ and $n = 3$. The three constraint planes represented by Eqs. (19.38), (19.39), and (19.41) intersect at only one point, where $\mathbf{x}^T = [2/3,4/3,4/3]$. This is the only solution, and of course $z = 8/3$.

The set of feasible solutions of the constraint equations is called the *solution space*. In these three examples the solution space is a plane, a line, and a point. The number of dimensions of this space is n-m. In each case the solution space is bounded by the planes representing the constraints, including the three planes $x_1 = 0$, $x_2 = 0$, $x_3 = 0$. Because of the feasibility requirement $x_i \geqslant 0$, the solution space lies in the first octant. Suppose the constraint equations include four variables instead of three. Each constraint now describes a 3-dimensional space or hyperplane. These hyperplanes lie in a 4-dimensional coordinate system having the axes x_1, x_2, x_3, and x_4. The solution space is in the first *orthant*. The intersection of two constraints is now a plane, and the intersection of three constraints is a line. The solution space can be a point, a line, a plane, or a 3-dimensional hyperplane or polyhedron, depending on the number of constraints. If there are five variables, the intersection of two constraints is a 3-dimensional hyperplane, and the solution space can have up to four dimensions. Although the physical picture is now impossible to see, two tentative generalizations are possible:

1. If there are m constraints and n variables, n-m of the coordinates of each vertex of the solution space are zero. That is, each vertex is a basic feasible solution of the constraints.

2. The optimal solution is a basic feasible solution.

19.6 Convex Sets

Another essential property of the solution space is that it is convex. An n-dimensional vector $\mathbf{y}$ is a *convex combination* of the vectors $\mathbf{x}_1$, $\mathbf{x}_2, \ldots \mathbf{x}_n$ if it is a linear combination of the $\mathbf{x}_i$'s, and the coefficients are all non-negative and add up to unity:

$$\mathbf{y} = k_1\,\mathbf{x}_1 + k_2\,\mathbf{x}_2 + \cdots + k_n\,\mathbf{x}_n\,, \tag{19.42}$$

$$k_1 + k_2 + \cdots + k_n = 1, \tag{19.43}$$

and

$$0 \leq k_i \leq 1, \quad i = 1,2, \ldots n\,. \tag{19.44}$$

Fig. 19.4 shows a two-dimensional vector $\mathbf{y}$ that is a convex combination of vectors $\mathbf{x}_1$ and $\mathbf{x}_2$:

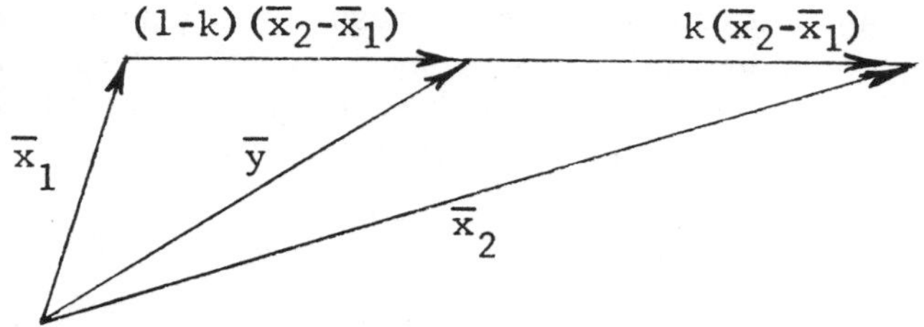

Fig. 19.4. Convex combination of vectors.

$$\mathbf{y} = k\,\mathbf{x}_1 + (1 - k)\,\mathbf{x}_2 \,. \tag{19.45}$$

This can be written as

$$\mathbf{y} = \mathbf{x}_1 + (1 - k)(\mathbf{x}_2 - \mathbf{x}_1) = \mathbf{x}_2 - k(\mathbf{x}_2 - \mathbf{x}_1)\,. \tag{19.46}$$

For any value of k between 0 and 1, the tip of vector $\mathbf{y}$ lies on the straight line joining vectors $\mathbf{x}_1$ and $\mathbf{x}_2$. The numbers representing the vectors are also the coordinates of their tips. Thus the point $\mathbf{y}$ is a convex combination of the two points $\mathbf{x}_1$ and $\mathbf{x}_2$ if it lies on the straight line segment joining them. A set of points is said to be convex if it contains every convex combination of every pair of its elements, i.e., if it includes every point on the line segment between any two points in the set. Fig. 19.5 shows the boundaries of two sets of points in two-dimensional

Fig. 19.5. Convex and non-convex sets.

space, only one of which is convex. In general, a set of points in n-dimensional space is convex if it contains every convex combination of every pair of its elements.

Fig. 19.5 shows that any point on a side of the convex polygon is a convex combination of two vertices, and every point within the polygon lies on a straight segment joining two sides. Thus every point is a convex combination of at most four vertices. A convex set of points in 3-dimensional space, whose boundaries are planes, is a polyhedron. Every point within the polyhedron is a convex combination of vertices. The preceding section explained that the solution space of a linear program is a multidimensional polyhedron, and decided tentatively that the vertices of the solution space are basic feasible solutions. The conclusion is that every feasible solution (i.e., every point within the polyhedron) is a convex combination of basic feasible solutions. References 19, 51, and 138 confirm this conclusion with algebraic proofs.

19.7 The Simplex Method

The objective function of a linear program is a hyperplane in the n-dimensional space. The optimal solution occurs when the hyperplane just touches a corner of the polyhedron that constitutes the solution space. A reader who has followed this argument therefore expects that the optimal solution of the program is a basic feasible solution. This expectation is correct. References 19, 51, and 138 prove algebraically that if a linear program is formulated so that the objective function has a minimum value, this value is given by a basic feasible solution of the constraints.

How is the optimal solution found? One way is to calculate all of the basic solutions by inverting the **B** matrix for each one, eliminate the non-feasible basic solutions, and calculate the value of the objective function for each of those remaining. Since the number of basic solutions is the number of combinations of n things taken m at a time, the calculation time for a large problem would be excessive. This brute-force approach is avoided by the simplex method, which searches for the optimal solution, and requires the calculation of only a few basic solutions. Furthermore, the calculation of each solution is relatively simple and does not require inverting the **B** matrix. Start with a known basic feasible solution and the constraints and objective function in canonical form for that solution. Then calculate a new basic feasible solution by setting one of the basic variables equal to zero, and bringing in as a basic variable one of the previously non-basic ones. The swap can be made in $m(n\text{-}m)$ ways. Choose the one that apparently decreases the objective function as much as possible. Ref. 19 (page 155) shows that this process of exchanging one basic variable for another in the basic feasible solution corresponds to moving between adjacent vertices of the solution space. The process is continued until the objective function cannot be reduced by bringing another variable into the basic feasible solution. Then the optimal solution has been achieved. The path from one vertex of the solution space to the next has led to the vertex that touches the hyperplane representing the minimum value of the objective function. Although the path does not necessarily have the smallest possible number of steps, the calculation is surprisingly fast and is vastly superior to the brute-force approach.

An example will illustrate the simplex method. Suppose a linear program has five variables and three constraints. The canonical form for the basic variables x_1, x_2, x_3 is

minimize $$z = z_0 + c_4 x_4 + c_5 x_5 \tag{19.47}$$

subject to $$x_1 + a_{14} x_4 + a_{15} x_5 = b_1 \tag{19.48}$$

$$x_2 + a_{24} x_4 + a_{25} x_5 = b_2 \tag{19.49}$$

$$x_3 + a_{34} x_4 + a_{35} x_5 = b_3 \tag{19.50}$$

and $$x_i \geqslant 0, \quad i = 1,2,3,4,5 . \tag{19.51}$$

Assume that the b_i's are non-negative: $b_i \geqslant 0$, $i = 1,2,3$. Then the basic solution $\mathbf{x}^T = [x_1,x_2,x_3,0,0]$ is feasible. (A method of preventing negative b_i's will be explained.) How can the objective function z be reduced? If c_4 and c_5 are both positive, raising x_4 or x_5 from zero will increase z, and the present basic feasible solution is optimal. If one or more of the c_i's is negative, bringing in its corresponding variable will decrease z. Choose the most negative c_i, because raising its variable x_i will produce the greatest decrease in z. Assume that c_4 is the most negative of the coefficients in z. Then reduce z by increasing x_4, until either x_1, x_2, or x_3 becomes zero. This step creates a new basic feasible solution and a lower objective function. The constraints can be written as

$$x_1 + a_{15}\,x_5 = b_1 - a_{14}\,x_4 \tag{19.52}$$

$$x_2 + a_{25}\,x_5 = b_2 - a_{24}\,x_4 \tag{19.53}$$

$$x_3 + a_{35}\,x_5 = b_3 - a_{34}\,x_4\,. \tag{19.54}$$

Remember that x_5 is a zero, non-basic variable. If all of the a_{i4}'s are positive, x_4 can rise until it is the minimum b_i/a_{i4}. Assume the minimum is b_1/a_{14}. Then $x_1 = 0$, and the new basic variables are x_2, x_3, x_4. If any of the a_{i4}'s is negative, the ith equation can be ignored because increasing x_4 increases x_i rather than forcing it toward zero. If all of the a_{i4}'s are negative, x_4 can be increased without bound, and the objective function z can be made as negative as desired. Such a problem is not "well posed." The solution might reveal, for example, the uninteresting news that a company's profit can be maximized by selling as many products as possible.

In the example x_4 was chosen to be the new basic variable because c_4 was the most negative coefficient in the objective function. Then x_4 was raised as far as possible, reducing the objective function by the amount c_4x_4. Possibly if x_5 had been chosen instead, it could have been raised high enough to make c_5x_5 larger than c_4x_4. Although c_ix_i could be calculated for all of the variables x_i in the objective function with negative coefficients, the simplex method does not include this complication.

Now the canonical form for the new basic variables can be calculated. Eq. (19.52) can be written as

$$x_4 = \frac{b_1}{a_{14}} - \frac{1}{a_{14}}x_1 - \frac{a_{15}}{a_{14}}x_5 \tag{19.55}$$

or

$$x_4 + \frac{1}{a_{14}}x_1 + \frac{a_{15}}{a_{14}}x_5 = \frac{b_1}{a_{14}}\,. \tag{19.56}$$

Substituting Eq. (19.55) into (19.53) gives

$$x_2 + a_{25}\,x_5 = b_2 - a_{24}\left(\frac{b_1}{a_{14}} - \frac{1}{a_{14}}\,x_1 - \frac{a_{15}}{a_{14}}\,x_5\right) \tag{19.57}$$

or

$$x_2 - \frac{a_{24}}{a_{14}}\,x_1 + \left(a_{25} - \frac{a_{24}a_{15}}{a_{14}}\right)x_5 = b_2 - \frac{a_{24}}{a_{14}}\,b_1\,. \tag{19.58}$$

Substituting Eq. (19.55) into (19.54) produces

$$x_3 + a_{35}\,x_5 = b_3 - a_{34}\left(\frac{b_1}{a_{14}} - \frac{1}{a_{14}}\,x_1 - \frac{a_{15}}{a_{14}}\,x_5\right) \tag{19.59}$$

or

$$x_3 - \frac{a_{34}}{a_{14}}\,x_1 + \left(a_{35} - \frac{a_{34}a_{15}}{a_{14}}\right)x_5 = b_3 - \frac{a_{34}}{a_{14}}\,b_1\,. \tag{19.60}$$

In terms of the new non-basic variables x_1 and x_5, the objective function is

$$\begin{aligned} z &= z_0 + c_4\left(\frac{b_1}{a_{14}} - \frac{1}{a_{14}}\,x_1 - \frac{a_{15}}{a_{14}}\,x_5\right) + c_5\,x_5 \\ &= z_0 + \frac{b_1}{a_{14}}\,c_4 - \frac{c_4}{a_{14}}\,x_1 + \left(c_5 - \frac{a_{15}}{a_{14}}\,c_4\right)x_5\,. \end{aligned} \tag{19.61}$$

This equation shows that moving from the vertex $[x_1,x_2,x_3,0,0]$ of the solution space to the adjacent vertex $[0,x_2,x_3,x_4,0]$ has decreased the objective function from z_0 to $z_0 + (b_1/a_{14})c_4$. For the first vertex, the constraints in canonical form were

$$\begin{bmatrix} 1 & 0 & 0 & a_{14} & a_{15} \\ 0 & 1 & 0 & a_{24} & a_{25} \\ 0 & 0 & 1 & a_{34} & a_{35} \end{bmatrix}\begin{bmatrix} x_1 \\ x_2 \\ x_3 \\ x_4 \\ x_5 \end{bmatrix} = \begin{bmatrix} b_1 \\ b_2 \\ b_3 \end{bmatrix}. \tag{19.62}$$

The new canonical form is

$$\begin{bmatrix} \dfrac{1}{a_{14}} & 0 & 0 & 1 & \dfrac{a_{15}}{a_{14}} \\ -\dfrac{a_{24}}{a_{14}} & 1 & 0 & 0 & a_{25} - \dfrac{a_{24}a_{15}}{a_{14}} \\ -\dfrac{a_{34}}{a_{14}} & 0 & 1 & 0 & a_{35} - \dfrac{a_{34}a_{15}}{a_{14}} \end{bmatrix}\begin{bmatrix} x_1 \\ x_2 \\ x_3 \\ x_4 \\ x_5 \end{bmatrix} = \begin{bmatrix} \dfrac{b_1}{a_{14}} \\ b_2 - \dfrac{a_{24}}{a_{14}}\,b_1 \\ b_3 - \dfrac{a_{34}}{a_{14}}\,b_1 \end{bmatrix}. \tag{19.63}$$

Notice that only a little simple arithmetic was required to calculate the new basic feasible solution.

The process can be generalized to include any number of variables n and constraints m. Let x_r be the old basic variable set to zero and x_s be the variable made basic. (In the example, $r = 1$ and $s = 4$.) New values will be denoted by an asterisk. In the **A** matrix,

$$a^*_{rs} = 1. \tag{19.64}$$

In the rest of column s,

$$a^*_{is} = 0\,, \quad i \neq r\,. \tag{19.65}$$

In the other columns,

$$a^*_{ij} = a_{ij} - a_{is}\, a^*_{rj}, \quad i \neq r\,. \tag{19.66}$$

In the rth row,

$$a^*_{rj} = \frac{a_{rj}}{a_{rs}}, \quad j \neq s\,. \tag{19.67}$$

The new coefficients in the objective function are

$$c^*_j = c_j - c_s\, a^*_{rj}\,. \tag{19.68}$$

The values of the new basic variables are

$$x_i = b^*_i = b_i - a_{is}\, b^*_r\,, \quad i \neq r \tag{19.69}$$

$$x_s = b^*_r = \frac{b_r}{a_{rs}}\,. \tag{19.70}$$

The new value of the objective function is

$$z^*_0 = z_0 + c_s\, b^*_r\,. \tag{19.71}$$

Now all of the formulas have been derived for the process of moving from one basic feasible solution to the next in the search for the optimal solution. The tool still needed is a way to start the solution.

19.8 Phase I

In order to start, the simplex algorithm requires the objective function and the constraints in canonical form for a basic feasible solution. They must be in the form of Eqs. (19.32) and (19.33), and the elements of the vector **b** (the right side of Eq. (19.33)) must all be non-negative. If the original problem is not in this form, take three steps:

1. If any of the b_i's is negative, multiply that constraint equation by -1 to make the b_i positive.

2. Introduce up to *m artificial variables* to make the constraints and objective function canonical.

3. Write a second objective function w, called the *infeasibility form*, that is the sum of the artificial variables.

As an example, start the solution of the problem given by Eqs. (19.23) thru (19.27). Multiply the first constraint by -1. The problem is now

$$\text{minimize} \quad z = -2x_1 - 3x_2 \tag{19.72}$$

$$\text{subject to} \quad -2x_1 + 3x_2 + x_3 = 6 \tag{19.73}$$

$$3x_1 + 2x_2 + x_4 = 6 \tag{19.74}$$

$$x_1 + x_2 - x_5 = 1 \tag{19.75}$$

$$\text{and} \quad x_i \geqslant 0\,, \quad i = 1,2,3,4,5\,. \tag{19.76}$$

The first two constraints are now in canonical form, but the third is not. Add the artificial variable x_6 to the third constraint to obtain

$$x_1 + x_2 - x_5 + x_6 = 1\,. \tag{19.77}$$

Now the constraints are in canonical form for the basic feasible solution $\mathbf{x}^T = [0,0,x_3,x_4,0,x_6] = [0,0,6,6,0,1]$. The infeasibility form $w = x_6$ must be written, as any canonical objective function, in terms of non-basic variables. Thus according to Eq. (19.77),

$$w = x_6 = 1 - x_1 - x_2 + x_5\,. \tag{19.78}$$

The three steps have produced a basic feasible solution of a new problem, whose constraints and objective function are in canonical form. The coefficients of the infeasibility form will be called d_i, so that in the original standard form like Eq. (19.18),

$$w = d_1 x_1 + d_2 x_2 + \cdots + d_6 x_6 = \mathbf{d}^T \mathbf{x}\,. \tag{19.79}$$

Comparison with Eqs. (19.68) and (19.71) shows that the new coefficients after each iteration are

$$d_j^* = d_j - d_s\, a_{rj}^* \tag{19.80}$$

and the new value of the infeasibility form is

$$w_0^* = w_0 + d_s\, b_r^*\,. \tag{19.81}$$

The new problem can be solved by the simplex method. If the original problem has a basic feasible solution with five variables, the new problem has the same basic feasible solution with an extra variable, the artificial variable being zero. The simplex method will find the latter solution, because it produces the minimum value of w, namely zero.

When this value is obtained, Phase I is complete. Dropping the artificial variable leaves a basic feasible solution of the original problem, with its constraints and objective function in canonical form. Phase II, the solution of the original problem, can then proceed.

19.9 The Simplex Tableau

Fig. 19.6 is a display of the variables and coefficients in the initial canonical form of the problem, including the artificial variables, and the values after one iteration. This *simplex tableau* is a help in calculating the new values by hand or with a desk calculator. The first column lists the values of the m basic variables and the two objective functions. The remaining columns are the coefficients of all of the variables in the constraint equations and the two objective functions. In the iteration shown, x_r is made zero and x_s is made non-zero. Therefore x_r and its coefficients are replaced by x_s and its coefficients in row r. The fact that the row numbers in the tableau do not correspond to the variable numbers is not a serious source of confusion. The element a_{rs} is called the *pivot element*. Marking its location is a help in calculating the new coefficients. A simplex tableau of the example is shown in Fig. 19.7. Coefficients of zero are omitted to avoid cluttering. To start Phase I, choose one of the two most negative coefficients in the infeasibility form, namely $d_1 = -1$. Raise x_1 until it reaches the minimum b_i/a_{i1} of all the positive a_{i1}'s. This minimum is $b_3/a_{31} = 1$. Coefficient a_{31} is the pivot element. The basic variable x_6 is replaced by x_1. The first iteration reduces w to zero, and produces the basic feasible solution $[x_1,0,x_3,x_4,0]$ of the original problem. Eliminate the column of coefficients of the artificial variable and the row of coefficients in the infeasibility form. Then Phase II is ready to start with the simplex tableau in Fig. 19.8.

Only one artificial variable was needed in the example because two of the constraints, Eqs. (19.73) and (19.74), were already in canonical form. No harm is done if an artificial variable is added to each constraint equation, without an inspection to see if it is needed. For example, the artificial variables x_6, x_7, and x_8 may be added to Eqs. (19.73), (19.74), and (19.75). The infeasibility form is then

$$w = x_6 + x_7 + x_8 \,. \tag{19.82}$$

It can be put into canonical form by adding the three new constraint equations together. Then

$$2\,x_1 + 6\,x_2 + x_3 + x_4 - x_5 + x_6 + x_7 + x_8 = 13\,, \tag{19.83}$$

and

$$w = x_6 + x_7 + x_8 = 13 - 2\,x_1 - 6\,x_2 - x_3 - x_4 + x_5\,. \tag{19.84}$$

Basic variables	x_1	x_2	. .	x_s	. .	x_n
$x_1 = b_1$	a_{11}	a_{12}	. .	a_{1s}	. .	a_{1n}
$x_2 = b_2$	a_{21}	a_{22}	. .	a_{2s}	. .	a_{2n}
: :	:	:	: :	:	: :	:
$x_r = b_r$	a_{r1}	a_{r2}	. .	$\boxed{a_{rs}}$	. .	a_{rn}
: :	:	:	: :	:	: :	:
$x_m = b_m$	a_{m1}	a_{m2}	. .	a_{ms}	. .	a_{mn}
$z = z_0$	c_1	c_2	. .	c_s	. .	c_n
$w = w_0$	d_1	d_2	. .	d_s	. .	d_n

$x_1=b_1-a_{1s}b_r^*$	$a_{11}-a_{1s}a_{r1}^*$	$a_{12}-a_{1s}a_{r2}^*$	. .	0	. .	$a_{1n}-a_{1s}a_{rn}^*$
$x_2=b_2-a_{2s}b_r^*$	$a_{21}-a_{2s}a_{r1}^*$	$a_{22}-a_{2s}a_{r2}^*$	. .	0	. .	$a_{2n}-a_{2s}a_{rn}^*$
: :	:	:	: :	:	: :	:
$x_s=b_r^*=b_r/a_{rs}$	$a_{r1}^*=a_{r1}/a_{rs}$	$a_{r2}^*=a_{r2}/a_{rs}$	. .	1	. .	$a_{rn}^*=a_{rn}/a_{rs}$
: : :	:	:	: :	:	: :	:
$x_m=b_m-a_{ms}b_r^*$	$a_{m1}-a_{ms}a_{r1}^*$	$a_{m2}-a_{ms}a_{r2}^*$	. .	0	. .	$a_{mn}-a_{ms}a_{rn}^*$
$z=z_0+c_sb_r^*$	$c_1-c_sa_{r1}^*$	$c_2-c_sa_{r2}^*$	. .	0	. .	$c_n-c_sa_{rn}^*$
$w=w_0+d_sb_r^*$	$d_1-d_sa_{r1}^*$	$d_2-d_sa_{r2}^*$	. .	0	. .	$d_n-d_sa_{rn}^*$

Fig. 19.6. Simplex tableau.

Basic variables	x_1	x_2	x_3	x_4	x_5	x_6
$x_3 = b_1 = 6$	-2	3	1			
$x_4 = b_2 = 6$	3	2		1		
$x_6 = b_3 = 1$	1	1			-1	1
$z = 0$	-2	-3				
$w = 1$	-1	-1			1	
$x_3 = b_1 = 8$		5	1		-2	2
$x_4 = b_2 = 3$		-1		1	3	-3
$x_1 = b_3 = 1$	1	1			-1	1
$z = -2$		-1			-2	2
$w = 0$						1

Fig. 19.7. Phase I of the example problem.

Basic variables	x_1	x_2	x_3	x_4	x_5
$x_3 = 8$		5	1		-2
$x_4 = 3$		-1		1	3
$x_1 = 1$	1	1			-1
$z = -2$		-1			-2

Fig. 19.8. Initial tableau for Phase II.

Basic variables	x_1	x_2	x_3	x_4	x_5	x_6	x_7	x_8
$x_6 = 6$	-2	3	1			1		
$x_7 = 6$	3	2		1			1	
$x_8 = 1$	1	1			-1			1
$z = 0$	-2	-3						
$w = 13$	-2	-6	-1	-1	1			
$x_6 = 3$	-5		1		3	1		-3
$x_7 = 4$	1			1	2		1	-2
$x_2 = 1$	1	1			-1			1
$z = -3$	1				-3			3
$w = 7$	4		-1	-1	-5			6
$x_5 = 1$	-5/3		1/3		1	1/3		-1
$x_7 = 2$	13/3		-2/3	1		-2/3	1	
$x_2 = 2$	-2/3	1	1/3			1/3		
$z = -6$	-4		1			1		
$w = 2$	-13/3		2/3	-1		5/3		1
$x_5 = 23/13$					1			
$x_1 = 6/13$	1		-2/13	3/13		-2/13	3/13	
$x_2 = 30/13$		1						
$z = -102/13$			5/13	12/13		5/13	12/13	
$w = 0$						1	1	1

Fig. 19.9. Solution of the example with a full Phase I.

The simplex tableau including the three artificial variables is shown in Fig. 19.9. Notice that after three iterations w is reduced to zero, and the coefficients c_i of the original objective function z happen to be all positive. For this example no Phase II is necessary, and the optimal value of z is $-102/13$.

19.10 The Revised Simplex Method

In a typical practical linear program, many of the coefficients of the original constraint equations are zero, and the original simplex tableau has corresponding zeros. As new tableaus are formed, the zeros are soon replaced by non-zeros, and a calculation is required for each coefficient in the program. Computation time is saved by the *revised simplex method*, which calculates the new coefficients at each iteration from the original coefficients. The zeros therefore reduce the computation time of each iteration. Furthermore, the revised method requires smaller tableaus for hand calculations and fewer storage registers for computer calculations, because most of the calculations are made for only the m basic variables, instead of all n variables. The revised simplex method is also called the *simplex method using multipliers*, or the *inverse matrix method*. Fig. 19.10, presented in Ref. 19, is a guide to choosing between the standard simplex method and the simplex method using multipliers.

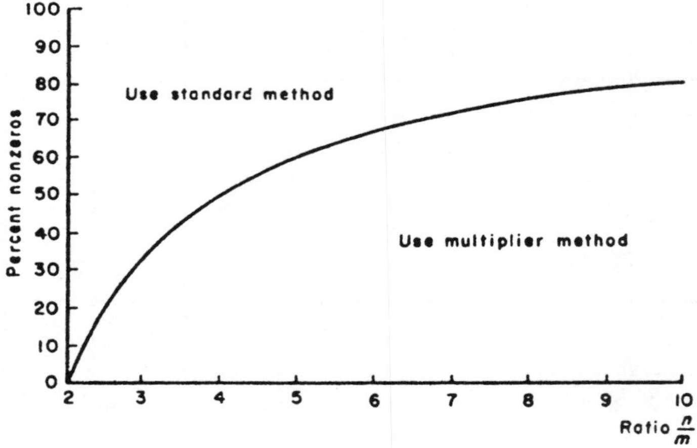

Fig. 19.10. Choice of methods of solution. (From *Linear Programming and Extensions* by George B. Dantzig, copyright 1963 by the RAND Corporation. Reprinted by permission of the publisher, Princeton University Press.)

To understand the revised method, first observe how it finds the canonical forms of the objective function and constraints for a new basis.

Suppose the original problem in standard form has $m = 2$ constraints and $n = 4$ variables. The objective function is

$$z = c_1 x_1 + c_2 x_2 + c_3 x_3 + c_4 x_4 \tag{19.85}$$

and the constraints are

$$a_{11} x_1 + a_{12} x_2 + a_{13} x_3 + a_{14} x_4 = b_1 \tag{19.86}$$

$$a_{21} x_1 + a_{22} x_2 + a_{23} x_3 + a_{24} x_4 = b_2 \,. \tag{19.87}$$

As an example, find the canonical forms for the basic variables x_1 and x_2. Multiply the first constraint by the constant π_1, and the second by π_2:

$$\pi_1 a_{11} x_1 + \pi_1 a_{12} x_2 + \pi_1 a_{13} x_3 + \pi_1 a_{14} x_4 = \pi_1 b_1 \tag{19.88}$$

$$\pi_2 a_{21} x_1 + \pi_2 a_{22} x_2 + \pi_2 a_{23} x_3 + \pi_2 a_{24} x_4 = \pi_2 b_2 \,. \tag{19.89}$$

Next add these two equations to the objective function and collect the coefficients of each x_i:

$$\begin{aligned}(c_1 + a_{11} \pi_1 + a_{21} \pi_2)x_1 + (c_2 + a_{12} \pi_1 + a_{22} \pi_2)x_2 \\ + (c_3 + a_{13} \pi_1 + a_{23} \pi_2)x_3 + (c_4 + a_{14} \pi_1 + a_{24} \pi_2)x_4 \\ = z + b_1 \pi_1 + b_2 \pi_2 \,.\end{aligned} \tag{19.90}$$

This will be the canonical form of the objective function for the basic variables x_1, x_2 if their coefficients are set at zero. Therefore

$$c_1 + a_{11} \pi_1 + a_{21} \pi_2 = 0 \tag{19.91}$$

$$c_2 + a_{12} \pi_1 + a_{22} \pi_2 = 0 \tag{19.92}$$

or

$$c_1 = -a_{11} \pi_1 - a_{21} \pi_2 \tag{19.93}$$

$$c_2 = -a_{12} \pi_1 - a_{22} \pi_2 \,. \tag{19.94}$$

According to Eq. (19.29), the **B** matrix consists of the coefficients of the basic variables in the original standard form of the constraints. Thus

$$\mathbf{B} = \begin{bmatrix} a_{11} & a_{12} \\ a_{21} & a_{22} \end{bmatrix} \quad \text{and} \quad \mathbf{B}^T = \begin{bmatrix} a_{11} & a_{21} \\ a_{12} & a_{22} \end{bmatrix} . \tag{19.95}$$

If vectors $\boldsymbol{\pi}$ and $\mathbf{c}$ are defined as

$$\boldsymbol{\pi} = \begin{bmatrix} \pi_1 \\ \pi_2 \end{bmatrix} \quad \text{and} \quad \mathbf{c} = \begin{bmatrix} c_1 \\ c_2 \end{bmatrix} , \tag{19.96}$$

Eqs. (19.93) and (19.94) can be written as

$$\mathbf{c} = -\,\mathbf{B}^T \boldsymbol{\pi} \tag{19.97}$$

and

$$\boldsymbol{\pi} = -(\mathbf{B}^T)^{-1}\,\mathbf{c}\,, \tag{19.98}$$

where **c** is the vector of coefficients of the basic variables in the original objective function. The constants π_1 and π_2 are called the *simplex multipliers* for the basic variables x_1 and x_2. In general there are m simplex multipliers, one for each constraint equation. The calculation of the first set of simplex multipliers is trivial if the solution is started with Phase I, because then $(\mathbf{B}^T)^{-1}$ is a unit matrix, and the elements of vector **c** are all zero.

The simplex multipliers for the same basic variables, calculated from the infeasibility form (the objective function of Phase I) are called σ_i and are found in the same way. If $\boldsymbol{\sigma}$ is the vector of these simplex multipliers and **d** is the vector of coefficients of the basic variables in the original infeasibility form,

$$\boldsymbol{\sigma} = -(\mathbf{B}^T)^{-1}\,\mathbf{d}\,. \tag{19.99}$$

The first set of σ_i's are all zero because the d_i's are all zero.

In the revised simplex method the coefficients a_i, c_i, and d_i are determined in each iteration from the original coefficients. The values of the basic variables, the inverse of the **B** matrix, and the simplex multipliers are found from the present coefficients. A distinction between original, present, and new values is necessary. Original values are unprimed, present values are primed, and new values have an asterisk.

When the original simplex multipliers are found by Eq. (19.98), the coefficients of the non-basic variables in the canonical objective function (19.90) can be found. For example, the coefficients of x_3 is

$$c_3' = c_3 + a_{13}\,\pi_1 + a_{23}\,\pi_2\,. \tag{19.100}$$

In general,

$$c_j' = c_j + \sum_{i=1}^{m} a_{ij}\,\pi_i' \tag{19.101}$$

and

$$d_j' = d_j + \sum_{i=1}^{m} a_{ij}\,\sigma_i'\,. \tag{19.102}$$

The constant term in the objective function, according to Eq. (19.90), is

$$z_0^* = -(b_1\pi_1 + b_2\pi_2)\,, \tag{19.103}$$

or in general,

$$z_0^* = -\sum_{i=1}^{m} b_i \pi_i' . \tag{19.104}$$

The constant term in the infeasibility form is

$$w_0^* = -\sum_{i=1}^{m} b_i \sigma_i' . \tag{19.105}$$

Eqs. (19.98), (19.101), and (19.103) can produce the canonical form of the objective function for any set of basic variables from the original statement of the problem.

The constraint equations also can be put into canonical form with the help of the inverse of the **B** matrix. Let the elements of this matrix be β_{ij}. For the example,

$$\mathbf{B}^{-1} = \begin{bmatrix} \beta_{11} & \beta_{12} \\ \beta_{21} & \beta_{22} \end{bmatrix} . \tag{19.106}$$

Multiply the first constraint, Eq. (19.86), by β_{11} and the second by β_{12}:

$$\beta_{11} a_{11} x_1 + \beta_{11} a_{12} x_2 + \beta_{11} a_{13} x_3 + \beta_{11} a_{14} x_4 = \beta_{11} b_1 \tag{19.107}$$

$$\beta_{12} a_{21} x_1 + \beta_{12} a_{22} x_2 + \beta_{12} a_{23} x_3 + \beta_{12} a_{24} x_4 = \beta_{12} b_2 . \tag{19.108}$$

The sum of these equations is

$$a_{11}' x_1 + a_{12}' x_2 + a_{13}' x_3 + a_{14}' x_4 = b_1' \tag{19.109}$$

where

$$\begin{aligned} a_{11}' &= \beta_{11} a_{11} + \beta_{12} a_{21} \\ a_{12}' &= \beta_{11} a_{12} + \beta_{12} a_{22} \\ a_{13}' &= \beta_{11} a_{13} + \beta_{12} a_{23} \\ a_{14}' &= \beta_{11} a_{14} + \beta_{12} a_{24} \end{aligned} \tag{19.110}$$

and

$$b_1' = \beta_{11} b_1 + \beta_{12} b_2 . \tag{19.111}$$

Next, multiply the first original constraint (19.86) by β_{21} and the second by β_{22}:

$$\beta_{21} a_{11} x_1 + \beta_{21} a_{12} x_2 + \beta_{21} a_{13} x_3 + \beta_{21} a_{14} x_4 = \beta_{21} b_1 \tag{19.112}$$

$$\beta_{22} a_{21} x_1 + \beta_{22} a_{22} x_2 + \beta_{22} a_{23} x_3 + \beta_{22} a_{24} x_4 = \beta_{22} b_2 . \tag{19.113}$$

The sum of these two equations is

$$a_{21}' x_1 + a_{22}' x_2 + a_{23}' x_3 + a_{24}' x_4 = b_2' \tag{19.114}$$

where

$$a'_{21} = \beta_{21}\, a_{11} + \beta_{22}\, a_{21}$$
$$a'_{22} = \beta_{21}\, a_{12} + \beta_{22}\, a_{22}\,, \tag{19.115}$$
etc.

and

$$b'_2 = \beta_{21}\, b_1 + \beta_{22}\, b_2\,. \tag{19.116}$$

Notice that

$$a'_{ij} = [\beta_{i1}, \beta_{i2}] \begin{bmatrix} a_{1j} \\ a_{2j} \end{bmatrix} = \sum_{k=1}^{2} \beta_{ik}\, a_{kj}\,, \tag{19.117}$$

or

$$a'_{ij} = \langle i\text{th row of } \mathbf{B}^{-1}, j\text{th column of } \mathbf{B} \rangle = \delta_{ij}\,, \qquad i = 1,2\,. \tag{19.118}$$

The two constraints (19.109) and (19.114) are now in canonical form for the basic variables x_1 and x_2:

$$x_1 \quad + a'_{13}\, x_3 + a'_{14}\, x_4 = b'_1 \tag{19.119}$$
$$x_2 + a'_{23}\, x_3 + a'_{24}\, x_4 = b'_2\,. \tag{19.120}$$

This method produces the m constraint equations in canonical form for any set of m basic variables, from the original statement of the problem. The new coefficients of the non-basic variables are

$$a'_{ij} = \sum_{k=1}^{m} \beta'_{ik}\, a_{kj}\,. \tag{19.121}$$

This section has shown how to obtain the canonical form of the objective function and constraints for any set of basic variables using the present simplex multipliers and inverse of the **B** matrix. The revised simplex method finds the optimal solution by moving from one basic feasible solution to the next according to the same searching procedure as that used by the simplex method. The revised method calculates the objective coefficients and constraint coefficients for each solution from the original problem statement, rather than from the preceding canonical form. Each solution needs the inverse of the **B** matrix. When the problem is started in Phase I, $\mathbf{B}^{-1}$ is a unit matrix. For the subsequent iterations it is not. Fortunately the **B** matrix does not have to be inverted for each solution. Ref. 19 shows that when basic variable x_s replaces x_r, the elements β^*_{ij} of the new $\mathbf{B}^{-1}$ are found from the elements β'_{ij} of the present $\mathbf{B}^{-1}$ by the simple formulas

$$\beta^*_{ij} = \beta'_{ij} - a'_{is}\,\beta^*_{rj}\,, \qquad i \neq r \tag{19.122}$$

and

$$\beta^*_{rj} = \frac{\beta'_{rj}}{a'_{rs}}\,. \tag{19.123}$$

Similarly, the new simplex multipliers are

$$\pi^*_i = \pi'_i - c'_s\,\beta^*_{ri} \tag{19.124}$$

and

$$\sigma^*_i = \sigma'_i - d'_s\,\beta^*_{ri}\,, \tag{19.125}$$

where c'_s and d'_s are coefficients in the present objective functions. Thus at each iteration the simplex multipliers and inverse **B** matrix are obtained from the coefficients in the present solution. Then the new coefficients are obtained from the original coefficients. The values of the two objective functions at each iteration could be obtained from Eqs. (19.104) and (19.105), and the values of the basic variables from equations like (19.111) and (19.116). Less arithmetic is required by Eqs. (19.69), (19.70), (19.71), and (19.81), that were derived for the simplex method:

$$b^*_i = b'_i - a'_{is}\,b^*_r\,, \qquad i \neq r \tag{19.126}$$

$$b^*_r = \frac{b'_r}{a'_{rs}} \tag{19.127}$$

$$z^*_0 = z'_0 + c'_s\,b^*_r \tag{19.128}$$

$$w^*_0 = w'_0 + d'_s\,b^*_r\,. \tag{19.129}$$

Unlike the simplex method, the revised method does not require calculation of all the constraint coefficients at each step. As in the simplex method, observe which of the negative coefficients in the objective function is the most negative, and now call it c'_s. The variable x_s will enter the basis. As in the simplex method, x_s will be raised to the lowest value of b'_i/a'_{is} of all of the i's for which a_{is} is positive. The i chosen is called r, and variable x_r leaves the basis. Since constraint coefficients are needed in the revised method only to make the choice of r, calculate only the column a'_{is}, $i = 1,2, \ldots m$, instead of all the constraint coefficients, using Eq. (19.121):

$$a'_{is} = \sum_{k=1}^{m} \beta'_{ik}\,a_{ks}\,. \tag{19.130}$$

Fortunately, this is the same column a'_{is} needed for the elements of the inverse **B** matrix, Eqs. (19.122) and (19.123), and the values of the basic variables, Eqs. (19.126) and (19.127).

19.11 Tableaus for the Revised Simplex Method

A hand solution of a linear program by the revised method requires three tables, showing

1. the original objective and constraint coefficients,
2. the objective coefficients for all of the variables at each iteration, and
3. the items that must be calculated for the basic variables during each iteration.

The last of these tables is illustrated in Fig. 19.11 for two successive iterations. Note again that the primed terms are present values, and the unprimed coefficients a_{is} are original values.

Now solve the sample problem again by the revised simplex method. The problem is

$$\text{minimize} \quad z = -2x_1 - 3x_2 \tag{19.131}$$

$$\text{subject to} \quad -2x_1 + 3x_2 + x_3 = 6 \tag{19.132}$$

$$3x_1 + 2x_2 + x_4 = 6 \tag{19.133}$$

$$x_1 + x_2 - x_5 = 1 \tag{19.134}$$

$$\text{and} \quad x_i \geqslant 0, \qquad i = 1,2,3,4,5\,. \tag{19.135}$$

The original canonical form, obtained by adding one artificial variable x_6, is tabulated in Fig. 19.12. The original infeasibility form, Eq. (19.78), is

$$w = x_6 = 1 - x_1 - x_2 + x_5\,. \tag{19.136}$$

Fig. 19.13 is the start of the table of coefficients of all the variables in both objective functions. Since the coefficient $d_1' = -1$ is the most negative in the infeasibility form, $s = 1$ and x_1 will enter the basis. Fig. 19.14 is the start of the table of iterations. The initial $\mathbf{B}^{-1}$ is a unit matrix. The initial simplex multipliers π_i and σ_i for the basis x_3, x_4, x_6, calculated by Eqs. (19.98) and (19.99), are all zero. Record $d_s' = d_1'$ and the corresponding c_1' in the lower right corner for use in the first iteration. To determine which variable will leave the basis, calculate each a_{i1}' according to Eq. (19.130) and fill the last column. The mini-

Basic variables	Inverse of the B matrix				a'_{is}
$x_1 = b'_i$	β'_{11}	β'_{12}	. .	β'_{1m}	$a'_{1s} = \sum \beta'_{1i} a_{is}$
$x_2 = b'_2$	β'_{21}	β'_{22}	. .	β'_{2m}	$a'_{2s} = \sum \beta'_{2i} a_{is}$
⋮ ⋮	⋮	⋮	⋮ ⋮	⋮	⋮
$x_r = b'_r$	β'_{r1}	β'_{r2}	. .	β'_{rm}	$a'_{rs} = \sum \beta'_{ri} a_{is}$
⋮ ⋮	⋮	⋮	⋮ ⋮	⋮	⋮
$x_m = b'_m$	β'_{m1}	β'_{m2}	. .	β'_{mm}	$a'_{ms} = \sum \beta'_{mi} a_{is}$
$z = z_0$	π'_1	π'_2	. .	π'_m	c'_s
$w = w_0$	σ'_1	σ'_2	. .	σ'_m	d'_s

$x_1=b'_1-a'_{1s}b^*_r$	$\beta'_{11}-a'_{1s}\beta^*_{r1}$	$\beta'_{12}-a'_{1s}\beta^*_{r2}$	. .	$\beta'_{1m}a'_{1s}\beta^*_{rm}$	Same as above, with present values of β_{ij}
$x_2=b'_2-a'_{2s}b^*_r$	$\beta'_{21}-a'_{2s}\beta^*_{r1}$	$\beta'_{22}-a'_{2s}\beta^*_{r2}$	. .	$\beta'_{2m}-a'_{2s}\beta^*_{rm}$	
⋮ ⋮	⋮	⋮	⋮ ⋮	⋮	
$x_s=b^*_r=b'_r/a'_{rs}$	$\beta^*_{r1}=\beta'_{r1}/a'_{rs}$	$\beta^*_{r2}=\beta'_{r2}/a'_{rs}$	. .	$\beta^*_{rm}=\beta'_{rm}/a'_{rs}$	
⋮ ⋮ ⋮	⋮	⋮	⋮ ⋮	⋮	
$x_m=b'_m-a'_{ms}b^*_r$	$\beta'_{m1}-a'_{ms}\beta^*_{r1}$	$\beta'_{m2}-a'_{ms}\beta^*_{r2}$	. .	$\beta'_{mm}-a'_{ms}\beta^*_{rm}$	
$z = z_0 + c'_s b^*_r$	$\pi'_1 - c'_s\beta^*_{r1}$	$\pi'_2 - c'_s\beta^*_{r2}$	. .	$\pi'_m - c'_s\beta^*_{rm}$	— —
$w = w_0 + d'_s b^*_r$	$\sigma'_1 - d'_s\beta^*_{r1}$	$\sigma'_2 - d'_s\beta^*_{r2}$	. .	$\sigma'_m - d'_s\beta^*_{rm}$	— —

Fig. 19.11. Revised simplex tableau.

mum b'_i/a'_{i1} for the positive values of a'_{i1} is 1, in row 3. Accordingly, $r = 3$, and x_6 will leave the basis.

Now the tableau for the first iteration can be established. In Fig. 19.15 the elements of $\mathbf{B}^{-1}$ are found by Eqs. (19.122) and (19.123). Thus in row $r = 3$,

$$\beta^*_{31} = \frac{\beta'_{31}}{a'_{31}} = 0 \qquad (19.137)$$

$$\beta^*_{32} = \frac{\beta'_{32}}{a'_{31}} = 0 \tag{19.138}$$

$$\beta^*_{33} = \frac{\beta'_{33}}{a'_{31}} = \frac{1}{1} = 1\,. \tag{19.139}$$

In row $i = 1$,

$$\beta^*_{11} = \beta'_{11} - a'_{11}\,\beta^*_{31} = 1 - (-2)(0) = 1 \tag{19.140}$$

$$\beta^*_{12} = \beta'_{12} - a'_{11}\,\beta^*_{32} = 0 - (-2)(0) = 0 \tag{19.141}$$

$$\beta^*_{13} = \beta'_{13} - a'_{11}\,\beta^*_{33} = 0 - (-2)(1) = 2\,. \tag{19.142}$$

b_i	x_1	x_2	x_3	x_4	x_5	x_6
6	-2	3	1			
6	3	2		1		
1	1	1			-1	1
c_i's	-2	-3				
d_i's	-1	-1			1	

Fig. 19.12. Original canonical form.

The two new sets of simplex multipliers are given by Eqs. (19.124) and (19.125):

$$\pi^*_1 = \pi'_1 - c'_1\,\beta^*_{31} = 0 - (-2)(0) = 0 \tag{19.143}$$

$$\pi^*_2 = \pi'_2 - c'_1\,\beta^*_{32} = 0 - (-2)(0) = 0 \tag{19.144}$$

$$\pi^*_3 = \pi'_3 - c'_1\,\beta^*_{33} = 0 - (-2)(1) = 2 \tag{19.145}$$

$$\sigma^*_1 = \sigma'_1 - d'_1\,\beta^*_{31} = 0 - (-1)(0) = 0 \tag{19.146}$$

$$\sigma^*_2 = \sigma'_2 - d'_1\,\beta^*_{32} = 0 - (-1)(0) = 0 \tag{19.147}$$

$$\sigma^*_3 = \sigma'_3 - d'_1\,\beta^*_{33} = 0 - (-1)(1) = 1\,. \tag{19.148}$$

Iteration	d_1'	d_2'	d_3'	d_4'	d_5'	d_6'
0	-1	-1			1	
1						

Iteration	c_1'	c_2'	c_3'	c_4'	c_5'
0	-2	-3			
1					

Fig. 19.13. Table of all the objective coefficients.

Basic variables	Inverse of B matrix			$a_{is}' = a_{i1}'$
$x_3 = b_1' = 6$	1			-2
$x_4 = b_2' = 6$		1		3
$x_6 = b_3' = 1$			1	1
$z = 0$	0	0	0	$c_1' = -2$
$w = 1$	0	0	0	$d_1' = -1$

Fig. 19.14. Start of the revised-simplex tableau.

Basic variables	Inverse of B matrix			a'_{i5}
$x_3 = b_1^* = 8$	1		2	-2
$x_4 = b_2^* = 3$		1	-3	3
$x_1 = b_3^* = 1$			1	-1
$z = -2$	0	0	2	$c'_5 = -2$
$w = 0$	0	0	1	

Fig. 19.15. First iteration.

The values of the new basic variables are found from Eqs. (19.126) and (19.127):

$$b_3^* = \frac{b'_3}{a'_{31}} = \frac{1}{1} = 1 \tag{19.149}$$

$$b_1^* = b'_1 - a'_{11}\, b_3^* = 6 - (-2)(1) = 8 \tag{19.150}$$

$$b_2^* = b'_2 - a'_{21}\, b_3^* = 6 - (-3)(1) = 3\,. \tag{19.151}$$

The values of the two objective functions are given by Eqs. (19.128) and (19.129):

$$z_0^* = z'_0 + c'_1\, b_3^* = 0 + (-2)(1) = -2 \tag{19.152}$$

$$w_0^* = w'_0 + d'_1\, b_3^* = 1 + (-1)(1) = 0\,. \tag{19.153}$$

Since the infeasibility form w has been reduced to zero, Phase I is complete and the artificial variable w_6 can be dropped.

All of the objective-function coefficients in the first iteration must now be added to Fig. 19.13. The coefficients of the new basic variables x_3, x_4, x_1 are of course zero. The coefficients of the non-basic variables are given by Eq. (19.101):

$$\begin{aligned} c'_2 &= c_2 + a_{12}\,\pi'_1 + a_{22}\,\pi'_2 + a_{32}\,\pi'_3 \\ &= -3 + (3)(0) + (2)(0) + (1)(2) = -1 \end{aligned} \tag{19.154}$$

$$\begin{aligned} c'_5 &= c_5 + a_{15}\,\pi'_1 + a_{25}\,\pi'_2 + a_{35}\,\pi'_3 \\ &= 0 + (0)(0) + (0)(0) + (-1)(2) = -2\,. \end{aligned} \tag{19.155}$$

These coefficients are the second row of c_i's in Fig. 19.16, the extension

Iteration	d_1'	d_2'	d_3'	d_4'	d_5'	d_6'
0	-1	-1			1	
1						1

Iteration	c_1'	c_2'	c_3'	c_4'	c_5'
0	-2	-3			
1		-1			-2
2		-5/3		2/3	
3			5/13	12/13	

Fig. 19.16. Complete table of objective coefficients.

of Fig. 19.13. The coefficients d_i of the infeasibility form for the first iteration, obtained from Eq. (19.102), are also included, although they are not needed. The second row of c_i's shows that the most negative is $c_5' = -2$. Therefore x_5 will become a basic variable. The present values of $a_{is}' = a_{i5}'$ are calculated next to complete Fig. 19.15. The second iteration can now begin. The objective coefficients and the tableaus for the three iterations necessary to complete the solution are shown in Figs. 19.16 and 19.17. Notice that the objective function z decreases monotonically from zero to $-102/13$, and the optimal basic feasible solution of the constraint equations is $\mathbf{x}^T = [6/13,30/13,0,0,23/13]$.

19.12 Computer Solutions

Several programs are available for computer solution of linear programs. One of these is the BASIC program LINPRO***, in the General Electric Mark III Library. LINPRO*** starts the solution with Phase I, and finds the optimal solution by the revised simplex method. Instructions for its use are listed in LPINST***, shown in Table 19.1. The user is requested not to enter coefficients for the slack, surplus, and artificial variables. (A *surplus* variable is the slack variable for a "greater-than" constraint.) These coefficients are generated by the computer. During the run, the user declares the number of original variables N, which is in general less than the number of variables n in the standard form of the program. LINPRO*** calculates the maximum value of the objective function (called the *cost function* in line 123 of the instructions). To minimize the objective function, the user must enter the objective coefficients with their signs reversed, and then reverse the sign of the maximum objective function printed in the results. The more recent BASIC program LINPR$*** has the same operating instructions, except that it does not require the user to reverse the signs of the objective coefficients. It asks the user whether the objective function is to be maximized or minimized.

Table 19.2 is a computer solution of the example problem, which of course agrees with the hand solution tabulated in Fig. 19.17. Table 19.3 is a computer solution of the oscillograph problem stated in Eqs. (19.1) thru (19.5). Notice that the optimal computer solution includes a slack variable, because three basic variables are required in a basic feasible solution of this problem, and the original problem statement contained only two variables. The minimum objective function given by the computer is $125,000. This result does not agree exactly with Eq. (19.9) in which the variables had been rounded to integral values.

	Basic variables	Inverse of B matrix			a'_{is}
0	$x_3 = 6$	1			-2
	$x_4 = 6$		1		3
	$x_6 = 1$			1	1
	$z = 0$	0	0	0	$c'_1 = -2$
	$w = 1$	0	0	0	$d'_1 = -1$

Fig. 19.17. Complete revised-simplex tableau.

Fig. 19.17. *(Continued)*

1

$x_3 = 8$	1		2	-2
$x_4 = 3$		1	-3	3
$x_1 = 1$			1	-1
$z = -2$	0	0	2	$c_5' = -2$
$w = 0$	0	0	1	

2

$x_3 = 10$	1	2/3		13/3
$x_5 = 1$		1/3	-1	-1/3
$x_1 = 2$		1/3		2/3
$z = -4$		2/3		$c_2' = -5/3$

3

$x_2 = 30/13$	3/13	2/13		---
$x_5 = 23/13$	1/13	5/13	-1	---
$x_1 = 6/13$	-2/13	3/13		---
$z = -102/13$	5/13	12/13		---

TABLE 19.1. INSTRUCTIONS FOR LINPRO***

```
LPINST              13:34EDT              05/12/75

100              -NOVEMBER 13,1969-
101 THESE INSTRUCTIONS ARE FOR LINPRO***
102
103
104 THIS CODE MAXIMIZES THE OBJECTIVE FUNCTION
105 BY THE TWO-PHASE METHOD.
106
107
108 ENTER DATA STARTING AT LINE 10000
109
110 FIRST-ARRANGE YOUR RESTRICTIONS SO THAT THE LESS
111 THAN INEQUALITIES PRECEDE THE STRICT EQUALITIES,
112 WHICH, IN TURN, PRECEDE THE GREATER THAN INEQUALITIES.
113
114 THEN-TYPE IN THE COEFFICIENTS OF THE RESTRICTIONS
115 ROW BY ROW.
116
117 DO NOT INCLUDE COEFFICIENTS FOR SLACK, SURPLUS,
118 OR ARTIFICIAL VARIABLES.
119
120 NEXT-TYPE IN THE B VECTOR (THE CONSTANTS OF THE
121 RESTRICTIONS.) THESE VALUES MUST BE NON-NEGATIVE.
122
123 FINALLY-TYPE IN THE COEFFICIENTS OF THE COST FUNCTION.
124
125
126 FOR A MINIMIZATION PROBLEM, REVERSE THE SIGNS OF THE
127 COEFFICIENTS OF THE OBJECTIVE FUNCTION.
128
129
130 AT RUN TIME YOU WILL BE ASKED TO:
131
132     (1) INDICATE THE LEVEL OF DETAIL FOR OUTPUT.
133
134     (2) INPUT THE NUMBER OF RESTRICTIONS AND VARIABLES
135         M AND N RESPECTIVELY.
136
137     (3) AND TO INPUT THE NUMBER OF LESS THAN INEQUALITIES,
138         STRICT EQUALITIES, AND GREATER THAN INEQUALITIES,
139         RESPECTIVELY.
140
141
142
143 REMEMBER TO ALWAYS TYPE ZEROS WHEN THEY ARE APPLICABLE.

READY
```

TABLE 19.2. COMPUTER SOLUTION OF THE EXAMPLE PROBLEM

```
OLD LINPRO***

READY
10000 DATA -2,3,1,0,0
10010 DATA 3,2,0,1,0
10020 DATA 1,1,0,0,-1
10030 DATA 6,6,1
10040 DATA 2,3,0,0,0
RUN
```

TABLE 19.2. *(Continued)*

```
LINPRO              14:53EDT              05/12/75

TYPE '2' FOR OUTPUT OF TABLEAUS AND BASIS
AT EACH ITERATION, '1' FOR THE BASIS ONLY,
OR '0' FOR JUST THE SOLUTION. WHICH? 0

WHAT ARE M AND N OF THE DATA MATRIX? 3,5

HOW MANY 'LESS THANS', 'EQUALS', 'GREATER THANS'? 0,3,0

       YOUR VARIABLES 1 THROUGH 5
ARTIFICIAL VARIABLES 6 THROUGH 8

ANSWERS:

VARIABLE            VALUE
 5                  1.76923
 1                  0.461538
 2                  2.30769

OBJECTIVE FUNCTION VALUE          7.84615
```

TABLE 19.3. COMPUTER SOLUTION OF THE OSCILLOGRAPH PROBLEM

```
OLD LINPRO***

READY
10000 DATA 1500,7000
10010  DATA 1,6
10020  DATA 1,-2
10030  DATA 200000,100,0
10040  DATA -1500,-7000
RUN

LINPRO              14:56EDT              05/12/75

TYPE '2' FOR OUTPUT OF TABLEAUS AND BASIS
AT EACH ITERATION, '1' FOR THE BASIS ONLY,
OR '0' FOR JUST THE SOLUTION. WHICH? 0

WHAT ARE M AND N OF THE DATA MATRIX? 3,2

HOW MANY 'LESS THANS', 'EQUALS', 'GREATER THANS'? 1,0,2

       YOUR VARIABLES 1 THROUGH 2
    SURPLUS VARIABLES 3 THROUGH 4
      SLACK VARIABLES 5 THROUGH 5
ARTIFICIAL VARIABLES 6 THROUGH 7

ANSWERS:

VARIABLE            VALUE
 5                  75000
 2                  12.5
 1                  25.

OBJECTIVE FUNCTION VALUE          -125000
```

Chapter 20

ANALOG COMPUTERS

20.1 Introduction

The analog computer solves systems of ordinary differential equations, both linear and nonlinear, and presents the solutions as curves on an oscilloscope screen or on graph paper. Compared to the digital computer, which solves differential equations by numerical integration, the analog computer requires more preparation before it can be run, especially if the equations are nonlinear. The advantage of the analog computer is that the output curves are available continuously. The effect of varying a parameter in the system, obtained merely by turning a knob on a potentiometer, is observable immediately. The performance of a system can be optimized faster by judicious knob "twiddling" on an analog computer than by printing out run after run on a digital computer.

In the mid-1960s the hybrid computer emerged, consisting of an analog computer interfaced with a digital computer. The combination allows easier representation of nonlinearities and reduction of the data obtained by the computer, such as Fourier analysis of the waveform. This chapter is devoted only to the fundamentals of analog computation.

20.2 Components of an Analog Computer

The circuitry of an analog computer needed to solve linear differential equations consists of operational amplifiers, resistor networks to convert the amplifiers to voltage summers and inverters, R-C networks to convert the amplifiers to integrators, potentiometers (properly called attenuators, but commonly called pots), and an oscilloscope or X-Y pen recorder to draw the output curves. The components available for solving nonlinear differential equations include multipliers, diodes, function generators, signal comparators, and track-store units. This chapter will concentrate on the linear components and multipliers, and in particular those used in the EAI (Electronic Associates, Inc.) TR-20 analog computer.

20.3 Operational Amplifiers

The TR-20 has 20 single-ended operational amplifiers, one of which is represented by Fig. 20.1. The forward and feedback impedances Z_1 and

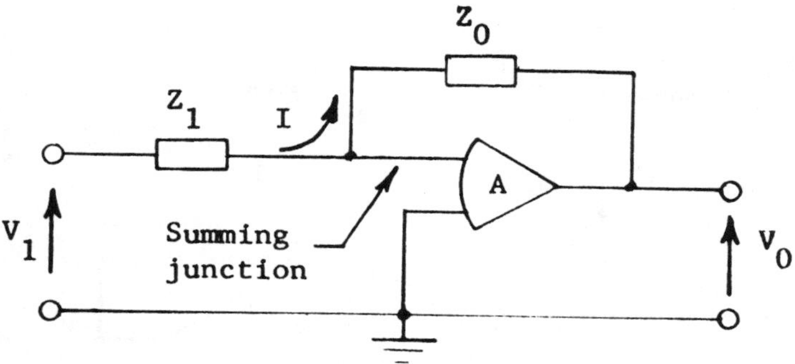

Fig. 20.1. Operational amplifier.

Z_0 are in general functions of s. For example, if the feedback component is a capacitor C, $Z_0 = 1/Cs$. Since the input impedance (between the summing junction and ground) is very high, the same current I flows in the forward impedance Z_1 and the feedback impedance Z_0. The difference between the input and output voltages is

$$V_1 - V_0 = I(Z_1 + Z_0)\,. \tag{20.1}$$

Since the open-loop gain of the amplifier A is very high, and the output voltage V_0 is finite, the input voltage is virtually zero:

$$V_1 - I Z_1 = 0\,. \tag{20.2}$$

Dividing Eq. (20.1) by Eq. (20.2) produces

$$\frac{V_1 - V_0}{V_1} = \frac{I(Z_1 + Z_0)}{I Z_1}$$

or

$$\frac{V_0}{V_1} = -\frac{Z_0}{Z_1}\,. \tag{20.3}$$

The transfer function of the amplifier is therefore determined by the forward and feedback impedances, not by its open-loop gain.

If several voltages are applied at the input of the amplifier, the circuit appears as in Fig. 20.2. Since the summing junction SJ is at nearly ground potential, the current thru the impedance Z_1 is V_1/Z_1. Similarly, the current thru Z_2 is V_2/Z_2. The sum of currents entering the summing junction is

$$\frac{V_1}{Z_1} + \frac{V_2}{Z_2} + \frac{V_3}{Z_3} + \cdots + \frac{V_0}{Z_0} = 0 \tag{20.4}$$

or

$$V_0 = -\left(\frac{Z_0}{Z_1}V_1 + \frac{Z_0}{Z_2}V_2 + \frac{Z_0}{Z_3}V_3 + \cdots\right). \tag{20.5}$$

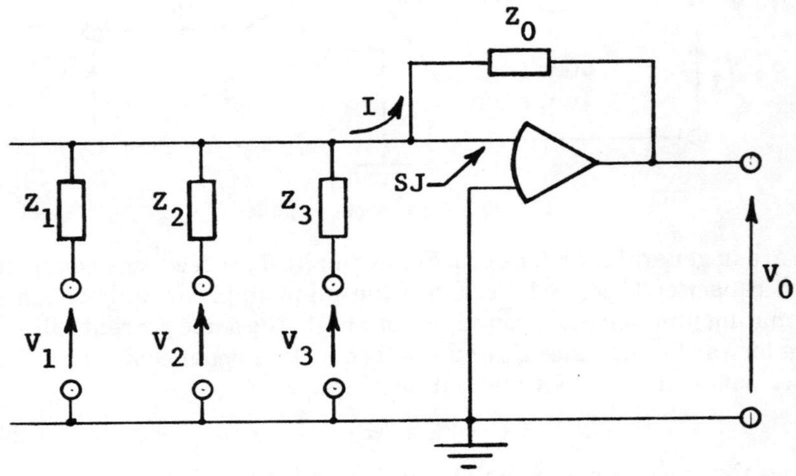

Fig. 20.2. Summing amplifier.

If all the impedances are resistors of equal value,

$$V_0 = -\left(\frac{R_0}{R_1}V_1 + \frac{R_0}{R_2}V_2 + \frac{R_0}{R_3}V_3 + \cdots\right) = -(V_1 + V_2 + V_3 + \cdots) \tag{20.6}$$

and the circuit is a summer. In the TR-20, R_0 is 100 $k\Omega$ and R_1, R_2, etc. are either 100 or 10 $k\Omega$. If the latter value is chosen, the amplifier also provides a gain of 10. Another simple connection provides an R_0 of 10 $k\Omega$ and an R_1 of 100 $k\Omega$, and therefore a gain of 0.1.

Frequently an amplifier is needed simply to invert the polarity of a signal. Then only one forward resistor R_1 is needed, equal to R_0, and $V_0 = -V_1$. An amplifier of the TR-20 is patched for gains of 1 or 10 by inserting a four-prong bottle plug onto its four upper terminals. All five outputs of the amplifier are available. One output is the lower right hole of the bottle plug.

20.4 Integrators

If the forward impedance in Fig. 20.1 is a resistor R and the feedback component is a capacitor C as in Fig. 20.3, and v_1 and v_0 are the input

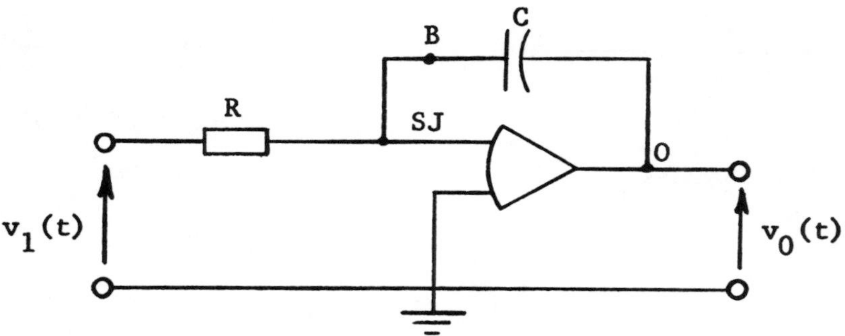

Fig. 20.3. Integrator.

and output voltages as functions of time, the sum of the currents flowing into the summing junction is

$$\frac{v_1(t)}{R} + C\frac{dv_0(t)}{dt} = 0 \tag{20.7}$$

and therefore

$$v_0(t) = -\frac{1}{RC}\int_0^t v_1(x)dx + v_0(0) \,. \tag{20.8}$$

The amplifier is now an integrator. In the TR-20, C is 10 μF and R is either 100 $k\Omega$ or 10 $k\Omega$. The amplifier therefore provides a gain of 1 or 10 in addition to integrating the input. The TR-20 has separate integrator networks that are patched to an amplifier by connecting the terminals marked SJ, B, and O on both components. The locations of these terminals in the circuit are shown in Fig. 20.3. Each integrator network also has a terminal marked IC, to which an initial integrator output voltage can be applied, if required by the problem. The +REF and −REF terminals provide +10 and −10 volts DC. A pot connected between one of these terminals and the IC terminal provides any initial condition between −10 and +10 volts. As Eq. (20.5) shows, an integrator can serve the dual purpose of summing and integrating. The standard symbols for an inverter, a summer, and an integrator are shown in Fig. 20.4. The identification number of the amplifier or pot is shown within its triangle or circle. The gain for each input is shown at the input terminal.

20.5 Potentiometers

The pots, one of which is shown in Fig. 20.5, multiply their input voltage by any fraction between zero and one. In the TR-20 the lower limit for reasonable accuracy is 0.01. The pots have 5000 ohms and 10

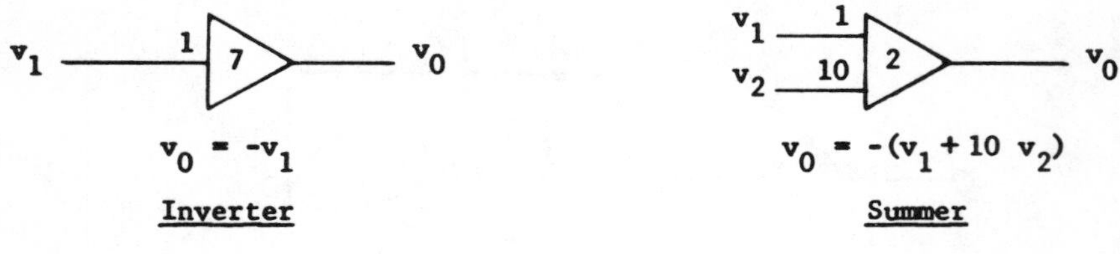

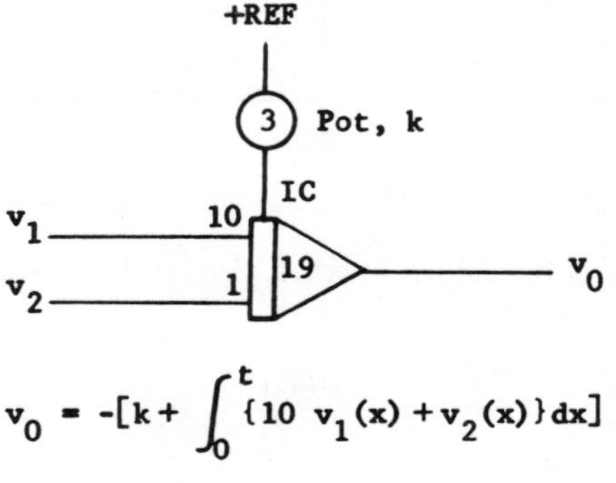

Fig. 20.4. Symbols for analog components.

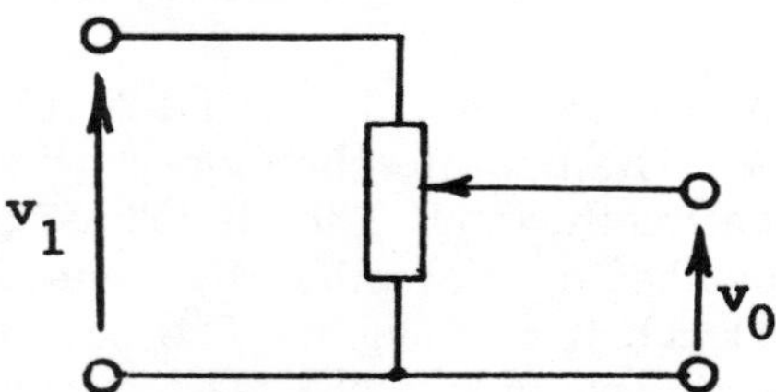

Fig. 20.5. Potentiometer.

turns. To prevent error due to loading of their outputs, pots should not be connected in cascade, and only one amplifier should be connected to the output of a pot, as in Fig. 20.6. The pot is represented by a circle

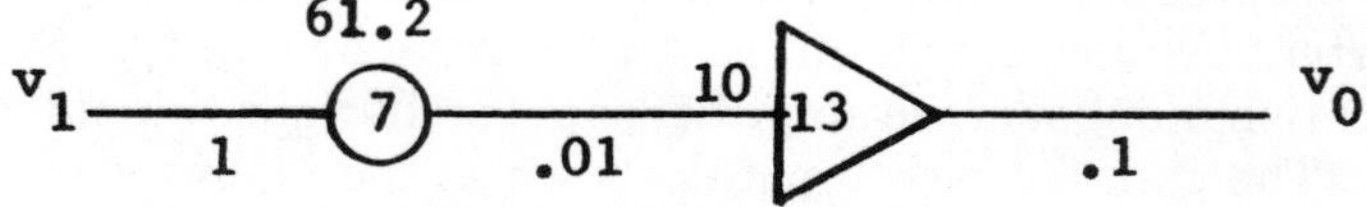

Fig. 20.6. Potentiometer connected into an amplifer.

containing its identification number, and its desired setting is shown next to it. The TR-20 has 20 pots, each of which can be set by first setting a calibrated master "null pot" to the desired setting. Its input voltage is 10 volts, as shown in Fig. 20.7. The operating pot is then disconnected

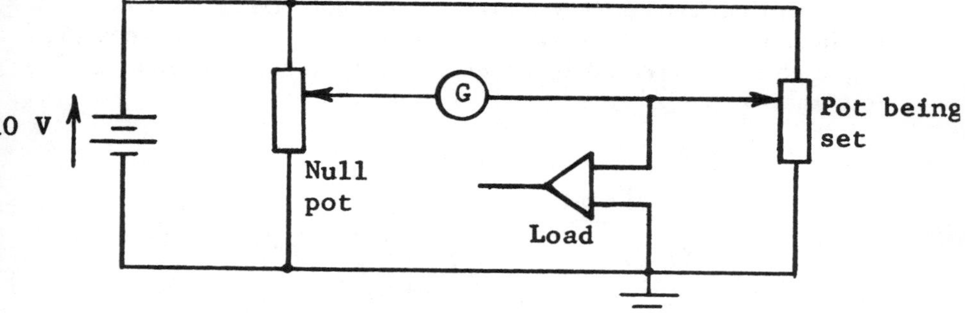

Fig. 20.7. Connection for setting a pot.

from its input and connected to the 10-volt supply. Its load is kept connected. At the same time the outputs of the two pots are connected to buck each other thru a galvanometer G. When the operating pot is adjusted to null the galvanometer, its setting is correct. This scheme eliminates the need for 20 calibrated dials, and corrects for the loading of each pot. If the gain of the amplifier to which the output of a pot is connected is changed from 1 to 10 or vice versa, the pot should be reset, because its load has changed.

20.6 Amplitude Scaling

Because the gains of the pots and amplifiers of an analog computer are of limited range, they must usually be scaled. This requirement, which is not made by a digital computer, makes analog computation seem formidable to the beginner. Scaling is not a straightforward process, but with a little practice can be accomplished with a reasonable amount of cutting and trying. *Amplitude scaling* is accomplished by changing the level of the voltage in various parts of the analog diagram. For example, suppose that in Fig. 20.6 the input voltage v_1 is at the arbitrary level 1. The output voltage of pot 7 should be 61.2 v_1. If the pot is set at the realistic value of 0.612, the output voltage is 0.612 v_1, or at level 0.01. No harm is done. This voltage is applied to a gain-of-10 terminal of amplifier 13, and therefore comes out at level 0.1. Other voltages can be added at the gain-of-10 inputs of the amplifier, if they are at level 0.01, or at gain-of-1 inputs if they are at level 0.1. The scaling must be carried throughout the block diagram, so that the levels at every amplifier input are correctly matched.

20.7 Time Scaling

An additional opportunity for getting pot settings into the usable range is provided by *time scaling*, namely making the model run faster or slower than the actual system. This technique can be explained with the help of two examples. First consider the simple feedback circuit of Fig. 20.8 to which the driving function $y = -a \sin \omega t$ is applied. The integrator input is

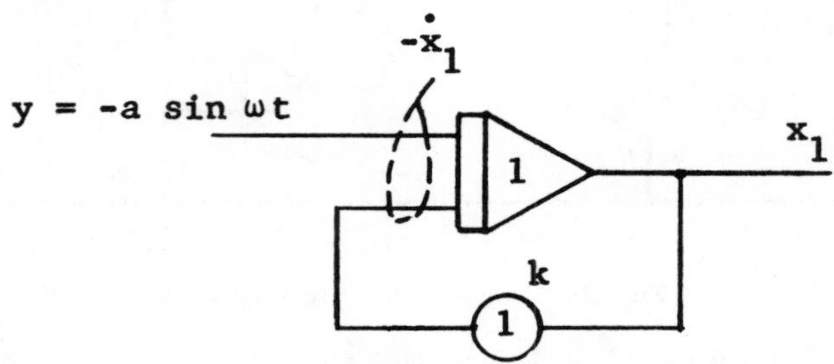

Fig. 20.8. Simple feedback circuit.

$$\dot{x}_1 = a \sin \omega t - k\, x_1 \,. \tag{20.9}$$

If the initial integrator output is zero, the subsequent output is

$$x_1(t) = \frac{a\,\omega}{k^2 + \omega^2}\, e^{-kt} + \frac{a}{\sqrt{k^2 + \omega^2}} \sin\left(\omega t - \tan^{-1}\frac{\omega}{k}\right) . \tag{20.10}$$

Suppose that a, ω, and k are decreased by a factor of 10. The coefficients of the two terms in Eq. (20.10) are unchanged, and so is the phase angle. Only the coefficients of time t change. They are reduced by 10. The output is now

$$x_2(t) = x_1(0.1\, t) \,. \tag{20.11}$$

The integrator output reaches the same values as before, but takes 10 times as long. The model is running one tenth as fast as the original system. The integrator input was originally

$$\dot{x}_1(t) = -\frac{k\,a\,\omega}{k^2 + \omega^2}\, e^{-kt} + \frac{\omega\, a}{\sqrt{k^2 + \omega^2}} \cos\left(\omega t - \tan^{-1}\frac{\omega}{k}\right) , \tag{20.12}$$

and after time scaling is

$$\dot{x}_2(t) = 0.1\, \dot{x}_1(0.1\, t) \,. \tag{20.13}$$

The level of the integrator input has decreased by 10, while the level of the integrator output has remained the same. Time scaling by a factor of 10 has caused the integrator to increase the voltage level of the signal passing thru it by 10.

An analog diagram containing two integrators is shown in Fig. 20.9.

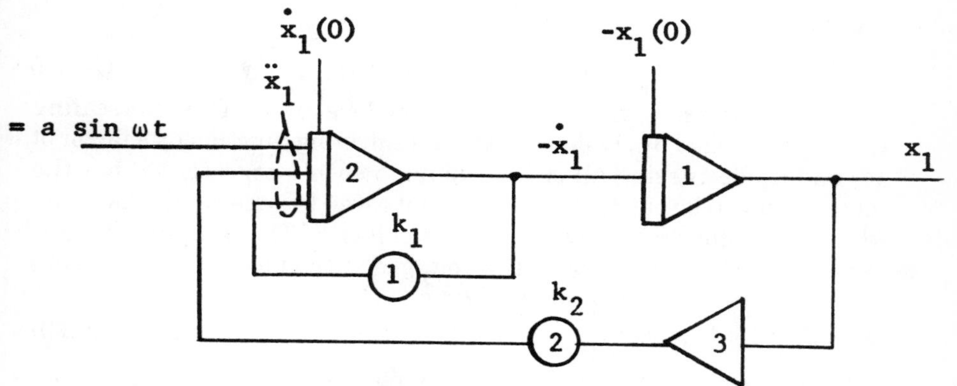

Fig. 20.9. Block diagram with two integrators.

The input to integrator 2 is

$$\ddot{x}_1 = a \sin \omega t - k_1 \dot{x}_1 - k_2 x_1 . \tag{20.14}$$

If the integrator outputs are initially zero, the solution of this differential equation is

$$x_1(t) = \frac{a\,\omega}{(c_1^2 + \omega^2)(c_2 - c_1)} e^{-c_1 t} + \frac{a\,\omega}{(c_2^2 + \omega^2)(c_1 - c_2)} e^{-c_2 t}$$

$$+ \frac{a}{\sqrt{(k_2 - \omega^2)^2 + (\omega\, k_1)^2}} \sin(\omega t + \theta) \tag{20.15}$$

where

$$c_1 = \frac{k_1 + \sqrt{k_1^2 - 4\,k_2}}{2}\,, \qquad c_2 = \frac{k_1 - \sqrt{k_1^2 - 4\,k_2}}{2}\,,$$

and

$$\theta = -\tan^{-1} \frac{\omega\, k_1}{k_2 - \omega^2} . \tag{20.16}$$

Now decrease ω and k_1 by 10, and a and k_2 by 100. The coefficients of the three terms in Eq. (20.15) are unchanged, and so is the phase angle θ. The output of integrator 1 is now

$$x_2(t) = x_1(0.1\, t) . \tag{20.17}$$

This model has been time scaled to run one tenth as fast as the unscaled model. The new inputs of integrators 1 and 2 are

$$\dot{x}_2(t) = 0.1\, \dot{x}_1(0.1\, t) \tag{20.18}$$

and

$$\ddot{x}_2(t) = 0.01\,\ddot{x}_1(0.1\,t)\,. \tag{20.19}$$

Each integrator now increases the voltage level by 10. The time scaling was accomplished by (1) slowing down the driving function by a factor of 10, and (2) decreasing all of the inputs to each integrator so that the input level will be one tenth of the output level. In general, the factor by which the solution is slowed down is called β. The *computer time* τ, namely the time required for the voltages in the model to reach given scaled values, is β times the *real time t*. Thus

$$\tau = \beta\,t\,. \tag{20.20}$$

Any nonzero initial condition of course has the same level as the integrator output. Suppose that in the diagram of Fig. 20.9, $k_1 = 5$, $k_2 = 60$, $x_1(0) = 0.02$, $\dot{x}_1(0) = 0.5$, and the driving function is $y = 3\sin 10t$. The diagram with numbers added is shown in Fig. 20.10. If β is chosen

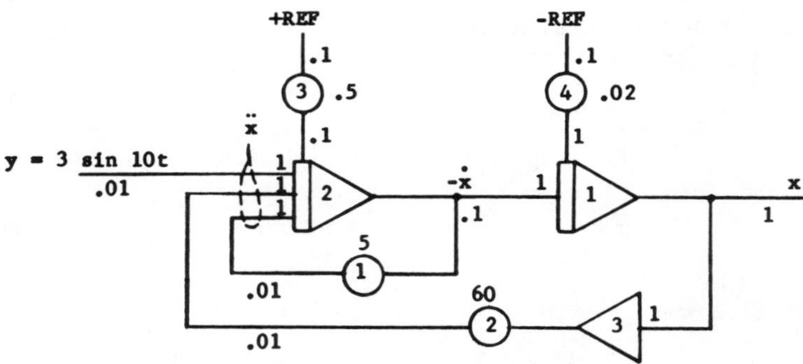

Fig. 20.10. Time-scaled diagram.

to be 10, and the voltage level at the output of integrator 1 is 1, the levels at the integrator inputs are .1 and .01. Each level is shown on the diagram. The scaled driving function is

$$y = 0.03\sin t\,. \tag{20.21}$$

The pot settings are calculated in Fig. 20.11. The voltage levels supplied by the +REF and −REF terminals must be the same because the magnitudes of these two voltages are the same, 10 volts. The levels there need not be 1, and are 0.1 in Fig. 20.10. Plus or minus 10 volts produces full-scale deflection of the oscilloscope with the TR-20. The initial output of integrator 1 will therefore be 20 percent of full scale, which represents 0.02 units of the variable x.

Pot No.	Input Level	Output Level	Pot Setting
1	.1	.01	$\frac{.01}{.1}$ (5) = .5
2	1	.01	$\frac{.01}{1}$ (60) = .6
3	.1	.1	$\frac{.1}{.1}$ (.5) = .5
4	.1	1	$\frac{1}{.1}$ (.02) = .2

Fig. 20.11. Pot settings.

A model with any number of integrators can be time scaled in an attempt to bring the pots into their useful range. Decide on the slow-down β desired. Each integrator will then increase the voltage level by β. Change each pot so that it transforms its input level to the correct output level. Choose the level of each IC to match the level of its integrator output. If a driving function is used, slow it down by a factor of β, and adjust its amplitude to match the level where it is connected.

20.8 Example 1. A Linear System

An example will illustrate the technique of scaling a large model. Fig. 20.12 is a simplified block diagram of a servo drive for aircraft instru-

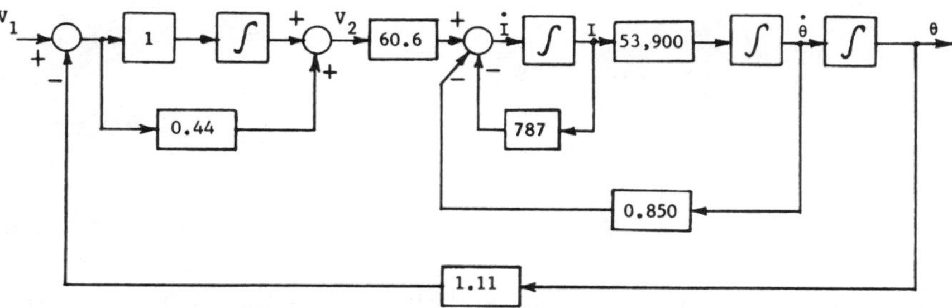

Fig. 20.12. Servo drive for aircraft instruments.

ments. The input voltage $V_1(t)$ is provided by a transducer such as a pressure gage or a tachometer. The output θ is the angular displacement of the pointer on the instrument. A diagram for determining the step response of the servo on an analog computer is shown in Fig. 20.13. Like the block diagram, it has four integrators. Although the block diagram has three summing junctions, the analog diagram needs only two summers because integrator 12 also serves as a summer. Fig. 20.13 needs three inverters, 10, 17, and 18, to correct polarities for summing. A 10-volt step is provided by any of the +REF terminals on the TR-20. Pot 18 is needed to lower the height of the step so that none of the amplifiers in the model will be overloaded. The output of amplifier 14, which is the angular deflection θ, is connected to the display oscilloscope.

Scaling this model is a challenge because the gains to be represented by pots range from 0.44 to 53,900. If pot 15 is to be set at the convenient value of 0.539, that pot will reduce the voltage level by a factor of 10^{-5}. The level can be recovered by the two integrators that follow pot 15 if the diagram is time scaled. A choice of $\beta = 100$ seems reasonable. Each integrator then raises the level by 100. The calculations of pot settings are tabulated in Fig. 20.13, and each voltage level is shown on the diagram. Notice that there is no absolute voltage level. The scaling would still be correct if all of the levels were multiplied by the same constant. The connections to +REF or −REF, for a step input or for initial conditions, may be made at any level, but the levels must all be the same.

20.9 Example 2. A Nonlinear System

A second example will demonstrate the use of a multiplier, and will also illustrate the remarkable balance of nature. Let x_1 be the number of rabbits in a forest and x_2 be the number of foxes. Initially there are 400 rabbits and 700 foxes. Assume that the number of encounters between foxes and rabbits in a given time is proportional to the product $x_1 x_2$. The relationship between the two populations can be represented approximately by the equations

$$\frac{dx_1}{dt} = 2\,x_1 - k\,x_1\,x_2 \tag{20.22}$$

and

$$\frac{dx_2}{dt} = -x_2 + k\,x_1\,x_2\,, \tag{20.23}$$

where $k = 0.01$. This coefficient and the other two, 2 and -1, seem reasonable and can be modified as desired. The analog diagram of the two equations is shown in Fig. 20.14. The multiplier, indicated by the box containing a cross, consists of a multiplier unit which has terminals marked B, O, +X, −X, +Y, and −Y, patched into one of the operational amplifiers as shown in Fig. 20.15. On the 7.137 multiplier units of the

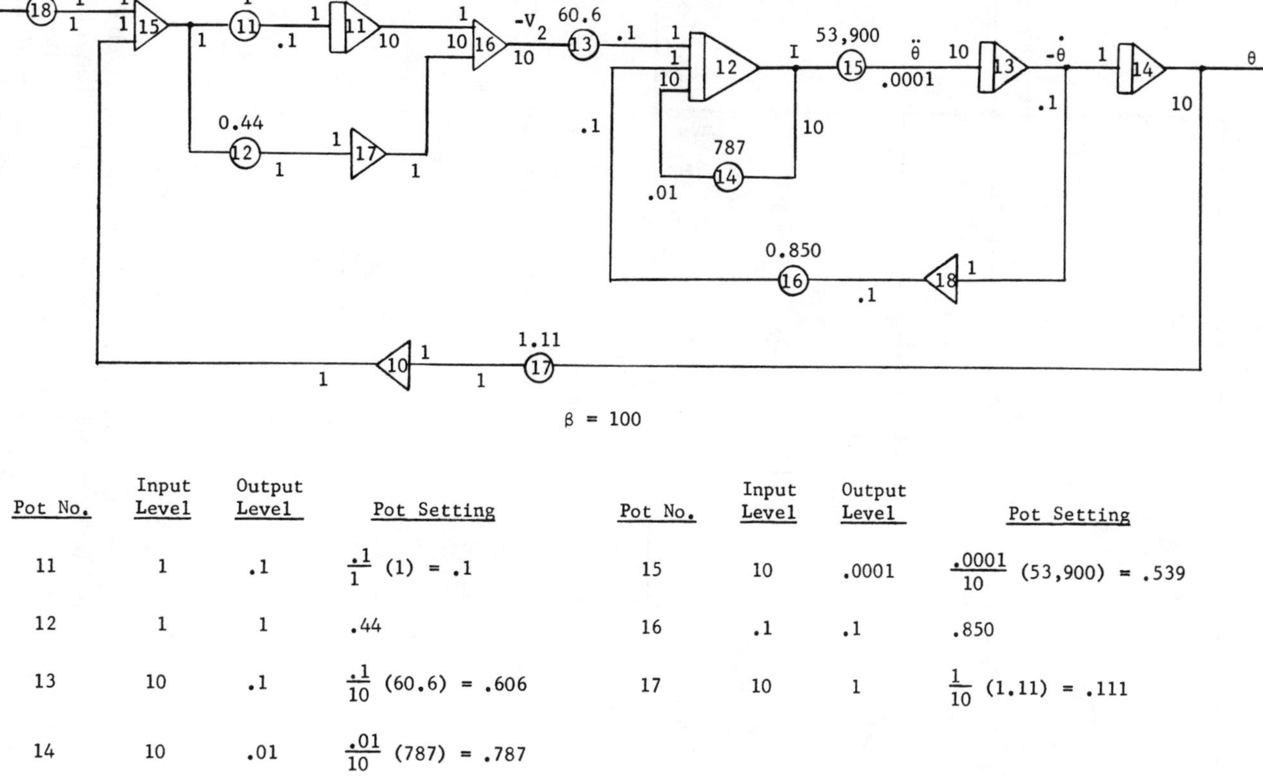

Pot No.	Input Level	Output Level	Pot Setting
11	1	.1	$\frac{.1}{1}$ (1) = .1
12	1	1	.44
13	10	.1	$\frac{.1}{10}$ (60.6) = .606
14	10	.01	$\frac{.01}{10}$ (787) = .787
15	10	.0001	$\frac{.0001}{10}$ (53,900) = .539
16	.1	.1	.850
17	10	1	$\frac{1}{10}$ (1.11) = .111

Fig. 20.13. Analog diagram of the servo drive.

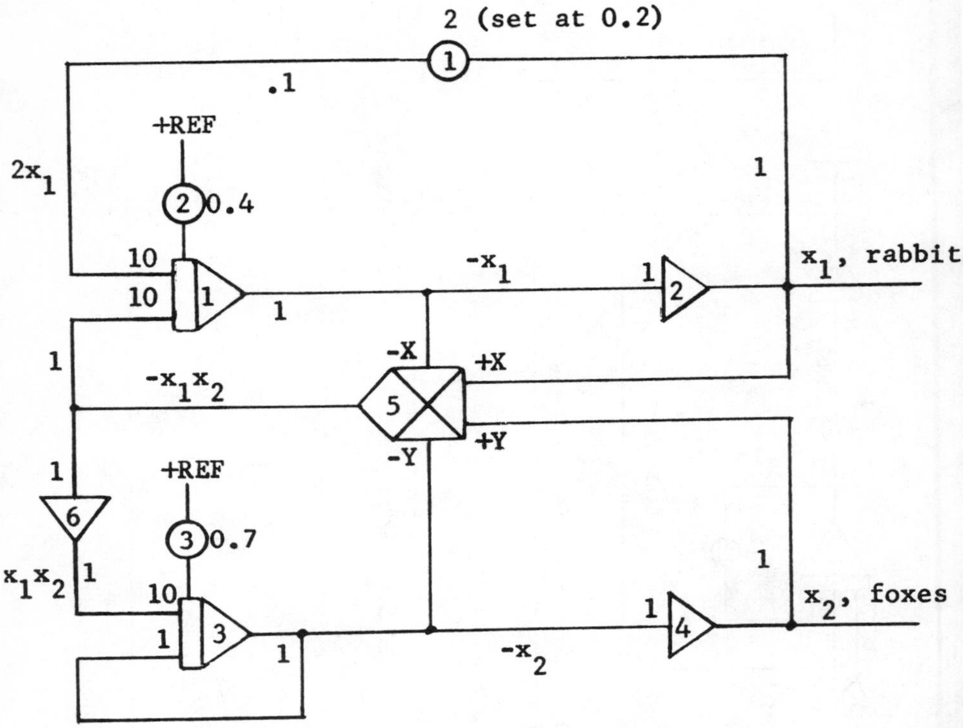

Fig. 20.14. Analog diagram of the rabbit and fox populations.

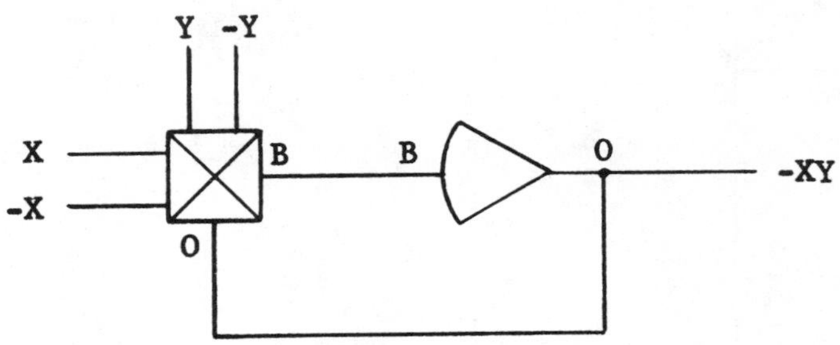

Fig. 20.15. Multiplier unit and its amplifier.

TR-20, leave bottle plugs on the 10 upper terminals. Remove the bottle plugs from the amplifier. Connect the B and O terminals of the multiplier unit and the amplifier. Both plus and minus X and Y signals must be connected to the multiplier unit. Sometimes, as in Fig. 20.14, all four signals are available. If not, extra inverters are needed. The output of the multiplier is one tenth of the product of the two inputs, if all three are measured in volts. If 10 volts are applied at X and Y, the output is 10 volts. If X and Y are measured in fractions of the reference voltage or *machine units*, the output is $-XY$ machine units. The level of the output is the product of the levels of X and Y.

Achieving this simple relationship in Fig. 20.14 requires a modification. The magnitudes of X and Y are the magnitudes of the outputs of the two integrators. If the initial conditions are to be expressed in machine units, they must of course be less than 1. Initially, however, $x_1 =$ 400 rabbits and $x_2 = 700$ foxes. This difficulty can be avoided by expressing x_1 and x_2 in kilorabbits and kilofoxes. Then they have the realistic initial values of 0.4 and 0.7. Since the numerical values of x_1 and x_2 are decreased by 1000, each term of Eqs. (20.22) and (20.23) decreases by 1000. The parameter k must be increased by 1000 to the new value of 10. These equations become

$$\frac{dx_1}{dt} = 2\,x_1 - 10\,x_1\,x_2 \tag{20.24}$$

$$\frac{dx_2}{dt} = -x_2 + 10\,x_1\,x_2\,, \tag{20.25}$$

and in this form were used to construct Fig. 20.14. The interesting result of plotting x_1 against x_2 on an *X-Y* plotter is shown in Fig. 20.16. Periodically the rabbits are nearly exterminated. They are saved from extinction by the sharp drop in the fox population. Starting from any initial conditions, the two populations spiral in to the steady-state values $x_1 = 0.1$ kilorabbits and $x_2 = 0.2$ kilofoxes.

20.10 Example 3. A Phase-Plane Plot

A plot of a variable versus its time derivative is called a *phase-plane plot*. It is a convenient display of the solution of a second-order differential equation, because it shows both state variables continuously. Phase-plane plots can be produced easily by an analog computer. For example, consider the van der Pol equation

$$\ddot{y} - \lambda(1 - y^2)\dot{y} + y = 0 \tag{20.26}$$

or

$$\ddot{y} = \lambda(\dot{y} - \dot{y}y^2) - y\,, \tag{20.27}$$

in which y is the charge flowing in an R-L-C circuit whose resistor is nonlinear. The resistance, proportional to $-\lambda(1 - y^2)$, is produced by a triode tube or tunnel diode. Eq. (20.27) is represented by the analog diagram of Fig. 20.17. This circuit overdrives amplifier 7. The trouble

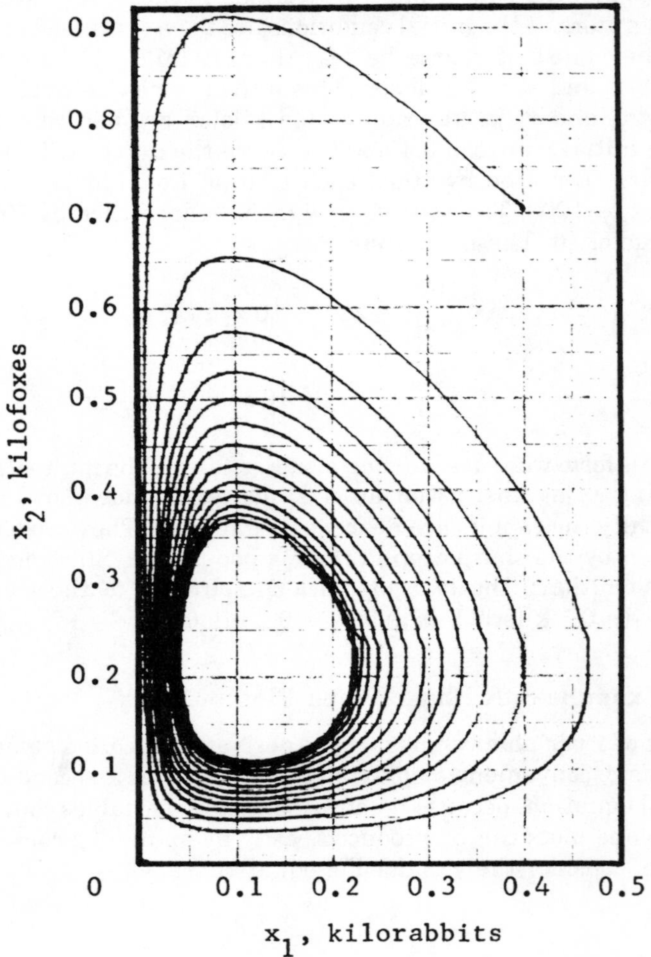

Fig. 20.16. The balance of nature.

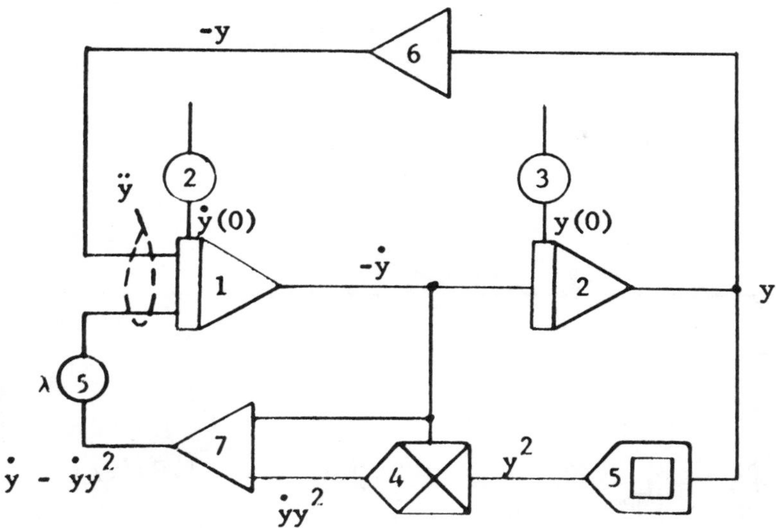

Fig. 20.17. First analog diagram of the van der Pol equation.

can be corrected by replacing y and $\dot{y}$ by $0.2y$ and $0.2\dot{y}$ as in Fig. 20.18. Calculation of the new variables shows that pot 4 is required, set at 0.4, and pot 5 now represents 0.25 λ. Inverters 3 and 8 are added because the multiplier needs both positive and negative values of its input variables. The symbol containing a square is a squarer, namely a multiplier to which the same signal is applied at both the X and Y terminals. In Fig. 20.18 the signal $0.2y$ (the output of integrator 2) is applied to the +X and −Y terminals, and $-0.2y$ (the output of inverter 6) to −X and +Y. Then the output of the squarer is $(0.2y)^2$ instead of $-(0.2y)^2$.

With $\lambda = 1$ and the initial conditions

$$0.2y(0) = -0.4 \qquad \text{and} \qquad 0.2\dot{y}(0) = 0.4\,, \qquad (20.28)$$

the phase-plane plot in Fig. 20.19 was drawn by an *X-Y* plotter. Notice that the state variables spiral in quickly to steady-state oscillations, and describe a *limit cycle*. For any initial conditions, either inside or outside of the limit cycle, the variables move quickly to the limit cycle.

20.11 Additional Instructions for Operating the TR-20

1. The amplifiers drift a little, and should be checked once in a while. Set the voltmeter function switch on BAL. Turn the AMPL SEL switch to the numbers of the amplifiers being used. If an amplifier is balanced,

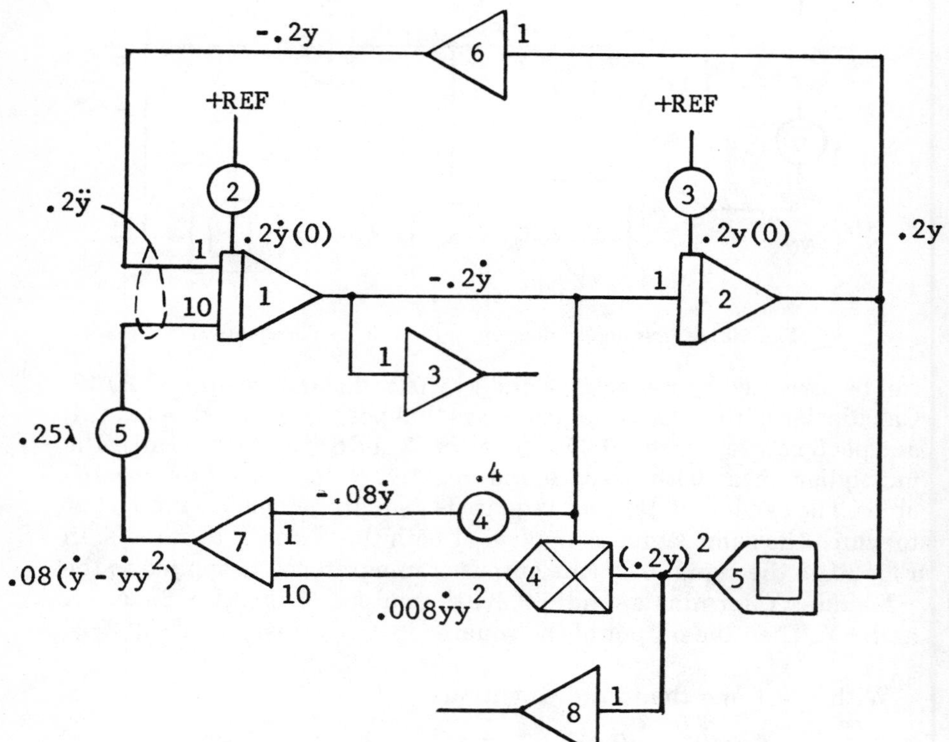

Fig. 20.18. Scaled diagram of the van der Pol equation.

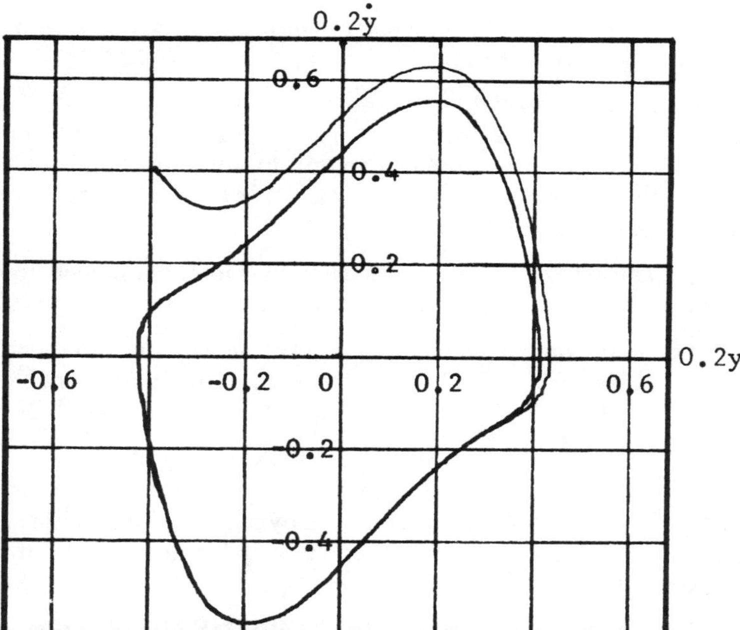

Fig. 20.19. Phase-plane plot of the van der Pol equation.

the panel meter reads zero. If necessary, open the drop-front panel below the controls, and adjust the balance pot of the amplifier to null the meter.

2. Before calibrating the pots, put the reference selector switch (+10, OFF, −10) at +10. Turn the COMPUTE TIME MILLISEC switch to OFF. The trace on the rep-op oscilloscope will stop. Turn off the rep-op unit or turn down the brightness, to keep the spot from burning the screen.

3. To set the pots, turn the voltmeter function switch to POT BUS. Set the NULL POT to the value desired for pot 1. Depress the small push-button next to pot 1, and adjust pot 1 to null the panel meter. Repeat the operation for the other pots.

4. To display a variable on the scope, jumper X_D and Λ on the DISPLAY terminals. Connect the variable to Y_1, Y_2, Y_3, or Y_4 and turn the CHANNEL switch on the rep-op unit to the same subscript. Set the FUNCTION switch on the rep-op unit at SWEEP. Put the rocker switch on the TR-20 at HOLD.

5. To display two, three, or four variables as functions of time, connect them to Y_1 thru Y_4, and turn the CHANNEL switch to ALL.

6. To display two variables x and y against each other, connect x to Y_4 and y to Y_1, Y_2, or Y_3. The jumper from X_D to Λ can stay on. Turn the CHANNEL switch to the same subscript as y. Put the FUNCTION switch at X PLOT.

7. When the TR-20 is used with the rep-op unit, the 10-μF feedback capacitor in each integrator is replaced by a 0.02-μF capacitor. According to Eq. (20.8), the computer then runs 500 times faster. This speed permits a convenient display on the scope.

8. The calibrations on the COMPUTER TIME MILLISEC switch are correct when the vernier is all the way counterclockwise. They indicate the computer time of each repetitive run, during which the scope trace sweeps 10 horizontal divisions. If for example the switch is at 20, and the model has been scaled with $\beta = 100$, ten horizontal divisions represent $(0.020)(500)/100 = 0.1$ real seconds.

9. The OVLD IND consists of 22 lamps that light if their corresponding amplifier is overloaded. Usually the cause of an overload is a patching mistake. If a correctly-patched amplifier overloads, for example, because a pot was turned up too high during a run, put the rocker switch at RESET to disconnect the integrator inputs and reset the initial integrator outputs.

10. When the TR-20 is used with an X-Y plotter or strip-chart recorder, put the COMPUTE TIME MILLISEC switch at OFF. Put the rocker switch at RESET. Connect the signals desired from the patchboard to the recorder terminals. When adjusting the initial X and Y positions of the plotter, remember that the initial conditions are on. When the rocker switch is turned to OPER, the solution starts, and continues until the switch is turned back to either HOLD or RESET. The HOLD position freezes the solution by removing the integrator inputs. Switching back to OPER restarts the solution where it left off.

Chapter 21

THE FIELD EQUATIONS OF ELASTICITY

21.1 Introduction

Stress is a defined quantity that can be neither observed nor measured and yet is responsible for most of the failures of manufactured products. A few structures, such as the floor of a building, fail because the static load is too heavy. Such failures are relatively few because symptoms of impending disaster are usually present. More often, products such as automobiles and airplanes fail because large impact loads are applied accidentally. Still more often, parts fail in fatigue under the application of repeated stress over a long time. Turbine buckets, generator stator bars, the tubes in a heat exchanger, and airplane wings have failed in fatigue. Any part that moves cyclically, whether intentionally or not, is potentially in danger of failure under repeated stress. The strength of a material specimen is tested in laboratories by (1) pulling it with a slowly-increasing tensile force until it breaks, (2) hitting it with hammer blows of known momentum, (3) applying a fixed load at elevated temperatures, and (4) vibrating the specimen at fixed amplitude. Much remains to be learned about correlating the results of one strength test with another and with survival of the material under operating conditions. The strength of a material is influenced in unknown ways by the part size and shape, finish smoothness, cleanliness, and the way in which the load is applied. This chapter and the following two are devoted to methods of calculating stresses and deflections of loaded structures. The engineer who becomes proficient in these methods still has the problem of deciding whether the stresses and deflections are acceptable.

The calculation of stress starts with the field equations: 15 equations relating the stresses, strains, and displacements at any point in a stressed body. When these quantities are known on boundaries of the body, the equations and the boundary conditions constitute a *boundary-value problem*. Its solution gives the values of the quantities at any point in the body. For irregularly-shaped three-dimensional bodies, the solution is formidable. Fortunately, for many structural shapes the equations can be reduced to two dimensions, and useful solutions can be obtained. In this chapter the three-dimensional field equations and their two-dimensional simplifications will be derived.

21.2 Stresses and Strains

Stress can be defined easily for a long bar of uniform cross section A, shown in Fig. 21.1. If the axial force P is applied, the *stress* in the bar is

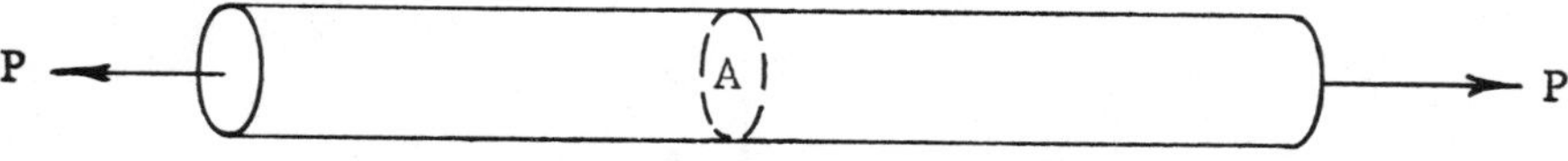

Fig. 21.1. Bar in tension.

the force per unit area:

$$\sigma = \frac{P}{A} \qquad \text{psi or pascals .} \tag{21.1}$$

Tests show that this quantity is uniform throughout the bar except near the grips at the ends. Tests also show that for many materials the fractional elongation or *strain* ε of the uniformly-stressed portion of the bar is proportional to the stress:

$$\sigma = E\, \varepsilon\ . \tag{21.2}$$

This is *Hooke's law* in one dimension. The constant of proportionality E is the *modulus of elasticity*. For steel, E is about 3×10^7 psi or about 2×10^{11} Pa, and is the same in tension or compression. The highest stress for which Hooke's law applies is called the *proportional limit*. For structural steel it is about 33,000 psi or 228 MPa.

If a part of a structure has an irregular shape, the stress in it is not uniform but varies from one point to another. The definition of stress is modified accordingly, to be the net load acting on an infinitesimal area of the part, divided by the area. Fig. 21.2A shows a stressed body cut

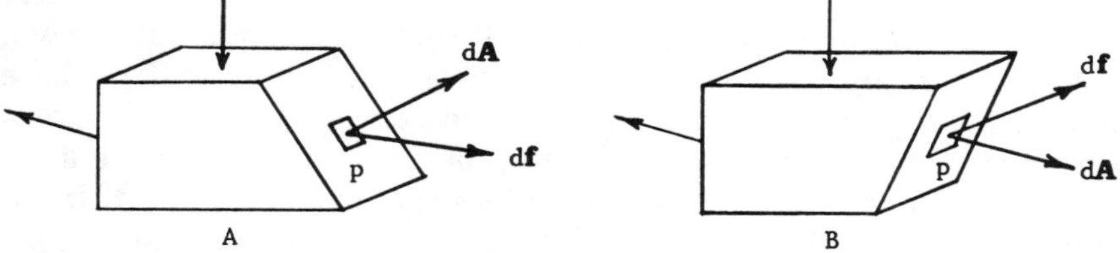

Fig. 21.2. Two cuts thru the point p in a stressed body.

along a plane thru the interior point p. The half that has been removed exerts a force at every point on the plane. The force $d\mathbf{f}$ is exerted on a differential area of the plane $d\mathbf{A}$ that encloses point p. Notice that $d\mathbf{f}$ and the surface vector $d\mathbf{A}$ are in general not in the same direction. The quantity $d\mathbf{f}/dA$ has the dimensions of stress. Since it is a vector, it can be resolved into three rectangular components. The component normal to the plane is called the *normal stress* σ, and components in the plane are called *shear stresses* τ. If the direction of the normal surface vector is x, the normal stress is called σ_x, as in Fig. 21.3. The y and z axes can be

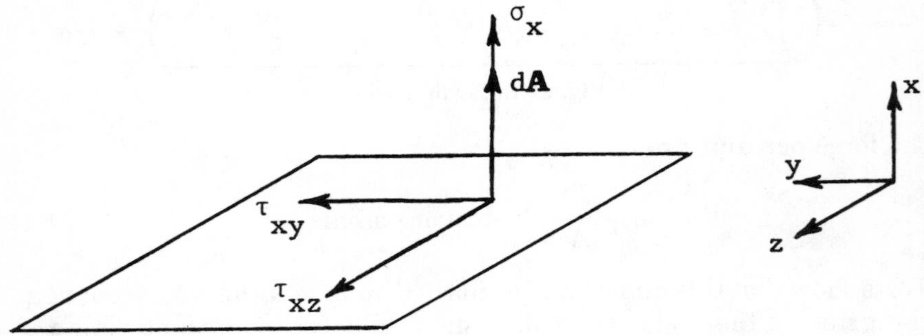

Fig. 21.3. Normal and shear stresses.

any two mutually-perpendicular axes in the plane. Shear stresses in the y and z directions are called τ_{xy} and τ_{xz}. The first subscript refers to the normal to the plane in which the shear stress lies, and the second denotes the direction of the shear stress.

Fig. 21.2B shows the same stressed body cut along a different plane thru the same point p. The magnitudes and directions of $d\mathbf{A}$ and $d\mathbf{f}$ are different. The quantity $d\mathbf{f}/dA$ is different, and so are its components normal and parallel to the new plane. Clearly the three stresses on and in a plane at a point in a body depend not only on the location of the point, but on the orientation of the plane. In order to describe the stresses at a point completely, nine or 3^2 components must be known, namely σ_x, σ_y, σ_z, τ_{xy}, τ_{yx}, τ_{xz}, τ_{zx}, τ_{yz}, and τ_{zy}. A field quantity whose description requires 3^r components is called a *tensor of rank r*. Stress is a second-rank tensor. The positive directions of the nine components of stress at a point are shown on the differential box of Fig. 21.4. If the normal stresses pull outward on the faces of the box, they are called positive or tensile. If they push inward, they are called negative or compressive. On the three faces for which the positive normal stress is in the positive coordinate direction, the positive sense of each shear stress is in the positive direction of its second subscript. On the other three faces the positive normal stress is in the negative coordinate direction, and the positive sense of each shear stress is in the negative direction of its second subscript.

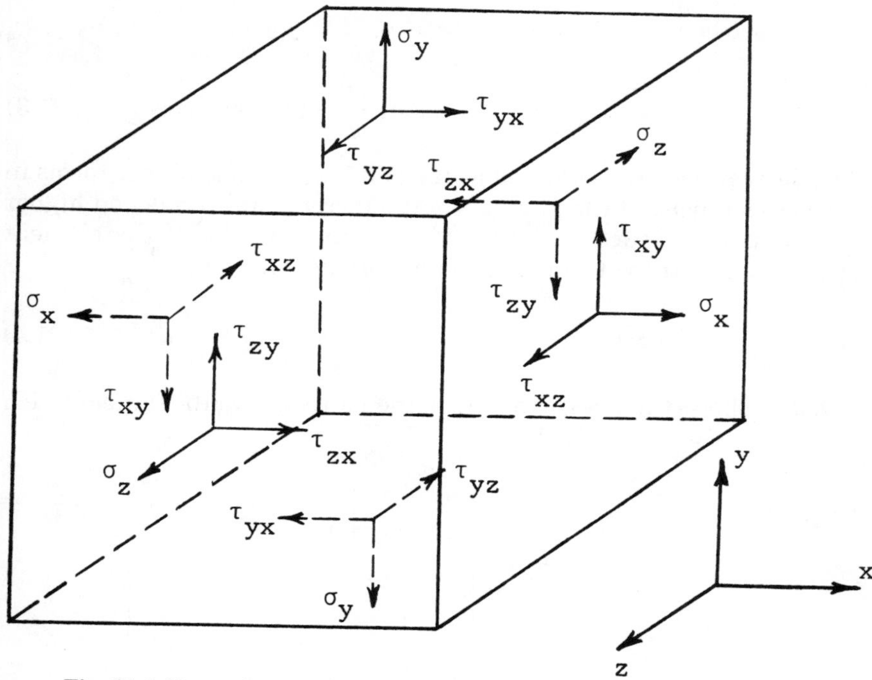

Fig. 21.4. Nomenclature of the stresses at a point.

21.3 The Stress-Equilibrium Equations

The derivation of the field equations begins with a small rectangular element of a stressed body, shown in Fig. 21.5. At the corner whose

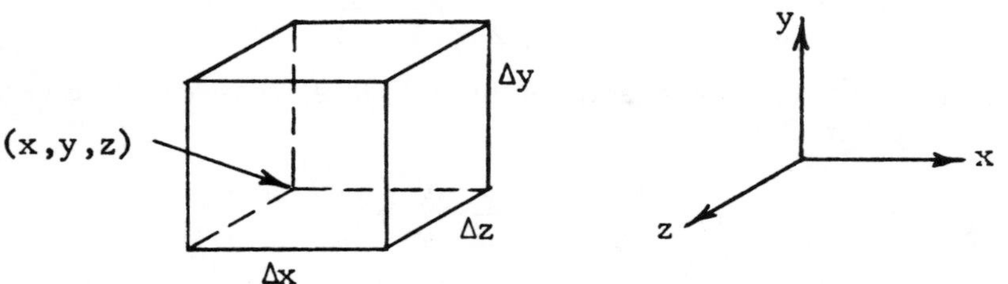

Fig. 21.5. Small rectangular element.

coordinates are x,y, and z, the stresses are σ_x, σ_y, σ_z, τ_{xy}, τ_{yx}, τ_{xz}, τ_{zx}, τ_{yz}, and τ_{zy}. These quantities at the point $(x + \Delta x, y + \Delta y, z + \Delta z)$ can be expressed by a Taylor series which for a function of three variables is

$$f(x + \Delta x, y + \Delta y, z + \Delta z) = f(x,y,z) + \Delta x \frac{\partial f}{\partial x} + \Delta y \frac{\partial f}{\partial y} + \Delta z \frac{\partial f}{\partial z} + \text{higher terms}\,. \qquad (21.3)$$

The derivatives are evaluated at the point (x,y,z). The higher terms in the series consist of the products of the incremental terms and higher derivatives of f, such as $\Delta x\, \Delta y\, \partial^2 f/\partial x\, \partial y$. As the sides of the element approach zero these terms become negligible, and

$$f(x + dx, y + dy, z + dz) = f(x,y,z) + \frac{\partial f}{\partial x} dx + \frac{\partial f}{\partial y} dy + \frac{\partial f}{\partial z} dz\,. \qquad (21.4)$$

Fig. 21.6 shows the stresses acting in the x direction at the center of each

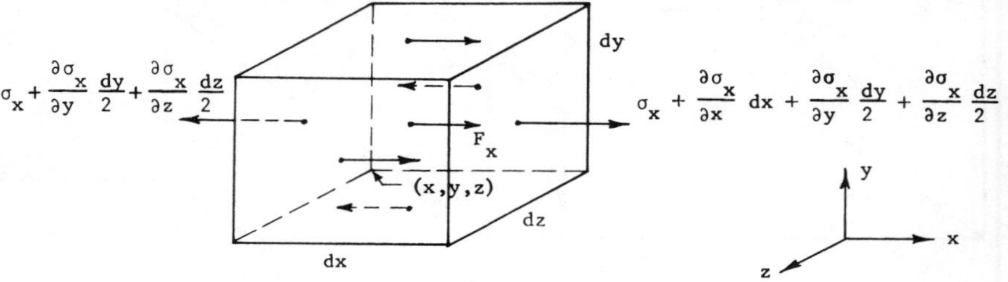

Fig. 21.6. Stresses on a differential element in the x direction.

face of a differential element. The normal stress at the corner (x,y,z) is σ_x. The coordinates of the center of the left face are x, $y + dy/2$, and $z + dz/2$. The normal stress at that point is therefore

$$\sigma_x + \frac{\partial \sigma_x}{\partial y}\frac{dy}{2} + \frac{\partial \sigma_x}{\partial z}\frac{dz}{2}\,.$$

The normal stress at the center of the right face, whose coordinates are $x + dx$, $y + dy/2$, $z + dz/2$, is

$$\sigma_x + \frac{\partial \sigma_x}{\partial x} dx + \frac{\partial \sigma_x}{\partial y}\frac{dy}{2} + \frac{\partial \sigma_x}{\partial z}\frac{dz}{2}\,.$$

Similarly, the shear stresses at the center of the bottom and top faces are

$$\tau_{yx} + \frac{\partial \tau_{yx}}{\partial x}\frac{dx}{2} + \frac{\partial \tau_{yx}}{\partial z}\frac{dz}{2} \quad \text{and} \quad \tau_{yx} + \frac{\partial \tau_{yx}}{\partial x}\frac{dx}{2} + \frac{\partial \tau_{yx}}{\partial y} dy + \frac{\partial \tau_{yx}}{\partial z}\frac{dz}{2}\,,$$

and the shear stresses at the center of the back and front faces are

$$\tau_{zx} + \frac{\partial \tau_{zx}}{\partial x}\frac{dx}{2} + \frac{\partial \tau_{zx}}{\partial y}\frac{dy}{2} \qquad \text{and} \qquad \tau_{zx} + \frac{\partial \tau_{zx}}{\partial x}\frac{dx}{2} + \frac{\partial \tau_{zx}}{\partial y}\frac{dy}{2} + \frac{\partial \tau_{zx}}{\partial z}dz\,.$$

Eq. (21.4) shows that each stress varies uniformly in the two directions across the face on which it acts. Therefore the total force on the face is the product of its area and the stress at its center. Sometimes a body force such as gravity or centrifugal force acts on each differential element of a stressed body. The body force per unit volume of the body is called F (N/m^3 or lb/in^3). In Fig. 21.6 its x component is F_x. The sum of the forces on the element in the x direction is zero:

$$\left(\frac{\partial \sigma_x}{\partial x}dx\right) dy\,dz + \left(\frac{\partial \tau_{yx}}{\partial y}dy\right) dx\,dz + \left(\frac{\partial \tau_{zx}}{\partial z}dz\right) dx\,dy + F_x dx\,dy\,dz = 0 \tag{21.5}$$

or

$$\frac{\partial \sigma_x}{\partial x} + \frac{\partial \tau_{yx}}{\partial y} + \frac{\partial \tau_{zx}}{\partial z} + F_x = 0\,. \tag{21.6}$$

A similar summation of the forces due to the stresses on the element in the y and z directions yields

$$\frac{\partial \sigma_y}{\partial y} + \frac{\partial \tau_{xy}}{\partial x} + \frac{\partial \tau_{zy}}{\partial z} + F_y = 0 \tag{21.7}$$

and

$$\frac{\partial \sigma_z}{\partial z} + \frac{\partial \tau_{xz}}{\partial x} + \frac{\partial \tau_{yz}}{\partial y} + F_z = 0\,. \tag{21.8}$$

The last three equations are called the *stress-equilibrium equations*, since they are obtained by adding all of the forces on the element, the sum of which is zero.

More useful information about the stresses is obtained by summing the moments caused by the shear stresses on the differential element. In Fig. 21.7 the shear stresses τ_{xy} and τ_{yx} act at the corner (x,y,z). The shear stresses at the center of the top, bottom, left, and right faces are shown. They cause moments about an axis thru the center of the element parallel to the z axis. Any off-center body force F_x, such as the weight per unit volume of a body whose density varies with y, contributes the moment $(F_x dx\,dy\,dz)(k\,dy)$ where k is between zero and 0.5. The sum of the moments is

$$\left(2\tau_{xy} + \frac{\partial \tau_{xy}}{\partial x}dx + \frac{\partial \tau_{xy}}{\partial y}dy + \frac{\partial \tau_{xy}}{\partial z}dz\right) dy\,dz\,\frac{dx}{2} - F_x dx\,dy\,dz\,k\,dy$$

$$- \left(2\tau_{yx} + \frac{\partial \tau_{yx}}{\partial x}dx + \frac{\partial \tau_{yx}}{\partial y}dy + \frac{\partial \tau_{yx}}{\partial z}dz\right) dx\,dz\,\frac{dy}{2} = 0\,. \tag{21.9}$$

The terms with four differentials are negligible compared to the two terms with three differentials. Therefore

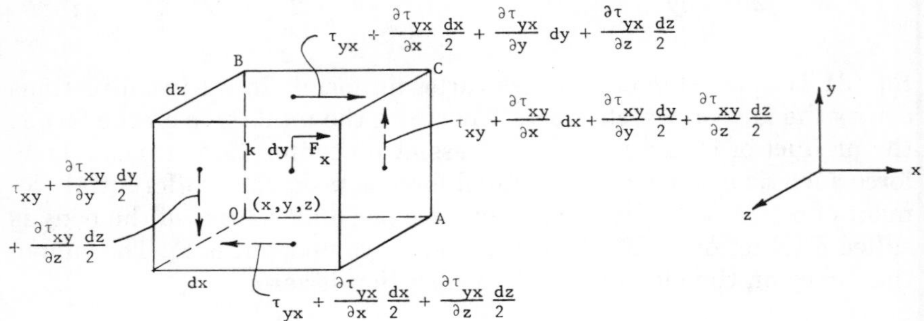

Fig. 21.7. Shear stresses on the differential element.

$$\tau_{xy} = \tau_{yx} \ . \tag{21.10}$$

A similar summation of the moments about the other two orthogonal axes thru the center of the element yields

$$\tau_{xz} = \tau_{zx} \qquad \text{and} \qquad \tau_{yz} = \tau_{zy} \ . \tag{21.11}$$

These results show that only three shear stresses instead of six need to be calculated in a boundary-value problem. From now on the two subscripts of a shear stress will be used interchangeably.

21.4 The Strain-Displacement Equations

When a structure such as a bridge or a turbine wheel is stressed, each particle in the structure is displaced a small distance from its unstressed position. In a rectangular coordinate system that is fixed with respect to the unstressed position of the structure, the particle originally at the point (x,y,z) moves the distances u, v, and w in the x, y, and z directions to the point $(x + u, y + v, z + w)$. In some practical boundary-value problems, one of the known boundary conditions is the displacements of the particles along part of the stressed body. Six more field equations will now be derived that relate the strains to the displacements of particles in a body, and permit the use of displacement boundary conditions. Refer again to a rectangular differential element of a body, shown in Fig. 21.8. The corner O is originally at the coordinates x, y, and z. When the loads are applied, its displacements are u, v, and w. Let the function f in Eq. (21.4) be the displacement of points in the x direction. The x displacement of point O is $f(x,y,z) = u$. Point A was at the point $(x + dx, y, z)$. Its x displacement is therefore

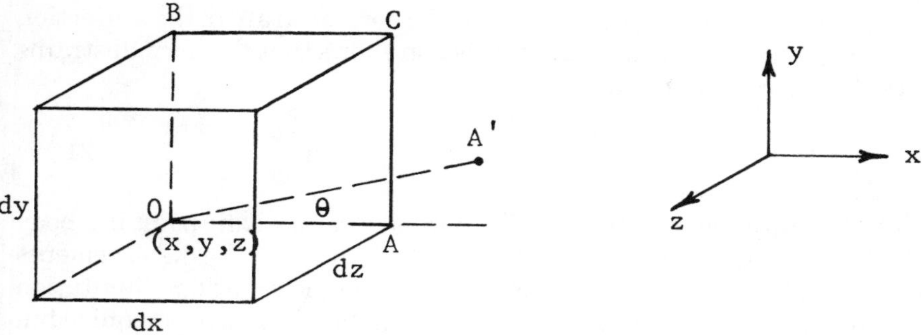

Fig. 21.8. Rectangular differential element of a body.

$$f(x + dx, y, z) = u + \frac{\partial u}{\partial x} dx + \frac{\partial u}{\partial y}(0) + \frac{\partial u}{\partial z}(0) = u + \frac{\partial u}{\partial x} dx . \tag{21.12}$$

The *normal strain* in any given direction at a point in a body is the change in length in that direction of a differential straight segment that is originally in that direction, divided by its original length. In Fig. 21.8 the segment OA moves to the position OA' when the load is applied. The normal strain in the x direction is

$$\varepsilon_x = \frac{OA' \cos \theta - OA}{OA}, \tag{21.13}$$

where θ is the angle between OA and OA'. According to Eq. (21.12) the normal strain of segment OA is

$$\varepsilon_x = \frac{f(x + dx, y, z) - f(x, y, z)}{dx} = \frac{\partial u}{\partial x} . \tag{21.14}$$

Similarly, the x displacements of points B and C are

$$f(x, y + dy, z) = u + \frac{\partial u}{\partial y} dy$$

and $$f(x + dx, y + dy, z) = u + \frac{\partial u}{\partial x} dx + \frac{\partial u}{\partial y} dy . \tag{21.15}$$

The normal strain along the segment BC is therefore

$$\varepsilon_x = \frac{f(x + dx, y + dy, z) - f(x, y + dy, z)}{dx} = \frac{\partial u}{\partial x} . \tag{21.16}$$

A little thought shows that along any edge of the differential element parallel to the x axis, or along any segment *in* the element parallel to the

x axis, the strain is $\partial u/\partial x$. This then is the normal strain in the x direction at the point (x,y,z). A similar calculation shows that the normal strains in the y and z directions are

$$\varepsilon_y = \frac{\partial v}{\partial y} \qquad \text{and} \qquad \varepsilon_z = \frac{\partial w}{\partial z} . \tag{21.17}$$

The last three equations relate the normal strains at any point in a body to the three displacements of that point. Notice that the displacements and strains do not have to be small. Eq. (21.3) shows the only limitation on the displacements $f(x,y,z)$. All of the higher derivatives required in the Taylor series, such as $\partial^2 f/\partial x\, \partial y$, must be finite. This limitation makes sense physically. For example, if x is normal to the interface of two materials with different moduli of elasticity, the derivative $\partial u/\partial x$ is discontinuous there, and the higher derivatives of u are infinite. Truncation of the Taylor series is not valid, and ε_x is not defined at the interface. In real structures the normal strains are usually small, but the displacements u, v, and w are frequently large. For example, the modulus of elasticity and proportional limit of structural steel are typically 2×10^{11} Pa and 2.28×10^8 Pa. The strain is a long bar as in Fig. 21.1 that is loaded axially up to its proportional limit is therefore only

$$\varepsilon = \frac{\sigma}{E} = \frac{2.28 \times 10^8}{2 \times 10^{11}} = 0.00114 . \tag{21.18}$$

The strains in a springboard are similarly small. The vertical deflections of points at the free end of the springboard can of course be several centimeters.

The *shear strain* at a point in a body is the decrease in angle of an originally right angle. Fig. 21.9 shows the back face *OACB* of the

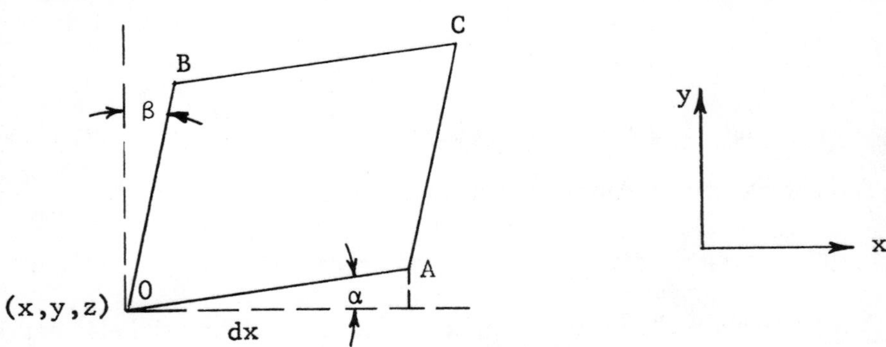

Fig. 21.9. Differential element in shear.

differential element of Fig. 21.7 after the shearing loads are applied. The shear strain in the xy plane is

$$\gamma_{xy} = \alpha + \beta \, . \tag{21.19}$$

To calculate the angle α, let the function f in Eq (21.4) be the displacement of points in the y direction. The y displacement of point O is $f(x,y,z) = v$. Since point A was originally at $(x + dx, y, z)$, its y displacement is

$$f(x + dx, y, z) = v + \frac{\partial v}{\partial x} dx \, . \tag{21.20}$$

If α and the normal strain in the x direction are small, the difference of the x displacements of points O and A is negligible compared to dx, and therefore

$$\tan \alpha = \alpha = \frac{f(x + dx, y, z) - f(x, y, z)}{dx} = \frac{\partial v}{\partial x} \, . \tag{21.21}$$

Similar calculations show that

1. $\tan \beta = \beta = \dfrac{\partial u}{\partial y}$ (21.22)

2. in any plane thru the differential element of Fig. 21.7 parallel to the xy plane, the angles α and β are given by Eqs. (21.21) and (21.22).

The shear strain in the xy plane at point (x,y,z) is therefore

$$\gamma_{xy} = \frac{\partial v}{\partial x} + \frac{\partial u}{\partial y} \, . \tag{21.23}$$

A similar analysis shows that the shear strains in the yz and xz planes are

$$\gamma_{yz} = \frac{\partial v}{\partial z} + \frac{\partial w}{\partial y} \tag{21.24}$$

$$\gamma_{xz} = \frac{\partial w}{\partial x} + \frac{\partial u}{\partial z} \, . \tag{21.25}$$

Notice that the last three equations are valid only if the shear and normal strains are small. Equations ((21.16), (21.17), and (21.23) thru (21.25) are the *strain-displacement equations*. They express the six strains at a point in terms of the three displacements.

21.5 Hooke's Law for Normal Stresses

The list of field equations will be completed by the six that express Hooke's law, which in one dimension is $\sigma = \varepsilon E$. Fig. 21.10 shows a

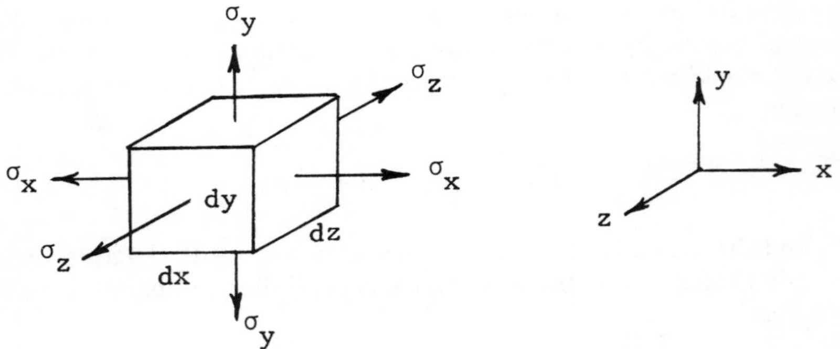

Fig. 21.10. Three-dimensional normal stresses.

differential rectangular element on whose left face the average normal stress is σ_x. The derivation of the stress-equilibrium equations showed that the normal stress on the right face is higher by the differential amount

$$\frac{\partial \sigma_x}{\partial x}\, dx \, .$$

In that analysis this term was important because the net force on the element was calculated. Now the small difference between the two stresses is of no concern, and the normal stress on the right face is also called σ_x. According to Hooke's law, if the only stress acting is σ_x, the normal strain of the element in the x direction is

$$\varepsilon_x = \frac{\sigma_x}{E} \, . \tag{21.26}$$

Suppose that the element is loaded only in the y direction, by a tensile pull. Since its volume tends to remain constant, it contracts in the lateral directions. Experiments show that within the proportional limit the lateral strain in the x direction is

$$\varepsilon_x = -\mu\, \varepsilon_y = -\mu \frac{\sigma_y}{E} \, . \tag{21.27}$$

The negative sign indicates that the strain is compressive if σ_y is tensile. The constant μ, called *Poisson's ratio*, is about 0.3 for steel, and is the same in both tension and compression. If the material is isotropic, so that μ is the same for lateral strains in all directions, a normal stress σ_z produces the strain

$$\varepsilon_x = -\mu \frac{\sigma_z}{E} \tag{21.28}$$

in the x direction. If the element is loaded in all three directions as shown in Fig. 21.10, the three normal stresses create three strains in the x direction: σ_x/E, $-\mu\, \sigma_y/E$, and $-\mu\, \sigma_z/E$. If the material is isotropic, and the deformations are small, and the stresses are within the proportional limit, the total strain in the x direction is the sum of the three components:

$$\varepsilon_x = \frac{1}{E}[\sigma_x - \mu(\sigma_y + \sigma_z)]\,. \tag{21.29}$$

Similarly, the total normal strains in the y and z directions are

$$\varepsilon_y = \frac{1}{E}[\sigma_y - \mu(\sigma_x + \sigma_z)] \tag{21.30}$$

and

$$\varepsilon_z = \frac{1}{E}[\sigma_z - \mu(\sigma_x + \sigma_y)]\,. \tag{21.31}$$

The last three equations state Hooke's law in three dimensions for normal stresses. Notice that the sum of the three normal strains is

$$\varepsilon_x + \varepsilon_y + \varepsilon_z = (\sigma_x + \sigma_y + \sigma_z)\left(\frac{1 - 2\mu}{E}\right). \tag{21.32}$$

A little thought will convince the reader that if the material is incompressible, $\varepsilon_x + \varepsilon_y + \varepsilon_z = 0$ and therefore $\mu = 0.5$. Since actual materials are compressible, their Poisson ratios are less than 0.5.

Although stresses cannot be measured, the normal strains on the surface of a body can be measured by resistance strain gages. If two gages are mounted at right angles, they measure strains that can be called ε_x and ε_y. On the surface of a body, $\sigma_z = 0$. The solution of Eqs. (21.29) and (21.30) for the stresses is

$$\sigma_x = \frac{E}{1 - \mu^2}(\varepsilon_x + \mu\, \varepsilon_y) \tag{21.33}$$

$$\sigma_y = \frac{E}{1 - \mu^2}(\varepsilon_y + \mu\, \varepsilon_x)\,. \tag{21.34}$$

These two equations are the workhorses of experimental stress analysis.

21.6 Hooke's Law for Shear Stresses

The relationships between shear stresses and shear strains are simpler than those for normal stresses and strains. Fig. 21.11 shows an *xy*

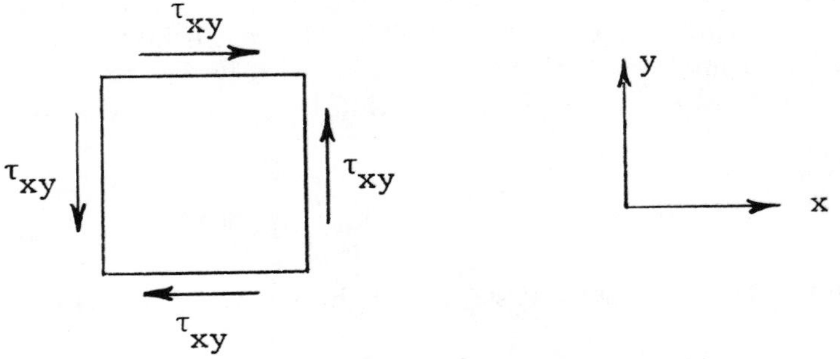

Fig. 21.11. Shear stress on a cubic differential element.

section of a cubic differential element in equilibrium when the shear stress τ_{xy} is applied to its top, bottom, left, and right faces. This stress deforms the section into a rhombus, creating the shear strain γ_{xy}. Clearly the shear stress does not deform the rectangular sections in the *yz* or *xz* planes, and therefore causes no shear strain γ_{yz} or γ_{xz}. Equally clearly, the shear stress τ_{xy} causes no normal stress in the *z* direction, σ_z. The same *xy* section appears in Fig. 21.12 with the *x* and *y* axes

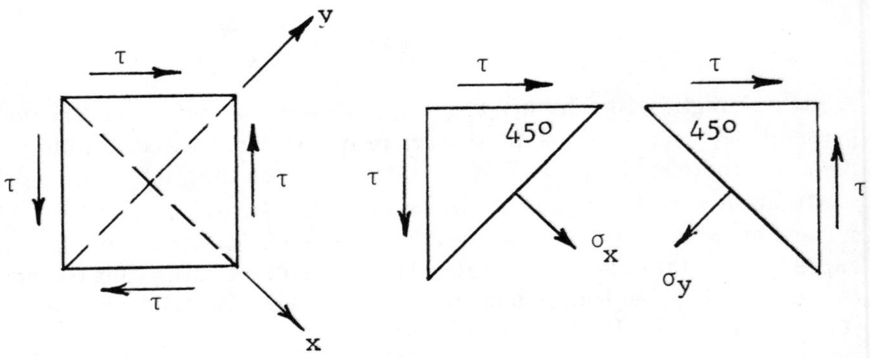

Fig. 21.12. Same cubic differential element with axes rotated.

rotated 45 degrees. Now the shear stress has no subscript. Two free-body diagrams are formed by cutting the element along its two diagonals. They show that $\sigma_y = -\sigma_x = \tau$. Fig. 21.13 shows the element

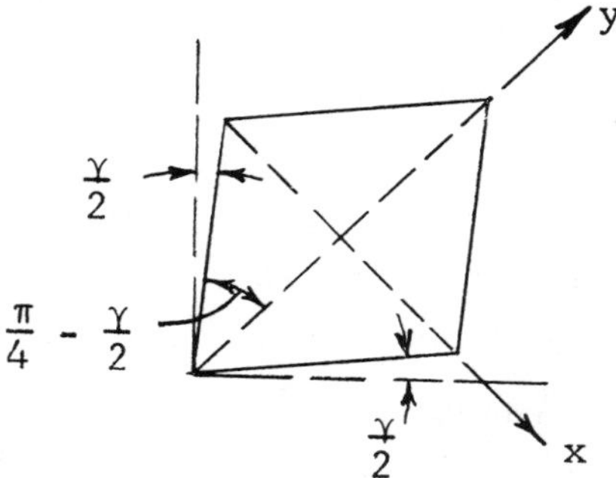

Fig. 21.13. Same cubic differential element after deformation.

with the shear strain γ exaggerated. The normal stresses σ_x and σ_y have produced the normal strains ε_x and ε_y. If the unstressed lengths of the two diagonals were unity, they are now $1 + \varepsilon_x$ and $1 + \varepsilon_y$. According to Fig. 21.13,

$$\tan\left(\frac{\pi}{4} - \frac{\gamma}{2}\right) = \frac{1 + \varepsilon_x}{1 + \varepsilon_y}. \tag{21.35}$$

Since $\sigma_z = 0$ and $\sigma_y = -\sigma_x = \tau$, Eqs. (21.29) and (21.30) reduce to

$$\varepsilon_x = \frac{1}{E}(\sigma_x - \mu\,\sigma_y) = -\frac{(1 + \mu)\tau}{E} \tag{21.36}$$

and

$$\varepsilon_y = \frac{1}{E}(\sigma_y - \mu\,\sigma_x) = \frac{(1 + \mu)\tau}{E}. \tag{21.37}$$

For any two angles A and B,

$$\tan(A - B) = \frac{\tan A - \tan B}{1 + \tan A \tan B}. \tag{21.38}$$

Since γ is small, $\tan \gamma/2$ is very nearly equal to $\gamma/2$, and

$$\tan\left(\frac{\pi}{4} - \frac{\gamma}{2}\right) = \frac{1 - \frac{\gamma}{2}}{1 + \frac{\gamma}{2}}. \tag{21.39}$$

Combining Eq. (21.39) with (21.35) thru (21.37) yields

$$\tau = \frac{E}{2(1 + \mu)}\gamma. \tag{21.40}$$

The constant

$$G = \frac{E}{2(1 + \mu)} \tag{21.41}$$

is called the *shear modulus* or *modulus of rigidity*. For steel with $\mu = 0.3$, $G = E/2.6$. If $E = 3 \times 10^7$ psi or 2×10^{11} Pa,

$$G = 1.15 \times 10^7 \text{ psi} \qquad \text{or} \qquad 7.7 \times 10^{10} \text{ Pa} . \tag{21.42}$$

The x and y axes can be rotated back to their position in Fig. 21.11. Then τ becomes τ_{xy} and γ becomes γ_{xy}, and Eq. (21.40) becomes

$$\tau_{xy} = G\,\gamma_{xy} . \tag{21.43}$$

A similar analysis shows that

$$\tau_{yz} = G\,\gamma_{yz} \qquad \text{and} \qquad \tau_{xz} = G\,\gamma_{xz} . \tag{21.44}$$

These three equations express Hooke's law for shear stresses.

21.7 The Saint-Venant Principle

Three more field equations are derived in Ref. 134, pages 213–214, that express the six stresses σ_x, τ_{xy}, etc. at a point in terms of the stress acting on any plane thru the point. Fig. 21.14 shows a differential

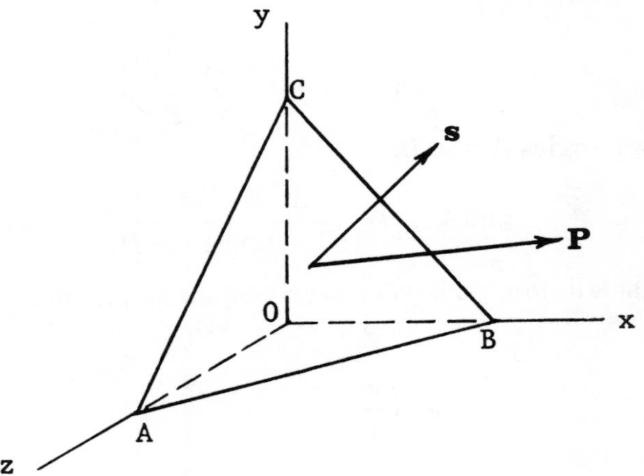

Fig. 21.14. Stresses at a point.

tetrahedron representing the point 0, formed by passing the inclined plane ABC thru a differential rectangular element. Let **s** be a vector normal to the plane ABC. Let α, β, and γ be the angles that **s** makes with the x, y, and z axes. Then the three components of the stress **P** acting on face ABC are

$$P_x = \sigma_x \cos\alpha + \tau_{xy} \cos\beta + \tau_{xz} \cos\gamma \tag{21.45}$$

$$P_y = \tau_{xy} \cos\alpha + \sigma_y \cos\beta + \tau_{yz} \cos\gamma \tag{21.46}$$

$$P_z = \tau_{xz} \cos\alpha + \tau_{yz} \cos\beta + \sigma_z \cos\gamma\,. \tag{21.47}$$

These are sometimes called *boundary-condition equations*, because they relate the stresses at the surface of a body to the pressure of the applied load. For example, suppose that plane ABC thru point 0 is part of the inner wall of a pipe containing water at pressure p. Let the x axis be normal to the wall at point 0. Then $\cos\alpha = 1$ and $\cos\beta = \cos\gamma = 0$. Since the hydrostatic pressure acts normal to the wall, $P_y = P_z = 0$ and $P_x = -p$. The last stress is negative because it is compressive. The boundary-condition equations show that $\tau_{xy} = \tau_{xz} = 0$ and $\sigma_x = -p$. Other boundary conditions are needed to determine σ_y, σ_z, and τ_{yz}.

Often the pressure distribution of the applied load is unknown. For example, if a woman is standing on the end of a cantilever beam as in Fig. 21.15, the applied stress varies with the flatness of her shoes and of

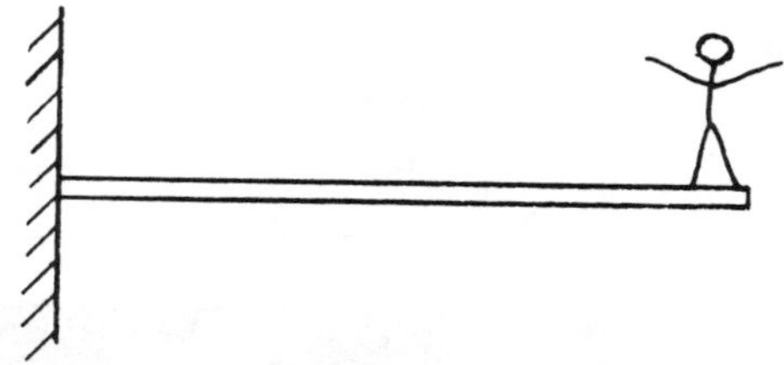

Fig. 21.15. Cantilever beam.

the beam, and with local yielding. Even if she is wearing golf shoes and applies very high local stresses under her feet, the important stress is elsewhere, next to the supporting wall. For calculation of the deflection and allowable weight of the woman, the distribution of the load under her feet is not important if the location of its centroid is known. A general rule, called the *Saint-Venant principle*, generalizes this idea: if the forces acting on a small portion of an elastic body are replaced by a statically-equivalent system on the same area, their effects on the stresses in the body are indistinguishable except near the loaded area. The principle is strikingly illustrated by photographs of the stress patterns in photoelastic specimens in Ref. 41, Vol. II, pages 27–30. Two of the photographs are shown in Figs. 21.16 and 21.17. In the former, rectangular struts are compressed by concentrated loads. In the center of the two longer struts the absence of black fringes indicates that the stress is axial and uniform. The center strut has a length-to-width ratio of about 2.5. Even in this stubby column, the stress distribution along the center cross section is the same as if the strut were compressed by a uniform load with the same magnitude.

Fig. 21.17 shows a beam to which bending stresses are applied by four concentrated vertical loads, each pair of which constitutes a bending moment. Between the loads the beam is in pure bending. The stress distribution there is the same as if the same moments were applied by clamps, distributed loads, or on extensions of the same beam.

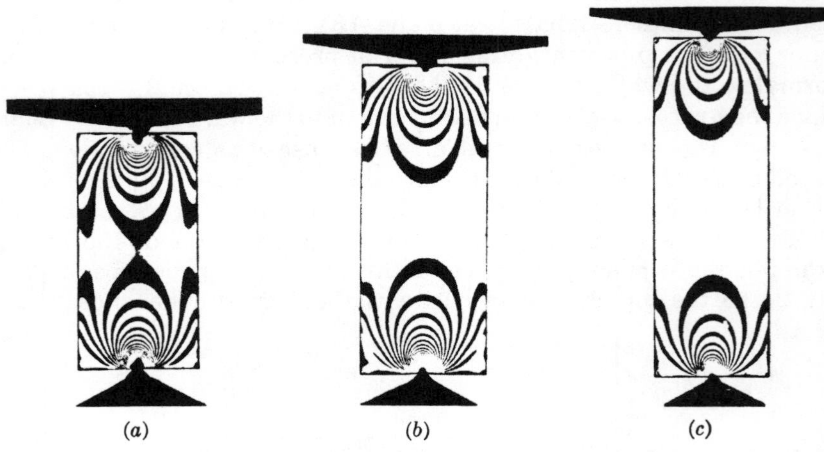

Fig. 21.16. Struts with concentrated compressive loads.

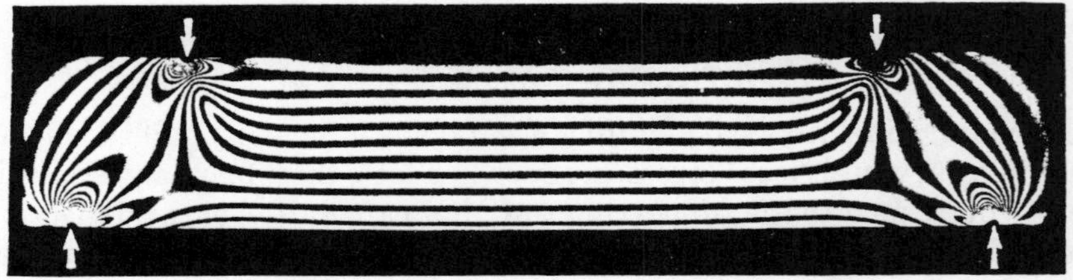

Fig. 21.17. Beam subjected to pure bending. (Figs. 21.16 and 21.17 are reprinted by permission from *Photoelasticity*, Volume II, by Max Mark Frocht, John Wiley & Sons, 1948.)

21.8 Summary of the Field Equations

The derivation of the field equations in rectangular coordinates is now complete. The equations are summarized here.

Stress-Equilibrium Equations

$$\frac{\partial \sigma_x}{\partial x} + \frac{\partial \tau_{xy}}{\partial y} + \frac{\partial \tau_{xz}}{\partial z} + F_x = 0 \tag{21.48}$$

$$\frac{\partial \sigma_y}{\partial y} + \frac{\partial \tau_{xy}}{\partial x} + \frac{\partial \tau_{yz}}{\partial z} + F_y = 0 \qquad (21.49)$$

$$\frac{\partial \sigma_z}{\partial z} + \frac{\partial \tau_{xz}}{\partial x} + \frac{\partial \tau_{yz}}{\partial y} + F_z = 0 \qquad (21.50)$$

Strain-Displacement Equations

$$\varepsilon_x = \frac{\partial u}{\partial x} \qquad \varepsilon_y = \frac{\partial v}{\partial y} \qquad \varepsilon_z = \frac{\partial w}{\partial z} \qquad (21.51)$$

$$\gamma_{xy} = \frac{\partial v}{\partial x} + \frac{\partial u}{\partial y} \qquad \gamma_{yz} = \frac{\partial v}{\partial z} + \frac{\partial w}{\partial y} \qquad \gamma_{xz} = \frac{\partial w}{\partial x} + \frac{\partial u}{\partial z} \qquad (21.52)$$

Hooke's-Law Equations

$$\varepsilon_x = \frac{1}{E}\left[\sigma_x - \mu(\sigma_y + \sigma_z)\right] \qquad (21.53)$$

$$\varepsilon_y = \frac{1}{E}\left[\sigma_y - \mu(\sigma_x + \sigma_z)\right] \qquad (21.54)$$

$$\varepsilon_z = \frac{1}{E}\left[\sigma_z - \mu(\sigma_x + \sigma_y)\right] \qquad (21.55)$$

$$\tau_{xy} = G\,\gamma_{xy} \qquad \tau_{yz} = G\,\gamma_{yz} \qquad \tau_{xz} = G\,\gamma_{xz} \qquad (21.56)$$

21.9 Field Equations in Cylindrical Coordinates

If an elastic body has cylindrical symmetry, the field equations are more convenient if expressed in the cylindrical coordinates r, θ, and z. If u, v, and w are the displacements of a point in the body in the r, θ, and z directions, the equations are as follows.

Stress-Equilibrium Equations

$$\frac{\partial \sigma_r}{\partial r} + \frac{1}{r}\frac{\partial \tau_{r\theta}}{\partial \theta} + \frac{\partial \tau_{rz}}{\partial z} + \frac{\sigma_r - \sigma_\theta}{r} + F_r = 0 \qquad (21.57)$$

$$\frac{\partial \tau_{r\theta}}{\partial r} + \frac{1}{r}\frac{\partial \sigma_\theta}{\partial \theta} + \frac{\partial \tau_{\theta z}}{\partial z} + 2\frac{\tau_{r\theta}}{r} + F_\theta = 0 \qquad (21.58)$$

$$\frac{\partial \tau_{rz}}{\partial r} + \frac{1}{r}\frac{\partial \tau_{\theta z}}{\partial \theta} + \frac{\partial \sigma_z}{\partial z} + \frac{\tau_{rz}}{r} + F_z = 0 \qquad (21.59)$$

Strain-Displacement Equations

$$\varepsilon_r = \frac{\partial u}{\partial r} \qquad \varepsilon_\theta = \frac{1}{r}\frac{\partial v}{\partial \theta} + \frac{u}{r} \qquad \varepsilon_z = \frac{\partial w}{\partial z} \tag{21.60}$$

$$\gamma_{r\theta} = \frac{1}{r}\frac{\partial u}{\partial \theta} + \frac{\partial v}{\partial r} - \frac{v}{r} \qquad \gamma_{\theta z} = \frac{\partial v}{\partial z} + \frac{1}{r}\frac{\partial w}{\partial \theta} \qquad \gamma_{rz} = \frac{\partial w}{\partial r} + \frac{\partial u}{\partial z} \tag{21.61}$$

Hooke's-Law Equations

$$\varepsilon_r = \frac{1}{E}[\sigma_r - \mu(\sigma_\theta + \sigma_z)] \tag{21.62}$$

$$\varepsilon_\theta = \frac{1}{E}[\sigma_\theta - \mu(\sigma_r + \sigma_z)] \tag{21.63}$$

$$\varepsilon_z = \frac{1}{E}[\sigma_z - \mu(\sigma_r + \sigma_\theta)] \tag{21.64}$$

$$\tau_{r\theta} = G\,\gamma_{r\theta} \qquad \tau_{\theta z} = G\,\gamma_{\theta z} \qquad \tau_{rz} = G\,\gamma_{rz} \tag{21.65}$$

21.10 Plane Stress

In many practical problems the stresses in a body justify these assumptions:

1. $\sigma_z = \tau_{xz} = \tau_{yz} = F_z = 0$. (21.66)
2. σ_x, σ_y, τ_{xy}, F_x, and F_y are independent of z. (21.67)

In cylindrical coordinates these assumptions are

1. $\sigma_z = \tau_{rz} = \tau_{\theta z} = F_z = 0$. (21.68)
2. σ_r, σ_θ, $\tau_{r\theta}$, F_r, and F_θ are independent of z. (21.69)

An example is the spinning thin disk in Fig. 21.18. If the centrifugal

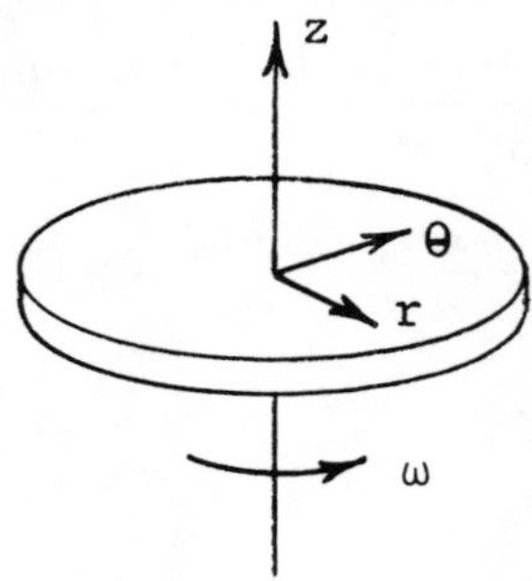

Fig. 21.18. Spinning thin disk.

force is large compared to gravity, the body force acts only in the r direction and is uniform in the z direction. Since no normal or tangential load acts on the top or bottom of the disk, σ_z, τ_{rz}, and $\tau_{\theta z}$ are zero there. Since the disk is thin, these stresses do not have a chance to build up to a significant value in the interior. A state of stress that obeys the two assumptions listed above is called *plane stress*. Assumption 1 reduces the field equations to the forms shown in Tables 21.1 and 21.2.

TABLE 21.1. PLANE-STRESS EQUATIONS IN RECTANGULAR COORDINATES

Stress Equilibrium

$$\frac{\partial \sigma_x}{\partial x} + \frac{\partial \tau_{xy}}{\partial y} + F_x = 0 \qquad (21.70)$$

$$\frac{\partial \sigma_y}{\partial y} + \frac{\partial \tau_{xy}}{\partial x} + F_y = 0 \qquad (21.71)$$

Strain-Displacement

$$\varepsilon_x = \frac{\partial u}{\partial x} \qquad \varepsilon_y = \frac{\partial v}{\partial y} \qquad \varepsilon_z = \frac{\partial w}{\partial z} \qquad (21.72)$$

$$\gamma_{xy} = \frac{\partial v}{\partial x} + \frac{\partial u}{\partial y} \qquad (21.73)$$

Hooke's Law

$$\varepsilon_x = \frac{1}{E}(\sigma_x - \mu\,\sigma_y) \qquad \varepsilon_y = \frac{1}{E}(\sigma_y - \mu\,\sigma_x) \qquad (21.74)$$

$$\varepsilon_z = -\frac{\mu}{E}(\sigma_x + \sigma_y) \qquad \tau_{xy} = G\,\gamma_{xy} \qquad (21.75)$$

TABLE 21.2. PLANE-STRESS EQUATIONS IN CYLINDRICAL COORDINATES

Stress Equilibrium

$$\frac{\partial \sigma_r}{\partial r} + \frac{1}{r}\frac{\partial \tau_{r\theta}}{\partial \theta} + \frac{\sigma_r - \sigma_\theta}{r} + F_r = 0 \qquad (21.76)$$

$$\frac{1}{r}\frac{\partial \sigma_\theta}{\partial \theta} + \frac{\partial \tau_{r\theta}}{\partial r} + 2\,\frac{\tau_{r\theta}}{r} + F_\theta = 0 \qquad (21.77)$$

Strain-Displacement

$$\varepsilon_r = \frac{\partial u}{\partial r} \qquad \varepsilon_\theta = \frac{1}{r}\frac{\partial v}{\partial \theta} + \frac{u}{r} \qquad \varepsilon_z = \frac{\partial w}{\partial z} \qquad (21.78)$$

$$\gamma_{r\theta} = \frac{1}{r}\frac{\partial u}{\partial \theta} + \frac{\partial v}{\partial r} - \frac{v}{r} \qquad (21.79)$$

Hooke's Law

$$\varepsilon_r = \frac{1}{E}(\sigma_r - \mu\,\sigma_\theta) \qquad \varepsilon_\theta = \frac{1}{E}(\sigma_\theta - \mu\,\sigma_r) \qquad (21.80)$$

$$\varepsilon_z = -\frac{\mu}{E}(\sigma_r + \sigma_\theta) \qquad \tau_{r\theta} = G\,\gamma_{r\theta} \qquad (21.81)$$

The plane-stress assumptions are valid for thin plates and wheels that are loaded parallel to their long dimensions. The reader is entitled to ask "how thin?" Fig. 21.19 provides a partial answer. The first-stage

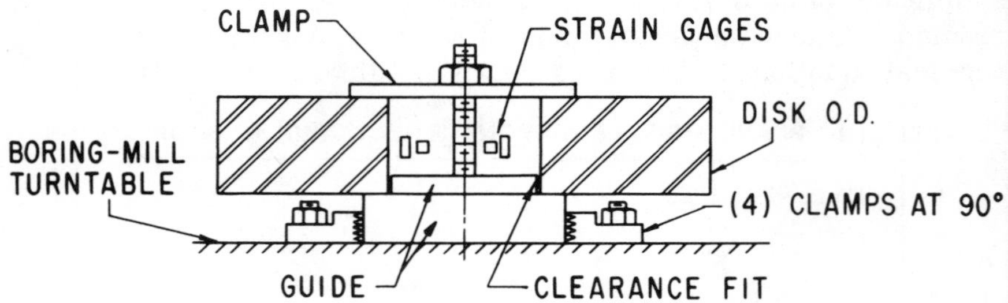

Fig. 21.19. Steel disk clamped on a boring mill.

wheel of a gas turbine was heated, spun, cooled and then stopped to introduce compressive residual stress σ_θ near its central bore hole. It was then cut into several pieces for various tests. The piece shown in Fig. 21.19 was a central disk of 14.75-in. outside diameter and 3-in. axial length. Strain gages were mounted in the bore hole of 4.56-in. diameter. The gages were read as the OD was turned off in successive cuts, so that the residual stresses throughout the disk could be calculated by the Sachs turning-down formula (Ref. 86). The tangential residual stress σ_θ varied from 9700 psi at the OD to $-41{,}400$ psi at the bore hole. Within the limits of experimental error, the axial residual stress σ_z was zero everywhere. Although the disk thickness was a fifth of its outside diameter, the disk was in plane stress.

21.11 Plane Strain

Another simplification of the field equations can be made for long cylinders of any uniform cross section loaded laterally by forces that do not vary in the z direction. An example is the pipe in Fig. 21.20, that is pressurized internally and built in at both ends. Since no particle of the pipe material can move in the z direction, $w = 0$. Since the loading is uniform in the z direction, the deflection u and v of points in the r and θ directions are independent of z, except near the ends. A state of strain that justifies the assumptions

$$u = u(r, \theta), \qquad v = v(r, \theta), \qquad \text{and} \qquad w = 0 \tag{21.82}$$

is called *plane strain*. A little thought shows that if a body force contributes to the plane strain, its z component must be zero, and its lateral components must be independent of z:

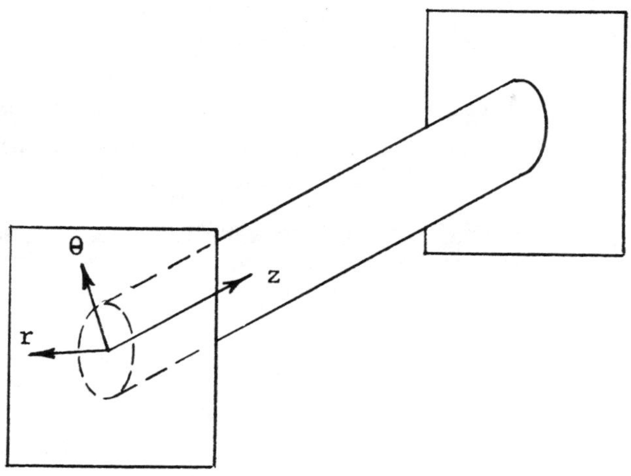

Fig. 21.20. Pipe in plane strain.

$$F_r = F_r(r, \theta) \qquad F_\theta = F_\theta(r, \theta) \qquad F_z = 0\,. \tag{21.83}$$

The plane-strain assumptions reduce the six strain-displacement equations (21.60) and (21.61) to the form

$$\varepsilon_r = \frac{\partial u}{\partial r} \qquad \varepsilon_\theta = \frac{1}{r}\frac{\partial v}{\partial \theta} + \frac{u}{r} \qquad \varepsilon_z = \gamma_{\theta z} = \gamma_{rz} = 0 \tag{21.84}$$

$$\gamma_{r\theta} = \frac{1}{r}\frac{\partial u}{\partial \theta} + \frac{\partial v}{\partial r} - \frac{v}{r}\,. \tag{21.85}$$

The Hooke's-law equation (21.64) reduces to

$$\sigma_z = \mu(\sigma_r + \sigma_\theta)\,. \tag{21.86}$$

When this is substituted into Eqs. (21.62) and (21.63), they become

$$\varepsilon_r = \frac{1+\mu}{E}\,[(1-\mu)\sigma_r - \mu\,\sigma_\theta] \tag{21.87}$$

$$\varepsilon_\theta = \frac{1+\mu}{E}\,[(1-\mu)\sigma_\theta - \mu\,\sigma_r]\,. \tag{21.88}$$

The last of Eqs. (21.84) reduces the other three Hooke's-law equations to

$$\tau_{r\theta} = G\,\gamma_{r\theta} \qquad \tau_{\theta z} = 0 \qquad \tau_{rz} = 0\,. \tag{21.89}$$

The first two stress-equilibrium equations (21.57) and (21.58) become

$$\frac{\partial \sigma_r}{\partial r} + \frac{1}{r}\frac{\partial \tau_{r\theta}}{\partial \theta} + \frac{\sigma_r - \sigma_\theta}{r} + F_r = 0 \tag{21.90}$$

$$\frac{\partial \tau_{r\theta}}{\partial r} + \frac{1}{r}\frac{\partial \sigma_\theta}{\partial \theta} + 2\frac{\tau_{r\theta}}{r} + F_\theta = 0 \,. \tag{21.91}$$

Every term in the third stress-equilibrium equation (21.59) is zero because of Eqs. (21.89) and (21.83). The plane-strain field equations are summarized in Tables 21.3 and 21.4. Notice that all of the stresses,

TABLE 21.3. PLANE-STRAIN EQUATIONS IN RECTANGULAR COORDINATES

Stress Equilibrium

$$\frac{\partial \sigma_x}{\partial x} + \frac{\partial \tau_{xy}}{\partial y} + F_x = 0 \tag{21.92}$$

$$\frac{\partial \sigma_y}{\partial y} + \frac{\partial \tau_{xy}}{\partial x} + F_y = 0 \tag{21.93}$$

Strain-Displacement

$$\varepsilon_x = \frac{\partial u}{\partial x} \qquad \varepsilon_y = \frac{\partial v}{\partial y} \qquad \varepsilon_z = 0 \qquad \gamma_{xy} = \frac{\partial v}{\partial x} + \frac{\partial u}{\partial y} \tag{21.94}$$

Hooke's Law

$$\varepsilon_x = \frac{1+\mu}{E}\left[(1-\mu)\sigma_x - \mu\,\sigma_y\right] \qquad \varepsilon_y = \frac{1+\mu}{E}\left[(1-\mu)\sigma_y - \mu\,\sigma_x\right] \tag{21.95}$$

$$\sigma_z = \mu(\sigma_x + \sigma_y) \qquad \tau_{xy} = G\,\gamma_{xy} \tag{21.96}$$

TABLE 21.4. PLANE-STRAIN EQUATIONS IN CYLINDRICAL COORDINATES

Stress Equilibrium

$$\frac{\partial \sigma_r}{\partial r} + \frac{\sigma_r - \sigma_\theta}{r} + \frac{1}{r}\frac{\partial \tau_{r\theta}}{\partial \theta} + F_r = 0 \tag{21.97}$$

$$\frac{1}{r}\frac{\partial \sigma_\theta}{\partial \theta} + \frac{\partial \tau_{r\theta}}{\partial r} + 2\frac{\tau_{r\theta}}{r} + F_\theta = 0 \tag{21.98}$$

Strain-Displacement

$$\varepsilon_r = \frac{\partial u}{\partial r} \qquad \varepsilon_\theta = \frac{1}{r}\frac{\partial v}{\partial \theta} + \frac{u}{r} \qquad \varepsilon_z = 0 \qquad \gamma_{r\theta} = \frac{1}{r}\frac{\partial u}{\partial \theta} + \frac{\partial v}{\partial r} - \frac{v}{r} \tag{21.99}$$

Hooke's Law

$$\varepsilon_r = \frac{1+\mu}{E}\left[(1-\mu)\sigma_r - \mu\,\sigma_\theta\right] \qquad \varepsilon_\theta = \frac{1+\mu}{E}\left[(1-\mu)\sigma_\theta - \mu\,\sigma_r\right] \tag{21.100}$$

$$\sigma_z = \mu(\sigma_r + \sigma_\theta) \qquad \tau_{r\theta} = G\,\gamma_{r\theta} \tag{21.101}$$

strains, displacements, and body forces in the plane-strain equations are functions of r and θ and are independent of z. To verify this conclusion, substitute Eqs. (21.82) into Eqs. (21.99) and observe the effect on the other equations. An assumption like (21.67) or (21.69) is not necessary for plane strain. Many structures of engineering importance are in plane strain, such as tunnels, dams, rollers bearing against each other, and a bar clamped in a vise.

21.12 An Example

The use of the field equations to solve a boundary-value problem can be illustrated by calculating the stresses in a straight thick-walled pipe carrying steam at pressure p, shown in Fig. 21.21. Normally such a pipe

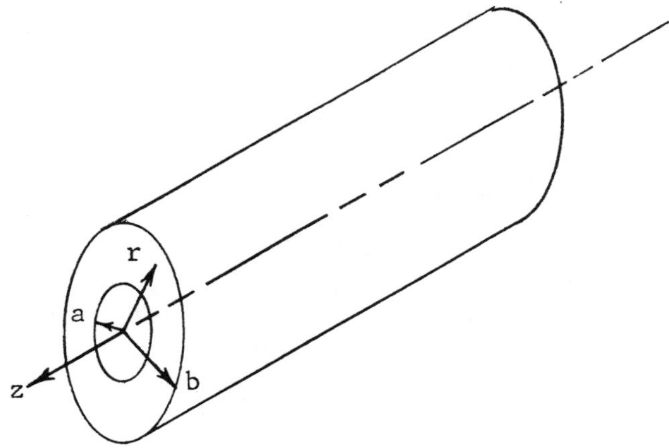

Fig. 21.21. Steam pipe.

has bends or loops at intervals along its length so that it can expand without constraint. Along a straight run of the pipe, σ_z is therefore nearly zero. Since the steam causes no twisting or shearing of the pipe, all of the shear stresses are zero. Clearly no body force is applied, and the normal stresses and strains are the same at every cross section and are independent of θ. The plane-stress equations can therefore be used, in the simplified form

$$\frac{\partial \sigma_r}{\partial r} + \frac{\sigma_r - \sigma_\theta}{r} = 0 \tag{21.102}$$

$$\varepsilon_r = \frac{\partial u}{\partial r} \tag{21.103}$$

$$\varepsilon_\theta = \frac{u}{r} \tag{21.104}$$

$$\varepsilon_r = \frac{1}{E}(\sigma_r - \mu\,\sigma_\theta) \tag{21.105}$$

$$\varepsilon_\theta = \frac{1}{E}(\sigma_\theta - \mu\,\sigma_r)\,. \tag{21.106}$$

Two boundary conditions are known: at $r = a$, $\sigma_r = -p$, and at $r = b$, $\sigma_r = 0$. The equations must be manipulated into an expression involving only r and σ_r so that the boundary conditions can be applied. Eq. (21.104) shows that

$$u = \varepsilon_\theta\, r \tag{21.107}$$

and

$$\frac{\partial u}{\partial r} = r\frac{\partial \varepsilon_\theta}{\partial r} + \varepsilon_\theta\,. \tag{21.108}$$

Substituting Eq. (21.108) into (21.103) yields

$$\varepsilon_r = r\frac{\partial \varepsilon_\theta}{\partial r} + \varepsilon_\theta\,. \tag{21.109}$$

According to Eq. (21.106),

$$\frac{\partial \varepsilon_\theta}{\partial r} = \frac{1}{E}\left(\frac{\partial \sigma_\theta}{\partial r} - \mu\,\frac{\partial \sigma_r}{\partial r}\right). \tag{21.110}$$

Now substitute (21.105), (21.106), and (21.110) into (21.109) to get

$$\frac{1}{E}(\sigma_r - \mu\,\sigma_\theta) = \frac{1}{E}\left(r\,\frac{\partial \sigma_\theta}{\partial r} - \mu\, r\,\frac{\partial \sigma_r}{\partial r}\right) + \frac{1}{E}(\sigma_\theta - \mu\,\sigma_r)\,. \tag{21.111}$$

According to Eq. (21.102),

$$\sigma_\theta = r\frac{\partial \sigma_r}{\partial r} + \sigma_r\,, \tag{21.112}$$

and therefore

$$\frac{\partial \sigma_\theta}{\partial r} = r\,\frac{\partial^2 \sigma_r}{\partial r^2} + 2\,\frac{\partial \sigma_r}{\partial r}\,. \tag{21.113}$$

Substituting (21.113) and (21.112) into (21.111) yields

$$r^2\,\frac{\partial^2 \sigma_r}{\partial r^2} + 3r\,\frac{\partial \sigma_r}{\partial r} = 0\,. \tag{21.114}$$

Since Eq. (21.114) has only one independent variable, it is an ordinary Euler differential equation:

$$r^2\frac{d^2\sigma_r}{dr^2} + 3r\frac{d\sigma_r}{dr} = 0\,, \tag{21.115}$$

and is the anticipated expression for σ_r in terms of r. The solution is

$$\sigma_r = k_1 + \frac{k_2}{r^2}\,. \tag{21.116}$$

The two constants, found by applying the two boundary conditions, are

$$k_1 = \frac{-p}{b^2\left(\dfrac{1}{b^2} - \dfrac{1}{a^2}\right)} \qquad \text{and} \qquad k_2 = \frac{p}{\dfrac{1}{b^2} - \dfrac{1}{a^2}}\,. \tag{21.117}$$

Thus

$$\sigma_r = \frac{pa^2}{b^2 - a^2}\left(1 - \frac{b^2}{r^2}\right). \tag{21.118}$$

Substitution of this result into Eq. (21.112) gives

$$\sigma_\theta = \frac{pa^2}{b^2 - a^2}\left(1 + \frac{b^2}{r^2}\right). \tag{21.119}$$

The last two equations express the radial and tangential stresses in the pipe, and are plotted in Fig. 21.22. Several interesting conclusions can be made.

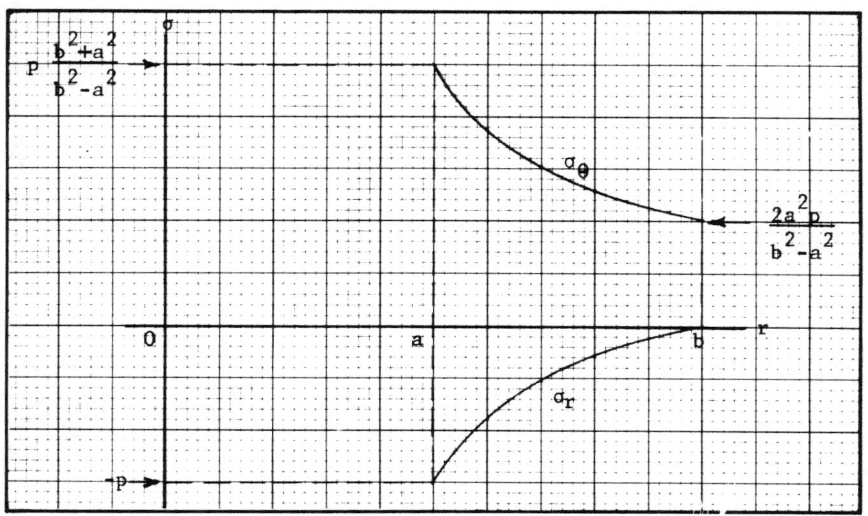

Fig. 21.22. Stresses in the pipe wall.

1. The radial stress is compressive, and the tangential stress is tensile, everywhere in the pipe.

2. The tangential stress is greater than the radial stress at every point.

3. The highest stress in the pipe is the tangential stress at the inner wall. This stress is of particular importance because it is tensile and can therefore start a destructive crack.

4. At every point the sum $\sigma_r + \sigma_\theta$ is the same constant. Hence, according to Eq. (21.81) the axial strain ε_z is uniform with the value

$$\varepsilon_z = -\frac{2\mu p a^2}{E(b^2 - a^2)} . \tag{21.120}$$

If the pipe wall is thin, the stress distributions are as shown in Fig. 21.23. Since now a, b, and r at points in the pipe material are approxi-

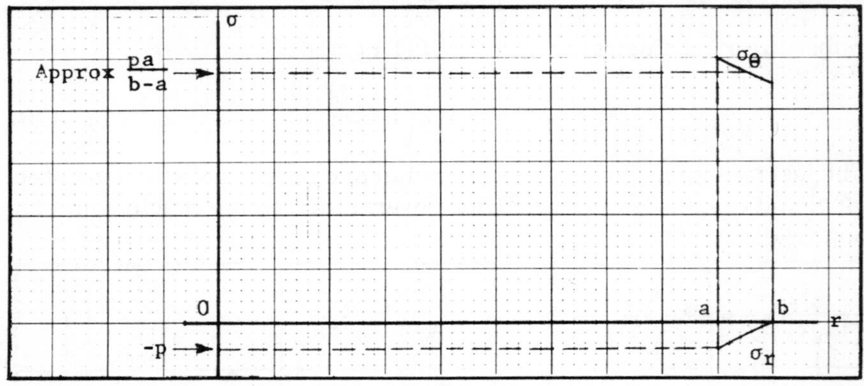

Fig. 21.23. Stresses in a thin-walled pipe.

mately equal, the tangential stress according to Eq. (21.119) is

$$\sigma_\theta = \frac{pa^2(r^2 + b^2)}{(b + a)(b - a)r^2} \approx \frac{pa}{b - a} . \tag{21.121}$$

This is also the value obtained by assuming a uniform tangential stress or "hoop stress" σ_θ in the pipe wall. A free-body diagram of half of a thin pipe is shown in Fig. 21.24. The total steam force on the left half of the pipe, per unit length of pipe, is $2ap$. It is balanced by the hoop force $2(b - a)\sigma_\theta$. Thus

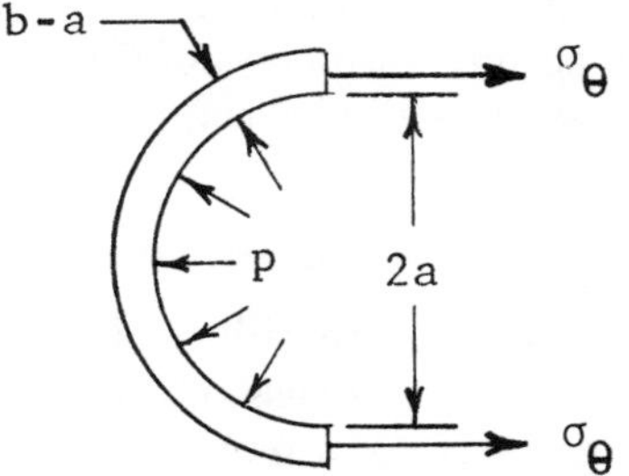

Fig. 21.24. Hoop stress in a thin pipe.

$$\sigma_\theta = \frac{pa}{b-a} = \frac{p}{(b/a)-1}, \tag{21.122}$$

which agrees with Eq. (21.121).

21.13 Superposition

If several loads are to be applied to a body, the resulting stresses, strains, and displacements can be calculated first for each load alone. Since the field equations are linear, the sum of these results is the same as the result when all of the loads are applied at once. If the body is regarded as a system whose inputs are various loads or boundary conditions and whose outputs are the resulting stresses, strains, and displacements, the system is linear and the inputs and outputs can be superposed. This superposition principle permits a calculation of the stresses and strains in the pipe by the plane-strain equations instead of the plane-stress equations. The former include

$$\varepsilon_z = 0 \qquad \text{and} \qquad \sigma_z = \mu(\sigma_r + \sigma_\theta), \tag{21.123}$$

and produce the same formulas for σ_r and σ_θ as before, Eqs. (21.118) and (21.119). The pipe, however, is unrestrained axially. There is an axial strain ε_z given by Eq. (21.120), and $\sigma_z = 0$. Table 21.5 shows the bound-

TABLE 21.5. BOUNDARY CONDITIONS OF THE PIPE

Actual	Plane Strain	Second Load
$\sigma_r(a) = -p$	$\sigma_r(a) = -p$	$\sigma_r(a) = 0$
$\sigma_r(b) = 0$	$\sigma_r(b) = 0$	$\sigma_r(b) = 0$
$\sigma_z = 0$	$\sigma_z = \mu(\sigma_r + \sigma_\theta)$	$\sigma_z = -\mu(\sigma_r + \sigma_\theta)$

ary conditions actually applied, and those applied in the plane-strain solution. To match the actual boundary conditions, a second load must be applied, which consists of an axial compressive force that produces the axial compressive stress

$$\sigma_z = -\mu(\sigma_r + \sigma_\theta)\,, \tag{21.124}$$

and no steam pressure. The results of this load are obtained easily. Since the pipe is long and straight, the stress in it is axial and uniform, as in the longest strut of Fig. 21.16, and now $\sigma_r = \sigma_\theta = 0$. The second load therefore has no effect on the values of σ_r and σ_θ calculated by the plane-strain equations. The additional strains are found from Eqs. (21.62) thru (21.64):

$$\varepsilon_r = \varepsilon_\theta = -\frac{\mu}{E}\sigma_z \qquad \text{and} \qquad \varepsilon_z = \frac{\sigma_z}{E}\,. \tag{21.125}$$

Eq. (21.124) shows that in terms of the total values of σ_r and σ_θ,

$$\varepsilon_r = \varepsilon_\theta = \frac{\mu^2}{E}(\sigma_r + \sigma_\theta) \qquad \text{and} \qquad \varepsilon_z = -\frac{\mu}{E}(\sigma_r + \sigma_\theta)\,. \tag{21.126}$$

When these strains are added to those obtained by the plane-strain equations (21.100), the results are the same as those obtained by the plane-stress equations (21.80) and (21.81). When the assumptions of plane strain, Eqs. (21.82), are amended to the form

$$u = u(r, \theta), \qquad v = v(r, \theta), \qquad \text{and} \qquad \varepsilon_z = \frac{\partial w}{\partial z} = k\,, \tag{21.127}$$

the body is in *generalized plane strain*. In the example, the constant k has the value given by Eq. (21.126).

Chapter 22

BENDING OF BEAMS

22.1 The Assumptions of Beam Theory

A *beam* is a long bar acted upon by transverse loads that cause it to bend. Many structural parts are beams, such as floor joists, turbine-generator rotors, railroad tracks, and the contact springs in a lever switch. Since the stresses, strains, and deflections of beams must be calculated often by engineers, a simplification of the elasticity field equations has evolved, called *beam theory*. In general, beam theory produces accurate results if the beam is long compared to its depth, bends in the direction of the load but does not buckle sideways, and does not bend very far. Specifically, the assumptions made for a typical beam, shown in Fig. 22.1, are as follows.

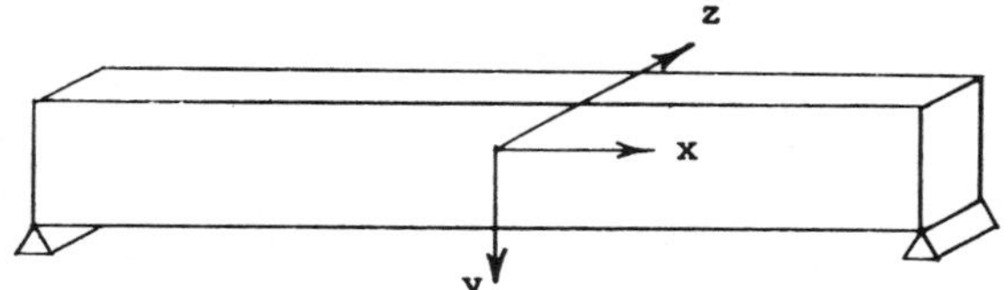

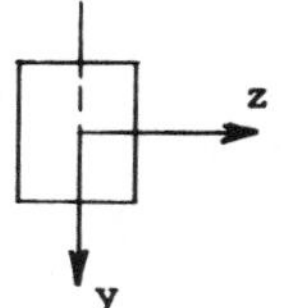

Fig. 22.1. A typical beam.

1. The beam is straight and symmetric about a central xy plane, and all applied loads lie in this plane, so that bending occurs only in the xy plane.

2. The vertical normal stress σ_y is negligible compared to the bending normal stress σ_x. Notice that σ_y is zero on the bottom of a beam, and equal to any distributed load on the top. Directly under a concentrated load it is large and violates Assumption 2, but diminishes rapidly away from the load.

3. The vertical displacement v of any particle in the beam is a function of x only.

4. For particles on the neutral plane (to be defined), the longitudinal or axial displacement u is zero.

5. Plane cross sections of the beam remain plane after bending.

6. Cross sections (yz planes) remain normal to sections in the xz planes after bending.

7. If a beam is narrow in the z direction the plane-stress simplifications apply, namely $\sigma_z = \tau_{xz} = \tau_{yz} = 0$, and σ_x, σ_y, and τ_{xy} are independent of z.

8. If a beam is wide in the z direction it is in plane strain. Then ε_z is zero but σ_z is not.

This long list of assumptions allows the derivation of simple formulas that produce accurate results and greatly simplify the work of the stress analyst.

22.2 Stress Resultants

The first result of the assumptions is shown with the help of Fig. 22.2.

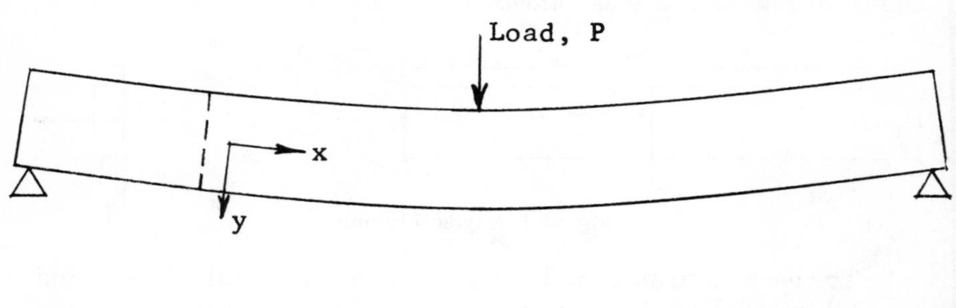

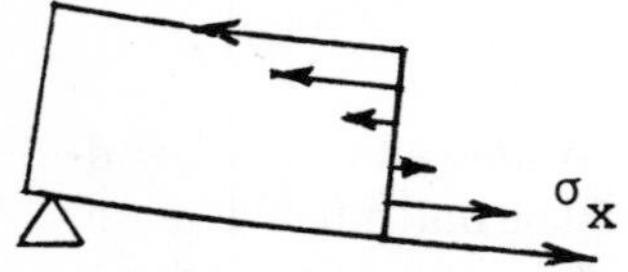

Fig. 22.2. Bending stress.

According to Assumptions 2 and 7, $\sigma_y = 0$ and if the beam is narrow, $\sigma_z = 0$. The only normal stress on a cross section of the beam is the *bending stress* or *fiber stress* σ_x, shown in Fig. 22.2. If the bending stress is tensile on the bottom portion of the section, it must be compressive on the top portion. On some xz plane near the middle of the beam σ_x must be zero. This plane of no stress is called the *neutral plane* or *neutral surface*. Its intersection with the plane of the cross section is the *neutral axis*. Hooke's law shows that for a narrow beam,

$$\varepsilon_x = \frac{1}{E}\left[\sigma_x - \mu(\sigma_y + \sigma_z)\right] = \frac{\sigma_x}{E}, \tag{22.1}$$

and

$$\varepsilon_y = \varepsilon_z = -\mu\frac{\sigma_x}{E}. \tag{22.2}$$

Accordingly, points on the neutral surface experience no normal strain, and therefore the neutral surface does not change in length or width. For beams with no axial load, the neutral axis will be designated as the z axis. The coordinate y of a particle in a beam will be measured from the neutral plane, and in agreement with the standard practice for beams, the positive direction of y will be *downward*. The sign conventions for stresses are explained in Section 21.2. The positive directions of the normal stress σ_x and shear stress τ_{xy} at a point in a beam are shown in Fig. 22.3. Some useful integrals of these stresses are called *stress resultants*, namely *thrust* T, transverse or *vertical shear force* V, and *bending moment* M. The positive directions of the stress resultants acting on the two ends of the hatched length in Fig. 22.4A are shown in Fig. 22.4B. The numerical values of the resultants at the two ends are of

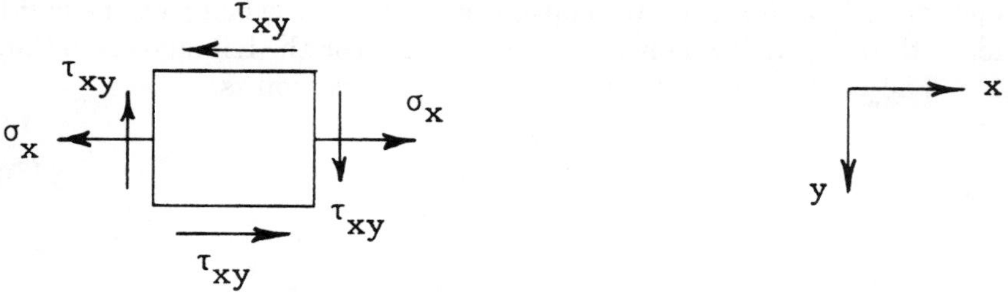

Fig. 22.3. Positive stresses at a point in a beam.

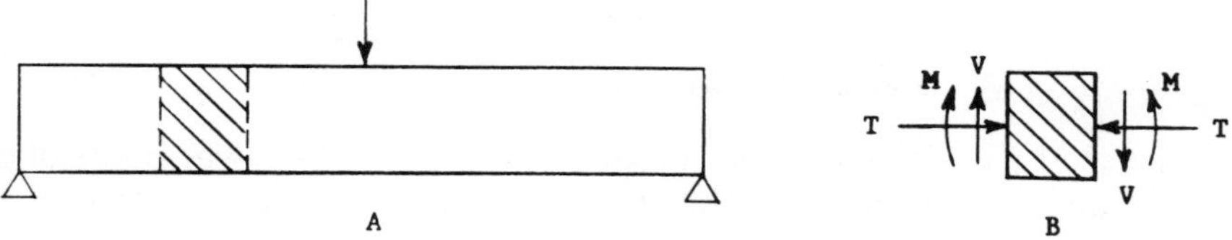

Fig. 22.4. Stress resultants.

course not necessarily equal. If there is an axial force or thrust on the beam, its value is

$$T = -\int_s \sigma_x \, ds, \tag{22.3}$$

where the surface integral extends over the area A of a cross section. A convenient choice of the differential area ds is shown in Fig. 22.5. Notice

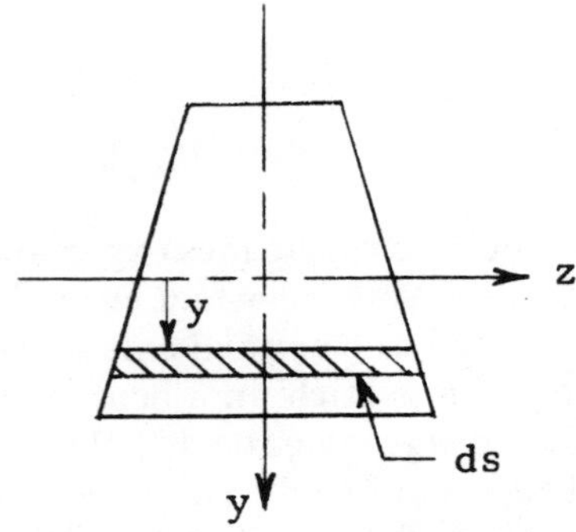

Fig. 22.5. Typical cross section of a beam.

that a compressive thrust is positive. The total vertical shear force acting on a cross section is

$$V = \int_s \tau_{xy}\, ds \,. \tag{22.4}$$

A positive shear force tends to push the portion of the beam on the right side of the section down lower than the portion on the left side, as in Fig. 22.6. The bending moment acting on a cross section is

$$M = \int_s \sigma_x\, y\, ds \,. \tag{22.5}$$

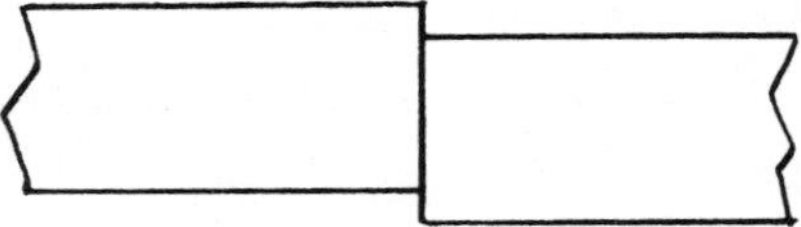

Fig. 22.6. Tendency of a positive shear force.

Notice that a positive moment produces tension in the lower fibers of a beam, and compression in the upper fibers, and therefore causes a "smiling beam" that is concave upward as in Fig. 22.2.

22.3 Bending of Narrow Beams

The way is now clear for the derivation of two simple formulas for the deflection and bending stress in beams, namely the moment-curvature formula and the flexure formula. Fig. 22.7 shows the side view of a cross

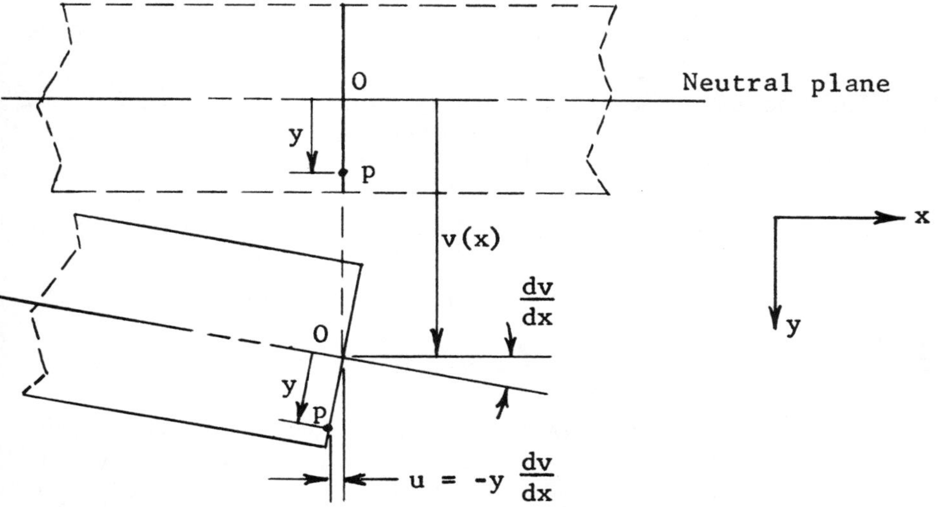

Fig. 22.7. Beam section before and after deflection.

section of a beam before and after deflection. According to Assumption 4, a particle 0 on the neutral plane has no horizontal displacement u. The slope of the beam is dv/dx, where v is the vertical displacement of particles in the beam. According to Assumptions 5 and 6 the cross section remains plane after bending and rotates thru the angle dv/dx. If the point p in the cross section is the distance y from the neutral plane, its horizontal displacement is

$$u = -y \frac{dv}{dx} . \tag{22.6}$$

The equations relating strains to displacements, derived in the preceding chapter, are

$$\varepsilon_x = \frac{\partial u}{\partial x} \qquad \text{and} \qquad \varepsilon_y = \frac{\partial v}{\partial y} . \tag{22.7}$$

Thus

$$\varepsilon_x = \frac{\partial u}{\partial x} = -y \frac{d^2 v}{dx^2} . \tag{22.8}$$

Note in passing that since v is assumed to be independent of y, $\varepsilon_y = 0$. This conclusion conflicts with Eq. (22.2). Other inconsistencies can be found in beam theory. The theory is used because experience shows that its simplified formulas produce accurate results. Substitution of Eq. (22.8) into (22.1), which is valid for narrow beams, yields

$$\sigma_x = E\,\varepsilon_x = -E\,y\,\frac{d^2v}{dx^2}\,. \tag{22.9}$$

This equation verifies that the bending stress in a narrow beam is zero at the neutral plane, where $y = 0$. When Eq. (22.9) is substituted into (22.3), the result is

$$T = -\int_s \sigma_x\,ds = -\int_s -E\,y\,\frac{d^2v}{dx^2}\,ds = E\,\frac{d^2v}{dx^2}\int_s y\,ds\,. \tag{22.10}$$

If there is no thrust on the beam, $T = 0$ and therefore

$$\int_s y\,ds = 0\,. \tag{22.11}$$

As Fig. 22.5 shows, this integral is the first moment of the area of a cross section about the z axis. Since the moment is zero, the z axis is the centroidal axis of the cross section. Consequently, the neutral axis at any cross section is also the centroidal axis. Substitution of Eq. (22.9) into the moment equation (22.5) yields

$$M = \int_s -E\,y\,\frac{d^2v}{dx^2}\,y\,ds = -E\,\frac{d^2v}{dx^2}\int_s y^2 ds\,. \tag{22.12}$$

Fig. 22.5 shows that the moment of inertia of the cross section about its centroidal axis is

$$I = \int_s y^2 ds\,. \tag{22.13}$$

Therefore

$$M = -E\,I\,\frac{d^2v}{dx^2} \qquad \text{or} \qquad \frac{d^2v}{dx^2} = -\,\frac{M}{E\,I}\,. \tag{22.14}$$

This ordinary differential equation is called the *moment-curvature formula,* since d^2v/dx^2 is the curvature or rate of change of slope of the beam. This formula applies for beams that are narrow, for which $\sigma_z = 0$. Notice that I is not necessarily constant, but can be a function of x. Frequently the bending moment M is known at every cross section of the beam as a function of x. Then if two boundary values of displacement v are known, Eq. (22.14) can be solved to produce a formula for the deflection of the beam.

A simple formula for the bending stress σ_x can now be found by combining Eqs. (22.9) and (22.14):

$$\sigma_x = (-E\,y)\left(-\,\frac{M}{E\,I}\right),$$

or

$$\sigma_x = \frac{M\,y}{I}. \tag{22.15}$$

This is the *flexure formula*. It shows that the bending stress is proportional to the distance y out from the centroidal axis. The distance out to the extreme fiber of the beam is called c, and the *section modulus* is defined as

$$Z = \frac{I}{c}. \tag{22.16}$$

The highest bending stress in the beam is the normal stress σ_x in the extreme fiber:

$$\sigma_x = \frac{M\,c}{I} = \frac{M}{Z}. \tag{22.17}$$

For a beam of rectangular cross section as in Fig. 22.8, the moment of

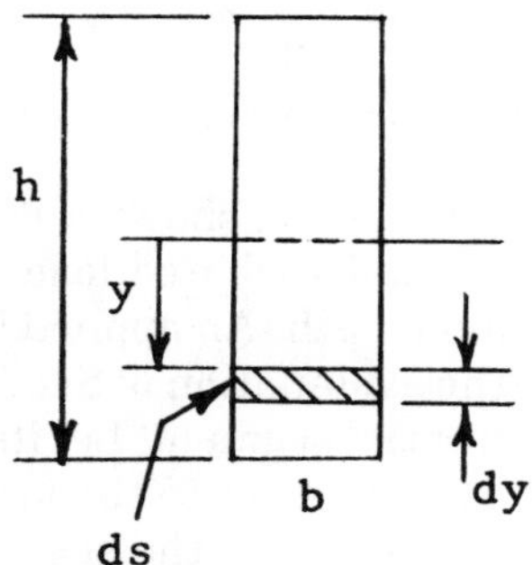

Fig. 22.8. Rectangular cross section of a beam.

inertia is

$$I = \int_s y^2 ds = b \int_{-h/2}^{h/2} y^2 dy = \frac{bh^3}{12}, \tag{22.18}$$

and since $c = h/2$,

$$Z = \frac{bh^2}{6}. \tag{22.19}$$

The values of I and Z for various beam cross sections are tabulated in engineering handbooks such as Refs. 7 and 30.

22.4 Deflection as a Function of Load

In addition to the moment-curvature formula (22.14), expressions for derivatives of displacement at a beam cross section in terms of the vertical shear force or applied load are also useful. Fig. 22.9 is the first

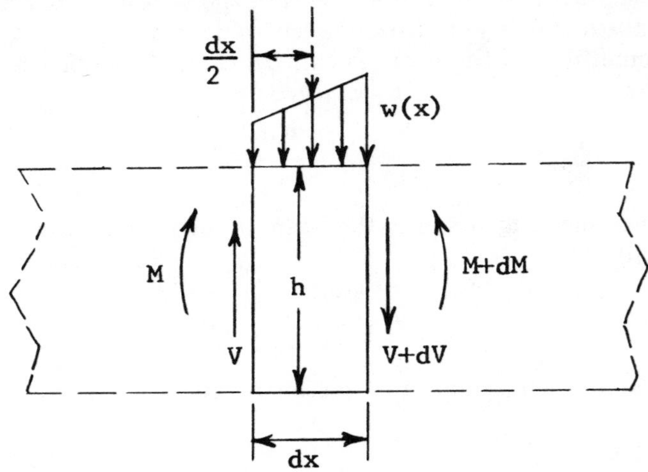

Fig. 22.9. Differential segment of a beam.

step in deriving these formulas. It shows a differential segment of a beam supporting the applied distributed load $w(x)$ pounds per foot or newtons per meter of beam length. An applied load directed downward is positive. According to the explanation in Section 21.3, this load varies uniformly along the differential segment. Let its average value over the segment be w. The load is equivalent to the force $w\,dx$ acting at about the distance $dx/2$ from either end of the segment. The vertical shear force V and bending moment M on the left and right ends differ by the amounts dV and dM. The sum of vertical forces on the segment is

$$w\,dx + V + dV - V = 0\,.$$

Therefore

$$\frac{dV}{dx} = -w\,. \tag{22.20}$$

The sum of moments about the right end of the segment is very nearly

$$M + dM + w\,dx\,\frac{dx}{2} - V\,dx - M = 0\,. \tag{22.21}$$

The moment arm $dx/2$ in the third term is an approximation. When the second-order differential in that term is ignored,

$$\frac{dM}{dx} = V . \tag{22.22}$$

Now differentiate the moment-curvature formula (22.14), and substitute in the derivatives of V and M. The results are

$$\frac{d}{dx}\left(E\,I\,\frac{d^2v}{dx^2}\right) = -\,\frac{dM}{dx} = -V \tag{22.23}$$

and

$$\frac{d^2}{dx^2}\left(E\,I\,\frac{d^2v}{dx^2}\right) = -\,\frac{dV}{dx} = w . \tag{22.24}$$

If the beam has a uniform cross section, I is constant. If the modulus of elasticity E is also uniform along the beam, the last two equations become

$$\frac{d^3v}{dx^3} = -\,\frac{V}{E\,I} \tag{22.25}$$

and

$$\frac{d^4v}{dx^4} = \frac{w}{E\,I} . \tag{22.26}$$

These are the desired expressions for beam deflection v as a function of vertical shear force and of applied load. The usefulness of Eq. (22.26) can be illustrated by computing the natural frequencies of the cantilever beam shown in Fig. 22.10. If the beam is vibrating up and down, the load

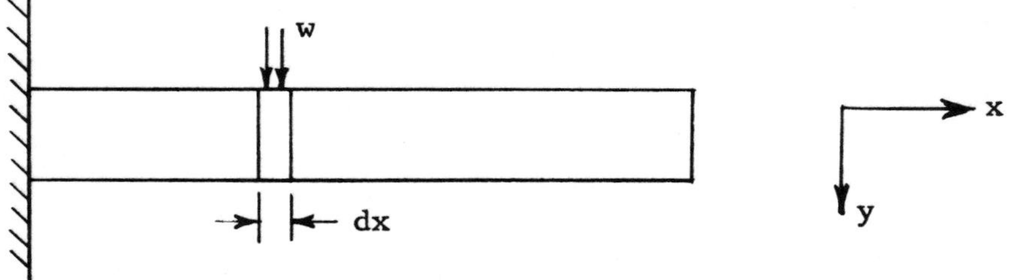

Fig. 22.10. Cantilever beam.

applied to a segment of length dx is its own inertial force:

$$w\,dx = -m\,dx\,\frac{\partial^2 v}{\partial t^2} , \tag{22.27}$$

where m is the mass of the beam per unit length. With the total derivative replaced by a partial derivative, Eq. (22.26) becomes

$$\frac{\partial^4 v}{\partial x^4} = - \frac{m}{E\,I} \frac{\partial^2 v}{\partial t^2} . \tag{22.28}$$

This partial differential equation can be solved by separation of variables.

22.5 Bending of Wide Beams

When a beam of narrow or intermediate width bends as in Fig. 22.11,

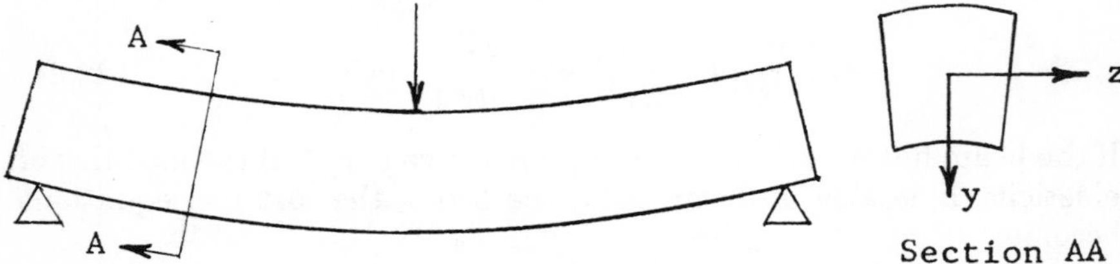

Fig. 22.11. Distortion of a beam cross section.

a rectangular cross section distorts, becoming wider at the top and narrower at the bottom. The reader can observe this distortion by bending a rectangular eraser. The beam experiences a lateral strain ε_z, which for narrow beams is given by Eq. (22.2). If the beam is wide, the displacement w of any particle in the z direction is restrained, except near the ends, by the adjacent particles. By bending a flat steel ruler, the reader can be convinced that the cross sections do not curl as in Fig. 22.11, but remain straight. Evidently $w = 0$, and the deflections u and v in the x and y directions are independent of z. A wide beam is in plane strain when it is loaded. According to the plane-strain equations in Table 21.3, Section 21.11,

$$\sigma_z = \mu(\sigma_x + \sigma_y) \tag{22.29}$$

and

$$\varepsilon_x = \frac{1 + \mu}{E} [(1 - \mu)\sigma_x - \mu\, \sigma_y] . \tag{22.30}$$

Since σ_y is negligible according to Assumption 2, $\sigma_z = \mu\, \sigma_x$. Therefore a wide beam, unlike a narrow beam, experiences a normal stress in the lateral or z direction. For a wide beam Eq. (22.30) reduces to

$$\varepsilon_x = \frac{1 - \mu^2}{E} \sigma_x , \tag{22.31}$$

which differs from Eq. (22.1) by the factor $1 - \mu^2$. Eq. (22.8) is valid for either narrow or wide beams. Now for wide beams,

$$\frac{1-\mu^2}{E}\sigma_x = -y\frac{d^2v}{dx^2} \tag{22.32}$$

or

$$\sigma_x = -\frac{E}{1-\mu^2}y\frac{d^2v}{dx^2}, \tag{22.33}$$

and the moment-curvature formula becomes

$$\frac{d^2v}{dx^2} = -\frac{1-\mu^2}{E}\cdot\frac{M}{I}. \tag{22.34}$$

The differential equations (22.23) thru (22.26) are the same as before, except that E has been replaced by $E/(1-\mu^2)$. A combination of Eqs. (22.33) and (22.34) shows that the flexure formula is unchanged:

$$\sigma_x = \left(-\frac{E}{1-\mu^2}y\right)\left(-\frac{1-\mu^2}{E}\cdot\frac{M}{I}\right) = \frac{My}{I}. \tag{22.35}$$

The differential equations and flexure formula that were derived for narrow beams are therefore applicable to wide beams if the modulus of elasticity E is replaced by $E/(1-\mu^2)$. A wide steel beam, for which $\mu = 0.3$, is therefore about 10 percent stiffer than a narrow beam with the same cross-sectional moment of inertia I. If the analyst forgets the factor $1-\mu^2$, deflections calculated by the differential equations will be about 10 percent too large. The bending stress calculated by the flexure formula will be unaffected.

22.6 Load, Shear, and Moment Diagrams

The calculation of the vertical shear force and bending moment in a beam is simplified by the construction of three diagrams. They are based on Eqs. (22.20) and (22.22) that are repeated here:

$$\frac{dV}{dx} = -w, \tag{22.36}$$

$$\frac{dM}{dx} = V. \tag{22.37}$$

To understand the method, consider the beam in Fig. 22.12 that is subjected to a concentrated load of 6 kN at one end and a distributed load of 6 kN/m at the other. The reactions at the two supports, found by summing the vertical forces and the moments about either support, are 18 and 24 kN. A free-body diagram of the beam or *load diagram* is shown

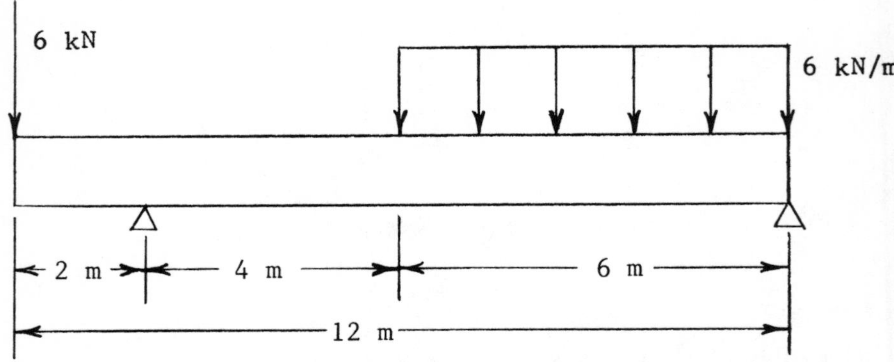

Fig. 22.12. A loaded beam.

in Fig. 22.13A. In agreement with Fig. 22.9 a downward distributed load w is positive. A concentrated load is an impulse of distributed load. The load distribution of Fig. 22.13A can be written as

$$w = 6\,\delta(x) - 18\,\delta(x-2) + 6[U(x-6) - U(x-12)] - 24\,\delta(x-12)\,, \tag{22.38}$$

where $\delta(x-a)$ and $U(x-a)$ are a unit impulse and a unit step at $x = a$. According to Eq. (22.36) the vertical shear force V is the negative integral of w. The *shear diagram* in Fig. 22.13B can be drawn by inspection. According to Eq. (22.37) the bending moment M is the integral of the shear force, and the slope of M equals the ordinate of V. Since the beam is not fixed at the left end, the initial value of M is zero. The *moment diagram*, Fig. 22.13C, consists of two straight lines and a parabola. Its peak ordinate at $x = 8$, which is the area under the shear diagram up to that distance, is

$$M = -12 + 48 + 12 = 48 \quad \text{N·m}\,. \tag{22.39}$$

The largest bending stress in the beam can now be found from the flexure formula, $\sigma_x = Mc/I$.

Formulas for the shear force and bending moment can be obtained by two integrations of Eq. (22.38). The integrals of a unit impulse and a unit step are

$$\int \delta(x-a)\,dx = U(x-a) \tag{22.40}$$

and

$$\int U(x-a)\,dx = (x-a)\,U(x-a)\,. \tag{22.41}$$

Therefore

$$V = -6 + 18\,U(x-2) - 6[(x-6)\,U(x-6) - (x-12)\,U(x-12)] + 24\,U(x-12) \tag{22.42}$$

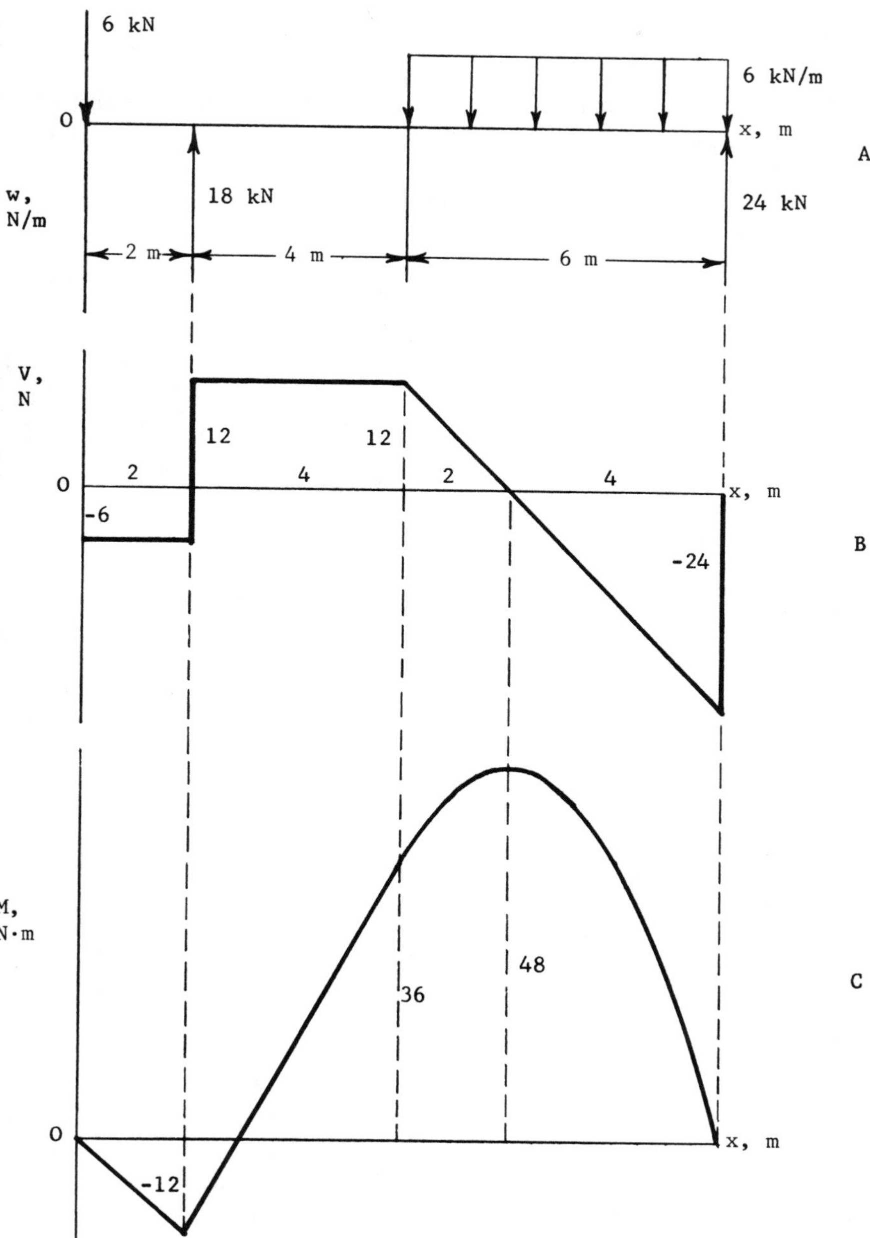

Fig. 22.13. Load, shear, and moment diagrams.

and

$$M = -6x + 18(x-2)\,U(x-2) - 3[(x-6)^2 U(x-6) \\ - (x-12)^2 U(x-12)] + 24(x-12)\,U(x-12)\,. \qquad (22.43)$$

The same information can be obtained in a different form by drawing free-body diagrams of various lengths of the beam. Fig. 22.14 shows

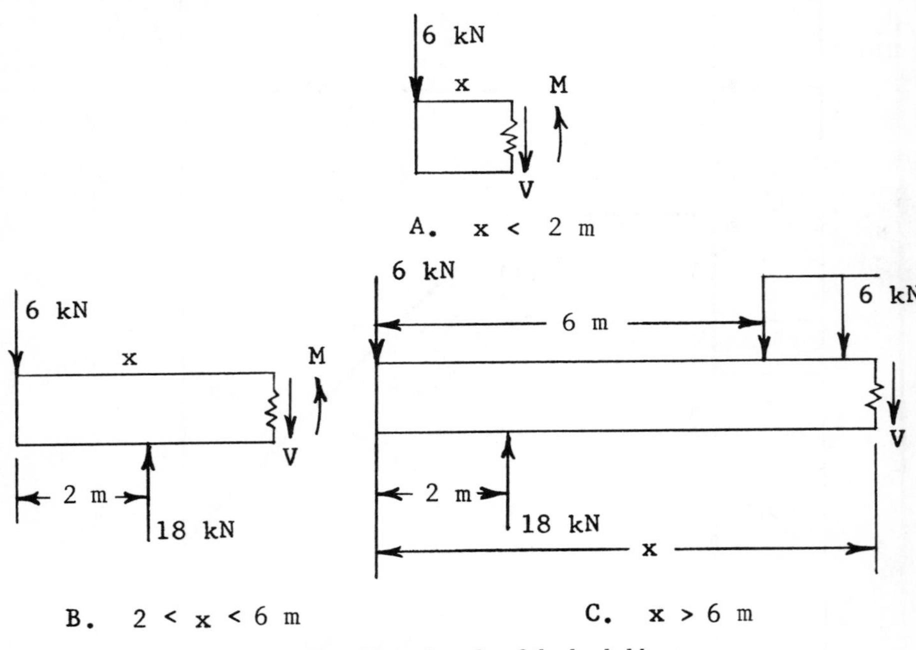

Fig. 22.14. Three lengths of the loaded beam.

three such diagrams of length x. Summation of the forces and the moments on the right end of each portion of the beam shows that

$$V = -6 \quad \text{and} \quad M = -6\,x\,, \qquad 0 \leqslant x \leqslant 2$$

$$V = 12 \quad \text{and} \quad M = 12\,x - 36\,, \qquad 2 \leqslant x \leqslant 6$$

$$V = 48 - 6\,x \quad \text{and} \quad M = -\,3\,x^2 + 48\,x - 144\,, \; 6 \leqslant x \leqslant 12\,.$$

These six equations agree with Eqs. (22.42) and (22.43). The shape of the deflected beam can be found with the moment-curvature formulas (22.14) or (22.34) and two more integrations of Eq. (22.43). Two boundary conditions on v are needed. Since the beam has no deflection at its supports, the two conditions are $v(2) = v(12) = 0$.

A second and simpler example will allow an easy calculation of the deflection shape. Fig. 22.15A shows a cantilever beam loaded by a

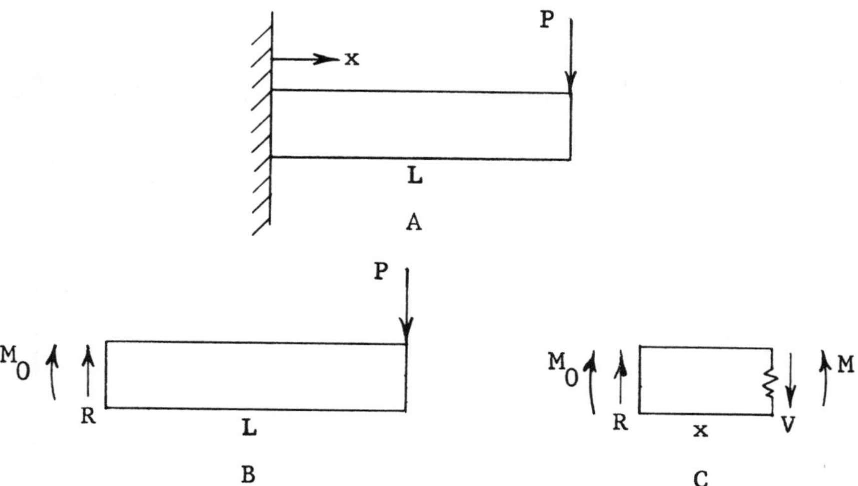

Fig. 22.15. Cantilever beam with a concentrated load.

concentrated force at the free end. The free-body diagram of Fig. 22.15B is kept in equilibrium by the reacting force R and the reacting moment M_0. The reactions are determined by summing the vertical forces, and the moments about the left end of the beam:

$$R = P\,, \qquad M_0 = -P\,L\,. \tag{22.44}$$

The load, shear, and moment diagrams are shown in Fig. 22.16. The bending moment at any distance x from the left end of the beam can be written by inspection of the moment diagram:

$$M = -P\,L + \frac{P\,L}{L}\,x = P(x - L)\,. \tag{22.45}$$

The bending moment can also be found from the free-body diagram of a portion of the beam of length x, shown in Fig. 22.15C. The sum of moments about the right end is

$$M = M_0 + R\,x = -P\,L + P\,x = P(x - L)\,. \tag{22.46}$$

This formula can be substituted into the moment-curvature formula (22.14) to produce the deflection shape of the beam:

$$\frac{d^2v}{dx^2} = -\frac{P}{E\,I}(x - L)\,. \tag{22.47}$$

The known boundary conditions for this differential equation are

$$v(0) = 0 \qquad \text{and} \qquad v'(0) = 0\,. \tag{22.48}$$

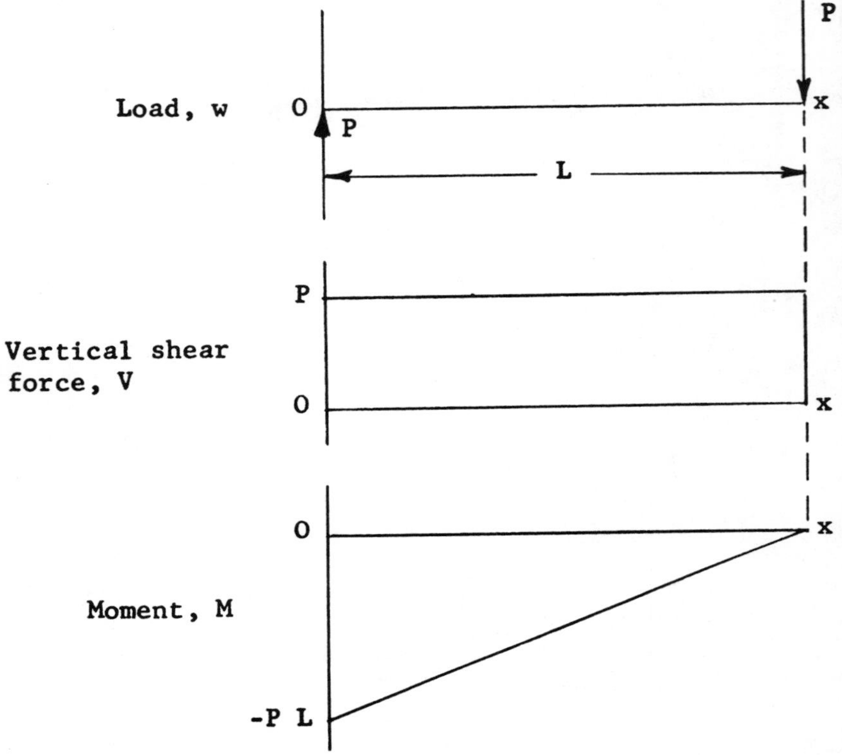

Fig. 22.16. Diagrams for the cantilever beam.

Two integrations of Eq. (22.47) produce

$$\frac{dv}{dx} = -\frac{P}{E\,I}\left(\frac{x^2}{2} - L\,x\right) \tag{22.49}$$

and

$$v = -\frac{P}{E\,I}\left(\frac{x^3}{6} - \frac{L\,x^2}{2}\right) = \frac{P\,x^2}{6\,E\,I}(3\,L - x)\,. \tag{22.50}$$

The last equation describes the shape of the cantilever beam when it is loaded. The deflection is a maximum at the free end where $x = L$, and is

$$v(L) = \frac{P\,L^2}{6\,E\,I}(3\,L - L) = \frac{P\,L^3}{3\,E\,I}\,. \tag{22.51}$$

This is the formula commonly given in engineering handbooks for the maximum deflection of a long cantilever beam with a load concentrated at the free end. If the beam is wide, E should be replaced by $E/(1 - \mu^2)$.

The slope of the beam at the free end is found from Eq. (22.49):

$$v'(L) = -\frac{P}{EI}\left(\frac{L^2}{2} - L^2\right) = \frac{PL^2}{2EI}. \tag{22.52}$$

Since the deflection v is positive downward, the positive value given by this equation is a negative slope. According to Assumption 6, if the end face of the beam was originally normal to the neutral surface it remains normal after bending. Since also the slope is small, $v'(L)$ is the angle thru which the end face has rotated.

22.7 Shear Stress in Rectangular Beams

The assumptions of beam theory lead to the conclusion that there is no shear stress in a beam. Eq. (22.6), based on these assumptions, is

$$u = -y\frac{dv}{dx}, \tag{22.53}$$

and therefore

$$\frac{\partial u}{\partial y} = -\frac{dv}{dx}. \tag{22.54}$$

One of the general strain-displacement equations derived in the preceding chapter is

$$\gamma_{xy} = \frac{\partial v}{\partial x} + \frac{\partial u}{\partial y}. \tag{22.55}$$

According to Assumption 3, $\partial v/\partial x = dv/dx$. Eq. (22.55) becomes

$$\gamma_{xy} = \frac{dv}{dx} - \frac{dv}{dx} = 0, \tag{22.56}$$

and accordingly,

$$\tau_{xy} = G\,\gamma_{xy} = 0. \tag{22.57}$$

Clearly this is wrong. According to Eq. (22.4) the total shear force V applied on any section of a beam is

$$V = \int_s \tau_{xy}\,ds. \tag{22.58}$$

A shear stress τ_{xy} is needed to equilibrate the shear force. A transverse shear stress τ_{xy} of course does exist in beams, and so does an equal accompanying longitudinal shear stress τ_{yx}. The effect of the latter is shown in Fig. 22.17. The beam in Fig. 22.17A consists of two pieces.

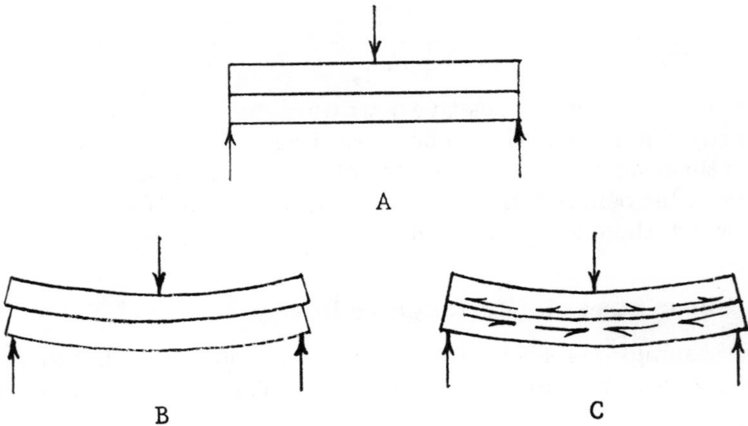

Fig. 22.17. Longitudinal shear in a beam.

When it is bent as in Fig. 22.17B, the lower surface of the upper piece is longer than the upper surface of the lower piece. If the two pieces are fastened together as in Fig. 22.17C by gluing or bolting, or are replaced by a single piece of double thickness, the two surfaces at the interface must be of equal length. The upper surface is shorter than its free length, and the lower surface is longer. The changes in length are caused by the longitudinal shear stress τ_{yx}.

The shear stress can be calculated without the assumptions of beam theory. Eqs. (21.70) and (21.92) show that if the beam is either narrow (and in plane stress) or wide (and in plane strain) and experiences no body force in the x direction,

$$\frac{\partial \sigma_x}{\partial x} + \frac{\partial \tau_{xy}}{\partial y} = 0 , \tag{22.59}$$

or

$$\frac{\partial \tau_{xy}}{\partial y} = - \frac{\partial \sigma_x}{\partial x} = - \frac{\partial}{\partial x}\left(\frac{M\,y}{I}\right) . \tag{22.60}$$

If the beam has a uniform cross section so that the moment of inertia I is independent of x,

$$\frac{\partial \tau_{xy}}{\partial y} = - \frac{y}{I} \cdot \frac{\partial M}{\partial x} = - \frac{Vy}{I} . \tag{22.61}$$

Since V is not a function of y, the integral of this equation is

$$\tau_{xy} = - \frac{V\,y^2}{2\,I} + f(x) . \tag{22.62}$$

To evaluate the function $f(x)$ for a beam with with a rectangular cross section as in Fig. 22.8, observe that the longitudinal shear stress τ_{yx} is zero along the top of the beam where $y = h/2$. Therefore

$$0 = -\frac{V}{2I}\left(\frac{h}{2}\right)^2 + f(x) . \tag{22.63}$$

For the same rectangular beam

$$I = \frac{bh^3}{12} , \tag{22.64}$$

the area of a cross section is

$$A = bh , \tag{22.65}$$

and the y coordinate of the extreme fiber is

$$c = \frac{h}{2} . \tag{22.66}$$

Eq. (22.62) becomes

$$\tau_{xy} = -\frac{V y^2}{2I} + \frac{V}{2I}\left(\frac{h}{2}\right)^2$$

or

$$\tau_{xy} = \frac{3V}{2A}\left[1 - \left(\frac{y}{c}\right)^2\right] . \tag{22.67}$$

Thus for either a narrow or a wide rectangular beam, the longitudinal and transverse shear stresses are distributed parabolically across a section as in Fig. 22.18. They have the maximum value

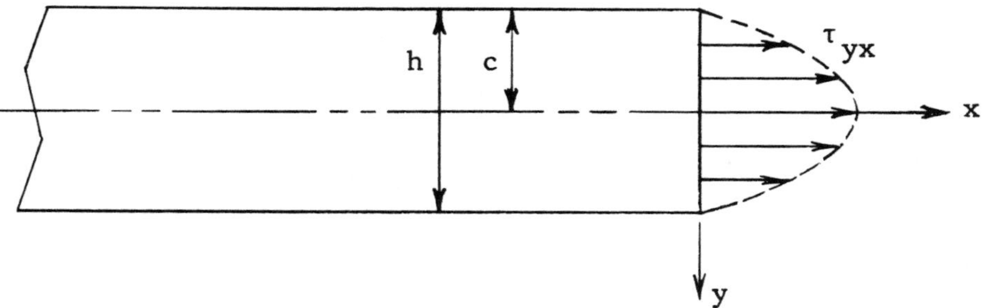

Fig. 22.18. Distribution of shear stress.

$$\tau_{\max} = \frac{3V}{2A} \tag{22.68}$$

at the neutral surface, which is 3/2 of the average shear stress over the section. Many of the ceiling beams of old houses and barns have failed in longitudinal shear by splitting along the grain near the neutral surface. The reader is invited to explain why they continue to hold up the ceiling.

22.8 Shear Stress in Beams of Any Cross Section

The method of calculating shear stress explained above assumes that the beam is in either plane stress or plane strain. Neither assumption is justified for a beam of square or circular cross section. A method will now be presented that works for any cross section, based on the assumption that the shear stress τ_{yx} is independent of z. This assumption is valid for either plane stress or plane strain, and for many beams whose cross sections are neither very narrow nor very wide. The method is explained with the help of Fig. 22.19A, which shows a segment of a beam of

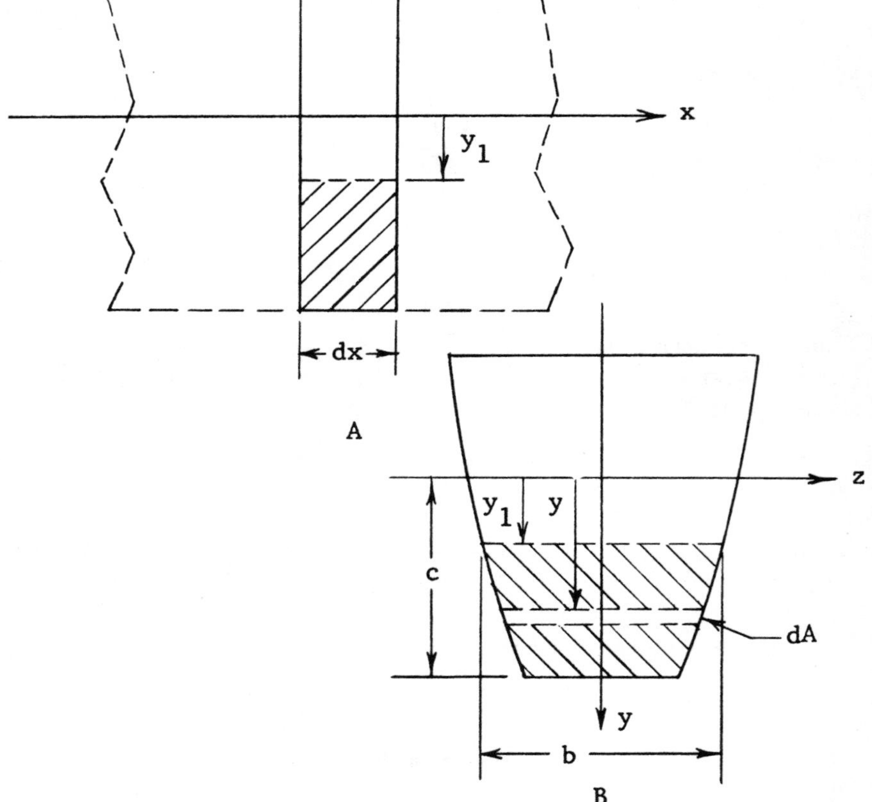

Fig. 22.19. Differential segment of a beam of general cross section.

differential length dx. Fig. 22.19B is the cross section of the segment, that can have any shape that is symmetrical about the y axis, to fulfill Assumption 1. The bending moments acting on the ends of the segment, and the distribution of bending stress, are shown in Fig. 22.20. A free-body diagram of the hatched volume, which extends from the depth y_1 to the extreme fiber, is shown in Fig. 22.21. Since the bending

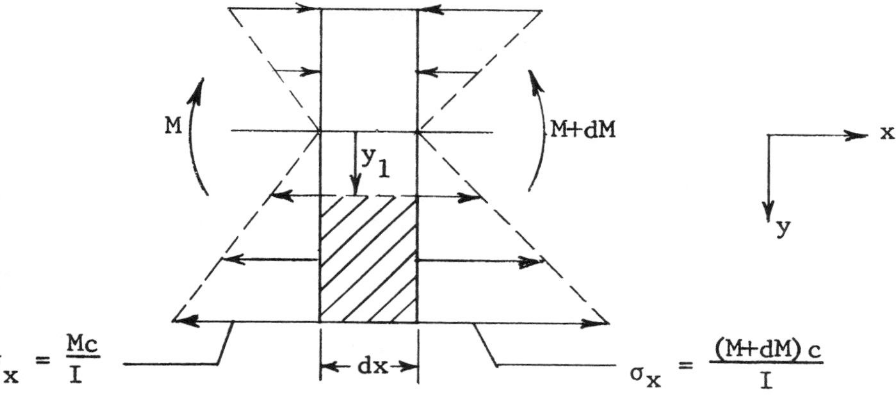

Fig. 22.20. Moments and bending stresses on the ends of the segment.

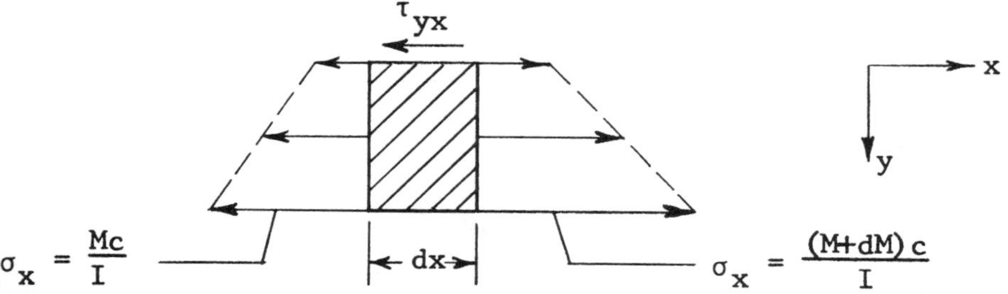

Fig. 22.21. Stresses on the hatched volume.

stresses at the two ends of the volume are not in general equal, a longitudinal shear stress τ_{yx} is required for equilibrium. The bending stresses on the left and right ends are

$$\sigma_x = \frac{M\,y}{I} \qquad \text{and} \qquad \sigma_x = \frac{(M + dM)\,y}{I},$$

where I is the moment of inertia of the entire cross section of the beam. The width of the beam at the top of the hatched volume is b. Since the shear stress τ_{yx} is assumed to be uniform across the width, the shear force on the top of the hatched volume is $\tau_{yx}\,b\,dx$. The sum of horizontal forces on the hatched volume is

$$\tau_{yx}\, b\, dx = \int_{y_1}^{c} (M + dM)\frac{y}{I}\, dA - \int_{y_1}^{c} M\frac{y}{I}\, dA$$

or

$$\tau_{yx}\, b\, dx = \frac{dM}{I}\int_{y_1}^{c} y\, dA\,, \tag{22.69}$$

where dA is the differential area in Fig. 22.19B, and c is the distance from the centroidal axis to the extreme fiber. Since

$$\frac{dM}{dx} = V\,, \tag{22.70}$$

Eq. (22.69) can be written as

$$\tau_{yx}(y_1) = \frac{dM}{dx}\cdot\frac{1}{b\,I}\int_{y_1}^{c} y\, dA \tag{22.71}$$

or

$$\tau_{yx}(y_1) = \frac{V}{b\,I}\int_{y_1}^{c} y\, dA\,. \tag{22.72}$$

This is the longitudinal or transverse shear stress in a beam at the depth y_1 from the centroidal axis, when b is the width of the beam at the depth y_1.

The usefulness of Eq. (22.72) can be illustrated by computing again the shear stress in the rectangular beam of Fig. 22.8. Since the beam has the uniform width b, and $dA = b\, dy$, and $c = h/2$, Eq. (22.72) becomes

$$\tau_{yx}(y_1) = \frac{V}{b\,I}\int_{y_1}^{c} b\, y\, dy = \frac{V}{2\,I}(c^2 - y_1^2) = \frac{3}{2}\frac{V}{A}\left[1 - \left(\frac{y_1}{c}\right)^2\right], \tag{22.73}$$

where A is the area of the cross section. This result of course agrees with Eq. (22.67). Calculation of the shear stress in a beam of circular cross section, shown in Fig. 22.22, is not much more difficult. Now

$$b = 2\sqrt{R^2 - y_1^2}\,,\quad I = \frac{\pi R^4}{4}\,,\quad y = R\cos\theta\,,\quad c = R\,,\quad A = \pi R^2\,,$$

and

$$dA = (2R\sin\theta)dy = (2R\sin\theta)(-R\sin\theta\, d\theta) = -2R^2\sin^2\theta\, d\theta\,. \tag{22.74}$$

Now

$$\int_{y_1}^{c} y\, dA = -2R^3\int_{\cos^{-1}(y_1/R)}^{0}\sin^2\theta\cos\theta\, d\theta = \frac{2}{3}R^3\sin^3\theta\Big|_0^{\cos^{-1}(y_1/R)}$$

$$= \frac{2}{3}R^3\left(\frac{\sqrt{R^2 - y_1^2}}{R}\right)^3 = \frac{2}{3}(R^2 - y_1^2)^{3/2}\,. \tag{22.75}$$

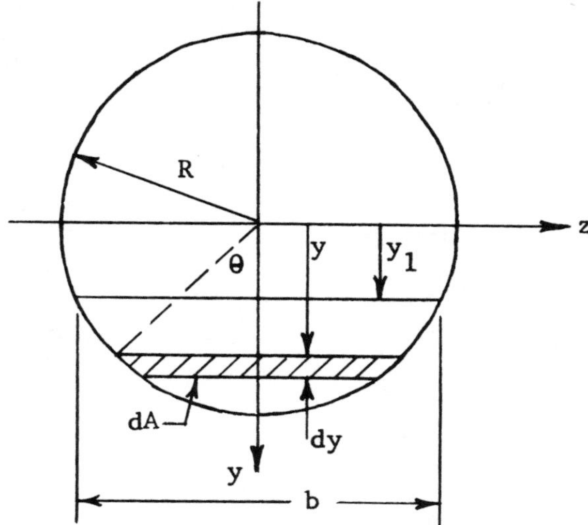

Fig. 22.22. Beam of circular cross section.

Eq. (22.72) becomes

$$\tau_{yx}(y_1) = \frac{4\,V}{(2\sqrt{R^2 - y_1^2})(\pi\,R^4)} \cdot \frac{2(R^2 - y_1^2)^{3/2}}{3} \tag{22.76}$$

or

$$\tau_{yx}(y_1) = \frac{4\,V}{3\,A}\left[1 - \left(\frac{y_1}{R}\right)^2\right]. \tag{22.77}$$

As in a rectangular beam, the shear stresses in a round beam are distributed parabolically across the section, and reach a maximum at the neutral surface. Their highest value is

$$\tau_{\max} = \frac{4\,V}{3\,A}, \tag{22.78}$$

which is 4/3 of the average shear stress over the section.

22.9 Deflection Due to Shear Stress

The deflection of a long beam is calculated by integrating the moment-curvature formula twice. With this method the maximum deflection of the cantilever beam in Fig. 22.15 was found to be

$$v(L) = \frac{P\,L^3}{3\,E\,I}. \tag{22.79}$$

The derivation of the moment-curvature formula requires Assumptions 5 and 6, which state that cross sections of the beam remain plane and normal to the neutral surface after bending. If a beam is short its cross sections become s-shaped as in Fig. 22.23, and the assumptions are

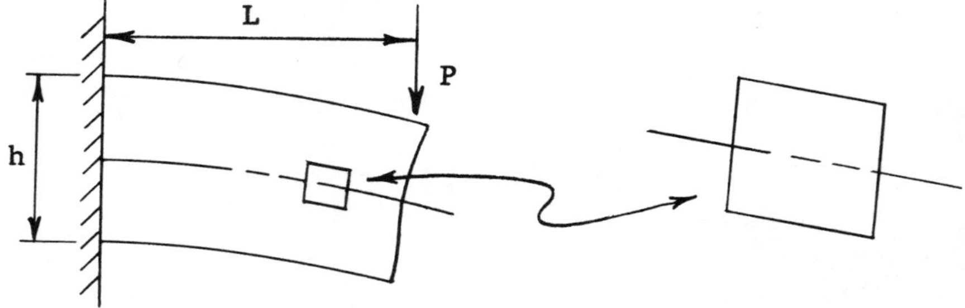

Fig. 22.23. Short cantilever beam.

violated. Along the neutral surface where the shear stress is the highest, a differential rectangular element is distorted into a rhomboid as shown in the enlargement. The shear strain increases the deflection of the beam above the amount given by Eq. (22.79). A method for calculating the total deflection will be explained in the next chapter. For the cantilever beam the total deflection is

$$v(L) = \frac{P L^3}{3 E I}\left[1 + \frac{3}{5}(1 + \mu)\left(\frac{h}{L}\right)^2\right]. \tag{22.80}$$

If $\mu = 0.3$ and the length-to-depth ratio L/h is greater than 4, the deflection due to shear stress is less than 5 percent of that due to bending stress. Observe that a simply-supported beam loaded in the middle is equivalent to two cantilever beams joined at their fixed ends. For this beam L/h must exceed 8 in order for the deflection error caused by neglecting shear stress to be less than 5 percent. In general, the shear deflection of a long or slender beam is negligible compared to the bending deflection.

22.10 Beams with Axial Loads

Until now the beams being considered have been subjected to only vertical or transverse loads. Some beams are loaded axially as well as transversely, and must act as columns as well as beams. What effect does the axial thrust have on the deflection of the beam? The thrust is included in the differential equation for displacement v, which must be solved again. The procedure is illustrated by the example shown in Fig. 22.24. It is the same cantilever beam as in Fig. 22.15, with the addition

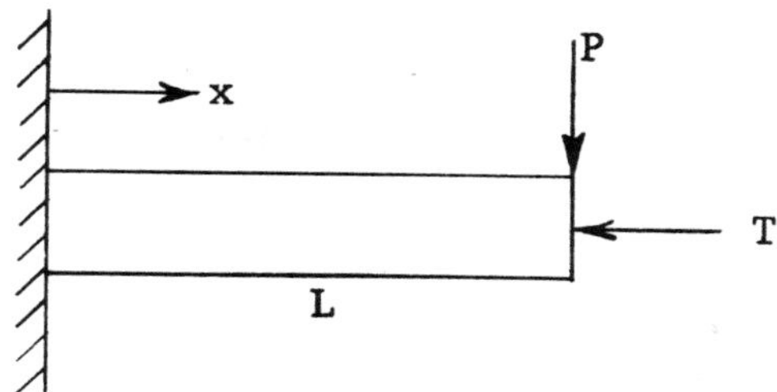

Fig. 22.24. Cantilever beam with axial thrust.

of an axial or longitudinal compressive thrust T, acting on the centroid of the end of the beam. The longitudinal normal stress σ_x on any cross section now consists of a uniform compressive component $-T/A$, and the bending stress. The distribution of σ_x is shown in Fig. 22.25A. The force

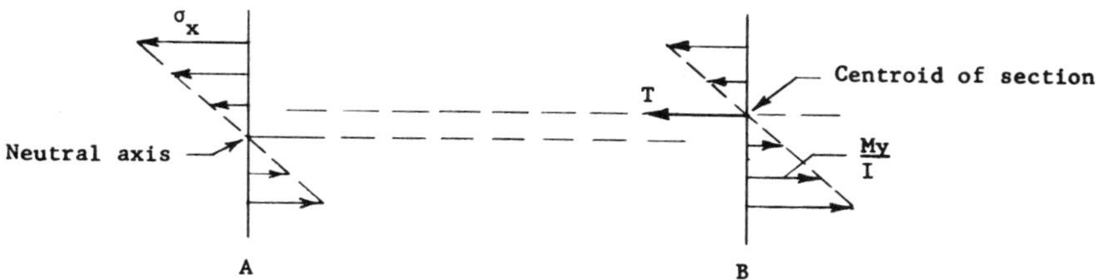

Fig. 22.25. Distribution of longitudinal normal stress σ_x.

due to the uniform component is equivalent to a concentrated force T acting thru the centroid of the section, not the neutral axis, as shown in Fig. 22.25B. The variable component of σ_x is the conventional bending stress My/I, where M is the total bending moment on the section, I is the moment of inertia of the section about its centroidal axis (not the neutral axis) and y is measured from the centroidal axis (not the neutral axis). Figs. 22.26A and B are free-body diagrams of the cantilever beam and a portion of length x. The latter figure shows that the bending moment at a distance x from the left end of the beam is

$$M = M_0 + T\,v(x) + P\,x\,. \tag{22.81}$$

In the moment-curvature formula

$$\frac{d^2v}{dx^2} = -\frac{M}{E\,I}, \tag{22.82}$$

I is still the moment of inertia of the section about its centroidal axis. These two equations produce the ordinary second-order differential equation

$$\frac{d^2v}{dx^2} + \frac{T}{E\,I}\,v = -\frac{1}{E\,I}\,(M_0 + P\,x)\,. \tag{22.83}$$

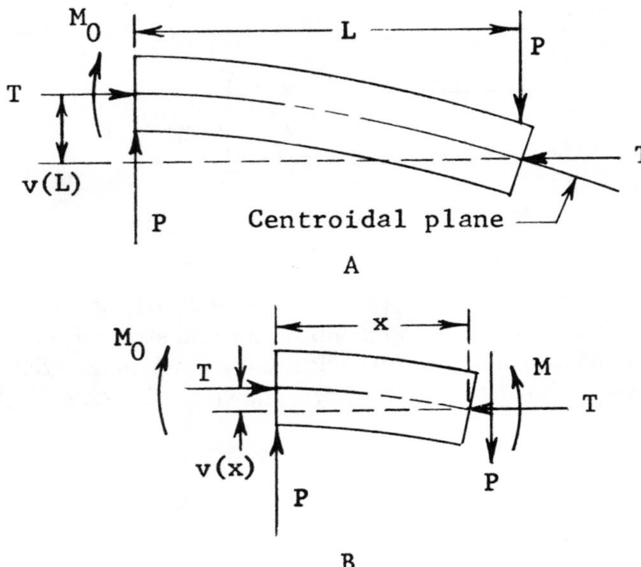

Fig. 22.26. Free-body diagrams of the cantilever beam.

Since the vertical deflection and slope of the beam are zero at its left end, and no moment acts on the free right end,

$$v(0) = 0\,, \qquad v'(0) = 0\,, \qquad \text{and} \qquad v''(L) = -\frac{M}{E\,I} = 0\,. \tag{22.84}$$

With the first two of these boundary conditions applied, the solution is

$$v = \frac{P}{a\,T}\sin ax + \frac{M_0}{T}\cos ax - \frac{M_0 + P\,x}{T}\,, \tag{22.85}$$

where

$$a = \sqrt{\frac{T}{E\,I}}\,. \tag{22.86}$$

According to Fig. 22.26A, the reacting moment on the fixed end of the beam is

$$M_0 = -P\,L - T\,v(L)\,. \tag{22.87}$$

Therefore

$$v = \frac{P}{a\,T}\sin ax - \frac{P\,L + T\,v(L)}{T}\cos ax + \frac{T\,v(L) + P(L - x)}{T}\,. \tag{22.88}$$

When $x = L$, this equation becomes

$$v(L) = \frac{P}{a\,T}\sin aL - \frac{P\,L + T\,v(L)}{T}\cos aL + v(L) \qquad (22.89)$$

or

$$v(L) = \frac{P}{T}\left(\frac{\tan aL}{a} - L\right). \qquad (22.90)$$

The same result is obtained by applying the third boundary condition to Eq. (22.88). Eqs. (22.88) and (22.90) constitute the rather complicated expression for the deflection of the cantilever beam at any axial position x. The maximum deflection, at the free end, is given by Eq. (22.90). It can be put into a more convenient form. Since $T = E\,I\,a^2$,

$$v(L) = \frac{P\,L^3}{3\,E\,I}\left[\frac{3}{(aL)^3}(\tan aL - a\,L)\right], \qquad (22.91)$$

or if

$$\alpha = a\,L = L\sqrt{\frac{T}{E\,I}}, \qquad (22.92)$$

$$v(L) = \frac{P\,L^3}{3\,E\,I}\left(3\,\frac{\tan\alpha - \alpha}{\alpha^3}\right). \qquad (22.93)$$

The term before the parentheses in Eq. (22.93) is the maximum deflection of the cantilever beam with no axial thrust, given by Eq. (22.51). The term in parentheses is a magnification factor produced by the thrust. Its magnitude is shown in Fig. 22.27. Notice that the magnification factor becomes infinite when $\alpha = \pi/2$. Then

$$L\sqrt{\frac{T}{E\,I}} = \frac{\pi}{2} \qquad \text{or} \qquad T = \frac{\pi^2\,E\,I}{4\,L^2}. \qquad (22.94)$$

With this value of thrust, the deflection given by Eq. (22.93) is infinite if the lateral load P has any value other than zero. For example, suppose that the hardware on a telephone pole is distributed so that the centroid of the load coincides with the axis of the pole. Assume that the pole is perfectly straight and vertical. If the load T has the value given by Eq. (22.94), and the pole can endure the compressive stress $-T/A$, the pole will stand. The first breath of wind or vibration of the ground, however, will cause the lateral load P to increase from zero, and the pole will collapse.

If the axial load on a beam is a tensile *pull*, the thrust T in Eq. (22.92) is negative, and α is imaginary. Let

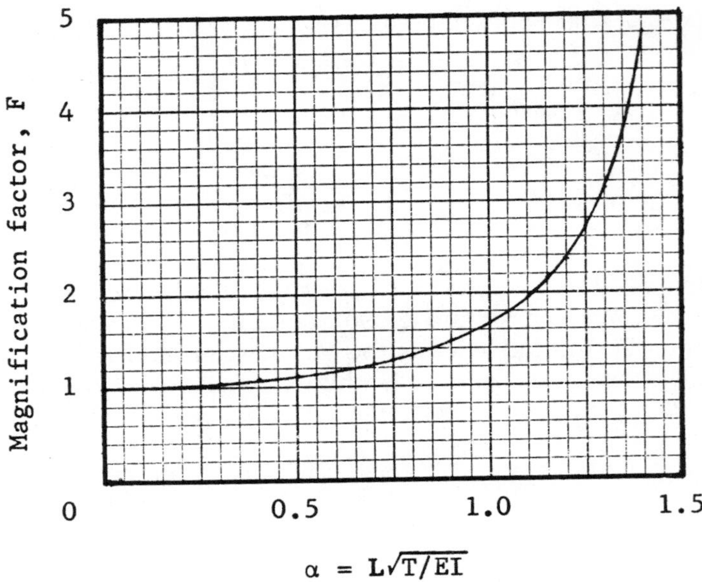

Fig. 22.27. Magnification of deflection caused by axial thrust.

$$\beta = L\sqrt{\frac{-T}{EI}} = j\alpha\,. \tag{22.95}$$

If T is negative, β is real. The new magnification factor is

$$F = 3\frac{\tan\alpha - \alpha}{\alpha^3} = 3\,\frac{\tan(-j\beta) + j\beta}{j\beta^3} = 3\,\frac{-j\tanh\beta + j\beta}{j\beta^3}$$

$$= 3\,\frac{\beta - \tanh\beta}{\beta^3}\,. \tag{22.96}$$

This factor starts at unity and decreases toward zero as the axial pull increases. The axial pull T therefore stiffens the beam. Even a rope becomes a beam, capable of supporting a lateral load, when it is stiffened by an axial pull.

22.11 Principal Stresses

At any point in a beam there are a normal stress σ_x and a shear stress τ_{xy}, and unless the beam is in plane stress, a normal stress σ_z. The preceding chapter showed that the stresses at a point in a body are determined by the stresses σ_x, σ_y, σ_z, τ_{xy}, τ_{xz}, and τ_{yz}. The magnitudes of the stresses on a plane at the point depend on the orientation of the plane. How can the combined effect of the normal and shear stresses be determined? Is there a plane on which the normal or shear stress is a maximum? To answer these questions, consider the stresses in a typical body, namely the narrow beam in Fig. 22.28. A rectangular differential element of the beam is shown enlarged in Fig. 22.29. Since the beam is

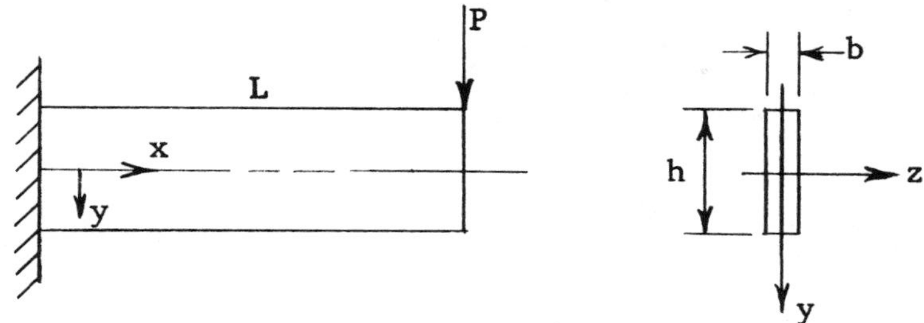

Fig. 22.28. Narrow beam.

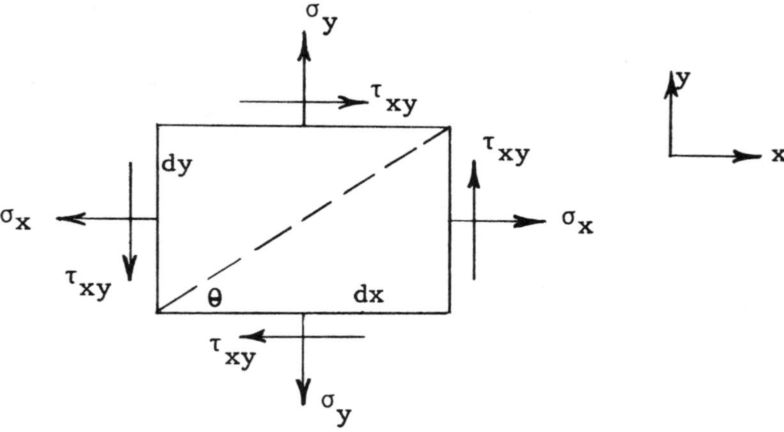

Fig. 22.29. Differential element in plane stress.

in plane stress, σ_z, τ_{xz}, and τ_{yz} are zero. According to the special formulas that have been derived for beams in this chapter,

$$\sigma_x = \frac{M\,y}{I}\,, \qquad \sigma_y = 0\,, \qquad \tau_{xy} = -\frac{3}{2}\frac{V}{A}\left[1 - \left(\frac{2y}{h}\right)^2\right]. \qquad (22.97)$$

The differential differences between the stresses on the left and right faces, and the top and bottom faces, are of no concern in this analysis. For this reason the stresses on opposite faces are labeled the same. Notice that the y axis is now pointing in the conventional upward direction, not the unconventional downward direction used for beams, because Fig. 22.29 represents a differential element of any body in plane stress. A half of the element made by a diagonal cut is shown in Fig. 22.30. The normal stress N and the shear stress S on any plane thru

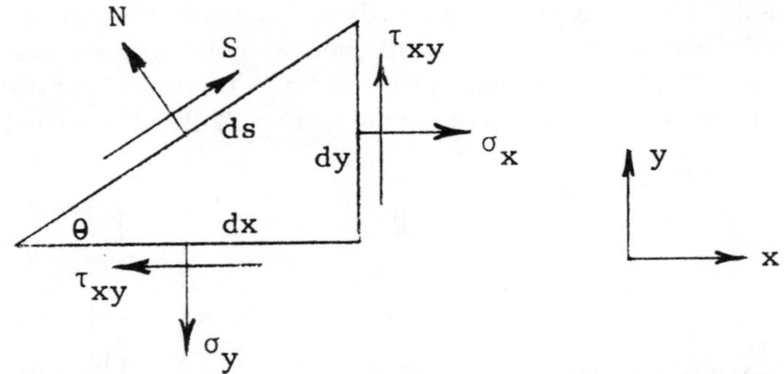

Fig. 22.30. Differential triangular element in plane stress.

the point represented by the differential element can be found by summing forces on the element. The sum of forces in the direction of N is

$$N\,ds\,dz = \sigma_x \sin\theta\,dy\,dz + \sigma_y \cos\theta\,dx\,dz - \tau_{xy}\cos\theta\,dy\,dz - \tau_{xy}\sin\theta\,dx\,dz\,. \tag{22.98}$$

Now

$$\frac{dx}{ds} = \cos\theta \qquad \text{and} \qquad \frac{dy}{ds} = \sin\theta\,. \tag{22.99}$$

Therefore

$$N = \sigma_x \sin^2\theta + \sigma_y \cos^2\theta - 2\,\tau_{xy}\sin\theta\cos\theta = \frac{1}{2}(\sigma_x + \sigma_y) - \frac{1}{2}(\sigma_x - \sigma_y)\cos 2\theta - \tau_{xy}\sin 2\theta\,. \tag{22.100}$$

The sum of forces in the direction of S is

$$S\,ds\,dz = \sigma_y \sin\theta\,dx\,dz - \sigma_x\cos\theta\,dy\,dz + \tau_{xy}\cos\theta\,dx\,dz - \tau_{xy}\sin\theta\,dy\,dz$$

or

$$S = (\sigma_y - \sigma_x)\sin\theta\cos\theta + \tau_{xy}(\cos^2\theta - \sin^2\theta) = -\frac{1}{2}(\sigma_x - \sigma_y)\sin 2\theta + \tau_{xy}\cos 2\theta\,. \tag{22.101}$$

The orientation of the planes on which the normal stress N has maximum and minimum values is found by differentiating Eq. (22.100):

$$\frac{dN}{d\theta} = (\sigma_x - \sigma_y)\sin 2\theta - 2\,\tau_{xy}\cos 2\theta = 0\,. \tag{22.102}$$

Then

$$\tan 2\theta = \frac{2\,\tau_{xy}}{\sigma_x - \sigma_y} \quad \text{or} \quad \frac{-2\,\tau_{xy}}{-(\sigma_x - \sigma_y)}. \tag{22.103}$$

The two values of 2θ, twice the angle of inclination of the plane on which the normal stress N is a maximum or minimum, are 180 degrees apart, as shown in Fig. 22.31. The maximum occurs where $dN/d\theta = 0$ and

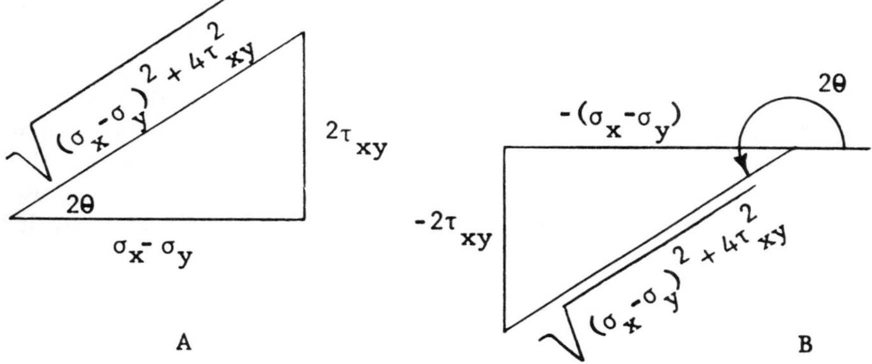

Fig. 22.31. Double angle of inclination of principal planes, 2θ.

$d^2N/d\theta^2$ is negative. Differentiating Eq. (22.102) shows that the second value of 2θ given by Eq. (22.103) makes $d^2N/d\theta^2$ negative. For this angle, shown in Fig. 22.31B,

$$\sin 2\theta = -\frac{2\,\tau_{xy}}{\sqrt{(\sigma_x - \sigma_y)^2 + 4\,\tau_{xy}^2}}$$

and

$$\cos 2\theta = -\frac{\sigma_x - \sigma_y}{\sqrt{(\sigma_x - \sigma_y)^2 + 4\,\tau_{xy}^2}}. \tag{22.104}$$

The maximum value of N is found by substituting these values into Eq. (22.100):

$$N = \sigma_1 = \frac{\sigma_x + \sigma_y}{2} + \sqrt{\left(\frac{\sigma_x - \sigma_y}{2}\right)^2 + \tau_{xy}^2}. \tag{22.105}$$

The value of 2θ shown in Fig. 22.31A makes $d^2N/d\theta^2$ positive. Substitution of the sine and cosine of this angle into Eq. (22.100) produces the minimum value of N:

$$\sigma_2 = \frac{\sigma_x + \sigma_y}{2} - \sqrt{\left(\frac{\sigma_x - \sigma_y}{2}\right)^2 + \tau_{xy}^2}. \tag{22.106}$$

The shear stress on the planes of maximum and minimum normal stress is found by substituting the two angles given by Eq. (22.103) into Eq. (22.101):

$$S = -\frac{1}{2}(\sigma_x - \sigma_y)\frac{\pm 2\,\tau_{xy}}{\sqrt{(\sigma_x - \sigma_y)^2 + 4\,\tau_{xy}^2}} + \tau_{xy}\frac{\pm(\sigma_x - \sigma_y)}{\sqrt{(\sigma_x - \sigma_y)^2 + 4\,\tau_{xy}^2}} = 0\,. \tag{22.107}$$

Two planes, 90 degrees apart, have been found on which the shear stress is zero and the normal stress is stationary (at a maximum or minimum). Ref. 15 shows that at any point in a stressed body there are three mutually-perpendicular planes on which the shear stresses are zero and the normal stress is stationary. These normal stresses are the *principal stresses*, their directions are the *principal axes*, and the planes on which they act are the *principal planes*. On any other plane thru the point the shear stress is non-zero and the normal stress is somewhere between the most positive and the most negative of the three principal stresses. In the example of Fig. 22.28 the z axis is the third principal axis, and the third principal stress is $\sigma_3 = \sigma_z = 0$.

Like the normal stress N, the shear stress S on a plane at a point in a body is a function of the angle of inclination θ of the plane. The maximum and minimum shear stress, found by differentiating Eq. (22.101), are

$$S = \tau_1 = \sqrt{\left(\frac{\sigma_x - \sigma_y}{2}\right)^2 + \tau_{xy}^2} \tag{22.108}$$

where

$$\tan 2\theta = \frac{-(\sigma_x - \sigma_y)}{2\,\tau_{xy}}\,, \tag{22.109}$$

and

$$S = \tau_2 = -\sqrt{\left(\frac{\sigma_x - \sigma_y}{2}\right)^2 + \tau_{xy}^2} \tag{22.110}$$

where

$$\tan 2\theta = \frac{\sigma_x - \sigma_y}{-2\,\tau_{xy}}\,. \tag{22.111}$$

These two values of tan 2θ are negative reciprocals of those given by Eq. (22.103), and therefore designate planes that are 90 degrees from those in Fig. 22.31. The planes of greatest shear stress are therefore 45 degrees from the principal planes. For example, suppose that σ_x is tensile, $\sigma_y = -\sigma_x$, and $\tau_{xy} = 0$, as in Fig. 22.32A. According to Eqs.

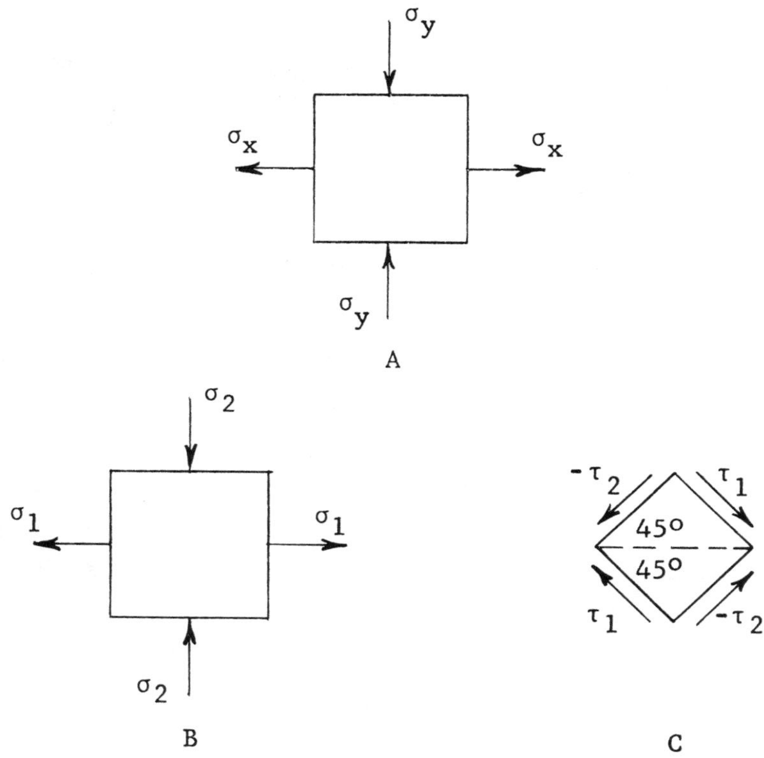

Fig. 22.32. Principal stresses at a point.

(22.105) and (22.106), $\sigma_1 = \sigma_x$ and $\sigma_2 = \sigma_y$ as shown in Fig. 22.32B. Eqs. (22.108) thru (22.111) show that the maximum and minimum shear stresses are

$$\tau_1 = \sigma_x \qquad \text{and} \qquad \tau_2 = -\sigma_x \, , \tag{22.112}$$

and that they act on planes inclined at ± 45 degrees, as in Fig. 22.32C.

Another interesting fact can be learned from Eq. (22.100), which is the formula for $N(\theta)$, the normal stress on the plane thru a point at an angle of inclination θ. This formula shows that

$$N(\theta) + N(\theta + 90°) = \sigma_x + \sigma_y \, . \tag{22.113}$$

Thus at a point in a body in plane stress, the sum of the normal stresses on any two planes at right angles is invariant. Ref. 15 (page 26) shows that for any orientation of the x, y, and z axes in any stressed body, the sum $\sigma_x + \sigma_y + \sigma_z$ is invariant.

22.12 Mohr's Circle for Stresses

For a body in plane stress, the relationships between the known σ_x, σ_y, and τ_{xy}, and the principal and maximum shear stresses can be shown graphically by Mohr's circle for stresses, shown in Fig. 22.33. To

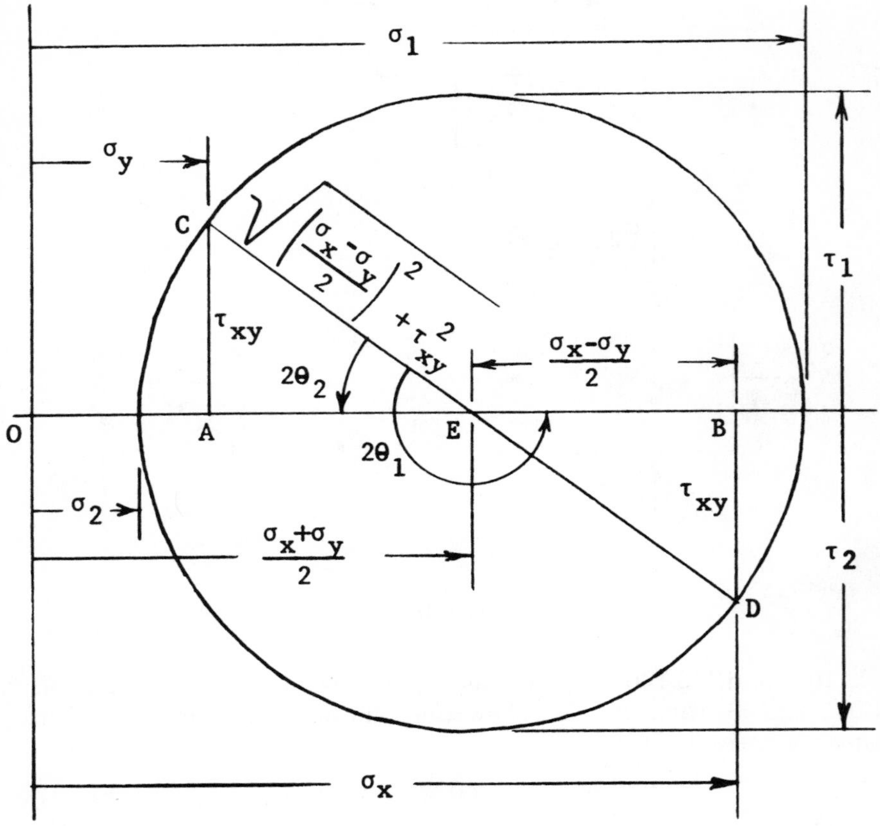

Fig. 22.33. Mohr's circle for stresses.

construct the circle, lay off the values of σ_x and σ_y along the horizontal axis. If τ_{xy} is positive, lay its value off vertically upward from *A* and downward from *B* (or vice versa, if τ_{xy} is negative). Then draw the circle with *CD* as a diameter. The principal stresses σ_1 and σ_2 and the maximum and minimum shear stresses τ_1 and τ_2 can be read directly. The angles of inclination θ_1 and θ_2 of the principal planes are shown as double angles measured from the radius *CE*.

The use of the Mohr circle is illustrated by a calculation of the stresses in the round shaft of Fig. 22.34A. The torque *T* applied to the ends pro-

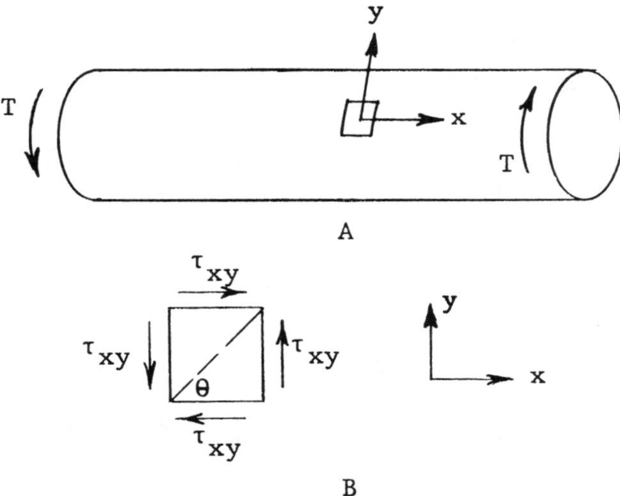

Fig. 22.34. Round shaft in pure torsion.

duces the known shear stress τ_{xy} at a point on the surface, enlarged in Fig. 22.34B. Since the shaft has no axial thrust or bending load, σ_x and σ_y are zero everywhere. The Mohr circle in Fig. 22.35 shows that

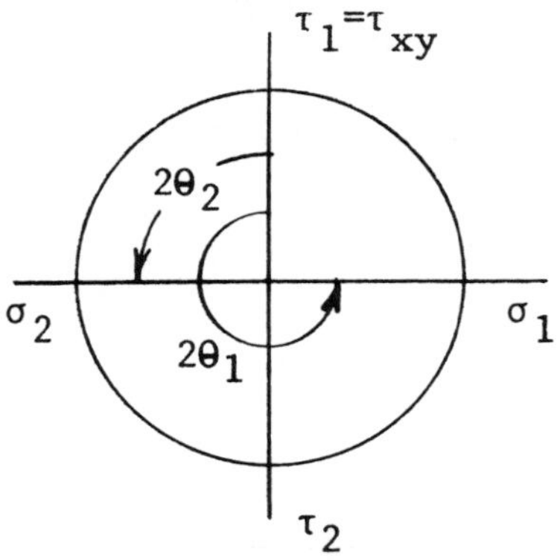

Fig. 22.35. Mohr circle for pure shear.

the maximum and minimum principal stresses are

$$\sigma_1 = \tau_{xy} \qquad \text{and} \qquad \sigma_2 = -\tau_{xy}\,, \tag{22.114}$$

and that σ_1 is normal to the plane at $\theta_1 = 135°$ as in Fig. 22.36. This stress condition is called *pure shear*. It is not truly "pure", of course, because normal stress acts on the planes at every angle of inclination except zero and 90 degrees. When a piece of chalk is twisted as in Fig.

22.34A, the tensile principal stress breaks it. The fracture is a spiral along a line at 135 degrees.

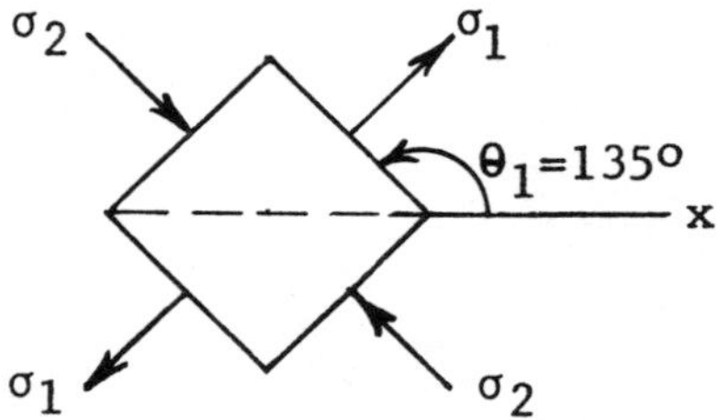

Fig. 22.36. Principal stresses for pure shear.

The principal stresses have been derived and the Mohr circle constructed for a body in plane stress. If it is not in plane stress, the stresses σ_z, τ_{xz}, and τ_{yz} are not necessarily zero. They still do not contribute to the net forces on the differential element of Fig. 22.30 in the *N* and *S* directions, and do not affect the subsequent formulas for σ_1 and σ_2. Since the three principal stresses are mutually perpendicular, σ_1 and σ_2 are principal stresses only if σ_z is the third principal stress, σ_3. Then the *xy* plane is a principal plane, and the Mohr circle of Fig. 22.33 can be drawn to determine the orientation of the other two principal planes. Now if the magnitude of σ_3 is known, a Mohr circle can be drawn for each of the other two principal planes. The circle in the plane normal to σ_1 lies between σ_3 and σ_2, and the circle in the plane normal to σ_2 lies between σ_3 and σ_1, as shown in Fig. 22.37. The largest shear stress at a point is therefore

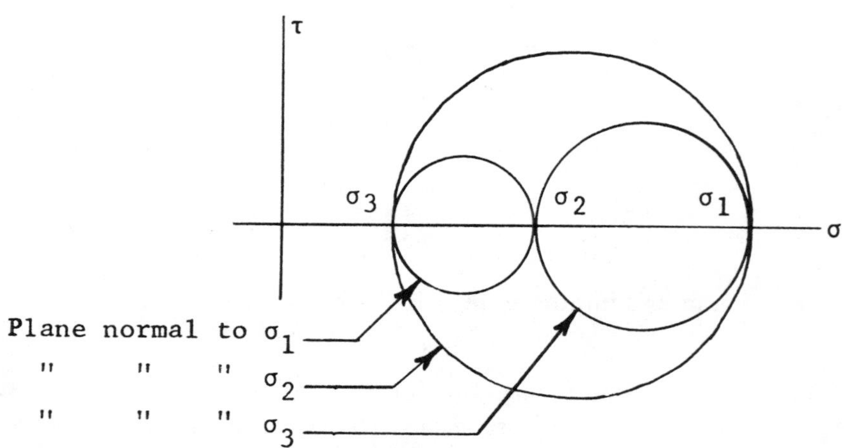

Fig. 22.37. Mohr circle for three-dimensional stress.

$$\tau_{max} = \frac{\sigma_1 - \sigma_3}{2}, \qquad (22.115)$$

where σ_1 and σ_3 are the most positive and most negative of the three principal stresses. The highest normal stress at the point is σ_1.

Frequently the direction of one of the three principal planes is known. In Fig. 22.28, the xy plane thru any point is a principal plane because the shear stresses on it, τ_{zx} and τ_{zy}, are zero. When a beam of circular cross section is bent as in Fig. 22.38, the vertical xy plane thru the axis is a

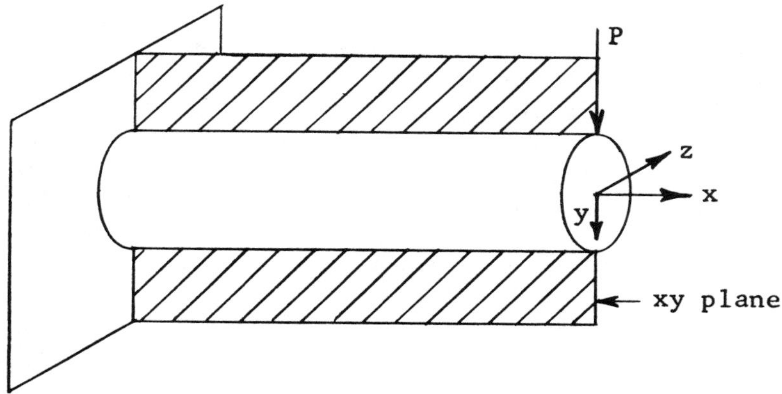

Fig. 22.38. Round cantilever beam.

principal plane, for the same reason. The plane tangent to any free surface of a body is a principal plane, because no shear stress acts on the surface.

22.13 Stresses Determined Experimentally

The preceding two sections have shown how to calculate the direction and magnitude of two principal stresses when the normal and shear stresses are known in two perpendicular directions parallel to one of the principal planes. In experimental work, stresses cannot be measured but normal strains can. The strains ε_1 and ε_2 in two perpendicular directions at the surface of a body can be measured by resistance strain gages as in Fig. 22.39. The stresses in these two directions can then be calculated with Hooke's law:

$$\sigma_1 = \frac{E}{1 - \mu^2} (\varepsilon_1 + \mu\, \varepsilon_2) \qquad (22.116)$$

$$\sigma_2 = \frac{E}{1 - \mu^2} (\varepsilon_2 + \mu\, \varepsilon_1)\,. \qquad (22.117)$$

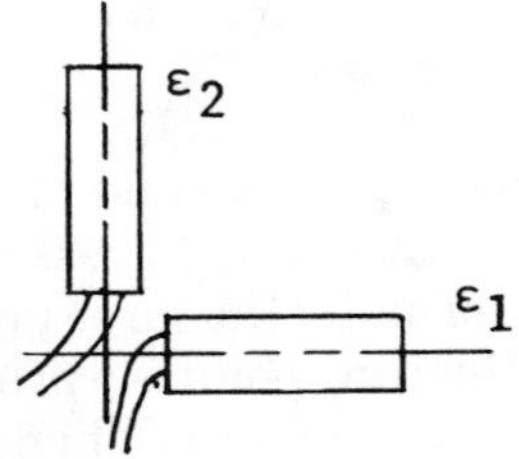

Fig. 22.39. Two perpendicular strain gages.

The surface is a principal plane, and the principal stress normal to it is zero. If the directions of the other two principal stresses parallel to the surface are known, as they are in many simple structural shapes, the gages are oriented in those directions, and σ_1 and σ_2 are the principal stresses. If the directions are not known, strains are measured by a rosette of three gages. One arrangement is shown in Fig. 22.40. The principal stresses lie at angles ϕ_1 and ϕ_2 counterclockwise from the axis of gage A, as in Fig. 22.41. Ref. 102 shows that $2\phi_1$ and $2\phi_2$ are the two angles, 180 degrees apart, for which

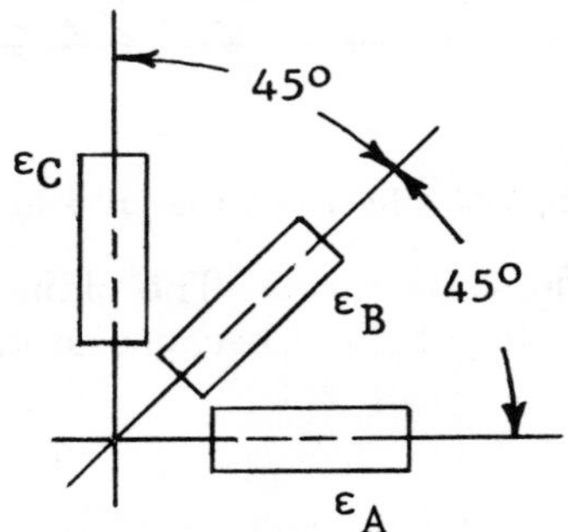

Fig. 22.40. Rosette of three strain gages.

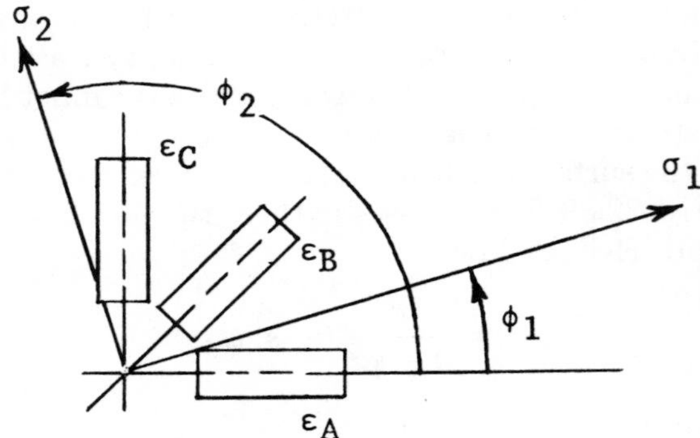

Fig. 22.41. Directions of principal stresses.

$$\tan 2\phi = \frac{2\,\varepsilon_B - \varepsilon_A - \varepsilon_C}{\varepsilon_A - \varepsilon_C}. \tag{22.118}$$

The strains in the directions of the principal stresses, called the *principal strains*, can be calculated from the formulas

$$\varepsilon_1 = \frac{\varepsilon_A + \varepsilon_C}{2} + \frac{\varepsilon_A - \varepsilon_C}{2}\cos 2\phi_1 + \frac{2\,\varepsilon_B - \varepsilon_A - \varepsilon_C}{2}\sin 2\phi_1\,, \tag{22.119}$$

$$\varepsilon_2 = \frac{\varepsilon_A + \varepsilon_C}{2} + \frac{\varepsilon_A - \varepsilon_C}{2}\cos 2\phi_2 + \frac{2\,\varepsilon_B - \varepsilon_A - \varepsilon_C}{2}\sin 2\phi_2\,. \tag{22.120}$$

The principal stresses are then computed from Hooke's law, Eqs. (22.116) and (22.117).

The relationships of Eqs. (22.118), (22.119), and (22.120) are shown graphically in Fig. 22.42. To construct the circle, lay off the known

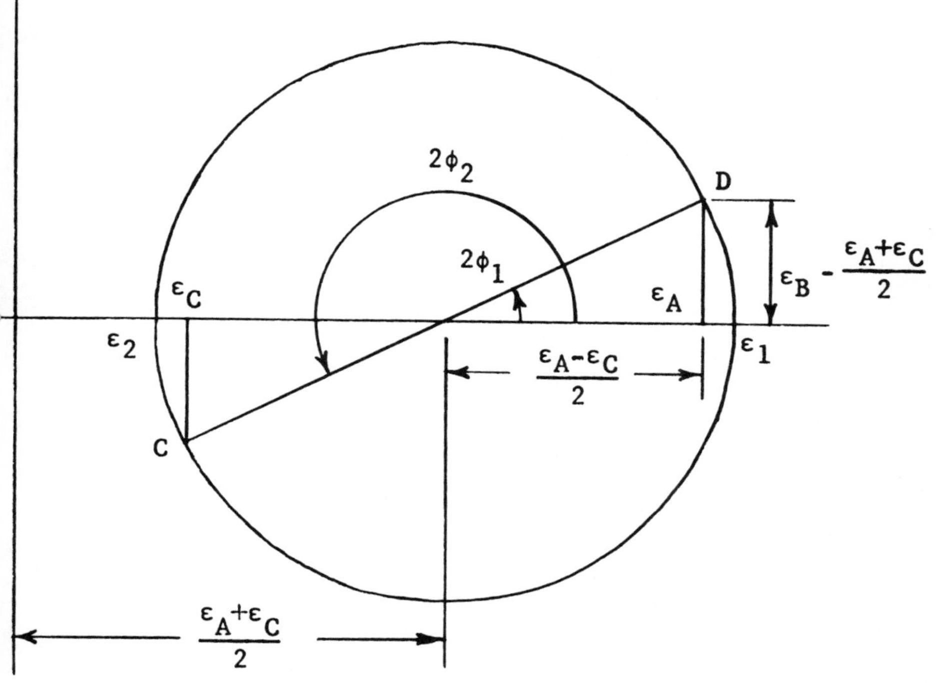

Fig. 22.42. Graphical calculation of principal strains.

strains ε_A and ε_C on the horizontal axis. Draw the known quantity $\varepsilon_B - (\varepsilon_A + \varepsilon_C)/2$ vertically from the ends of ε_A and ε_C, upward from ε_A if the quantity is positive. Then draw the circle with *CD* as a

Rosettes of two and three strain gages are used by the thousands in industry to measure strains in irregular shapes such as turbine buckets, pressure vessels, airplane wings, and bridge trusses. The output of strain gages mounted on a ship's propeller shaft can be calibrated to measure torque. If that signal is multiplied by a signal proportional to shaft speed, the product is proportional to power transmitted. Strain gages have even been mounted on the oars of a rowing shell to measure the effort of the oarsmen.

Chapter 23

STATIC ENERGY METHODS IN ELASTICITY

23.1 Introduction

Stress in materials, vibration frequency, voltage, and many other quantities in engineering are commonly calculated by "classical" methods. The physical law governing either the desired variable, or a variable from which the desired one can be found, is formulated as an ordinary or partial differential equation. The boundary conditions are specified, and the differential equation solved. For many problems energy methods offer an alternate solution that is sometimes simpler. The total energy stored in a field or system is calculated. The variable of interest is determined by minimizing the total energy, differentiating it, or equating the maximum potential and kinetic energies. In stress analysis, energy methods are used to calculate the loads that cause buckling of columns and plates, the deflection curves of beams, and the stresses in statically-indeterminate structures. In the computer era, the finite-element method has been developed to compute the stresses in structures of all kinds. This energy method, in which a continuous field is approximated by small interconnected elements, is now being applied to fluid, magnetic, and other continuous fields.

This chapter is devoted to the modest task of calculating the deflections of beams with redundant reactions. The tool for this purpose is an energy method: the simple and powerful theorem of Alberto Castigliano (1847–1884).

23.2 Castigliano's Theorem

An interesting approach to the derivation of Castigliano's theorem will lead past a reciprocity theorem and a handy theorem by B.P.E. Clapeyron. To begin the approach, consider the forces F_1, F_2, . . F_n applied to a body as in Fig. 23.1. The forces are applied slowly, so that all of the work done on the body is converted into strain energy in the body, and none into kinetic energy. Assume that the body is elastic and that the material does not yield, so that none of the applied work is converted into heat. Let x_{jj} be the deflection of the body at the point of application of force F_j, in the direction of that force. Let x_{ij} be the deflection at the point of application of force F_i due to force F_j, in the direction of force F_i. Suppose a force F is applied, increasing from zero

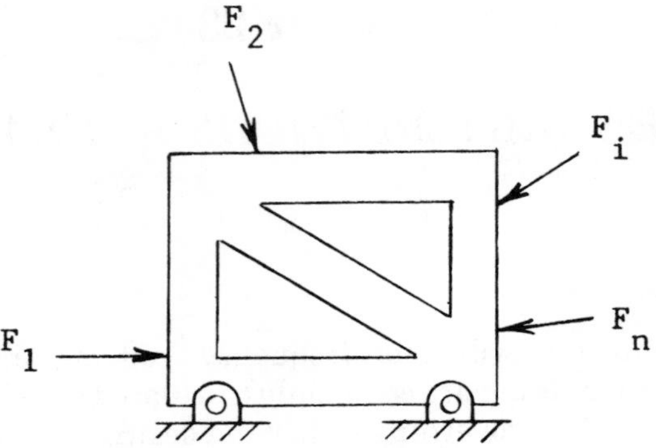

Fig. 23.1. Forces applied to a body.

up to its final value F_1. The resulting deflection x increases from zero to x_{11}. If the deflection is proportional to the force causing it,

$$F(x) = \frac{F_1}{x_{11}} x \,, \tag{23.1}$$

and the energy stored in the body is

$$\int_0^{x_{11}} F(x)dx = \frac{F_1}{x_{11}} \int_0^{x_{11}} x\,dx = \frac{F_1 x_{11}}{2} \,. \tag{23.2}$$

Now the load F_2 is applied, causing a deflection x_{22} under it, and also a deflection x_{12} at load F_1 in the direction of F_1. While F_2 is being applied, F_1 is constant and does the work $F_1 x_{12}$ on the body. The total energy stored in the body is now

$$U = \frac{1}{2} F_1 x_{11} + F_1 x_{12} + \frac{1}{2} F_2 x_{22} \,. \tag{23.3}$$

If the two loads were applied in the reverse order, the stored energy would be

$$U = \frac{1}{2} F_2 x_{22} + F_2 x_{21} + \frac{1}{2} F_1 x_{11} \,. \tag{23.4}$$

If each deflection is assumed to be proportional to the force causing it, regardless of the other forces already applied, the two stored energies are the same, and

$$F_1 x_{12} = F_2 x_{21} \,. \tag{23.5}$$

In general,

$$F_i x_{ij} = F_j x_{ji} \,. \tag{23.6}$$

This is a statement of reciprocity that will be needed in the following derivation.

Now apply all n of the loads on the body that are independent of each other, and calculate the total strain energy. As will be explained soon, the number n includes all of the applied loads plus all of the reactions, less the number of equations of static equilibrium that relate the forces and moments. The n loads can be any combination of applied loads and reactions. If they are applied in numerical order, the total strain energy is

$$\begin{aligned} U &= \frac{1}{2} F_1 x_{11} \\ &+ \frac{1}{2} F_2 x_{22} + F_1 x_{12} \\ &+ \frac{1}{2} F_3 x_{33} + F_1 x_{13} + F_2 x_{23} \\ &+ \cdots \\ &+ \frac{1}{2} F_n x_{nn} + F_1 x_{1n} + F_2 x_{2n} + \cdots + F_{n-1} x_{n-1,n} \,. \end{aligned} \tag{23.7}$$

With the help of Eq. (23.6), this expression can be put into the form

$$\begin{aligned} U &= \frac{1}{2} F_1 (x_{11} + x_{12} + x_{13} + \cdots + x_{1n}) \\ &+ \frac{1}{2} F_2 (x_{21} + x_{22} + x_{23} + \cdots + x_{2n}) \\ &+ \cdots \\ &+ \frac{1}{2} F_n (x_{n1} + x_{n2} + x_{n3} + \cdots + x_{nn}) \,. \end{aligned} \tag{23.8}$$

Each of the terms in parentheses is the total deflection at a load caused by all of the loads. If the total deflection at load F_i is x_i,

$$x_i = x_{i1} + x_{i2} + x_{i3} + \cdots + x_{in} \,, \tag{23.9}$$

and

$$\begin{aligned} U &= \frac{1}{2} (F_1 x_1 + F_2 x_2 + F_3 x_3 + \cdots + F_n x_n) \\ &= \frac{1}{2} \sum_{i=1}^{n} F_i x_i \,. \end{aligned} \tag{23.10}$$

This is *Clapeyron's theorem.* It shows that the total energy stored in the body is the same as if each load produced the total deflection under it.

Now define the *influence coefficient* a_{ij} by the formula

$$x_{ij} = a_{ij} F_j \, . \tag{23.11}$$

Notice that a_{ij} is the deflection under force F_i caused by a unit force F_j. Eq. (23.8) can be written as

$$\begin{aligned} U = {} & \frac{1}{2} F_1(a_{11}F_1 + a_{12}F_2 + \cdots + a_{1n}F_n) \\ & + \frac{1}{2} F_2(a_{21}F_1 + a_{22}F_2 + \cdots + a_{2n}F_n) \\ & + \cdots \\ & + \frac{1}{2} F_n(a_{n1}F_1 + a_{n2}F_2 + \cdots + a_{nn}F_n) \, . \end{aligned} \tag{23.12}$$

Eq. (23.6) shows that

$$\frac{x_{ij}}{F_j} = \frac{x_{ji}}{F_i} \tag{23.13}$$

or

$$a_{ij} = a_{ji} \, . \tag{23.14}$$

Eq. (23.12) can therefore be written as

$$\begin{aligned} U = {} & \frac{1}{2} (a_{11}F_1{}^2 + a_{12}F_1F_2 + a_{13}F_1F_3 + \cdots + a_{1n}F_1F_n) \\ & + \frac{1}{2} (a_{12}F_1F_2 + a_{22}F_2{}^2 + a_{23}F_2F_3 + \cdots + a_{2n}F_2F_n) \\ & + \frac{1}{2} (a_{13}F_1F_3 + a_{23}F_2F_3 + a_{33}F_3{}^2 + \cdots + a_{3n}F_3F_n) \\ & + \cdots \\ & + \frac{1}{2} (a_{1n}F_1F_n + a_{2n}F_2F_n + a_{3n}F_3F_n + \cdots + a_{nn}F_n{}^2) \\ = {} & \frac{1}{2} (a_{11}F_1{}^2 + a_{22}F_2{}^2 + \cdots + a_{nn}F_n{}^2) \\ & + (a_{12}F_1F_2 + a_{13}F_1F_3 + \cdots + a_{1n}F_1F_n) \end{aligned}$$

$$+ (a_{23}F_2F_3 + a_{24}F_2F_4 + \cdots + a_{2n}F_2F_n)$$
$$+ \cdots$$
$$+ a_{n-1,n}F_{n-1}F_n \,. \tag{23.15}$$

Now differentiate the energy U stored in the body with respect to one of the applied forces, say F_1. Since the forces are all independent of each other,

$$\frac{\partial U}{\partial F_1} = a_{11}F_1 + a_{12}F_2 + a_{13}F_3 + \cdots + a_{1n}F_n$$
$$= x_{11} + x_{12} + x_{13} + \cdots + x_{1n} = x_1 \,. \tag{23.16}$$

In general,

$$\frac{\partial U}{\partial F_i} = x_i \,. \tag{23.17}$$

This is *Castigliano's theorem*. It applies to bodies whose deflections are proportional to the forces producing them. It states that the derivative of the strain energy in a body with respect to one of the statically-independent forces acting on the body equals the total deflection under that force caused by all of the forces. If the independent force F_i is a reaction at a fixed support, the deflection x_i is zero. This fact, as examples will show, is useful in solving beam problems.

23.3 Strain Energy

Castigliano's theorem is useful for engineering calculations if the strain energy in a body is expressed as a function of the stresses in the body, which in turn can be expressed as functions of the known applied loads. To accomplish the first of these goals, consider the differential cube of Fig. 23.2, that is loaded in uniaxial tension by the force F_x. If the

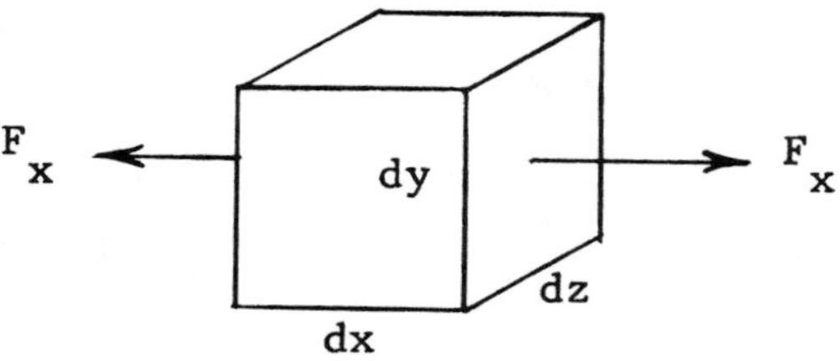

Fig. 23.2. Differential cube in tension.

material obeys Hooke's law, the elongation u in the direction of the force is proportional to the force: $F_x = ku$. As the force increases to the value

F, the elongation increases to δ, and the strain energy stored in the cube becomes

$$dU_x = \int_0^\delta ku\,du = \frac{k\delta^2}{2} = \frac{F\delta}{2}. \tag{23.18}$$

Since the cube is small, the normal stress σ_x can be considered uniform over the right and left faces, and $F = \sigma_x dydz$. If the modulus of elasticity of the material is E, the strain in the x direction is σ_x/E, and $\delta = \sigma_x dx/E$. Eq. (23.18) becomes

$$dU_x = \frac{1}{2}(\sigma_x dy\,dz)\left(\frac{\sigma_x dx}{E}\right) = \frac{\sigma_x^{\,2}}{2E}\,dx\,dy\,dz\,. \tag{23.19}$$

If the cube is loaded in tension in all three directions, the normal stresses σ_y and σ_z act on the top and bottom, and on the front and back. According to Hooke's law in three dimensions, the strain in the x direction is now

$$\varepsilon_x = \frac{1}{E}[\sigma_x - \mu(\sigma_y + \sigma_z)]\,, \tag{23.20}$$

where μ is Poisson's ratio. Notice that the strain ε_x is not proportional to the stress σ_x, and the deflection in the x direction is not proportional to the force. How can the strain energy be calculated? Clapeyron's theorem provides the answer by showing that the total strain energy stored in a body is the same as if each force acted alone in producing the total deflection under it, and was proportional to that deflection. Thus the strain energy credited to the force $\sigma_x dy\,dz$ and the deflection $\varepsilon_x dx$ is

$$\begin{aligned} dU_x &= \frac{1}{2}(\sigma_x dy\,dz)\cdot\frac{1}{E}[\sigma_x - \mu(\sigma_y + \sigma_z)]dx \\ &= \frac{1}{2E}(\sigma_x^{\,2} - \mu\sigma_x\sigma_y - \mu\sigma_x\sigma_z)dx\,dy\,dz\,. \end{aligned} \tag{23.21}$$

Similarly, the energies credited to the stresses and strains in the y and z directions are

$$dU_y = \frac{1}{2E}(\sigma_y^{\,2} - \mu\sigma_y\sigma_x - \mu\sigma_y\sigma_z)dx\,dy\,dz \tag{23.22}$$

and

$$dU_z = \frac{1}{2E}(\sigma_z^{\,2} - \mu\sigma_z\sigma_x - \mu\sigma_z\sigma_y)dx\,dy\,dz\,. \tag{23.23}$$

The total strain energy stored in the differential cube in tension is the sum of the three contributions. The total tensile-strain energy in any body is therefore the volume integral

$$U_t = \int_v \frac{1}{2E} [(\sigma_x^2 + \sigma_y^2 + \sigma_z^2) - 2\mu(\sigma_x\sigma_y + \sigma_x\sigma_z + \sigma_y\sigma_z)]dx\,dy\,dz\,. \tag{23.24}$$

To calculate the strain energy stored in a body in shear, start with the differential cube whose front face is shown in Fig. 23.3. The shear force

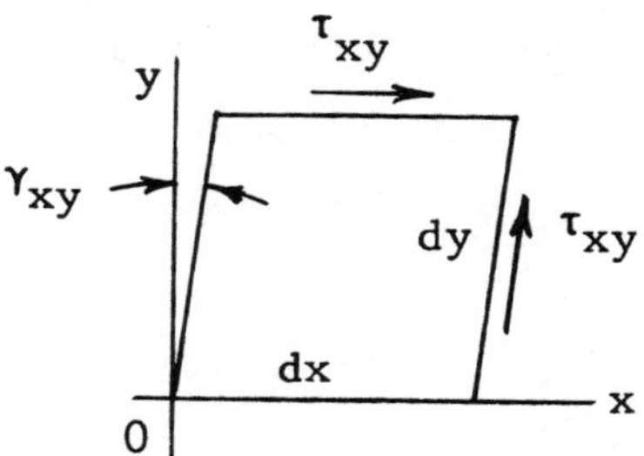

Fig. 23.3. Differential cube in shear.

$\tau_{xy}dx\,dz$ on the top face acts thru the distance $\gamma_{xy}dy$. If the material obeys Hooke's law, the displacement is proportional to the force, and the strain energy stored in the cube is

$$dU_{xy} = \frac{1}{2}(\tau_{xy}dx\,dz)(\gamma_{xy}dy)\,. \tag{23.25}$$

Since

$$\gamma_{xy} = \frac{\tau_{xy}}{G} \tag{23.26}$$

where G is the shear modulus of elasticity,

$$dU_{xy} = \frac{1}{2G}\tau_{xy}^2 dx\,dy\,dz\,. \tag{23.27}$$

Similarly, the strain energies stored in the cube by the other two shear stresses are

$$dU_{xz} = \frac{1}{2G}\tau_{xz}^2 dx\,dy\,dz\,, \qquad \partial U_{yz} = \frac{1}{2G}\tau_{yz}^2 dx\,dy\,dz\,. \tag{23.28}$$

The total shear-strain energy in a body is therefore the volume integral

$$U_s = \int_v \frac{1}{2G} (\tau_{xy}{}^2 + \tau_{xz}{}^2 + \tau_{yz}{}^2) dx\, dy\, dz\,. \tag{23.29}$$

The total strain energy in a body that obeys Hooke's law is the sum of the tensile and shear-strain energies: $U = U_t + U_s$.

23.4 Strain Energy in Simple Shapes

The next step in preparation for the use of Castigliano's theorem to solve engineering problems is calculation of the strain energy in a few simple structural members in terms of the applied loads.

Bar loaded in tension. Fig. 23.4 shows a bar of length L to which the

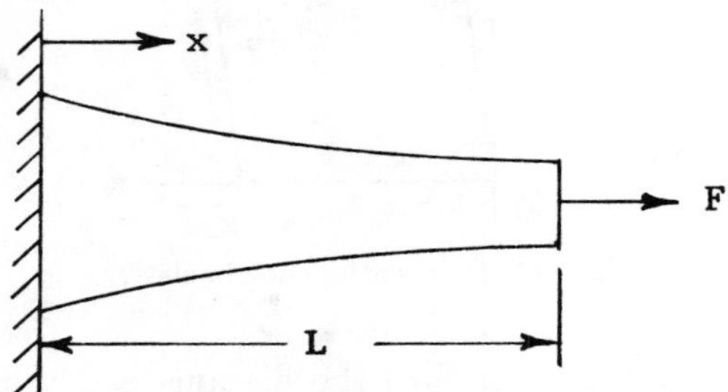

Fig. 23.4. Bar loaded in tension.

axial force F is applied. The cross-sectional area A may vary along the length of the bar in the x direction. If the bar is narrow in the y and z directions, all of the stresses in Eqs. (23.24) and (23.29) are zero except σ_x, and the bar contains no shear-strain energy. The tensile-strain energy is

$$U = \int_v \frac{\sigma_x{}^2}{2E} dx\, dy\, dz = \int_0^L \frac{F^2}{2AE} dx\,. \tag{23.30}$$

Round shaft loaded in torsion. Fig. 23.5 shows a round shaft of radius R, cross-sectional area A, polar moment of inertia J, and length L, to the ends of which the torque T is applied. The area A and moment of inertia J can be functions of the distance z along the shaft. The only one of the six stresses present in the shaft is the shear stress $\tau_{z\theta}$. At the distance r from the axis of the shaft,

$$\tau_{z\theta} = \frac{Tr}{J}\,. \tag{23.31}$$

According to Eq. (23.29), the strain energy in the shaft is

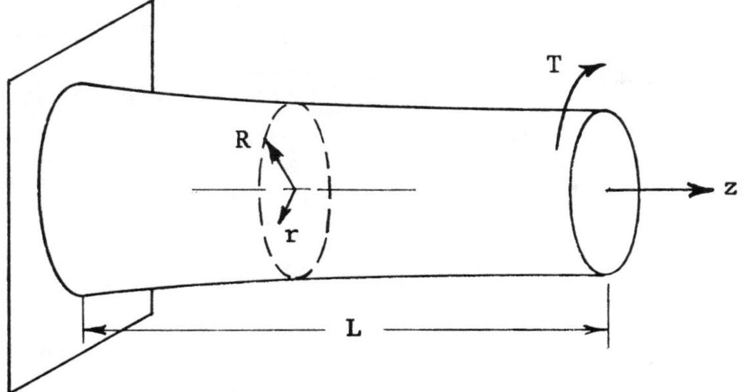

Fig. 23.5. Round shaft loaded in torsion.

$$U = \int_{v} \frac{\tau_{z\theta}{}^{2}}{2G}\, dv = \int_{0}^{L} \frac{T^2}{2J^2G}\left(\int_{A} r^2 dA\right) dz = \int_{0}^{L} \frac{T^2}{2JG}\, dz\,. \tag{23.32}$$

23.5 Strain Energy in a Beam

Fig. 23.6 shows a uniform rectangular beam of length L, cross-sectional area A, height h, and width b. The vertical shear force Q acts on a cross section located at the distance x from the origin. In general (although not in Fig. 23.6), Q is a function of x. The stresses of interest in

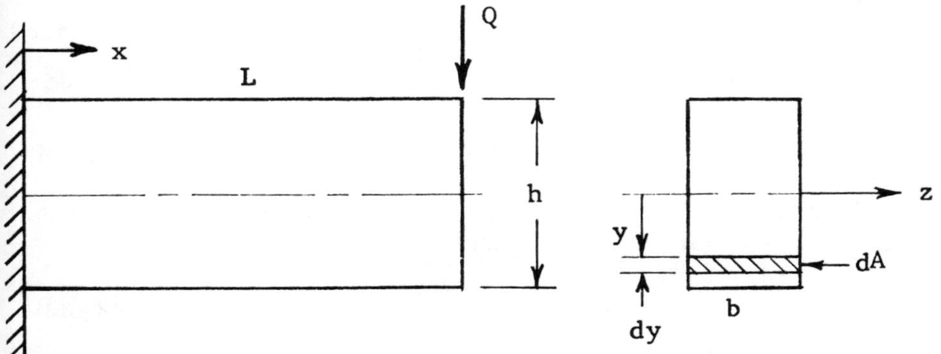

Fig. 23.6. A typical beam.

the beam are τ_{xy} and σ_x. The other four stresses in Eqs. (23.24) and (23.29) are assumed to be zero. According to Eq. (22.67) the shear stress at a point in the cross section is

$$\tau_{xy} = \frac{3Q}{2A}\left[1 - 4\left(\frac{y}{h}\right)^2\right], \tag{23.33}$$

where y is the distance of the point from the neutral axis. According to Eq. (23.29), the shear-strain energy in the beam is

$$
\begin{aligned}
U_s &= \frac{9}{8}\int_v \frac{Q^2}{A^2G}\left[1 - 4\left(\frac{y}{h}\right)^2\right]^2 dv \\
&= \frac{9}{8}\int_0^L \frac{Q^2 b}{A^2G}\left[\int_{-h/2}^{h/2}\left\{1 - 8\left(\frac{y}{h}\right)^2 + 16\left(\frac{y}{h}\right)^4\right\} dy\right] dx \\
&= \frac{9}{8}\int_0^L \frac{Q^2 b}{A^2G}\left(\frac{8h}{15}\right) dx = \frac{6}{5}\int_0^L \frac{Q^2}{2AG}\, dx\,. \qquad (23.34)
\end{aligned}
$$

Similar formulas can be derived for beams with cross sections other than rectangular. In general, the shear stress is

$$\tau_{xy} = f(y,z)\,\frac{Q}{A}\,. \qquad (23.35)$$

Then

$$U_s = \int_v \frac{Q^2}{2A^2G} f^2(y,z)dv = \int_0^L \frac{Q^2}{2A^2G}\left[\int_z\int_y f^2(y,z)dy\, dz\right] dx\,. \qquad (23.36)$$

With the definition

$$\alpha = \frac{1}{A}\int_z\int_y f^2(y,z)dy\, dz\,, \qquad (23.37)$$

Eq. (23.36) becomes

$$U_s = \alpha\int_0^L \frac{Q^2}{2AG}\, dx\,. \qquad (23.38)$$

The coefficient α is called the *shear form factor*. Eq. (23.34) shows that for a rectangular cross section it is 1.2.

To calculate the tensile-strain energy in a beam due to bending stress, observe first that the bending stress at any cross section is

$$\sigma_x = \frac{My}{I}\,, \qquad (23.39)$$

where M is the bending moment at the cross section, and I is the moment of inertia of the cross section about the neutral axis:

$$I = \int_A y^2 dA\,. \qquad (23.40)$$

Eq. (23.24) shows that if the beam is long and narrow so that $\sigma_y = \sigma_z = 0$, the tensile-strain energy is

$$U_t = \int_v \frac{M^2 y^2}{2EI^2} dv = \int_0^L \frac{M^2}{2EI^2}\left[\int_A y^2 dA\right] dx = \int_0^L \frac{M^2}{2EI} dx \,. \quad (23.41)$$

If the beam is wide enough to experience plane strain and long enough so that σ_y is negligible, then $\sigma_z = \mu\sigma_x$ and Eq. (23.24) becomes

$$U_t = \int_v \frac{1}{2E}[(\sigma_x{}^2 + \mu^2\sigma_x{}^2) - 2\mu(\mu\sigma_x{}^2)]dv = \int_v (1-\mu^2)\frac{\sigma_x{}^2}{2E} dv \,,$$

and Eq. (23.41) becomes

$$U_t = \int_v (1-\mu^2)\left(\frac{My}{I}\right)^2 \frac{1}{2E} dv = \int_0^L \frac{(1-\mu^2)M^2}{2EI} dx \,. \quad (23.42)$$

Eq. (23.41) is therefore valid for wide beams if the modulus of elasticity E is replaced by $E/(1-\mu^2)$.

23.6 The Importance of Shear-Strain Energy

An example will illustrate the use of Castigliano's theorem to calculate the deflection of a beam, and will also show the relative contributions of the tensile and shear-strain energies to the result. Calculate the deflection of a cantilever beam with a uniform rectangular cross section, to which a concentrated load Q is applied at the end, as in Fig. 23.6. According to Castigliano's theorem, Eq. (23.17), the deflection δ under the load is $\partial U/\partial Q$. If only the tensile-strain energy is considered,

$$\delta_t = \frac{\partial U_t}{\partial Q} = \frac{\partial}{\partial Q}\int_0^L \frac{M^2}{2EI} dx = \frac{1}{EI}\int_0^L M \frac{\partial M}{\partial Q} dx \,. \quad (23.43)$$

Differentiating before integrating avoids the tedium of squaring M, which usually contains several terms. The bending moment at any cross section is

$$M = -Q(L-x) \,. \quad (23.44)$$

Then

$$\delta_t = \frac{1}{EI}\int_0^L -Q(L-x)(-L+x)dx = \frac{Q}{EI}\int_0^L (L^2 - 2Lx + x^2)dx$$

$$= \frac{QL^3}{3EI} \,. \quad (23.45)$$

The contribution of the shear-strain energy to the deflection under the load is

$$\delta_s = \frac{\partial U_s}{\partial Q} = \frac{6}{5} \cdot \frac{\partial}{\partial Q} \int_0^L \frac{Q^2}{2AG}\, dx = \frac{6}{5} \int_0^L \frac{Q}{AG}\, dx = \frac{6QL}{5AG}. \quad (23.46)$$

The moment of inertia I for the rectangular section of the beam is

$$I = \frac{bh^3}{12}, \quad (23.47)$$

and the relationship between the tensile and shear moduli of elasticity is

$$G = \frac{E}{2(1 + \mu)}. \quad (23.48)$$

The ratio of the two components of deflection is therefore

$$\frac{\delta_s}{\delta_t} = \frac{6QL}{5bh} \cdot \frac{2(1 + \mu)}{E} \cdot \frac{3Ebh^3}{12QL^3} = \frac{3}{5}(1 + \mu)\left(\frac{h}{L}\right)^2. \quad (23.49)$$

If $\mu = 0.3$ and $\delta_t/\delta_s = 9$, $L/h = 2.65$. Thus if the length of the cantilever is more than 2.65 times its depth, the deflection calculated by ignoring the shear-strain energy is in error by less than 10 percent. Tables of beam deflections in handbooks are usually based on calculations that ignore the shear strain, and therefore list Eq. (23.45) as the deflection of a cantilever beam with a concentrated load at its free end.

23.7 A Beam with a Redundant Reaction

Now calculate the deflection of the beam in Fig. 23.7 under the known

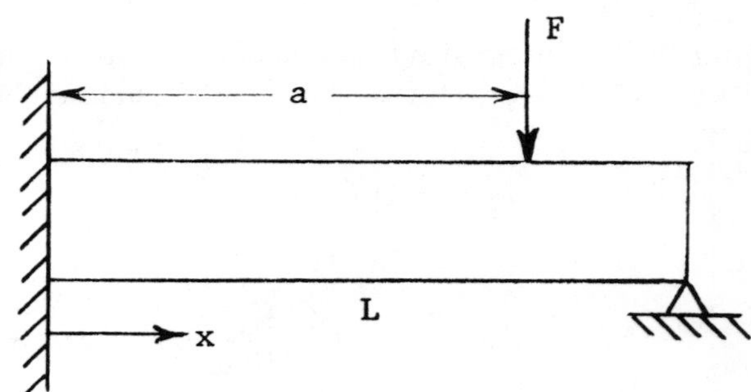

Fig. 23.7. A beam with a redundant reaction.

load F. The support at the free end just touches the beam before the load is applied. The beam has one redundant load, and cannot be analyzed simply by equating forces and moments. Fortunately, Castigliano's theorem makes the job easy. Fig. 23.8 is a free-body diagram of the beam including the reacting moment M_1 and reacting forces R_1 and R_2. The redundant reaction R_1 can be regarded as an applied force that produces a deflection of zero under it. The bending moment M at any section is

$$M = R_1(L - x) - F(a - x)\,, \qquad 0 \leqslant x \leqslant a$$
$$M = R_1(L - x)\,, \qquad a \leqslant x \leqslant L\,. \tag{23.50}$$

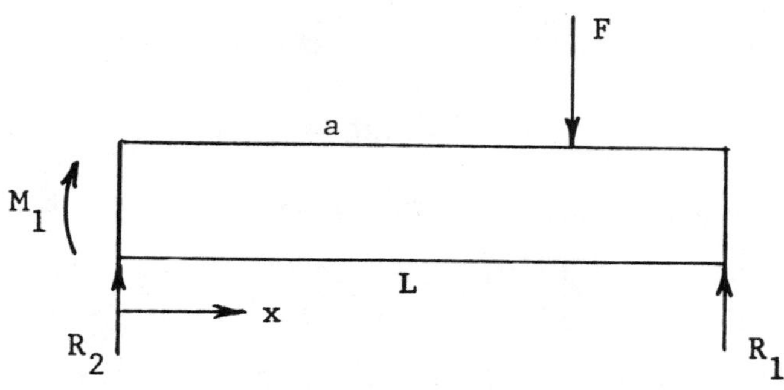

Fig. 23.8. Free-body diagram of the beam.

Use Castigliano's theorem and Eq. (23.41) to calculate the deflection under the load F. If the shear-strain energy is negligible,

$$\begin{aligned}\delta_F &= \frac{\partial U_t}{\partial F} = \frac{\partial}{\partial F}\int_0^L \frac{M^2}{2EI}\,dx = \frac{1}{EI}\int_0^L M\frac{\partial M}{\partial F}\,dx \\ &= \frac{1}{EI}\int_0^a [R_1(L - x) - F(a - x)](x - a)dx \\ &= \frac{a^2}{6EI}[2Fa - R_1(3L - a)]\,. \end{aligned}\tag{23.51}$$

This result contains the unknown reaction R_1. To determine the latter, apply Castigliano's theorem again, this time at the location of R_1 where the deflection δ_{R_1} is known to be zero:

$$\begin{aligned}\delta_{R_1} &= \frac{\partial U_t}{\partial R_1} = \frac{1}{EI}\int_0^L M\frac{\partial M}{\partial R_1}\,dx \\ &= \frac{1}{EI}\int_0^a [R_1(L - x) - F(a - x)](L - x)dx \\ &+ \frac{1}{EI}\int_a^L R_1(L - x)(L - x)dx = 0\,. \end{aligned}\tag{23.52}$$

This can be rearranged to the more convenient form

$$\delta_{R_1} = -\frac{F}{EI}\int_0^a (a-x)(L-x)dx + \frac{R_1}{EI}\int_0^L (L-x)^2 dx = 0\,. \quad (23.53)$$

The result of performing the integration is

$$\frac{F}{EI}\left(\frac{a^3}{6} - \frac{La^2}{2}\right) + \frac{R_1 L^3}{3EI} = 0 \quad (23.54)$$

or

$$R_1 = \frac{Fa^2}{2L^3}(3L - a)\,. \quad (23.55)$$

Now R_1 is known in terms of F. Eq. (23.51) becomes

$$\delta_F = \frac{a^2}{6EI}\left[2Fa - \frac{Fa^2}{2L^3}(3L-a)^2\right] = \frac{a^3 F}{6EI}\left[2 - \frac{a(3L-a)^2}{2L^3}\right]. \quad (23.56)$$

This deflection was found by applying Castigliano's theorem twice, once to find the deflection as a function of the known load F and the unknown reaction R_1, and again to find R_1 in terms of F.

23.8 Traps to Avoid

The preceding example led around a trap that cannot in general be escaped without effort. The redundant beam of Fig. 23.9 will display the

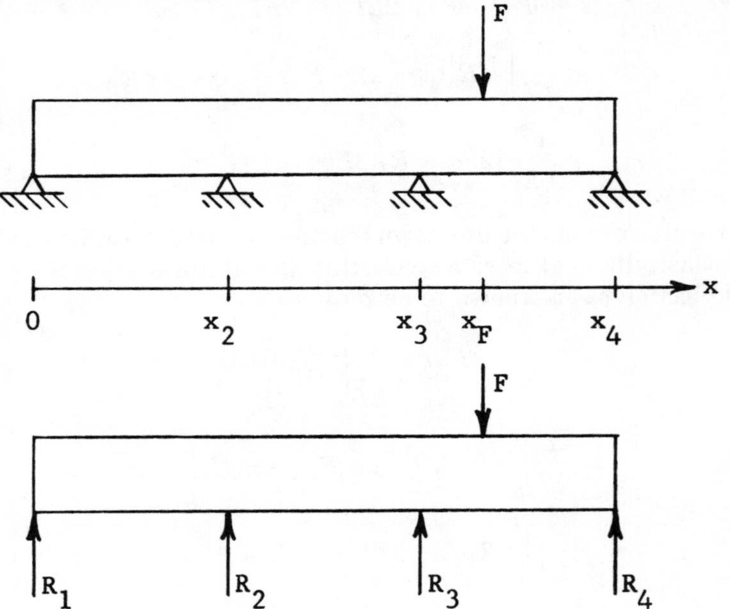

Fig. 23.9. A floor joist and its free-body diagram.

trap more clearly. The beam represents, for example, a floor joist with a concentrated load F at a distance x_F from the left end. The bending moment at any section of the beam can be expressed by the formulas

$$\begin{aligned} M &= R_1 x \,, & 0 \leqslant x \leqslant x_2 \\ M &= R_1 x + R_2(x - x_2) \,, & x_2 \leqslant x \leqslant x_3 \\ M &= R_4(x_4 - x) - F(x_F - x) \,, & x_3 \leqslant x \leqslant x_F \\ M &= R_4(x_4 - x) \,, & x_F \leqslant x \leqslant x_4 \,. \end{aligned} \tag{23.57}$$

If the shear-strain energy is ignored, the deflection under the load F is

$$\delta_F = \frac{1}{EI} \int_0^{x_4} M \frac{\partial M}{\partial F} \, dx \,. \tag{23.58}$$

The trap is sprung by substituting Eqs. (23.57) into this equation. The value of δ_F thus obtained is wrong. How can the trap be avoided? Remember that the forces applied to the body in Eq. (23.15) account for all of the strain energy and are independent of each other. When the energy is differentiated with respect to one of the forces, the terms not including that force drop out, leaving Castigliano's theorem. If Eq. (23.15) included *all* of the forces on the body including the reactions, they would not be independent because they are related by the force and moment equations of static equilibrium. As a simple example, suppose that for a given body Eq. (23.15) is

$$U = F_1^2 + F_2^2 + F_3^2 \,. \tag{23.59}$$

An uncritical application of Castigliano's theorem yields

$$\delta_{F_1} = \frac{\partial U}{\partial F_1} = 2F_1 \,. \tag{23.60}$$

Suppose that the free-body diagram of the body shows that $F_3 = 2F_1$. Because of this static dependence, Eq. (23.59) becomes

$$U = 5F_1^2 + F_2^2 \,,$$

and the true deflection under F_1 is

$$\delta_{F_1} = \frac{\partial U}{\partial F_1} = 10F_1 \,. \tag{23.61}$$

The deflection δ_F under the load F in Fig. 23.9 was incorrect because the four forces R_1, R_2, F, and R_4 substituted into Eq. (23.58) are statically dependent. The beam has five loads and two equations of equilibrium:

$$R_1 + R_2 + R_3 + R_4 = F \tag{23.62}$$

$$x_2R_2 + x_3R_3 + x_4R_4 = x_FF\,. \tag{23.63}$$

Any two of the five forces can be expressed in terms of the other three. The latter three are statically independent. The strain energy, written in terms of these three forces, is in the correct form of Eq. (23.15). For example, solve for R_2 and R_1:

$$R_2 = \frac{1}{x_2}\,(x_FF - x_3R_3 - x_4R_4) \tag{23.64}$$

$$R_1 = F - \frac{1}{x_2}\,(x_FF - x_3R_3 - x_4R_4) - R_3 - R_4\,. \tag{23.65}$$

These values are substituted into Eqs. (23.57) to obtain expressions for the bending moment M in terms of R_3, R_4, and F. Castigliano's theorem then provides the three equations

$$\delta_{R_3} = \frac{\partial U}{\partial R_3} = 0\,, \qquad \delta_{R_4} = \frac{\partial U}{\partial R_4} = 0\,, \qquad \delta_F = \frac{\partial U}{\partial F}\,. \tag{23.66}$$

The first two yield R_3 and R_4 in terms of F. Substituting these values into the third equation produces the desired deflection δ_F as a function of F. The same result is obtained by using F and any two of the other four forces as the three independent forces. Of course F must be one of the three forces used. If it were not, Eq. (23.58) would produce zero instead of δ_F.

The beam in Fig. 23.7 has one applied force, two reacting forces, and one reacting moment. Two of these four loads are statically independent. That problem was solved correctly because luckily the bending moment was written in Eqs. (23.50) as a function of two statically-independent loads. The deflection was known at one, and wanted at the other.

The requirement of statically-independent loads creates a second trap, that is encountered only if the analyst is determined to do more work than necessary. In the example of Fig. 23.7 the strain energy U was a function of the forces F and R_1. Now

$$dU = \frac{\partial U}{\partial F}\,dF + \frac{\partial U}{\partial R_1}\,dR_1\,, \tag{23.67}$$

and

$$\frac{dU}{dF} = \frac{\partial U}{\partial F} + \frac{\partial U}{\partial R_1}\,\frac{dR_1}{dF}\,. \tag{23.68}$$

Castigliano's theorem produced a formula for R_1 as a function of F, Eq. (23.55). Suppose that this expression were substituted into the formula for U to eliminate R_1 before differentiation to obtain $\delta_F = \partial U/\partial F$. This move would destroy the independence of R_1 and F, and create the term dR_1/dF in Eq. (23.68). The differentiation would produce dU/dF instead of $\partial U/\partial F$, which is not the correct deflection δ_F. Of course if the deflection at R_1 is zero (as it is in this example), the term $\partial U/\partial R_1$ is zero, and $dU/dF = \partial U/\partial F$. A safer and easier practice is to perform each partial differentiation required by Castigliano's theorem before eliminating any of the statically-independent loads.

23.9 Summary

The follow list of rules is presented for calculating the deflection of structures.

1. Draw a free-body diagram of the structure, including all of the applied and reacting forces and moments.

2. Write the m applicable equations of static equilibrium to determine the dependency between the loads.

3. Use these equations to eliminate m of the loads (forces or moments). Keep the loads, either applied or reacting, at which the deflections are wanted or known.

4. Write the total strain energy in terms of the statically-independent loads. For long beams, only the bending moment is required.

5. Apply Castigliano's theorem at as many loads as necessary. Each application produces either a deflection, or if the deflection is known, an additional relationship between the loads.

23.10 Deflection at a Point Not Under a Force

Castigliano's theorem gives the deflection only under a concentrated load. The deflection at some other location can be calculated by adding a fictitious force, and later letting it be zero in the formula for the deflection. For example, calculate the deflection at the center of the simply-supported beam in Fig. 23.10. The beam is L meters long and is uniformly loaded with a pressure of w N/m. Add the fictitious force P at the center. Summing the moments about the center discloses that $R_1 = R_2$. The equation of vertical forces is

$$wL + P = R_1 + R_2 = 2R_1\,. \tag{23.69}$$

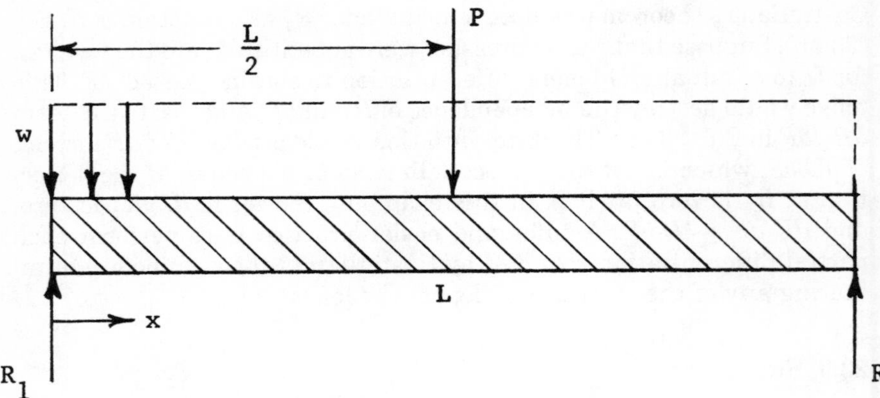

Fig. 23.10. Uniformly-loaded beam.

Any two of the four loads are statically independent. The logical choices are wL, which is known, and P, at which the deflection is wanted. The bending moment in the beam is

$$M = R_1 x - \frac{wx^2}{2} = (P + wL)\frac{x}{2} - \frac{wx^2}{2}, \qquad 0 \leqslant x \leqslant \frac{L}{2}. \tag{23.70}$$

The symmetry of the beam shows that the left half contains half of the strain energy. Therefore if the shear-strain energy is ignored,

$$\begin{aligned} \delta_P &= \frac{2}{EI}\int_0^{L/2} M\frac{\partial M}{\partial P}\,dx = \frac{2}{EI}\int_0^{L/2}\left[(P + wL)\frac{x}{2} - \frac{wx^2}{2}\right]\frac{x}{2}\,dx \\ &= \frac{PL^3}{48EI} + \frac{5wL^4}{384EI}. \end{aligned} \tag{23.71}$$

Now letting the fictitious force P be zero reduces this result to

$$\delta_P = \frac{5wL^4}{384EI}, \tag{23.72}$$

which is the correct value of the deflection.

23.11 Castigliano's Theorem for Moments

The loads applied to a beam consist of a combination of forces and moments, and might even consist entirely of moments. Fortunately, Castigliano's theorem can be written in the form

$$\frac{\partial U}{\partial M_i} = \theta_i, \tag{23.73}$$

where U is the total strain energy in the beam, and θ_i is the angular rotation of the section of the beam at which the moment M_i is applied. To illustrate the use of this form of the theorem, recalculate the bending moment in the beam of Fig. 23.8 in terms of M_1 and F. Summing the moments about the left end of the beam shows that

$$M_1 + aF = LR_1 \qquad \text{or} \qquad R_1 = \frac{M_1 + aF}{L} . \tag{23.74}$$

Eqs. (23.50) express the bending moment M at any section in terms of R_1 and F. After the second of Eqs. (23.74) is inserted, M is expressed in terms of M_1 and F:

$$\begin{aligned} M &= \frac{M_1 + aF}{L}(L - x) - F(a - x) , && 0 \leqslant x \leqslant a \\ M &= \frac{M_1 + aF}{L}(L - x) , && a \leqslant x \leqslant L . \end{aligned} \tag{23.75}$$

The cross section of the beam at its left end does not rotate when the beam deflects. Therefore according to Eq. (23.73),

$$\frac{\partial U}{\partial M_1} = \frac{\partial}{\partial M_1}\int_0^L \frac{M^2}{2EI}\,dx = \frac{1}{EI}\int_0^L M\frac{\partial M}{\partial M_1}\,dx = 0 , \tag{23.76}$$

or

$$\int_0^L \frac{M_1 + aF}{L}(L - x)\frac{L - x}{L}\,dx - \int_0^a F(a - x)\frac{L - x}{L}\,dx = 0 . \tag{23.77}$$

Integrating and simplifying produce the result

$$M_1 = \left[\frac{3}{2}\left(\frac{a}{L}\right) - \frac{1}{2}\left(\frac{a}{L}\right)^2 - 1\right] aF . \tag{23.78}$$

Now M_1 is known in terms of F. The deflection under the load F is obtained by applying Castigliano's theorem again:

$$\delta_F = \frac{\partial U_t}{\partial F} = \frac{1}{EI}\int_0^L M\frac{\partial M}{\partial F}\,dx . \tag{23.79}$$

Since M is a function of M_1 and F, Eq. (23.79) produces the deflection δ_F as a function of M_1 and F. Eq. (23.78) is then used to eliminate M_1, leaving the expression

$$\delta_F = \frac{a^3F}{6EI}\left[2 - \frac{a(3L - a)^2}{2L^3}\right] \tag{23.80}$$

which of course agrees with Eq. (23.56).

For some redundantly-loaded beams no deflection is known. An example is the ring shown in Fig. 23.11, to which three equally-spaced

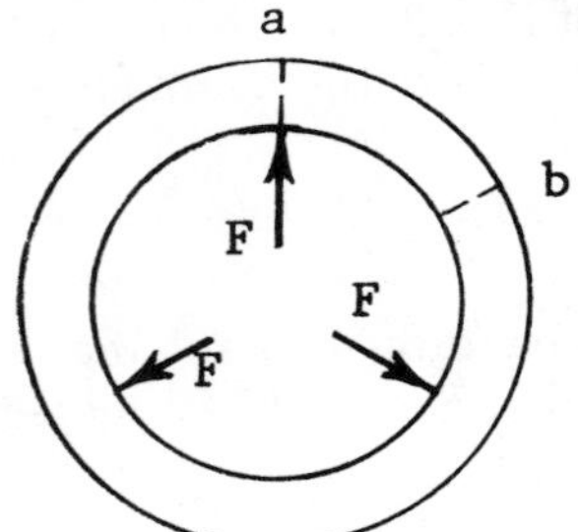

Fig. 23.11. Toroidal beam loaded internally.

equal forces F are applied. What *is* known is that under a load and at midspan between two loads, the cross sections a and b do not rotate when the loads are applied. Eq. (23.73) provides the relationships between the forces and moments that are needed to evaluate the deflections.

23.12 The Corollary to Castigliano's Theorem

Castigliano's theorem is based on the assumption that the deflections of a body are proportional to the forces causing them. If they are not, the deflections can sometimes be calculated with the use of a corollary of the theorem. To derive the corollary, apply all of the forces to the body in Fig. 23.1 again. As each force $F_i(x)$ increases from zero to its final value $F_i = F_i(x_i)$, the deflection under the force increases from zero to x_i. The total strain energy in the body is

$$U = \int_0^{x_1} F_1(x)dx + \int_0^{x_2} F_2(x)dx + \cdots + \int_0^{x_n} F_n(x)dx \,. \qquad (23.81)$$

Notice that U is a function of x_1, x_2, . . . x_n. Since the derivative of a definite integral with respect to its upper limit is the integrand evaluated at the upper limit,

$$\frac{\partial U}{\partial x_i} = F_i \,. \qquad (23.82)$$

This is the corollary to Castigliano's theorem. Its use requires that the strain energy be expressed as a function of the deflections instead of the loads. Although this is not always possible, the following example is a useful application of the corollary.

Fig. 23.12 shows two bars of original length L, each pin-connected at

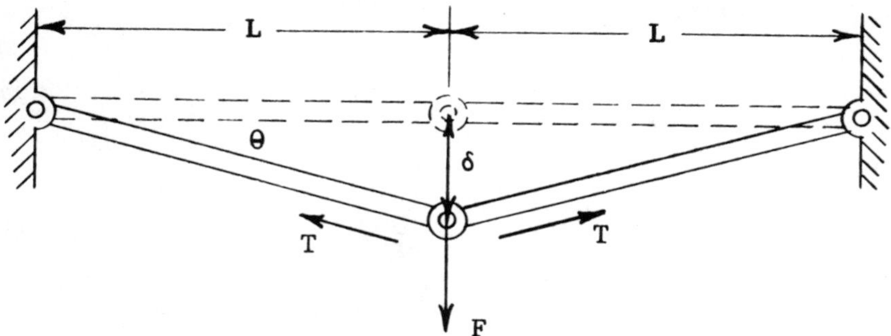

Fig. 23.12. Two bars loaded where they join.

both ends. Before loading, the bars are horizontal, and the stress in each bar is zero. Then a load F is suspended from the center pin. What is the deflection δ at the load? Castigliano's theorem cannot be used because the deflection is not proportional to the load. Instead, express the strain energy as a function of the deflection, and use the corollary. If T is the tensile force in a bar, and A is its cross-sectional area, the tensile stress is T/A. If ΔL is the increase in length of a bar, the tensile strain is $\Delta L/L$. Then

$$\frac{T}{A} = E\,\frac{\Delta L}{L}\,. \tag{23.83}$$

The diagram in Fig. 23.13 shows that $\delta/L = \tan\theta$, and if θ is small,

$$\sin\frac{\theta}{2} \approx \frac{\Delta L}{\delta}\,. \tag{23.84}$$

In general, if θ is small,

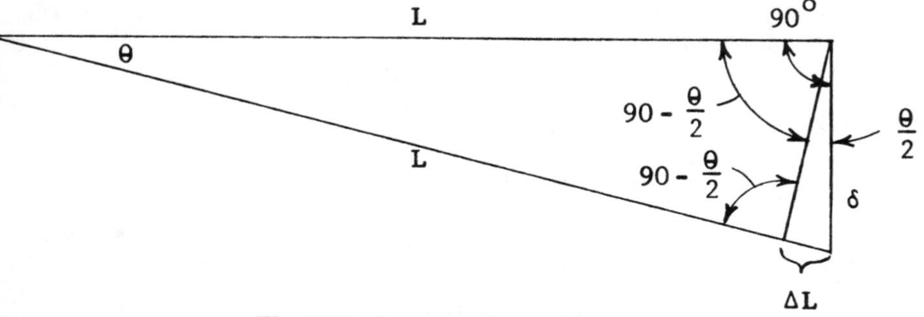

Fig. 23.13. Geometry of one of the bars.

$$\sin\frac{\theta}{2} \approx \tan\frac{\theta}{2} \approx \frac{1}{2}\tan\theta\,. \tag{23.85}$$

Thus for small values of θ,

$$\tan\theta = \frac{2\,\Delta L}{\delta} = \frac{\delta}{L}, \tag{23.86}$$

and

$$\Delta L = \frac{\delta^2}{2L}. \tag{23.87}$$

Combining this equation with (23.83) produces

$$T = \frac{AE\delta^2}{2L^2}. \tag{23.88}$$

According to Eq. (23.30) the strain energy in the two bars is

$$U = 2\int_0^L \frac{T^2}{2AE}\,dx = \frac{T^2 L}{AE} = \frac{AE\delta^4}{4L^3}. \tag{23.89}$$

Now the strain energy has been expressed as a function of the deflection, and the corollary to Castigliano's theorem shows that

$$F = \frac{\partial U}{\partial \delta} = \frac{AE\delta^3}{L^3}. \tag{23.90}$$

The deflection is therefore

$$\delta = L\left(\frac{F}{AE}\right)^{1/3}. \tag{23.91}$$

Although the stress and strain in the bars obey Hooke's law, the deflection δ is not proportional to the force F.

The strain energy can be expressed in terms of F by substituting Eq. (23.91) into (23.89):

$$U = \frac{AEL}{4}\left(\frac{F}{AE}\right)^{4/3}. \tag{23.92}$$

According to Castigliano's theorem,

$$\frac{\partial U}{\partial F} = \frac{L}{3}\left(\frac{F}{AE}\right)^{1/3}. \tag{23.93}$$

As expected, this is not the deflection δ.

23.13 Complementary Energy

An alternate form of Castigliano's theorem can be used when the deflections of a body are not proportional to the loads causing them. Consider the straight bar shown in Fig. 23.14. When an axial load F is

Fig. 23.14. Straight bar loaded axially.

applied, the bar stretches the amount x. The curve of force vs. displacement, shown in Fig. 23.15, is nonlinear. The energy stored in the bar is

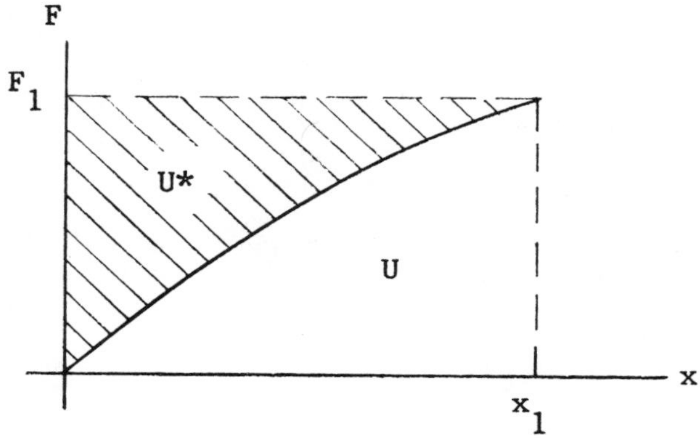

Fig. 23.15. Nonlinear deflection curve.

$$U = \int_0^{x_1} F(x)dx \, . \tag{23.94}$$

The *complementary energy* is defined as the hatched area:

$$U^* = \int_0^{F_1} x(F)dF \, . \tag{23.95}$$

If a body such as the one in Fig. 23.1 is subjected to n loads, the complementary energy is

$$U^* = \int_0^{F_1} x_1(F)dF + \int_0^{F_2} x_2(F)dF + \cdots + \int_0^{F_n} x_n(F)dF \, , \tag{23.96}$$

where $x_i(F)$ is the deflection that increases from zero to its final value x_i as the loads are applied. Now U^* is a function of $F_1, F_2, \ldots F_n$. Therefore

$$\frac{\partial U^*}{\partial F_i} = x_i \, . \tag{23.97}$$

This form of Castigliano's theorem does not require that the deflections be proportional to the loads.

Fig. 23.15 shows that if the straight bar obeys Hooke's law, $U = U^*$. Is this true for the body in Fig. 23.1 loaded by n forces, if the deflections are proportional to the forces? To find out, apply the forces in numerical order. Fig. 23.16 shows the values of U and U^* created by the deflections

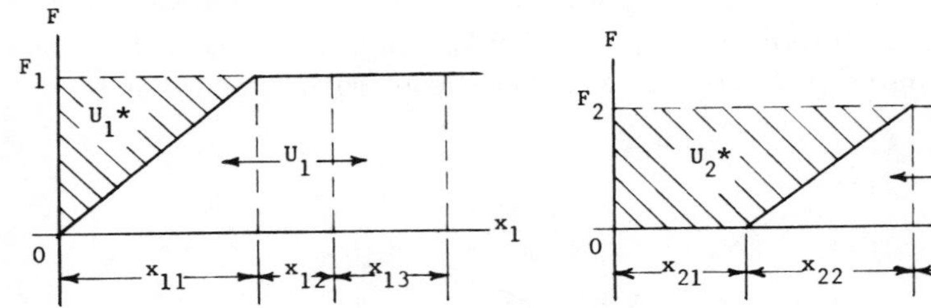

Fig. 23.16. Linear load-deflection curves.

at F_1 and F_2, as the first three loads are applied. After all the loads have been applied, the total deflection at each location is $x_i = x_{i1} + x_{i2} + \cdots + x_{in}$. The total complementary energy is

$$\begin{aligned} U^* &= \frac{1}{2} F_1 x_{11} \\ &+ \frac{1}{2} F_2 x_{22} + F_2 x_{21} \\ &+ \frac{1}{2} F_3 x_{33} + F_3(x_{31} + x_{32}) \\ &+ \frac{1}{2} F_4 x_{44} + F_4(x_{41} + x_{42} + x_{43}) \\ &+ \cdots \\ &+ \frac{1}{2} F_n x_{nn} + F_n(x_{n1} + x_{n2} + \cdots + x_{n,n-1}) . \end{aligned} \tag{23.98}$$

With the help of the reciprocal relation given by Eq. (23.6), namely

$$F_i x_{ij} = F_j x_{ji} ,$$

the terms can be rearranged into the form

$$U^* = \frac{1}{2}(F_1 x_1 + F_2 x_2 + \cdots + F_n x_n) = \frac{1}{2} \sum_{i=1}^{n} F_i x_i . \tag{23.99}$$

This is Clapeyron's theorem again. Comparing it with Eq. (23.10) shows that as expected, $U = U^*$. Thus if the deflections of a body are proportional to the forces producing them, Eq. (23.97) can be written as

$$\frac{\partial U}{\partial F_i} = x_i \,. \tag{23.100}$$

This second proof of Castigliano's theorem is a bonus for the investigation of complementary energy.

23.14 Conclusion

The last three chapters have explained the field equations of elasticity, plane stress and plane strain, beam theory, and Castigliano's theorem for determining deflections. Much remains to be said about stress analysis. The interested reader can learn about (1) stresses in plates, shells, twisted bars, and curved beams, (2) state vectors, transfer matrices, and the finite-element method of computing stresses in large interconnected structures, (3) the derivation of the elastic field equations in tensor notation, and (4) plastic deformation of materials, and theories of failure. Of the vast literature on stress analysis, the references at the end of this book include a small sample.

Chapter 24

FLUID-MECHANICS FUNDAMENTALS

24.1 Introduction

The difference between a solid and a fluid is that while a solid deforms by a fixed amount under a steady applied force, a fluid flows continuously. All gases and the common liquids are fluids. A tensile specimen of lead at room temperature or aluminum at about 200°C exhibits continuous elongation or creep under load, and is therefore a fluid. For the most common fluids, called *newtonian*, the continuity of flow and Newton's second law are applied to derive the Navier-Stokes equation. With simplifying assumptions, it reduces to the Euler and Bernoulli equations, with which many practical fluid-flow problems can be solved.

24.2 Vorticity

A person sitting on the bank of a river probably sees no relationship between the linear velocity **v** of the water particles and their angular velocity $\boldsymbol{\omega}$. A relationship exists, however, that is surprisingly simple and of fundamental importance in the calculations of fluid flow. Consider the differential element of a particle of a fluid shown in Fig. 24.1. At time t its xy section is a square. At time $t + dt$ the square has

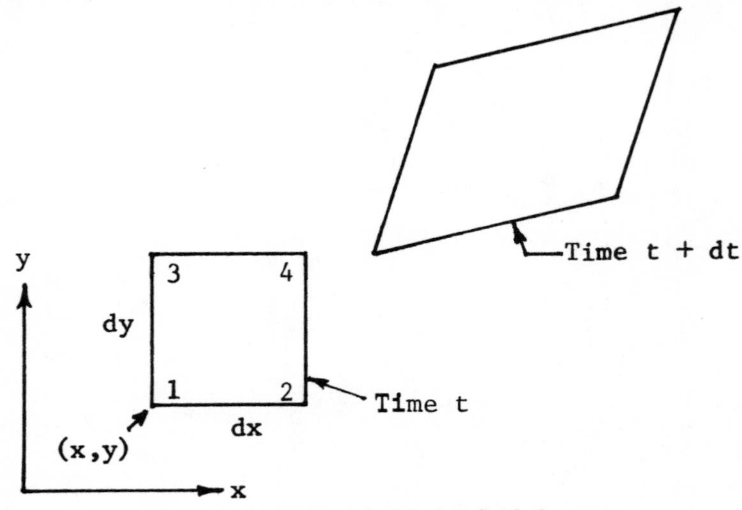

Fig. 24.1. Distortion of a moving fluid element.

translated, rotated, grown in size, and deformed. The displacements of the corners can be written conveniently as a Taylor series. For any function $f(x, y)$,

$$f(x + dx, y + dy) = f(x, y) + \frac{\partial f(x, y)}{\partial x} dx + \frac{\partial f(x, y)}{\partial y} dy + \cdots \quad (24.1)$$

The higher terms in the series contain products of differentials and are therefore negligible.The velocity of corner 1 of the square is

$$\mathbf{v} = \mathbf{1}_x v_x + \mathbf{1}_y v_y + \mathbf{1}_z v_z \,. \quad (24.2)$$

The horizontal displacement of that corner in the xy plane is

$$f(x, y) = v_x dt \,. \quad (24.3)$$

The horizontal displacement of corner 2 is

$$f(x + dx, y) = v_x dt + \frac{\partial v_x}{\partial x} dt\, dx \,. \quad (24.4)$$

The new horizontal length of the bottom of the square is therefore

$$dx + f(x + dx, y) - f(x, y) = dx + \frac{\partial v_x}{\partial x} dt\, dx \,. \quad (24.5)$$

The horizontal displacements of corners 3 and 4 are

$$f(x, y + dy) = v_x dt + \frac{\partial v_x}{\partial y} dt\, dy \quad (24.6)$$

and

$$f(x + dx, y + dy) = v_x dt + \frac{\partial v_x}{\partial x} dt\, dx + \frac{\partial v_x}{\partial y} dt\, dy \,. \quad (24.7)$$

The new horizontal length of the top of the square is

$$dx + f(x + dx, y + dy) - f(x, y + dy) = dx + \frac{\partial v_x}{\partial x} dt\, dx \,, \quad (24.8)$$

which is the same as the length of the bottom. Similar analyses show that the new horizontal lengths of the left and right sides are equal, and the vertical lengths of the top and bottom and the left and right sides are equal. The rectangle has become a rhomboid with parallel sides. The new horizontal and vertical lengths of the bottom and left side are shown in Fig. 24.2. If the rotations of the bottom and left sides are $d\alpha$ and $d\beta$,

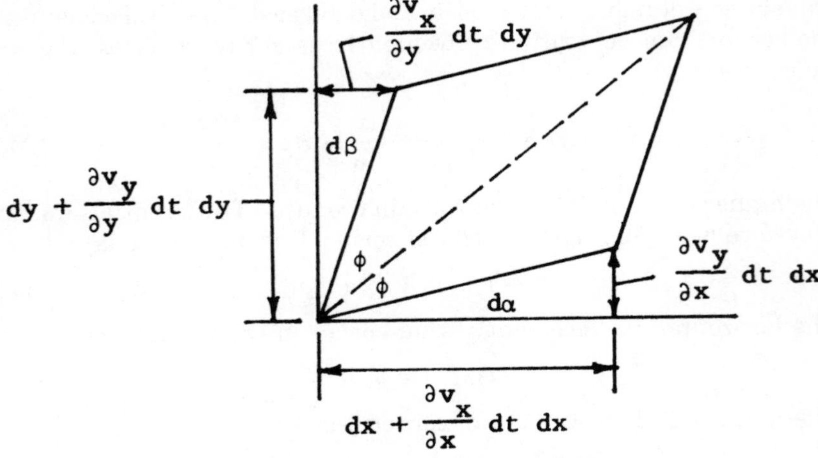

Fig. 24.2. New lengths of the particle's sides.

$$2\phi + d\alpha + d\beta = 90° \tag{24.9}$$

and the counterclockwise rotation of the dotted diagonal is

$$d\Omega_z = \phi + d\alpha - 45° \, . \tag{24.10}$$

Therefore

$$d\Omega_z = \frac{1}{2}(d\alpha - d\beta) \, . \tag{24.11}$$

Another simple calculation shows that the other diagonal has rotated the same amount, which is therefore the amount by which the fluid particle has rotated about the z axis. According to Fig. 24.2,

$$d\alpha = \frac{\dfrac{\partial v_y}{\partial x}\, dt\, dx}{dx + \dfrac{\partial v_x}{\partial x}\, dt\, dx} = \frac{\partial v_y}{\partial x}\, dt \tag{24.12}$$

and

$$d\beta = \frac{\dfrac{\partial v_x}{\partial y}\, dt\, dy}{dy + \dfrac{\partial v_y}{\partial y}\, dt\, dy} = \frac{\partial v_x}{\partial y}\, dt \, . \tag{24.13}$$

The z component of fluid angular velocity is therefore

$$\omega_z = \frac{d\Omega_z}{dt} = \frac{1}{2}\left(\frac{\partial v_y}{\partial x} - \frac{\partial v_x}{\partial y}\right) . \tag{24.14}$$

When the analysis is repeated to find the other two components of angular velocity, the results are

$$\omega_x = \frac{1}{2}\left(\frac{\partial v_z}{\partial y} - \frac{\partial v_y}{\partial z}\right) \tag{24.15}$$

and

$$\omega_y = \frac{1}{2}\left(\frac{\partial v_x}{\partial z} - \frac{\partial v_z}{\partial x}\right) . \tag{24.16}$$

Now

$$\nabla \times \mathbf{v} = \begin{vmatrix} \mathbf{1}_x & \mathbf{1}_y & \mathbf{1}_z \\ \dfrac{\partial}{\partial x} & \dfrac{\partial}{\partial y} & \dfrac{\partial}{\partial z} \\ v_x & v_y & v_z \end{vmatrix} = \mathbf{1}_x\left(\frac{\partial v_z}{\partial y} - \frac{\partial v_y}{\partial z}\right) + \mathbf{1}_y\left(\frac{\partial v_x}{\partial z} - \frac{\partial v_z}{\partial x}\right) + \mathbf{1}_z\left(\frac{\partial v_y}{\partial x} - \frac{\partial v_x}{\partial y}\right) . \tag{24.17}$$

Eqs. (24.14), (24.15), and (24.16) can therefore be combined into one vector equation:

$$\nabla \times \mathbf{v} = 2\,\boldsymbol{\omega} . \tag{24.18}$$

The vector $2\boldsymbol{\omega}$, twice the angular velocity of a fluid particle, is called the *vorticity* of the fluid at that point. If the particles of a fluid are not rotating, the curl of velocity is zero, and the flow is *irrotational.* This concept extends to other fields. For example, an electric field is called rotational when the curl of its field intensity **E** is nonzero, even though the curl does not represent an angular velocity. Near the banks of a river the particles of water are rotating and the flow is rotational. In a vortex such as a whirlpool or tornado, the particles of fluid do not rotate about their own axes. This flow, counter to intuition, is irrotational.

24.3 Viscosity

The viscosity of a fluid is a property that relates the applied shear stress to the resulting rate of strain. To find the relationship, temporarily regard Fig. 24.2 as the section of a solid rectangular particle. Its shear strain in the xy plane is defined as

$$\gamma_{xy} = d\alpha + d\beta . \tag{24.19}$$

Now if the particle is fluid, it strains continuously under an applied shear stress. The rate of strain is

$$\dot{\gamma}_{xy} = \frac{d\alpha}{dt} + \frac{d\beta}{dt} = \frac{\partial v_y}{\partial x} + \frac{\partial v_x}{\partial y} . \tag{24.20}$$

In the device shown in Fig. 24.3 a fluid is sheared between a fixed lower

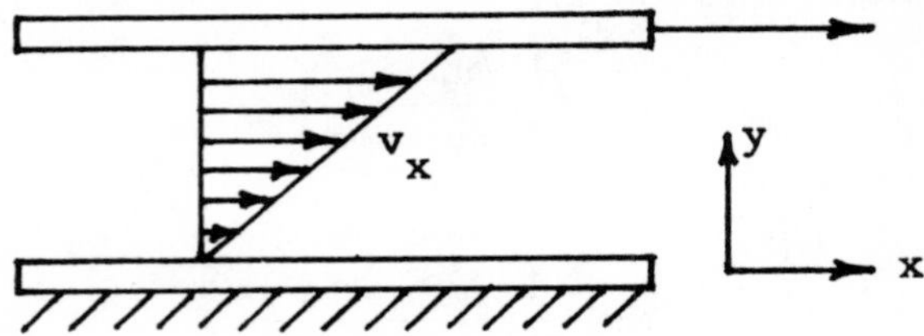

Fig. 24.3. Measurement of viscosity.

plate and a moving upper plate. Since the velocity has only an x component that varies only in the y direction, the rate of shear strain is

$$\dot{\gamma}_{xy} = \frac{dv_x}{dy} . \tag{24.21}$$

After the fluid has reached steady velocity, the shear stress τ_{xy} must be uniform throughout the fluid. Experiments have shown that for all of the common fluids, the steady-state velocity distribution is linear as in Fig. 24.3. Therefore, according to Eq. (24.21) the strain rate $\dot{\gamma}_{xy}$ is uniform throughout the fluid. It is some function of the uniform shear stress:

$$\tau_{xy} = f(\dot{\gamma}_{xy}) . \tag{24.22}$$

If this relationship is linear, the fluid is called *newtonian*, and

$$\tau_{xy} = \mu \, \dot{\gamma}_{xy} = \mu \, \frac{dv_x}{dy} . \tag{24.23}$$

The proportionality constant μ is the *viscosity*, measured in N·s/m^2. Water, oils, and gases are newtonian fluids. Notice that if the two plates in Fig. 24.3 are moved closer together, dv_x/dy increases and the shear stress therefore increases. For this reason racing boats avoid shallow water. An even better reason is the danger of scraping the propeller, keel, or oars on the bottom.

For nonnewtonian fluids the relationship of Eq. (24.22) is nonlinear, and no viscosity can be assigned. Plastics, heated metals, pastes, slurries, and all kinds of gunky and gooey materials are nonnewtonian. Many materials exhibit a fixed strain at low stresses but creep continuously under high stresses. They can be regarded as partly solid and partly fluid.

24.4 The Continuity Equation

The derivation of the Navier-Stokes equation begins with a mathematical statement of the continuity of fluid flow. Fig. 24.4 shows a

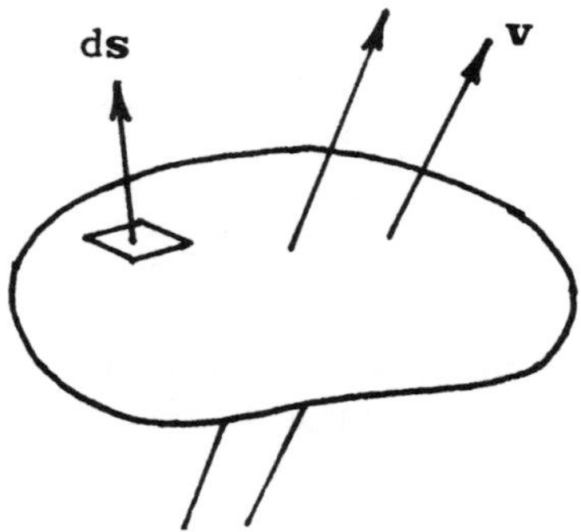

Fig. 24.4. Control volume in a fluid flow.

stationary control volume, thru which fluid of density ρ kg/m^3 is flowing with velocity **v** m/s. Both ρ and **v** may be functions of x, y, z, and t. The vector ρ**v**, measured in kg/s·m^2, can be considered as fluid flux density. Its integral over a surface is fluid flux, namely the rate of mass flow thru the surface, in kg/s. The net flow rate of fluid out of the closed surface s enclosing the volume v is

$$\begin{bmatrix}\text{rate of mass}\\ \text{flow out}\end{bmatrix} - \begin{bmatrix}\text{rate of mass}\\ \text{flow in}\end{bmatrix} = \oint_s (\rho\mathbf{v}) \cdot d\mathbf{s} \,. \tag{24.24}$$

The mass of the fluid in the control volume is

$$m = \int_v \rho \, dv \,. \tag{24.25}$$

If the density ρ changes with time, additional mass can be stored in the volume. The rate of mass storage is

$$\dot{m} = \int_v \frac{\partial \rho}{\partial t} \, dv \,. \tag{24.26}$$

Since no mass is created or destroyed,

$$\begin{bmatrix}\text{rate of mass}\\ \text{flow out}\end{bmatrix} - \begin{bmatrix}\text{rate of mass}\\ \text{flow in}\end{bmatrix} + \begin{bmatrix}\text{rate of mass}\\ \text{storage}\end{bmatrix} = 0 \tag{24.27}$$

or

$$\oint_s (\rho\mathbf{v}) \cdot d\mathbf{s} + \int_v \frac{\partial \rho}{\partial t} \, dv = 0 \,. \tag{24.28}$$

If the surface integral is converted to a volume integral with the help of Gauss's divergence theorem, this equation becomes

$$\int_v \nabla \cdot (\rho \mathbf{v})\, dv + \int_v \frac{\partial \rho}{\partial t}\, dv = 0 \tag{24.29}$$

or

$$\frac{\partial \rho}{\partial t} + \nabla \cdot (\rho \mathbf{v}) = 0\,. \tag{24.30}$$

This is the *equation of continuity* or conservation of mass of fluid flow. To write it in another convenient form, observe that the total differential of fluid density is

$$d\rho(x,y,z,t) = \frac{\partial \rho}{\partial x}\, dx + \frac{\partial \rho}{\partial y}\, dy + \frac{\partial \rho}{\partial z}\, dz + \frac{\partial \rho}{\partial t}\, dt\,. \tag{24.31}$$

Then the total derivative is

$$\frac{d\rho}{dt} = \frac{\partial \rho}{\partial x}\frac{dx}{dt} + \frac{\partial \rho}{\partial y}\frac{dy}{dt} + \frac{\partial \rho}{\partial z}\frac{dz}{dt} + \frac{\partial \rho}{\partial t}\,. \tag{24.32}$$

If dx/dt, dy/dt, and dz/dt are interpreted as the components of fluid velocity v_x, v_y, and v_z, the total derivative becomes the *substantial* or *material* derivative, designated by capital D's:

$$\frac{D\rho}{Dt} = v_x \frac{\partial \rho}{\partial x} + v_y \frac{\partial \rho}{\partial y} + v_z \frac{\partial \rho}{\partial z} + \frac{\partial \rho}{\partial t} \tag{24.33}$$

or

$$\frac{D\rho}{Dt} = \mathbf{v} \cdot \nabla \rho + \frac{\partial \rho}{\partial t}\,. \tag{24.34}$$

It is also called the "derivative following the motion," because it is the rate of change of the density of a particle of fluid as it flows along a stream line. The first three terms of the substantial derivative in Eq. (24.33) are called the *convective derivative*, because they exist if the fluid is moving and its density varies with distance. The last term is called the *local derivative*, because it is not concerned with fluid velocity or spatial variation of the density. When the driver of a car encounters a rainstorm, he or she observes the substantial derivative of the rain intensity. He cannot tell whether he drove into the squall, causing a convective derivative, or whether the squall started at his location, creating a local derivative.

The substantial derivative can be used to rewrite the continuity equation (24.30), which in its present form is

$$\frac{\partial \rho}{\partial t} + \nabla \cdot (\rho \mathbf{v}) = \frac{\partial \rho}{\partial t} + \frac{\partial}{\partial x}(\rho v_x) + \frac{\partial}{\partial y}(\rho v_y) + \frac{\partial}{\partial z}(\rho v_z)$$
$$= \frac{\partial \rho}{\partial t} + \rho \frac{\partial v_x}{\partial x} + v_x \frac{\partial \rho}{\partial x} + \rho \frac{\partial v_y}{\partial y} + v_y \frac{\partial \rho}{\partial y} + \rho \frac{\partial v_z}{\partial z} + v_z \frac{\partial \rho}{\partial z} = 0 . \tag{24.35}$$

Now

$$\rho \frac{\partial v_x}{\partial x} + \rho \frac{\partial v_y}{\partial y} + \rho \frac{\partial v_z}{\partial z} = \rho(\nabla \cdot \mathbf{v}) . \tag{24.36}$$

The continuity equation can therefore be written as

$$\frac{D\rho}{Dt} + \rho(\nabla \cdot \mathbf{v}) = 0 . \tag{24.37}$$

If the fluid is incompressible, ρ is constant. Then $D\rho/Dt$ is zero, and

$$\nabla \cdot \mathbf{v} = 0 . \tag{24.38}$$

If the flow is irrotational, $\nabla \times \mathbf{v} = 0$. Since for any scalar potential ϕ

$$\nabla \times \nabla\phi = 0 , \tag{24.39}$$

the fluid velocity $\mathbf{v}$ can be expressed as the gradient of a *velocity potential* ϕ. Then

$$\nabla \cdot \mathbf{v} = \nabla \cdot \nabla\phi = \nabla^2\phi = 0 , \tag{24.40}$$

and all of the techniques for solving Laplace's equation are available for calculating the velocity potential ϕ and therefore the fluid velocity $\mathbf{v}$. The irrotational flow of an incompressible fluid, which is governed by Eq. (24.40), is called a *potential flow*. Notice that zero viscosity is not a requirement of potential flow. The flow of a real fluid with viscosity can be irrotational. For example, a vortex in water is irrotational and is potential flow because water is essentially incompressible. The flow of an ideal nonviscous fluid is always irrotational, because its molecules have no way to exert the shear stress needed to make their neighbors rotate.

24.5 The Navier-Stokes Equation

Now the conservation of momentum, rather than mass, will be considered. Newton's second law states that the net force on a body equals the rate of change of its momentum:

$$\mathbf{f} = \frac{d}{dt}(m\mathbf{v}) = m\frac{d\mathbf{v}}{dt} + \mathbf{v}\frac{dm}{dt} , \tag{24.41}$$

where $\mathbf{v}$ is the velocity of the body. The first term on the right is the rate of change of momentum of a solid body of mass m. The second term is the rate of momentum flow of fluid out of a body or control volume, if the fluid moves with a steady velocity v and mass-flow rate dm/dt. The force causing the change in momentum can be caused by the fluid pressure, viscous shear between the fluid molecules, or a body force such as gravity. For example, if water in a pipe flows around a 180-degree bend as in Fig. 24.5, a brace is required to provide a reacting force of $2\,v\,dm/dt$, which is equal to the net centrifugal force on the water.

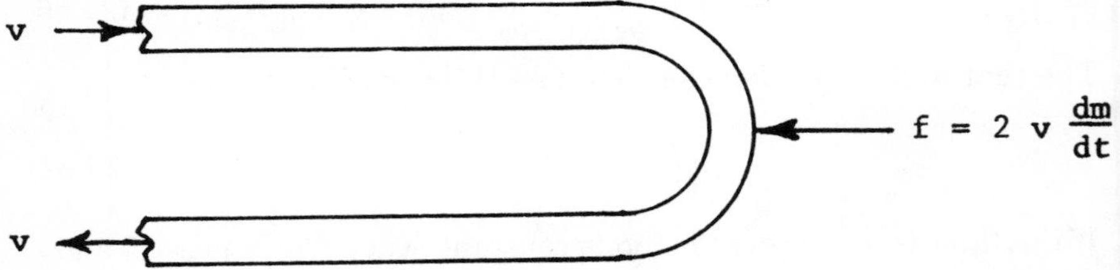

Fig. 24.5. Flow around a bend.

The rate of momentum flow of a fluid, steady or not, can be calculated with the help of Fig. 24.4. At any point on the surface surrounding the control volume, the fluid flux density is $p\mathbf{v}$ kg/s·m^2. It is the mass flow rate per unit area. The rate of mass flow thru a differential element of the surface $d\mathbf{s}$ is

$$\frac{dm}{dt} = \rho\mathbf{v} \cdot d\mathbf{s} \qquad \text{kg/s}\,. \tag{24.42}$$

The rate of momentum flow thru the differential surface is

$$\mathbf{v}\,\frac{dm}{dt} = \mathbf{v}(\rho\mathbf{v} \cdot d\mathbf{s}) \qquad \text{N}\,, \tag{24.43}$$

and the rate of flow of the x component of momentum is

$$v_x\,\frac{dm}{dt} = v_x(\rho\mathbf{v} \cdot d\mathbf{s}) = \rho v_x\mathbf{v} \cdot d\mathbf{s}\,. \tag{24.44}$$

The quantity $\rho v_x\mathbf{v}$, measured in N/m^2, can be regarded as a momentum flux density. Its integral over the entire surface is momentum flux, namely the rate of momentum flow thru the surface, in newtons. The net flow rate of the x component of momentum out of the control volume is

$$\begin{bmatrix}\text{rate of flow of the } x\\ \text{component of momentum out}\end{bmatrix} - \begin{bmatrix}\text{rate of flow of the } x\\ \text{component of momentum in}\end{bmatrix}$$

$$= \oint_s (\rho v_x\mathbf{v}) \cdot d\mathbf{s} \qquad \text{N}\,. \tag{24.45}$$

This difference in the rates of flow of momentum in and out of the control volume can exist because either momentum is being stored in the volume, or force is being exerted on it. To calculate the former, observe that at any point within the volume the x component of the fluid momentum per unit volume is ρv_x kg·m/s per m³. This momentum increases if the fluid is accelerating or if the density is increasing. The rate of increase is

$$\frac{\partial}{\partial t}(\rho v_x) \qquad \text{N/m}^3 .$$

The total rate of momentum storage within the control volume is the volume integral

$$\int_v \frac{\partial}{\partial t}(\rho v_x) dv \qquad \text{N} .$$

Now consider the forces acting on the fluid that cause the changes in momentum. If the x component of body force at a point in the fluid is F_x measured in N/kg, the total body force acting on the control volume in the x direction is

$$\int_v \rho F_x dv \qquad \text{N} .$$

The force caused by the fluid pressure can be found by inspection of a differential element of the control volume, shown in Fig. 24.6. If the

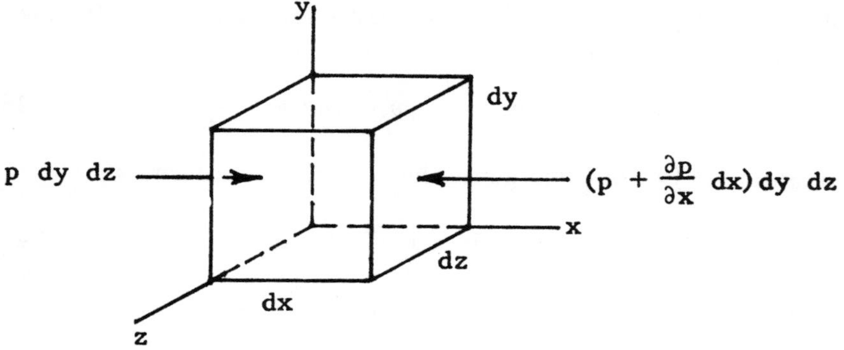

Fig. 24.6. Force due to fluid pressure p.

pressure at the center of the left face is p, the inward normal force on the left face is $p\,dy\,dz$, and the inward normal force on the right face is

$$(p + \frac{\partial p}{\partial x} dx) dy\, dz .$$

The net force in the x direction at the point represented by Fig. 24.6 is

$$-\frac{\partial p}{\partial x}\,dx\,dy\,dz = -\frac{\partial p}{\partial x}\,dv\,, \tag{24.46}$$

and the net force in the x direction on the control volume due to fluid pressure is

$$-\int_v \frac{\partial p}{\partial x}\,dv\,.$$

For the fluid in the control volume, Newton's second law for the forces and rates of change of momentum in the x direction is

$$\begin{bmatrix}\text{net applied}\\ \text{force}\end{bmatrix} = \begin{bmatrix}\text{rate of momentum}\\ \text{flow out}\end{bmatrix} - \begin{bmatrix}\text{rate of momentum}\\ \text{flow in}\end{bmatrix} + \begin{bmatrix}\text{rate of momentum}\\ \text{storage}\end{bmatrix}. \tag{24.47}$$

Notice that the net applied force does not include any force devoted to mechanical or shaft work. For example, the pressure of the steam in a turbine, acting thru a distance, produces shaft work but does not increase the momentum of the steam. Notice also that Eq. (24.47) does not include any momentum change due to the addition of heat to the fluid. Heating steam in the superheater of a boiler increases its volume and therefore its momentum.

With these restrictions in mind, the reader can insert the mathematical expressions into Eq. (24.47). The viscous-shear force on the fluid will be neglected temporarily. The equation becomes

$$\int_v \rho F_x dv - \int_v \frac{\partial p}{\partial x}\,dv = \oint_s (\rho v_x \mathbf{v})\cdot d\mathbf{s} + \int_v \frac{\partial}{\partial t}(\rho v_x)dv\,. \tag{24.48}$$

According to Gauss's divergence theorem, the third term is

$$\oint_s (\rho v_x \mathbf{v})\cdot d\mathbf{s} = \int_v [\nabla\cdot(\rho v_x \mathbf{v})]dv\,. \tag{24.49}$$

Since the integrands of the volume integrals must be equal,

$$\nabla\cdot(\rho v_x \mathbf{v}) + \frac{\partial}{\partial t}(\rho v_x) = \rho F_x - \frac{\partial p}{\partial x}\,. \tag{24.50}$$

The left side of this equation can be expanded to the form

$$\frac{\partial}{\partial x}(\rho v_x v_x) + \frac{\partial}{\partial y}(\rho v_x v_y) + \frac{\partial}{\partial z}(\rho v_x v_z) + \rho\frac{\partial v_x}{\partial t} + v_x\frac{\partial \rho}{\partial t} \qquad \text{(continued)}$$

$$= v_x \left[\frac{\partial}{\partial x} (\rho v_x) + \frac{\partial}{\partial y} (\rho v_y) + \frac{\partial}{\partial z} (\rho v_z) + \frac{\partial \rho}{\partial t} \right]$$

$$+ \rho \left[v_x \frac{\partial v_x}{\partial x} + v_y \frac{\partial v_x}{\partial y} + v_z \frac{\partial v_x}{\partial z} + \frac{\partial v_x}{\partial t} \right] . \tag{24.51}$$

According to the continuity equation in the form of Eq. (24.35), the first term in brackets is zero. The second bracketed term is Dv_x/Dt. Eq. (24.50) becomes

$$\frac{Dv_x}{Dt} = F_x - \frac{1}{\rho} \frac{\partial p}{\partial x} . \tag{24.52}$$

Similar equations can be derived for the forces and momentum rates in the y and z directions:

$$\frac{Dv_y}{Dt} = F_y - \frac{1}{\rho} \frac{\partial p}{\partial y} \tag{24.53}$$

$$\frac{Dv_z}{Dt} = F_z - \frac{1}{\rho} \frac{\partial p}{\partial z} . \tag{24.54}$$

The three can be combined into one vector equation. Since the substantial derivative of the velocity vector is

$$\frac{D\mathbf{v}}{Dt} = \frac{D}{Dt} (\mathbf{1}_x v_x + \mathbf{1}_y v_y + \mathbf{1}_z v_z) = \mathbf{1}_x \frac{Dv_x}{Dt} + \mathbf{1}_y \frac{Dv_y}{Dt} + \mathbf{1}_z \frac{Dv_z}{Dt} , \tag{24.55}$$

Eqs. (24.52) thru (24.54) become

$$\frac{D\mathbf{v}}{Dt} = \mathbf{F} - \frac{1}{\rho} \nabla p , \tag{24.56}$$

where **F** is the total body force at a point in the fluid, in N/kg. This is the *Euler equation of motion*, namely Newton's second law for a fluid if the effect of viscosity is negligible. Including the effect of viscous-shear force converts the Euler equation to the complicated *Navier-Stokes equation*. A good derivation is provided in Ref. 144, pages 65–71. If the fluid is newtonian, and the density ρ and viscosity μ of the fluid are constant, the Navier-Stokes equation has the simple form

$$\frac{D\mathbf{v}}{\mathrm{Dt}} = \mathbf{F} - \frac{1}{\rho} \nabla p + \frac{\mu}{\rho} \nabla^2 \mathbf{v} \qquad \text{N/kg} , \tag{24.57}$$

where in rectangular coordinates,

$$\nabla^2 \mathbf{v} = \mathbf{1}_x \nabla^2 v_x + \mathbf{1}_y \nabla^2 v_y + \mathbf{1}_z \nabla^2 v_z . \tag{24.58}$$

Eq. (24.57) is used when viscosity is important, as in the analysis of bearings. It is accurate for liquids at uniform temperature and gases with uniform compression. It is not accurate for a liquid whose temperature is nonuniform, because the viscosities of many liquids are highly temperature dependent.

24.6 A Different Form of the Substantial Derivative

An alternate form of the substantial derivative of a vector is needed for the derivation of the useful Bernoulli equation. For any vector property $\mathbf{A}$ of a fluid,

$$
\begin{aligned}
\frac{D\mathbf{A}}{Dt} &= \mathbf{1}_x \frac{DA_x}{Dt} + \mathbf{1}_y \frac{DA_y}{Dt} + \mathbf{1}_z \frac{DA_z}{Dt} \\
&= \mathbf{1}_x \left(v_x \frac{\partial A_x}{\partial x} + v_y \frac{\partial A_x}{\partial y} + v_z \frac{\partial A_x}{\partial z} + \frac{\partial A_x}{\partial t} \right) \\
&\quad + \mathbf{1}_y \left(v_x \frac{\partial A_y}{\partial x} + v_y \frac{\partial A_y}{\partial y} + v_z \frac{\partial A_y}{\partial z} + \frac{\partial A_y}{\partial t} \right) \\
&\quad + \mathbf{1}_z \left(v_x \frac{\partial A_z}{\partial x} + v_y \frac{\partial A_z}{\partial y} + v_z \frac{\partial A_z}{\partial z} + \frac{\partial A_z}{\partial t} \right) \\
&= v_x \left(\mathbf{1}_x \frac{\partial A_x}{\partial x} + \mathbf{1}_y \frac{\partial A_y}{\partial x} + \mathbf{1}_y \frac{\partial A_z}{\partial x} \right) + v_y \left(\mathbf{1}_x \frac{\partial A_x}{\partial y} + \mathbf{1}_y \frac{\partial A_y}{\partial y} + \mathbf{1}_z \frac{\partial A_z}{\partial y} \right) \\
&\quad + v_z \left(\mathbf{1}_x \frac{\partial A_x}{\partial z} + \mathbf{1}_y \frac{\partial A_y}{\partial z} + \mathbf{1}_z \frac{\partial A_z}{\partial z} \right) + \left(\mathbf{1}_x \frac{\partial A_x}{\partial t} + \mathbf{1}_y \frac{\partial A_y}{\partial t} + \mathbf{1}_z \frac{\partial A_z}{\partial t} \right) \\
&= v_x \frac{\partial}{\partial x} (\mathbf{1}_x A_x + \mathbf{1}_y A_y + \mathbf{1}_z A_z) + v_y \frac{\partial}{\partial y} (\mathbf{1}_x A_x + \mathbf{1}_y A_y + \mathbf{1}_z A_z) \\
&\quad + v_z \frac{\partial}{\partial z} (\mathbf{1}_x A_x + \mathbf{1}_y A_y + \mathbf{1}_z A_z) + \frac{\partial}{\partial t} (\mathbf{1}_x A_x + \mathbf{1}_y A_y + \mathbf{1}_z A_z) \\
&= v_x \frac{\partial \mathbf{A}}{\partial x} + v_y \frac{\partial \mathbf{A}}{\partial y} + v_z \frac{\partial \mathbf{A}}{\partial z} + \frac{\partial \mathbf{A}}{\partial t} .
\end{aligned}
\tag{24.59}
$$

This form is exactly the same as the definition of the substantial derivative of a scalar, Eq. (24.33). If the operator

$$
\nabla = \mathbf{1}_x \frac{\partial}{\partial x} + \mathbf{1}_y \frac{\partial}{\partial y} + \mathbf{1}_z \frac{\partial}{\partial z}
\tag{24.60}
$$

is treated as a vector, Eq. (24.59) can be written as

$$\frac{D\mathbf{A}}{Dt} = \left(v_x \frac{\partial}{\partial x} + v_y \frac{\partial}{\partial y} + v_z \frac{\partial}{\partial z}\right)\mathbf{A} + \frac{\partial \mathbf{A}}{\partial t}$$

or

$$\frac{D\mathbf{A}}{Dt} = (\mathbf{v} \cdot \nabla)\,\mathbf{A} + \frac{\partial \mathbf{A}}{\partial t}. \tag{24.61}$$

This is the alternate form that was needed. It is almost the same as the substantial derivative of a scalar in the form of Eq. (24.34). The Navier-Stokes equation (24.57) can now be written as

$$(\mathbf{v} \cdot \nabla)\mathbf{v} + \frac{\partial \mathbf{v}}{\partial t} = \mathbf{F} - \frac{1}{\rho}\nabla p + \frac{\mu}{\rho}\nabla^2 \mathbf{v}. \tag{24.62}$$

24.7 Reduction to the Bernoulli Equation

The Navier-Stokes equation can be simplified by assumptions that are valid for many engineering problems. First assume that the only body force on the fluid is gravity. The potential energy of the fluid at elevation h in a gravitational field with the gradient g N/kg is $g\,h$, in J/kg. The gravitational force is

$$\mathbf{F} = -\nabla(gh) \qquad \text{N/kg}. \tag{24.63}$$

The minus sign is needed because the gradient is directed upward, in the direction of the maximum rate of increase of potential, and the force is downward. The first and last terms of Eq. (24.62) can be rewritten according to vector identities:

$$\begin{aligned}(\mathbf{v} \cdot \nabla)\mathbf{v} &= \frac{1}{2}\nabla(\mathbf{v} \cdot \mathbf{v}) + (\nabla \times \mathbf{v}) \times \mathbf{v} \\ &= \frac{1}{2}\nabla(v^2) + (\nabla \times \mathbf{v}) \times \mathbf{v}\,,\end{aligned} \tag{24.64}$$

and

$$\nabla^2 \mathbf{v} = \nabla(\nabla \cdot \mathbf{v}) - \nabla \times (\nabla \times \mathbf{v}). \tag{24.65}$$

With the introduction of the last three equations, the Navier-Stokes equation (24.62) becomes

$$\begin{aligned}\frac{1}{2}\nabla(v^2) + (\nabla \times \mathbf{v}) \times \mathbf{v} + \frac{\partial \mathbf{v}}{\partial t} &= -\nabla(gh) - \frac{1}{\rho}\nabla p \\ &+ \frac{\mu}{\rho}[\nabla(\nabla \cdot \mathbf{v}) - \nabla \times (\nabla \times \mathbf{v})].\end{aligned} \tag{24.66}$$

It will be simplified by two different sets of assumptions.

1. *Irrotational flow, etc.* The fluid has already been assumed to be newtonian with constant density ρ and constant viscosity μ. The continuity equation (24.37) shows that $\nabla \cdot \mathbf{v} = 0$ if ρ is a constant. Assume now that the flow is irrotational, so that $\nabla \times \mathbf{v} = 0$. Now it is a potential flow, and the velocity can be expressed as the gradient of a velocity potential ϕ. Then

$$\frac{\partial \mathbf{v}}{\partial t} = \frac{\partial}{\partial t}(\nabla \phi) = \nabla \left(\frac{\partial \phi}{\partial t}\right), \tag{24.67}$$

and Eq. (24.66) becomes

$$\frac{1}{2}\nabla(v^2) + \nabla\left(\frac{\partial \phi}{\partial t}\right) + \nabla(gh) + \frac{1}{\rho}\nabla p = \nabla\left(\frac{v^2}{2} + \frac{\partial \phi}{\partial t} + gh + \frac{p}{\rho}\right) = 0 \tag{24.68}$$

or

$$\frac{\partial \phi}{\partial t} + \frac{p}{\rho} + \frac{v^2}{2} + gh = \text{constant}\ . \tag{24.69}$$

This is the *Bernoulli equation* for the unsteady, irrotational flow of an incompressible newtonian fluid with constant viscosity.

2. *Negligible viscosity, etc.* Assume that the flow is rotational, but the viscosity of the fluid is so low that the last term of the Navier-Stokes equation (24.57) is negligible. That equation becomes the Euler equation (24.56), for which the assumptions of a newtonian fluid with constant density were unnecessary. The Euler equation becomes Eq. (24.66) with the last term set at zero:

$$\frac{1}{2}\nabla(v^2) + (\nabla \times \mathbf{v}) \times \mathbf{v} + \frac{\partial \mathbf{v}}{\partial t} + \nabla(gh) + \frac{1}{\rho}\nabla p = 0\ . \tag{24.70}$$

Forming the inner product of each of these vectors with the differential length $d\ell$ produces the equation

$$\nabla\left(\frac{v^2}{2}\right) \cdot d\ell + [(\nabla \times \mathbf{v}) \times \mathbf{v}] \cdot d\ell + \frac{\partial \mathbf{v}}{\partial t} \cdot d\ell + \nabla(gh) \cdot d\ell + \frac{1}{\rho}\nabla p \cdot d\ell = 0\ . \tag{24.71}$$

For any scalar potential U,

$$\nabla U \cdot d\ell = \frac{\partial U}{\partial x}dx + \frac{\partial U}{\partial y}dy + \frac{\partial U}{\partial z}dz = dU\ . \tag{24.72}$$

Eq. (24.71) can therefore be written in the form

$$d\left(\frac{v^2}{2}\right) + [(\nabla \times \mathbf{v}) \times \mathbf{v}] \cdot d\ell + \frac{\partial \mathbf{v}}{\partial t} \cdot d\ell + d(gh) + \frac{dp}{\rho} = 0 . \qquad (24.73)$$

The second term is zero if one of two assumptions is made:

a. The differential length $d\ell$ is measured along a stream line, in the direction of the velocity $\mathbf{v}$. Since $(\nabla \times \mathbf{v}) \times \mathbf{v}$ is perpendicular to $\mathbf{v}$ it is perpendicular to $d\ell$, and therefore the inner product is zero.

b. The curl of $\mathbf{v}$ is in the direction of the stream line. This is called *Beltrami* or *helicoidal* flow.

Then Eq. (24.73) becomes

$$\frac{\partial \mathbf{v}}{\partial t} \cdot d\ell + \frac{dp}{\rho} + d\left(\frac{v^2}{2}\right) + d(gh) = 0 , \qquad (24.74)$$

which can be integrated from one point in the fluid to another:

$$\int_1^2 \frac{\partial \mathbf{v}}{\partial t} \cdot d\ell + \int_1^2 \frac{dp}{\rho} + \frac{1}{2}(v_2^2 - v_1^2) + g(h_2 - h_1) = 0 . \qquad (24.75)$$

This is an alternate form of the Bernoulli equation for unsteady, rotational flow of a low-viscosity fluid when either (a) the integration is along a stream line, or (b) the flow is helicoidal. Notice that both sets of assumptions accomplished the same task, namely elimination of the second and last terms of the Navier-Stokes equation (24.66). With that accomplished the first set, like the second, leads directly to the Bernoulli equation in the form of Eq. (24.75), and permits integration between any two points in the fluid.

If the flow is steady, the fluid velocity at any point does not vary with time. Then

$$\frac{\partial \mathbf{v}}{\partial t} = 0 \qquad \text{and} \qquad \frac{\partial \phi}{\partial t} = \text{constant} . \qquad (24.76)$$

According to Eq. (24.69), a steady flow that obeys the first set of assumptions is governed by the simple equation

$$\frac{p}{\rho} + \frac{v^2}{2} + gh = \text{constant} . \qquad (24.77)$$

If steady flow and constant density are added to the second set of assumptions, Eq. (24.75) becomes

$$\frac{1}{\rho}(p_2 - p_1) + \frac{1}{2}(v_2^2 - v_1^2) + g(h_2 - h_1) = 0 \tag{24.78}$$

or

$$\frac{p}{\rho} + \frac{v^2}{2} + gh = \text{constant}\,. \tag{24.79}$$

Eq. (24.77) or (24.79) is the familiar *Bernoulli equation for steady flow*. It is a special case of the Navier-Stokes equation, which in turn is Newton's second law applied to the fluid.

Notice that the terms of Eq. (24.79) are measured in J/kg. It is an energy equation, because it was obtained by integrating forces per unit mass with respect to distance. In the application of Newton's second law that lead to the Euler equation of motion (24.56), the net force on the fluid was equated to its rate of change of momentum. None of this force was used for external or shaft work, and none of the momentum change was due to the addition of heat. The Bernoulli equation (24.79) expresses the conservation of energy in the flow of a fluid that does no shaft work, receives no heat, and obeys the assumptions already listed.

The reader may appreciate a review of the assumptions used in the derivations. The Euler equation of motion, the Navier-Stokes equation, and the simplified versions that follow them are based on the assumption that

1. the fluid does no shaft work and receives no heat.

In addition, the Navier-Stokes equation in the form of Eq. (24.57) assumes that

2. the fluid is newtonian and has constant density and constant viscosity.

The Bernoulli equation for unsteady flow, (24.75), assumes that

3. the only body force on the fluid is gravity, and either

4. { a. the fluid is newtonian, has constant density and constant viscosity, and the flow is irrotational, or

   b. the fluid has negligible viscosity and either (i) the path of integration follows a stream line, or (ii) the flow is helicoidal. }

In addition, the Bernoulli equation for steady flow, (24.79), assumes that

5. the flow is steady and the fluid is incompressible.

24.8 An Example

To illustrate the use of the Bernoulli equation for unsteady flow, consider the water pump in Fig. 24.7, that lifts water 50 meters thru 100 meters of pipe. For the distance $L_1 = 60$ m the cross-sectional area is A_1, and for the remaining distance $L_2 = 40$ m it is $A_1/4$. The piston is

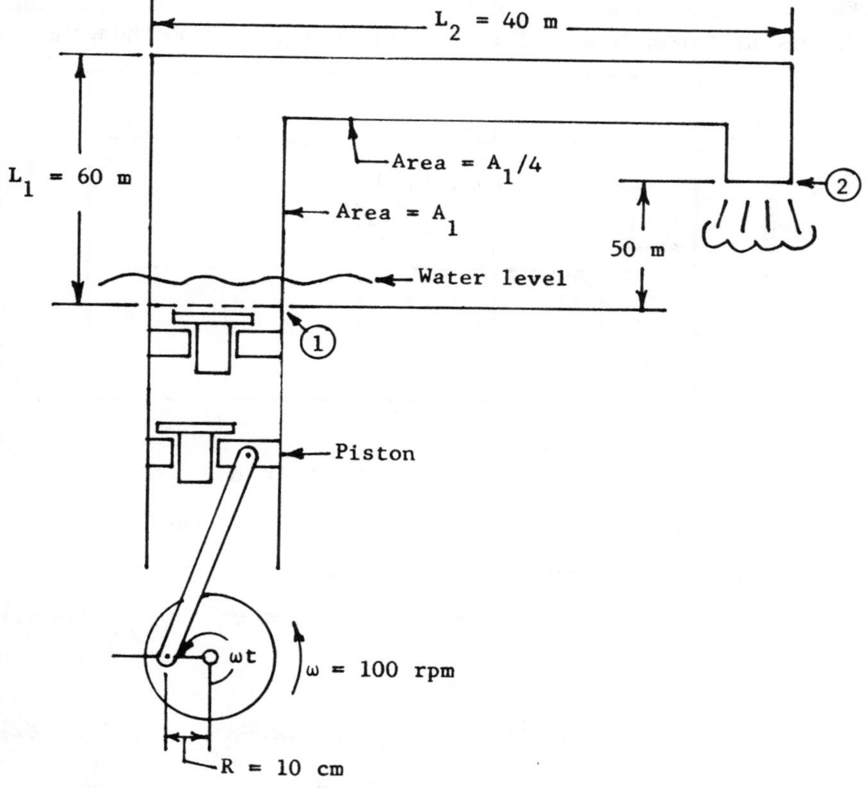

Fig. 24.7. Water pump.

driven by a crank of radius $R = 10$ cm, turning at an angular velocity ω of 100 rpm. What is the water pressure p_1 just above the pump valves at position 1? The water above the pump does no shaft work and receives no heat. The only body force on the fluid is gravity. Since the work required to overcome friction in the pipe is small compared to the other components of the energy of the water, its viscosity can be neglected. The integration from one end of the pipe to the other will follow a stream line. Since assumptions 1, 3, and 4b are valid but 5 is not, the pressure will be calculated by Eq. (24.75), the Bernoulli equation for unsteady flow.

Position 2 in the diagram is the pipe outlet, where the water pressure is atmospheric. Measured as gage pressure, $p_2 = 0$. The vertical displacement of the piston from its lowest position is approximately

$$x = R(1 - \cos \omega t) \ . \tag{24.80}$$

This is also the displacement of the water in the first 60 m of pipe during the first upstroke, shown in Fig. 24.8. During a downstroke the water in

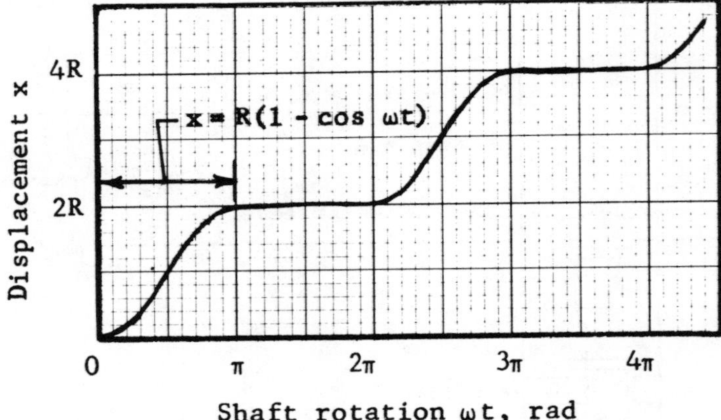

Fig. 24.8. Displacement of the water above the pump.

the pipe stands still. The velocity of the water is

$$v_1 = R\,\omega \sin \omega t \ , \qquad 0 \leqslant \omega t \leqslant \pi \ , \tag{24.81}$$

and its acceleration is

$$\frac{dv_1}{dt} = R\,\omega^2 \cos \omega t \ , \qquad 0 \leqslant \omega t \leqslant \pi \ . \tag{24.82}$$

The velocity of the water in the last 40 m of pipe is $v_2 = 4\,v_1$. The first term of Eq. (24.75) becomes

$$\int_1^2 \frac{\partial \mathbf{v}}{\partial t} \cdot d\ell = \frac{dv_1}{dt} L_1 + \frac{dv_2}{dt} L_2 = 60\,\frac{dv_1}{dt} + 40\,\frac{d}{dt}(4v_1) = 220\,\frac{dv_1}{dt}$$

$$= 220\,R\,\omega^2 \cos \omega t \ . \tag{24.83}$$

Since water is nearly incompressible, the second term of Eq. (24.75) is

$$\int_1^2 \frac{dp}{\rho} = \frac{1}{\rho}(0 - p_1) = -\frac{p_1}{\rho}. \qquad (24.84)$$

The Bernoulli equation becomes

$$220\,R\,\omega^2 \cos \omega t - \frac{p_1}{\rho} + \frac{(4v_1)^2 - v_1^2}{2} + 50\,g = 0 \qquad (24.85)$$

or

$$p_1 = \rho\left[\frac{15}{2}(R\omega)^2 \sin^2 \omega t + 220\,R\,\omega^2 \cos \omega t + 50\,g\right]. \qquad (24.86)$$

With the numerical values $\rho = 1000$ kg/m^3 and $g = 9.81$ N/kg, this equation becomes

$$p_1 = 8225 \sin^2 \omega t + 2{,}412{,}570 \cos \omega t + 490{,}500 \qquad \text{Pa}. \qquad (24.87)$$

Let the coefficients be a, b, and c. Then

$$p_1 = a \sin^2 \omega t + b \cos \omega t + c. \qquad (24.88)$$

To find the peak value of the pressure p_1, write

$$\frac{dp_1}{dt} = 2\,\omega\,a \sin \omega t \cos \omega t - \omega\,b \sin \omega t = 0 \qquad (24.89)$$

or

$$\omega \sin \omega t(2\,a \cos \omega t - b) = 0, \qquad 0 \leqslant \omega t \leqslant \pi. \qquad (24.90)$$

Since b is larger than $2\,a$, the term in parentheses is never zero. This equation is satisfied only by $\sin \omega t = 0$, for which $\omega t = 0$ or π. Eq. (24.87) shows that the first of these gives the higher peak pressure, which is

$$\text{peak } p_1 = 2{,}412{,}570 + 490{,}500 = 2{,}903{,}070 \text{ Pa}$$
$$= 421.0 \text{ psig}. \qquad (24.91)$$

The largest contributor to the water pressure is the $\cos \omega t$ term in Eq. (24.87), which comes from the first term in the Bernoulli equation (24.75). It is the pressure required to accelerate all of the water in the pipe at the same time. The next largest contributor is the constant term of Eq. (24.87), which is the pressure needed to lift the water 50 meters. The $\sin^2 \omega t$ term of Eq. (24.87) is the smallest. It is the pressure required to speed the water up at the reduction in pipe area. It contributes nothing to the peak pressure, because it is zero when the $\cos \omega t$ term is at a maximum.

Chapter 25

POTENTIAL FLUID FLOW

25.1 Introduction and Review

Why does a baseball curve? What makes an airplane wing lift? What does streamlining accomplish? This chapter develops the theory that answers these questions, namely *potential flow*. Potential flow is fluid flow whittled down to Laplace's equation. The whittling is accomplished by assuming that the flow is irrotational and the fluid is incompressible. The preceding chapter derived the relationship between the linear velocity $\mathbf{v}$ and angular velocity $\boldsymbol{\omega}$ of a fluid, namely

$$\nabla \times \mathbf{v} = 2\,\boldsymbol{\omega}\,. \tag{25.1}$$

The vector $2\boldsymbol{\omega}$ is called the *vorticity* of the fluid. If the vorticity is zero, the flow is called *irrotational*. Any flow of an ideal nonviscous fluid is irrotational, because its particles cannot exert the viscous shear stress necessary to make their neighbors turn. Some flows of real fluids are irrotational. In either case, $\nabla \times \mathbf{v} = 0$, and the velocity $\mathbf{v}$ can be expressed as the gradient of a scalar potential ϕ, called *velocity potential*, because for any scalar ϕ,

$$\nabla \times \nabla\phi = 0\,. \tag{25.2}$$

Section 24.4 showed that if a fluid is incompressible its velocity does not diverge:

$$\nabla \cdot \mathbf{v} = 0\,. \tag{25.3}$$

Since $\mathbf{v} = \nabla\phi$,

$$\nabla \cdot \nabla\phi = \nabla^2\phi = 0\,. \tag{25.4}$$

The flow of a fluid whose velocity potential satisfies Laplace's equation (25.4) is a potential flow. Although the velocity potential ϕ has no physical significance, it can be calculated by the several techniques available for the solution of Laplace's equation. The velocity can then be found by differentiating ϕ. The irrotational flow of a fluid, for which $\nabla \times \mathbf{v} = 0$, is called *conservative*, by analogy to a field of force. An example is the force $\mathbf{E}$ on a unit positive charge in an electrostatic field, in which $\nabla \times \mathbf{E} = 0$. According to Stokes' theorem,

$$\int_s (\nabla \times \mathbf{E}) \cdot d\mathbf{s} = \oint \mathbf{E} \cdot d\ell = 0\,. \tag{25.5}$$

Since $\nabla \times \mathbf{E}$ is zero in the electrostatic field, no net work is done when the charge is moved around a closed path. The energy in the field is conserved.

If a jar of honey is rotated at an angular velocity $\boldsymbol{\omega}$, each particle of honey rotates with the same angular velocity. The flow is therefore rotational, and no velocity potential exists. The flow of water along a channel is rotational near the walls because the particles drag on each other, causing each other to rotate. A paddle wheel placed horizontally in the water indicates vorticity by turning. In a vortex such as a whirlpool or tornado, the particles of fluid do not rotate about their own axes. This flow, counter to intuition, is irrotational.

25.2 The Stream Function

The analysis of a two-dimensional fluid flow is expedited by deriving a *stream function*. Fig. 25.1 shows two points in the plane two-dimen-

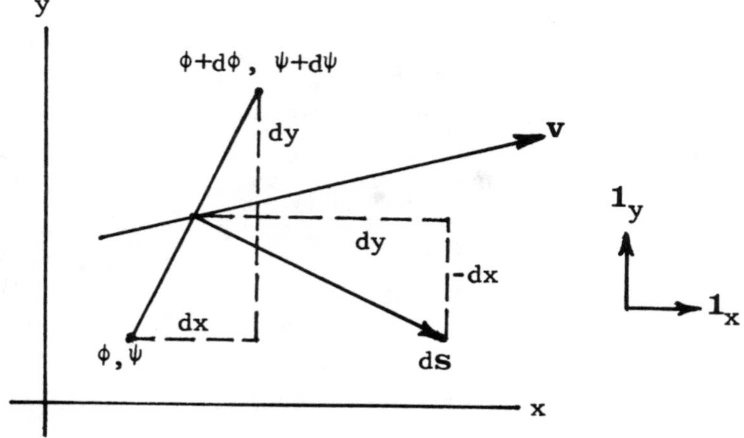

Fig. 25.1. Points in a planar flow.

sional flow of a fluid, that for simplicity will be called *planar* flow. The points are separated by the differential distance $\mathbf{1}_x\,dx + \mathbf{1}_y\,dy$, and are at the velocity potentials ϕ and $\phi + d\phi$. The components of the fluid velocity $\mathbf{v}$ are v_x and v_y. If the fluid is irrotational, $\mathbf{v} = \nabla\phi$, which can be written as

$$\mathbf{1}_x\,v_x + \mathbf{1}_y\,v_y = \mathbf{1}_x\,\frac{\partial\phi}{\partial x} + \mathbf{1}_y\,\frac{\partial\phi}{\partial y}\,. \tag{25.6}$$

Therefore

$$v_x = \frac{\partial \phi}{\partial x} \qquad \text{and} \qquad v_y = \frac{\partial \phi}{\partial y} . \tag{25.7}$$

The fluid velocity $\mathbf{v}$ m/s can be regarded as fluid flux density in m^3/s per m^2. The *Lagrange stream* or *flux function* ψ is now defined for planar flow so that the difference in the value of this function at two points is the amount of flux (in m^3/s) flowing across a surface of unit depth extending between the points. The values of the stream function at the two points in Fig. 25.1 are ψ and $\psi + d\psi$. The surface drawn between the points is plane and is represented by the vector

$$d\mathbf{s} = \mathbf{1}_x\, dy - \mathbf{1}_y\, dx . \tag{25.8}$$

This vector points to the right of the surface drawn in the direction of increasing ψ. The flux flowing to the right across the surface is

$$d\psi = \mathbf{v} \cdot d\mathbf{s} = (\mathbf{1}_x\, v_x + \mathbf{1}_y\, v_y) \cdot (\mathbf{1}_x\, dy - \mathbf{1}_y\, dx)$$

or

$$d\psi = v_x\, dy - v_y\, dx . \tag{25.9}$$

Now $d\psi$ can be written as a total differential:

$$d\psi = \frac{\partial \psi}{\partial x} dx + \frac{\partial \psi}{\partial y} dy . \tag{25.10}$$

Therefore

$$v_x = \frac{\partial \psi}{\partial y} \qquad \text{and} \qquad v_y = -\frac{\partial \psi}{\partial x} , \tag{25.11}$$

and

$$\nabla \cdot \mathbf{v} = \frac{\partial v_x}{\partial x} + \frac{\partial v_y}{\partial y} = 0 . \tag{25.12}$$

The divergence of velocity is zero, and therefore the fluid is incompressible. Because of the way in which the stream function has been defined, the stream function exists only if the fluid is incompressible. According to Eqs. (25.11) and (25.7),

$$\frac{\partial \phi}{\partial x} = \frac{\partial \psi}{\partial y} \qquad \text{and} \qquad \frac{\partial \phi}{\partial y} = -\frac{\partial \psi}{\partial x} . \tag{25.13}$$

These are the *Cauchy-Riemann equations*. If the first one is differentiated with respect to x and the second with respect to y, and the two are added, the result is

$$\frac{\partial^2 \phi}{\partial x^2} + \frac{\partial^2 \phi}{\partial y^2} = 0 , \tag{25.14}$$

which agrees with Eq. (25.4). In the derivation of both equations the assumptions of irrotational flow and incompressible fluid were required. If the first and second Cauchy-Riemann equations are differentiated with respect to y and x, respectively, and the second is subtracted from the first, the result is

$$\frac{\partial^2 \psi}{\partial x^2} + \frac{\partial^2 \psi}{\partial y^2} = 0 . \tag{25.15}$$

Thus the stream function in a planar flow, like the velocity potential, satisfies Laplace's equation.

A function that satisfies Laplace's equation is called a *harmonic function.* Two functions ϕ and ψ that are related by the Cauchy-Riemann equations are called *conjugate harmonic functions.* Every harmonic function has a harmonic conjugate, that can be calculated with the use of the Cauchy-Riemann equations. These useful equations also show that lines of constant ϕ and constant ψ are perpendicular where they intersect. To clarify this fact, observe that along the line $\phi = k_1$ in Fig. 25.2,

$$d\phi = \frac{\partial \phi}{\partial x}\, dx + \frac{\partial \phi}{\partial y}\, dy = 0 , \tag{25.16}$$

and therefore the slope of this line is

$$\frac{dy}{dx} = - \frac{\partial \phi / \partial x}{\partial \phi / \partial y} . \tag{25.17}$$

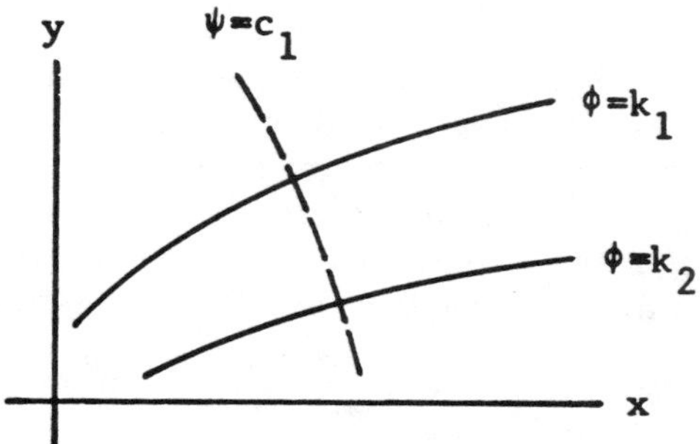

Fig. 25.2. Lines of constant ϕ and ψ.

Likewise, the slope of the line $\psi = c_1$ is

$$\frac{dy}{dx} = - \frac{\partial \psi / \partial x}{\partial \psi / \partial y} = \frac{\partial \phi / \partial y}{\partial \phi / \partial x} . \tag{25.18}$$

Since the product of the slopes of the two lines where they intersect is -1, lines of constant velocity potential and constant stream function are perpendicular to each other. Since the fluid velocity $\mathbf{v} = \nabla\phi$ is also perpendicular to lines of constant ϕ, lines of constant ψ are *stream lines*. No fluid crosses a stream line. If the viscosity of a fluid is neglected, so that the fluid is considered to be irrotational even near the side walls, the walls are lines of constant ψ.

The Cauchy-Riemann equations and the velocity components in planar potential flows are summarized in Fig. 25.3.

	Rectangular coordinates	Polar coordinates	
Velocity components	$v_x = \frac{\partial\phi}{\partial x}$	$v_r = \frac{\partial\phi}{\partial r}$	(25.19)
	$v_y = \frac{\partial\phi}{\partial y}$	$v_\theta = \frac{1}{r}\frac{\partial\phi}{\partial\theta}$	(25.20)
Cauchy-Riemann equations	$\frac{\partial\phi}{\partial x} = \frac{\partial\psi}{\partial y}$	$\frac{\partial\phi}{\partial r} = \frac{1}{r}\frac{\partial\psi}{\partial\theta}$	(25.21)
	$\frac{\partial\phi}{\partial y} = -\frac{\partial\psi}{\partial x}$	$\frac{1}{r}\frac{\partial\phi}{\partial\theta} = -\frac{\partial\psi}{\partial r}$	(25.22)

Fig. 25.3. Summary of equations for planar potential flow.

25.3 Uniform Flow

The potential flow around obstacles in a stream, such as airplane wings, turbine blades, and submarine hulls, can frequently be represented, and handled with ease mathematically, as a combination of basic potential flows. The potential and stream functions of a few basic planar flows will now be developed, and then the process of combining them will be illustrated. First consider the *uniform flow* illustrated in Fig. 25.4. If the uniform velocity U is in the x direction,

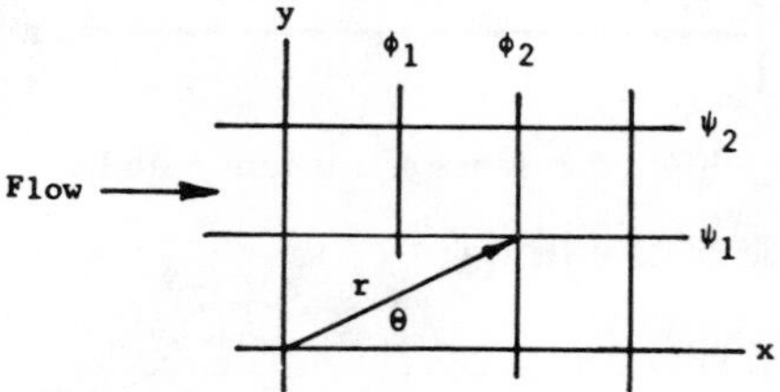

Fig. 25.4. A uniform flow.

$$v_x = \frac{\partial \phi}{\partial x} = U \qquad \text{and} \qquad v_y = \frac{\partial \phi}{\partial y} = 0 \,. \tag{25.23}$$

Notice that this velocity potential ϕ satisfies Laplace's equation. Since ϕ is a function of x only,

$$\frac{d\phi}{dx} = U \,, \tag{25.24}$$

and

$$\phi = U\,x + k_1 = U\,r \cos\theta + k_1 \,. \tag{25.25}$$

According to the Cauchy-Riemann equations (25.21) and (25.22),

$$\frac{\partial \psi}{\partial y} = \frac{\partial \phi}{\partial x} = U \tag{25.26}$$

and

$$\frac{\partial \psi}{\partial x} = -\frac{\partial \phi}{\partial y} = 0 \,. \tag{25.27}$$

Since ψ is a function of y only,

$$\frac{d\psi}{dy} = U \tag{25.28}$$

and the Lagrange stream function of a uniform flow in the x direction is

$$\psi = U\,y + k_2 = U\,r \sin\theta + k_2 \,. \tag{25.29}$$

The constants k_1 and k_2 are usually not important and will be ignored for all of the basic flows, because ϕ and ψ are later differentiated to obtain the velocity or pressure desired.

Notice that the velocity potential was calculated from the fluid velocity, and tested to make sure it is a harmonic function. Then the stream function was calculated by applying the Cauchy-Riemann equations, and is therefore guaranteed to be a harmonic function. This procedure will be followed in the development of each of the first three basic planar flows.

25.4 Source and Sink

The next basic potential flow is a *source*, namely the flow in a plane two-dimensional field emanating uniformly from a line that is straight in the z direction, as shown in Fig. 25.5. The rate of the radial flow is Q m^3/s per meter of depth, or m^2/s. The name "source" is given not only

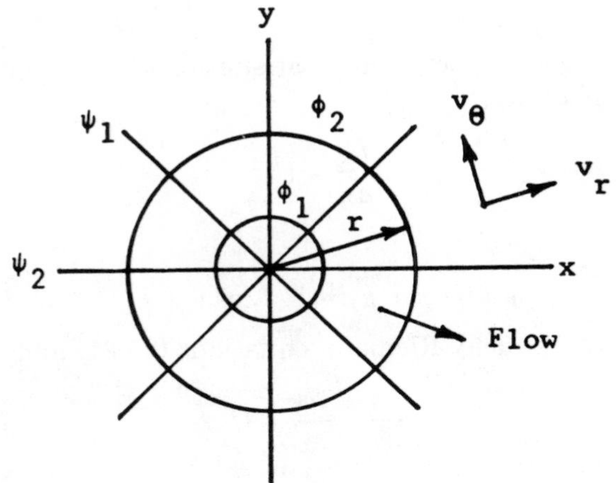

Fig. 25.5. A source or sink.

to the flow, but also to the line from which it emanates. Lines of constant ϕ and ψ are shown in Fig. 25.5. The fluid flux or flow rate is

$$Q = \oint_s \mathbf{v} \cdot d\mathbf{s} . \tag{25.30}$$

If the surface of integration is the cylinder represented by the circle of radius r, at which the radial and tangential components of fluid velocity are v_r and v_θ,

$$Q = v_r \cdot 2 \pi r \tag{25.31}$$

or

$$v_r = \frac{Q}{2\pi r} \qquad \text{and} \qquad v_\theta = 0 . \tag{25.32}$$

According to Eqs. (25.19) and (25.20),

$$\frac{\partial \phi}{\partial r} = v_r = \frac{Q}{2\pi r} \qquad \text{and} \qquad \frac{1}{r}\frac{\partial \phi}{\partial \theta} = v_\theta = 0 . \tag{25.33}$$

Notice that this potential ϕ satisfies Laplace's equation, which in polar coordinates is

$$\frac{1}{r}\frac{\partial}{\partial r}\left(r\frac{\partial \phi}{\partial r}\right) + \frac{1}{r^2}\frac{\partial^2 \phi}{\partial \theta^2} = 0 . \tag{25.34}$$

Since ϕ is a function of r only,

$$\frac{d\phi}{dr} = \frac{Q}{2\pi r} \tag{25.35}$$

and the velocity potential of a source is

$$\phi = \frac{Q}{2\pi} \ln r \, . \tag{25.36}$$

According to the Cauchy-Riemann equations (25.21) and (25.22),

$$\frac{\partial \psi}{\partial r} = -\frac{1}{r}\frac{\partial \phi}{\partial \theta} = 0 \qquad \text{and} \qquad \frac{\partial \psi}{\partial \theta} = r\frac{\partial \phi}{\partial r} = \frac{Q}{2\pi} \, . \tag{25.37}$$

Since ψ is a function of θ only,

$$\frac{d\psi}{d\theta} = \frac{Q}{2\pi} \tag{25.38}$$

and

$$\psi = \frac{Q\,\theta}{2\pi} \, . \tag{25.39}$$

Thus the stream lines of a source are radial, and the lines of constant potential are concentric circles. A *sink* is the flow draining into the central line in a plane two-dimensional field. The sign of v_r is negative. The formulas for the potential and stream functions are therefore

$$\phi = -\frac{Q}{2\pi} \ln r \qquad \text{and} \qquad \psi = -\frac{Q\,\theta}{2\pi} \, . \tag{25.40}$$

25.5 Vortex

A third interesting basic flow is a *vortex* or plane two-dimensional whirlpool. The fluid flows circumferentially about the center as in Fig. 25.6. Stream lines are concentric circles, and equipotential lines are radial. A quantity that will be useful in the calculation of ϕ and ψ is the *circulation* of the vortex, defined as the counterclockwise line integral

$$\Gamma = \oint \mathbf{v} \cdot d\ell \, , \tag{25.41}$$

for which the path of integration encloses the center of the vortex. The analysis will soon show that integration around any such path produces the same value of Γ. If the path is one of the concentric circles of radius r, along which the velocity is v_θ,

$$\Gamma = 2\,\pi\, r\, v_\theta \, , \tag{25.42}$$

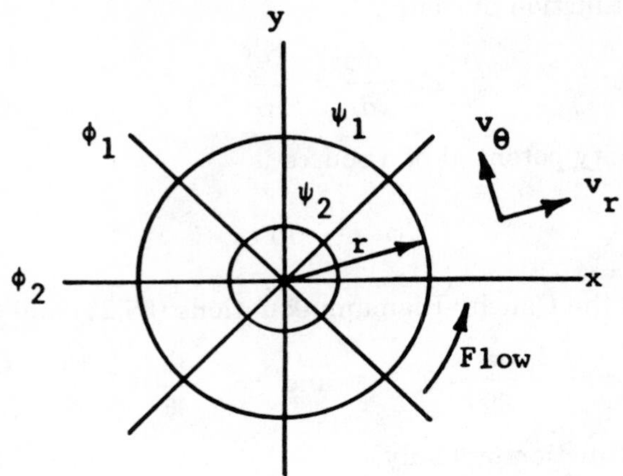

Fig. 25.6. A counterclockwise vortex.

and therefore

$$v_\theta = \frac{1}{r}\frac{\partial\phi}{\partial\theta} = \frac{\Gamma}{2\pi r} \qquad \text{and} \qquad v_r = \frac{\partial\phi}{\partial r} = 0\,. \tag{25.43}$$

Notice that the velocity is inversely proportional to radius, and is infinite at the center of the vortex. The potential function ϕ satisfies Laplace's equation. Since ϕ is a function of θ only,

$$\frac{1}{r}\frac{d\phi}{d\theta} = \frac{\Gamma}{2\pi r} \tag{25.44}$$

and

$$\phi = \frac{\Gamma\theta}{2\pi}\,. \tag{25.45}$$

According to the Cauchy-Riemann equations,

$$\frac{\partial\psi}{\partial r} = -\frac{1}{r}\frac{\partial\phi}{\partial\theta} = -\frac{\Gamma}{2\pi r} \qquad \text{and} \qquad \frac{\partial\psi}{\partial\theta} = r\frac{\partial\phi}{\partial r} = 0\,. \tag{25.46}$$

Since ψ is a function of r only,

$$\frac{d\psi}{dr} = -\frac{\Gamma}{2\pi r} \tag{25.47}$$

and

$$\psi = -\frac{\Gamma}{2\pi}\ln r\,. \tag{25.48}$$

Eqs. (25.45) and (25.48) show the velocity potential and stream function for a counterclockwise vortex. For a clockwise vortex the sign of v_θ is negative, and therefore the signs of ϕ and ψ are reversed.

Since a potential flow is conservative, $\nabla \times \mathbf{v} = 0$, and the observant reader can reasonably ask "Why is Γ as defined by Eq. (25.41) not zero?" The reason can be explained by applying Stokes' theorem:

$$\Gamma = \oint \mathbf{v} \cdot d\ell = \int_s (\nabla \times \mathbf{v}) \cdot d\mathbf{s} = \int_s 2\,\boldsymbol{\omega} \cdot d\mathbf{s}\,, \qquad (25.49)$$

where the surface integral extends over the surface bounded by the path of the line integral. Since the field is plane, $d\mathbf{s}$ and $\boldsymbol{\omega}$ are directed normal to the paper, and

$$\int_s 2\,\boldsymbol{\omega} \cdot d\mathbf{s} = \int_s 2\,\omega\, ds = \Gamma \int_s \frac{2\omega}{\Gamma}\, ds = \Gamma \int_s \delta(r) ds\,. \qquad (25.50)$$

In an ideal vortex the magnitude 2ω of the vorticity vector is zero everywhere except at the center of the vortex, where it is infinite. The quantity

$$\delta(r) = \frac{2\omega}{\Gamma} \qquad (25.51)$$

is an example of a two-dimensional *Dirac delta function*, defined by the equations

$$\int_s \delta(r) ds = 1 \qquad (25.52)$$

if the surface of integration includes the origin (the right side is zero otherwise), and

$$\delta(r) = \begin{cases} 0, & r \neq 0 \\ \infty, & r = 0\,. \end{cases} \qquad (25.53)$$

The integral in Eq. (25.41) or (25.49) has the value Γ if the path of integration encloses the vortex center, and the value zero if it does not. In the vortex flow of a real fluid such as water, viscosity prevents the tangential velocity v_θ and the angular velocity ω from becoming infinite at the center. Except for the small core in which the viscous shear forces are large, the flow is irrotational and the velocity is given by Eq. (25.43). One method of producing a vortex of known circulation in a viscous fluid will be shown in the next section.

An analog of the fluid velocity $\mathbf{v}$ in a vortex is the magnetic field intensity $\mathbf{H}$ surrounding a wire carrying the direct current I. For this field

$$I = \oint \mathbf{H} \cdot d\ell = \int_s (\nabla \times \mathbf{H}) \cdot d\mathbf{s} = \int_s \mathbf{J} \cdot d\mathbf{s} \qquad (25.54)$$

where **J** is the current density. The field is conservative because $\nabla \times \mathbf{H} = 0$ everywhere except in the wire. Still the line integral is I, not zero, if it encloses the wire.

25.6 Vortex in a Viscous Fluid

A vortex can be created by rotating a cylinder in a real, viscous fluid. This fact has practical importance. To prove the fact, first consider two concentric cylinders with vertical axes, shown in Fig. 25.7, whose annu-

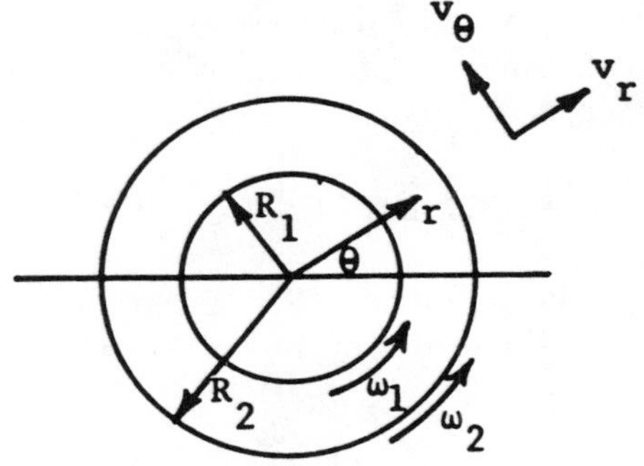

Fig. 25.7. Viscous fluid between concentric cylinders.

lar space is filled with a newtonian fluid of constant density and viscosity. For such a fluid the Navier-Stokes equation has the form of Eq. (24.57):

$$\frac{D\mathbf{v}}{Dt} = \mathbf{F} - \frac{1}{\rho}\nabla p + \frac{\mu}{\rho}\nabla^2\mathbf{v}\,. \tag{25.55}$$

Assume that the cylinders are infinitely long, to make the flow two dimensional. Ref. 79, page 51, shows that in polar coordinates the r and θ components of the vector equation (25.55) are

$$\frac{\partial v_r}{\partial t} + v_r\frac{\partial v_r}{\partial r} + \frac{v_\theta}{r}\frac{\partial v_r}{\partial \theta} - \frac{v_\theta^2}{r} = F_r - \frac{1}{\rho}\frac{\partial p}{\partial r}$$
$$+ \frac{\mu}{\rho}\left(\frac{\partial^2 v_r}{\partial r^2} + \frac{1}{r}\frac{\partial v_r}{\partial r} - \frac{v_r}{r^2} + \frac{1}{r^2}\frac{\partial^2 v_r}{\partial \theta^2} - \frac{2}{r^2}\frac{\partial v_\theta}{\partial \theta}\right) \tag{25.56}$$

and

$$\frac{\partial v_\theta}{\partial t} + v_r\frac{\partial v_\theta}{\partial r} + \frac{v_\theta}{r}\frac{\partial v_\theta}{\partial \theta} + \frac{v_r v_\theta}{r} = F_\theta - \frac{1}{\rho r}\frac{\partial p}{\partial \theta}$$
$$+ \frac{\mu}{\rho}\left(\frac{\partial^2 v_\theta}{\partial r^2} + \frac{1}{r}\frac{\partial v_\theta}{\partial r} - \frac{v_\theta}{r^2} + \frac{1}{r^2}\frac{\partial^2 v_\theta}{\partial \theta^2} + \frac{2}{r^2}\frac{\partial v_r}{\partial \theta}\right). \tag{25.57}$$

When the cylinders rotate at steady speeds ω_1 and ω_2, the fluid has no radial velocity v_r, and the tangential velocity v_θ and the pressure p are functions of r but not θ. The Navier-Stokes equations reduce to

$$-\frac{v_\theta^2}{r} = F_r - \frac{1}{\rho}\frac{\partial p}{\partial r} \tag{25.58}$$

and

$$0 = F_\theta + \frac{\mu}{\rho}\left(\frac{\partial^2 v_\theta}{\partial r^2} + \frac{1}{r}\frac{\partial v_\theta}{\partial r} - \frac{v_\theta}{r^2}\right). \tag{25.59}$$

The radial body force F_r is centrifugal force, $r\omega^2$ N/kg. Gravity does not contribute a body force F_θ, and if no pathological source of F_θ is permitted, Eq. (25.59) becomes

$$r^2\frac{d^2 v_\theta}{dr^2} + r\frac{dv_\theta}{dr} - v_\theta = 0\,. \tag{25.60}$$

The solution of this Euler equation is

$$v_\theta = k_1 r + \frac{k_2}{r}\,. \tag{25.61}$$

Because the fluid is viscous its velocity at the inner and outer cylinders must be the tangential velocities of the cylinders:

$$v_\theta(R_1) = R_1\,\omega_1 \qquad \text{and} \qquad v_\theta(R_2) = R_2\,\omega_2\,. \tag{25.62}$$

When these two boundary conditions are used to evaluate k_1 and k_2, Eq. (25.61) becomes

$$v_\theta = \frac{\omega_2 R_2^2 - \omega_1 R_1^2}{R_2^2 - R_1^2}\, r + \frac{(\omega_1 - \omega_2)R_1^2 R_2^2}{R_2^2 - R_1^2}\cdot\frac{1}{r}\,. \tag{25.63}$$

This is the velocity of the fluid in the space between the two cylinders. The pressure distribution in the fluid with gravity neglected can now, if desired, be found by integrating Eq. (25.58). If the cylinders rotate with the same angular velocity ω, Eq. (25.63) becomes

$$v_\theta = \omega\, r\,, \tag{25.64}$$

and the fluid rotates as a solid mass, not as a vortex. If the inner cylinder rotates with angular velocity ω_1, and the outer cylinder is removed by letting its radius R_2 approach infinity and its angular velocity ω_2 be zero,

$$v_\theta = \frac{\omega_1 R_1^2}{r}\,. \tag{25.65}$$

According to Eqs. (25.43) the velocities in a vortex are

$$v_\theta = \frac{\Gamma}{2\pi r} \qquad \text{and} \qquad v_r = 0\,. \tag{25.66}$$

Now it is clear that a cylinder of radius R, rotating counterclockwise at an angular velocity ω in a viscous fluid, produces a vortex of circulation

$$\Gamma = 2\,\pi\,\omega\,R^2\,. \tag{25.67}$$

According to Eq. (25.48) the stream function of this vortex is

$$\psi = -\frac{\Gamma}{2\pi}\ln r = -\omega\,R^2\ln r\,. \tag{25.68}$$

This vortex created by a rotating cylinder is an example of a potential flow of a real, viscous fluid.

25.7 Doublet

The last basic planar flow to be considered is a *doublet* or *dipole*. It consists of a source and a sink of strengths Q and $-Q$, whose centers are the distance d apart. They are moved together until the centers coincide, while the dipole moment Qd is kept constant. Surprisingly the fields do not cancel, and the direction of their axis, namely the line from the sink to the source shown in Fig. 25.8, is preserved. To show this,

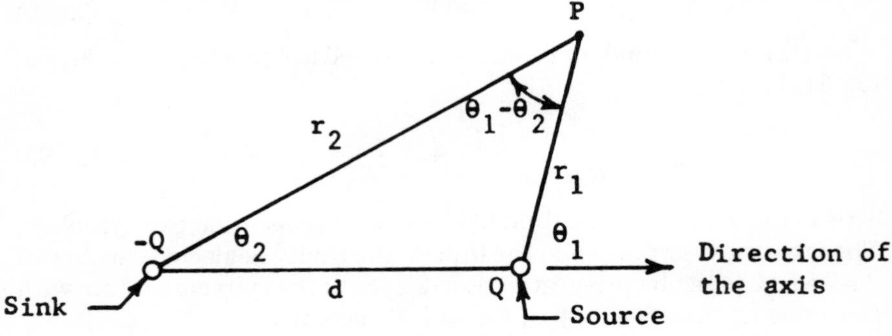

Fig. 25.8. A source and sink of equal strength.

observe first that if ψ_1 and ψ_2 are two stream functions, both of which satisfy Laplace's equation,

$$\nabla^2(\psi_1 + \psi_2) = \nabla^2\psi_1 + \nabla^2\psi_2 = 0\,. \tag{25.69}$$

The sum of two potential flows is therefore also a potential flow. At any point P in Fig. 25.8 the stream function of the source and sink is

$$\psi = \frac{Q\,\theta_1}{2\pi} - \frac{Q\,\theta_2}{2\pi} = \frac{Q\,d}{2\pi d}\,(\theta_1 - \theta_2)\,. \tag{25.70}$$

According to the law of sines,

$$\frac{r_2}{\sin\theta_1} = \frac{d}{\sin(\theta_1 - \theta_2)} \tag{25.71}$$

or

$$d = \frac{r_2 \sin(\theta_1 - \theta_2)}{\sin\theta_1}\,. \tag{25.72}$$

Now Eq. (25.70) can be written as

$$\psi = \frac{Q\,d}{2\pi} \cdot \frac{(\theta_1 - \theta_2)\sin\theta_1}{r_2 \sin(\theta_1 - \theta_2)}\,. \tag{25.73}$$

As d approaches zero, r_1 and r_2 approach the same length r, and θ_1 and θ_2 approach the same angle θ. If the dipole moment Qd is held constant,

$$\lim_{d \to 0} \psi = \frac{Q\,d \sin\theta}{2\pi r}\,. \tag{25.74}$$

This is the Lagrange stream function of a doublet. It can be shown to be harmonic by either (1) substituting it into Laplace's equation in polar coordinates or (2) referring to Eq. (25.69). The velocity potential ϕ is found from either Cauchy-Riemann equation. If Eq. (25.21) is used,

$$\frac{1}{r}\,\frac{\partial\psi}{\partial\theta} = \frac{Q\,d\cos\theta}{2\pi r^2} = \frac{\partial\phi}{\partial r}\,. \tag{25.75}$$

Therefore

$$\phi = -\,\frac{Q\,d\cos\theta}{2\pi r} + f(\theta)\,, \tag{25.76}$$

where $f(\theta)$ is an unknown function of θ. To evaluate it, apply the other Cauchy-Riemann equation (25.22), which is

$$\frac{1}{r}\,\frac{\partial\phi}{\partial\theta} = -\,\frac{\partial\psi}{\partial r}\,. \tag{25.77}$$

Substituting Eqs. (25.76) and (25.74) into this equation produces

$$\frac{Q\,d\sin\theta}{2\pi r^2} + \frac{f'(\theta)}{r} = \frac{Q\,d\sin\theta}{2\pi r^2} \tag{25.78}$$

or

$$f(\theta) = \text{constant} . \tag{25.79}$$

As usual, the constant will be chosen to be zero. The velocity potential of a doublet is therefore

$$\phi = -\frac{Q\,d\cos\theta}{2\pi r} . \tag{25.80}$$

Lines of constant ϕ and constant ψ are families of eccentric circles, all tangent at the origin, as shown in Fig. 25.9. Even if the distance d between the source and the sink is not zero, Eqs. (25.74) and (25.80) are accurate at distances r that are large compared to d. They are called the far-field equations.

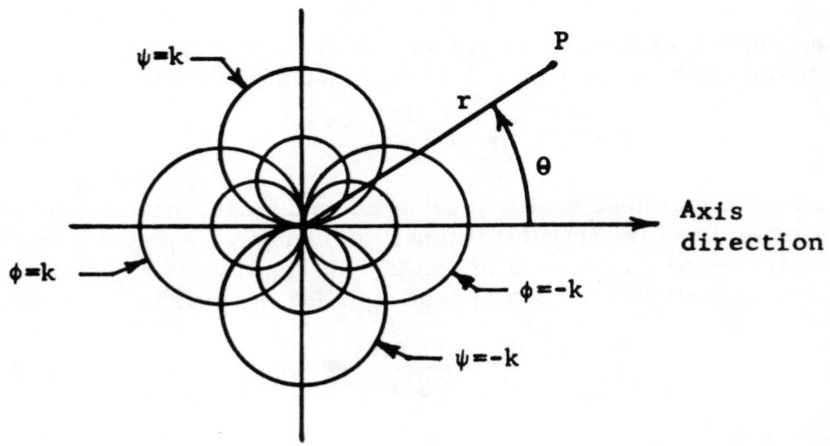

Fig. 25.9. Field of a doublet.

25.8 Flow Around a Cylinder

A sum of basic potential flows having physical significance is a uniform flow in the positive x direction and a doublet oriented in the negative x direction. The stream function of the latter is the negative of that given by Eq. (25.74). The stream function of the composite flow is

$$\psi = U\,r\sin\theta - \frac{Q\,d\sin\theta}{2\pi r} . \tag{25.81}$$

For convenience, let

$$\frac{Q\,d}{2\pi U} = R^2 . \qquad (25.82)$$

Then

$$\psi = U \sin\theta \left(r - \frac{R^2}{r} \right) . \qquad (25.83)$$

Notice that $\psi = 0$ for $r = R, \theta = 0$, and $\theta = 180°$. Therefore the x axis and the circle of radius R constitute a stream line as shown in Fig. 25.10. The

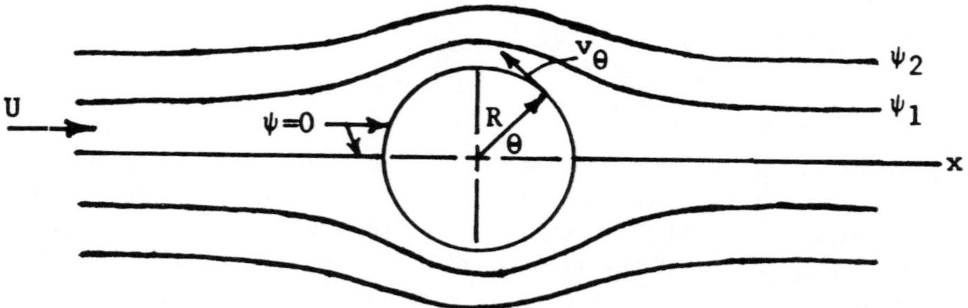

Fig. 25.10. Stream lines of a uniform flow and a doublet.

circle can be replaced by a cylindrical boundary. At the boundary the velocity is tangential, and is

$$v_\theta(R,\theta) = -\left.\frac{\partial\psi}{\partial r}\right|_{r=R} = -2\,U \sin\theta . \qquad (25.84)$$

A calculation of the force exerted by the fluid on the cylinder will produce an interesting and temporarily discouraging result. To calculate this force, consider first that the potential flow around a cylinder, like any potential flow, is based on the assumptions that the fluid is incompressible and the flow is irrotational. If in addition the fluid is newtonian with constant viscosity and the flow is steady, the Bernoulli equation for steady flow, (24.79), can be used to calculate the pressure distribution on the cylinder. If the cylinder is vertical in a horizontal uniform stream, the flow is not affected by gravity and the Bernoulli equation becomes

$$\frac{p}{\rho} + \frac{v^2}{2} = \text{constant} \qquad (25.85)$$

or

$$\frac{p}{\rho} + \frac{v^2}{2} = \frac{p_\infty}{\rho} + \frac{U^2}{2} = \frac{p_o}{\rho}, \tag{25.86}$$

where p_∞ is the pressure of the fluid far upstream or downstream where the velocity is U, p and v are the pressure and velocity anywhere, and ρ is the density of the fluid. The pressure

$$p_o = p_\infty + \frac{\rho U^2}{2} \tag{25.87}$$

produced by reducing the velocity to zero is called the *total* or *stagnation pressure*. At any point in the flow,

$$p = p_o - \frac{\rho v^2}{2}. \tag{25.88}$$

A point at which $p = p_o$ is called a *stagnation point*. The flow in Fig. 25.10 has two stagnation points, at $r = R$, $\theta = 0$ and $r = R$, $\theta = 180°$. According to Eq. (25.88), the fluid pressure can be negative. Actually this is impossible. If the velocity of a liquid is increased until the pressure is reduced to the vapor pressure (the pressure at which the liquid boils), the liquid usually *cavitates*, i.e., forms bubbles of its gaseous phase. If the velocity of a gas is increased to a substantial fraction of the speed of sound, its density decreases appreciably, violating the assumption of incompressibility on which Eq. (25.85) is based. The pressure drops, but never goes negative.

A useful dimensionless measure of pressure is the *pressure coefficient*:

$$C_p = \frac{p - p_\infty}{\rho U^2/2} = 1 - \left(\frac{v}{U}\right)^2, \tag{25.89}$$

which is zero far upstream or downstream from an obstacle in a uniform flow, is unity at a stagnation point, and can have large negative values. The pressure coefficient on the cylinder of Fig. 25.10 is found by substituting the fluid velocity given by Eq. (25.84) into Eq. (25.89):

$$C_p = 1 - \left(\frac{-2\,U \sin\theta}{U}\right)^2 = 1 - 4\sin^2\theta. \tag{25.90}$$

The distribution of this pressure coefficient over the surface of the cylinder is shown in Fig. 25.11.

What force does the nonviscous fluid exert on the cylinder in Fig. 25.10? According to Eq. (25.84) and Fig. 25.11, the magnitude of the fluid velocity at the surface of the cylinder is the same at angles θ, $-\theta$,

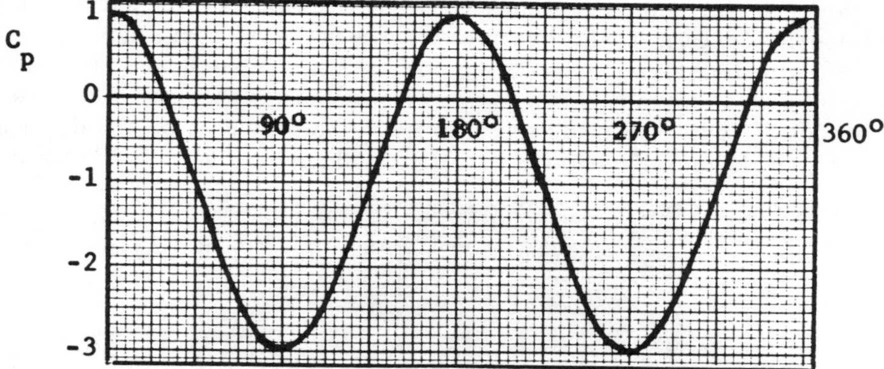

Fig. 25.11. Pressure coefficient C_p on a cylinder in a uniform flow.

$180° - \theta$, and $180° + \theta$. The Bernoulli equation in the form of Eq. (25.88) shows that the pressure on the cylinder is the same at all four points. Each quadrant of the cylinder has the same pressure distribution. There is therefore no net force on the cylinder. Of course, a cylinder placed in a uniform flow of a real fluid experiences a *drag* force in the direction of the uniform flow. As the particles of fluid approach the body, they are pushed away by the body, crowded together, and speeded up. The assumptions of potential flow are intact. The fluid particles should slow down and fill in smoothly behind the body, to maintain the potential flow. Unfortunately, the force required to shove them into smooth stream lines like those on the upstream side is not available. Instead, the fluid particles are swept along and rotated, as shown in Fig. 25.12,

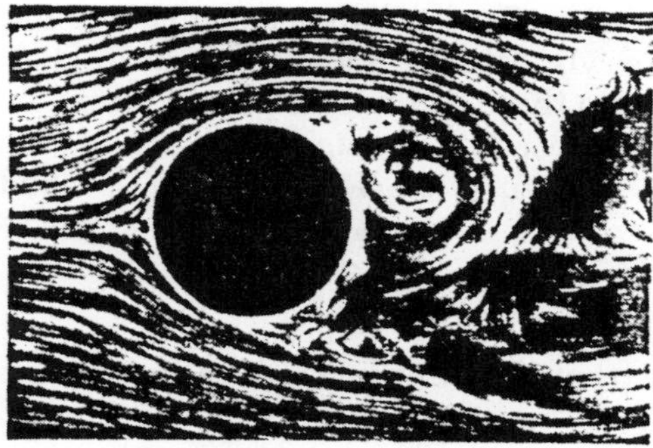

Fig. 25.12. Actual flow around a cylinder.

by the shear force applied by their faster neighbors. The flow behind the cylinder is turbulent, the velocity is high, and the pressure is low. The integral of pressure over the circumference of the cylinder is a *pressure drag* directed downstream. Streamlining is an attempt to shape the body so that the smooth flow does not separate from the body. If it were completely successful, the pressure would be recovered on the downstream side, and the net pressure drag would be zero. Fig. 25.13 shows

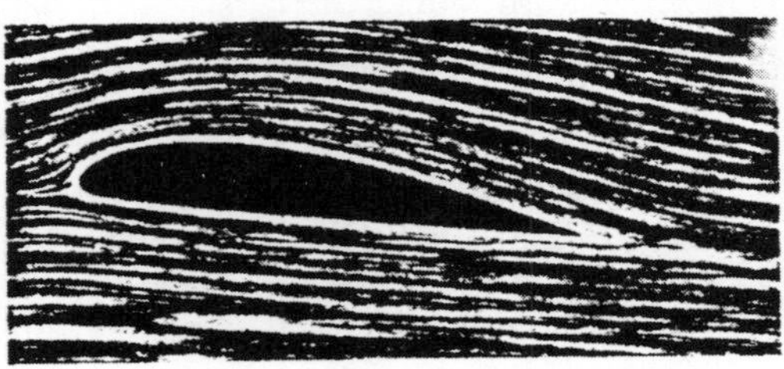

Fig. 25.13. Flow around an airfoil.

that the air flow around the streamlined cross section of an airplane wing suffers almost no separation, and therefore causes little pressure drag. Since the air has viscosity, the particles of air touching the wing do not move. Across a thin boundary layer the velocity builds up to the free-stream velocity of potential flow. According to Eq.(24.23), the high velocity gradient causes a shear stress, whose integral over the body is *friction drag* or *skin friction*. If a streamlined shape is made longer so that it tapers more gradually, the friction drag increases. The optimal shape minimizes the sum of pressure and friction drags.

25.9 Lift

The preceding sections have shown that (1) the potential flow around a cylinder in a uniform flow can be represented by a uniform flow and a doublet, and (2) a cylinder rotating in a viscous fluid produces a vortex. It seems reasonable that the flow around a rotating cylinder in a uniform flow can be represented by a unifor[illegible] and a vortex centered on a doublet. The stream function of the uniform flow and doublet in Fig. 25.10 is

$$\psi = U \sin\theta \left(r - \frac{R^2}{r} \right) . \tag{25.91}$$

Eq. (25.68) shows that if a cylinder of radius R rotates clockwise with the angular velocity ω, the stream function of the vortex it creates is

$$\psi = \omega R^2 \ln r . \tag{25.92}$$

The stream function of a cylinder rotating clockwise in a uniform flow is therefore

$$\psi = U \sin\theta \left(r - \frac{R^2}{r} \right) + \omega R^2 \ln r\,. \tag{25.93}$$

The stream lines can be plotted by calculating r as a function of θ for fixed values of ψ. The calculated flows for $\omega R/U$ of 0, 1, 2, and 3 are shown in Fig. 25.14. Included for comparison are photographs of the actual flow of water around a rotating cylinder.

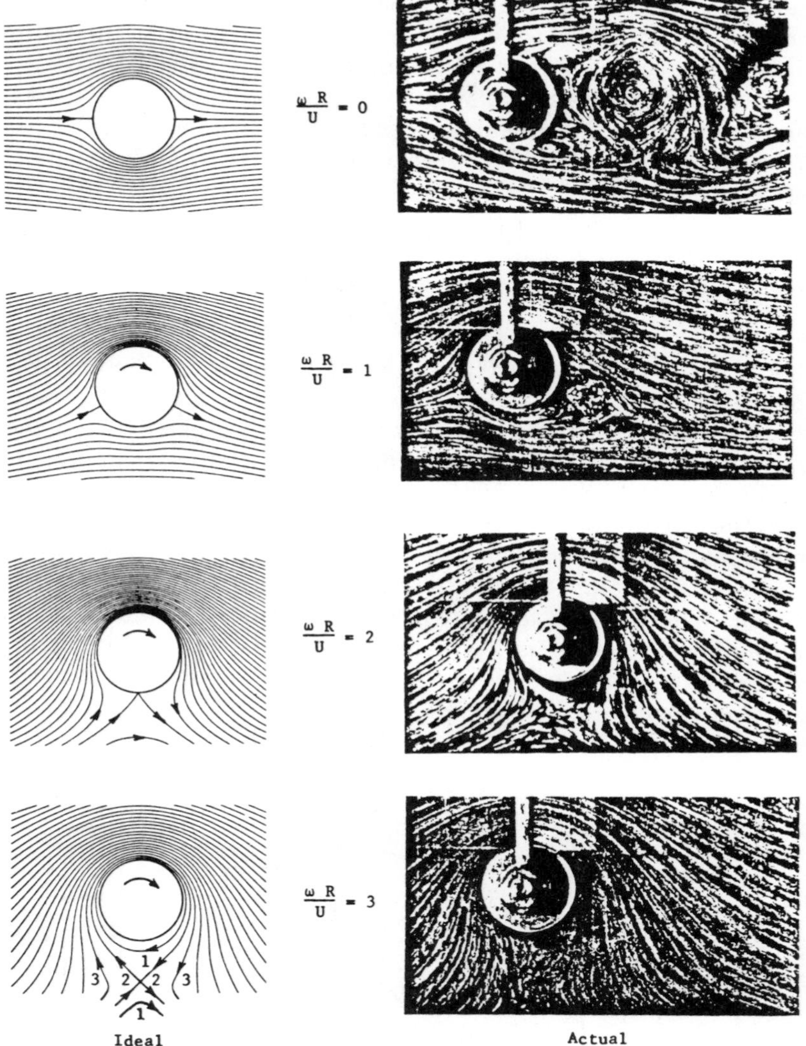

Fig. 25.14. Ideal and actual flows around a spinning cylinder in a uniform flow. (Adapted by permission of the United Engineering Trustees, Inc. from *Applied Hydro- and Aeromechanics* by L. Prandtl and O. G. Tietjens, McGraw-Hill, 1934.)

According to Eq. (25.93) the velocity of the fluid along the surface of the cylinder is

$$v_\theta(R,\theta) = -\left.\frac{\partial\psi}{\partial r}\right|_{r=R} = -2\,U\sin\theta - \omega\,R\,. \tag{25.94}$$

This is the velocity the fluid would have if it were nonviscous. Water or any real fluid is dragged around by the cylinder, so that at $r = R$ the fluid velocity v_θ is $-\omega\,R$. Nature reconciles the difference by providing a boundary layer, across which the fluid velocity adjusts to the requirements of the potential-flow stream function.

Notice that as the angular velocity of the cylinder increases, the two stagnation points in the ideal flow approach each other. Their locations can be found from Eq. (25.94). Since the velocity is zero at the stagnation points,

$$-2\,U\sin\theta - \omega\,R = 0 \tag{25.95}$$

or

$$\sin\theta = -\frac{\omega\,R}{2U}\,. \tag{25.96}$$

When $\omega\,R/U = 1$, $\sin\theta = -0.5$, and $\theta = 210°$ and $330°$ as in Fig. 25.14. When $\omega\,R/U = 2$, $\sin\theta = -1$, and θ has only the value $270°$. The two stagnation points have coalesced. When $\omega\,R/U$ is greater than 2, θ has no real value. The stagnation point has left the cylinder and now constitutes a *saddle point* in the fluid. As the numbered stream lines show, the stream function increases to the left and right of the saddle point, and decreases above and below. For any value of $\omega\,R/U$ greater than 2, a ring of fluid is trapped and rotates permanently around the cylinder. Where the stream lines are close together, the fluid velocity is high and the pressure is low according to Eq. (25.85). The cylinder therefore experiences a force upward, toward the crowded stream lines. This phenomenon, called the *Magnus effect*, explains why a baseball curves. It is also the basis of the design of a ship, shown in Fig. 25.15,

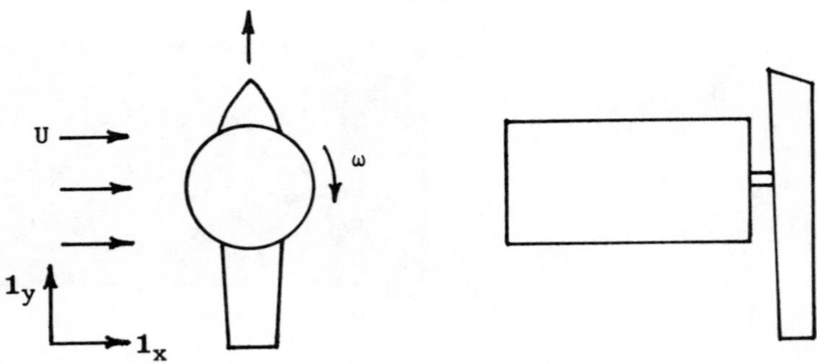

Fig. 25.15. Flettner rotorship.

with a cylindrical sail called a *Flettner rotor*, turned by an engine. In 1927 the rotor ship *Barbara* crossed the Atlantic twice. It had three Flettner rotors, 23 feet in diameter and 98 feet high, rotating at 150 rpm.

The ideal force on a spinning cylinder in a uniform flow can be calculated easily. Fig. 25.16 shows a cross section of the cylinder of

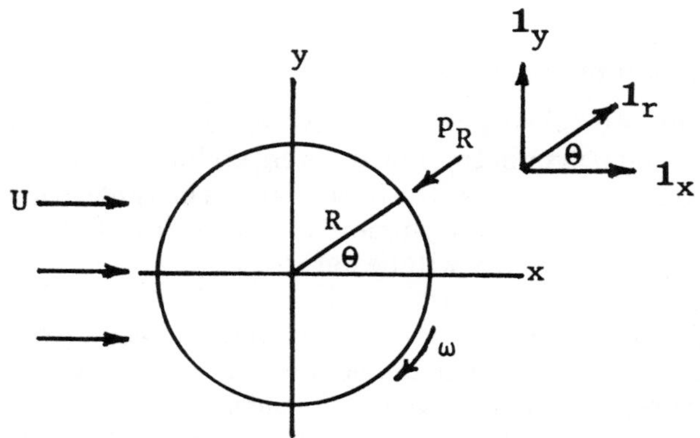

Fig. 25.16. Cross section of a spinning cylinder in a uniform flow.

radius R. The pressure on its surface is

$$p_R = p_o - \frac{\rho\, v_\theta^2(R,\theta)}{2} = p_o - \frac{\rho}{2}(-2\,U \sin\theta - \omega\, R)^2\,. \qquad (25.97)$$

The pressure is directed radially inward, opposite to the direction of

$$\mathbf{1}_r = \mathbf{1}_x \cos\theta + \mathbf{1}_y \sin\theta\,. \qquad (25.98)$$

Therefore an element of force (per unit length) on the cylinder is

$$d\mathbf{f} = -\mathbf{1}_r\, p_R\, R\, d\theta\,. \qquad (25.99)$$

Integration of this force around the periphery of the cylinder yields

$$\mathbf{f} = \mathbf{1}_y\, 2\,\pi\,\rho\, U\,\omega\, R^2 = \mathbf{1}_y\,\rho\, U\,\Gamma\,, \qquad (25.100)$$

where Γ is the circulation of the vortex. The ship in Fig. 25.15 is driven forward by this force, which is called *lift*, because a force calculated similarly produces the lift on airplane wings. For each Flettner rotor on the *Barbara*, R = 11.5 ft, the height h is 98 ft, and $\omega = 5\pi$ rad/s. The density of dry air at atmospheric pressure and 71°F is 0.0747 lb_m/ft^3. If the wind is blowing from the side at U = 30 ft/s, the ideal lift on each rotor is

$$F = \frac{2\,\pi\,\rho\,U\,\omega\,R^2\,h}{g} = \frac{(2\pi)(0.0747)(30)(5\pi)(11.5)^2(98)}{32.2}$$

$$= 89{,}024\ \mathrm{lb_f}\,. \tag{25.101}$$

This is almost twice the maximum thrust of the largest aircraft jet engines, such as the General Electric CF6.

25.10 Axisymmetric Flow

This chapter until now has been devoted to potential flows with plane two-dimensional symmetry. Many potential flows with axial symmetry are also important, because the flow around a body of revolution pointed into a uniform flow is axisymmetric. The stream functions for three basic axisymmetric flows will be derived, so that the reader can calculate the flow around submarines, dirigibles, bullets, rockets, and balls. To start the derivation, recall that the Lagrange stream or flux function ψ for planar flow was defined in Section 25.2 so that the difference in the values of this function at two points is the amount of flux flowing across a surface of unit depth extending between the points. The vector $d\mathbf{s}$ representing the surface points to the right of the surface drawn in the direction of increasing ψ. For example, Fig. 25.17 shows two points in a

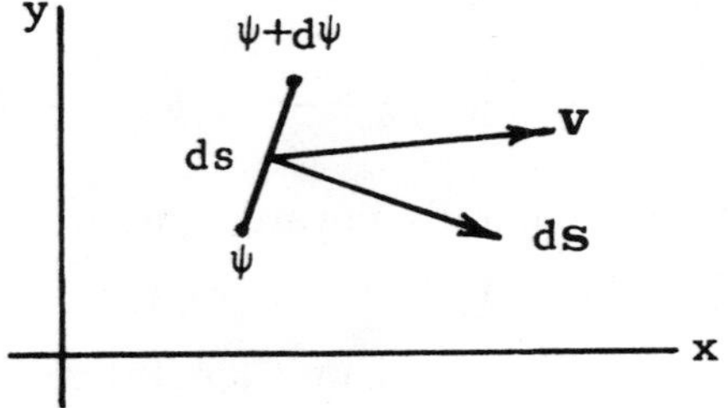

Fig. 25.17. Stream function for planar flow.

planar flow separated by the plane surface ds, represented by the vector $d\mathbf{s}$ normal to it. The fluid velocity is the flux density $\mathbf{v}$ m/s. The total flux flowing to the right across the surface is

$$d\psi = \mathbf{v} \cdot d\mathbf{s} = v_n\, ds \qquad \mathrm{m^2/s}\,, \tag{25.102}$$

where v_n is the component of velocity normal to ds.

The stream function for axisymmetric flows, invented by G. G. Stokes and named for him, is similar but not identical. Fig. 25.18 shows two of the stream surfaces, or surfaces across which no fluid flows, in an axi-

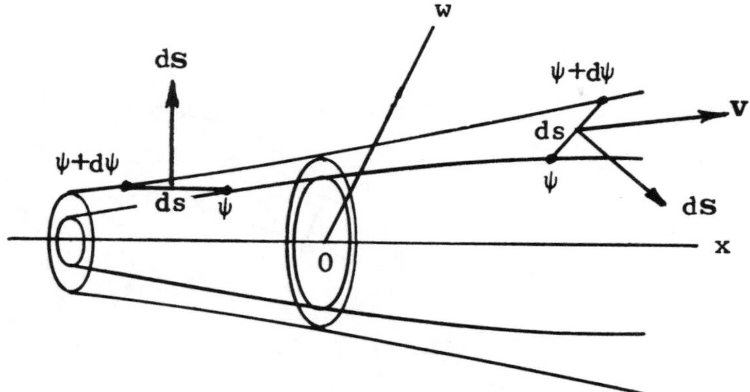

Fig. 25.18. Axisymmetric stream surfaces.

symmetric flow. The Stokes stream function can be expressed conveniently in the two cylindrical coordinates x and w. The w axis can rotate about the x axis. No angular coordinate is needed. The intersections of the stream surfaces with the xw or *meridian plane* are stream lines. The Stokes stream function for an axisymmetric flow is defined so that 2π times the difference in its values at two points, which represent two concentric circles, is the amount of flux flowing thru the annulus between the circles. The construction on the right side of Fig. 25.18 shows a differential surface of width ds and unit depth in the circumferential direction, drawn between two stream surfaces in the direction of increasing ψ. As in the planar case, the vector $d\mathbf{s}$ representing the differential surface points to the right of it. The flux flowing to the right thru the annular space is

$$2\,\pi\,d\psi = (2\,\pi\,w)(\mathbf{v}\cdot d\mathbf{s}) = 2\,\pi\,w\,v_n\,ds \tag{25.103}$$

or

$$v_n = \frac{1}{w}\,\frac{d\psi}{ds}\,. \tag{25.104}$$

The 2π is included in the definition of the stream function so that it will not appear in Eq. (25.104). If the surface ds extends radially outward so that $d\mathbf{s}$ is positive axially, $ds = dw$, $v_n = v_x$, and

$$v_x = \frac{1}{w}\,\frac{\partial\psi}{\partial w}\,. \tag{25.105}$$

If the surface ds extends axially to the left as on the left side of Fig. 25.18, $d\mathbf{s}$ is radially outward, $ds = -dx$, $v_n = v_w$, and

$$v_w = -\frac{1}{w}\frac{\partial\psi}{\partial x}. \qquad (25.106)$$

In Fig. 25.19 the spherical coordinates r and θ have been added to the

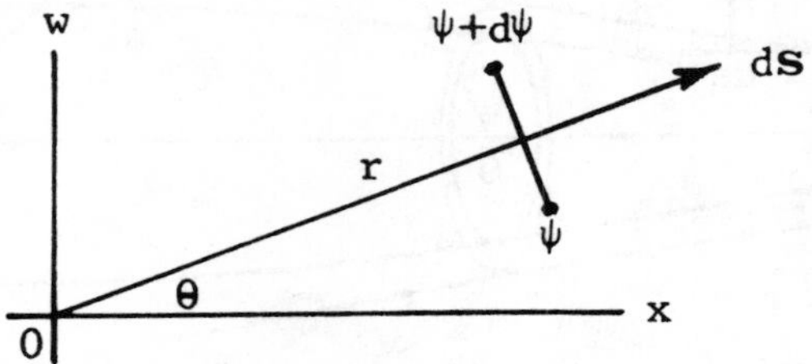

Fig. 25.19. Addition of spherical coordinates.

cylindrical coordinates x and w. If the surface ds extends in the θ direction, $ds = r\,d\theta$, $v_n = v_r$, and

$$v_r = \frac{1}{w}\frac{d\psi}{r\,d\theta} = \frac{1}{r^2 \sin\theta}\frac{\partial\psi}{\partial\theta}. \qquad (25.107)$$

Similarly,

$$v_\theta = -\frac{1}{r\sin\theta}\frac{\partial\psi}{\partial r}. \qquad (25.108)$$

These components of fluid velocity will now be used to calculate the Stokes stream functions of three basic flows.

25.11 Axisymmetric Uniform Flow, Source, and Doublet

For the planar basic flows the velocity potential ϕ was derived from the fluid velocity, and then the stream function ψ was found with the help of the Cauchy-Riemann equations. For the axisymmetric flows, the stream function will be obtained directly from the velocity, and the potential will not be calculated at all. Equations like the Cauchy-Riemann equations will be derived that relate ϕ and ψ, so that ϕ can be obtained if needed.

First, the Stokes stream function of a uniform flow in the x direction will be derived. If the fluid velocity is U,

$$v_x = U = \frac{1}{w}\frac{\partial\psi}{\partial w} \qquad \text{and} \qquad v_w = 0 = -\frac{1}{w}\frac{\partial\psi}{\partial x}. \qquad (25.109)$$

Since ψ is a function of w only,

$$\frac{d\psi}{dw} = U\,w$$

and

$$\psi = \frac{U\,w^2}{2}\,. \tag{25.110}$$

This is the Stokes stream function for a uniform flow in the x direction. Notice that it is not the same as the Lagrange stream function for a uniform flow given by Eq. (25.29).

In an axisymmetric flow a source and a sink are the flows out of and into a point at a constant rate Q m^3/s. Suppose that a source emanates from the origin in Fig. 25.19. Since the fluid flows radially away from the point in all directions, the strength of the source is

$$Q = 4\,\pi\,r^2\,v_r\,, \tag{25.111}$$

where v_r is the radial velocity at radius r. The Stokes stream function of the source is found by substituting Eq. (25.107) into (25.111):

$$Q = 4\,\pi\,r^2\,\frac{1}{r^2\,\sin\,\theta}\,\frac{\partial\psi}{\partial\theta}\,. \tag{25.112}$$

A little thought shows that since the fluid velocity is radial, ψ is a function of θ only. Therefore

$$\frac{d\psi}{d\theta} = \frac{Q\,\sin\,\theta}{4\pi}\,, \tag{25.113}$$

and the Stokes stream function of an axisymmetric source is

$$\psi = -\,\frac{Q\,\cos\,\theta}{4\pi} = -\,\frac{Q\,x}{4\pi r}\,. \tag{25.114}$$

The Stokes stream function of an axisymmetric sink is of course

$$\psi = \frac{Q\,\cos\,\theta}{4\pi}\,. \tag{25.115}$$

An axisymmetric doublet is the flow between a source and a sink of strengths Q and $-Q$, separated by the distance d, when d is reduced to zero while the product Qd is kept constant. In Fig. 25.20 the stream function at point P of the source and sink is

$$\psi = \frac{Q}{4\pi}\,(\cos\,\theta_2 - \cos\,\theta_1) = \frac{Q\,d}{4\pi d}\,(\cos\,\theta_2 - \cos\,\theta_1)\,. \tag{25.116}$$

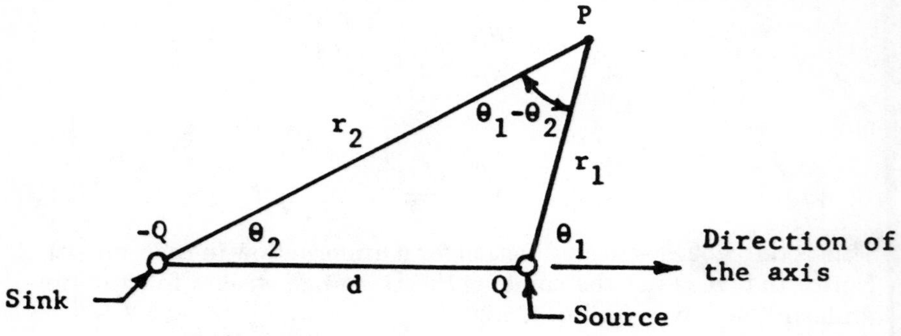

Fig. 25.20. Doublet geometry.

According to the law of sines,

$$\frac{r_1}{\sin \theta_2} = \frac{d}{\sin(\theta_1 - \theta_2)} \tag{25.117}$$

or

$$d = \frac{r_1 \sin(\theta_1 - \theta_2)}{\sin \theta_2} . \tag{25.118}$$

Therefore

$$\psi = \frac{Q\, d(\cos \theta_2 - \cos \theta_1) \sin \theta_2}{4\, \pi\, r_1 \sin(\theta_1 - \theta_2)} . \tag{25.119}$$

Now

$$\cos \theta_2 - \cos \theta_1 = -2 \sin \frac{\theta_2 + \theta_1}{2} \sin \frac{\theta_2 - \theta_1}{2} \tag{25.120}$$

and

$$\sin(\theta_1 - \theta_2) = 2 \sin \frac{\theta_1 - \theta_2}{2} \cos \frac{\theta_1 - \theta_2}{2} . \tag{25.121}$$

Therefore

$$\psi = \frac{Q\, d \sin \dfrac{\theta_1 + \theta_2}{2}}{4\, \pi\, r_1 \cos \dfrac{\theta_1 - \theta_2}{2}} \sin \theta_2 . \tag{25.122}$$

As d approaches zero, r_1 and r_2 approach the same length r, and θ_1 and θ_2 approach the same angle θ. If the dipole moment Qd is held constant,

$$\lim_{d\to 0} \psi = \frac{Q\,d}{4\pi r} \sin^2 \theta \,. \tag{25.123}$$

This is the Stokes stream function of an axisymmetric doublet. As Fig. 25.19 shows,

$$\sin^2 \theta = \frac{w^2}{r^2} \,. \tag{25.124}$$

If the doublet strength Qd is called m, the stream function of the axisymmetric doublet is

$$\psi = \frac{m\,w^2}{4\pi r^3} \,. \tag{25.125}$$

Notice that the Stokes stream functions of a uniform flow, source, and doublet, given by Eqs. (25.110), (25.114), and (25.123) are different from the Lagrange stream functions given by Eqs. (25.29), (25.39), and (25.74).

25.12 Axisymmetric Potential and Stream Functions

For axisymmetric as well as planar flow, the velocity potential ϕ of an irrotational fluid is defined by the relation

$$\mathbf{v} = \nabla\phi \,. \tag{25.126}$$

In the cylindrical coordinates x and w,

$$\nabla\phi = \mathbf{1}_w \frac{\partial\phi}{\partial w} + \mathbf{1}_x \frac{\partial\phi}{\partial x} \,. \tag{25.127}$$

Therefore

$$v_x = \frac{\partial\phi}{\partial x} \qquad \text{and} \qquad v_w = \frac{\partial\phi}{\partial w} \,. \tag{25.128}$$

If the fluid is incompressible, the potential obeys Laplace's equation:

$$\nabla \cdot \mathbf{v} = \nabla^2\phi = \frac{\partial^2\phi}{\partial w^2} + \frac{1}{w}\frac{\partial\phi}{\partial w} + \frac{\partial^2\phi}{\partial x^2} = 0 \,. \tag{25.129}$$

According to Eqs. (25.105) and (25.106),

$$v_x = \frac{1}{w}\frac{\partial\psi}{\partial w} \qquad \text{and} \qquad v_w = -\frac{1}{w}\frac{\partial\psi}{\partial x} \,. \tag{25.130}$$

Therefore

$$\frac{\partial \phi}{\partial x} = \frac{1}{w}\frac{\partial \psi}{\partial w} \qquad \text{and} \qquad \frac{\partial \phi}{\partial w} = -\frac{1}{w}\frac{\partial \psi}{\partial x}. \tag{25.131}$$

Notice that these are not the Cauchy-Riemann equations. The axisymmetric potential and stream functions ϕ and ψ are not conjugate harmonic function, and ψ does not satisfy Laplace's equation. The equation that ψ *does* satisfy is obtained from the knowledge that the fluid is irrotational. In the cylindrical coordinates w, Φ, x,

$$\nabla \times \mathbf{v} = \mathbf{1}_\Phi \left(\frac{\partial v_w}{\partial x} - \frac{\partial v_x}{\partial w} \right) = 0 \tag{25.132}$$

or

$$\frac{\partial v_w}{\partial x} - \frac{\partial v_x}{\partial w} = 0\,. \tag{25.133}$$

Substituting Eqs. (25.130) into this equation produces

$$\frac{\partial^2 \psi}{\partial w^2} - \frac{1}{w}\frac{\partial \psi}{\partial w} + \frac{\partial^2 \psi}{\partial x^2} = 0\,. \tag{25.134}$$

This is like Laplace's equation (25.129) except that the sign of the second term is reversed. Robertson (Ref. 111, page 82) abbreviates this equation as

$$D^2 \psi = 0\,. \tag{25.135}$$

The equations relating the potential and stream functions, and the velocity components for axisymmetric potential flow, are tabulated in Fig. 25.21.

The astute reader will observe that no effort has been made to show that an axisymmetric uniform flow, source, or doublet is a potential flow. The proofs are now simple. First, an axisymmetric uniform flow is identical to a planar uniform flow, which has already been shown to be a potential flow. Second, the only component of the fluid velocity of an axisymmetric source is radial. Eq. (25.111) shows that this component is

$$v_r = \frac{Q}{4\pi r^2}. \tag{25.136}$$

In spherical coordinates the divergence of the radial fluid velocity is simply

$$\nabla \cdot \mathbf{v} = \frac{1}{r^2}\frac{\partial}{\partial r}(r^2 v_r)\,. \tag{25.137}$$

Relations between ϕ and ψ	$\frac{\partial \phi}{\partial x} = \frac{1}{w}\frac{\partial \psi}{\partial w}$
	$\frac{\partial \phi}{\partial w} = -\frac{1}{w}\frac{\partial \psi}{\partial x}$
Velocity components	$v_x = \frac{1}{w}\frac{\partial \psi}{\partial w}$
	$v_w = -\frac{1}{w}\frac{\partial \psi}{\partial x}$
	$v_r = \frac{1}{r^2 \sin\theta}\frac{\partial \psi}{\partial \theta}$
	$v_\theta = -\frac{1}{r \sin\theta}\frac{\partial \psi}{\partial r}$
Laplace's equation for potential	$\nabla^2\phi = \frac{\partial^2 \phi}{\partial w^2} + \frac{1}{w}\frac{\partial \phi}{\partial w} + \frac{\partial^2 \phi}{\partial x^2} = 0$
Equation for stream function	$D^2\psi = \frac{\partial^2 \psi}{\partial w^2} - \frac{1}{w}\frac{\partial \psi}{\partial w} + \frac{\partial^2 \psi}{\partial x^2} = 0$

Fig. 25.21. Summary of equations for axisymmetric potential flow.

For an axisymmetric source, therefore,

$$\nabla^2\phi = \nabla \cdot \mathbf{v} = 0\,, \tag{25.138}$$

which proves that the source is a potential flow. And third, since the sum of two potential flows is a potential flow, and an axisymmetric doublet is the sum of a source and a sink, the doublet is a potential flow.

In an axisymmetric flow, as in a planar flow, surfaces of constant potential and stream function are perpendicular to each other. This can be seen by observing that since $\mathbf{v} = \nabla\phi$, the velocity vector is normal to surfaces of constant ϕ. Since surfaces of constant ψ are stream surfaces, $\mathbf{v}$ is tangent to ψ surfaces. Therefore surfaces of constant ϕ and ψ are orthogonal. The mathematical proof is the same as that for planar flow, except that it uses Eqs. (25.131) instead of the Cauchy-Riemann equations.

Chapter 26

THERMODYNAMICS

26.1 Introduction

Thermodynamics is the study of the mechanical effects of heat. It received much attention in the nineteenth century, first for the design of steam engines, and later for internal-combustion engines, steam and gas turbines, refrigerators, heat pumps, and the analysis of chemical reactions. During that century Carnot, Mayer, Joule, Clausius, Kelvin, Maxwell, Planck, Boltzmann, and Gibbs contributed to the theory. The last two were largely responsible for statistical thermodynamics, which attempts to predict the properties of a fluid by statistical analysis of individual particles. The development of statistical thermodynamics has continued up to the present. This chapter is devoted to the classical theory including the first and second laws of thermodynamics, the mysterious concept of entropy, and applications to steam turbines.

26.2 The First Law

The *first law of thermodynamics* is a statement of the conservation of energy: the energy entering a system, minus the energy leaving, is equal to the change in energy stored in the system. For a *closed system* or *control mass*, namely a system that has no substance flowing into or out of it, the first law is

$$dq - dw = du + d(PE) + d(KE)\ , \tag{26.1}$$

where q is the heat added, w is the work done by the system, u is its internal energy, and PE and KE are its potential and kinetic energies. Each term is energy per unit mass, measured in J/kg. The *internal energy* of a substance is the energy of its particles on a molecular level. It includes the kinetic and potential energy due to the motion of the molecules and the attractive forces between them. When a chemical reaction occurs, the internal energy of the substances changes because the atoms are rearranged within the molecules. In a nuclear reaction, the internal energy changes because the structure of the atoms is changed. Changes in internal energy of the fluid in a heat engine are manifested as changes in temperature and pressure and in boiling and condensing. If the changes in potential and kinetic energy are ignored, Eq. (26.1) becomes

$$dq - dw = du \,. \tag{26.2}$$

This is the first law for *stationary* closed systems. In this equation dw is the work that affects the internal energy but not the motion of the system. For example, if a system consists of the fluid in a cylinder, dw does not include any work required to raise or accelerate the cylinder. Fig. 26.1 shows a typical stationary closed system consisting of the gas in an insulated box. When the weight descends, it turns the propeller and does the work dw on the gas. The gas does the work $-dw$ on the weight. If no heat is added from an external source, $dq = 0$. Eq. (26.2) shows that $-(-dw) = du$ or $dw = du$. The increase in internal energy du is of course apparent in the temperature rise of the gas. If the gas is allowed to cool to its original internal energy, $du = 0$. Then $dq - (-dw) = 0$ or $dw = -dq$. The mechanical work was converted to an equal amount of heat, which left the box.

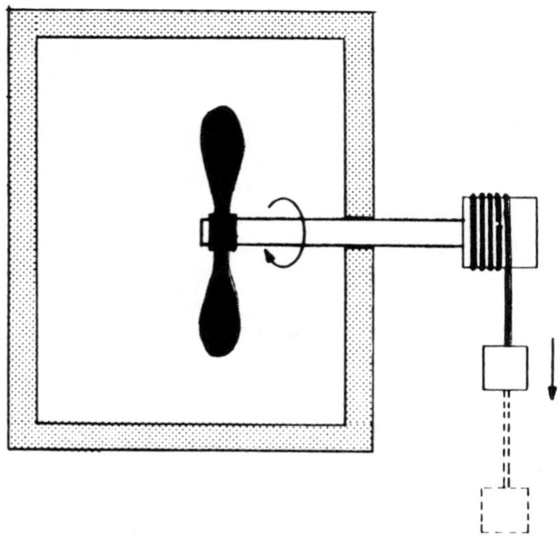

Fig. 26.1. A closed system.

Fig. 26.2 shows another stationary control mass consisting of the gas in a cylinder. As the cylinder moves a differential distance, the gas does the work

$$dw = p\, dv \,, \tag{26.3}$$

where p is the gas pressure (Pa) and v is *specific volume* or volume per unit mass (m^3/kg). The work done by an expanding volume of gas of any shape is given by Eq. (26.3). For the closed system of Fig. 26.2 the first law becomes

$$dq - p\, dv = du \,. \tag{26.4}$$

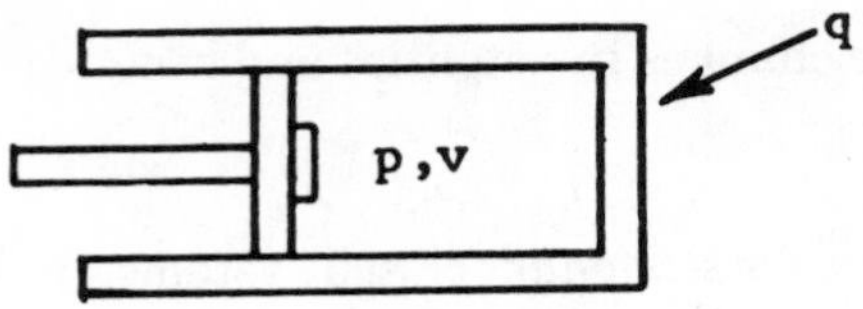

Fig. 26.2. Expanding gas in a cylinder.

Another important example of a control mass is a designated mass of the gas flowing along a duct of changing cross-sectional area. If the work required to change the kinetic and potential energies of the mass is ignored, it obeys the first law for a stationary control mass, Eq. (26.2). If the gas has no viscosity and therefore experiences no frictional drag, none of the work w is required to keep it moving. It does the work $w = p\,dv$ on the surrounding gas when the duct area changes or when it is heated, and obeys Eq. (26.4).

An *open system* or *control volume* is a volume with fixed boundaries across which fluid can flow. Fig. 26.3 shows an open system consisting of the gas in a tank. Fluid enters the tank at elevation z_1, pressure p_1, specific volume v_1, and velocity V_1, thru an inlet pipe of area A_1. Its entering potential and kinetic energies per unit mass are

$$PE = g\,z_1 \qquad \text{and} \qquad KE = V_1^2/2\,. \tag{26.5}$$

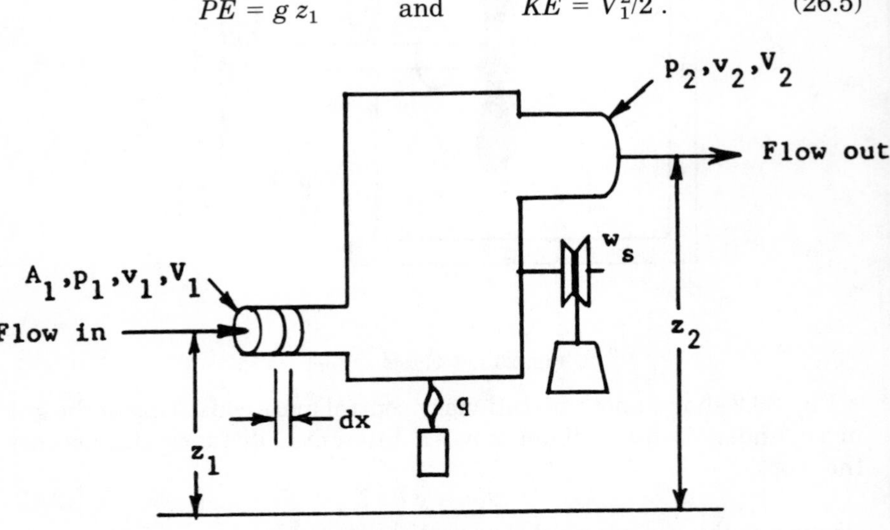

Fig. 26.3. An open system.

The work done on the system when a differential element of fluid of length dx is pushed into the inlet pipe is

$$dW_1 = p_1 A_1 dx \qquad \text{joules} . \tag{26.6}$$

If dm is the mass of the fluid in the length dx, the work per unit mass is

$$w_1 = p_1 A_1 \frac{dx}{dm} \qquad \text{J/kg} . \tag{26.7}$$

But

$$\frac{dm}{dx} = \frac{A_1}{v_1} \qquad \text{kg/m} . \tag{26.8}$$

Therefore

$$w_1 = p_1 v_1 \qquad \text{J/kg} . \tag{26.9}$$

This work is called *flow work*. If the exhaust pressure and specific volume are p_2 and v_2, the flow work done by the system in pushing fluid out of the system is $p_2 v_2$.

The first law for steady-state open systems is used widely in engineering practice. An open system is in steady state if

1. the inlet and outlet values of p, v, V, and z are constant,

2. the states of the fluid at all points in the fluid are either constant or return periodically and simultaneously to their previous values,

3. either the rates at which heat and work cross the boundaries of the system are constant, or the amounts of heat and work in each cycle are constant, and

4. either the rates of fluid flow into and out of the system are constant and equal, or the amounts are equal in succeeding cycles and equal to each other.

If these requirements are met, the sum of the heat q added to the system, external or shaft work w_s done by the system, internal energy u, flow work pv, potential energy gz, and kinetic energy $V^2/2$ is

$$q - w_s + (u_1 + p_1 v_1 + g\, z_1 + V_1^2/2) - (u_2 + p_2 v_2 + g\, z_2 + V_2^2/2) = 0 . \tag{26.10}$$

This is the first law for steady-state open systems, or the *energy equation of steady flow*. It expresses the energies of the fluid in a steam or gas turbine, or in a reciprocating steam engine or pump. A useful sum that is frequently used in calculations in *enthalpy* (the accent is on either the first or the second syllable), defined as

$$h = u + pv . \tag{26.11}$$

With enthalpy included, the steady-flow equation becomes

$$q - w_s = h_2 - h_1 + g(z_2 - z_1) + \frac{1}{2}(V_2^2 - V_1^2)\,. \qquad (26.12)$$

As an example of the use of the steady-flow equation, consider the energy in a steam power plant. Water at state 1 is heated, boiled, and superheated in the boiler to state 2. Normally the changes in potential and kinetic energy of the water between the boiler inlet and outlet are negligible compared to the change in enthalpy. The heat added in the boiler is therefore

$$q = h_2 - h_1 \qquad \text{J/kg}\,. \qquad (26.13)$$

When the steam passes thru the turbine from state 2 to state 3, little heat is lost thru the turbine shell to the atmosphere. Again, the differences between the initial and final potential and kinetic energies are negligible. The shaft work produced by the turbine is

$$w_s = h_2 - h_3\,. \qquad (26.14)$$

In general, the various components of heat and work in a heat engine can be calculated conveniently with the aid of the steady-flow energy equation, in terms of enthalpy. Tables of the enthalpy of steam will be presented and used later in the chapter.

Another interesting open system is the stream line leading to a thermocouple in an insulated pipe carrying gas, shown in Fig. 26.4. The

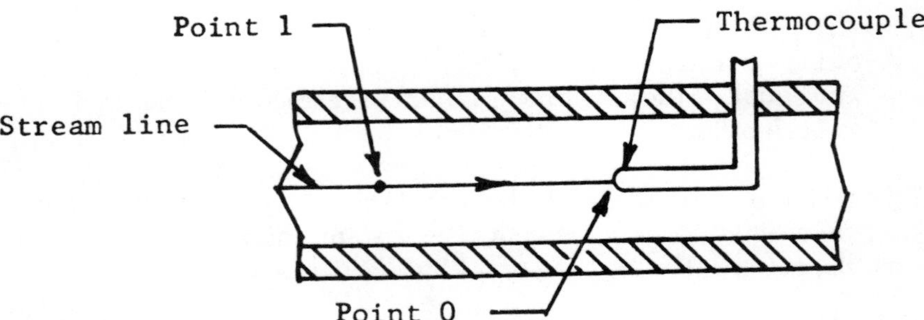

Fig. 26.4. Thermocouple in an insulated pipe.

inlet is any point 1 along the stream line, at which the velocity and enthalpy of the gas are V and h. The outlet is a stagnation point 0 at the thermocouple, where the velocity is zero. From that point the gas drifts laterally into the moving stream and flows out of the system. No shaft work w_s is done by the gas between points 1 and 0. If the heat lost to the surrounding gas is neglected, Eq. (26.12) becomes

$$h_o = h + \frac{1}{2} V^2 , \qquad (26.15)$$

where h_o is the *total* or *stagnation* enthalpy of the gas, namely the enthalpy obtained by bringing the gas to rest without adding or subtracting heat or mechanical work.

As a final example of the use of the steady-flow energy equation, consider the steady flow of a nonviscous, incompressible fluid along a pipe of varying cross section and elevation. No heat is added or removed from the pipe, and the fluid does no shaft work. Water and lightweight oil flowing in pipes of moderate length fulfill these requirements. Since q and w_s are zero, Eq. (26.10) becomes

$$u + pv + gz + V^2/2 = \text{constant} . \qquad (26.16)$$

Now a nonviscous fluid flowing in a duct obeys Eq. (26.4), namely

$$dq - p\, dv = du . \qquad (26.17)$$

Since the fluid is incompressible, $dv = 0$. Since dq is zero also, Eq. (26.17) shows that $du = 0$. The internal energy remains constant. Eq. (26.16) becomes

$$pv + gz + V^2/2 = \text{constant} . \qquad (26.18)$$

The specific volume of the fluid v, in m^3/kg, is the reciprocal of the density ρ, in kg/m^3. Eq. (26.18) can be written in the form

$$p/\rho + gz + V^2/2 = \text{constant} . \qquad (26.19)$$

This is the familiar *Bernoulli equation for steady flow*, that was derived in section 24.7 by simplifying the Navier-Stokes equation.

26.3 Reversible Processes

A process is called *reversible* if the system and its environment can be completely restored to their initial state after the process has occurred. The swing of a frictionless pendulum is reversible, because when the pendulum completes the swing, its potential and kinetic energies return to their original values. Real or natural processes are irreversible, because friction, windage, or electrical resistance is always present. A few irreversible processes are

1. flow of current thru a resistor

2. compression of a spring

3. flow of a fluid in a pipe

4. motion of a car, even in neutral

5. any chemical reaction

6. mixing of hot and cold water

7. mixing gin and vermouth.

As an example of a chemical reaction, consider the burning of hydrogen to form water. If the heat produced by the reaction could be completely converted to electrical energy, and if the electric current could be conducted without loss to electrodes in the water tank, etc., the hydrogen and its original environment could be restored. The "if's" of course cannot be accomplished.

Thermodynamic reversible processes are used to measure the efficiency of real processes. An example is a *reversible isothermal expansion*, illustrated by Fig. 26.5. Heat flows from a source at absolute temperature T_1, thru a perfectly conducting cover into the fluid in a perfectly insulated cylinder at temperature T_0. While T_0 is kept in-

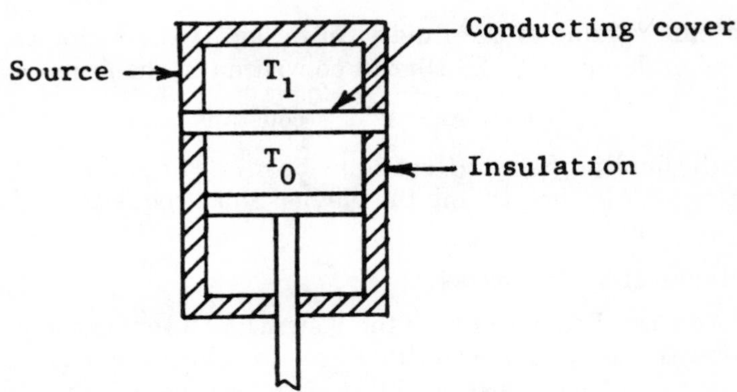

Fig. 26.5. A reversible isothermal expansion.

finitesimally lower than T_1, so that heat flows into the cylinder, the piston is lowered. The piston is frictionless, and moves so slowly that at any part of the stroke the gas is at equilibrium, i.e., its properties are uniform throughout. This is a reversible isothermal expansion. When it is reversed, with T_0 infinitesimally higher than T_1, the heat flows back to the source. When the piston is back to its original position, the fluid pressure, specific volume, and enthalpy have returned to their original values, and no net work was needed from the environment.

Another example is a *reversible adiabatic expansion.* "Adiabatic" (Greek *adiabatos*, impassable) means "occurring without the addition or removal of heat." Replace the conducting cover in Fig. 26.5 with a perfectly insulating cover, and allow the fluid to expand from temperature T_1 down to T_2 with no friction, turbulence, or temporary storage of heat in the cylinder wall. The last requirement is neccesary so that the fluid will not store heat in the wall when it is warmer than the wall, and reclaim the heat when it is cooler than the wall. This adiabatic expansion is reversible. When the piston is returned under the same ideal conditions to its original position, no net work is required and the original fluid conditions are restored. Reversible constant-pressure and constant-volume processes can also be described, with similar requirements of no friction or turbulence and only a differential temperature drop across the conducting cover.

26.4 The Carnot Cycle

A heat engine is a device that receives heat at high temperatures, does work, and rejects heat at low temperatures. N.L.S. Carnot (1795-1832) invented a cycle of four reversible processes that describe the most efficient heat engine possible. This cycle is used as a measure of the relative efficiency of real engines operating between the same inlet and exhaust temperatures. The four processes are shown in Fig. 26.6, and their pressure-volume diagram in Fig. 26.7A.

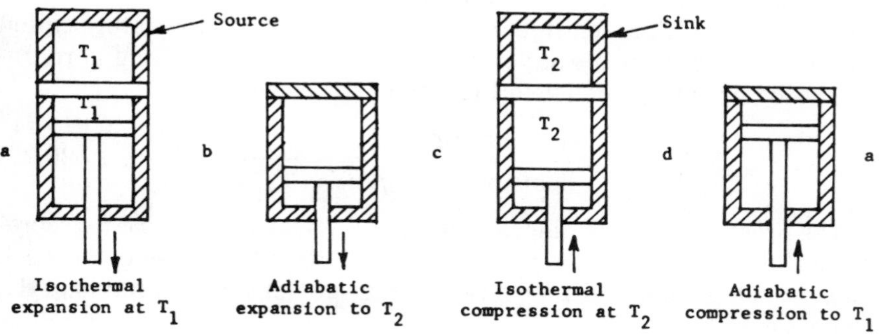

Fig. 26.6. Carnot cycle.

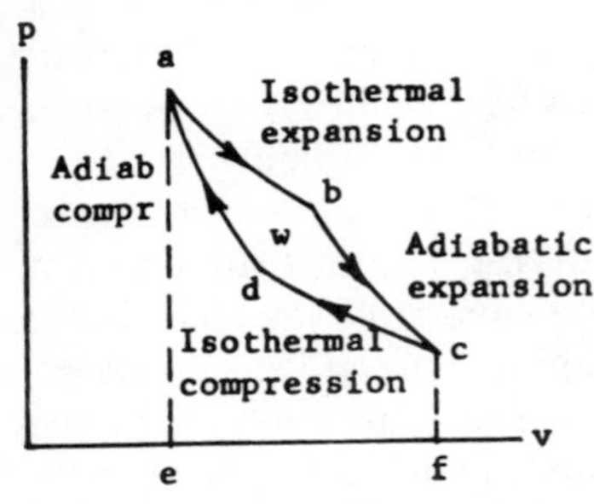

A. Pressure-volume diagram

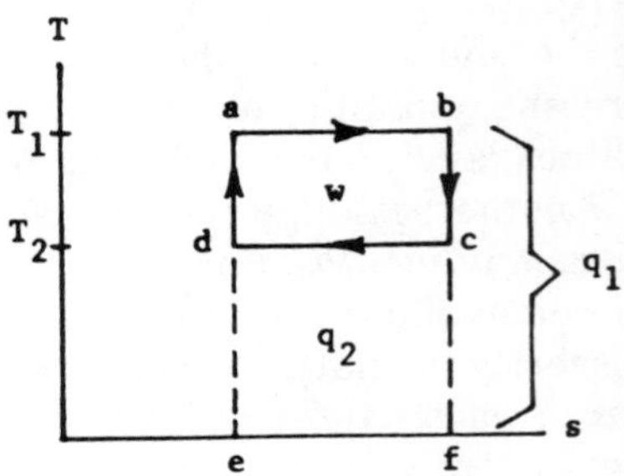

B. Temperature-entropy diagram

Fig. 26.7. Diagrams of the Carnot cycle.

For calculation of the efficiency of the Carnot cycle, a property of the fluid called *entropy* is needed. For a reversible process, a differential change in the entropy s is defined as

$$ds = \frac{dq}{T} \tag{26.20}$$

or

$$Q = \int T\, ds\ , \tag{26.21}$$

where dq is the heat added and T is the absolute temperature. The temperature-entropy diagram of the Carnot cycle is shown in Fig. 26.7B. During the reversible isothermal expansion the heat $a\ b\ f\ e$ or q_1 is added to the fluid. During the reversible adiabatic expansion no heat is added to the fluid, and the entropy remains constant. During the reversible isothermal compression the heat $c\ d\ e\ f$ or q_2 is rejected to the sink. During the reversible adiabatic compression the entropy remains constant again. A reversible adiabatic process is appropriately called *isentropic*. The work output $w = q_1 - q_2$ of the Carnot cycle is represented by area $a\ b\ c\ d$. The efficiency of the cycle is

$$\eta = \frac{\text{work output}}{\text{heat input}} = \frac{w}{q_1} = \frac{T_1 - T_2}{T_1}\ . \tag{26.22}$$

In the pressure-volume diagram of Fig. 26.7A, the area $a\ b\ c\ f\ e$ represents the work done *by* the piston, the area $c\ d\ a\ e\ f$ represents the work done *on* the piston, and $a\ b\ c\ d$ represents the net work output w of the Carnot cycle.

If the Carnot engine is reversed, the compression strokes become expansions and vice versa, the arrowheads in Figs. 26.6 and 26.7 reverse direction, and the engine becomes a refrigerator or air conditioner. For the latter, the sink is the cool inside of the house, and the source is the warm outside. The air conditioner removes the heat q_2 from inside, adds the work w, and pumps their sum q_1 outside. A good air conditioner removes much heat and requires little energy. It is therefore judged by its *coefficient of performance*, which for a Carnot air conditioner or refrigerator is

$$\text{Cooling } COP = \frac{q_2}{w} = \frac{T_2}{T_1 - T_2} . \tag{26.23}$$

A heat pump, like a refrigerator, removes heat at a low temperature (outdoors) and pumps it to a high temperature (indoors). A Carnot heat pump has the same cycle as a Carnot refrigerator. Since its purpose is to pump as much heat as possible into the high-temperature indoors, its measure of performance is

$$\text{Heating } COP = \frac{q_1}{w} = \frac{T_1}{T_1 - T_2} , \tag{26.24}$$

which is the reciprocal of the engine efficiency given by Eq. (26.22). An electric heater converts the electric energy w into the indoor heat q_1. Considered as a heat pump, it has a heating *COP* of unity. A Carnot heat pump, taking heat from outdoors at 0°C or 273 K and delivering it indoors at 293 K, achieves the spectacular

$$\text{Heating } COP = \frac{T_1}{T_1 - T_2} = \frac{293}{20} = 14.65 . \tag{26.25}$$

A real heat pump, such as the General Electric Weathertron, achieves a relatively modest heating *COP* between 2 and 3, and still offers an economic advantage over straight electric heating.

26.5 The Second Law

Your ordinary perpetual-motion machine produces work without requiring any input of energy or material. In the early days of the industrial revolution, it also produced a separation of credulous investors from their money. According to the first law for closed systems, such a machine cannot exist. A *perpetual-motion machine of the second kind* takes heat from a reservoir at some fixed temperature and delivers an equal amount of work. This machine would be even more useful than an ordinary perpetual-motion machine. If the reservoir were the inside of a refrigerator, the machine could keep the food cold and also provide energy for the rest of the house. The *second law of thermodynamics* states that a perpetual-motion machine of the second kind cannot be built. Specifically, the *Kelvin-Planck statement* of the second law is

> *It is impossible to construct a cyclic engine that will absorb heat from a single reservoir and produce an equal amount of work.*

The second law, like the first, is a postulate that has been proved only by the failure of all efforts to disprove it. A second and equivalent statement of the second law is the *Clausius statement*:

> *It is impossible to construct a cyclic engine whose only effect is to transfer heat from one reservoir to another at a higher temperature.*

This statement guarantees that a refrigerator needs a motor. The Kelvin-Planck and Clausius statements are equivalent. The proof consists of showing that if it were possible to violate one statement of the law, the other could be violated also. A violation of the Kelvin-Planck statement is shown in Fig. 26.8A. The engine on the left receives the heat q_1 from a single reservoir at temperature T_1 and produces the work $w = q_1$. This work is used to drive the refrigerator on the right. If the refrigerator works at all, its cooling *COP* is greater than zero. It pumps a little heat q_2 from the lower reservoir (such as the inside of a refrigerator) at the lower temperature T_2, adds the mechanical work $w = q_1$, and delivers the sum $q_1 + q_2$ to the upper reservoir (such as the kitchen). The two machines working together pump the heat q_2 from the low to the high-temperature reservoir without requiring any external work. They therefore violate the Clausius statement.

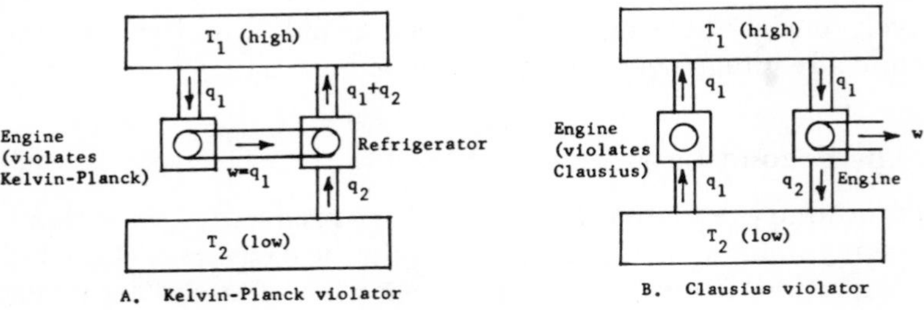

Fig. 26.8. Equivalence of the Kelvin-Planck and Clausius statements.

Fig. 26.8B shows the converse situation. The engine on the left pumps the heat q_1 between the low and high-temperature reservoirs and requires no external source of energy. This heat pump violates the Clausius statement. The engine on the right is designed to take the heat q_1 from the upper reservoir. It does the work w and rejects the heat

$q_2 = q_1 - w$ to the lower reservoir. The upper reservoir is unaffected by the heat transfer, and can be replaced by a pipe between the two engines. The two engines working together therefore absorb the heat $q_1 - q_2 = w$ from the remaining reservoir, do the external work w, and therefore violate the Kelvin-Planck statement.

It is interesting to digress and philosophize about this proof. The equivalence of the two statements of the second law is a special case of this more general proposition: *The statements "A is impossible" and "B is impossible" are equivalent.* The proposition is proved by proving that

1. If A is possible, B is possible.

2. If B is possible, A is possible.

Another example of the general proposition is: *The statements "I can't lift this weight" and "you can't lift this weight" are equivalent.* If the two steps of the proof are true, you and I obviously have the same strength. In this and nearly every example that comes to mind, the two steps of the proof not only prove the proposition, but also show *why* the two statements are equivalent. An exception is the proof for the Kelvin-Planck and Clausius statements. Since they are both postulates, the proof does not indicate a more fundamental reason for why they are equivalent.

26.6 Corollaries of the Second Law

The second law has several corollaries whose proofs contribute to an understanding of thermodynamics. Consider a reversible engine, namely one whose cycle consists of reversible processes, such as a Carnot engine. The *first corollary* states that *a reversible engine has the highest possible efficiency for engines operating between the same two temperatures.* To prove it, observe first that if an engine receives the heat q_1, rejects the heat q_2, and does the work $w = q_1 - q_2$, its efficiency is

$$\eta = \frac{w}{q_1}. \tag{26.26}$$

If the engine is reversible, its cycle can be reversed to make it a refrigerator that receives the same heat q_2, adds the same work w, and rejects the heat $q_1 = q_2 + w$. Fig. 26.9 shows a reversible engine R being driven as a refrigerator by a real or irreversible engine I, that is assumed to be more efficient than the reversible engine. Then

$$\frac{w}{q_3} > \frac{w}{q_1}, \qquad \text{or} \qquad q_1 > q_3 . \tag{26.27}$$

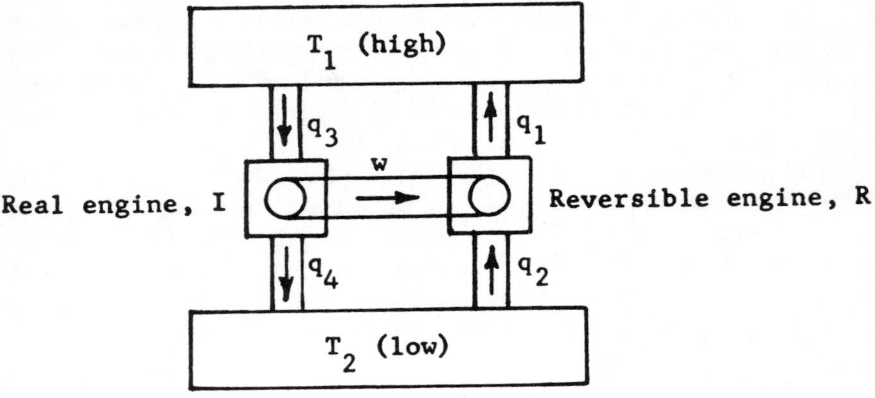

Fig. 26.9. Test of engine efficiency.

Since

$$q_4 = q_3 - w \qquad \text{and} \qquad q_2 = q_1 - w \,, \tag{26.28}$$

$$q_2 > q_4 \,. \tag{26.29}$$

The two engines working together extract the heat $q_2 - q_4$ from the low-temperature reservoir, and deliver the equal amount $q_1 - q_3$ to the high-temperature reservoir. They therefore violate the Clausius statement of the second law. If the real engine is less efficient than the reversible engine, the three inequality signs above are reversed. Then heat flows from the high to the low-temperature reservoir, as in nature. The conclusion is that no heat engine is more efficient than a reversible engine operating between the same two temperatures.

Beside the Carnot cycle there are other reversible cycles consisting of reversible processes. One is the ideal cycle for the Stirling engine, consisting of two isothermal and two constant-volume processes, shown in Fig. 26.10. Another is the ideal cycle for the Ericsson engine, consisting of two isothermal and two constant-pressure processes, shown in Fig. 26.11. Suppose that two reversible engines with different cycles are put in the test stand of Fig. 26.9. If the engine on the left is more efficient than the one on the right, the system pumps heat and violates the second law. If the engine on the right is more efficient, interchange them, and the system still violates the second law. The conclusion is the *second corollary* of the second law: *all reversible engines have the same efficiency when working between the same two temperatures*, namely

$$\eta = \frac{T_1 - T_2}{T_1} \,. \tag{26.30}$$

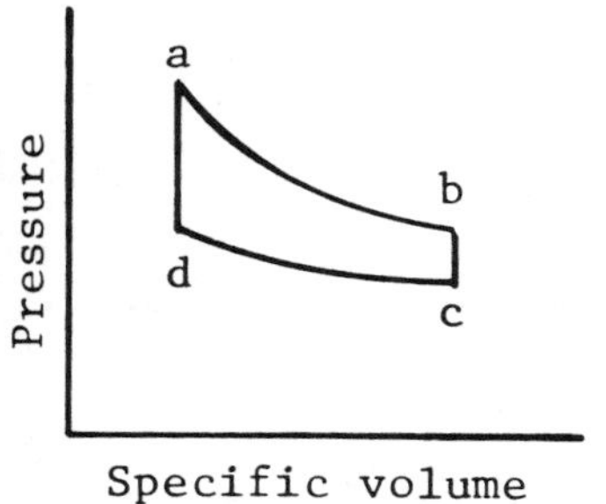

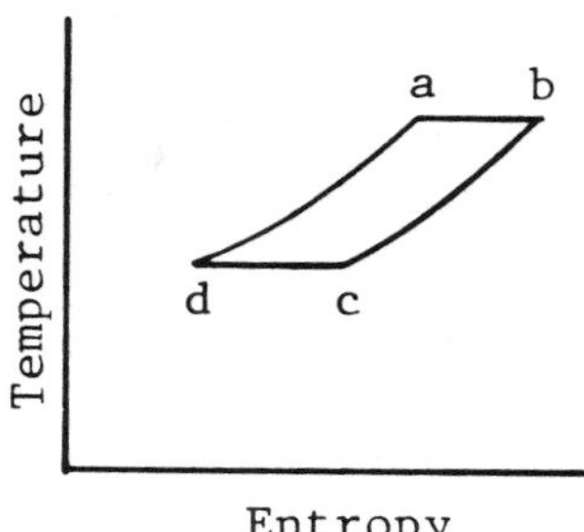

Fig. 26.10. Ideal cycle of the Stirling engine.

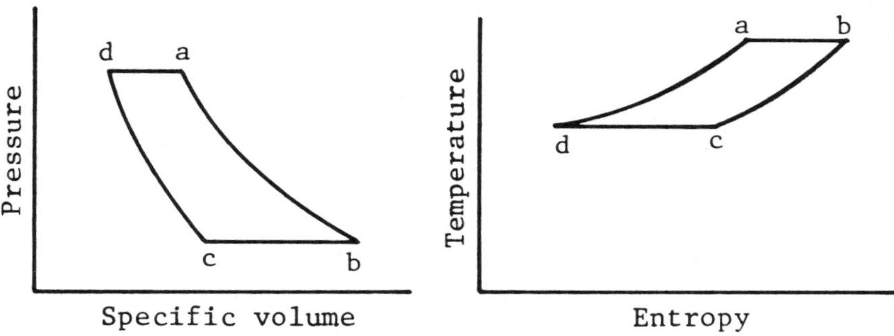

Fig. 26.11. Ideal cycle of the Ericsson engine.

Until now, all of the engines considered receive heat at one constant temperature T_1 and reject heat at another constant temperature T_2. In most real engines such as internal-combustion engines, and in the boiler of a steam turbine, the temperature of the fluid varies while heat is being received or rejected. Let dq be the amount of heat received by the engine at temperature T. The *third corollary* of the second law states that *when a system executes a complete cycle of processes, the integral of dq/T around the cycle is negative, or in the limit, zero.* It can be proved with the help of Fig. 26.12. During one cycle an engine receives heat from two reservoirs, first the heat q_1 at temperature T_1, and then q_2 at temperature T_2. The engine does the work w_0 and rejects the heat $-q_0$ into a lower-temperature reservoir at T_0. The arrow representing q_0 points upward, so that a positive value of q_0 represents heat flow out of the reservoir. Two reversible Carnot refrigerators R are connected between the reservoirs, to restore the heat removed from the upper two reservoirs. The upper reservoirs could be replaced by pipes. Together with the three machines, they constitute a system that receives the heat $q_0 + q_{01} + q_{02}$ from the lower reservoir and does the equivalent

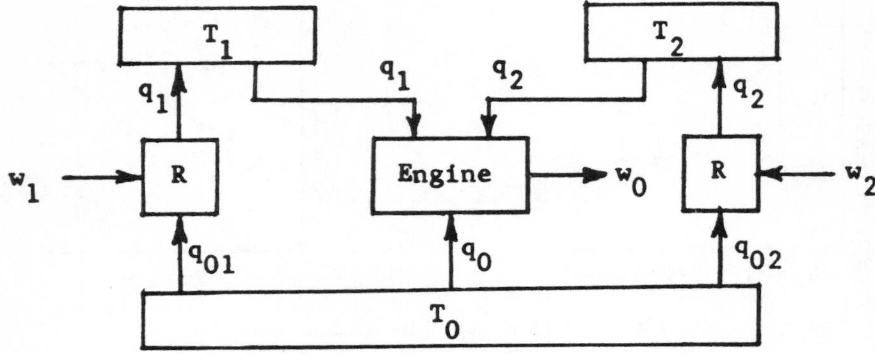

Fig. 26.12. Proof of the Clausius inequality.

amount of work $w_0 - w_1 - w_2$. Clearly the system violates the Kelvin-Planck statement of the second law unless both the heat and the work are negative or zero. A system can *receive* work and *give* an equivalent amount of heat to a single reservoir. The system in Fig. 26.1 is an example. If the system in Fig. 26.12 is real,

$$q_0 + q_{01} + q_{02} \leqslant 0\,. \tag{26.31}$$

The engine efficiencies of the two Carnot refrigerators are

$$\frac{q_1 - q_{01}}{q_1} = \frac{T_1 - T_0}{T_1} \quad \text{and} \quad \frac{q_2 - q_{02}}{q_2} = \frac{T_2 - T_0}{T_2}\,. \tag{26.32}$$

Therefore

$$q_{01} = T_0\left(\frac{q_1}{T_1}\right) \quad \text{and} \quad q_{02} = T_0\left(\frac{q_2}{T_2}\right)\,. \tag{26.33}$$

Inequality (26.31) becomes

$$q_0 + T_0\left(\frac{q_1}{T_1}\right) + T_0\left(\frac{q_2}{T_2}\right) \leqslant 0 \tag{26.34}$$

or

$$\frac{q_0}{T_0} + \frac{q_1}{T_1} + \frac{q_2}{T_2} \leqslant 0\,. \tag{26.35}$$

This result shows that the algebraic sum of the heats received by the engine during one cycle, divided by the temperatures at which they are received, is nonpositive. The number of reservoirs and Carnot refrigerators can be made arbitrarily large. If each reservoir in turn delivers the heat dq to the engine at temperature T, inequality (26.35) becomes

$$\oint \frac{dq}{T} \leqslant 0\,. \tag{26.36}$$

The closed line integral indicates summation around a closed cycle of the engine. Alternatively, the differential amounts of heat can be delivered or removed by one or two reservoirs whose temperatures T vary with time. Fig. 26.13, for example, shows the ideal cycle of the Otto engine, the ordinary four-stroke-cycle gasoline engine. Heat is delivered to the engine by the burning gasoline along the constant-volume line *bc*, and rejected out thru the exhaust valve along the constant-volume line *da*. Inequality (26.36) is called the *inequality of Clausius*.

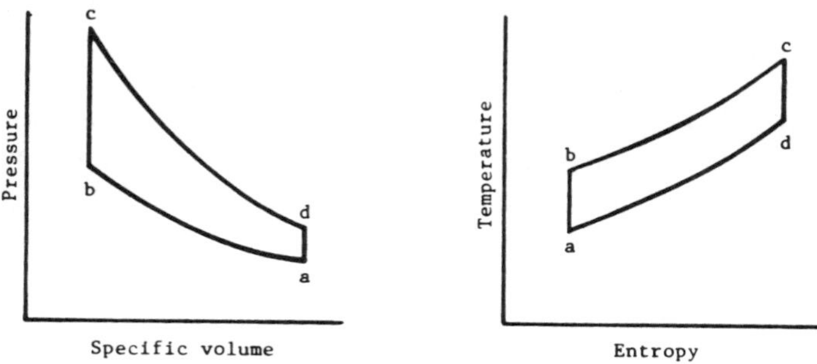

Fig. 26.13. Ideal cycle of the Otto engine.

The Clausius inequality can be verified by a numerical example. Suppose that a heat engine operates between reservoirs at 500 K and 300 K, with an efficiency of 30 percent. During one cycle the engine receives 1000 joules at 500 K, does 300 J of work, and exhausts 700 J at 300 K. Then

$$\oint \frac{dq}{T} = \frac{1000}{500} - \frac{700}{300} = -0.33 \qquad \text{J/K}\,, \tag{26.37}$$

which is a negative number. A Carnot engine operating between the same two temperatures has an efficiency of 40 percent. If it receives 1000 J, it rejects 600 J, and

$$\oint \frac{dq}{T} = \frac{1000}{500} - \frac{600}{300} = 0\,. \tag{26.38}$$

This result can be generalized. If the engine in Fig. 26.12 is reversible, its cycle can be reversed to make it a refrigerator with the same components of heat and work. The two Carnot refrigerators can be reversed and run as engines. Then all of the components of heat and work reverse in sign and stay the same in magnitude, and

$$\frac{q_0}{T_0} + \frac{q_1}{T_1} + \frac{q_2}{T_2} \geqslant 0 \tag{26.39}$$

and Ineq. (26.36) becomes

$$\oint \frac{dq}{T} \geqslant 0 . \qquad (26.40)$$

Inequalities (26.40) and (26.36) can both be true only if

$$\oint \frac{dq}{T} = 0 . \qquad (26.41)$$

This result is the *fourth corollary* of the second law: *the integral of dq/T around a reversible cycle is zero.*

Two more corollaries remain to be proved. The pressure-volume diagram of some reversible cycle is shown in Fig. 26.14. According to Eq. (26.41), if the upper path from state 1 to state 2 is A and the lower path is B,

$$\int_A \frac{dq}{T} - \int_B \frac{dq}{T} = 0 \qquad (26.42)$$

or

$$\int_A \frac{dq}{T} = \int_B \frac{dq}{T} \quad . \qquad (26.43)$$

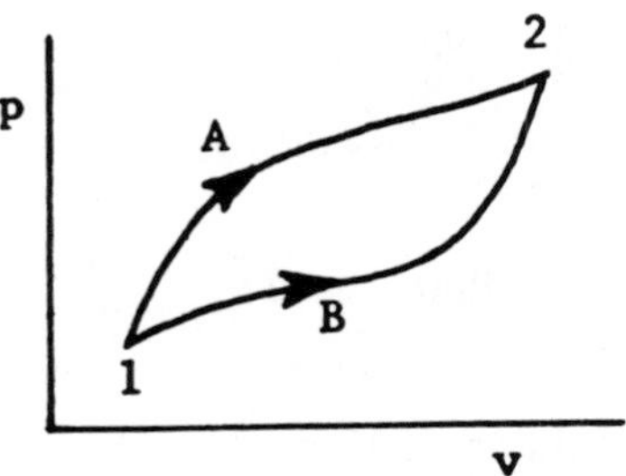

Fig. 26.14. A reversible cycle.

The integral is the same along path A or B, or along any reversible path between the two states. The quantity dq/T is an exact differential of a function s, because along any reversible path between the two states,

$$\int_1^2 \frac{dq}{T} = \int_1^2 ds = s_2 - s_1 . \qquad (26.44)$$

The quantity s is called *entropy*. When a reference state 1 is arbitrarily chosen with zero entropy, a value of s can be calculated for every other state 2, by integrating between them with any convenient reversible processes. Entropy, like pressure or temperature, is therefore a property of the system. Lines of constant entropy could be added in Fig. 26.14 for convenience in solving problems. Notice that entropy on a pressure-volume or temperature-pressure diagram is analogous to a scalar potential in space. The potential has a unique value at every point in space. Entropy has a unique value at every point on the *p-v* diagram, i.e., at every state of the system.

The *fifth corollary* of the second law has now been proved: *the integral of dq/T for a reversible process between a reference state 1 and another state 2 is a property of the system in state 2, namely its entropy.*

26.7 The Principle of the Increase of Entropy

The sixth and final corollary, namely the principle of the increase of entropy, can now be proved. Fig. 26.15 is a property diagram of a system, whose coordinates are any two properties that define the state of the system, such as pressure and specific volume, or enthalpy and entropy. The dotted line is the path of a natural or irreversible process of the system between two equilibrium states 1 and 2. The dotted line only approximates a locus of states, because during a natural process the fluid in a system is turbulent, the parts are unequally heated, etc., and the system does not have a unique state. The system is insulated from its surroundings so that no heat can enter or leave. Therefore during the natural process,

$$\int_{1N}^{2} \frac{dq}{T} = 0 . \tag{26.45}$$

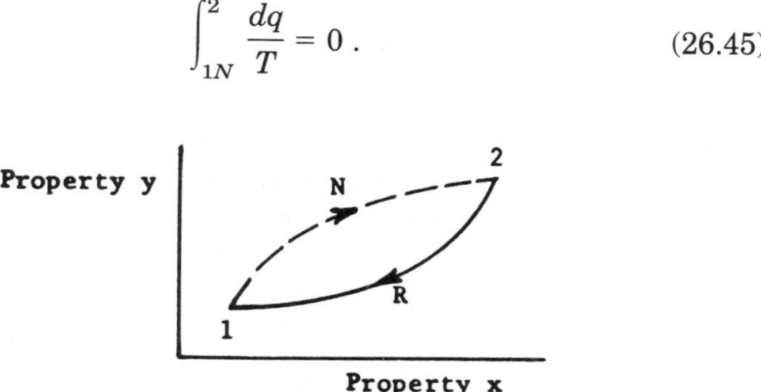

Fig. 26.15. Reversible and natural processes.

The solid line represents a reversible process by which the system is returned to state 1. During this process the insulation is removed. The system can exchange heat and work with outside sources, like the fluid in a Carnot engine. The two processes constitute a complete cycle. It is irreversible, because one of the processes is irreversible. According to the inequality of Clausius (26.36),

$$\int_{1N}^{2} \frac{dq}{T} + \int_{2R}^{1} \frac{dq}{T} < 0\,. \tag{26.46}$$

Therefore

$$\int_{2R}^{1} \frac{dq}{T} < 0 \tag{26.47}$$

and according to Eq. (26.44),

$$s_1 - s_2 < 0 \qquad \text{or} \qquad s_2 > s_1\,. \tag{26.48}$$

The entropy of the system in state 2, reached by an arbitrary natural process, is higher than in state 1. The conclusion is that the entropy of an adiabatic system increases in every natural process. An *isolated system* is a system that is adiabatic, and in addition cannot exchange work with its surroundings. A less general but more popular statement of the conclusion is the *sixth corollary: the entropy of an isolated system increases in every natural process*. This conclusion leads to several others with interesting philosophical implications:

1. Entropy cannot be destroyed, but it can be created.

2. The entropy of the universe is continually increasing.

3. An isolated system cannot move to a state of lower entropy. This knowledge helps a chemist to decide whether a proposed chemical reaction will occur or not. If the reaction would result in a decrease in entropy, it cannot occur.

An example will show how the change in entropy during a natural process can be calculated. Fig. 26.16 shows a system consisting of two perfectly insulated tanks, each containing 1 kg of water, at temperatures 273 K and 373 K. When they are brought together, and their adjacent walls are replaced by a conducting sheet, the water in both tanks eventually reaches equilibrium at 323 K. Notice that the final

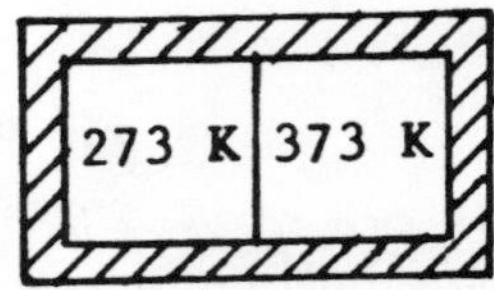

Fig. 26.16. Cooling and heating of water.

state would be the same if the conducting sheet were not used, and the two bodies of water were allowed to mix. The sheet is used, however, so that the two bodies can be identified throughout the process. What is the change in entropy of the system during this irreversible process? Since entropy is a property of the system, and its change can be calculated by Eq. (26.44) for any reversible path between the states, the change can be calculated by devising a convenient reversible path. Let a subsystem consist of the water in the left tank. The water can be heated reversibly by placing it in contact with a heat source that is infinitesimally warmer than 273 K. If the specific heat of the water is the constant c, the heat

$$dq = c\,dT \tag{26.49}$$

will be added. Since the process is reversible, the increase in entropy is

$$ds = \frac{dq}{T} = c\frac{dT}{T}. \tag{26.50}$$

Replace the source with another that is dT warmer than the first. Continue the process, using an infinite number of sources, until the water temperature reaches 323 K. Since the specific heat of water is 4186 J/kg·K, the total increase in entropy of the subsystem is

$$s_2 - s_1 = \int_{T_1}^{T_2} c\frac{dT}{T} = c\ln\frac{T_2}{T_1} = 4186\ln\frac{323}{273} = 704\text{ J/kg·K}. \tag{26.51}$$

A second subsystem consists of the water in the right tank. Its entropy increase, when it is cooled from 373 to 323 K by an infinite sequence of heat sinks, is

$$s_2 - s_1 = 4186\ln\frac{323}{373} = -602\text{ J/kg·K}. \tag{26.52}$$

The increase in entropy of the entire system is

$$704 - 602 = 102\text{ J/K}, \tag{26.53}$$

which verifies the principle of the increase of entropy.

Since the change in entropy of the water is the same for the natural and the reversible processes of equalizing the temperatures, it might seem unnecessary to make a distinction. There is an important difference, however. In the natural process, the two kilograms of water constitute an isolated system whose entropy increases by 51 J/kg·K, or a total of 102 J/K. Since no other body is involved, the entropy of the *universe* increases by 102 J/K. In the reversible process, each change of entropy of the water of dq/T is accompanied by a change of $-dq/T$ in the entropy of a heat source or sink. Although the total change in entropy of the water, 102 J/K, is the same as in the natural process, the change in entropy of the universe is *zero*. The entropy of an isolated system consisting of the two water tanks and the heat reservoirs does not change. The principle of the increase of entropy is not violated, because the process that occurred within the system was reversible.

The term "irreversible" is misleading, because an irreversible process can be reversed! After the two tanks of water have reached 323 K by natural heat conduction thru the sheet, they can be separated, and one heated and one cooled back to their original temperatures. But at what price? If the right tank is heated reversibly back to 373 K by the infinite sequence of heat sources, its entropy increases by

$$4186 \ln \frac{373}{323} = 602 \text{ J/kg·K} , \tag{26.54}$$

and the entropy of the heat sources decreases by the same amount. When the left tank is cooled to 273 K by the heat sinks, its entropy increases by

$$4186 \ln \frac{273}{323} = -704 \text{ J/kg·K} , \tag{26.55}$$

and the entropy of the sinks increases by +704 J/kg·K. The total entropy of the water has been reduced by 51 J/kg·K or 102 J/K, and is back at the value it had before the initial mixing. The irreversible process has been reversed. The entropy of the heat reservoirs, however, has been increased by 102 J/K. While the increase in entropy of the water has been eliminated, the increase has just been passed along to the reservoirs. The isolated system being considered must include the reservoirs. In the cycle of mixing and separating the heats in the water, the first process was natural. The result was an increase in the entropy of the system, as foretold by the principle of the increase of entropy. The fundamental significance of reversibility is now apparent: *a reversible process is one that does not increase the entropy of the universe.*

26.8 More About Natural Processes

Before the two tanks of water were joined an opportunity to run a heat engine existed. An engine could have been constructed that would receive heat from the hot water, reject heat to the cold water, and do useful work. After the heats of the two tanks were mixed, the water constituted a single reservoir, which according to the Kelvin-Planck statement of the second law is unable to operate a heat engine. Although the mixing produced an increase in entropy and no change in energy, it also produced a loss of *opportunity*, namely the opportunity to convert heat to mechanical work. Any natural process within a heat engine reduces this opportunity and lowers the efficiency. A second example is provided by an engine that works like a Carnot engine except that its strokes are natural instead of reversible. The *T-s* diagram of this engine and an ideal Carnot engine whose cycle begins at the same state *a* are shown in Fig. 26.17. Consider first the isothermal expansions *a b*, during which the pistons descend the same distance and draw heat from a reservoir. In the ideal engine the reservoir is at the same temperature as the fluid in the cylinder, T_2. Because the process is reversible, the increase in entropy of the fluid is

$$s_2 - s_1 = \int \frac{dq}{T_2} = \frac{q_1}{T_2}, \tag{26.56}$$

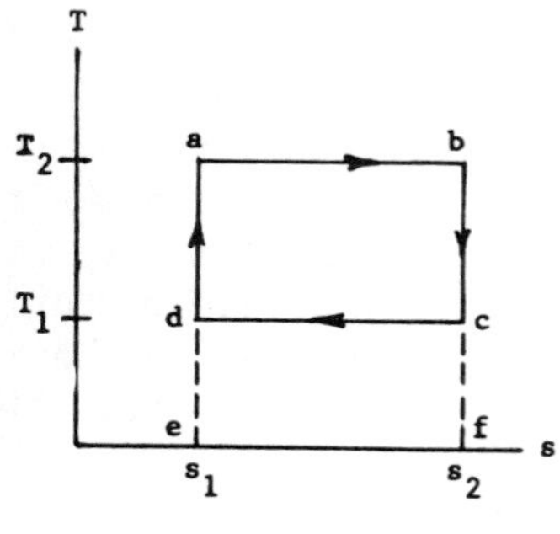

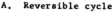

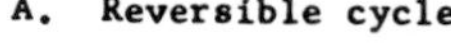
A. Reversible cycle

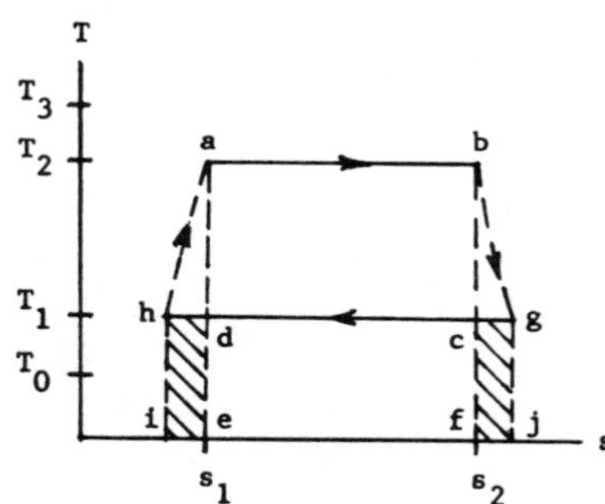

B. Natural cycle

Fig. 26.17. Ideal and natural Carnot cycles.

where q_1 is the heat added to the fluid. The entropy of the heat source decreases by the same amount. In the natural Carnot engine the temperature of the source, T_3, is higher than the temperature of the fluid, T_2. During the isothermal expansion the source loses the entropy q_1/T_3, and the increase in entropy of the universe is

$$\Delta s = \frac{q_1}{T_2} - \frac{q_1}{T_3}, \tag{26.57}$$

which of course is a positive number. Although the changes in entropy of the heat source in the two engines during the isothermal expansion are different, the changes in the state of the fluid in the two cylinders are identical. Heat enters both cylinders at temperature T_2. If the same amount of heat enters both cylinders, areas *a b f e* in Figs. 26.17A and B are identical, and the entropy increase during the natural as well as the reversible isothermal expansion is given by Eq. (26.56). Similar reasoning for other processes leads to this rule: adding or removing heat from a fluid across a temperature drop changes its entropy by the same amount as if the process were reversible, and produces the same path on the *T-s* diagram of the fluid. An important example is the boiling of water and superheating of steam in a boiler at constant pressure. Such a process, that is reversible within a system even though the flow of heat into the system is irreversible, is said to be *internally reversible*. The isothermal expansion *a b* in Fig. 26.17B is internally reversible.

A heat engine can convert to useful work only a part of the heat it receives, and must reject the rest. *Available energy* is the part of the heat added to or removed from a system that could be converted into work by a reversible engine. *Unavailable energy* is the remainder of the heat, namely the smallest amount that must be rejected. In Figs. 26.17A and B, the available part of the heat supplied to the engine is represented by the area *a b c d*, and the unavailable part by *c d e f*. The natural cycle of Fig. 26.17B includes an adiabatic expansion *b g* and an adiabatic compression *h a*, neither of which is isentropic. During each stroke the entropy of the fluid increases, according to the sixth corollary. As a result, the heat rejected to the sink is represented by the large area *g h i j*. If the temperature T_0 of the sink is only slightly below that of the fluid T_1, there is no opportunity to convert this heat into work. The heat removed from the engine is all unavailable. Notice that the natural adiabatic strokes cause an increase in the unavailable energy. In general, a natural process causes a loss of availability of energy.

The work output of the natural cycle is the heat added, *a b f e*, less the heat rejected, *g h i j*, which is less than the area *a b c d* of the reversible cycle. The difference between the work outputs of the reversible and natural cycles is the two hatched areas in Fig. 26.17B. The areas under the paths of the two adiabatic processes do not have physical significance. They do not represent heat, because the formula

$$q = \int T\,ds$$

applies only for reversible processes.

26.9 The Rankine Cycle

Because the Carnot cycle is an unrealistic goal for steam-turbine power plants, the ideal *Rankine cycle* is provided as a more encouraging measure of performance. This cycle is the path *a b c d e* shown in Fig. 26.18, taken by the state of the steam as it flows thru the components in Fig. 26.19. In the boiler, water is heated at constant pressure p_2 along *a b*, boiled along *b c*, and superheated at the same pressure along *c d*. Because the heating process is internally reversible, the area *a b c d f g* represents the heat added to the water in the boiler. In this ideal cycle the steam expands isentropically in the turbine along *d e*. As it passes thru the stages of buckets its temperature and pressure decrease and its specific volume increases. In a typical turbine, the steam leaves the

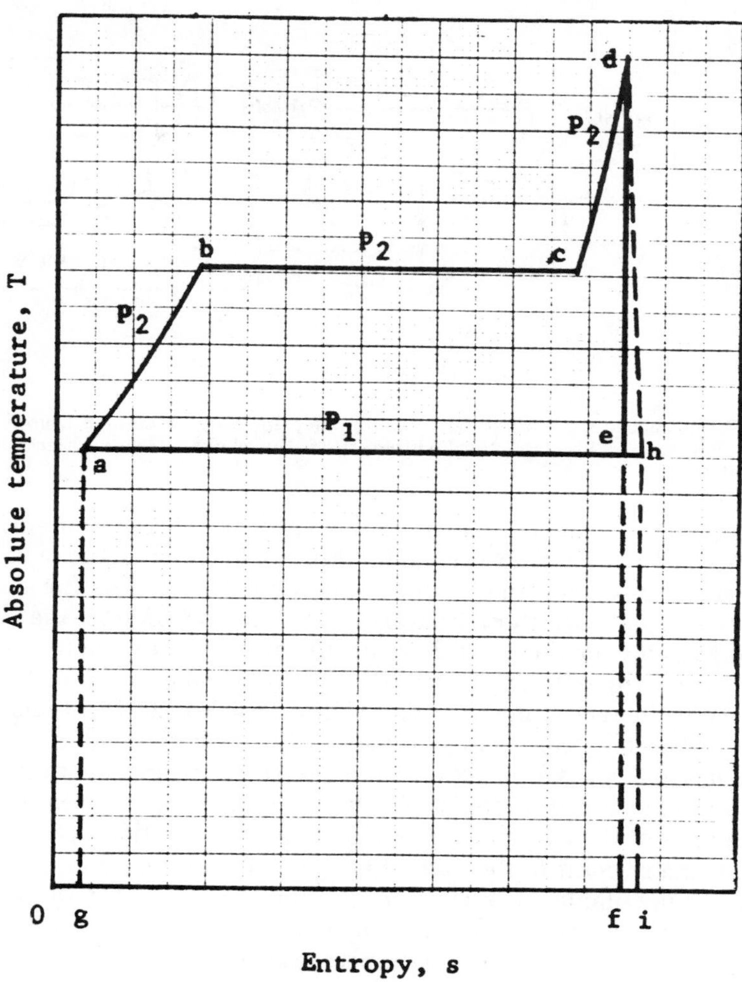

Fig. 26.18. Rankine cycle.

last stage at a pressure p_1 of 3.4 kPa (1 inch of mercury). It is no longer superheated, but is *saturated*, i.e., at the boiling temperature for that pressure, 26.2°C. The steam is wet, because some of it has condensed. Its *quality*, the concentration of vapor by weight, is 87 percent, and its moisture content is 13 percent. The steam enters the condenser, where it is condensed at the low pressure p_1, and the heat *e a g f* is rejected to the cooling water. The removal of heat is an internally-reversible process, and is represented by the line *e a*. At point *a*, the water is pumped back up to the boiler pressure p_2 by the boiler feed pump driven by a small

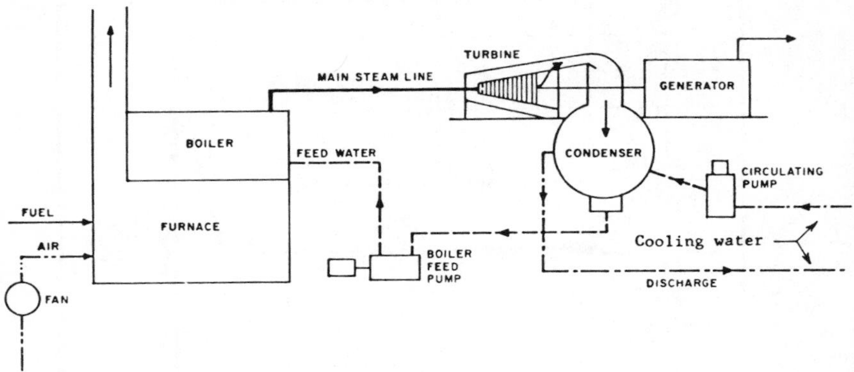

Fig. 26.19. Basic steam-turbine power plant. (Reprinted by permission from *Electric Utility Systems and Practices*, third edition, H. M. Rustebakke, General Electric Company, 1974.)

steam turbine, without appreciable change in temperature or entropy. The *thermal efficiency* of the ideal Rankine cycle is the energy available for mechanical work (the available energy *a b c d e* less the energy required by the feedwater pump) divided by the heat added to the water, *a b c d f g*. The calculation of thermal efficiency will be explained soon.

In a real turbine the expansion of the steam is not isentropic. Instead, the entropy increases along the dotted line *d h* of Fig. 26.18, because the steam encounters friction in passing thru the buckets and diaphragms. Some of its energy is used in overcoming the friction, and is converted to heat and reabsorbed by the steam as the temperature decreases. The availability of the energy therefore decreases. When the steam leaves the turbine at point *h*, the extra energy *h e f i*, called *waste heat*, has become unavailable. It is the energy that was converted to heat by friction in the turbine. The unavailable heat *h a g i* is rejected in the condenser. *Turbine efficiency* is the percentage of the available energy *a b c d e* that is converted to useful mechanical work in turning the generator. Because the waste heat must be deducted, and because of friction in the shaft bearings, the turbine efficiencies of high and low-pressure large steam turbines are about 85 and 90 percent, respectively.

26.10 Increasing Efficiency by Resuperheating

Modern steam plants employ several devices to increase their thermal efficiency over that of the Rankine cycle. An explanation starts with the *T*-*s* diagram for water, Fig. 26.20. The curve 0 *a b c d e f* is called the *saturation line*. The left half 0 *a b c* shows the state of *saturated water*, namely water that is at the boiling temperature corresponding to

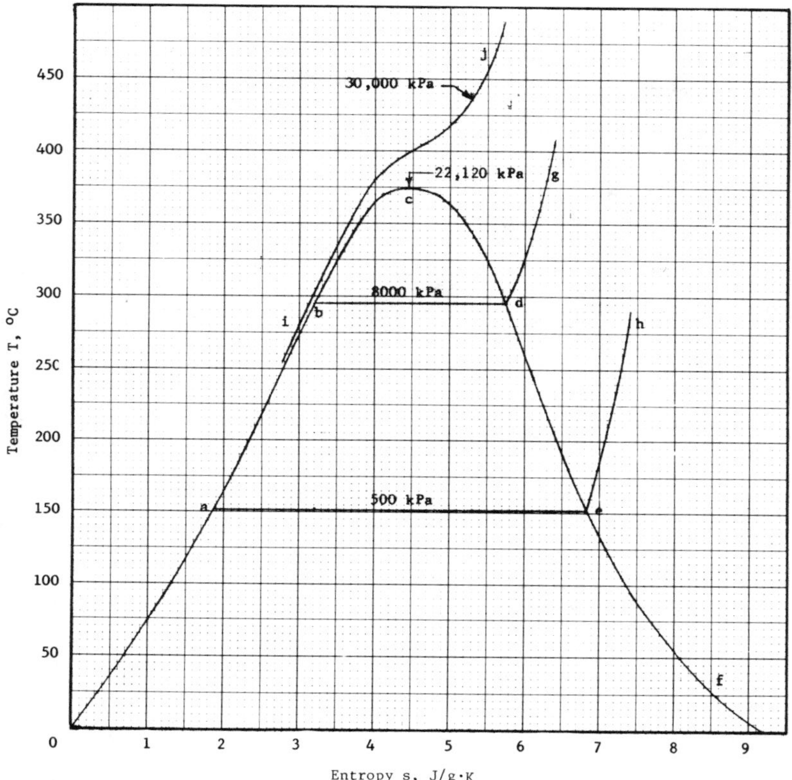

Fig. 26.20. Properties of water and steam.

its pressure. The zero for entropy is that of saturated water at 0.01°C, for which the pressure is 0.6112 kPa. The right half of the saturation line shows the steam of *saturated steam*, namely dry steam that is at the boiling temperature corresponding to its pressure. When cool water is pumped into a high-pressure boiler, it is initially below the boiling temperature and is said to be *compressed*. Because the specific heat of liquid water is nearly independent of pressure, its entropy and enthalpy are nearly independent of pressure. Therefore for any moderate boiler pressure the state of the compressed water follows the segment 0 *a b c* as the water warms up. When the water reaches the boiling or saturation temperature, it starts to evaporate at constant temperature. For example, if the boiler pressure is 500 kPa, the state of the water-steam mixture follows the horizontal line *a e*. At any point under the "steam dome" formed by the saturation line, the water is a mixture of liquid and vapor. When the water is completely evaporated, as at point *e*, it is still saturated and is now dry, with 100 percent quality and zero percent moisture. In fossil-fueled plants the dry steam is heated further in a superheater. The steam temperature rises along a line such as *e h*.

When boiler pressure is increased, the saturation temperature of course rises, and the latent heat of evaporation (the area under the line *a e* or *b d* down to absolute zero temperature) decreases. When the pressure increases to 22,120 kPa, the saturation temperature is 374.15°C, the latent heat reduces to zero, and the state of the water is at the top of the steam dome, point *c*. This is called the *critical point*, and the saturation temperature and pressure there are called the critical temperature and pressure. In boilers operating at pressures higher than the critical pressure, there is no distinction between liquid and evaporated water. At very high pressures, the specific heat of compressed water decreases somewhat. Less heat must be added to the water in the boiler to raise its temperature. As a result, the line representing the state of the water lies to the left or above the saturation line, as shown in Fig. 26.20 by the line *i j* for a pressure of 30,000 kPa. In a modern fossil-fueled power plant the boiler pressure is typically 24,200 kPa (3500 psig). The water is in the *supercritical* region of the *T*-*s* diagram, outside of the steam dome.

The cycle of another typical supercritical steam power plant is shown in Fig. 26.21. The water is heated at a pressure of 23,091 kPa (3349 psia) to a temperature of 538°C (1000°F) at point *b*, and enters the high-pressure turbine. If the steam expanded isentropically down to the exhaust temperature of 41°C at point *j*, its moisture content would be 27 percent. In a real turbine the entropy would increase slightly to about the location of point *i*, where the moisture content of the exhaust steam is 23 percent. The water particles in the steam passing thru the latter stages of the turbine would subject the buckets and diaphragms to intolerable abrasion. For this reason the steam is allowed to expand only to 354°C and 6578 kPa at point *c* in the high-pressure turbine, where it is still dry and superheated. It then returns to a *reheater* and is resuperheated to 552°C and 6137 kPa at point *d*. Next the steam enters an intermediate-pressure turbine and expands down to 408°C and 2393 kPa at point *e*, where it is still dry. Again it is reheated to 566°C and 2151 kPa at point *f*. Finally, it expands thru more intermediate and low-pressure stages to point *g*, where it enters the condenser saturated at 41°C and 7.8 kPa, with 5 percent moisture. The steam is wet only in the last stage, and the leading edges of the last-stage buckets are specially treated to resist abrasion.

Notice that because the turbines are designed to be highly efficient, the three expansions *b c*, *d e*, and *f g* are nearly isentropic. The three lines represent irreversible processes, however. They are dotted as a reminder that the area under them does not have physical significance. The other segments of the cycle represent internally-reversible processes, and the areas under them represent heat added or rejected.

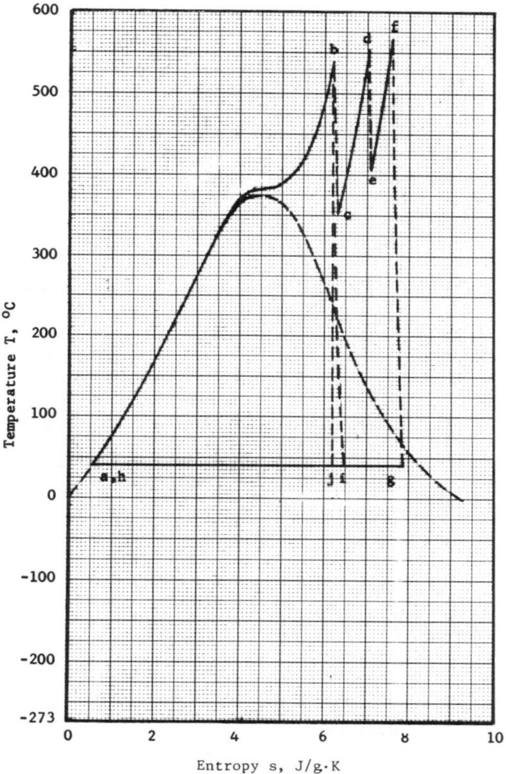

Fig. 26.21. Typical double-reheat cycle.

Single and double-reheat cycles are commonly used in steam-power plants, for two reasons. First, as has been shown, reheating the steam decreases its moisture content in the last turbine stages, and therefore decreases abrasion of the buckets. And second, reheating increases the average temperature at which heat is absorbed by the steam, and therefore increases the thermal efficiency. The efficiencies of the cycle in Fig. 26.21 with and without reheating are 42.6 and 40.9 percent. They will be calculated later.

26.11 Extraction Heating of the Feedwater

The efficiency of a steam power plant is also increased by *regenerative heating* of the feedwater. Consider the ideal Rankine cycle without superheat, $a\ b\ c\ d\ a$, shown in Fig. 26.22. Water is heated to 200°C, evaporated to make dry, saturated steam, expanded isentropically in a frictionless turbine down to 40°C, condensed to saturated water at 40°C, and pumped back to the boiler. The physical components of this cycle are

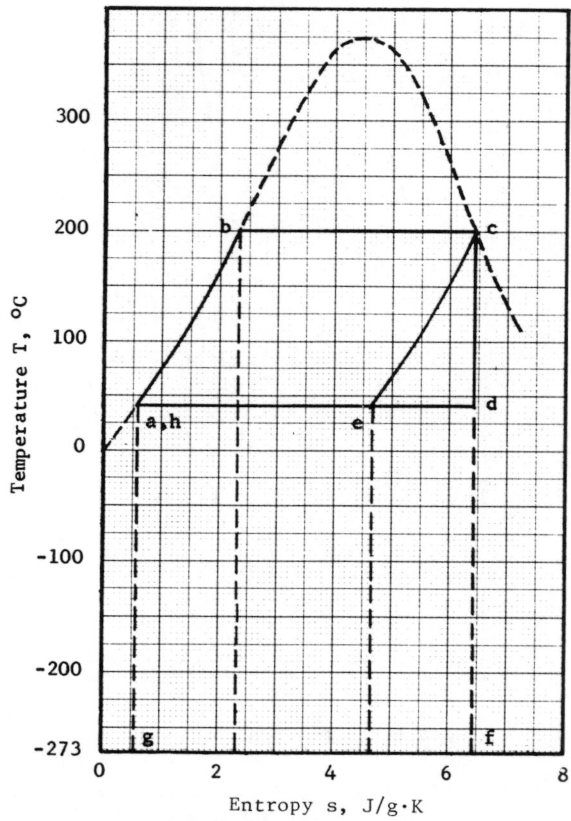

Fig. 26.22. Regenerative heating of feedwater.

shown in Fig. 26.19. The thermal efficiency of the cycle, area $a\ b\ c\ d\ a$ divided by area $a\ b\ c\ f\ g\ a$, is 30.1 percent. Now let the system be rebuilt so that the condensate, instead of returning directly to the boiler, passes first thru a counterflow heat exchanger or *regenerator* that surrounds the turbine. The condensate flowing one way is warmed by the steam flowing the other way thru the turbine. The turbine shell is a perfect heat conductor, so that at any point along the regenerator the temperature difference between the condensate and the steam is negligible. The heating of the condensate along $a\ b$ and the cooling of the steam along $c\ e$

in Fig. 26.22 are reversible processes, and the two paths are parallel. The ideal regenerative cycle is *a b c e a*. A little geometry shows that the efficiency of this ideal cycle, 33.8 percent, is that of a Carnot engine operating between 40 and 200°C. Although the ideal regenerator is not practical, its effect in increasing efficiency can be approximated by *extraction heating* of the feedwater. At several locations along the steam path in the turbine, steam is extracted and passed thru a feedwater heater, in which it warms the condensate or feedwater on its way to the boiler. The heaters operate at successively higher temperatures, thereby warming the feedwater in steps that approximate the continuous warming along *a b* in Fig. 26.22.

The additional components used to increase the efficiency of the basic power plant of Fig. 26.19 are shown in Fig. 26.23. This plant has six feedwater heaters. The superheater and reheater are in the furnace in

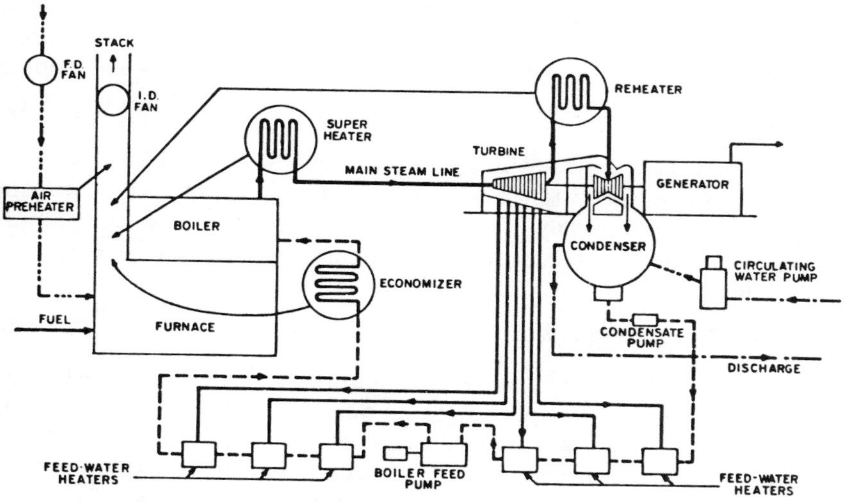

Fig. 26.23. Additional components in a power plant. (Reprinted by permission from *Electric Utility Systems and Practices*, third edition, H. M. Rustebakke, General Electric Company, 1974.)

addition to the boiler. The air preheater and economizer are two more heat exchangers, located near the stack, that preheat the combustion air and feedwater, respectively. Both cool the flue gas and minimize the loss of heat up the stack. They restrict the flow of air and gas, and require a forced-draft fan for the combustion air and an induced-draft fan for the flue gas. The overall efficiency of such a power plant, namely the fraction of the energy content of the fuel that is converted to electricity, can be as high as 40 percent. Most of the remaining 60 percent is rejected to the cooling water.

26.12 Steam Tables

The calculations of efficiencies and the heat added or removed in each component of a steam power plant are accomplished with the help of the *steam tables* in Ref. 90. Table 1 of these steam tables lists the pressure, specific volume, enthalpy, and entropy of saturated water and saturated steam as a function of temperature, up to the critical temperature. Table 2 provides the same information as a function of pressure. This table shows, for example, that the temperature and entropy of saturated water at a pressure of 500 kPa are 151.84°C and 1.8604 kJ/kg·K. Fig. 26.20 confirms these numbers. The table and Fig. 26.20 agree that the entropy of saturated steam at the same pressure is 6.8192 kJ/kg·K. Eq. (26.13) shows that when water is boiled, the heat added equals the increase in its enthalpy. The heat added to saturated water is also proportional to the fraction of the water that is boiled, until it is all converted to steam. Therefore the enthalpy of evaporation of a partially-boiled mixture or wet steam is proportional to its quality. For example, the enthalpy of steam at 500 kPa with a moisture content of 8 percent is

$$h = h_f + 0.92\, h_{fg} = 640.1 + (0.92)(2107.4) = 2578.9 \text{ kJ/kg}\,, \qquad (26.58)$$

where h_f and h_{fg} are the enthalpy of saturated fluid and the enthalpy of evaporation from fluid to gas. Because the boiling occurs at constant temperature, the entropy of evaporation of wet steam is also proportional to its quality. The entropy of steam at 500 kPa with 8 percent moisture is

$$s = s_f + 0.92\, s_{fg} = 1.8604 + (0.92)(4.9588) = 6.4225 \text{ kJ/kg·K}\,. \qquad (26.59)$$

Table 7 in Ref. 90 lists the specific volume, enthalpy, and entropy of compressed water and superheated steam as functions of pressure and temperature. The states described by these coordinates are outside of the "steam dome" of Fig. 26.20. The table shows, for example, that when water at 500 kPa is superheated to 260°C, its entropy is 7.3115 kJ/kg·K. This state is on the 500 kPa line in Fig. 26.20. Table 7 shows that compressed water at 30,000 kPa and 295°C has an entropy of about 3.13 kJ/kg·K. Table 2, on the other hand, shows that the entropy of saturated water at 8000 kPa and 295°C is 3.21. If the specific heat of water were independent of pressure, the two entropies would be equal. Table 7 was used to plot the states of water at 30,000 kPa in Fig. 26.20. Water in these states is not exactly compressed water or superheated steam. It is best described as *supercritical water or steam.*

The steam tables can be used to calculate the thermal efficiency of the ideal Rankine cycle *a b c d a* in Fig. 26.22. The temperature and pressure of the water or steam at each point in the cycle are listed in Fig. 26.24. Table 1 or 7 lists the enthalpy at each point except *d*, whose enthalpy is

Point	State of the fluid	Temperature, °C	Pressure, kPa	Enthalpy, kJ/kg	Entropy, kJ/kg·K	Table No.
a	compressed water	40	1554.9	168.8	0.5715	7
b	saturated water	200	1554.9	852.37	2.3307	1
c	saturated steam	200	1554.9	2790.9	6.4278	1
d	wet steam	40	7.375	2001.2	6.4278	1
h	saturated water	40	7.375	167.45	0.5721	1

Fig. 26.24. Properties of the steam in the ideal Rankine cycle.

calculated as follows. The entropies at points c and d are equal, because the expansion in the turbine is isentropic. The entropy at point c, found in Table 1, is 6.4278. If x is the quality of the exhaust steam at point d,

$$6.4278 = 0.5721 + 7.6861\,x \tag{26.60}$$

or

$$x = 0.76186\,. \tag{26.61}$$

The enthalpy at point d is therefore

$$h_d = 167.45 + (2406.9)(0.76186) = 2001.2 \text{ kJ/kg}\,. \tag{26.62}$$

As explained by Eq. (26.13), the heat q added to the water in the boiler is

$$q = h_c - h_a\,, \tag{26.63}$$

or area $a\ b\ c\ f\ g\ a$. The energy available for mechanical work by the turbine is $h_c - h_d$, or area $a\ b\ c\ d\ a$. The feedwater pump adds the energy $h_a - h_h$ to the water. If its efficiency is 100 percent, it requires that much work at the expense of the turbine output. The thermal efficiency of the cycle is therefore

$$\eta = \frac{h_c - h_d - (h_a - h_h)}{h_c - h_a} = \frac{h_c - h_d - (h_a - h_h)}{h_c - h_h - (h_a - h_h)}\,. \tag{26.64}$$

The enthalpies in Fig. 26.24 show that the term in parentheses is small and can be neglected. Eq. (26.64) becomes

$$\eta = \frac{h_c - h_d}{h_c - h_h} = \frac{2790.9 - 2001.2}{2790.9 - 167.45} = \frac{789.7}{2623.45} = 0.301\,. \tag{26.65}$$

This is the thermal efficiency of the ideal Rankine cycle, reported earlier.

26.13 The Mollier Diagram

The tedium of interpolating the tables and calculating the enthalpy of wet steam is avoided by the use of the *Mollier diagram* or enthalpy-entropy diagram in the centerfold of Ref. 90. Superimposed on the grid lines are lines of constant pressure, running upward and to the right. The heavy curve in the bottom third is the saturation line. Running above and roughly parallel to it are lines of constant superheat temperature. The other dotted lines are lines of constant temperature. In the area below the saturation line or "steam dome" the steam is wet. Below and roughly parallel to the saturation line are lines of constant percentage of moisture. Constant-temperature lines are not needed in this region, because they coincide with the constant-pressure lines.

The usefulness of the Mollier diagram can be illustrated by a calculation of the thermal efficiency of the supercritical double-reheat cycle of Fig. 26.21. The measured temperature and pressure at each point, and the moisture at point g, are tabulated in Fig. 26.25. The enthalpies at

Point	Temperature, °C	Pressure, kPa	Enthalpy, kJ/kg	Remarks
a	41	23,091	192	Table 7
b	538	23,091	3322	
c	354	6578	3045	
d	552	6137	3543	
e	408	2393	3260	
f	566	2151	3610	
g	41	7.8	2456	Moisture 5 percent
h	41	7.8	172	Table 1

Fig. 26.25. Properties of the steam in the double-reheat cycle.

points b thru g are found on the Mollier diagram. Four-place accuracy was obtained with the use of a General Electric TL-1281 Mollier Chart, which has horizontal and vertical scales about 2.7 times as large as those in Ref. 90. States a and h are not on the diagram. Their enthalpies were found by interpolating Tables 7 and 1. Fig. 26.21 shows that the heat added in the furnace is

$$q_1 = (h_b - h_a) + (h_d - h_c) + (h_f - h_e)$$
$$= (h_b - h_h) + (h_d - h_c) + (h_f - h_e) - (h_a - h_h) . \qquad (26.66)$$

The energy required by the feedwater pump is

$$w_1 = h_a - h_h = 192 - 172 = 20 \text{ kJ/kg} . \qquad (26.67)$$

Therefore

$$q_1 = 3322 - 172 + 3543 - 3045 + 3610 - 3260 - w_1$$
$$= 3998 - 20 = 3978 \text{ kJ/kg} . \qquad (26.68)$$

The heat rejected in the condenser is

$$q_2 = h_g - h_h = 2456 - 172 = 2284 \text{ kJ/kg} . \qquad (26.69)$$

Fig. 26.21 shows that the work done by the turbines is

$$(h_b - h_c) + (h_d - h_e) + (h_f - h_g) .$$

The work done by the turbines, less the energy used by the feedwater pump, is therefore

$$w_2 = h_b - h_c + h_d - h_e + h_f - h_g - w_1 . \qquad (26.70)$$

Comparison of this equation with (26.66), (26.68), and (26.69) shows that

$$w_2 = q_1 - q_2 = 3978 - 2284 = 1694 \text{ kJ/kg} . \qquad (26.71)$$

The thermal efficiency of the cycle is

$$\eta = \frac{w_2}{q_1} = \frac{1694}{3978} = 0.426 . \qquad (26.72)$$

If the energy w_1 required by the feedwater pump is neglected, the efficiency is

$$\eta = \frac{1714}{3998} = 0.429 . \qquad (26.73)$$

Even in this high-pressure plant, the effect of the feedwater pump on the thermal efficiency is small.

If the supercritical power plant did not have reheaters, the steam would expand adiabatically to a point such as i in Fig. 26.21, at which the temperature is 41°C and the moisture content is 23 percent. The enthalpy h_i, found on the Mollier diagram, is 2023 kJ/kg. The thermal efficiency of this simplified cycle is

$$\eta = \frac{(h_b - h_i) - (h_a - h_h)}{(h_b - h_h) - (h_a - h_h)} = \frac{1299 - 20}{3150 - 20} = 0.409 . \qquad (26.74)$$

This result confirms the statement made earlier, that reheating increases the thermal efficiency of a steam cycle, as well as decreasing the moisture content in the last turbine stages.

So far the Mollier diagram has been used only to find the enthalpy of steam at states where two other properties were known. The diagram can also be used to avoid the calculation of a constant-enthalpy process. An example is provided by the *throttling calorimeter* shown in Fig. 26.26, which measures the moisture content of wet steam. A small, continuous amount of steam at pressure p_s is throttled by expansion thru an orifice down to almost atmospheric pressure. No mechanical

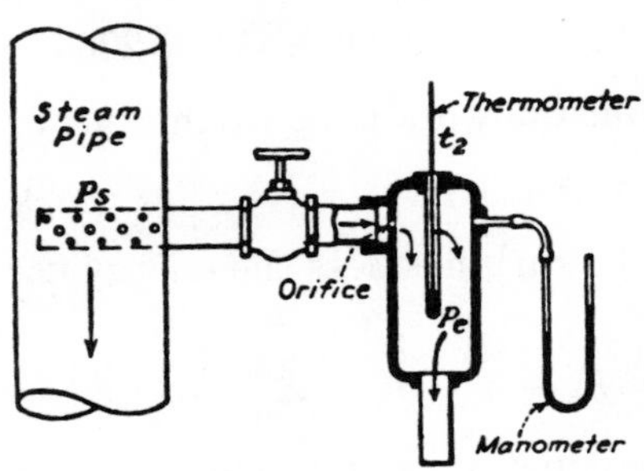

Fig. 26.26. Throttling calorimeter. (From *Thermodynamics* by J. E. Emswiler and F. L. Schwartz, copyright 1943 by McGraw-Hill. Used with the permission of the McGraw-Hill Book Company.)

work is done, and if the calorimeter is well insulated, no heat is lost. The energy equation of steady flow, Eq. (26.12), shows that if the differences between initial and final elevations and velocities are negligible, the throttling does not change the enthalpy of the steam. If the steam in the calorimeter is dry, its enthalpy can be determined from its pressure p_e and temperature t_2. In a typical application the wet steam at a pressure p_s of 1500 kPa is throttled to a temperature of 140°C and a pressure of 110 kPa. The Mollier diagram shows that the enthalpy of the steam in the calorimeter is 2755 kJ/kg. The state of the wet steam is found by moving horizontally from that point to the 1500-kPa constant-pressure line. The diagram shows that the moisture content of the wet steam is 1.8 percent. Notice that the throttling calorimeter works only if the throttled steam is superheated, so that its state can be determined by its temperature and pressure. The Mollier diagram shows that if the exhaust pressure p_e is atmospheric, the calorimeter can measure moisture contents only up to about 7 percent.

26.14 Perfect Gases

Engineers design machines that use air, hydrogen, ammonia, and other gases in addition to steam. How can the states of these gases be calculated? A simple equation of state, requiring no table or diagram, is available that applies over a wide range of states for many gases. It is based on a fortunate property of all known *simple* substances, namely those not under the influence of motion, fluid shear, capillarity, anisotropic stress, or body force. All of these substances become gaseous at sufficiently low pressures, and for each gas the ratio pv/T approaches a limit as the pressure approaches zero:

$$R = \lim_{p \to 0} \frac{pv}{T} \qquad \text{J/kg·K} . \tag{26.75}$$

The limit R is called the *gas constant*. The *molecular mass* of a gas is the dimensionless number

$$M = 32 \frac{R_0}{R} \tag{26.76}$$

where R_0 is the gas constant of atmospheric oxygen. The molecular mass is proportional to the mass of the individual molecules of the gas. A *mole* of a gas is a mass numerically equal to the molecular mass. Eq. (26.76) shows that one mole of oxygen is 32 kg. The constant

$$MR = 32\, R_0 = 8314.9 \qquad \text{J/K·mole} \tag{26.77}$$

is called the *universal gas constant*. An *ideal* or *perfect gas* is one whose equation of state is the *perfect-gas law*:

$$pv = RT , \tag{26.78}$$

where

$$R = \frac{8314.9}{M} \qquad \text{J/kg·K} \tag{26.79}$$

or

$$R = \frac{1545.3}{M} \qquad \text{ft·lb}_f/\text{lb}_m\text{·°R} . \tag{26.80}$$

In general, Eq. (26.78) is accurate for real gases with low molecular masses at low pressures and high temperatures. Even steam obeys the perfect-gas law at high superheats.

Eq. (26.78) can be written as

$$pv = \frac{8314.9\, T}{M} \tag{26.81}$$

or

$$Mv = 8314.9 \frac{T}{p} \qquad \text{m}^3\text{/mole} . \tag{26.82}$$

For a given temperature and pressure, the volume occupied by a mole of any perfect gas is the same. Since the mass of a mole is proportional to the mass of a molecule, the volume occupied by one molecule is the same for any perfect gas. The conclusion is *Avogadro's law*: *In all perfect gases at the same temperature and pressure, the number of molecules in a given volume is the same*. The number of molecules in 32 kg of oxygen is *Avogadro's number*, 6.0232×10^{26}. This is the number of molecules in a mole of any gas.

26.15 Specific Heats of Gases

James P. Joule conducted an experiment to demonstrate an important property of a perfect gas, namely that its internal energy is a function of temperature only. The apparatus is shown in Fig. 26.27. Two tanks, one filled with air at about 22 atmospheres and one evacuated, were immersed in a tank of water. When the air, tanks, and water were all at room temperature, the valve between the two air tanks was opened. Air rushed into the empty tank, bringing the pressure in each tank to 11 atmospheres. Joule observed no change in the water temperature as a result of the changes in pressure and specific volume of the air.

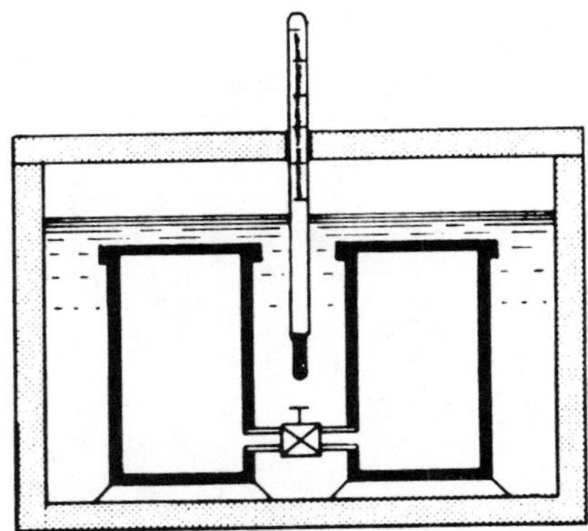

Fig. 26.27. Joule's experiment.

Evidently the temperature of the air did not change, and no heat was transferred to or from the air. The air of course did no external work. According to Eq. (26.2), the internal energy u of the air did not change. Joule concluded that

$$\left(\frac{\partial u}{\partial v}\right)_T = 0 \,. \tag{26.83}$$

The subscript T is a reminder that temperature is held constant for the partial derivative. Experience has shown that the state of a simple substance like a gas is determined by the value of two independent properties such as temperature, pressure, and specific volume. The internal energy of a gas can therefore be expressed as a function of T and v:

$$u = u(T,v) . \tag{26.84}$$

Then

$$du = \left(\frac{\partial u}{\partial T}\right)_v dT + \left(\frac{\partial u}{\partial v}\right)_T dv . \tag{26.85}$$

The second term on the right is zero, the remaining partial derivative therefore becomes total, and u is now identified as a function of T only:

$$du = \left(\frac{du}{dT}\right)_v dT . \tag{26.86}$$

The *specific heat at constant volume* is defined as

$$c_v = \left(\frac{dq}{dT}\right)_v \qquad \text{J/kg·K} , \tag{26.87}$$

the volume of the substance being held constant as the heat dq is applied. Since no work is done by a quantity of gas that is heated at constant volume, $dq = du$, and

$$c_v = \left(\frac{du}{dT}\right)_v . \tag{26.88}$$

This result shows that c_v, like u, is a function of T only. Eq. (26.86) now becomes

$$du = c_v dT . \tag{26.89}$$

This analysis of Joule's experiment indicates that the internal energy of a gas is a function of temperature only. Later, more accurate investigation showed that the temperature of the water changes slightly when a real gas expands in the tanks. Joule's experiment, however, was followed by mathematical analysis (such as in Ref. 72, p. 326) that proved Eq. (26.83) for perfect gases. For any real gas that obeys the perfect-gas law $pv = RT$ closely, Eq. (26.89) is valid also.

A similar derivation will show that the enthalpy of a perfect gas, like its internal energy, is a function of temperature only. The enthalpy can be expressed as a function of the two independent properties T and p:

$$h = h(T,p) . \tag{26.90}$$

Therefore

$$dh = \left(\frac{\partial h}{\partial T}\right)_p dT + \left(\frac{\partial h}{\partial p}\right)_T dp . \tag{26.91}$$

Enthalpy is defined by Eq. (26.11) as

$$h = u + pv \,. \tag{26.92}$$

Therefore

$$\begin{aligned} dh &= du + d(pv) = du + d(RT) \\ &= du + R\,dT \,. \end{aligned} \tag{26.93}$$

Since the right side is a function of T only, the enthalpy h of a perfect gas is only temperature dependent. The second term on the right side of Eq. (26.91) is therefore zero, and the remaining partial derivative becomes total:

$$dh = \left(\frac{dh}{dT}\right)_p dT \,. \tag{26.94}$$

The *specific heat at constant pressure* is defined as

$$c_p = \left(\frac{dq}{dT}\right)_p \,. \tag{26.95}$$

Eq. (26.4) shows that during a constant-pressure heating of a quantity of gas,

$$dq = du + p\,dv = dh \,. \tag{26.96}$$

Therefore

$$c_p = \left(\frac{dh}{dT}\right)_p \,, \tag{26.97}$$

and according to Eq. (26.94),

$$dh = c_p dT \,. \tag{26.98}$$

Notice that c_p, like c_v, is a function of T only. If the gas is perfect, $pv = RT$, and

$$p\,dv = R\,dT - v\,dp \,. \tag{26.99}$$

Since $du = c_v dT$ and for this constant-pressure process $dp = 0$, Eq. (26.96) becomes

$$dq = c_v dT + R\,dT = (c_v + R)dT \,. \tag{26.100}$$

According to this equation and (26.95),

$$c_p = c_v + R \,. \tag{26.101}$$

The gas constant R of a perfect gas is therefore the difference between its specific heats.

Unfortunately c_v and c_p are not constant, but vary somewhat with temperature. Fig. 26.28 shows the variation of c_p for several gases at

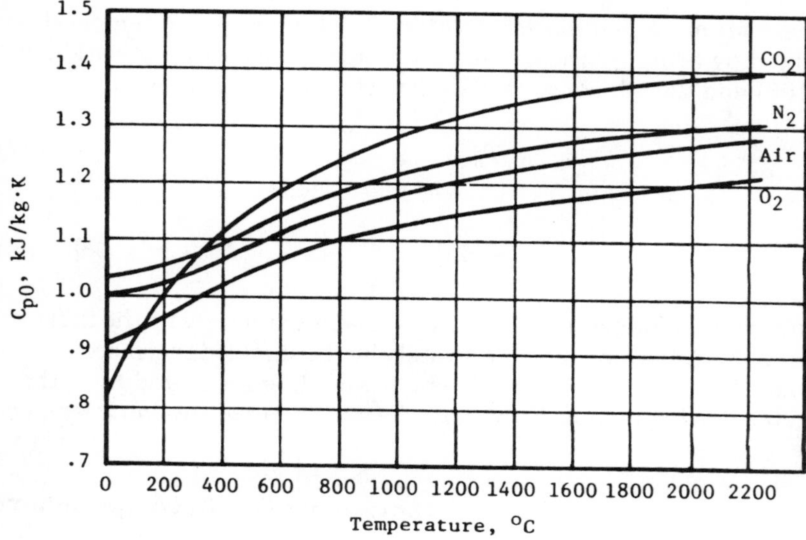

Fig. 26.28. Zero-pressure specific heats, c_{p0}.

very low pressures, at which they act as perfect gases. These are called *zero-pressure specific heats*, and are designated as c_{p0}. Empirical equations for these curves and similar curves of c_v for gases at large specific volumes are available (in Ref. 72, p. 167, for example), with which changes in internal energy and enthalpy of a perfect gas can be obtained by integrating Eqs. (26.89) and (26.98):

$$\Delta u = \int c_v(T)dT \tag{26.102}$$

and

$$\Delta h = \int c_p(T)dT\,. \tag{26.103}$$

Within limited temperature ranges the specific heats of these gases are nearly constant. Then

$$\Delta u = c_v \Delta T \tag{26.104}$$

and

$$\Delta h = c_p \Delta T\,. \tag{26.105}$$

If u and h are arbitrarily chosen to be zero at $T = 0$,

$$u = c_v T \qquad \text{and} \qquad h = c_p T\,. \tag{26.106}$$

If steam were a perfect gas with constant c_p, the constant-temperature lines in the Mollier diagram of Ref. 90 would be horizontal and evenly spaced, according to Eq. (26.105). The fact that this is true in the upper right portion of the diagram indicates that superheated steam behaves as a perfect gas.

The *total* or *stagnation temperature* T_o of a gas is the temperature obtained by bringing the gas to rest adiabatically with no work. Eqs. (26.106) and (26.15) show that for a perfect gas with constant c_p,

$$c_p T_o = c_p T + \frac{V^2}{2} \tag{26.107}$$

or

$$T_o = T + \frac{V^2}{2c_p} . \tag{26.108}$$

The stagnation temperature is measured approximately by the thermocouple in Fig. 26.4, and more accurately by the shielded thermocouple in Fig. 26.29. The temperature T, which would be measured by a thermometer moving at velocity V with the gas, is called the *static temperature*.

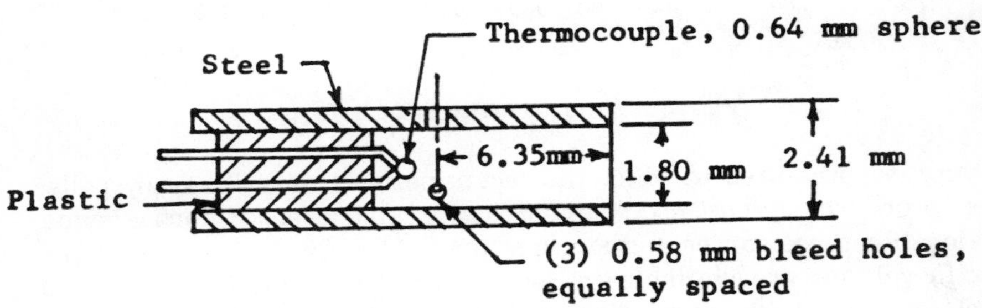

Fig. 26.29. Stagnation-temperature probe.

26.16 Flow of a Perfect Gas

The flow of gases thru turbines, nozzles, and ducts is often nearly frictionless and adiabatic, and is therefore nearly isentropic. The relationships between temperature, pressure, and specific volume in an isentropic flow are therefore important in engineering, and will be derived now for a perfect gas with constant specific heats. The first law for the frictionless flow of a gas is given by Eq. (26.4):

$$dq - p\,dv = du . \tag{26.109}$$

Since

$$d(pv) = p\,dv + v\,dp , \tag{26.110}$$

$$dq = d(pv) - v\,dp + du = d(pv + u) - v\,dp = dh - v\,dp . \tag{26.111}$$

If the gas is perfect,

$$dh = c_p dT \qquad \text{and} \qquad v = \frac{RT}{p} . \tag{26.112}$$

Therefore

$$dq = c_p dT - \frac{RT}{p}\,dp\,. \tag{26.113}$$

For any reversible process such as a frictionless flow,

$$ds = \frac{dq}{T}\,. \tag{26.114}$$

Therefore

$$ds = c_p\frac{dT}{T} - R\,\frac{dp}{p}\,. \tag{26.115}$$

The difference in entropy between states 1 and 2 is obtained by integrating this equation. If c_p is constant,

$$\begin{aligned} s_2 - s_1 &= c_p \ln\frac{T_2}{T_1} - R\ln\frac{p_2}{p_1} = c_p\ln\frac{T_2}{T_1} - c_p\ln\left(\frac{p_2}{p_1}\right)^{R/c_p} \\ &= c_p\ln\frac{T_2/T_1}{(p_2/p_1)^{R/c_p}}\,. \end{aligned} \tag{26.116}$$

Now

$$\frac{R}{c_p} = \frac{c_p - c_v}{c_p} = 1 - \frac{c_v}{c_p}\,. \tag{26.117}$$

The ratio of specific heats is

$$k = \frac{c_p}{c_v} \tag{26.118}$$

and is constant if c_p and c_v are constant. Fig. 26.30 shows that for air, k is 1.40 at near-room temperatures. Eq. (26.116) can be written as

$$s_2 - s_1 = c_p\ln\frac{T_2/T_1}{(p_2/p_1)^{(k-1)/k}}\,. \tag{26.119}$$

This result shows the change in entropy in any reversible process of a perfect gas with constant specific heats. Since entropy has a unique value at every state, this equation can be used to calculate the change in entropy of a natural or irreversible process of the gas, if the initial and final temperature and pressure are known.

If a frictionless flow is also adiabatic, it is isentropic, and Eq. (26.119) becomes

$$c_p\ln\frac{T_2/T_1}{(p_2/p_1)^{(k-1)/k}} = 0 \tag{26.120}$$

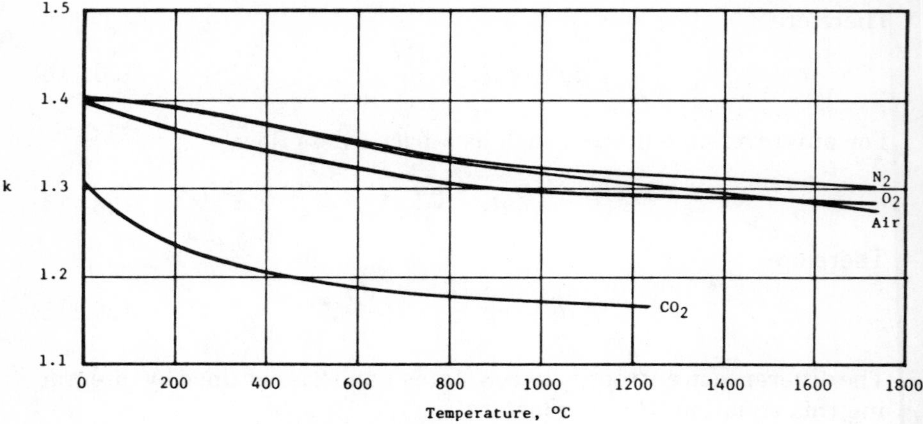

Fig. 26.30. Specific-heat ratios k for various gases.

or

$$\frac{T_2}{T_1} = \left(\frac{p_2}{p_1}\right)^{(k-1)/k} . \tag{26.121}$$

Then

$$\frac{T^{k/(k-1)}}{p} = \text{constant} . \tag{26.122}$$

The T-v and p-v relationships, obtained by combining this equation with the perfect-gas law, are

$$T\, v^{k-1} = \text{constant} \tag{26.123}$$

and

$$p\, v^{k} = \text{constant} . \tag{26.124}$$

To illustrate the usefulness of these relationships, consider the tank of air with a small vent, shown in Fig. 26.31. The pressure and temperature of the air in the tank are

$$p_1 = 150 \text{ kPa} \qquad \text{and} \qquad T_1 = 298 \text{ K} ,$$

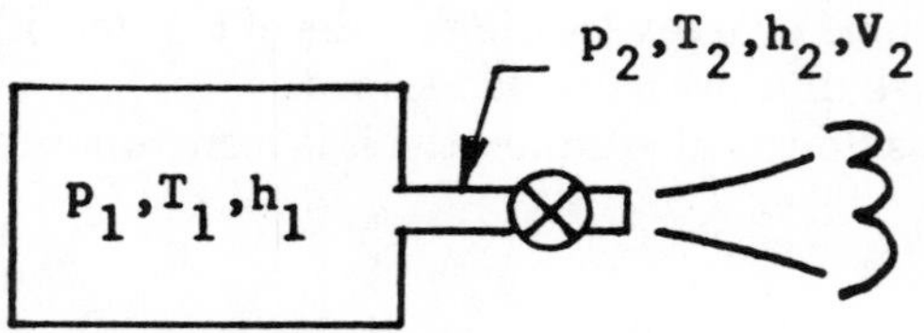

Fig. 26.31. Air tank with a vent.

and the atmospheric pressure p_2 is 101.3 kPa. If the air escapes isentropically, what is its velocity V_2? The flow is governed by the energy equation of steady flow, Eq. (26.12). With no heat q added, no shaft work w_s done, and no change in potential energy gz of the air, the equation becomes

$$h_1 = h_2 + \frac{V_2^2}{2} \tag{26.125}$$

where h_2 is the enthalpy of the air in the vent pipe at velocity V_2. Since the air is nearly a perfect gas, and the specific heats c_p and c_v and their ratio k remain nearly constant while the air is escaping,

$$h = c_p T = c_p \left(\frac{pv}{R}\right). \tag{26.126}$$

According to Eq. (26.101),

$$R = c_p - c_v\,. \tag{26.127}$$

Therefore

$$h = pv\,\frac{c_p}{c_p - c_v} = \frac{pv}{1 - \dfrac{1}{k}} = pv\,\frac{k}{k-1} \tag{26.128}$$

and Eq. (26.125) becomes

$$V_2^2 = 2(h_1 - h_2) = \frac{2k}{k-1}(p_1 v_1 - p_2 v_2) = \frac{2k}{k-1}\,p_1 v_1 \left(1 - \frac{p_2 v_2}{p_1 v_1}\right). \tag{26.129}$$

According to Eq. (26.124),

$$p^{1/k} v = \text{constant}\,, \tag{26.130}$$

or

$$\frac{v_2}{v_1} = \left(\frac{p_1}{p_2}\right)^{1/k} = \left(\frac{p_2}{p_1}\right)^{-1/k}. \tag{26.131}$$

Therefore

$$\frac{p_2 v_2}{p_1 v_1} = \left(\frac{p_2}{p_1}\right)^{(k-1)/k}, \tag{26.132}$$

and since $pv = RT$, Eq. (26.129) becomes

$$V_2 = \sqrt{\frac{2kRT_1}{k-1}\left[1 - \left(\frac{p_2}{p_1}\right)^{(k-1)/k}\right]}. \tag{26.133}$$

For air, $R = 286.8$ J/kg·K and $k = 1.40$. Then

$$V_2 = \sqrt{\frac{(2)(1.40)(286.8)(298)}{0.40}\left[1 - \left(\frac{101.3}{150}\right)^{(0.40/1.40)}\right]}$$

$$= 251.9 \text{ m/s} . \tag{26.134}$$

Since the actual flow is not isentropic, the actual velocity is somewhat slower. The temperature of the escaping air, if the flow is isentropic, is obtained with the help of Eq. (26.122). Since

$$\frac{T_1^{k/(k-1)}}{p_1} = \frac{T_2^{k/(k-1)}}{p_2} , \tag{26.135}$$

$$T_2 = T_1 \left(\frac{p_2}{p_1}\right)^{(k-1)/k} = (298)\left(\frac{101.3}{150}\right)^{0.4/1.4} = 266.4 \text{ K} . \tag{26.136}$$

This result confirms the familiar experience of cold air escaping from a pressure vessel such as an automobile tire.

Chapter 27

ONE-DIMENSIONAL COMPRESSIBLE FLOW

27.1 Introduction

The flow of liquids and the potential flow of gases that have been studied in the last three chapters have been based on the assumption that the fluid is incompressible. In this chapter the assumption of constant density will be relaxed, so that the high-velocity flow of gases can be analyzed. For simplicity three new assumptions will be added: the flow is one dimensional and steady, and the fluid is nonviscous. The flow in a duct whose cross section changes slowly with length, and whose radius of curvature is large compared to its width, can be considered one dimensional. That is, all of the fluid properties are uniform over any cross section. Even with this assumption, much of the flow in nozzles, diffusers, wind tunnels, and jet engines can be analyzed. The goals of this chapter are to (1) list the equations of continuity, momentum, and energy for the steady, one-dimensional flow of a compressible, perfect gas, (2) use these equations to derive expressions for the properties of a perfect gas in a steady, isentropic, one-dimensional flow in terms of its Mach number, and (3) show applications to the design of supersonic nozzles and wind tunnels.

27.2 Continuity Equation

Fig. 27.1 shows a stationary control volume in a duct, in which the

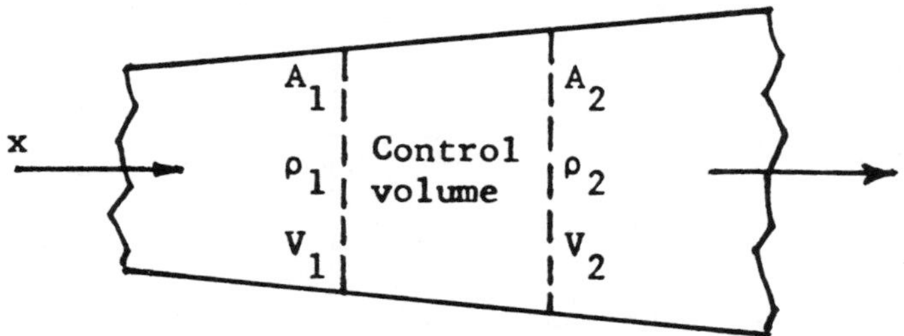

Fig. 27.1. Control volume in a duct.

flow of a fluid is steady and one dimensional in the x direction. The cross-sectional area A, density ρ, and velocity V vary as the fluid crosses the control volume. The rate of mass flow $\dot{m}$ is the same entering and leaving the control volume:

$$\dot{m} = \rho_1 V_1 A_1 = \rho_2 V_2 A_2 = \text{constant}\,, \tag{27.1}$$

and at any cross section,

$$\dot{m} = \rho\, V\, A = \text{constant}\,. \tag{27.2}$$

If ρ is in kg/m^3, V in m/s, and A in m^2, $\dot{m}$ is in kg/s. This is the continuity equation for steady, one-dimensional flow. The perceptive reader may wonder whether it can be obtained from the general equation of continuity (24.30), which for steady flow reduces to

$$\nabla \cdot (\rho\, \mathbf{v}) = 0\,, \tag{27.3}$$

where $\mathbf{v}$ is the fluid velocity. The answer is "not easily," for two reasons. First, $\mathbf{v}$ includes all three components of velocity at any point in the fluid, while V is the average value of the x component of velocity over a cross section. And second, if the area A is changing, the velocity $\mathbf{v}$ must have a y or z component. These components do not appear in Eq. (27.2) but are needed in Eq. (27.3).

27.3 Momentum Equation

The control volume in the duct is shown again in Fig. 27.2, this time

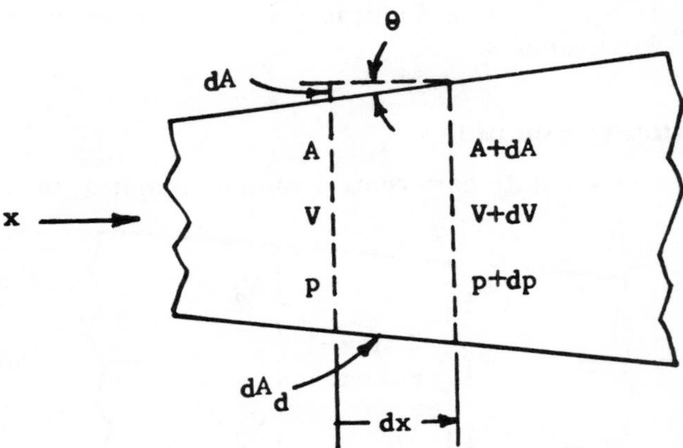

Fig. 27.2. Control volume of differential length.

with a differential length dx. A momentum equation can be obtained by applying Newton's second law to the fluid in the control volume. If the fluid pressure at the inlet and outlet are p and $p + dp$, the forces in the x direction on the left and right ends of the fluid are pA and

$(p + dp)(A + dA)$. The duct wall also exerts a force on the fluid. Let the angle of expansion of the duct be θ, and the area of the duct wall surrounding the control volume be dA_d. A little thought shows that

$$dA_d \sin\theta = dA \, . \tag{27.4}$$

The average pressure exerted by the duct wall on the fluid is $p + dp/2$. The force that the duct wall exerts on the fluid in the x direction is therefore

$$\left(p + \frac{dp}{2}\right) dA_d \sin\theta = \left(p + \frac{dp}{2}\right) dA \, . \tag{27.5}$$

Since the fluid is nonviscous the duct exerts no shear force on it. If no body force such as gravity is applied, the net force on the fluid within the control volume in the x direction is

$$p\,A + \left(p + \frac{dp}{2}\right) dA - (p + dp)(A + dA) = -A\,dp \, . \tag{27.6}$$

The second-order products of differentials are ignored. Since the flow is steady, the rate of change of momentum of the fluid in the control volume is simply

$$\dot{m}(V + dV - V) = \dot{m}\,dV \qquad \text{kg·m/s}^2 \quad \text{or} \quad \text{N} \, . \tag{27.7}$$

According to Newton's second law, the net force on the fluid equals the rate of change of its momentum, or

$$-A\,dp = \dot{m}\,dV \, . \tag{27.8}$$

Since

$$\dot{m} = \rho\,V\,A \, , \tag{27.9}$$

$$\rho\,V\,A\,dV + A\,dp = 0 \tag{27.10}$$

or

$$V\,dV + \frac{dp}{\rho} = 0 \, . \tag{27.11}$$

This is the momentum equation for the steady, one-dimensional flow of a nonviscous fluid to which no body force is applied .

The same result can be obtained from the Euler equation of motion that for flow in the x direction is Eq. (24.52):

$$\frac{Dv_x}{Dt} = F_x - \frac{1}{\rho}\frac{\partial p}{\partial x} \, , \tag{27.12}$$

where v_x is the x component of velocity, now called V, and F_x is the body force in the x direction, now zero. Since the flow is steady, the substantial derivative is simply

$$\frac{Dv_x}{Dt} = v_x \frac{\partial v_x}{\partial x} = V \frac{dV}{dx} , \tag{27.13}$$

and Eq. (27.12) becomes

$$V \frac{dV}{dx} + \frac{1}{\rho} \frac{dp}{dx} = 0 \tag{27.14}$$

or

$$V\, dV + \frac{dp}{\rho} = 0 , \tag{27.15}$$

which agrees with Eq. (27.11).

If the duct is a cylinder, its cross-sectional area is constant. The wall exerts no force on the fluid in the x direction, and a simple alternate momentum equation can be written. If the duct in Fig. 27.1 is a cylinder of cross-sectional area A, the net force on the fluid in the control volume is $p_1A - p_2A$, and the rate of change of momentum of the fluid is $\dot{m}(V_2 - V_1)$. Then

$$p_1A - p_2A = \dot{m}\, V_2 - \dot{m}\, V_1 \tag{27.16}$$

or

$$p_1A + \dot{m}\, V_1 = p_2A + \dot{m}\, V_2 \tag{27.17}$$

or at any cross section of the duct,

$$p\, A + \dot{m}\, V = \text{constant} . \tag{27.18}$$

This is the momentum equation for the steady, one-dimensional flow of a nonviscous fluid without body force in a cylinder.

27.4 Energy Equation

The control volume in the duct is shown for the third time in the form of Fig. 27.3, to aid the derivation of an energy equation. Heat is added to the fluid in the control volume at the rate of dq J/kg. The pressure, velocity, temperature, and enthalpy of the fluid entering the control volume are p, V, T, and h. The properties of the fluid leaving are $p + dp$, etc. No external work is done by the fluid, and any elevation change is ignored. According to the energy equation of steady flow, Eq. (26.12), the sums of energy per unit mass of fluid entering and leaving the control volume are

$$dq + h + \frac{1}{2} V^2 = h + dh + \frac{1}{2} (V + dV)^2 . \tag{27.19}$$

Since the second-order differential is negligible, this equation becomes

$$dq = dh + V\, dV . \tag{27.20}$$

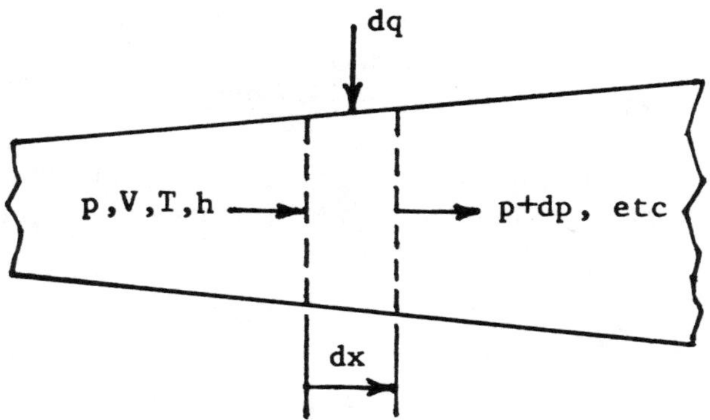

Fig. 27.3. Control volume with heat added.

If the fluid is a perfect gas, $dh = c_p dT$, and

$$dq = c_p\, dT + V\, dV\,. \tag{27.21}$$

This is the energy equation for the steady, one-dimensional flow of a perfect gas that does no external work.

The total or stagnation enthalpy h_o of a fluid is the enthalpy obtained by stopping the fluid adiabatically with no external work. Integrating Eq. (27.20) between the enthalpy limits of h and h_o, and the velocity limits of V and zero, with no heat input, produces the result

$$0 = \int_h^{h_o} dz + \int_V^0 z\, dz \tag{27.22}$$

or

$$h_o = h + \frac{1}{2} V^2\,. \tag{27.23}$$

Integrating Eq. (27.20) between the limits of h_1 and h_2, and V_1 and V_2, yields

$$0 = \int_{h_1}^{h_2} dz + \int_{V_1}^{V_2} z\, dz \tag{27.24}$$

or

$$h_1 + \frac{V_1^2}{2} = h_2 + \frac{V_2^2}{2} = h_o = \text{constant}\,. \tag{27.25}$$

Eq. (27.23) confirms Eq. (26.15), and Eq. (27.25) shows that during an adiabatic, no-work process, the stagnation enthalpy of a fluid remains constant. If the fluid is a perfect gas whose specific heat c_p is constant, $h = c_p T$. Eq. (27.23) becomes

$$T_o = T + \frac{V^2}{2c_p}\,, \tag{27.26}$$

where T_o is the stagnation temperature, and Eq. (27.25) becomes

$$c_p T_1 + \frac{V_1^2}{2} = c_p T_2 + \frac{V_2^2}{2} = c_p T_o = \text{constant} . \tag{27.27}$$

Eq. (27.26) confirms Eq. (26.108), and Eq. (27.27) shows that during an adiabatic, no-work process of a perfect gas with constant c_p, the stagnation temperature T_o remains constant.

27.5 The Speed of Sound

The first goal of this chapter has been accomplished. Now a formula is needed for the speed of sound waves in a perfect gas, so that the properties of the gas can be expressed in terms of its Mach number. The formula will be derived for a plane wave, namely a wave that varies only in the direction of its propagation. A sound or a radio wave that has traveled a long way from its source without reflection is a plane wave. It constitutes a large sphere, a small portion of which is essentially a plane normal to the direction of propagation. Imagine a plane sound wave traveling in the x direction in a perfect gas. The particles are at rest before the wave arrives, and then move to and fro with small amplitude and the velocity v_x as the wave passes with the speed c. Observation of such longitudinal waves shows that v_x is small compared to c. Since the particles in a plane normal to the direction of motion all have the same velocity, they experience no viscous shear force. The momentum equation for the gas particles has the form of the Euler equation (24.52). For flow in the x direction with no body force on the gas, this equation is

$$\frac{\partial v_x}{\partial t} + v_x \frac{\partial v_x}{\partial x} + \frac{1}{\rho} \frac{\partial p}{\partial x} = 0 . \tag{27.28}$$

The continuity equation (24.30) shows that for the gas particles in the path of the sound wave,

$$\frac{\partial \rho}{\partial t} + \frac{\partial (\rho v_x)}{\partial x} = 0$$

or

$$\frac{\partial \rho}{\partial t} + \rho \frac{\partial v_x}{\partial x} + v_x \frac{\partial \rho}{\partial x} = 0 . \tag{27.29}$$

Because the temperature of the gas varies only slightly and the wave passes quickly, the heat transferred to or from the gas particles is negligible, and the process is nearly adiabatic. Since the gas properties fluctuate only slightly and the particles experience little friction, the process is nearly reversible. It can therefore be considered isentropic, and the gas obeys the equation of isentropic flow of a perfect gas, Eq. (26.124):

$$p\,v^k = p/\rho^k = \text{constant}\,, \tag{27.30}$$

where k is the ratio of specific heats, c_p/c_v. Although ρ is a function of x and t in the sound wave, Eq. (27.30) shows that p is a function of ρ only. Therefore

$$\frac{\partial p}{\partial x} = \frac{dp}{d\rho}\frac{\partial \rho}{\partial x}\,. \tag{27.31}$$

The momentum equation (27.28) reduces to

$$\frac{\partial v_x}{\partial t} + v_x\frac{\partial v_x}{\partial x} + \frac{1}{\rho}\frac{dp}{d\rho}\frac{\partial \rho}{\partial x} = 0\,. \tag{27.32}$$

The continuity and momentum equations (27.29) and (27.32) are too complicated to solve simultaneously for ρ and v_x. They can be simplified by the fundamental idea of perturbation theory, namely the assumption that each of the gas properties consists of an undisturbed value that is either large or zero, with a small perturbation superimposed on it. Thus

$$p = p_o + p' \tag{27.33}$$

$$\rho = \rho_o + \rho' \tag{27.34}$$

$$v_x = 0 + v_x'\,, \tag{27.35}$$

where the subscript o indicates the undisturbed value in the gas ahead of the sound wave, and the primed value is the perturbation. Substituting these expressions into Eqs. (27.29) and (27.32) gives

$$\frac{\partial \rho'}{\partial t} + (\rho_o + \rho')\frac{\partial v_x'}{\partial x} + v_x'\frac{\partial \rho'}{\partial x} = 0 \tag{27.36}$$

and

$$\frac{\partial v_x'}{\partial t} + v_x'\frac{\partial v_x'}{\partial x} + \frac{1}{(\rho_o + \rho')}\frac{\partial p}{\partial \rho}\frac{\partial \rho'}{\partial x} = 0\,. \tag{27.37}$$

Since the amplitude of a sound wave is small,

1. the term $\rho_o + \rho'$ is nearly equal to ρ_o,

2. the slope of the curve of p vs. ρ varies little from its steady value of $(dp/d\rho)_o$, and

3. the two terms containing v_x' as a multiplier are negligible.

For convenience, let $(dp/d\rho)_o = c^2$. According to the three statements, Eqs. (27.36) and (27.37) reduce to two simultaneous partial differential equations with constant coefficients:

$$\frac{\partial \rho'}{\partial t} + \rho_o \frac{\partial v_x'}{\partial x} = 0 \tag{27.38}$$

and

$$\frac{\partial v_x'}{\partial t} + \frac{c^2}{\rho_o} \frac{\partial \rho'}{\partial x} = 0 \, . \tag{27.39}$$

To solve them for ρ', differentiate the first with respect to t and the second with respect to x, multiply the second by ρ_o, and subtract the second from the first. The result is

$$\frac{\partial^2 \rho'}{\partial t^2} = c^2 \frac{\partial^2 \rho'}{\partial x^2} \, . \tag{27.40}$$

Solving the simultaneous equations for v_x' produces the result

$$\frac{\partial^2 v_x'}{\partial t^2} = c^2 \frac{\partial^2 v_x'}{\partial x^2} \, . \tag{27.41}$$

The last two equations are examples of the *wave equation* in one space dimension, commonly called the one-dimensional wave equation. The solution, of Eq. (27.40) for example, is

$$\rho' = \rho_f'(x - ct) + \rho_b'(x + ct) \, , \tag{27.42}$$

where ρ_f' and ρ_b' are any functions of their arguments $x - ct$ and $x + ct$. This solution can be verified by substituting it back into the differential equation.

To understand why the solution represents traveling waves, consider the density perturbation $\rho_f'(x - ct)$, plotted as a function of its argument in Fig. 27.4. The ordinate $\rho_f'(k)$ of any abscissa $x - ct = k$ is of course

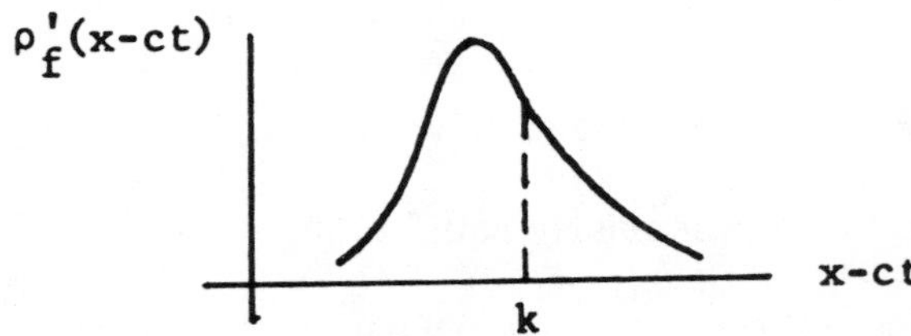

Fig. 27.4. Traveling wave.

constant. Therefore as time increases, x must increase to keep k constant. The conclusion is that $\rho_f'(x - ct)$ is a wave that travels in the positive x direction. Since

$$x = ct + k \,, \tag{27.43}$$

the velocity of the forward-traveling wave is

$$\frac{dx}{dt} = c \,. \tag{27.44}$$

Similarly, $\rho_b'(x + ct)$ is a backward-traveling wave, moving in the negative x direction with velocity c. Backward-traveling waves are normally produced by reflection. If a wave propagates outward from its transmitter without reflection, $\rho_b' = 0$. The velocity perturbation in the sound wave behaves like the density perturbation and travels at the same speed, which is now seen to be the speed of sound, c.

The speed of sound can be put into a form that is more convenient than its definition

$$c^2 = \left(\frac{dp}{d\rho}\right)_o \,. \tag{27.45}$$

According to Eq. (27.30),

$$\frac{p}{\rho^k} = \frac{p_o}{\rho_o^k} \tag{27.46}$$

where k is the ratio of specific heats of the gas, c_p/c_v. Then

$$p = \frac{p_o}{\rho_o^k}\,\rho^k \,, \tag{27.47}$$

and

$$\frac{dp}{d\rho} = k\,\frac{p_o}{\rho_o^k}\,\rho^{k-1} = k\,\frac{p}{\rho^k}\,\rho^{k-1} = k\,\frac{p}{\rho} \,. \tag{27.48}$$

Since the gas obeys the perfect-gas law $p = \rho RT$,

$$\frac{dp}{d\rho} = k\,\frac{\rho RT}{\rho} = k\,R\,T \tag{27.49}$$

and

$$c^2 = \left(\frac{dp}{d\rho}\right)_o = k\,R\,T_o \,, \tag{27.50}$$

where T_o is the absolute temperature of the undisturbed gas. Since any difference between the gas temperature T and its undisturbed value T_o is negligible, the subscript o will be dropped. Eq. (27.50) becomes

$$c = \sqrt{k R T} . \tag{27.51}$$

This is the speed of sound in a perfect gas. The formula is surprisingly simple, and shows that counter to intuition, the speed is independent of the pressure and density of the gas.

27.6 The Gas Equations in Differential Form

Now begins a long, unexciting, but necessary manipulation of the definition of Mach number, the perfect-gas law, and the continuity, momentum, and energy equations. First, the five equations will be expressed in terms of the six variables p, ρ, V, T, A, and M, and the parameter k. The final result will be useful expressions for the variables in a steady, isentropic, one-dimensional flow of a perfect gas in terms of its Mach number. The manipulation begins with the definition of the Mach number of a fluid:

$$M = V/c , \tag{27.52}$$

where V is the fluid velocity and c is the local speed of sound in the fluid. Inserting the hard-won Eq. (27.51) into this definition produces the form

$$M = \frac{V}{\sqrt{k R T}} , \tag{27.53}$$

or

$$\ln M = \ln V - \ln \sqrt{k R} - \frac{1}{2} \ln T . \tag{27.54}$$

Now differentiate both sides, to put the Mach-number equation into the form

$$\frac{dM}{M} = \frac{dV}{V} - \frac{dT}{2T} . \tag{27.55}$$

Similarly, the perfect-gas law

$$p = \rho R T \tag{27.56}$$

can be converted to the form

$$\ln p = \ln \rho + \ln R + \ln T \tag{27.57}$$

and then

$$\frac{dp}{p} - \frac{d\rho}{\rho} - \frac{dT}{T} = 0 . \tag{27.58}$$

The continuity of steady, one-dimensional flow is expressed by Eq. (27.2):

$$\dot{m} = \rho V A . \tag{27.59}$$

Since $d\dot{m}/dt = 0$, it can be written with separated variables as

$$\frac{d\rho}{\rho} + \frac{dV}{V} + \frac{dA}{A} = 0 . \tag{27.60}$$

To put the momentum equation (27.11) into a similar form, first divide by V^2, to get

$$\frac{dV}{V} + \frac{dp}{\rho V^2} = 0 . \tag{27.61}$$

For a perfect gas,

$$\rho = \frac{p}{RT} . \tag{27.62}$$

Then

$$\frac{dV}{V} + \frac{RT}{V^2} \cdot \frac{dp}{p} = 0 . \tag{27.63}$$

According to Eqs. (27.55) and (27.53),

$$\frac{dV}{V} = \frac{dM}{M} + \frac{dT}{2T} \tag{27.64}$$

and

$$V^2 = k R T M^2 . \tag{27.65}$$

Substituting the last two equations into (27.63) yields

$$\frac{dM}{M} + \frac{dT}{2T} + \frac{1}{kM^2} \frac{dp}{p} = 0 . \tag{27.66}$$

This is an alternate form of the momentum equation for the steady, one-dimensional flow of a perfect, nonviscous gas with no body force.

Finally, the energy equation (27.21) can be put into similar form by first dividing by c_pT. If the flow is adiabatic, $dq = 0$, and

$$\frac{V^2}{c_pT} \cdot \frac{dV}{V} + \frac{dT}{T} = 0 . \tag{27.67}$$

The opportunity to eliminate V is provided by Eqs. (27.64) and (27.65) again. The latter contains the unwanted R, which can be eliminated by observing that

$$c_p = \frac{k}{k-1} R . \tag{27.68}$$

With these three substitutions, Eq. (27.67) becomes

$$\frac{k\,R\,T\,M^2}{\dfrac{k}{k-1}R\,T}\left(\frac{dM}{M}+\frac{dT}{2T}\right)+\frac{dT}{T}=0 \tag{27.69}$$

or

$$(k-1)M\,dM+\left(\frac{k-1}{2}M^2+1\right)\frac{dT}{T}=0\,. \tag{27.70}$$

This is the energy equation for the steady, one-dimensional, adiabatic, no-work flow of a perfect gas.

Now five equations in differential form have been derived, that relate the six variables p, ρ, V, T, A, and M. The equations are summarized here:

Mach number
$$\frac{dM}{M}=\frac{dV}{V}-\frac{dT}{2T} \tag{27.71}$$

Perfect gas
$$\frac{dp}{p}-\frac{d\rho}{\rho}-\frac{dT}{T}=0 \tag{27.72}$$

Continuity
$$\frac{d\rho}{\rho}+\frac{dV}{V}+\frac{dA}{A}=0 \tag{27.73}$$

Momentum
$$\frac{dM}{M}+\frac{dT}{2T}+\frac{1}{kM^2}\frac{dp}{p}=0 \tag{27.74}$$

Energy
$$(k-1)M\,dM+\left(\frac{k-1}{2}M^2+1\right)\frac{dT}{T}=0\,. \tag{27.75}$$

27.7 One-Dimensional Isentropic Flow

The five equations will now be manipulated to express each of five variables in terms of Mach number. The equations are based on the assumptions that the fluid is a perfect gas that is nonviscous and therefore flows without friction, and that the flow is one dimensional, steady, and adiabatic. A frictionless, adiabatic flow is isentropic. Even with these restrictions the equations will be useful. The air and many other gases that flow in a nozzle or diffuser are nearly perfect, and the flow is frequently steady. If the cross section varies slowly with distance, the flow can be considered one dimensional. If the duct is short and smooth, little heat enters or leaves thru the walls, and the friction loss is small. The flow is nearly isentropic. The first of the five variables to be considered is temperature, which can be expressed in terms of Mach number directly with the help of the energy equation (27.75):

$$\frac{dT}{T} = -\frac{2\,M\,dM}{\dfrac{2}{k-1} + M^2} . \tag{27.76}$$

This equation is ready to integrate. The integration will be postponed until expressions for the other four variables have been obtained. An expression for pressure can be obtained by substituting Eq. (27.76) into the momentum equation (27.74):

$$\frac{dp}{p} = -\frac{2k}{k-1} \cdot \frac{M\,dM}{\dfrac{2}{k-1} + M^2} . \tag{27.77}$$

The last two equations provide the useful bonus information that

$$\frac{dp}{p} = \frac{k}{k-1} \cdot \frac{dT}{T} . \tag{27.78}$$

If this equation is integrated between two sections 1 and 2 in a duct, the result is

$$\frac{p_2}{p_1} = \left(\frac{T_2}{T_1}\right)^{k/(k-1)} \tag{27.79}$$

or

$$\frac{T^{k/(k-1)}}{p} = \text{constant} . \tag{27.80}$$

And since for a perfect gas $pv = RT$,

$$p\,v^k = \text{constant} . \tag{27.81}$$

This short digression constitutes an alternate derivation of Eq. (27.30), the equation of isentropic flow of a perfect gas.

An expression for velocity in terms of Mach number can be obtained by eliminating temperature from the Mach-number equation (27.71) with the help of Eq. (27.76). The result is

$$\frac{dV}{V} = \frac{dM}{M} - \frac{M\,dM}{\dfrac{2}{k-1} + M^2} . \tag{27.82}$$

The perfect-gas equation (27.72) provides an expression for density:

$$\frac{d\rho}{\rho} = \frac{dp}{p} - \frac{dT}{T} = -\frac{2}{k-1} \cdot \frac{M\,dM}{\dfrac{2}{k-1} + M^2}. \tag{27.83}$$

Finally, an expression for cross-sectional area is obtained from the continuity equation (27.73):

$$\frac{dA}{A} = \frac{k+1}{k-1} \cdot \frac{M\,dM}{\dfrac{2}{k-1} + M^2} - \frac{dM}{M}. \tag{27.84}$$

The equations for the five variables T, p, V, ρ, and A are ready to integrate. Each integral can be written in the form of either

$$\int_{x_1}^{x_2} \frac{dx}{x} = \ln \frac{x_2}{x_1} \tag{27.85}$$

or

$$\int_{x_1}^{x_2} \frac{x\,dx}{k + x^2} = \frac{1}{2} \ln \frac{k + x_2^2}{k + x_1^2}. \tag{27.86}$$

The integrals of the five equations are

$$\frac{T_2}{T_1} = \frac{1 + \dfrac{k-1}{2} M_1^2}{1 + \dfrac{k-1}{2} M_2^2} \tag{27.87}$$

$$\frac{p_2}{p_1} = \left(\frac{1 + \dfrac{k-1}{2} M_1^2}{1 + \dfrac{k-1}{2} M_2^2} \right)^{k/(k-1)} \tag{27.88}$$

$$\frac{V_2}{V_1} = \frac{M_2}{M_1} \left(\frac{1 + \dfrac{k-1}{2} M_1^2}{1 + \dfrac{k-1}{2} M_2^2} \right)^{1/2} \tag{27.89}$$

$$\frac{\rho_2}{\rho_1} = \left(\frac{1 + \dfrac{k-1}{2} M_1^2}{1 + \dfrac{k-1}{2} M_2^2} \right)^{1/(k-1)} \tag{27.90}$$

and

$$\frac{A_2}{A_1} = \frac{M_1}{M_2}\left(\frac{1 + \dfrac{k-1}{2}M_2^2}{1 + \dfrac{k-1}{2}M_1^2}\right)^{[(k+1)/(k-1)]/2} \tag{27.91}$$

These five equations show the variations in the properties of a gas flowing along a duct, as a function of Mach number. A review of the derivations shows that each equation requires the assumptions of a one-dimensional, steady, adiabatic flow of a perfect gas. In addition, the equations for pressure, density, and area require a frictionless and therefore isentropic flow. The equations for temperature and velocity are valid even if the fluid has viscosity.

27.8 Nozzles and Diffusers

Eq. (27.91) shows how the cross-sectional area of a duct must be varied to achieve any arbitrary variation of Mach number. The accompanying distribution of temperature, pressure, velocity, and density can be found from Eqs. (27.87) thru (27.90). For a duct that is already built, the area profile A_2/A_1 is known. If the duct carries air for which $k = 1.40$, Eq. (27.91) becomes

$$\frac{A_2}{A_1} = \frac{M_1}{M_2}\left(\frac{1 + 0.2\,M_2^2}{1 + 0.2\,M_1^2}\right)^3 \tag{27.92}$$

or

$$\frac{(1 + 0.2\,M_2^2)^3}{M_2} = \frac{(1 + 0.2\,M_1^2)^3}{M_1} \cdot \frac{A_2}{A_1}. \tag{27.93}$$

With a given entrance Mach number M_1, the value of the right side of Eq. (27.93) can be calculated for any area ratio A_2/A_1. The left side is plotted as a function of M_2 in Fig. 27.5. The curve has one positive real extreme value, namely a minimum value of 1.728 at $M_2 = 1$. The right side of Eq. (27.93) can therefore go no lower than 1.728. There is a minimum allowable area ratio for any given M_1. To understand the physical meaning of this restriction, rewrite Eq. (27.84) as

$$\frac{dM}{M} = \left(\frac{1 + \dfrac{k-1}{2}M^2}{M^2 - 1}\right)\frac{dA}{A}. \tag{27.94}$$

Notice that dA/A and dM/M are the fractional changes in cross-sec-

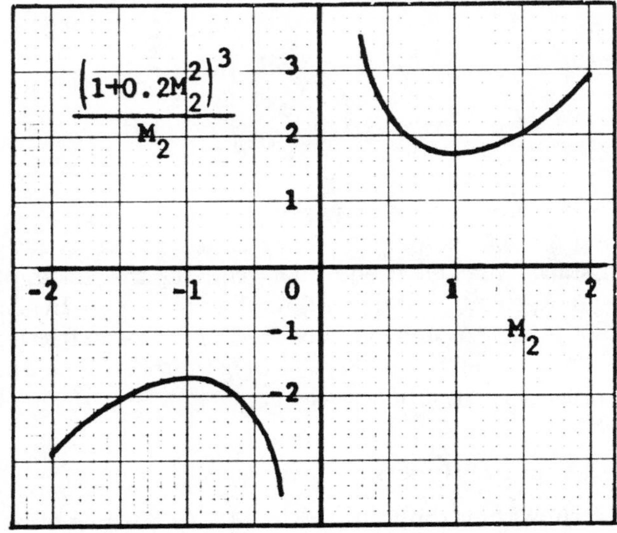

Fig. 27.5. Plot of the left side of Eq. (27.93).

tional area and Mach number as the gas moves the distance dx along the duct. If $M < 1$ the multiplier in parentheses is negative, and a decrease in area causes an increase in gas velocity. A converging duct is a nozzle that accelerates the gas, and a diverging duct is a diffuser that decelerates the gas. If $M > 1$ the multiplier is positive. Then contrary to intuition, a converging duct is a diffuser that decelerates the gas, and a diverging duct is a nozzle that accelerates it. These conclusions are summarized in Fig. 27.6.

Fig. 27.6. Converging and diverging ducts.

What happens if a converging and diverging air duct are connected together as in Fig. 27.7? The cross-sectional area of the duct at the tank outlet is very large, so that the initial Mach number M_o is zero. The tank pressure is p_o. When the back pressure (the pressure outside the exit) is lowered slightly to p_1, a subsonic air flow is established. The

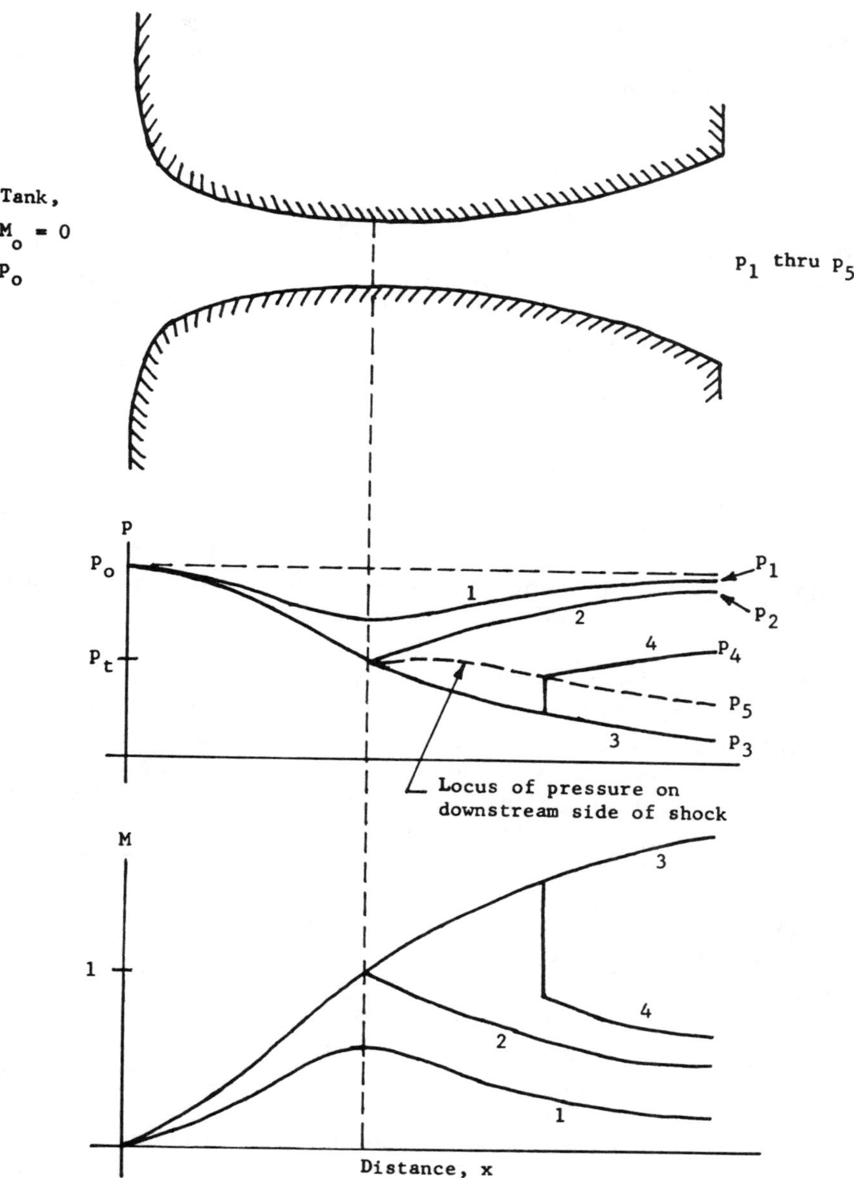

Fig. 27.7. Air flow in a converging-diverging duct.

Mach number increases in the converging section and decreases in the diverging section. The pressure and Mach number follow curves 1 in Fig. 27.7. The flow rate can be varied by varying the back pressure. A slight reduction in the back pressure to p_2 brings the Mach number up to unity at the throat. Then according to Eq. (27.88) the ratio of throat pressure p_t to tank pressure p_o is

$$\frac{p_t}{p_o} = \left(\frac{1}{1.2}\right)^{3.5} = 0.528 \,. \tag{27.95}$$

When the back pressure is lowered below p_2, one might expect the velocity at the throat to become supersonic. The Mach number would have to be 1 at a section upstream from the throat, and increase as the area decreases. But a converging duct cannot accelerate a supersonic flow. The Mach number remains unity at the throat. Since a diverging duct *does* accelerate a supersonic flow, the Mach number now increases in the diverging section. If the flow obeys Eq. (27.91), the exit-plane Mach number can be calculated for a duct of known cross-sectional areas. The corresponding exit-plane pressure, called the *design pressure*, can then be calculated with Eq. (27.88). If the back pressure is lowered so that it equals the design pressure p_3, the pressure and Mach number follow curves 3 in Fig. 27.7. If the back pressure is lowered below p_3, the flow in the duct is unaffected. The air leaves the duct at pressure p_3 and expands down to the back pressure in oblique expansion waves.

If the back pressure is somewhere between p_2 and p_3, it is too high to allow supersonic flow throughout the diverging section, and too low to permit subsonic flow throughout. Nature solves this dilemma by providing a *normal shock wave* in the duct downstream from the throat. A typical normal shock is shown in Fig. 27.8. It is a discontinuity in the fluid properties that extends across the duct roughly normal to the flow. The straight line is a reference wire outside the duct. For a back pressure such as p_4 in Fig. 27.7, the flow between the throat and the shock is supersonic. At the shock the Mach number steps down to a subsonic value and the pressure steps up. (Because of boundary-layer thickening and separation discussed in Ref. 122, p. 141, the step is somewhat ragged.) Then the diverging section of the duct becomes a diffuser, and the pressure rises to equal the back pressure at the exit. As the back pressure is decreased from p_2 toward p_5, the shock moves downstream, its downstream pressure following the dotted line. When the back pressure reaches p_5, the shock is standing in the exit plane of the duct. When the back pressure is lowered still more, toward p_3, the flow throughout the diverging section is supersonic at the design conditions. The exit-plane pressure p_3 is lower than the back pressure. The air is compressed up to the back pressure outside of the duct in oblique shock waves. The operation of the converging-diverging duct can be summarized as follows.

Fig. 27.8. Normal shock wave. (Reprinted by permission from *The Dynamics and Thermodynamics of Compressible Fluid Flow*, Volume I, by Ascher H. Shapiro, Ronald Press, 1953.)

1. If the back pressure is higher than p_2, the flow within the duct is subsonic, and the flow rate varies with the back pressure.

2. If the back pressure is lower than p_2, the flow rate is independent of the back pressure, and the flow pattern upstream from the normal shock is unaffected by changes in the back pressure.

3. If the back pressure is lower than p_5, the flow pattern throughout the duct is the same as that for the design pressure p_3.

The design conditions for isentropic air flow in a converging-diverging nozzle with an initial Mach number of zero are plotted in Figs. 27.9 thru 27.12, according to Eqs. (27.87) thru (27.91). The subscript *o* designates the initial conditions. Fig. 27.9 shows the interesting fact that for one-dimensional flow at velocities up to about Mach 0.3, air can be assumed to be incompressible. These curves help to explain the counter-intuitive fact that a diverging duct accelerates a supersonic flow. According to Eq. (27.2),

$$\rho V A = \text{constant} . \tag{27.96}$$

Figs. 27.9 and 27.12 show that when air is supersonic in a diverging duct, the density ρ decreases faster than the area A increases. The velocity V therefore increases.

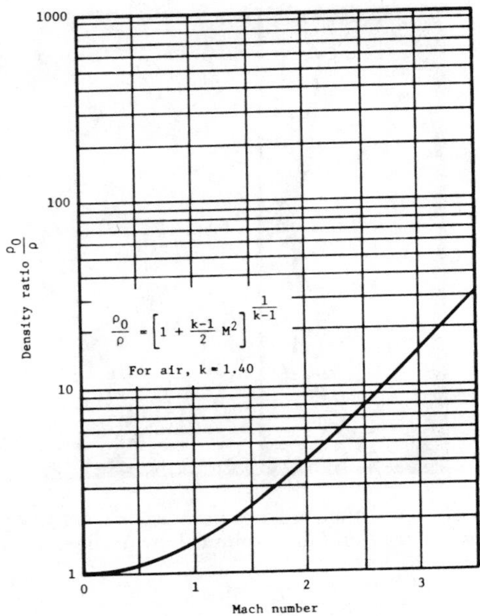

Fig. 27.9. Variation of density ratio during the isentropic expansion of air.

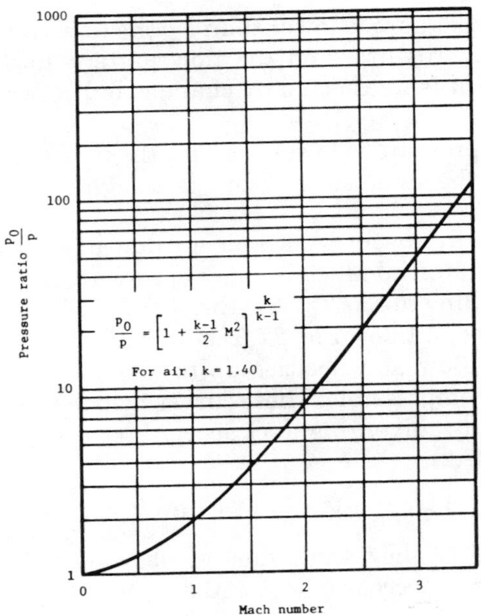

Fig. 27.10. Variation of pressure ratio during the isentropic expansion of air.

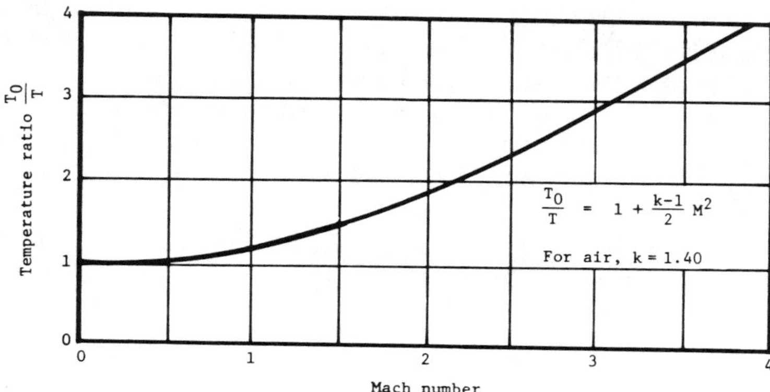

Fig. 27.11. Variation of temperature ratio during the adiabatic (not necessarily isentropic) expansion of air.

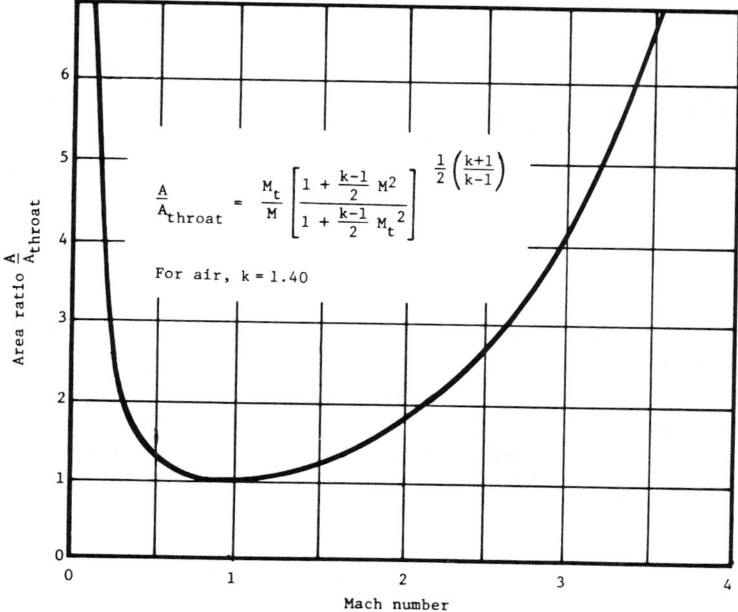

Fig. 27.12. Variation of cross-sectional area ratio during the isentropic expansion of air.

27.9 Stagnation Temperature and Pressure

What temperatures and pressures are measured in a one-dimensional flow? Eq. (27.27) shows that during an adiabatic, no-work process of a perfect gas with constant specific heat c_p, the stagnation temperature T_o remains constant. If the gas moving at velocity V and static temperature T in an insulated duct is stopped, for example by letting it enter a large insulated tank, its temperature rises to

$$T_o = T + \frac{V^2}{2c_p} = T\left(1 + \frac{V^2}{2c_pT}\right) = T\left(1 + \frac{k-1}{2}M^2\right) \tag{27.97}$$

or

$$\frac{T_o}{T} = 1 + \frac{k-1}{2}M^2 . \tag{27.98}$$

The flow does not have to be frictionless. This ratio of stagnation to static temperature is also obtained from Eq. (27.87) by letting M_2 be zero. That equation was derived by assuming that the flow is adiabatic, but again, the assumption of frictionless flow was not required. Neither, incidentally, was the assumption of constant specific heat, although that assumption was made in the first derivation of Eq. (27.98).

A similar formula can be obtained for pressures. Eq. (27.88) shows that if M_2 is zero and the corresponding pressure is p_o, and p is the gas pressure at Mach number M,

$$\frac{p_o}{p} = \left(1 + \frac{k-1}{2}M^2\right)^{k/(k-1)} . \tag{27.99}$$

The pressure p_o is called *stagnation* or *total pressure*, and p is called *static pressure*. Eq. (27.88) required the assumption of isentropic flow. The stagnation pressure of a moving gas is recovered only by stopping it without either friction or heating. In a real adiabatic, no-work process the total pressure drops. For example, in Fig. 27.7 the air leaving the converging-diverging duct comes to rest at the back pressure, which is its final total pressure. This is always less than the initial total pressure p_o. If the duct is well insulated, however, the stagnation temperatures at the inlet and outlet are equal.

In supersonic flows the stagnation pressure p_{o2} is measured by a pitot tube as shown in Fig. 27.13. A curved shock wave stands upstream from the mouth of the tube. Since the flow thru the shock wave is not isentropic, the stagnation pressure p_{o2} is lower than the stagnation pressure p_{o1} upstream from the shock. The static pressure p_1 ahead of the shock is measured by a pressure tap in the duct wall. The free-

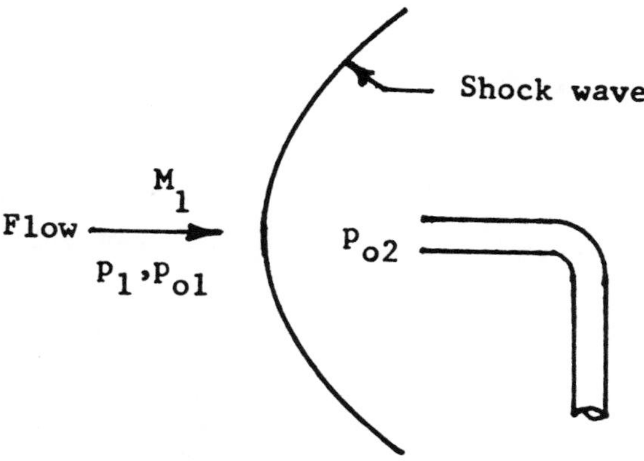

Fig. 27.13. Pitot tube.

stream Mach number M_1 can be calculated from p_1 and p_{o2} by a formula derived in Ref. 122, page 154. For subsonic flows there is no shock wave, and Eq. (27.99) can be used to calculate the Mach number of the gas.

27.10 Heating a Wind Tunnel

The calculation of stagnation temperature in a practical application produces a surprising result. Fig. 27.14 shows a wind tunnel that simu-

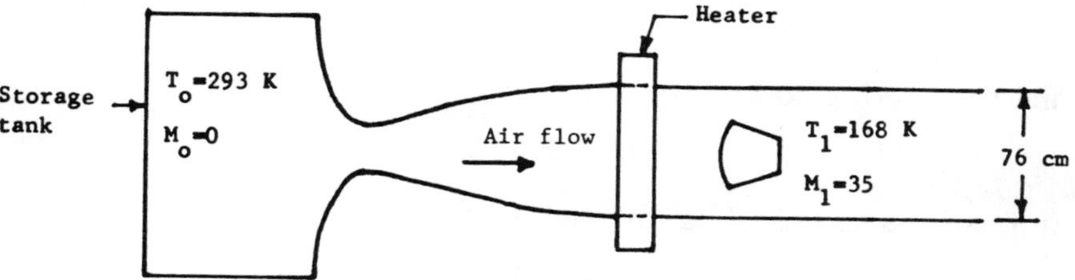

Fig. 27.14. Supersonic wind tunnel.

lates the air flow around a spaceship entering the earth's atmosphere at Mach 35 at an altitude of 91.5 km. The air temperature T_1 there is 168 K, the air density ρ is 2.5×10^{-6} kg/m^3, the specific heat of the air c_p is 1007 J/kg · K, and the ratio of specific heats k is 1.41. The test section of the wind tunnel is a cylinder with a diameter d of 76 cm. The required flow of air is

$$\dot{m} = \rho\, V A = \rho\, V \pi\, d^2/4\,. \tag{27.100}$$

Since the Mach number is

$$M = \frac{V}{\sqrt{k\,R\,T}}\,, \tag{27.101}$$

$$\dot{m} = \pi\, d^2\, \rho\, M \sqrt{k\,R\,T}\,/4\,. \tag{27.102}$$

For air, $R = 286.8$ J/kg · K. The rate of air flow provided by the wind tunnel must therefore be

$$\dot{m} = (\pi)(0.76)^2(2.5 \times 10^{-6})(35)\sqrt{(1.41)(286.8)(168)}/4 = 0.0103 \text{ kg/s}\,. \tag{27.103}$$

The air enters the tunnel from a storage tank in which its stagnation temperature T_o is 293 K. The air is accelerated in a converging-diverging nozzle. Before entering the test section it flows thru a heater, where its stagnation temperature is increased to T_2. The increase in stagnation temperature is ΔT, and the increase in stagnation enthalpy is $c_p\Delta T$. When the air reaches the test section, its static temperature T_1 is 168 K and its Mach number M_1 is 35. According to Eq. (27.97) its stagnation enthalpy is

$$c_pT_2 = c_p(T_o + \Delta T) = c_pT_1\left(1 + \frac{k-1}{2}M_1^2\right). \tag{27.104}$$

The increase in stagnation enthalpy is

$$c_p\Delta T = c_p\left[T_1\left(1 + \frac{k-1}{2}M_1^2\right) - T_o\right] \tag{27.105}$$

and the heating power required is

$$Q = \dot{m}\, c_p\, \Delta T\,. \tag{27.106}$$

If $\dot{m}$ is in kg/s, c_p in J/kg · K, and ΔT in K, Q is in watts. Therefore

$$\begin{aligned} q &= (0.0103)(1007)\left[168\left\{1 + \frac{1.41 - 1}{2}(35)^2\right\} - 293\right](10^{-3}) \\ &= 436 \text{ kw}\,. \end{aligned} \tag{27.107}$$

The addition of this much power to the air in the wind tunnel is a challenging engineering problem. One solution is an electric arc thru which the air passes. The arc is established between the wall of the cylindrical duct and a smaller cylinder concentric with the duct. The arc is made to rotate like the spokes of a wheel by a magnetic field directed axially thru the arc.

The stagnation temperature of the air after heating by the arc is

$$T_2 = T_1\left(1 + \frac{k-1}{2} M_1^2\right) = (168)\left[1 + \frac{1.41 - 1}{2}(35)^2\right]$$

$$= 42{,}357\ \text{K}\,. \tag{27.108}$$

Clearly the static temperature cannot be allowed to approach this number. Since the static temperature of the air with this stagnation temperature and Mach number M is

$$T = \frac{T_2}{1 + \dfrac{k-1}{2} M^2}\,, \tag{27.109}$$

the heat must be added when the air is nearly up to speed.

Chapter 28

HEAT TRANSFER BY CONDUCTION

28.1 Introduction

A knowledge of heat transfer is of great importance to engineers because heat is the final form of all energy. The success of an engine, an electronic package, or an air conditioner depends largely on the skill with which heat in the device is moved from one place to another. Heat can be transferred by conduction, convection, or radiation. Conduction is the transfer of kinetic energy from one molecule of a material to another while the material remains in place. Convection is the transfer of heat between two materials, one of which, a gas or a liquid, is sweeping past the other. Although the fundamental process is still the exchange of kinetic energy between molecules, the fluid flow makes engineering calculations more difficult. The difficulty is tolerable because convection increases dramatically the amount of heat that can be moved from one place to another. Thermal radiation is electromagnetic energy, emitted from any heated body. In a typical engineering problem all three modes of heat transfer must be considered. The reader is invited to identify the modes, in their order of importance, that contribute to

a. heating of a room by a hot-water "radiator",

b. heating of a room by an electric heater whose element glows red,

c. cooling of a beer can packed in crushed ice.

This chapter will consider only conduction. The partial differential equation that governs conductive heat flow, called the Fourier-Biot equation, will be derived, and some practical techniques for solving it will be presented. Although the solutions offer many opportunities for mathematical virtuosity, the physical concepts are simple. The subject of conductive heat transfer consists of (a) finding the amount of heat conducted between bodies whose temperatures and rates of heat generation are known, or (b) calculating the temperatures when the rates of heat generation and heat conduction are known. Although the subject may seem limited, its engineering importance is enormous.

28.2 Fourier's Law

The study of conductive heat transfer begins with Fourier's law. Its derivation starts with Fig. 28.1, a wall of thickness L and area A, whose faces are at a high temperature T_1 and a low temperature T_2. Experiments show that the amount of heat flowing thru the wall in time t is

$$Q = k\,\frac{(T_1 - T_2)At}{L}\,. \tag{28.1}$$

The proportionality constant k is called *thermal conductivity*. In SI units Q is in joules, T_1 and T_2 in kelvins, A in square meters, t in seconds, L in meters, and k in W/m·K. The rate of flow of heat in the n direction, normal to the faces of the wall, is

$$\frac{dQ}{dt} = q = \frac{kA}{L}\,(T_1 - T_2) \qquad \text{watts}\,. \tag{28.2}$$

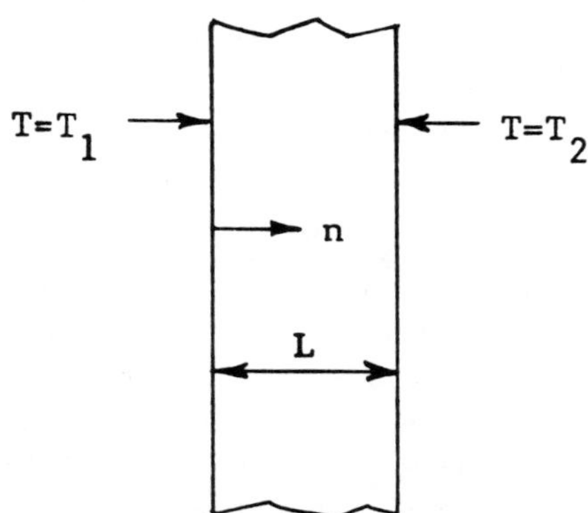

Fig. 28.1. One-dimensional conduction.

Over a short length of the path in the n direction, the distance is dn and the temperature drop is dT. Eq. (28.2) becomes

$$q = -k\,A\,\frac{dT}{dn}\,. \tag{28.3}$$

The minus sign is used to make q positive when $T_1 > T_2$, because then dT/dn is negative. Eq. (28.3) is generally attributed to Jean Fourier (1768–1830) and is called *Fourier's law* for one dimension. Regard q as heat flux and define $\mathbf{q}''$ as the heat flux-density vector, measured in W/m^2. Then

$$\mathbf{q}'' = \lim_{A \to 0} \frac{q}{A} = -\mathbf{n}\,k\,\frac{dT}{dn} \tag{28.4}$$

where **n** is a unit vector in the n direction. Since

$$\nabla T = \mathbf{n}\frac{dT}{dn}, \tag{28.5}$$

$$\mathbf{q}'' = -k\,\nabla T\,. \tag{28.6}$$

This is the three-dimensional form of Fourier's law. It shows that heat flux flows in the direction of the negative gradient of temperature. Fourier's law makes heat transfer a "cleaner" subject than electromagnetic theory or fluid mechanics. The latter two have the analogous formulas

$$\mathbf{D} = -\varepsilon\,\nabla V$$

in which **D** is electric flux density, ε is permittivity, and V is electrostatic potential, and

$$\mathbf{v} = \nabla\phi$$

where **v** is fluid velocity and ϕ is velocity potential. These formulas are not always valid, because V exists only if the magnetic flux density is time invariant, and ϕ exists only if the fluid is irrotational. The potential T, however, always exists, and Fourier's law (28.6) is always valid.

28.3 The Fourier-Biot Equation

Fourier's law will now be converted to a form that is useful for solving engineering problems. First determine the rate of heat flow entering, stored in, generated in, and leaving a differential volume. Instead of drawing the usual small rectangular solid and calculating the flux entering and leaving thru the various faces, draw a control volume and invoke the power of vector analysis. Fig. 28.2 shows a volume v enclosed

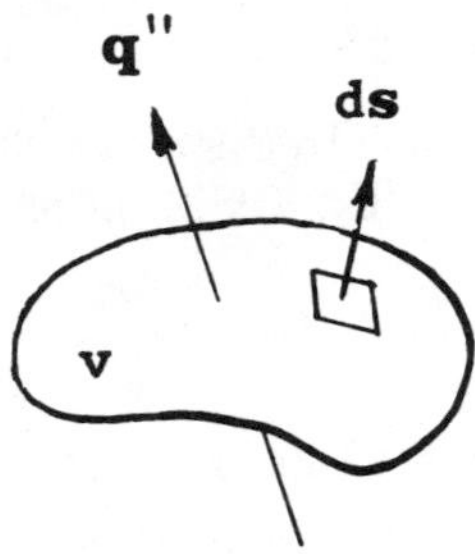

Fig. 28.2. Closed surface.

by a surface s thru which heat is flowing. A differential area of the surface is represented by the vector $d\mathbf{s}$. If q_{in} and q_{out} are the amounts of heat flux entering and leaving the surface, the net flow of flux out of the surface is

$$q_{out} - q_{in} = \oint_s \mathbf{q}'' \cdot d\mathbf{s} \qquad \text{watts} . \tag{28.7}$$

If heat is being stored within the volume, the temperature at any point is rising at the rate $\partial T/\partial t$. The rate of heat storage is

$$q_{stored} = \int_v \rho\, c \frac{\partial T}{\partial t}\, dv \qquad \text{watts} , \tag{28.8}$$

where ρ is the density of the material in kg/m^3, c is its specific heat in J/kg·K, and v is its volume in m^3. Heat might be generated within the volume, at the rate of γ W/m^3. Examples are the heat generated in a current-carrying conductor as I^2R loss, in a transformer core by the hysteresis and eddy currents, in the fuel elements of an atomic reactor, in the flame of a burning fuel, and in curing concrete. The total heat generated in the volume is

$$q_{gen} = \int_v \gamma\, dv . \tag{28.9}$$

Since

$$q_{out} - q_{in} = q_{gen} - q_{stored} , \tag{28.10}$$

$$\oint_s \mathbf{q}'' \cdot d\mathbf{s} = \int_v \left(\gamma - \rho\, c \frac{\partial T}{\partial t}\right) dv . \tag{28.11}$$

According to Gauss's divergence theorem, the left side can be written as

$$\oint_s \mathbf{q}'' \cdot d\mathbf{s} = \int_v (\nabla \cdot \mathbf{q}'') dv , \tag{28.12}$$

where the volume integral extends throughout the volume enclosed by the surface integral. Eq. (28.11) becomes

$$\int_v (\nabla \cdot \mathbf{q}'') dv = \int_v \left(\gamma - \rho\, c \frac{\partial T}{\partial t}\right) dv . \tag{28.13}$$

Since this equation is true for any volume v, the integrands must be equal:

$$\nabla \cdot \mathbf{q}'' = \gamma - \rho\, c \frac{\partial T}{\partial t} . \tag{28.14}$$

Substituting Eq. (28.6) into this equation yields

$$\nabla \cdot (-k\, \nabla T) = \gamma - \rho\, c \frac{\partial T}{\partial t} . \tag{28.15}$$

If the thermal conductivity is independent of position, it can be brought out of the divergence derivative, and then

$$\nabla^2 T = \frac{\rho c}{k}\frac{\partial T}{\partial t} - \frac{\gamma}{k}. \tag{28.16}$$

The parameter

$$\alpha = \frac{k}{\rho c} \qquad \text{m}^2/\text{s} \tag{28.17}$$

is called *thermal diffusivity*. With it included, Eq. (28.16) is

$$\nabla^2 T = \frac{1}{\alpha}\frac{\partial T}{\partial t} - \frac{\gamma}{k}. \tag{28.18}$$

This is the general heat-conduction equation, often called the *Fourier equation* or the *Fourier-Biot equation*. The properties α, ρ, c, and k for various materials are tabulated in books on heat transfer, such as Refs. 26, 47, and 125.

In a region in which no heat is generated, the Fourier-Biot equation reduces to

$$\nabla^2 T = \frac{1}{\alpha}\frac{\partial T}{\partial t}, \tag{28.19}$$

which is an example of the *diffusion equation*. If the temperatures in a body do not vary with time, the Fourier-Biot equation becomes

$$\nabla^2 T = -\frac{\gamma}{k}, \tag{28.20}$$

which is an example of the *Poisson equation*. For a material with steady temperatures and no internal heat generation, the temperature is governed by *Laplace's equation:*

$$\nabla^2 T = 0. \tag{28.21}$$

The last four partial differential equations are encountered in many branches of engineering and science. The analytical study of conductive heat transfer consists of the study of ways of solving these equations with various boundary conditions.

28.4 Steady-State Conduction

All of the tools for solving Laplace's equation are available for calculating steady temperatures where heat is not being generated. These include flux plotting, separation of variables, Green's functions, iterative solutions with difference equations, and electrical analogs, both continuous and lumped. The last of these is obtained by solving Laplace's equation for the one-dimensional heat flow in Fig. 28.1 with $n = x$:

$$\frac{d^2T}{dx^2} = 0 . \tag{28.22}$$

The solution is

$$T = A\,x + B . \tag{28.23}$$

With the boundary conditions $T(0) = T_1$ and $T(L) = T_2$, it becomes

$$T = T_1 - (T_1 - T_2)\frac{x}{L} . \tag{28.24}$$

The heat flow thru the wall is obtained by applying Fourier's law, Eq. (28.3):

$$q = -k\,A\frac{\partial T}{\partial x} = \frac{kA}{L}(T_1 - T_2) , \tag{28.25}$$

which agrees with Eq. (28.2). The last equation is analogous to Ohm's law:

$$I = \frac{1}{R}(V_1 - V_2) . \tag{28.26}$$

The quantity L/kA is analogous to the electrical resistance R. To illustrate the use of this analogy, calculate the heat flow thru the three-layer wall in Fig. 28.3. The conductivities of the layers are k_1, k_2, and k_3, and

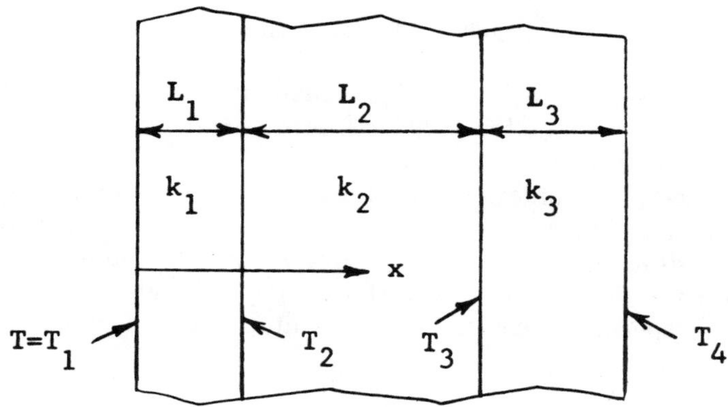

Fig. 28.3. Three-layer wall.

the heat flows in the x direction. According to Eq. (28.25) the rates of heat flow thru the three layers are

$$q_1 = k_1 A \frac{T_1 - T_2}{L_1}, \quad q_2 = k_2 A \frac{T_2 - T_3}{L_2}, \quad q_3 = k_3 A \frac{T_3 - T_4}{L_3}, \tag{28.27}$$

where A is the wall area. Since $q_1 = q_2 = q_3$, call them q and write

$$T_1 - T_2 = \frac{L_1}{k_1 A} q, \quad T_2 - T_3 = \frac{L_2}{k_2 A} q, \quad T_3 - T_4 = \frac{L_3}{k_3 A} q, \tag{28.28}$$

or

$$T_1 - T_4 = \left(\frac{L_1}{k_1 A} + \frac{L_2}{k_2 A} + \frac{L_3}{k_3 A}\right) q. \tag{28.29}$$

The heat-flow path is analogous to the electrical circuit of Fig. 28.4 in which

$$R_1 = \frac{L_1}{k_1 A}, \quad R_2 = \frac{L_2}{k_2 A}, \quad R_3 = \frac{L_3}{k_3 A}. \tag{28.30}$$

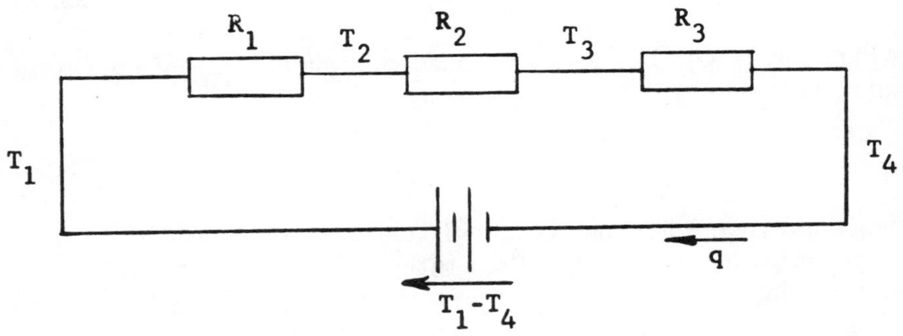

Fig. 28.4. Electrical analog.

The rate of heat flow q can be calculated easily if any two temperatures are known, and all of the temperatures can be calculated if q and one temperature are known.

Lumped electrical analogs are useful when the equivalent resistors are in parallel as well as in series. For example, the heat generated in the rotor winding of a motor can flow axially along the conductor to the end of the rotor or radially out to the air gap. The electrical analog constitutes a special-purpose analog computer, whose parameters are easily changed.

28.5 Heat Generation

In a region of heat generation, steady temperature is governed by Eq. (28.20). For example, suppose that heat is being generated uniformly throughout the wall in Fig. 28.1, at the rate of γ W/m^3. In one dimension, Eq. (28.20) is

$$\frac{d^2T}{dx^2} = -\frac{\gamma}{k}. \tag{28.31}$$

This is an example of Poisson's equation, so simple that it can be solved by integrating twice. Thus,

$$T = -\frac{\gamma x^2}{2k} + A\,x + B. \tag{28.32}$$

Applying the boundary conditions $T(0) = T_1$ and $T(L) = T_2$ to evaluate the two constants produces the result

$$T = T_1 - (T_1 - T_2)\frac{x}{L} + \frac{\gamma}{2k}(L - x)x. \tag{28.33}$$

The heat flow is obtained from Fourier's law:

$$q = -k\,A\frac{\partial T}{\partial x} = \frac{kA}{L}(T_1 - T_2) - \frac{A\gamma}{2}(L - 2x). \tag{28.34}$$

Fig. 28.5 shows the temperature distribution in the wall with and without heat generation, for the parameters $L = 1$ m, $\gamma/2k = 40$°C/m^2, $T_1 = 20$°C, and $T_2 = 10$°C. Since the heat flow is proportional to $-dT/dx$, its direction is the same as that of a ball rolling down the curve. Fig. 28.5 shows that the heat generation γ is great enough to make the heat flow out of both faces of the wall.

Frequently one or more boundary conditions of the Fourier-Biot equation are temperature gradients instead of temperatures. An example is provided by a stainless-steel pressure tube in a nuclear test reactor. Heat is generated uniformly throughout the steel by neutron flux and is removed by cooling water which flows thru the tube, keeping the inner surface at a temperature T_0. The outside of the tube is surrounded by a jacket containing a layer of hydrogen that is about as thick as the tube wall. If the diameter of the tube is large compared to its wall thickness L, the heat flow is one dimensional in the plane shown in Fig. 28.6. The thermal conductivities of hydrogen and stainless steel are about 0.2 and 16 W/m·K. Since the thermal resistance L/kA of the hydrogen is therefore about 80 times that of the steel, the hydrogen prevents heat flow radially outward to the reactor water. Assume that at $x = L$, $q = -kA\,\partial T/\partial x = 0$. Stated elegantly, the problem is

$$\frac{d^2T}{dx^2} = -\frac{\gamma}{k}, \qquad 0 \leqslant x \leqslant L \tag{28.35}$$

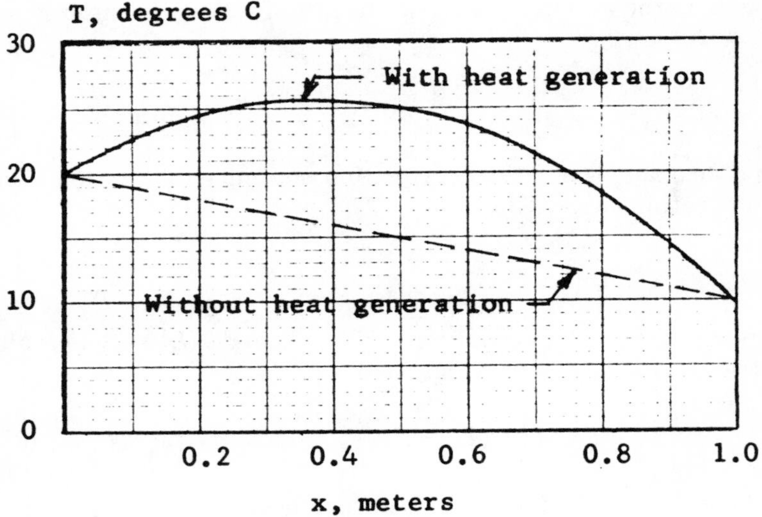

Fig. 28.5. Temperature distribution in the wall.

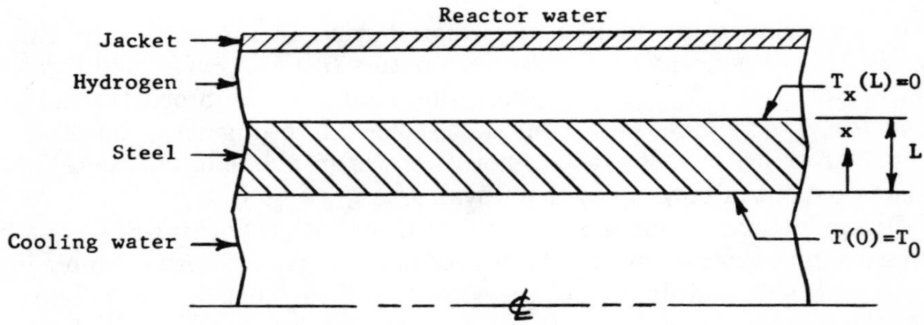

Fig. 28.6. Reactor pressure tube.

with the boundary conditions

$$T(0) = T_0\,, \quad \left.\frac{\partial T}{\partial x}\right|_{x=L} = 0\,. \tag{28.36}$$

Mathematicians frequently denote partial derivatives by subscripts. The second boundary condition can be written more simply as $T_x(L) = 0$. The solution of Eq. (28.35) is Eq. (28.32):

$$T = -\frac{\gamma x^2}{2k} + A\,x + B\,. \tag{28.37}$$

The first boundary condition shows that $B = T_0$. According to the second,

$$T_x(L) = -\frac{\gamma L}{k} + A = 0\,. \tag{28.38}$$

The temperature at any point in the wall of the pressure tube is therefore

$$T = -\frac{\gamma x^2}{2k} + \frac{\gamma L}{k}x + T_0 = T_0 + \frac{\gamma L^2}{2k}\left[2\frac{x}{L} - \left(\frac{x}{L}\right)^2\right]. \tag{28.39}$$

This parabola is shown in Fig. 28.7. Notice again that the heat flows "down the curve" at a rate proportional to the slope.

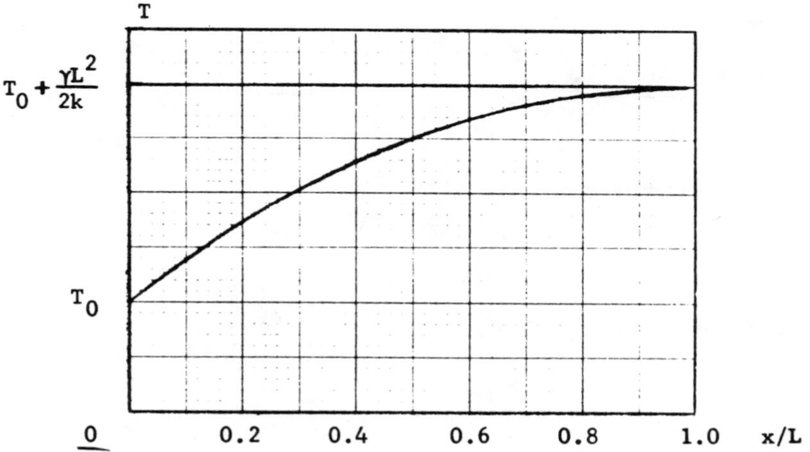

Fig. 28.7. Temperature distribution in the pressure-tube wall.

28.6 Heat Flow in a Composite Structure

In many practical problems, heat flows by conduction between materials of different thermal conductivities. As an illustration, calculate the temperature distribution in a fuel plate of a nuclear reactor shown in Fig. 28.8. The plate might consist of a layer 0.3 inches thick of UO_2

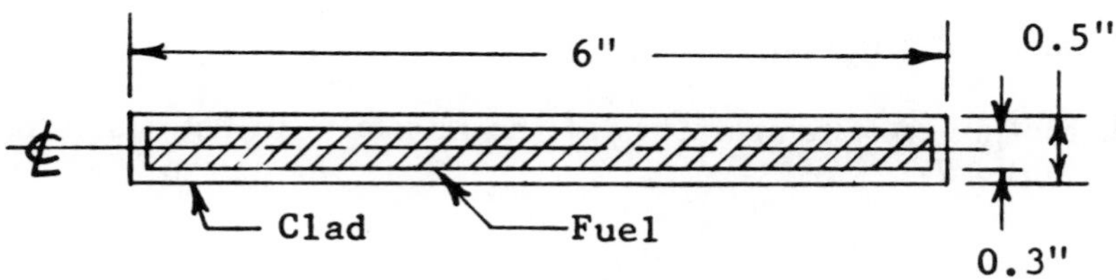

Fig. 28.8. Reactor fuel plate.

fuel, clad with zircalloy. The overall dimensions might be 6 × 0.5 × 40 inches. Heat generated in the fuel is removed by water flowing past the plate at temperature T_0. Since the plate is thin, the heat flow is vertical except near the edges. And since the plate is symmetrical, no heat flows across the horizontal central plane. The heat flow across the interface between the fuel and clad is continuous. If the two materials are bonded tightly together, the temperature drop in the gap between them is negligible. The temperature is then continuous at the interface. Fig. 28.9 shows a small portion of Fig. 28.8 in which the thermal conductivi-

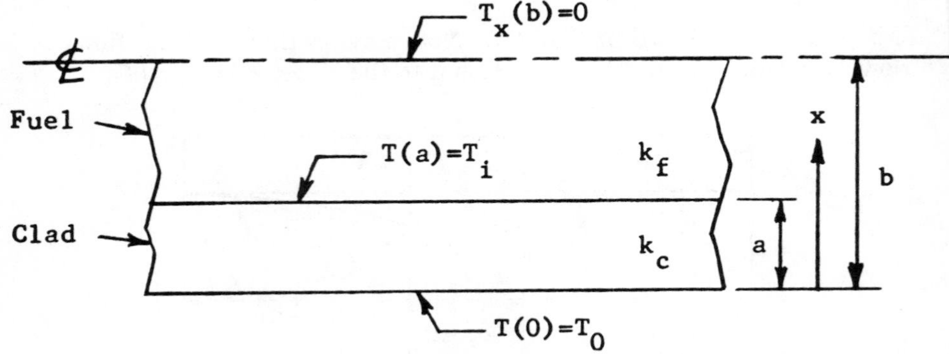

Fig. 28.9. Blown-up piece of the fuel plate.

ties of the fuel and clad are k_f and k_c. The temperature in the clad is governed by Laplace's equation, which in one dimension is

$$\frac{d^2T}{dx^2} = 0\,, \quad 0 \leqslant x < a \tag{28.40}$$

and in the fuel by the Poisson equation in one dimension:

$$\frac{d^2T}{dx^2} = -\frac{\gamma}{k_f}, \quad a < x \leqslant b\,. \tag{28.41}$$

The boundary conditions consist of

1. the known temperature $T(0) = T_0$.

2. the known gradient $T_x(b) = 0$.

3. continuity of temperature at the interface. In both materials, $T(a) = T_i$.

4. continuity of heat flow at the interface.

The temperature of the fuel can be obtained by solving Eq. (28.41) and applying boundary conditions 2 and 3. The result is the same as Eq. (28.39) with appropriate changes in the nomenclature:

$$T = T_i + \frac{\gamma(b-a)^2}{2k_f}\left[2\frac{x-a}{b-a} - \left(\frac{x-a}{b-a}\right)^2\right], \quad a \leqslant x \leqslant b\,. \tag{28.42}$$

The temperature of the clad is obtained from Eq. (28.40) and boundary conditions 1 and 3. The result, written by inspection, is

$$T = T_0 + \frac{T_i - T_0}{a}x\,, \quad 0 \leqslant x \leqslant a\,. \tag{28.43}$$

To evaluate the interface temperature T_i, apply the fourth boundary condition. If T_f and T_c are the temperatures in the fuel and the clad,

$$q''(a) = -k_f \left.\frac{\partial T_f}{\partial x}\right|_{x=a} = -k_c \left.\frac{\partial T_c}{\partial x}\right|_{x=a} \tag{28.44}$$

or

$$\gamma(b-a) = k_c \frac{T_i - T_0}{a} \tag{28.45}$$

or

$$T_i = T_0 + \frac{\gamma a(b-a)}{k_c}\,. \tag{28.46}$$

The temperatures are plotted in Fig. 28.10 for these representative parameters:

$k_f = 0.2$ Btu/hr·in·°F	$\gamma = 1{,}500$ Btu/hr·in^3
$k_c = 1.02$ Btu/hr·in·°F	$a = 0.1$ in
$T_0 = 500$°F	$b = 0.25$ in

The curve illustrates dramatically that the temperature gradient $\partial T/\partial x$ is not continuous at the interface between the two materials. The heat flux density $q''(x) = -k\,\partial T/\partial x$ and the temperature $T(x)$ *are* continuous.

28.7 An Electric-Field Analogy

An interesting analogy exists between Eq. (28.6), namely

$$\mathbf{q}'' = -k\,\nabla T \qquad \text{W/m}^2 \tag{28.47}$$

and the definition of electric flux density

$$\mathbf{D} = -\varepsilon\,\nabla V \qquad \text{coulombs/meter}^2\,, \tag{28.48}$$

where V is electric potential in volts, and ε is the permittivity of the medium in farads/meter. The quantity $\mathbf{E} = -\nabla V$ is called *electric field*

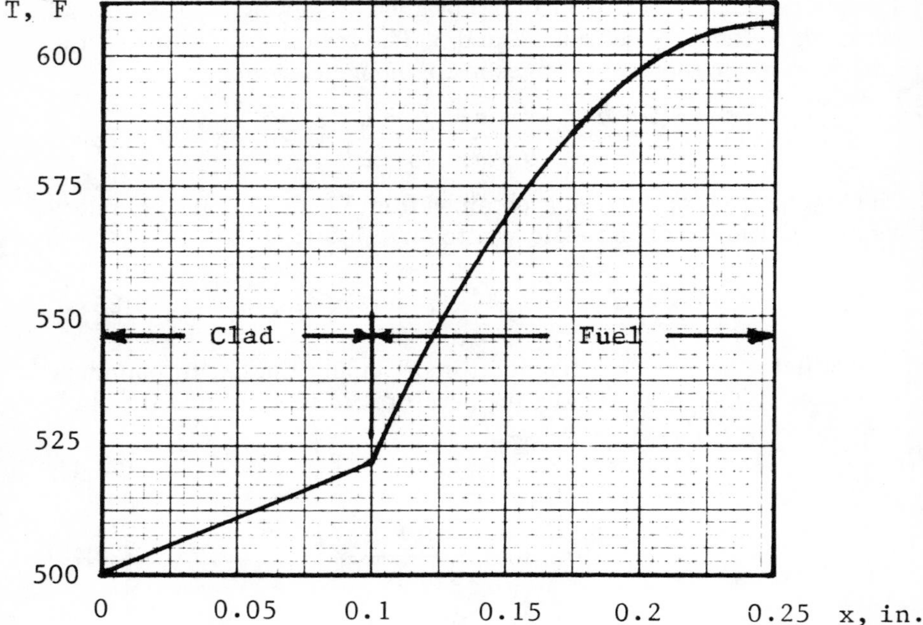

Fig. 28.10. Temperature distribution in the fuel plate.

intensity and has physical significance. It is the force on a positive one-coulomb charge in an electrostatic field. The analogous quantity equal to the negative of the temperature gradient ∇T, which might be called *thermal field intensity*, lacks physical significance, and does not have a standard symbol. Ref. 85 shows that at the interface between two materials of different permittivities ε_1 and ε_2, the electric flux-density vector $\mathbf{D}$ and the potential-gradient vector ∇V refract so that the relationship of Eq. (28.48) is preserved in both materials. Similarly, at the interface of two materials of different thermal conductivities, the heat flux-density vector $\mathbf{q}''$ and the temperature-gradient vector ∇T refract to preserve Eq. (28.47) in both materials. Fig. 28.11 shows these vectors at the interface of two materials with thermal conductivities k_1 and k_2 whose ratio is 3. For convenience the vectors in material 1, $\mathbf{q}_1''$ and $-\nabla T_1$, are drawn with equal lengths. To show how the vectors refract, calculate the normal components of $\mathbf{q}''$ and the tangential components of $-\nabla T$ on both sides of the interface. Since the curl of any gradient is zero, $\nabla \times \nabla T = 0$. According to Stokes' theorem,

$$\int_s (\nabla \times \nabla T) \cdot d\mathbf{s} = \oint \nabla T \cdot d\ell = 0\,, \tag{28.49}$$

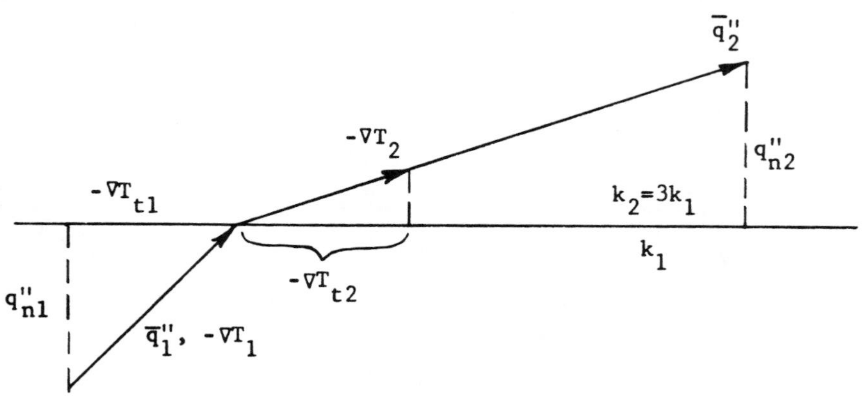

Fig. 28.11. Refraction of heat flux density and temperature gradient.

where the surface integral extends over any surface terminating on the path of the line integral. If the line integral in Fig. 28.12 proceeds for any distance between points a and b along the interface of the two

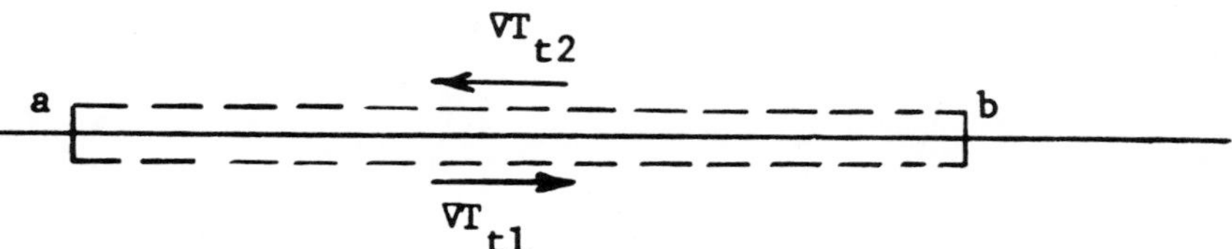

Fig. 28.12. Path of integration of ∇T.

materials just inside material 1, and back just inside material 2, the result is

$$\oint \nabla T \cdot d\ell = \int_a^b \nabla T_{t1} d\ell + \int_b^a \nabla T_{t2} d\ell = 0 \, , \tag{28.50}$$

where ∇T_{t1} and ∇T_{t2} are the tangential components of ∇T in the two materials. Since the equation is true for any a and b, the integrands must be equal:

$$\nabla T_{t1} = \nabla T_{t2} \, . \tag{28.51}$$

Thus the tangential component of temperature gradient ∇T is continuous across the boundary between two materials with unequal thermal conductivities.

Now examine the heat flux density $\mathbf{q}''$ at the boundary, and integrate $\mathbf{q}''$ over a closed surface lying just below and just above the interface as shown in Fig. 28.13. Eq. (28.11) is

$$\oint_s \mathbf{q}'' \cdot d\mathbf{s} = \int_v \left(\gamma - \rho\, c \frac{\partial T}{\partial t}\right) dv\,. \tag{28.52}$$

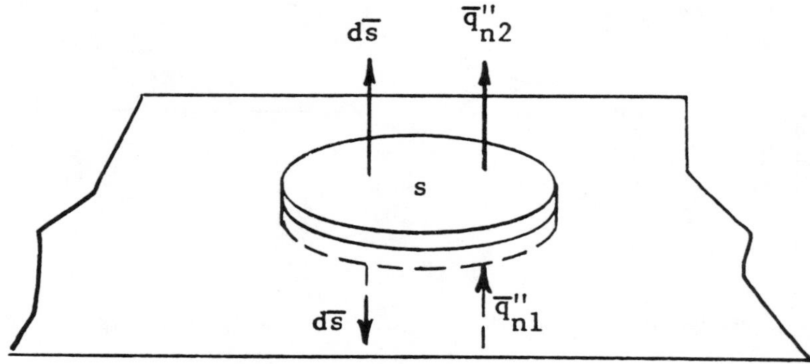

Fig. 28.13. Surface of integration of $\mathbf{q}''$.

The integrand of the volume integral is always a finite number. Therefore as the top and bottom faces of area s are moved arbitrarily close together, the volume integral approaches zero, and

$$\oint \mathbf{q}'' \cdot d\mathbf{s} = \int_s q''_{n2} ds - \int_s q''_{n1} ds = 0\,, \tag{28.53}$$

where q''_{n1} and q''_{n2} are the normal components of $\mathbf{q}''$ in the two materials at their interface. Since this equation is true for any surface area s, the integrands must be equal:

$$q''_{n1} = q''_{n2}\,. \tag{28.54}$$

Thus the normal component $q''_n = -k\ \partial T/\partial n$ of heat flux density $\mathbf{q}''$ is continuous across the boundary of two materials with unequal thermal conductivities:

$$k_1(\partial T/\partial n)_1 = k_2(\partial T/\partial n)_2\,. \tag{28.55}$$

The normal component $\partial T/\partial n$ of temperature gradient is *not* continuous.

In order to satisfy Eqs. (28.54), (28.51), and (28.47), the vectors $\mathbf{q}''$ and $-\nabla V$ must refract at the interface as shown in Fig. 28.11. If material 2 is a good conductor of heat such as copper or silver (see Fig. 28.14), and material 1 is a poor conductor such as wood or water, the temperature gradient ∇T_2 is much lower than ∇T_1. Since ∇T_{t2} is small, ∇T_{t1} is small at the interface. Since the normal component of ∇T_1 is not small, the vector ∇T_1 is nearly perpendicular to the interface. If material 2 is a perfect heat conductor with $k_2 = \infty$, the gradient ∇T_1 and heat flux

Material	Conductivity, W/m·K
wood	0.1-0.2
water	0.597
copper	386
silver	407

Fig. 28.14. Conductivities of materials at 20°C.

density $\mathbf{q}_1''$ in material 1 are perpendicular to the interface where they enter it.

28.8 The General Fourier-Biot Equation

The examples shown thus far have illustrated only steady heat flow. Now solve the Fourier-Biot equation by separation of variables in its most general form:

$$\nabla^2 T = \frac{1}{\alpha}\frac{\partial T}{\partial t} - \frac{\gamma}{k} . \quad (28.56)$$

The boundary conditions, which must be known on all of the boundaries of the region of interest, may be either the temperature T, the normal derivative of temperature $\partial T/\partial n$, or a weighted sum of the two: $aT + b\,\partial T/\partial n$. The latter boundary condition is frequently known when heat flows by both conduction and convection. This analysis will consider only time-independent boundary conditions, and will assume that the initial temperature distribution throughout the region is known. The procedure for solving Eq. (28.56) is as follows.

1. Write the temperature $T(x, y, z, t)$ as the sum of a steady and a transient component:

$$T(x,y,z,t) = T_s(x,y,z) + T_t(x,y,z,t) . \quad (28.57)$$

2. Calculate the steady-state temperature, governed by the Poisson equation

$$\nabla^2 T_s = -\frac{\gamma}{k} . \quad (28.58)$$

Apply the boundary conditions of the actual problem.

3. Calculate the transient temperature by solving the diffusion equation

$$\nabla^2 T_t = \frac{1}{\alpha} \frac{\partial T_t}{\partial t} \tag{28.59}$$

with all of the boundary conditions set at zero:

$$T_t = 0 \,, \quad \partial T_t/\partial n = 0 \,, \quad a\, T_t + b\, \partial T_t/\partial n = 0 \,. \tag{28.60}$$

These are called *homogeneous* boundary conditions. Notice that the sum $T_s + T_t$ satisfies the Fourier-Biot equation and also fulfills the boundary conditions. Some of the constants in the product solution of the diffusion equation will still not be evaluated.

4. To evaluate the remaining constants, equate the sum $T_s + T_t$ at $t = 0$, namely $T_s(x, y, z) + T_t(x, y, z, 0)$, to the known initial temperature distribution $T(x, y, z, 0)$.

To illustrate the method, calculate the transient temperature distribution in the reactor pressure tube of Fig. 28.6, shown again in Fig. 28.15. Heat flows in the x direction only. At $x = L$ the tube is insulated so that $\partial T/\partial x$ is zero there. Initially the tube and the cooling water are at the ambient temperature, T_1. Then the reactor is started up. Uniform heat generation of γ W/m^3 begins in the tube, and the temperature of the cooling water rises abruptly from T_1 to T_0. Assume that the temperature of the tube surface at $x = 0$ also rises abruptly to T_0 and stays there.

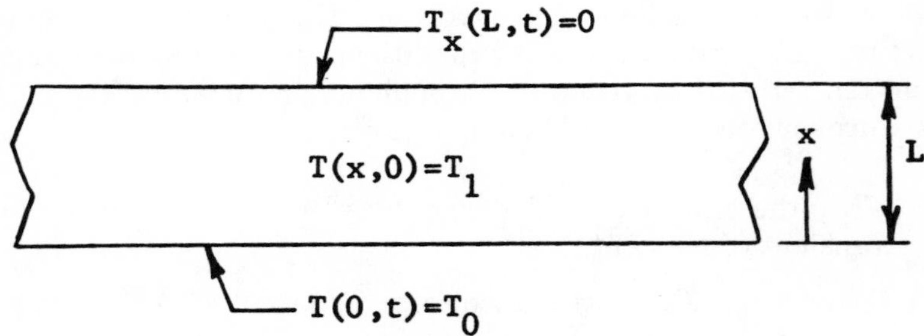

Fig. 28.15. Reactor pressure tube with transient heating.

Stated elegantly, the problem consists of solving

$$\frac{\partial^2 T}{\partial x^2} = \frac{1}{\alpha} \frac{\partial T}{\partial t} - \frac{\gamma}{k}, \qquad 0 \leqslant x \leqslant L \tag{28.61}$$

subject to the boundary conditions

$$T(0,t) = T_0 , \qquad t > 0 , \tag{28.62}$$

$$T_x(L,t) = 0 , \qquad t \geqslant 0 , \tag{28.63}$$

and the initial condition

$$T(x,0) = T_1 , \qquad 0 \leqslant x \leqslant L . \tag{28.64}$$

The temperature in the tube is the sum of the steady-state and transient components:

$$T(x,t) = T_s(x) + T_t(x,t) . \tag{28.65}$$

The steady-state temperature is governed by Poisson's equation, which in one dimension is

$$\frac{d^2T_s}{dx^2} = -\frac{\gamma}{k} . \tag{28.66}$$

The solution of this equation with the same boundary conditions is given by Eq. (28.39):

$$T_s = T_0 + \frac{\gamma L^2}{2k}\left[2\frac{x}{L} - \left(\frac{x}{L}\right)^2\right] . \tag{28.67}$$

The transient temperature obeys the diffusion equation

$$\frac{\partial^2 T_t}{\partial x^2} = \frac{1}{\alpha}\frac{\partial T_t}{\partial t} . \tag{28.68}$$

Assume the product solution

$$T_t = X(x)Y(t) \tag{28.69}$$

and substitute it back into Eq. (28.68) to get

$$\frac{1}{X}\frac{\partial^2 X}{\partial x^2} = \frac{1}{\alpha Y}\frac{\partial Y}{\partial t} = -\lambda^2 . \tag{28.70}$$

Then

$$\frac{d^2X}{dx^2} + \lambda^2 X = 0 , \tag{28.71}$$

and

$$X = A \sin \lambda x + B \cos \lambda x . \tag{28.72}$$

Also

$$\frac{dY}{dt} + \lambda^2 \alpha Y = 0 , \tag{28.73}$$

and

$$Y = e^{-\lambda^2 \alpha t} . \tag{28.74}$$

The product solution is

$$T_t = \sum_{\lambda} e^{-\lambda^2 \alpha t}(A_\lambda \sin \lambda x + B_\lambda \cos \lambda x) . \tag{28.75}$$

The solution with $\lambda = 0$, namely $T_t = A_0 x + B_0$, is included in the steady-state solution, Eq. (28.67), and need not be included here. To evaluate the constants in Eq. (28.75), apply the homogeneous boundary conditions $T(0, t) = 0$ and $T_x(L, t) = 0$. According to the first of these, $B_\lambda = 0$, and Eq. (28.75) reduces to

$$T_t = \sum_{\lambda} A_\lambda e^{-\lambda^2 \alpha t} \sin \lambda x . \tag{28.76}$$

According to the second homogeneous boundary condition,

$$\frac{\partial T_t(L,t)}{\partial x} = \sum_{\lambda} \lambda A_\lambda e^{-\lambda^2 \alpha t} \cos \lambda L = 0 , \tag{28.77}$$

which requires that

$$\cos \lambda L = 0$$

or

$$\lambda = \frac{n\pi}{2L}, \qquad n = 1,3,5, \ldots \tag{28.78}$$

The transient temperature is therefore

$$T_t = \sum_{n=1,3}^{\infty} A_n e^{-(n\pi/2L)^2 \alpha t} \sin \frac{n\pi x}{2L}, \qquad n \text{ odd} . \tag{28.79}$$

The actual temperature in the pressure tube is the sum of the steady-state and transient temperatures:

$$T = T_s + T_t = T_0 + \frac{\gamma L^2}{2k}\left[2\frac{x}{L} - \left(\frac{x}{L}\right)^2\right] + \sum_{n=1,3}^{\infty} A_n e^{-(n\pi/2L)^2 \alpha t} \sin \frac{n\pi x}{2L} . \tag{28.80}$$

Now according to the initial condition $T(x, 0) = T_1$,

$$T_1 = T_0 + \frac{\gamma L^2}{2k}\left[2\frac{x}{L} - \left(\frac{x}{L}\right)^2\right] + \sum_{n=1,3}^{\infty} A_n \sin \frac{n\pi x}{2L} . \tag{28.81}$$

The constants A_n can be evaluated by taking advantage of the orthogonality of the functions $\sin (n\pi x/2L)$. Multiplying both sides of Eq. (28.81) by $\sin (m\pi x/2L)$ and integrating with respect to x from 0 to L produces

$$\int_0^L (T_1 - T_0)\sin\frac{m\pi x}{2L}\,dx = \frac{\gamma L^2}{2k}\int_0^L \left[2\frac{x}{L} - \left(\frac{x}{L}\right)^2\right]\sin\frac{m\pi x}{2L}\,dx$$

$$+ \int_0^L \sin\frac{m\pi x}{2L}\sum_{n=1}^{\infty} A_n \sin\frac{n\pi x}{2L}\,dx\,, \qquad n \text{ odd}\,. \tag{28.82}$$

If m is an odd integer,

$$\int_0^L (T_1 - T_0)\sin\frac{m\pi x}{2L}\,dx = \frac{2L}{m\pi}(T_1 - T_0)\,, \tag{28.83}$$

and if m and n are both odd integers,

$$\int_0^L \sin\frac{m\pi x}{2L}\sin\frac{n\pi x}{2L}\,dx = \frac{L}{2}\,\delta_{mn}\,. \tag{28.84}$$

For odd integral values of m, the last integral of Eq. (28.82) reduces to $A_m L/2$. Then

$$A_n = \frac{2}{L}\left[\frac{2L}{n\pi}(T_1 - T_0) - \frac{\gamma L^2}{2k}\int_0^L \left[2\frac{x}{L} - \left(\frac{x}{L}\right)^2\right]\sin\frac{n\pi x}{2L}\,dx\right]. \tag{28.85}$$

Eqs. (28.80) and (28.85) constitute the solution of the problem. Notice that after the transient has subsided, Eq. (28.80) agrees with Eq. (28.39).

If no heat is being generated in the region of interest, the Fourier-Biot equation reduces to the diffusion equation

$$\nabla^2 T = \frac{1}{\alpha}\frac{\partial T}{\partial t}\,. \tag{28.86}$$

The solution proceeds as before. The steady-state temperature now obeys Laplace's equation

$$\nabla^2 T_s = 0\,. \tag{28.87}$$

For the pressure tube the solution is obtained by either (a) separation of variables, (b) setting γ equal to zero in Eq. (28.67), or (c) observing the physical picture in Fig. 28.15, which shows that $T_s = T_0$. The solution for the transient temperature T_t is the same as before down to Eq. (28.79). From there on the procedure is the same but involves fewer terms because γ is zero.

The reader is invited to test his or her understanding by calculating the temperatures in a large, thin, flat steel plate shown in Fig. 28.16. The plate is initially at temperature T_0 throughout. Starting at time zero it is cooled by immersion in a tank of oil at temperature T_1. What is

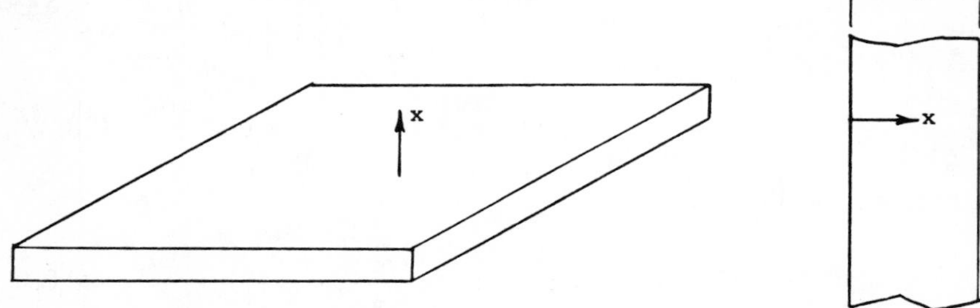

Fig. 28.16. Large plate of thickness L.

the subsequent temperature distribution as a function of distance x and time t? Assume that

$$T(0,t) = T(L,t) = T_1 , \qquad t > 0 . \tag{28.88}$$

The temperature of the surfaces is actually higher than T_1. The temperature drop between the surfaces of the plate and the oil is caused by convective heat transfer, the subject of Chapter 30.

28.9 An Interesting Transient Analog

Heat-transfer problems can be solved by separation of variables only if the boundaries of the region are regular. Numerical, graphical, or analog methods of solution must be used if the shapes are irregular. A clever analog method of solving the diffusion equation was developed in 1962 by Leo Hoogenboom of the General Electric Materials and Processes Laboratory in Schenectady, N.Y. (Ref. 62). He employed the method in a study of stresses in the buckets of a gas turbine. When a turbine is started up, the buckets are initially at ambient temperature. Then hot gas surrounds them, raising their surface temperature nearly to the gas temperature. During the time of heating, the temperature is not uniform throughout each bucket. The unequal transient temperatures cause unequal thermal expansion and therefore thermal stresses. The latter can be calculated if the temperature distribution in the bucket is known as a function of location and time. Assume that the temperature does not vary in the radial direction in the bucket. Thus if x and y are coordinates in the plane of a cross section of the bucket,

$$\nabla^2 T(x,y,t) = \frac{1}{\alpha} \frac{\partial T}{\partial t} . \tag{28.89}$$

If the ambient temperature is T_0, the initial condition is $T(x, y, 0) = T_0$. For a first solution assume as a boundary condition that after $t = 0$, the temperature everywhere on the bucket surface is the stagnation temperature of the gas, T_1.

The analog of a gas-turbine bucket, which will illustrate the method in general, is shown in Fig. 28.17. A sandwich is made of a sheet of resistance paper (called Teledeltos paper) and a sheet of conducting paper such as aluminum foil, insulated from each other electrically by a thin sheet of Mylar. The outline of the bucket is painted on the resistance paper with paint made of silver, having a high electrical conductivity. To ensure that the painted outline is an equipotential line, a bare copper wire is laid along the silver line and held against it every few

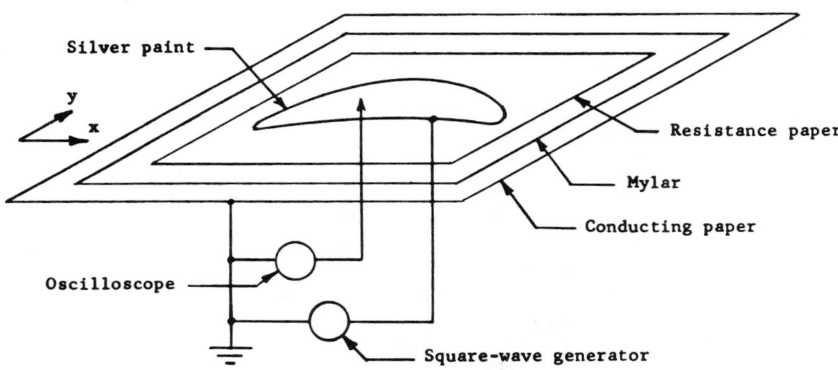

Fig. 28.17. Hoogenboom's transient heat transfer analog.

inches with a thumbtack. Then a step of voltage is applied between the conducting paper, which is at ground potential, and the bucket outline. The voltage to ground at any point within the bucket outline on the resistance paper is $V(x, y, t)$. A sheet of current flows in the resistance paper, with a density **J** amperes per meter. According to Ohm's law,

$$\mathbf{J} = \sigma \mathbf{E}\,, \tag{28.90}$$

where σ is the conductivity of the resistance paper and **E** is the electric field intensity. In this electric field the magnetic flux is negligible and $\mathbf{E} = -\nabla V$. Therefore

$$\mathbf{J} = -\sigma \nabla V\,. \tag{28.91}$$

Comparing this equation with Fourier's law

$$\mathbf{q}'' = -k \nabla T \tag{28.92}$$

shows that the electrical conductivity σ is analogous to the thermal conductivity k of the bucket. The current density **J** is analogous to the heat flux density $\mathbf{q}''$ within the bucket. Fig. 28.18 shows a differential rectangle on the resistance paper, and the x and y components of the two-dimensional current density. The difference between the currents flowing out and in is

$$I_{out} - I_{in} = \frac{\partial J_x}{\partial x}\, dx\, dy + \frac{\partial J_y}{\partial y}\, dx\, dy\,. \tag{28.93}$$

The resistance paper and conducting paper act like the plates of a capacitor of capacitance C farads per square meter of sandwich, with a voltage V between them. The current flow between the plates of the differential-size capacitor of Fig. 28.18 is

$$I_{thru} = C\, dx\, dy\, \frac{\partial V}{\partial t}\,. \tag{28.94}$$

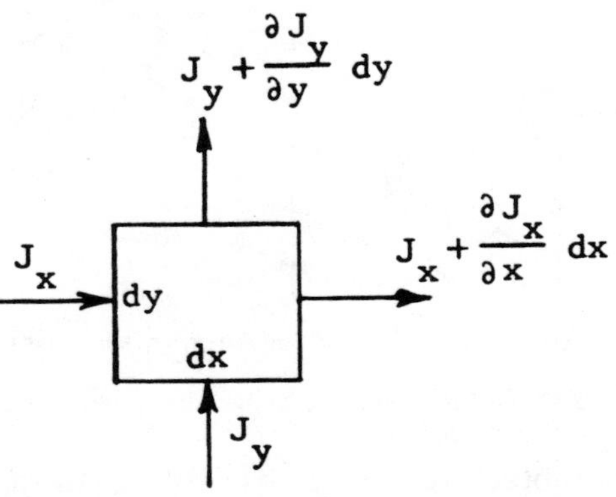

Fig. 28.18. Current density in a differential rectangle.

Since

$$I_{in} = I_{out} + I_{thru}\,, \tag{28.95}$$

$$\frac{\partial J_x}{\partial x} + \frac{\partial J_y}{\partial y} = -\,C\,\frac{\partial V}{\partial t}\,, \tag{28.96}$$

or

$$\nabla \cdot \mathbf{J} = -\,C\,\frac{\partial V}{\partial t}\,. \tag{28.97}$$

Substituting in Eq. (28.91) produces

$$\nabla \cdot (-\sigma\, \nabla V) = -\,C\,\frac{\partial V}{\partial t}\,. \tag{28.98}$$

Since the conductivity σ of the resistance paper is homogeneous and nearly isotropic,

$$\nabla^2 V = \frac{C}{\sigma} \frac{\partial V}{\partial t}. \tag{28.99}$$

This is a diffusion equation, analogous to Eq. (28.89). To obtain the analog of temperature as a function of time at any point within the bucket, connect a probe at that point to an oscilloscope as shown in Fig. 28.17. The oscilloscope displays $V(x, y, t)$. A photograph of its trace is the desired curve. A series of photographs taken with the probe at various locations within the bucket provides the information necessary for calculating thermal stresses.

This method was not practical until oscilloscopes with very fast sweeps became available. The quantity σ/C, in units of $m^2/F{\cdot}\Omega$, is very large, even when the Mylar is as thin as possible. The corresponding thermal diffusivity α is large, and the analog of the transient heating occurs very quickly. When a step of voltage corresponding to surface temperature T_1 is applied in Fig. 28.17, a slow oscilloscope displays the voltage $V(t)$ at any point within the bucket as another step. If the leading edge of the wave of $V(t)$ is displayed on a fast oscilloscope with a sweep time of 0.5 μs/cm, it appears as in Fig. 28.19. The picture can be

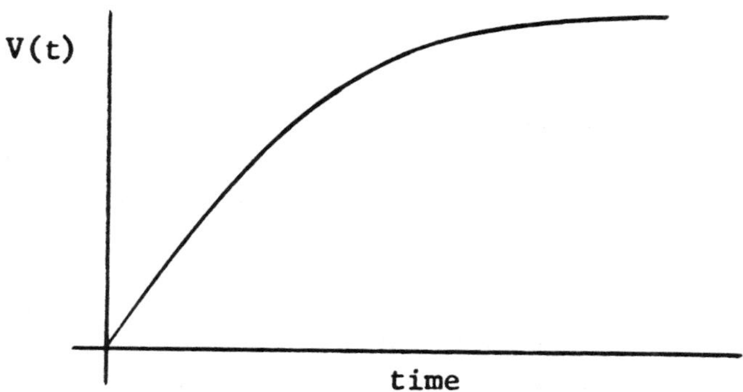

Fig. 28.19. Step response at a point within the bucket.

made repetitive by applying a periodic square wave of voltage to the model instead of a step of voltage.

Hoogenboom's analog method can be used to find the transient temperature distribution in a two-dimensional body of any cross-sectional shape. Ref. 62 shows how the model can be modified to account for the temperature drop in the boundary layer between the body and the surrounding fluid.

Chapter 29

RADIANT HEAT TRANSFER

29.1 Introduction

Thermal radiation is electromagnetic energy, that travels at the speed of light. As Fig. 29.1 shows, its wavelengths λ occupy the portion

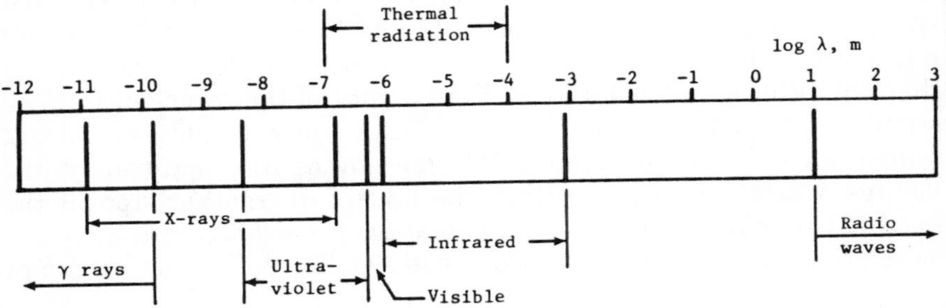

Fig. 29.1. Electromagnetic spectrum.

of the spectrum between about 10^{-7} and 10^{-4} meters. Every physical body emits thermal radiation over a continuous band of wavelengths that varies with the temperature of the body. Unlike the heat transferred by conduction or convection, radiant heat propagates in a vacuum. A thermos jug can never be a perfect insulator, because the coffee in the inner bottle always loses heat by radiation to the outer bottle. The space program has stimulated interest in radiant heat transfer, because earth satellites and space ships are heated and cooled only by radiation. Although the basic laws of radiant heat transfer are simple, the important parameters called emissivity and absorptivity that appear in the laws vary in complicated ways. Their variability makes calculated results only approximate, and increases the need for experimental testing. On the other hand, this same variability provides the opportunity to design greenhouses that stay warm at night and satellites that remain cool even when exposed continuously to the sun. The variability of emissivity and absorptivity has another advantage that far outweighs the disadvantage of imprecise calculations. If these parameters were independent of wavelength, the color of every physical object would be gray.

The adjectives *spectral, directional, total* and *hemispherical* will be used to describe emissivity, absorptivity and the density of heat power

(W/m^2) emitted or received by a body. The meanings are

spectral:	per unit wavelength
directional:	per unit of solid angle
total:	measured over all wavelengths
hemispherical:	measured over all directions.

29.2 Planck's Law

The law relating radiant power to temperature was derived by Max Planck, who invented quantum theory for the purpose. He postulated that radiant energy occurs in quanta of size $h\nu$ joules, called photons, where $\nu = c/\lambda$ is the frequency of the radiation in hertz, c is the speed of light, 2.9979×10^8 m/s, and h is Planck's constant, 6.6236×10^{-34} J·s. Planck found that there is a maximum amount of radiant power $E_{b\lambda}$ that can be emitted from a body at a given temperature at a given wavelength. This amount, expressed by *Planck's law*, is

$$E_{b\lambda} = \frac{2\pi hc^2}{\lambda^5(e^{hc/\lambda kT}-1)} \qquad \text{W/m}^3\,, \tag{29.1}$$

where k is Boltzmann's constant, 1.3802×10^{-23} J/K, and T is the absolute temperature of the body in kelvins. A body that emits this much power is said to be *black*. Although some real bodies radiate almost at the rate $E_{b\lambda}$ W/m^2 per meter of wavelength, no real body is perfectly black. Fig. 29.2 shows curves of $E_{b\lambda}$, plotted as a function of wavelength λ on log-log paper, for various temperatures. The density of the power emitted by a body in the wavelength range of λ to $\lambda + d\lambda$ is $E_{b\lambda}d\lambda$ watts per square meter of surface area. The ordinate $E_{b\lambda}$ is called by physicists the *spectral emissive power* of the black body. (The full name is *hemispherical spectral emissive power*.) An engineer might be more comfortable with the name *wavelength distribution of power density*. The curves show that a black body radiates power with a continuous spectrum of wavelengths. The peak of the curve shifts to the left as the temperature increases. The dotted line joining the peaks is a straight line, indicating that the peak value of $E_{b\lambda}$ is inversely proportional to some power of the wavelength λ_{max} at the peak. In addition, λ_{max} is inversely proportional to temperature. This fact is *Wien's displacement law*:

$$\lambda_{\max} T = 2.898 \times 10^{-3} \qquad \text{m·K}\,. \tag{29.2}$$

Fig. 29.3 shows the spectral emissive power of black-body radiation at various temperatures in the visible range of wavelengths. The ordinates

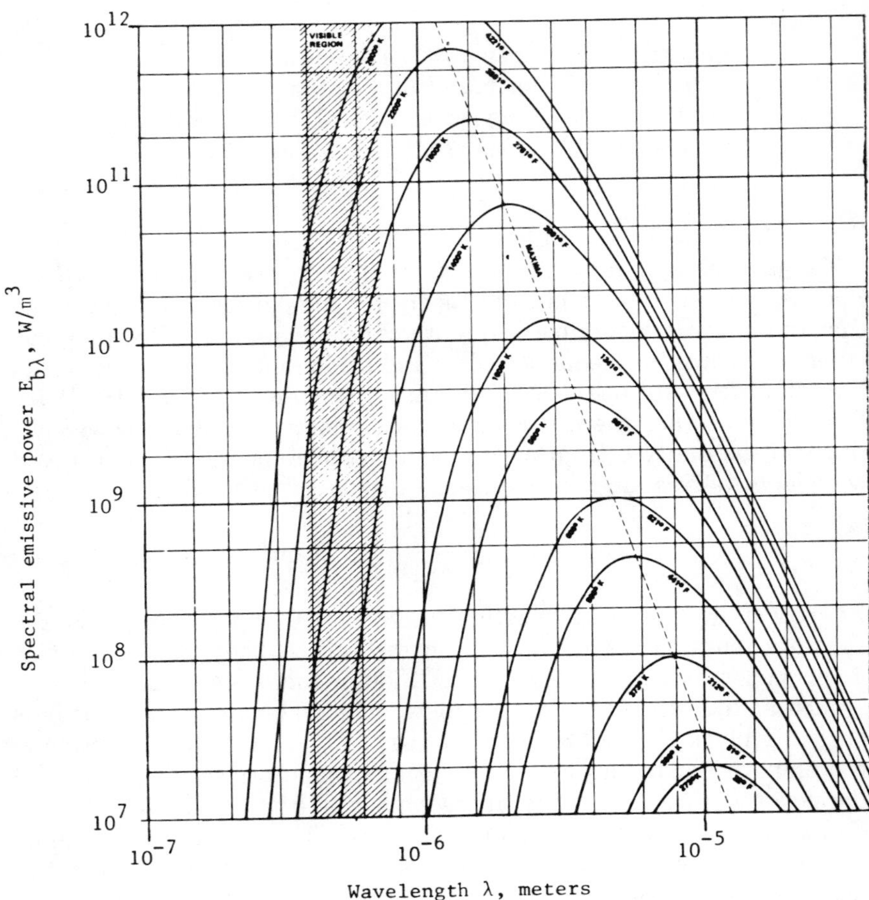

Fig. 29.2. Distribution of energy in black-body radiation. (Reprinted with permission from the *Handbook of Tables for Applied Engineering Science*, Second Edition, by R.E. Bolz and G.L. Tuve. Copyright The Chemical Rubber Co., CRC Press, Inc.)

have been normalized so that each curve has a height of 1 at 0.56 μm. The curves show why an incandescent body changes color as its temperature increases. At the lower temperatures it emits power at predominately long wavelengths that the eye sees as red. When the spectrum becomes nearly uniform over the visible range, the eye sees white. As the temperature increases still more, the power density becomes higher and is predominately in the short wavelengths. Then the bright incandescent body appear bluish-white.

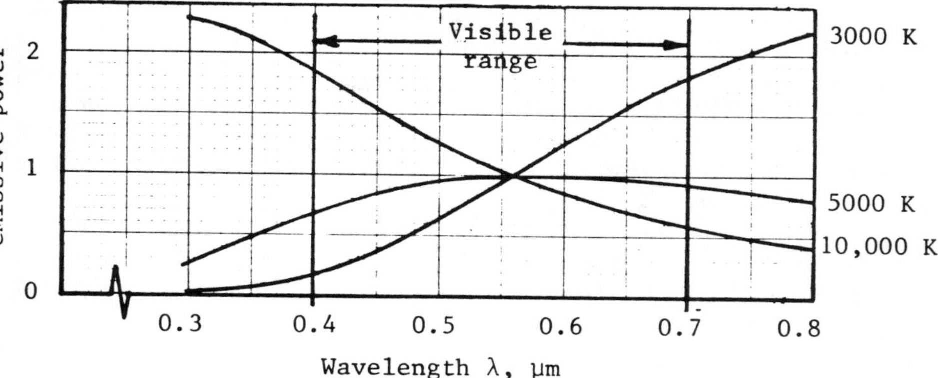

Fig. 29.3. Shift of the power spectrum with temperature.

29.3 The Stefan-Boltzmann Law

The *emissive power* E_b (more precisely called *hemispherical total emissive power*) radiated from a black body at a given temperature is the area under one of the curves in Fig. 29.2. In 1879 the Austrian physicist Stefan deduced from experimental data that

$$E_b = \sigma T^4 \qquad \text{W/m}^2 , \tag{29.3}$$

where σ is the Stefan-Boltzmann constant. This is the *Stefan-Boltzmann law*. The numerical value of σ can be determined accurately by integrating Eq. (29.1). The integration, performed in Section 29.14, produces the result

$$E_b = \int_0^\infty E_{b\lambda} d\lambda = \sigma T^4 , \tag{29.4}$$

where

$$\sigma = \frac{2 \pi^5 k^4}{15 h^3 c^2} = 5.669 \times 10^{-8} \qquad \text{W/m}^2\text{·K}^4 . \tag{29.5}$$

This calculation is an example of science at its best. The calculated value of σ obtained from Planck's analytical work verifies Stefan's value obtained earlier experimentally. In general, analytical verification of an experimental result is more difficult and more credible than vice versa. The remarkably simple Stefan-Boltzmann law shows that the power radiated from a black body is a function of its temperature only. For T = 273 K, E_b = 314.9 W/m². A black potato at 0°C radiates 315 W/m² whether it is in a freezer or a hot oven.

The heat power transferred between two bodies by conduction or convection is proportional to the temperature difference between them.

Since the power transferred by radiation is proportional to the difference in the fourth powers of temperature, the relative importance of radiation increases with the temperature difference. An interesting demonstration of this fact is obtained by pouring two cups of hot coffee at the same time. If cream is added to one cup immediately, and to the other cup after a few minutes, the mixture in the latter cup will be slightly cooler.

Another unexpected effect of the Stefan-Boltzmann law is illustrated by the radiation between two infinite, parallel, black plates at absolute temperatures T_1 and T_2, shown on edge in Fig. 29.4A. Assume that the

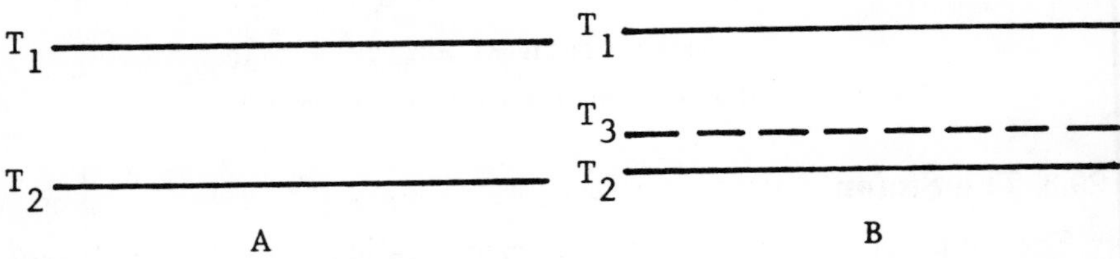

Fig. 29.4. Parallel black plates.

space between the plates is a vacuum, to avoid heat transfer by conduction or convection. If $T_1 > T_2$, the net power density transmitted from the upper plate to the lower is

$$E = \sigma\,(T_1^4 - T_2^4) \qquad \text{W/m}^2\,. \tag{29.6}$$

Now a thin, black sheet of a good heat conductor is inserted between the plates as in Fig. 29.4B, and assumes the temperature T_3. Try to answer these questions in advance:

- What is the formula for T_3?
- Is T_3 affected by the position of the sheet?
- Does the sheet reduce the heat transferred between the plates?

The answers are not obvious. To answer the first two questions, observe that the net power density received by the sheet from the upper plate must equal that which it sends to the lower plate:

$$E = \sigma\,(T_1^4 - T_3^4) = \sigma\,(T_3^4 - T_2^4)\,. \tag{29.7}$$

Therefore

$$T_3 = \left(\frac{T_1^4 + T_2^4}{2}\right)^{1/4}, \tag{29.8}$$

which is independent of the position of the sheet. The net power density transmitted from the upper plate thru the sheet to the lower plate is now

$$E = \sigma\,(T_1^4 - T_3^4) = \sigma\left(T_1^4 - \frac{T_1^4 + T_2^4}{2}\right) = \sigma\left(\frac{T_1^4 - T_2^4}{2}\right), \qquad (29.9)$$

which is half the amount that was transmitted before the sheet was inserted. It is interesting to note that this result would be obtained if the Stefan-Boltzmann law were

$$E = \sigma\,T^n\,, \qquad (29.10)$$

where n is any number.

Radiation shields similar to the thin black sheet have practical use in reducing the radiation between bodies of unequal temperature. For example, if a thermocouple is used to measure the temperature of a hot gas flowing in a cool pipe, the heat radiated to the pipe wall by the thermocouple bead cools the latter, and causes it to read too low a temperature. The error is reduced by placing a cylindrical shield around the thermocouple. Several concentric shields reduce the error still more.

29.4 Black Bodies

Several interesting properties can be deduced from the definition of a black body, namely a body that emits the maximum amount of radiation at a given temperature.

1. Suppose that a black body is put in an enclosed cavity such as an oven, with black walls, and the body and walls are allowed to reach the same steady temperature. Both radiated heat at the rate E_b. No matter how the body is oriented, its temperature remains constant. It must receive the same power density E_b W/m^2 from all directions. The conclusion is that the radiation filling a black enclosure of uniform wall temperature is isotropic, i.e., it consists of heat flux that is uniform in all directions. The black body can be considered to be part of the enclosure. It intercepts some of the black-body radiation from the walls. To maintain isotropic radiation, it must emit an equal amount in the return direction. *The radiation from a black body is therefore isotropic.*

2. Since the power density E_b incident upon the black body equals the power density that it radiates, and since its temperature remains constant, it must absorb all of the power incident upon it. *A black body is alternately defined as a body that absorbs all of the energy incident upon it.*

3. *The walls of an enclosed cavity appear thermally black, no matter what color they are painted*, because they eventually absorb every photon that is incident upon them. Any photon not absorbed when it first reaches a wall is reflected back and forth until it is eventually absorbed. The cavity is filled with black-body radiation, some of which is produced by emission and some by reflection of photons from the walls. Walls made of real materials of course emit less than black-body radiation.

4. Since the radiation emitted from a black body is isotropic, the intensity of the radiation is the same in all directions. The surface of such a body, or the body itself, is said to be *diffuse*. The amount of power in watts emitted from the body in a given direction depends on the projected area of the body in that direction. Fig. 29.5 shows a hemisphere of unit radius enclosing an element dA of a black surface. The

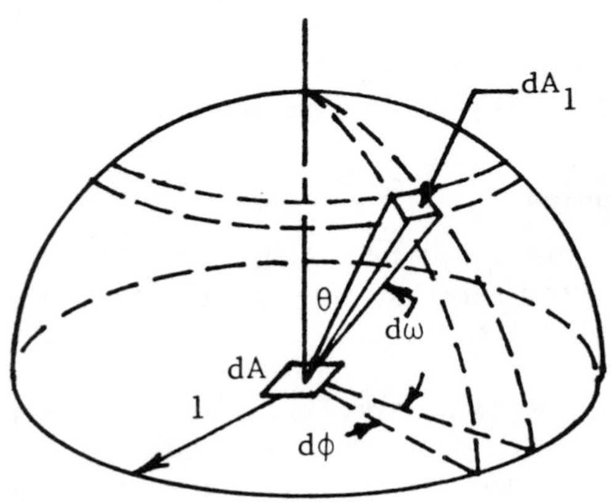

Fig. 29.5. Intensity of radiation from a black surface.

spectral intensity $i'_{b\lambda}$ of the black element is the power radiated per unit of solid angle $d\omega$ in the θ direction, per unit of wavelength, per unit of projected area normal to the θ direction. For a black body it is independent of θ and ϕ. The prime and the subscript λ denote a single direction and a single wavelength. The same quantity expressed per unit of actual area of the element, instead of projected area, is called the *directional spectral emissive power*, $E'_{b\lambda}$. The power per unit wavelength of the radiation in the solid angle $d\omega$ in Fig. 29.5 is

$$E'_{b\lambda} d\omega \, dA = i'_{b\lambda} d\omega \, dA \cos\theta \, , \tag{29.11}$$

and therefore

$$E'_{b\lambda} = i'_{b\lambda} \cos\theta \, . \tag{29.12}$$

The *hemispherical spectral emissive power* of a black body, expressed by Planck's law, Eq. (29.1), is the density of the power radiated in all directions by the elemental black surface, per unit wavelength. It is obtained by integrating the directional spectral emissive power over the hemisphere in Fig. 29.5:

$$E_{b\lambda} = \int_{\omega} E'_{b\lambda} d\omega = \int_{\omega} i'_{b\lambda} \cos\theta \, d\omega \, . \tag{29.13}$$

The solid angle $d\omega$ is equal to the area dA_1 that the angle intercepts on the hemisphere of unit radius. Thus

$$d\omega = d\theta \, (d\phi \sin\theta) \tag{29.14}$$

and

$$E_{b\lambda} = \int_{\phi=0}^{2\pi} \int_{\theta=0}^{\pi/2} i'_{b\lambda} \sin\theta \cos\theta \, d\theta \, d\phi \, . \tag{29.15}$$

Since for a black body the spectral intensity is independent of θ and ϕ, $i'_{b\lambda}$ can be brought out of the integral, and

$$E_{b\lambda} = 2\,\pi\, i'_{b\lambda} \int_0^1 \sin\theta \, d(\sin\theta) = \pi\, i'_{b\lambda} \, . \tag{29.16}$$

Thus the hemispherical spectral emissive power of a black body is π times its spectral intensity. The *hemispherical total emissive power* of a black body is obtained by integrating the hemispherical spectral emissive power over all wavelengths as in Eq. (29.4):

$$E_b = \int_0^{\infty} E_{b\lambda} d\lambda = \pi \int_0^{\infty} i'_{b\lambda} d\lambda = \pi\, i'_b \qquad \text{W/m}^2 \, , \tag{29.17}$$

where i'_b is the *total intensity* of radiation from the black surface. Like $i'_{b\lambda}$, i'_b is the same in all directions. For this reason, if a black surface is heated to incandescence, it appears equally bright from any angle. An incandescent black sphere therefore appears uniformly bright. According to Planck's law and the Stefan-Boltzmann law, Eqs. (29.1) and (29.3), the emissive powers $E_{b\lambda}$ and E_b are functions of temperature. Accordingly, the intensities $i'_{b\lambda}$ and i'_b are also functions of temperature.

29.5 Kirchhoff's Law

Until now the properties of only black bodies have been considered. The properties of real bodies are more complicated and more interesting, and make possible the design of useful heating and cooling surfaces. A real body radiates less power than a black body at the same temperature. In addition, its surface is not perfectly diffuse. Its spectral and total intensities of radiation are therefore directional, and are designated as i'_λ and i'. The corresponding emissive powers (directional spectral E'_λ and directional total E') of a real body are related to the intensities by the same simple geometry as for a black body:

$$E'_\lambda = i'_\lambda \cos\theta \qquad \text{and} \qquad E' = i' \cos\theta \,. \tag{29.18}$$

The ratio of the radiation from a real body to the radiation from a black body at the same temperature is called *emissivity*. The *directional spectral emissivity* of a surface is

$$\varepsilon'_\lambda = \frac{i'_\lambda}{i'_{b\lambda}} = \frac{E'_\lambda}{E'_{b\lambda}} \,. \tag{29.19}$$

Again, a prime and a subscript λ indicate a single direction and a single wavelength. The *directional total emissivity* is

$$\varepsilon' = \frac{i'}{i'_b} = \frac{E'}{E'_b} \,. \tag{29.20}$$

Although E'_b has not been defined, the reader should be able to define it and express its relationship to i'_b. Each of the emissivities is unity for a black body and less than 1 for a real body. Figs. 29.6 and 29.7 are polar plots of the directional total emissivity ε' for several real materials. For the electric nonconductors represented in Fig. 29.6 this emissivity decreases at polar angles near 90°. An incandescent sphere of one of these materials appears brighter near the center than at the edges. For electric conductors as illustrated in Fig. 29.7, ε' is larger at the larger angles. A heated sphere made of an electric conductor is brighter near the edges than at the center. If the elemental area dA in Fig. 29.5 is part of a real surface, the power per unit wavelength emitted from it in the solid angle $d\omega$ is

$$dq'_{\lambda e} = E'_\lambda \, d\omega \, dA = i'_\lambda \cos\theta \, d\omega \, dA = \varepsilon'_\lambda \, i'_{b\lambda} \cos\theta \, d\omega \, dA \,. \tag{29.21}$$

Although a black body absorbs all of the radiation that is incident upon it, a real body absorbs somewhat less. The *absorptivity* of a surface is the fraction of the incident radiation that is absorbed. To obtain a formula for absorptivity, observe the differential surface dA in Fig. 29.8, receiving radiation in the solid angle $d\omega_1$. The differential area dA_1 is on a unit hemisphere at the vertex of the solid angle. Radiation from a distant body passes thru dA_1 on its way to dA. The spectral intensity of this radiation coming from the θ, ϕ direction, at the location of dA_1, is $i'_{\lambda i}$. The power per unit wavelength incident on the element dA from the θ, ϕ direction is

$$dq'_{\lambda i} = i'_{\lambda i} dA_1 d\omega_1 = i'_{\lambda i} dA_1 dA \cos\theta \,. \tag{29.22}$$

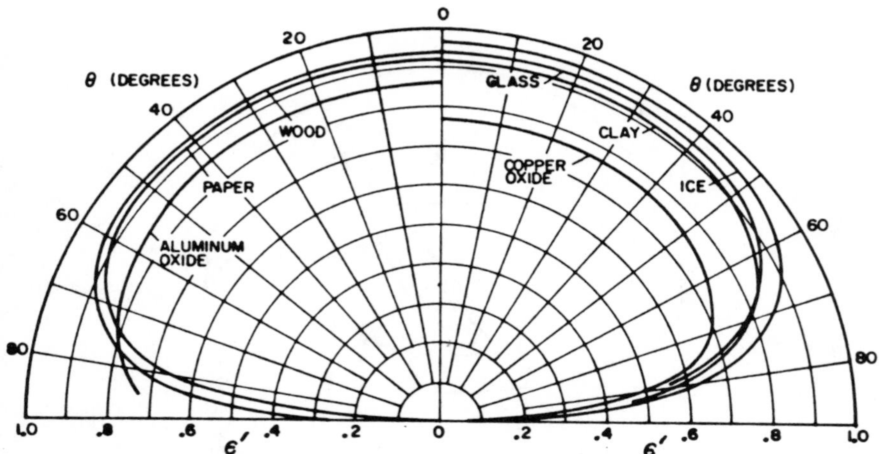

Fig.29.6. Directional total emissivity ε′ of several electric nonconductors. (From *Radiation Heat Transfer*, by E.M. Sparrow and R.D. Cess. Copyright ©1966 by Wadsworth, Inc. Reprinted by permission of the publisher, Brooks/Cole Publishing Company, Monterey, California.)

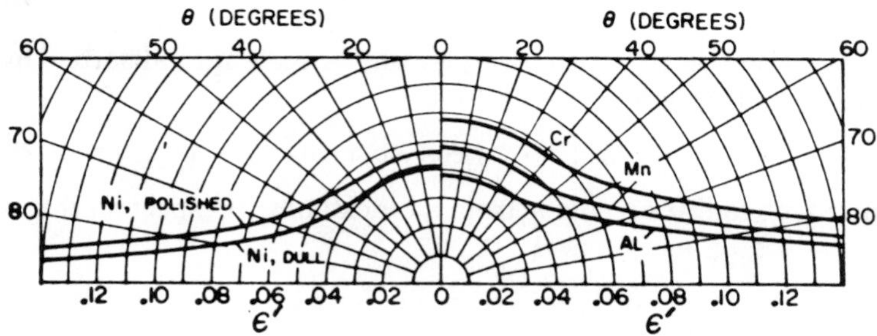

Fig. 29.7. Directional total emissivity ε′ of several metals. (From *Radiation Heat Transfer*, by E.M. Sparrow and R.D. Cess. Copyright ©1966 by Wadsworth, Inc. Reprinted by permission of the publisher, Brooks/Cole Publishing Company, Monterey, California.)

Of this power, the amount absorbed is designated as $dq'_{\lambda a}$. The fraction of the incident power that is absorbed by the surface dA is the *directional spectral absorptivity* of the surface:

$$\alpha'_\lambda = \frac{dq'_{\lambda a}}{dq'_{\lambda i}}. \qquad (29.23)$$

A comparison of absorbed and emitted powers will be easier if the solid angle in Fig. 29.8 is turned around to the position in Fig. 29.5. This is accomplished in one step. Since

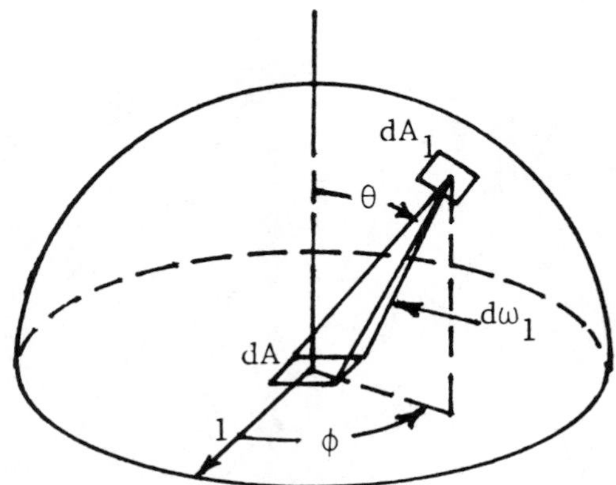

Fig. 29.8. Intensity of radiation upon an elemental surface.

$$d\omega = dA_1 \,, \tag{29.24}$$

then

$$dq'_{\lambda i} = i'_{\lambda i} \cos\theta \; d\omega \; dA \,. \tag{29.25}$$

According to Eq. (29.23), the power per unit wavelength absorbed by dA from the θ, ϕ direction is

$$dq'_{\lambda a} = \alpha'_\lambda i'_{\lambda i} \cos\theta \; d\omega \; dA \,. \tag{29.26}$$

If the incident radiation comes from a black body, its spectral intensity can be designated as $i'_{b\lambda i}$, and

$$dq'_{\lambda a} = \alpha'_\lambda i'_{b\lambda i} \cos\theta \; d\omega \; dA \,. \tag{29.27}$$

Suppose that the surface element dA in Fig. 29.5 is completely enclosed by bodies that are at the same temperature as dA. Since the radiation from any enclosed cavity with walls of uniform temperature is thermally black, the intensity of the radiation incident upon dA is $i'_{b\lambda i}$. The power unit wavelength emitted by dA in the θ, ϕ direction is given by Eq. (29.21):

$$dq'_{\lambda e} = \varepsilon'_\lambda i'_{b\lambda} \cos\theta \; d\omega \; dA \,. \tag{29.28}$$

Since the surface dA is at the same temperature as its surroundings, the emitting intensity $i'_{b\lambda}$ in this equation is the same as the receiving intensity $i'_{b\lambda i}$ in Eq. (29.27). The radiation in the enclosed cavity is isotropic. In order to preserve the isotropy the powers absorbed and emitted by surface dA in the θ, ϕ direction must be equal. Accordingly, Eqs. (29.27) and (29.28) shows that

$$\varepsilon_\lambda{}' = \alpha'_\lambda \,. \tag{29.29}$$

This equality of absorptivity and emissivity is *Kirchhoff's law*. It has been proved only for the directional spectral properties, and only for a body in thermal equilibrium with its surroundings. It is only approximately true when the body and its surroundings are at different temperatures. According to Ref. 124, page 60, α'_λ and ε'_λ are nearly equal in most applications, are determined primarily by the temperature of the body, and are not affected significantly by the temperature of the surroundings.

29.6 Kirchhoff's Law for Hemispherical and Total Properties

Kirchhoff's law for the integrated emissivities and absorptivities is as valid as Eq. (29.29) only under special conditions. The hemispherical properties of an elemental surface, such as the one in Fig. 29.5, are obtained by integrating the directional properties over the entire solid angle of 2π subtended by the hemisphere. The *hemispherical spectral emissive power* E_λ of an element of a real body is obtained by integrating the directional spectral emissive power E'_λ:

$$E_\lambda = \int_\omega E'_\lambda \, d\omega \, . \tag{29.30}$$

The *hemispherical spectral emissivity* is

$$\varepsilon_\lambda = \frac{E_\lambda}{E_{b\lambda}} \, . \tag{29.31}$$

The *hemispherical spectral absorptivity* α_λ of a surface is the fraction of the incident power from all directions per unit wavelength that is absorbed. The incident power is obtained by integrating Eq. (29.25) over the hemisphere of Fig. 29.5:

$$q_{\lambda i} = \int_\omega i'_{\lambda i} \cos\theta \, dA \, d\omega \, , \tag{29.32}$$

and the power absorbed is $q_{\lambda a}$, the integral of Eq. (29.26). Then

$$\alpha_\lambda = \frac{q_{\lambda i}}{q_{\lambda a}} \, . \tag{29.33}$$

Kirchhoff's law for the hemispherical spectral properties is

$$\varepsilon_\lambda = \alpha_\lambda \, . \tag{29.34}$$

A little calculation (Ref. 124, p. 62) shows that this law is as accurate as Eq. (29.29) only if

1. the incident spectral intensity is uniform in all directions, i.e., $i'_{\lambda i}$ is a function of λ but not of θ, or

2. the directional spectral properties a'_{λ} and ε'_{λ} of the surface, which are equal, are independent of θ. Such a surface is diffuse, but not necessarily black.

The directional total emissivity ε' was defined by Eq. (29.20). The *directional total absorptivity* α' of a surface is the fraction of the incident power over all wavelengths per unit angle that is absorbed. The numerator and denominator of this fraction are obtained by integrating Eqs. (29.26) and (29.25) over all wavelengths. Kirchhoff's law for the directional total properties is

$$\varepsilon' = \alpha' . \tag{29.35}$$

Ref. 124, p. 61 shows that this law is as accurate as Eq. (29.29) only when

1. at any angle θ the spectral distribution of the incident intensity $i'_{\lambda i}$ is proportional to $i'_{b\lambda i}$, i.e., the curve of $i'_{\lambda i}$ vs. λ is a scaled-down version of the black-body curve, or

2. the properties ε'_{λ} and α'_{λ} of the surface are independent of λ. This condition exists if the curve of emitting intensity i'_{λ} vs. λ at any angle θ is a scaled-down version of the black-body curve.

The hemispherical total emissive power E of a real surface is the density of power emitted in all directions to the hemisphere and over all wavelengths:

$$E = \int_{\omega} E' d\omega = \int_{0}^{\infty} E_{\lambda} d\lambda \qquad \text{W/m}^2 . \tag{29.36}$$

The *hemispherical total emissivity*, usually called just *emissivity*, is the ratio of this emission to that of a black body at the same temperature:

$$\varepsilon = \frac{E}{E_b} = \frac{E}{\sigma T^4} . \tag{29.37}$$

The *hemispherical total absorptivity* α of a surface, or just *absorptivity*, is the fraction of the power density incident from all directions and over all wavelengths that is absorbed. The numerator and denominator of the fraction are obtained by integrating Eqs. (29.26) and (29.25) over all angles of the hemisphere and all wavelengths. Kirchhoff's law for the hemispherical total properties is

$$\varepsilon = \alpha . \tag{29.38}$$

Ref. 124, p. 65 shows that this most general form of Kirchhoff's law is as valid as Eq. (29.29) only if

1. the incident radiation $i'_{\lambda i}$ is uniform in all directions, and its variation with λ is a scaled-down version of the black-body curve, or

2. the incident radiation $i'_{\lambda i}$ is uniform in all directions, and the properties ε'_λ and α'_λ of the surface, which are equal, are independent of λ (i.e., the curve of emitting intensity i'_λ vs. λ is a scaled-down version of the black-body curve), or

3. the incident radiation varies with angle θ, but its spectral distribution at any angle is a scaled-down version of the black-body curve, and ε'_λ (which equals α'_λ) is independent of angle, or

4. the equal surface properties ε'_λ and α'_λ are independent of angle and wavelength.

29.7 Emissivities of Real Bodies

Suppose that the hemispherical spectral emissive power E_λ of a surface at a given temperature is a scaled-down version of the black-body spectral emissive power $E_{b\lambda}$, as in Fig. 29.9. Then since

$$E_\lambda = \varepsilon_\lambda E_{b\lambda}\ , \tag{29.39}$$

the hemispherical spectral emissivity ε_λ is independent of wavelength. Such a surface, for which ε_λ and α_λ are independent of λ, is called *gray*. Since the emissivity ε is the ratio of the areas under the two curves, $\varepsilon = \varepsilon_\lambda$ for a gray body. As illustrated in Fig. 29.9, the spectral density curve of a real surface lies below the black-body curve, and has a different shape. The ratio ε_λ of the ordinates of the two curves is a function of wavelength. Some typical values of hemispherical spectral emissivity ε_λ for various materials are shown in Figs. 29.10A and 29.10B. Clearly real surfaces are not gray. For metals ε_λ decreases with wavelength, while for electric nonconductors (including the oxide on the surface of anodized aluminum) it increases irregularly with wavelength. Notice that for wavelengths beyond about 5 μm, bare aluminum is approximately gray, and white enamel is nearly black. The hemispherical spectral emissivity ε_λ of materials varies not only with wavelength, but also with the temperature of the body and its surface finish. The latter variation is illustrated in Fig. 29.10A. The curves apply for a limited range of temperatures.

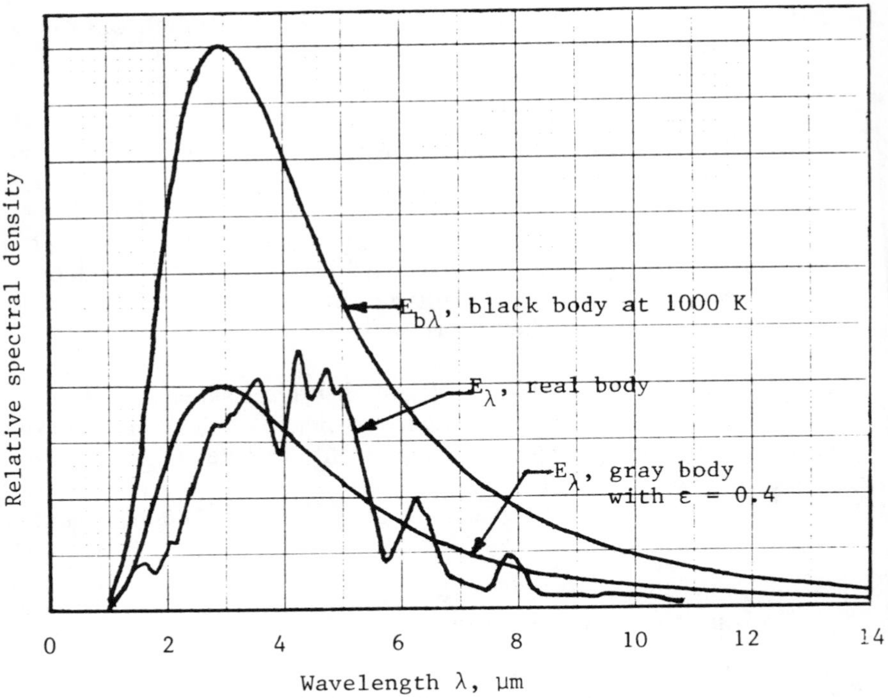

Relative spectral density

$E_{b\lambda}$, black body at 1000 K

E_{λ}, real body

E_{λ}, gray body with $\varepsilon = 0.4$

0 2 4 6 8 10 12 14

Wavelength λ, μm

Fig. 29.9. Hemispherical spectral emissive powers.

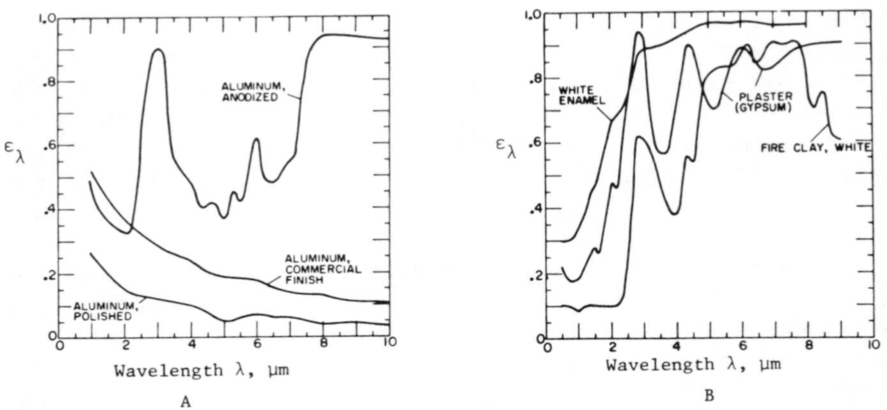

Fig. 29.10. Dependence of ε_λ on wavelength. (From *Radiation Heat Transfer*, by E.M. Sparrow and R.D. Cess. Copyright ©1966 by Wadsworth, Inc. Reprinted by permission of the publisher, Brooks/Cole Publishing Company, Monterey, California.)

According to Kirchhoff's law, the hemispherical spectral absorptivity α_λ is approximately equal to ε_λ, and therefore describes irregular curves like those in Fig. 29.10. For this reason, the hemispherical total absorptivity α depends on the spectrum of the incident radiation. If the incident radiation is intense in the range of wavelengths where α_λ is large, and low where α_λ is low, the power absorbed by the surface is larger than if the incident radiation is low where α_λ is high and vice versa, and α is accordingly higher. This dependence of α on the spectrum of the incident radiation is a nuisance that is frequently assumed away in engineering calculations. For some applications, on the other hand, the variation of α_λ and ε_λ is turned to advantage. For example, clear lacquer on the aluminum surface of a satellite has a hemispherical spectral absorptivity α_λ that is low at the short wavelengths that predominate in sunlight, and high at the long wavelengths that predominate in low-temperature radiation. As a result the satellite remains cool even when exposed continuously to the sun. It is able to radiate the heat generated by its internal electronics, while absorbing only a small fraction of the incident sunlight.

The (hemispherical total) emissivity ε of a surface is the ratio of the areas under the curves of E_λ and $E_{b\lambda}$ in Fig. 29.9. These emissivities for various surfaces are listed in Fig. 29.11. Notice that lampblack and flat black lacquer, that appear black in the narrow visible range of the spectrum, are nearly black over the entire spectrum. Asbestos board and water, on the other hand, are nearly thermally black but do not look black.

Suppose that the directional total emissivity and absorptivity ε' and α' of a surface are the same in all directions. The surface is said to be *diffuse*. Any black surface is diffuse. A little thought shows that if a surface is both diffuse and gray, ε'_λ and α'_λ are independent of both direction and wavelength. Then the fourth justification of Kirchhoff's law $\varepsilon = \alpha$ applies, and all of the emissivities and absorptivities are equal:

$$\varepsilon'_\lambda = \varepsilon_\lambda = \varepsilon' = \varepsilon = \alpha'_\lambda = \alpha_\lambda = \alpha' = \alpha \,. \tag{29.40}$$

In many calculations of radiant heat transfer, surfaces are assumed to be diffuse and gray. Then the tabulated emissivities such as those in Fig. 29.11 are also absorptivities, and are independent of the spectrum or direction of the incident radiation.

29.8 Reflectivity and Transmissivity

Since the absorptivity of any real surface is less than unity, some of the power incident upon the surface is reflected. The fraction of the

Surface	Temp, °C	Emissivity ε
Aluminium:		
Highly polished plate, 98·3% pure	237–576	0·039–0·057
Rough polish	100	0·18
Commercial sheet	100	0·09
Heavily oxidized	93–505	0·20–0·31
Al-surfaced roofing	38	0·216
Brass:		
Highly polished, 73·2 Cu, 26·7 Zn	247–357	0·028–0·031
Polished	100	0·06
Rolled plate, natural surface	22	0·06
Chromium, polished	100	0·075
Copper:		
Carefully polished electrolytic copper	80	0·018
Polished	100	0·052
Molten	1076–1278	0·16–0·13
Iron and steel:		
Steel, polished	100	0·066
Iron, polished	427–1028	0·14–0·38
Cast iron, polished	200	0·21
Cast iron, newly turned	22	0·44
Wrought iron, highly polished	38–249	0·28
Iron plate, completely rusted	19	0·69
Sheet steel, shiny oxide layer	24	0·82
Steel plate, rough	38–372	0·94–0·97
Cast iron, molten	1300–1400	0·29
Steel, molten	1522–1650	0·43–0·40
Stainless steel, polished	100	0·074
Lead, grey oxidized	24	0·28
Magnesium oxide	278–827	0·55–0·20
Nichrome wire, bright	49–1000	0·65–0·79
Nickel-silver, polished	100	0·135
Platinum filament	27–1230	0·036–0·192
Silver, polished, pure	227–627	0·02–0·032
Tin, bright tinned iron	23	0·043, 0·064
Tungsten filament	3320	0·39
Zinc, galvanized sheet iron, fairly bright	28	0·23
Asbestos board	23	0·96
Brick:		
Red, rough	21	0·93
Building	1000	0·45
Fireclay	1000	0·75
Magnesite, refractory	1000	0·38
Candle soot	97–272	0·952
Lampblack, other blacks	50–1000	0·96
Graphite, pressed, filed surface	249–516	0·98
Concrete tiles	1000	0·63
Enamel, white fused, on iron	19	0·90
Glass, smooth	22	0·94
Oak, planed	21	0·90
Flat black lacquer	38–94	0·96–0·98
Oil paints, 16 different, all colours	100	0·92–0·96
Aluminium paints, various	100	0·27–0·67
Radiator paint, bronze	100	0·51
Paper, thin, pasted on blackened plate	19	0·92, 0·94
Plaster, rough lime	10–87	0·91
Roofing paper	21	0·91
Water (calculated from spectral data)	0–100	0·95–0·963

Fig. 29.11. Emissivities of various surfaces. (From *Heat Transmission*, Third Edition by W.H. McAdams. Copyright 1954 by W.H. McAdams. Used with the permission of McGraw-Hill Book Company.)

power incident from all directions and all wavelengths that is reflected is the hemispherical total reflectivity or simple *reflectivity,* ρ. For an opaque surface, $\alpha + \rho = 1$. Transparent materials can absorb, reflect, or transmit radiation. If *transmissivity* τ is defined as the fraction of the incident power that is transmitted, then

$$\alpha + \rho + \tau = 1 . \tag{29.41}$$

The hemispherical spectral properties have the same relationship:

$$\alpha_\lambda + \rho_\lambda + \tau_\lambda = 1 . \tag{29.42}$$

Some kinds of glass have a transmissivity that makes them band-pass filters of light. Fig. 29.12 shows the spectral transmissivity τ_λ of a piece of Corning No. 556 blue glass, 5 mm thick. Also included is the spectral emissive power E_λ of sunlight. The density of the power passing thru the glass is

$$E = \int_0^\infty \tau_\lambda E_\lambda d\lambda \qquad \text{W/m}^2 , \tag{29.43}$$

which has wavelengths only in the pass band of the glass filter. Electrical engineers will recognize the similarity to the calculation of the power output of an electrical filter. The spectra of the input and output voltages are called $S_{xx}(\omega)$ and $S_{yy}(\omega)$, and are expressed as functions of frequency ω instead of wavelength λ. The transfer function of the filter is $H(\omega)$. Then

$$S_{yy}(\omega) = |H(\omega)|^2 S_{xx}(\omega) . \tag{29.44}$$

If the load on the filter is a one-ohm resistor, the total power at the filter output is

$$P = \frac{1}{2\pi}\int_{-\infty}^{\infty} S_{yy}(\omega)d\omega = \frac{1}{2\pi}\int_{-\infty}^{\infty} |H(\omega)|^2 S_{xx}(\omega)d\omega \qquad \text{watts} , \tag{29.45}$$

which is analogous to Eq. (29.43). The latter equation, for solar power, is simpler and has clearer physical meaning. The reader is invited to explain, with the help of Fig. 29.12, why a greenhouse can get warm on a cold, sunny winter day, and stay warm at night. Carbon dioxide has a pass band something like that of the glass in Fig. 29.12. Some scientists are concerned that the greenhouse effect will raise the temperature of the earth, because carbon dioxide is produced in huge quantities by the burning of hydrocarbon fuels.

29.9 Shape Factors

The exchange of radiant heat between bodies can be calculated with the help of the Stefan-Boltzmann law and a knowledge of their absorp-

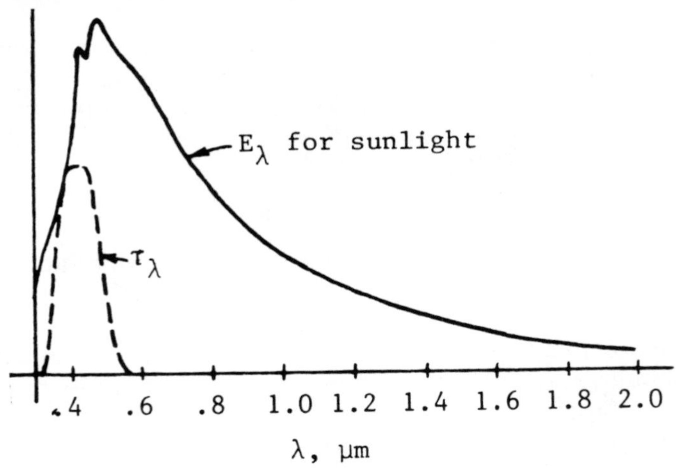

Fig. 29.12. Transmissivity of blue glass.

tivities and emissivities. Another useful tool is the *shape* or *configuration factor*, namely the fraction of the power radiated from one black body that reaches another. To start the derivation of shape factors, consider an element dA of a heated black surface shown in Fig. 29.13. The element is enclosed by a hemisphere of radius r. The total intensity of radiation from the element is i_b' watts per unit solid angle $d\omega$ per unit of area dA projected normal to the θ direction. The power reaching the area dA_1 of the hemisphere is

$$dq = i_b' \, dA \cos\theta \, d\omega \qquad \text{watts} . \tag{29.46}$$

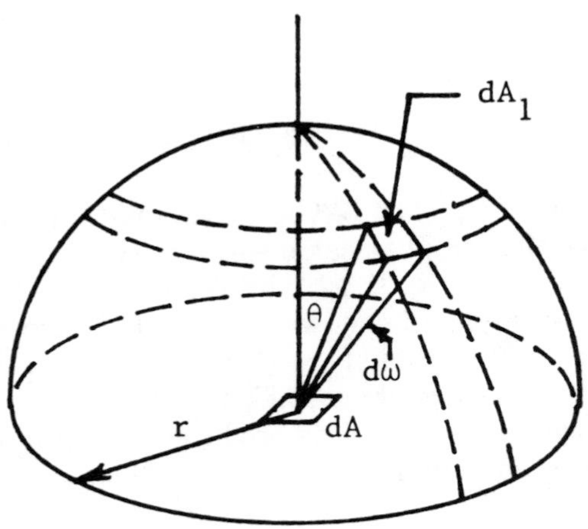

Fig. 29.13. Heated element of a black surface.

Since

$$d\omega = \frac{dA_1}{r^2}, \tag{29.47}$$

the density of the power received by a surface facing the heated element at the distance r is

$$J = \frac{dq}{dA_1} = \frac{i_b' dA \cos\theta}{r^2} \qquad \text{W/m}^2 . \tag{29.48}$$

Eq. (29.17) shows that the hemispherical total emissive power of a black body is

$$E_b = \pi i_b' \qquad \text{W/m}^2 . \tag{29.49}$$

Therefore

$$J = \frac{E_b dA \cos\theta}{\pi r^2} . \tag{29.50}$$

This is *Lambert's cosine law*, that applies exactly for black bodies, but only approximately for real bodies whose intensity of radiation i' is directional. It helps to explain why the choice location near a fireplace on a cold winter's night is in front rather than at the side.

Now consider the radiant power exchanged between the two differential black surfaces in Fig. 29.14, separated by the distance r, that are identified by the surface vectors $d\mathbf{A}_1$ and $d\mathbf{A}_2$. Element 1 radiates the power $E_{b1}dA_1$ watts. The density of this radiation at the location of element 2 is

$$J = \frac{E_{b1} dA_1 \cos\theta_1}{\pi r^2} . \tag{29.51}$$

If this power density is regarded as a flux density and represented by a vector $\mathbf{J}$ in the direction of the line between the two elements, the power from element 1 that reaches element 2 is

$$dq_{12} = \mathbf{J} \cdot d\mathbf{A}_2 = J\, dA_2 \cos\theta_2 = \frac{E_{b1} \cos\theta_1 \cos\theta_2\, dA_1 dA_2}{\pi r^2} . \tag{29.52}$$

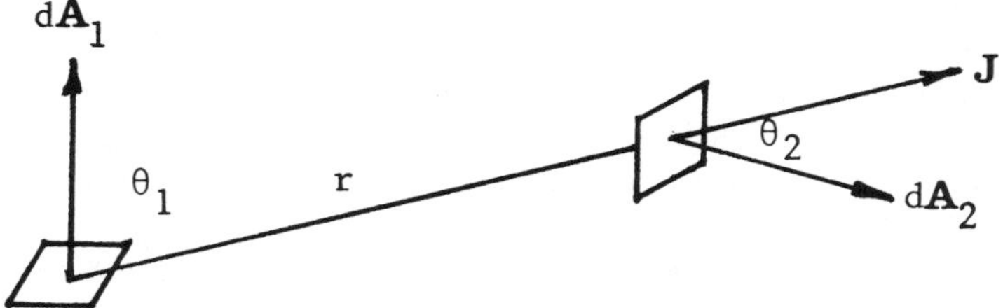

Fig. 29.14. Two black surface elements.

Likewise, the side of element 2 facing element 1 radiates the power $E_{b2}dA_2$. The power from element 2 reaching element 1 is

$$dq_{21} = \frac{E_{b2} \cos \theta_1 \cos \theta_2 \, dA_1 dA_2}{\pi r^2} . \tag{29.53}$$

The net power transferred from element 1 to element 2 is

$$dq = dq_{12} - dq_{21} = (E_{b1} - E_{b2}) \frac{\cos \theta_1 \cos \theta_2 \, dA_1 dA_2}{\pi r^2} . \tag{29.54}$$

According to the Stefan-Boltzmann law, Eq. (29.3),

$$E_{b1} = \sigma T_1^4 \qquad \text{and} \qquad E_{b2} = \sigma T_2^4 , \tag{29.55}$$

where T_1 and T_2 are the absolute temperatures of the two elements. Therefore

$$dq = \frac{\sigma}{\pi r^2} (T_1^4 - T_2^4) \cos \theta_1 \cos \theta_2 \, dA_1 dA_2 . \tag{29.56}$$

A calculation of the radiant power exchanged between two black bodies of uniform temperatures, such as two spheres, requires a summation of the contributions of all the differential elements of both bodies. The process is a double integration that is tedious for all but simple geometries. For example, the power from body 1 that reaches body 2 is

$$q_{12} = \frac{\sigma T_1^4}{\pi} \int_{A_2} \int_{A_1} \frac{\cos \theta_1 \cos\theta_2 \, dA_1 dA_2}{r^2} . \tag{29.57}$$

When the total powers q_{12} and q_{21} have been determined, shape factors can be determined easily. Let the shape factor F_{12} be defined as the fraction of the power $E_{b1}A_1$ radiated from a black body 1 at temperature T_1 that reaches black body 2:

$$F_{12} = \frac{q_{12}}{E_{b1}A_1} = \frac{q_{12}}{\sigma T_1^4 A_1} \tag{29.58}$$

or

$$q_{12} = \sigma T_1^4 F_{12} A_1 . \tag{29.59}$$

Notice that when Eq. (29.57) is substituted into (29.58), σ and T_1^4 cancel out. The calculation of F_{12}, or any shape factor, is just a geometry problem. In the derivation of the shape factor F_{12}, the two bodies were assumed to be black. A review of the derivation shows that body 1 needs to be only diffuse. The only restriction placed on body 2 is that it does not reflect any of the power from body 1 back to body 1, thereby giving the power a second chance to reach body 2.

29.10 Calculation of Shape Factors

The numerical evaluation of shape factors is frequently simplified by a useful reciprocity relationship that is derived as follows. If F_{21} is the fraction of the power $E_{b2}A_2$ radiated from black body 2 at temperature T_2 that reaches body 1,

$$q_{21} = \sigma T_2^4 F_{21} A_2 . \qquad (29.60)$$

The net power transferred from body 1 to body 2 is

$$q = q_{12} - q_{21} = \sigma T_1^4 F_{12} A_1 - \sigma T_2^4 F_{21} A_2 . \qquad (29.61)$$

Either Eq. (29.56) or common sense shows that if $T_1 = T_2$, no heat is exchanged between the bodies. Then the left side of Eq. (29.61) is zero, and the right side shows that

$$F_{12} A_1 = F_{21} A_2 . \qquad (29.62)$$

This useful reciprocity relationship will be used to calculate a difficult F_{21} with an F_{12} that is obtained easily.

Many shape factors have been calculated and tabulated. References 130 and 124 contain appendices with formulas for the factor for 15 and 32 common configurations of bodies with various dimensions. Ref. 130 also includes curves. One family of these, the shape factor for two parallel, equal, opposite rectangles, is shown in Fig. 29.15. The reader is

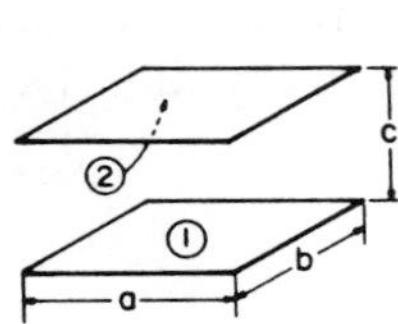

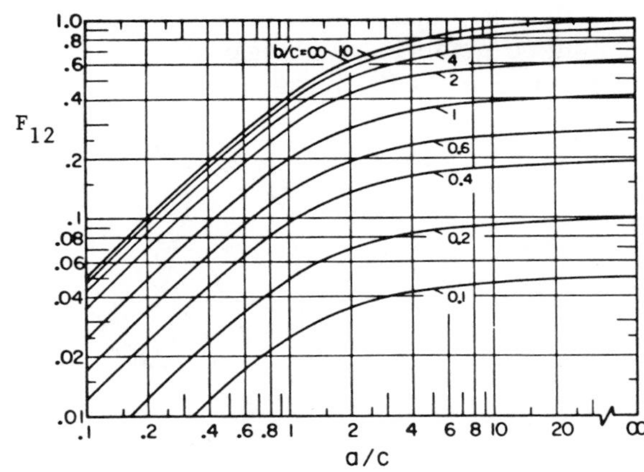

Fig. 29.15. Shape factor for parallel rectangles. (From *Radiation Heat Transfer*, by E.M. Sparrow and R.D. Cess. Copyright ©1966 by Wadsworth, Inc. Reprinted by permission of the publisher, Brooks/Cole Publishing Company, Monterey, California.)

invited to test his or her engineering judgment. Suppose that the rectangles are black squares separated so that $a = b = c$. Estimate the fraction of the radiation from the lower plate that reaches the upper, and then read the correct value.

A shape factor is the fraction of the power radiated from one black body that reaches another. If body 1 radiates heat to several other bodies numbered 2, 3, etc.,

$$F_{11} + F_{12} + F_{13} + \cdots = 1\,, \tag{29.63}$$

if a shape factor is included for each of the bodies and the space between them, as in Fig. 29.16. The factor F_{11} is needed if body 1 has a concave

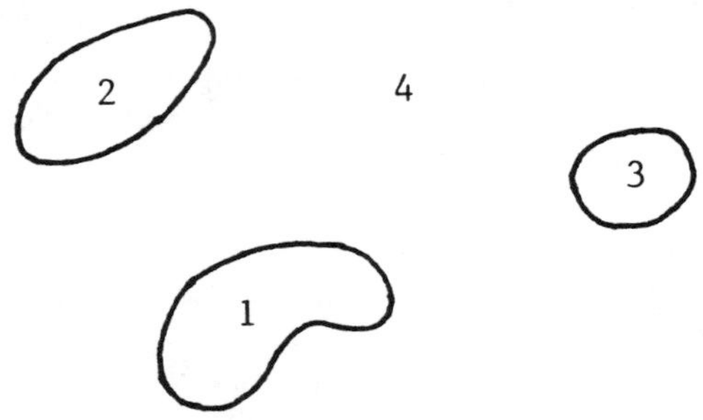

Fig. 29.16. Several bodies.

surface and therefore intercepts some of its own radiation. Eq. (29.63) and the reciprocity relationship (29.62) permit an easy calculation of the shape factors for two long concentric cylinders whose cross section is shown in Fig. 29.17, that avoids the difficult integration in Eq. (29.57).

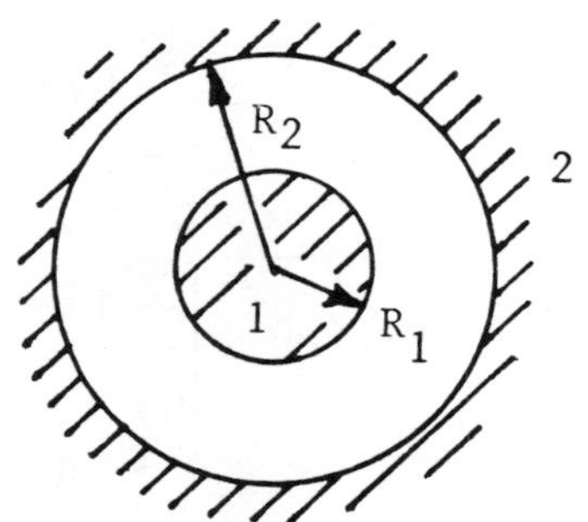

Fig. 29.17. Concentric cylinders.

Clearly $F_{12} = 1$, and since $F_{12}A_1 = F_{21}A_2$,

$$F_{21} = F_{12}\frac{A_1}{A_2} = F_{12}\frac{R_1}{R_2} = \frac{R_1}{R_2}\,. \tag{29.64}$$

Now since

$$F_{21} + F_{22} = 1 , \tag{29.65}$$

the fraction of its own radiation that the outer cylinder intercepts is

$$F_{22} = 1 - F_{21} = 1 - \frac{R_1}{R_2} . \tag{29.66}$$

The factors F_{21} and F_{22} are not obvious, even for this simple example.

29.11 Radiation Between Diffuse, Gray Bodies

Real bodies are not black, and a calculation of the radiant heat exchanged between them must account for their emissivities. For example, consider the two bodies in Fig. 29.18 that are far apart. If body 1

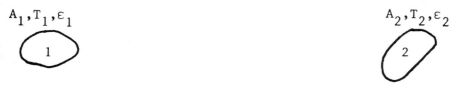

Fig. 29.18. Two bodies far apart.

were black, the power emitted from it would be $\sigma A_1 T_1^4$ watts. If its emissivity is ε_1, the emitted power is $\sigma A_1 \varepsilon_1 T_1^4$. If it is diffuse, its shape factors calculated on the assumption of black-body radiation can be used. The power emitted by body 1 that reaches body 2 is then $\sigma A_1 F_{12} \varepsilon_1 T_1^4$. Since the bodies are far apart, none of this power is reflected back to body 1 and then back to body 2. Furthermore, none of the radiation from body 2 is reflected back to it from body 1. If the absorptivity of body 2 is α_2, the total power absorbed by body 2 is $\sigma A_1 F_{12} \varepsilon_1 \alpha_2 T_1^4$. If for one of the four reasons listed earlier body 2 obeys Kirchhoff's law for the hemispherical total properties, $\alpha_2 = \varepsilon_2$, and the power absorbed by body 2 is

$$q_{12} = \sigma A_1 F_{12} \varepsilon_1 \varepsilon_2 T_1^4 . \tag{29.67}$$

Similary, if body 2 is diffuse and body 1 obeys Kirchhoff's law, the power radiated from body 2 that is absorbed by body 1 is

$$q_{21} = \sigma A_2 F_{21} \varepsilon_1 \varepsilon_2 T_2^4 = \sigma A_1 F_{12} \varepsilon_1 \varepsilon_2 T_2^4 . \tag{29.68}$$

A single assumption that justifies both equations is that both bodies are diffuse and gray. The net power exchanged between the two bodies is

$$q = q_{12} - q_{21} = \sigma A_1 F_{12} \varepsilon_1 \varepsilon_2 (T_1^4 - T_2^4) . \tag{29.69}$$

If a small body at temperature T_1 is enclosed in a large cavity as in Fig. 29.19, it does not disturb the black-body radiation at temperature T_2 from the cavity walls. The power incident on the small body is $\sigma A_2 F_{21} T_2^4$. The small body absorbs the power

$$q_{21} = \sigma A_2 F_{21} \varepsilon_1 T_2^4 = \sigma A_1 F_{12} \varepsilon_1 T_2^4 . \qquad (29.70)$$

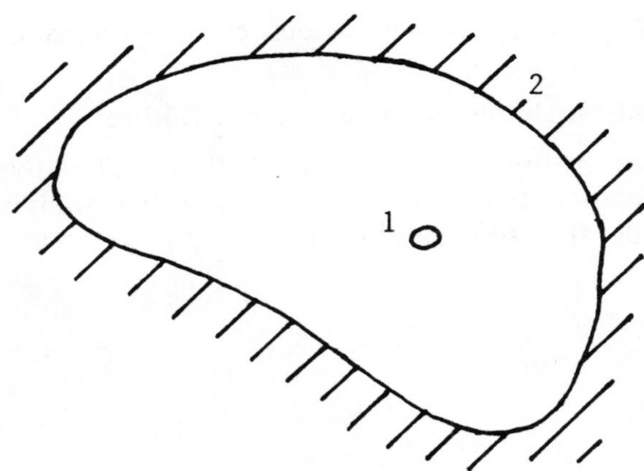

Fig. 29.19. Small body in a large cavity.

This is the same as Eq. (29.68) with $\varepsilon_2 = 1$. The latter emissivity verifies the fact that a large cavity appears black. The actual emissivity of pieces of the cavity wall is not important. The usefulness of shape factors will be illustrated by a calculation of radiant heat transfer. Fig. 29.20 shows two square plates whose areas A_1 are each 1 cm^2, opposite

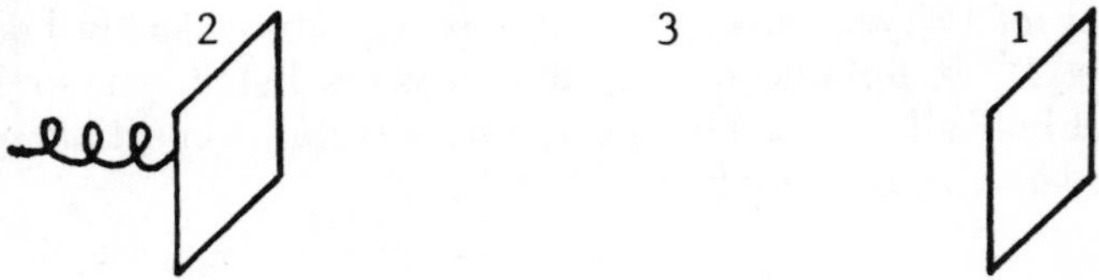

Fig. 29.20. Two square plates.

and parallel to each other at a distance of 5 cm, located in the vacuum of a spaceship. The plates are gray and diffuse, with emissivities ε_1 and ε_2 of 0.9, and are good heat conductors. Plate 2 is heated electrically to 1000 K. The surroundings are at a temperature T_3 of 300 K. What temperature does plate 1 reach?

The answer will be obtained by equating the components of radiant power absorbed and emitted by plate 1. The latter component is obtained easily. Since plate 1 has two side of area A_1, the power radiated from it is

$$q_1 = 2\sigma A_1 \varepsilon_1 T_1^4 \qquad \text{watts} . \tag{29.71}$$

To obtain the absorbed components, let the subscripts $f1$, $b1$, 2, and 3 denote the front and back sides of plate 1, plate 2, and the surroundings. The fraction of the power radiated from plate 2 that reaches the front of plate 1 is $F_{2,f1}$. Since the separation of the plates is large compared to their areas, and their absorptivities are high, it is reasonable to assume that none of the power radiated from one plate to the other is reflected back to its source. Since also the bodies are diffuse and gray, the power radiated from plate 2 that is absorbed by the front of plate 1 is

$$q_{2,1} = \sigma A_2 F_{2,f1} \varepsilon_1 \varepsilon_2 T_2^4 = \sigma A_1 F_{f1,2} \varepsilon_1 \varepsilon_2 T_2^4 . \tag{29.72}$$

Fig. 29.15 shows that $F_{f1,2} = 0.012$. The surroundings constitute a large enclosed cavity, and therefore appear black. The power radiated from the surroundings that is absorbed by the back of plate 1 is

$$q_{3,b1} = \sigma A_3 F_{3,b1} \varepsilon_1 T_3^4 . \tag{29.73}$$

Although neither A_3 nor $F_{3,b1}$ is known, the reciprocity relationship (29.62) saves the day:

$$q_{3,b1} = \sigma A_1 F_{b1,3} \varepsilon_1 T_3^4 . \tag{29.74}$$

Clearly $F_{b1,3} = 1$. The power radiated from the surroundings that is absorbed by the front of plate 1 is

$$q_{3,f1} = \sigma A_3 F_{3,f1} \varepsilon_1 T_3^4 = \sigma A_1 F_{f1,3} \varepsilon_1 T_3^4 . \tag{29.75}$$

The unknown $F_{f1,3}$ can be found indirectly with ease. Eq. (29.63) provides the relationship

$$F_{f1,2} + F_{f1,3} = 1 , \tag{29.76}$$

so that

$$q_{3,f1} = \sigma A_1 (1 - F_{f1,2}) \varepsilon_1 T_3^4 , \tag{29.77}$$

and $F_{f1,2}$ has already been determined.

Now the components of power radiated and absorbed by plate 1 can be equated:

$$q_1 = q_{2,1} + q_{3,f1} + q_{3,b1} \tag{29.78}$$

or

$$2\sigma A_1 \varepsilon_1 T_1^4 = \sigma A_1 \varepsilon_1 \left[F_{f1,2} \varepsilon_2 T_2^4 + (1 - F_{f1,2}) T_3^4 + T_3^4\right] . \tag{29.79}$$

Thus

$$T_1^4 = \frac{F_{f1,2}\varepsilon_2 T_2^4 + (2 - F_{f1,2})T_3^4}{2} \tag{29.80}$$

and

$$T_1 = \left[\frac{(0.012)(0.9)(1000)^4 + (1.988)(300)^4}{2}\right]^{1/4} = 341 \text{ K} . \tag{29.81}$$

This is the steady-state temperature of plate 1. Notice that it is independent of ε_1. This result is not surprising. If the ability of plate 1 to absorb heat from plate 2 is impaired by reducing α_1, its ability to radiate heat to the surroundings is impaired by an equal reduction in ε_1.

29.12 Emissivity Factors

When heated bodies are close together, the radiant power reflects back and forth between them, complicating the calculation of heat transfer. For determining the net heat exchange between two real bodies, the effects of reflection and nonblack emissivities can be lumped into a convenient emissivity factor. Eqs. (29.61) and (29.62) show that if two bodies 1 and 2 were black, the net power exchanged between them would be

$$q = \sigma A_1 F_{12}(T_1^4 - T_2^4) , \tag{29.82}$$

where F_{12} is the shape factor. Since real bodies are not black, the net power exchanged is

$$q = \sigma A_1 F_{12} F_\varepsilon (T_1^4 - T_2^4) , \tag{29.83}$$

where F_ε is the *emissivity factor*, namely the ratio of the power exchanged between the bodies to the power that would be exchanged if they were black. According to Eq. (29.69), the emissivity factor for two diffuse, gray bodies that are far apart is

$$F_\varepsilon = \varepsilon_1 \varepsilon_2 . \tag{29.84}$$

If a small body at temperature T_1 is enclosed in a large cavity at temperature T_2, the small body absorbs the power $\sigma A_2 F_{21} \varepsilon_1 T_2^4$ and radiates the power $\sigma A_1 F_{12} \varepsilon_1 T_1^4$. The net power emitted by the small body is therefore

$$q = \sigma A_1 F_{12} \varepsilon_1 (T_1^4 - T_2^4) . \tag{29.85}$$

The emissivity factor for a small body in a large enclosure is therefore

$$F_\varepsilon = \varepsilon_1 . \tag{29.86}$$

To illustrate the calculation of F_ε for bodies that are close together, consider two diffuse, gray, parallel plates with emissivities ε_1 and ε_2, shown in Fig. 29.21. The area A of each plate is so large compared to the

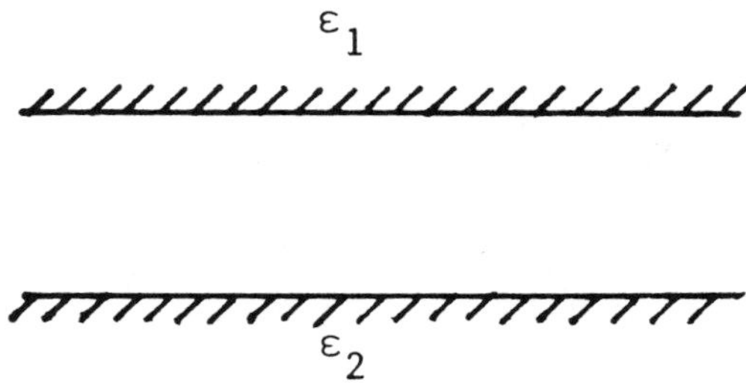

Fig. 29.21. Diffuse, gray, parallel plates.

separation between them that the heat lost at the sides is negligible. The power radiated from plate 1 is $\sigma T_1^4 A\varepsilon_1$. The fraction ε_2 of this power is absorbed by plate 2, and the fraction $1-\varepsilon_2$ is reflected back to plate 1. The fraction ε_1 of the latter amount, which is the fraction $\varepsilon_1(1-\varepsilon_2)$ of the original power, is absorbed by plate 1, and the remainder is reflected. The fractions of the original power absorbed and reflected are tabulated in Fig. 29.22. An infinite number of reflections and absorptions produces the sum at the bottom of each column. According to the third column, the power radiated from plate 1 and absorbed by plate 2 is

$$q_{12} = \sigma T_1^4 A\varepsilon_1\varepsilon_2 \sum_{n=0}^{\infty} [(1-\varepsilon_1)(1-\varepsilon_2)]^n . \tag{29.87}$$

This expression can be simplified by the fact that if $|x| < 1$,

$$\sum_{n=0}^{\infty} x^n = \frac{1}{1-x} . \tag{29.88}$$

Absorbed by plate 1	Reflected by plate 1	Absorbed by plate 2	Reflected by plate 2
		ε_2	$1-\varepsilon_2$
$\varepsilon_1(1-\varepsilon_2)$	$(1-\varepsilon_1)(1-\varepsilon_2)$	$\varepsilon_2(1-\varepsilon_1)(1-\varepsilon_2)$	$(1-\varepsilon_1)(1-\varepsilon_2)^2$
$\varepsilon_1(1-\varepsilon_1)(1-\varepsilon_2)^2$	$(1-\varepsilon_1)^2(1-\varepsilon_2)^2$	$\varepsilon_2(1-\varepsilon_1)^2(1-\varepsilon_2)^2$	$(1-\varepsilon_1)^2(1-\varepsilon_2)^3$
$\varepsilon_1(1-\varepsilon_1)^2(1-\varepsilon_2)^3$	$(1-\varepsilon_1)^3(1-\varepsilon_2)^3$	$\varepsilon_2(1-\varepsilon_1)^3(1-\varepsilon_2)^3$	$(1-\varepsilon_1)^3(1-\varepsilon_2)^4$
⋮			
$\varepsilon_1\sum_{n=0}^{\infty}(1-\varepsilon_1)^n(1-\varepsilon_2)^{n+1}$	$\sum_{n=1}^{\infty}[(1-\varepsilon_1)(1-\varepsilon_2)]^n$	$\varepsilon_2\sum_{n=0}^{\infty}[(1-\varepsilon_1)(1-\varepsilon_2)]^n$	$\sum_{n=0}^{\infty}(1-\varepsilon_1)^n(1-\varepsilon_2)^{n+1}$

Fig. 29.22. Fractions of the original power $\sigma T_1^4 A\varepsilon_1$.

Since $|(1-\varepsilon_1)(1-\varepsilon_2)|$ is less than 1 for any emissivities ε_1 and ε_2,

$$\sum_{n=0}^{\infty} [(1-\varepsilon_1)(1-\varepsilon_2)]^n = \frac{1}{1-(1-\varepsilon_1)(1-\varepsilon_2)} = \frac{1}{\varepsilon_1\varepsilon_2\left(\dfrac{1}{\varepsilon_1}+\dfrac{1}{\varepsilon_2}-1\right)}, \tag{29.89}$$

and Eq. (29.87) becomes

$$q_{12} = \frac{\sigma T_1^4 A}{\dfrac{1}{\varepsilon_1}+\dfrac{1}{\varepsilon_2}-1}. \tag{29.90}$$

Similarly, the power radiated from plate 2 and absorbed by plate 1 is

$$q_{21} = \frac{\sigma T_2^4 A}{\dfrac{1}{\varepsilon_1}+\dfrac{1}{\varepsilon_2}-1}. \tag{29.91}$$

The net power exchanged between the plates is

$$q = q_{12} - q_{21} = \frac{\sigma A(T_1^4 - T_2^4)}{\dfrac{1}{\varepsilon_1}+\dfrac{1}{\varepsilon_2}-1}. \tag{29.92}$$

The emissivity factor F_ε is defined by Eq. (29.83):

$$q = \sigma A_1 F_{12} F_\varepsilon (T_1^4 - T_2^4). \tag{29.93}$$

For the parallel plates $A_1 = A$ and $F_{12} = 1$. Therefore

$$F_\varepsilon = \frac{1}{\dfrac{1}{\varepsilon_1}+\dfrac{1}{\varepsilon_2}-1}. \tag{29.94}$$

This is the emissivity factor for two diffuse, gray, parallel plates whose spacing is small compared to their area.

The accounting of absorbed and reflected power in Fig. 29.22 verifies the assertion made earlier, that the walls of an enclosed cavity appear thermally black, no matter what color they are painted. To show this, observe that the two gray plates in Fig. 29.21 can be regarded as the walls of a long, closed oven. The power leaving plate 1 consists of three components:

1. the power radiated from plate 1: $q_1 = \sigma T_1^4 A \varepsilon_1$. (29.95)

2. *the power originally radiated from plate 1 and reflected from plate 1. According to column 2 of Fig. 29.22, this is*

$$q_2 = q_1 \sum_{n=1}^{\infty} [(1-\varepsilon_1)(1-\varepsilon_2)]^n = q_1 \left\{ \sum_{n=0}^{\infty} [(1-\varepsilon_1)(1-\varepsilon_2)]^n - 1 \right\}$$

$$= \sigma T_1^4 A \varepsilon_1 \left(\frac{1}{\varepsilon_1 + \varepsilon_2 - \varepsilon_1 \varepsilon_2} - 1 \right). \tag{29.96}$$

3. the power q_3 originally radiated from plate 2 that is reflected from plate 1. It is obtained by interchanging the subscripts 1 and 2 in column 4 of Fig. 29.22:

$$q_3 = \sigma T_2^4 A \varepsilon_2 \sum_{n=0}^{\infty} (1-\varepsilon_1)^{n+1} (1-\varepsilon_2)^n$$

$$= \sigma T_2^4 A \varepsilon_2 (1-\varepsilon_1) \sum_{n=0}^{\infty} [(1-\varepsilon_1)(1-\varepsilon_2)]^n$$

$$= \frac{\sigma T_2^4 A \varepsilon_2 (1-\varepsilon_1)}{\varepsilon_1 + \varepsilon_2 - \varepsilon_1 \varepsilon_2}. \tag{29.97}$$

If the two plates are at the same temperature T, the sum of the three components is

$$q = q_1 + q_2 + q_3$$

$$= \sigma T^4 A \left\{ \varepsilon_1 \left[1 + \frac{1}{\varepsilon_1 + \varepsilon_2 - \varepsilon_1 \varepsilon_2} - 1 \right] + \frac{\varepsilon_2 (1-\varepsilon_1)}{\varepsilon_1 + \varepsilon_2 - \varepsilon_1 \varepsilon_2} \right\}$$

$$= \sigma T^4 A . \tag{29.98}$$

The density of the power leaving plate 1 is therefore

$$\frac{q}{A} = \sigma T^4 , \tag{29.99}$$

which is the emissive power of a black surface. Regardless of the emissivities ε_1 and ε_2 of the plates, plate 1 supplies power to the oven as if it were black. Interchanging the roles of plates 1 and 2 in the preceding five equations shows that plate 2 also acts as if it were black.

29.13 Heat Loss in a Thermos Bottle

The use of emissivity factors can be shown by calculating the rate of cooling of the coffee in the thermos bottle shown in Fig. 29.23. The walls of the inner and outer bottles facing the vacuum are polished aluminum,

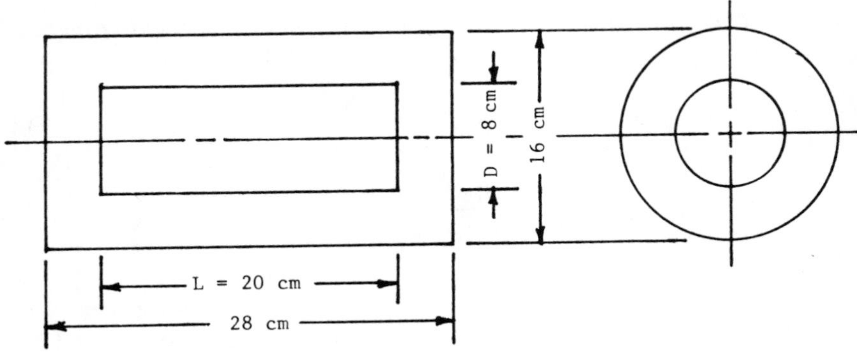

Fig. 29.23. A thermos bottle.

assumed to be diffuse and gray, with an emissivity ε of 0.04. The vacuum has a transmissivity of unity, and the temperature drops thru the walls of the inner and outer bottles are negligible. The inner bottle is full of coffee with a specific heat c of 4184 J/kg·K, at a temperature of 343 K, and the outer bottle is buried in snow at 273 K. The heat transferred between the bottles by conduction thru the structure supporting the inner bottle is assumed to be negligible. At what rate is the coffee losing heat by radiation, and how fast is its temperature dropping?

The solution will be obtained by evaluating all of the terms in Eq. (29.83). First, the surface area of the inner bottle is

$$A_1 = \pi DL + 2\pi R^2 = (\pi)(8)(20) + (2)(\pi)(4)^2$$
$$= 603 \text{ cm}^2 = 0.0603 \text{ m}^2 . \tag{29.100}$$

Since all of the power radiated from the inner bottle reaches the outer, $F_{12} = 1$. If the inner bottle were very small, the emissivity factor would be given by Eq. (29.86): $F_\varepsilon = \varepsilon$. If the inner bottle were almost as large as the outer, the two bottles would approximate parallel planes, and the emissivity factor would be given by Eq. (28.94):

$$F_\varepsilon = \frac{1}{\dfrac{1}{\varepsilon_1} + \dfrac{1}{\varepsilon_2} - 1} = \frac{1}{\dfrac{2}{\varepsilon} - 1} . \tag{29.101}$$

For the actual inner bottle the emissivity factor lies somewhere between, and

$$\varepsilon > F_\varepsilon > \frac{1}{\dfrac{2}{\varepsilon} - 1} , \tag{29.102}$$

or

$$0.04 > F_\varepsilon > 0.0204\,. \tag{29.103}$$

The last term needed for Eq. (29.83) is

$$T_1^4 - T_2^4 = (343)^4 - (273)^4 = 8.29 \times 10^9 \qquad \mathrm{K}^4\,. \tag{29.104}$$

The net power radiated from the inner bottle to the outer is

$$\begin{aligned} q &= \sigma A_1 F_{12} F_\varepsilon (T_1^4 - T_2^4) \\ &= (5.669 \times 10^{-8})(0.0603)(8.29 \times 10^9) F_\varepsilon = 28.3 F_\varepsilon \qquad \text{watts}\,. \end{aligned} \tag{29.105}$$

The coffee is therefore losing heat at a rate somewhere between

$$(28.3)(0.04) = 1.13\ \mathrm{W} \qquad \text{and} \qquad (28.3)(0.0204) = 0.58\ \mathrm{W}\,. \tag{29.106}$$

The density ρ of the coffee is 1000 kg/m^3, and its volume is

$$V = \pi R^2 L = (\pi)(4)^2(20) = 1005\ \mathrm{cm}^3 = 1.005 \times 10^{-3} \qquad \mathrm{m}^3\,. \tag{29.107}$$

The rate of cooling of the coffee is

$$\begin{aligned} r &= \frac{q}{c\rho V} = \frac{28.3\,F_\varepsilon}{(4184)(1000)(1.005 \times 10^{-3})} \\ &= 6.73 \times 10^{-3}\,F_\varepsilon \qquad \mathrm{K/s} \\ &= 24.2 F_\varepsilon \qquad \mathrm{K/hr}\,. \end{aligned} \tag{29.108}$$

If

$$F_\varepsilon = 0.04, \qquad r = 0.97\ \mathrm{K/hr}. \tag{29.109}$$

If

$$F_\varepsilon = 0.0204, \qquad r = 0.49\ \mathrm{K/hr}. \tag{29.110}$$

Clearly this is a high-quality thermos bottle, that was made ideal by the assumptions. Although the assumed emissivity is realistic, the assumptions of a perfect vacuum and no heat conduction between the bottles distinguish this product from those obtainable at the hardware store.

29.14 Appendix. Evaluation of the Stefan-Boltzmann Constant

The emissive power E_b of a black body at a given temperature is found by integrating the equation expressing Planck's law, Eq. (29.1):

$$E_b = \int_0^\infty \frac{2\pi hc^2 d\lambda}{\lambda^5 (e^{hc/\lambda kT} - 1)}. \tag{29.111}$$

Let

$$A = 2\pi hc^2\,, \qquad B = \frac{hc}{kT}\,, \qquad \text{and} \qquad x = \frac{hc}{\lambda kT} = \frac{B}{\lambda}\,. \tag{29.112}$$

Then

$$d\lambda = -\frac{Bdx}{x^2} \tag{29.113}$$

and

$$E_b = \frac{A}{B^4}\int_0^\infty \frac{x^3dx}{e^x - 1}\,. \tag{29.114}$$

Now let $u = e^x$. Long division shows that

$$\frac{1}{e^x - 1} = \frac{1}{u - 1} = \frac{1}{u} + \frac{1}{u^2} + \frac{1}{u^3} + \cdots \tag{29.115}$$

This Laurent series converges for $u > 1$ *or* $x > 0$, which is always the case. Therefore

$$E_b = \frac{A}{B^4}\int_0^\infty \left(\frac{x^3}{e^x} + \frac{x^3}{e^{2x}} + \frac{x^3}{e^{3x}} + \cdots\right) dx\,. \tag{29.116}$$

A table of integrals shows that

$$\int_0^\infty \frac{x^3}{e^{ax}}\, dx = \frac{3!}{a^4}\,, \qquad a > 0\,. \tag{29.117}$$

Therefore

$$E_b = \frac{A\cdot 3!}{B^4}\left(\frac{1}{1^4} + \frac{1}{2^4} + \frac{1}{3^4} + \cdots\right). \tag{29.118}$$

Ref. 148, p. 133 shows that the value of the series is

$$\frac{1}{1^4} + \frac{1}{2^4} + \frac{1}{3^4} + \cdots = \frac{\pi^4}{90}\,. \tag{29.119}$$

Therefore

$$E_b = \frac{6A\pi^4}{90B^4} = \frac{2\pi^5k^4T^4}{15\,h^3c^2}\,. \tag{29.120}$$

The Stefan-Boltzmann law is

$$E_b = \sigma\, T^4\,. \tag{29.121}$$

Since $k = 1.3802 \times 10^{-23}$ J/K, $h = 6.6236 \times 10^{-34}$ J·s, and $c = 2.9979 \times 10^{8}$ m/s, the Stefan-Boltzmann constant is

$$\sigma = \frac{2\pi^5}{15}\left(\frac{k}{h}\right)^3 \frac{k}{c^2} = 5.669 \times 10^{-8} \qquad \mathrm{W/m^2 \cdot K^4}\,. \qquad (29.122)$$

The computer was asked to calculate $(k/h)^3 k$ instead of k^4/h^3, because h^3 makes the denominator of Eq. (29.122) too small to handle accurately.

Chapter 30

CONVECTIVE HEAT TRANSFER

30.1 The Heat-Transfer Coefficient

Convective heat transfer is the exchange of heat between a solid surface and a fluid flowing past it. The flow may be forced by a fan or pump. Free or natural convection, on the other hand, is produced by changes in density of the fluid caused by the heat transfer. For example, a house with steam or hot-water piping is warmed by free convection. The air next to a convector (confusingly called a "radiator") is heated, expands, gains buoyancy, floats upward, and is replaced by cooler air from below. The result is a continuous free-convection current. Similarly, the light bulb in a lamp establishes a natural convection of air up thru the shade, and the fire in a fireplace pumps outdoor air in thru the cracks in the doors and windows, thru the rooms, and up the chimney. For either free or forced convection, the heat transfer cannot be calculated by Fourier's law of conduction

$$\mathbf{q}'' = -k\,\nabla T \qquad (30.1)$$

where k is the thermal conductivity of the fluid, T is its temperature, and $\mathbf{q}''$ is a vector representing the heat flux density in W/m^2. The reason is that the temperature gradient ∇T is an unknown function of distance away from the surface. If the heat flows in one direction for a distance L across a temperature drop $T_1 - T_2$, thru a material of cross-sectional area A and thermal conductivity k, the rate of heat flow according to Fourier's law of conduction is

$$q = \frac{k\,A}{L}(T_1 - T_2) \qquad \text{watts}\,. \qquad (30.2)$$

Again, this formula cannot be used to calculate the rate of heat transfer from a body into a flowing fluid because the temperature drop $T_1 - T_2$ across any given distance L is unknown. Instead, a formula is used that was suggested by Newton in 1701:

$$q = h\,A\,(T_w - T_\infty)\,, \qquad (30.3)$$

where T_w is the temperature of the surface or wall, T_∞ is the temperature of the fluid out beyond the thermal boundary layer, A is the area of the surface, and h is the *heat-transfer coefficient,* $W/m^2{\cdot}K$. This simple formula is used to calculate the three-dimensional flow of heat by convection to and from bodies of all sizes and shapes. The difficult part is the determination of h. Analytical calculation of h for any given configuration requires the solution of the differential equations of fluid flow and conduction, and is prohibitively difficult for all but a few cases. Almost all of the values of h have been determined by a combination of dimensional analysis and experimentation.

30.2 Dimensional Analysis

The technique of dimensional analysis does not solve differential equations or produce numerical results, but simplifies the experimenter's work of finding empirical solutions. It is a process of reducing the number of variables with which the experimenter must be concerned. An example will be worked to show how the technique is used in calculating a heat-transfer coefficient. What value of h should be used in Eq. (30.3) for the transfer of heat between a pipe of inside diameter D and the fluid pumped thru it with an average velocity V, shown in Fig. 30.1? To begin the dimensional analysis, list all of the

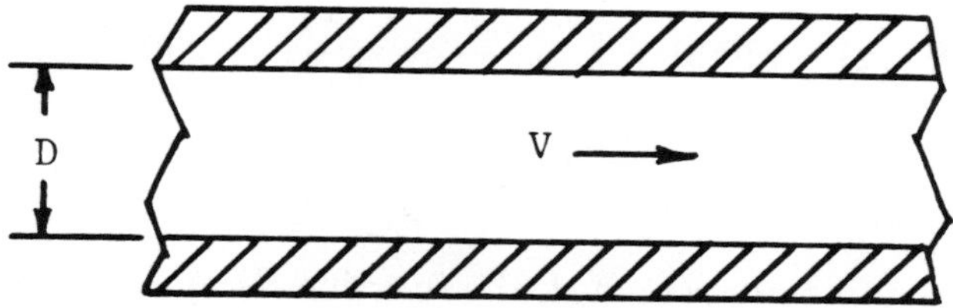

Fig. 30.1. Fluid flowing in a pipe.

variables upon which h depends. Certainly the thermal conductivity k of the fluid is a factor. The rate of heat transfer depends upon the temperature gradient and therefore upon the thickness of the thermal boundary layer across which the temperature drop $T_w - T_\infty$ occurs. The boundary-layer thickness depends upon the pipe inside diameter D and the velocity V and viscosity μ of the fluid. These three variables belong on the list. So do the specific heat c_p and the density ρ of the fluid, because their product $c_p\rho$, whose units are J/K·m^3, is a measure of the heat required to warm the fluid. If $c_p\rho$ is lowered, less heat is required. As the fluid flows along near a hot pipe wall, it heats faster and decreases the temperature gradient. The value of h applicable for the length of the pipe is reduced accordingly. Therefore h depends on c_p and ρ.

The problem now is to find the relationship among the seven variables h, D, ρ, V, μ, c_p, and k. A useful aid to the search is an observation well known to engineers and stated as a postulate by Hunsaker and Rightmire (Ref. 65, p. 106): "Any equation describing a physical phenomenon can be so formulated that its validity is independent of the size of the units of the primary quantities. Such an equation is called a *complete physical equation*." For example, Newton's second law $f - ma = 0$ is valid when written in either SI or English units. The complete physical equation relating the seven variables can be written as

$$\phi(h, D, \rho, V, \mu, c_p, k) = 0 \,. \tag{30.4}$$

The unknown relationship will be simplified by *Buckingham's Pi Theorem*: a relationship among n physical variables can be reduced to a relationship among m dimensionless products $\pi_1, \pi_2, \ldots \pi_m$ of the variables, of the form

$$\psi(\pi_1, \pi_2, \ldots \pi_m) = 0 \,. \tag{30.5}$$

The theorem is useful because m is smaller than n. To prove the theorem, observe first that if the function ϕ involved only two physical variables such as x_1 and x_2, it could be written as a Maclaurin series:

$$\phi(x_1,x_2) = \phi(0,0) + \frac{1}{1!}\left(x_1 \frac{\partial}{\partial x_1} + x_2 \frac{\partial}{\partial x_2}\right) \phi(0,0) + \frac{1}{2!}\left(x_1 \frac{\partial}{\partial x_1} + x_2 \frac{\partial}{\partial x_2}\right)^2 \phi(0,0) + \cdots = 0 \,. \tag{30.6}$$

If the constants are renamed, the function becomes the power series

$$\phi(x_1,x_2) = a_1 + a_2x_1 + a_3x_2 + a_4x_1x_2 + a_5x_1{}^2x_2 + a_6x_1x_2{}^2 + a_7x_1{}^2x_2{}^2 + \cdots = 0 \,, \tag{30.7}$$

in which the a's are constants. In general,

$$\phi(x_1,x_2) = a_1x_1{}^{b_{11}}x_2{}^{b_{21}} + a_2x_1{}^{b_{12}}x_2{}^{b_{22}} + a_3x_1{}^{b_{13}}x_2{}^{b_{23}} + \cdots = 0 \,, \tag{30.8}$$

in which the b's are non-negative integers. If the function ϕ contains n physical variables such as the seven in Eq. (30.4),

$$\phi(x_1,x_2, \ldots x_n) = a_1x_1{}^{b_{11}}x_2{}^{b_{21}} \cdots x_n{}^{b_{n1}} + a_2x_1{}^{b_{12}}x_2{}^{b_{22}} \cdots x_n{}^{b_{n2}} + \cdots = 0 \,. \tag{30.9}$$

Since this complete physical equation represents physical quantities, each term in the series must have the same dimensions as ϕ. Some of the products of the variables in the series have the same dimensions as ϕ and therefore have dimensionless coefficients. The remaining products have dimensions other than those of ϕ, and their coefficients have dimensions. These coefficients depend on the system of units, cannot appear in the complete physical equation, and are therefore all zero. A simple example is Newton's second law, that can be written as

$$f - ma = 0 = a_1 + a_2 f + a_3 m + a_4 a + a_5 fm + a_6 fa + a_7 ma + a_8 fma + \cdots \tag{30.10}$$

The only products of the variables in this series with nonzero coefficients are the ones with the dimensions of force: f and ma.

To put the complete physical equation (30.9) into a more convenient form, divide thru by one of the remaining terms such as the jth, to get

$$\frac{a_1}{a_j} x_1^{k_{11}} x_2^{k_{21}} \cdots x_n^{k_{n1}} + \frac{a_2}{a_j} x_1^{k_{12}} x_2^{k_{22}} \cdots x_n^{k_{n2}} + \cdots + 1 + \cdots = 0\,, \tag{30.11}$$

where each $k_{rs} = b_{rs} - b_{rj}$ is a positive or negative integer, the products of variables are all dimensionless, and their coefficients are all dimensionless. Now define the dimensionless product

$$\pi_i = x_1^{k_{1i}} x_2^{k_{2i}} \cdots x_n^{k_{ni}}\,, \tag{30.12}$$

in which each exponent k is an integer. The function ϕ, in the modified form of Eq. (30.11), can be written as

$$\psi = \frac{a_1}{a_j}\pi_1 + \frac{a_2}{a_j}\pi_2 + \cdots + 1 + \frac{a_{j+1}}{a_j}\pi_{j+1} + \cdots = 0\,. \tag{30.13}$$

The original relationship among n physical variables has been converted to an infinite series of dimensionless products of the variables. The advantage of this move will be apparent soon.

30.3 Determination of the π's

Although Eq. (30.13) appears to include an infinity of π's, their number is drastically and fortunately reduced by the requirement that they be dimensionless products. How the number and form of the π's are determined can be shown by continuing the example of forced convection in a pipe. Each dimensionless product π_i is a function of seven variables, which according to Eq. (30.12) is

$$\pi_i = h^{k_{1i}} D^{k_{2i}} \rho^{k_{3i}} V^{k_{4i}} \mu^{k_{5i}} c_p^{k_{6i}} k^{k_{7i}}\,. \tag{30.14}$$

Each of the seven variables can be expressed in terms of four dimensions, namely mass M, length L, time T, and temperature θ, as shown in Fig. 30.2. The equation of the dimensions of the variables is

$$M^0L^0T^0\theta^0 = (M\,T^{-3}\theta^{-1})^{k_{1i}}(L)^{k_{2i}}(M\,L^{-3})^{k_{3i}}(L\,T^{-1})^{k_{4i}}(M\,L^{-1}T^{-1})^{k_{5i}} \cdot (L^2T^{-2}\theta^{-1})^{k_{6i}}(M\,L\,T^{-3}\theta^{-1})^{k_{7i}}\,. \qquad (30.15)$$

Variable	SI units	Dimensions
h	$W/m^2\cdot K$ or $kg/s^3\cdot K$	$MT^{-3}\theta^{-1}$
D	m	L
ρ	kg/m^3	ML^{-3}
V	m/s	LT^{-1}
μ	$N\cdot s/m^2$ or $kg/m\cdot s$	$ML^{-1}T^{-1}$
c_p	$J/kg\cdot K$ or $m^2/s^2\cdot K$	$L^2T^{-2}\theta^{-1}$
k	$W/m\cdot K$ or $kg\cdot m/s^3\cdot K$	$MLT^{-3}\theta^{-1}$

Fig. 30.2. Dimensions of physical variables.

The exponents in Eq. (30.14) must be chosen so that the product π_i is dimensionless. Equating the exponents of each dimension in Eq. (30.15) yields

$$\begin{aligned}
M:&\quad k_{1i} + k_{3i} + k_{5i} + k_{7i} = 0\\
L:&\quad k_{2i} - 3k_{3i} + k_{4i} - k_{5i} + 2k_{6i} + k_{7i} = 0\\
T:&\quad -3k_{1i} - k_{4i} - k_{5i} - 2k_{6i} - 3k_{7i} = 0\\
\theta:&\quad -k_{1i} - k_{6i} - k_{7i} = 0
\end{aligned} \qquad (30.16)$$

or

$$\begin{bmatrix} 1 & 0 & 1 & 0 & 1 & 0 & 1 \\ 0 & 1 & -3 & 1 & -1 & 2 & 1 \\ -3 & 0 & 0 & -1 & -1 & -2 & -3 \\ -1 & 0 & 0 & 0 & 0 & -1 & -1 \end{bmatrix} \begin{bmatrix} k_{1i} \\ k_{2i} \\ k_{3i} \\ k_{4i} \\ k_{5i} \\ k_{6i} \\ k_{7i} \end{bmatrix} = \begin{bmatrix} 0 \\ 0 \\ 0 \\ 0 \end{bmatrix} \qquad (30.17)$$

or

$$\mathbf{A}\,\mathbf{k}_i = \mathbf{0}\,. \tag{30.18}$$

The matrix **A** is called the *dimensional matrix*. The number of physical variables n is also the number of elements in the vector $\mathbf{k}_i$ and the number of columns of **A**. Let r be the rank of **A**. The rows of **A** span an r-dimensional space. The matrix has a null space of $n-r$ dimensions, and $n-r$ linearly-independent vectors $\mathbf{k}_i$ can be chosen that lie in the null space, are orthogonal to the rows of **A**, and therefore satisfy Eq. (30.18). In the example $n = 7$, $r = 4$, and $n - r = 3$. Each of the three vectors $\mathbf{k}_1$, $\mathbf{k}_2$, and $\mathbf{k}_3$ produces a dimensionless product according to Eq. (30.14):

$$\begin{aligned}\pi_1 &= h^{k_{11}}D^{k_{21}}\rho^{k_{31}}V^{k_{41}}\mu^{k_{51}}{c_p}^{k_{61}}k^{k_{71}}\\ \pi_2 &= h^{k_{12}}D^{k_{22}}\rho^{k_{32}}V^{k_{42}}\mu^{k_{52}}{c_p}^{k_{62}}k^{k_{72}}\\ \pi_3 &= h^{k_{13}}D^{k_{23}}\rho^{k_{33}}V^{k_{43}}\mu^{k_{53}}{c_p}^{k_{63}}k^{k_{73}}\,.\end{aligned} \tag{30.19}$$

Any vector $\mathbf{k}_i$ that is a linear combination of $\mathbf{k}_1$, $\mathbf{k}_2$, and $\mathbf{k}_3$ lies in the null space of matrix **A** and satisfies Eq. (30.18). An infinite number of dimensionless products π_i can therefore be found. How many π's are in the complete physical equation for ψ, Eq. (30.13)? Evidently π_1, π_2, and π_3 are included, but perhaps more are necessary or fewer are enough. First consider the possibility that one of the three is just a product of powers of the other two. Then ψ is a function of only two π's. This possibility is tested by the formula

$$\pi_1^{\,c_1}\pi_2^{\,c_2}\pi_3^{\,c_3} = 1\,. \tag{30.20}$$

One π is a product of powers of the other two unless all of the constants c are zero. (The case of only one nonzero c does not arise because the π's are not constants). To find out whether or not they are all zero, substitute Eqs. (30.19) into (30.20), to get

$$(h^{k_{11}}\,D^{k_{21}}\cdots k^{k_{71}})^{c_1}(h^{k_{12}}\,D^{k_{22}}\cdots k^{k_{72}})^{c_2}(h^{k_{13}}\,D^{k_{23}}\cdots k^{k_{73}})^{c_3} = 1 \tag{30.21}$$

or

$$h^{k_{11}c_1 + k_{12}c_2 + k_{13}c_3}\,D^{k_{21}c_1 + k_{22}c_2 + k_{23}c_3}\cdots k^{k_{71}c_1 + k_{72}c_2 + k_{73}c_3} = 1\,. \tag{30.22}$$

Since the left side must be dimensionless like the right side, this equation is satisfied only if each exponent is zero:

$$\begin{aligned}k_{11}c_1 + k_{12}c_2 + k_{13}c_3 &= 0\\ k_{21}c_1 + k_{22}c_2 + k_{23}c_3 &= 0\\ &\cdot\\ &\cdot\\ &\cdot\\ k_{71}c_1 + k_{72}c_2 + k_{73}c_3 &= 0\end{aligned} \tag{30.23}$$

or

$$\begin{bmatrix} k_{11} & k_{12} & k_{13} \\ k_{21} & k_{22} & k_{23} \\ \cdot & \cdot & \cdot \\ \cdot & \cdot & \cdot \\ k_{71} & k_{72} & k_{73} \end{bmatrix} \begin{bmatrix} c_1 \\ c_2 \\ c_3 \end{bmatrix} = \begin{bmatrix} 0 \\ 0 \\ \cdot \\ \cdot \\ 0 \end{bmatrix} \tag{30.24}$$

or

$$\mathbf{k}_1 c_1 + \mathbf{k}_2 c_2 + \mathbf{k}_3 c_3 = \mathbf{0} \, . \tag{30.25}$$

This result requires that all of the c's be zero, because the three vectors $\mathbf{k}_i$ were chosen to be linearly independent. Since the c's are all zero, Eq. (30.20) shows that none of the π's is a product of powers of the other two, and the complete physical equation (30.13) is a relationship among at least three dimensionless products.

Now suppose that a fourth solution $\mathbf{k}_4$ of Eq. (30.18) is found and used to generate a fourth dimensionless product of the physical variables, π_4. To see if it is a product of powers of the first three π's, test it in the formula

$$\pi_1{}^{c_1} \pi_2{}^{c_2} \pi_3{}^{c_3} \pi_4{}^{c_4} = 1 \, . \tag{30.26}$$

Eq. (30.25) becomes

$$\mathbf{k}_1 c_1 + \mathbf{k}_2 c_2 + \mathbf{k}_3 c_3 + \mathbf{k}_4 c_4 = \mathbf{0} \, . \tag{30.27}$$

Since all four of these vectors lie in the three-dimensional null space of matrix $\mathbf{A}$, they are linearly dependent. The vector $\mathbf{k}_4$ is a linear combination of the other three. The c's are not all zero. According to Eq. (30.26), π_4 is just a product of powers of the first three π's:

$$\pi_4 = \pi_1{}^{-c_1/c_4} \pi_2{}^{-c_2/c_4} \pi_3{}^{-c_3/c_4} \, . \tag{30.28}$$

Similarly, any other π whose vector $\mathbf{k}_i$ satisfies Eq. (30.18) is a product of powers of the first three π's. Eq. (30.13) can therefore be written as

$$\psi = \frac{a_1}{a_j} \pi_1 + \frac{a_2}{a_j} \pi_2 + \frac{a_3}{a_j} \pi_3 + \frac{a_4}{a_j} \pi_1{}^{-c_1/c_4} \pi_2{}^{-c_2/c_4} \pi_3{}^{-c_3/c_4} + \cdots + 1$$

$$+ \frac{a_{j+1}}{a_j} \pi_1{}^{-c_1/c_{j+1}} \pi_2{}^{-c_2/c_{j+1}} \pi_3{}^{-c_3/c_{j+1}} + \cdots = 0 \, . \tag{30.29}$$

This strange-looking series with unknown a's and c's represents some function of π_1, π_2, and π_3 that will be abbreviated to the general form

$$\psi(\pi_1, \pi_2, \pi_3) = 0 \, . \tag{30.30}$$

The right number of π's in the relationship among the π's is now known.

The original infinite number in Eq. (30.13) has been reduced to $n-r$. Buckingham's Pi Theorem can now be stated more precisely:

A relationship among n physical variables can be reduced to a relationship among $n-r$ dimensionless products of the variables:

$$\psi(\pi_1,\pi_2, \ldots \pi_{n-r}) = 0 , \qquad (30.31)$$

where r is the rank of the dimensional matrix.

30.4 Choice of Dimensionless Products

How can the $n-r$ linearly-independent vectors $\mathbf{k}_i$ be obtained, with which to generate the $n-r$ dimensionless products? For the example, $n - r = 3$, and the three vectors are found by solving the four equations (30.16) with seven unknowns. The procedure is to choose any three of the elements of each vector arbitrarily, and then solve Eqs. (30.16) for the other four by inverting the remaining 4×4 matrix. One convenient choice of the arbitrary elements is shown in Fig. 30.3. With this choice the elements of the vectors $\mathbf{k}_i$ are as shown in Fig. 30.4. The choice of the arbitrary elements fulfills four requirements:

	k_{1i}	k_{2i}	k_{7i}
For π_1 (i = 1)	1	1	-1
π_2	0	1	0
π_3	0	0	1

Fig. 30.3. Arbitrary elements of the vectors $\mathbf{k}_i$.

	k_{1i}	k_{2i}	k_{3i}	k_{4i}	k_{5i}	k_{6i}	k_{7i}
For π_1	1	1	0	0	0	0	-1
π_2	0	1	1	1	-1	0	0
π_3	0	0	0	0	-1	-1	1

Fig. 30.4. Elements of the vectors $\mathbf{k}_i$.

1. A column in Fig. 30.4 must not be all zeros. If it were, a physical variable would be missing from each of the π's in Eqs. (30.19), and would be left out of Eq. (30.31).

2. Only one of the elements in the first column of Fig. 30.3, which are the coefficients of h in Eqs. (30.19), is nonzero. This choice puts h in only one of the π's, and will simplify the calculation of h when the relationship between the π's has been determined.

3. All of the elements in Fig. 30.4 are integers, as specified by Eq. (30.11).

4. The three vectors $\mathbf{k}_i$ are linearly independent.

Substituting these elements into Eqs. (30.19) produces three dimensionless products with well-known names:

$$\text{Nusselt number,} \qquad \pi_1 = N_{Nu} = hD/k \tag{30.32}$$

$$\text{Reynolds number,} \qquad \pi_2 = N_{Re} = D\rho V/\mu \tag{30.33}$$

$$\text{Prandtl number,} \qquad 1/\pi_3 = N_{Pr} = \mu c_p/k\ . \tag{30.34}$$

The relationship among the three dimensionless products is

$$\psi(hD/k,\ D\rho V/\mu,\ \mu c_p/k) = 0 \tag{30.35}$$

or

$$\psi(N_{Nu}, N_{Re}, N_{Pr}) = 0\ . \tag{30.36}$$

Now the usefulness of dimensional analysis is apparent. The heat-transfer coefficient h does not have to be expressed as a function of six other variables as in Eq. (30.4). Instead, Nusselt's number can be expressed as a function of only two other dimensionless products, neither of which contains h. Data from many experimental determinations of h with various pipes and various fluids can be expressed in terms of the Nusselt, Reynolds, and Prandtl numbers, and plotted on log-log paper. Such correlation of experimental data has produced several specific forms of Eq. (30.36). A form frequently used for turbulent flow in smooth pipes is

$$hD/k = 0.023(D\rho V/\mu)^{0.8}(\mu c_p/k)^{0.4} \tag{30.37}$$

or

$$N_{Nu} = 0.023\, {N_{Re}}^{0.8}{N_{Pr}}^{0.4}\ . \tag{30.38}$$

In this formula the fluid properties ρ, μ, c_p, and k are evaluated at the *bulk temperature* of the fluid, which is the temperature the fluid would reach if it were collected and allowed to mix. Other choices of the three arbitrary elements of the vectors $\mathbf{k}_i$ will of course produce different dimensionless products π_i. The products N_{Nu}, N_{Re}, and N_{Pr} are popular because they have physical meanings.

30.5 Free Convection

If the flow of fluid in a pipe is not forced, but is induced by the heating of the fluid, the velocity V is not an independent variable. Instead, V depends on the other six original variables plus three more: the temperature difference $\Delta T = T_w - T_\infty$ between the pipe wall and the fluid, the coefficient of expansion β of the fluid, and the body force on the fluid, normally g N/kg. Eq.(30.14), with D replaced by L for the reason explained below, becomes

$$\pi_i = h^{k_{1i}} L^{k_{2i}} \rho^{k_{3i}} \mu^{k_{4i}} c_p^{\ k_{5i}} k^{k_{6i}} \Delta T^{k_{7i}} \beta^{k_{8i}} g^{k_{9i}} \,. \tag{30.39}$$

These variables govern the heat transfer by free convection of a fluid past any heated or cooled body, not just a circular pipe. For this reason the inside diameter D is replaced by the characteristic dimension L. For any configuration this dimension must be recognized as the one that affects the heat-transfer coefficient h. If more than one dimension affects h, they must all be included in Eq. (30.39). For example, if a fluid flows between two concentric cylinders, both the outside diameter of the inner cylinder and the inside diameter of the outer cylinder must be included. The reader is invited to perform a dimensional analysis starting with Eq.(30.39), and show that

$$\psi(hL/k,\ \mu c_p/k,\ L^3\rho^2\Delta T\ \beta\ g/\mu^2,\ \beta\ \Delta T,\ c_p/L\ \beta\ g) = 0\,. \tag{30.40}$$

Notice that since $n = 9$ and $r = 4$, the number of dimensionless products $n - r$ in this relationship is 5. Experience has shown that the last two do not affect h substantially. The first two are the Nusselt and Prandtl numbers. The product

$$N_{Gr} = L^3\rho^2\Delta T\ \beta\ g/\mu^2 \tag{30.41}$$

is called the *Grashof number.*

McAdams (Ref. 88, pages 172 and 180) presents experimentally-determined formulas for the external heating and cooling of plates and cylinders by natural convection. All are of the form

$$N_{Nu} = k_1(N_{Gr}N_{Pr})^{k_2}\,. \tag{30.42}$$

Since $N_{Nu} = hL/k$, the heat-transfer coefficient h can be found when N_{Nu} is calculated, and then used in Eq. (30.3) to calculate the rate of flow of heat. The values of k_1 and k_2 for various configurations are shown in Fig. 30.5. The fluid properties ρ, μ, c_p, k, and β used to determine the three dimensionless products are evaluated at the *average film temperature* T_f, namely the average of the wall temperature T_w and temperature of the fluid T_∞ out beyond the boundary layer. For horizontal cylinders the characteristic dimension L in the Grashof and Nusselt numbers is the diameter. For horizontal plates L is the average

	$N_{Gr}N_{Pr}$	k_1	k_2
Horizontal cylinders	10^3-10^9	0.53	0.25
Vertical plates and cylinders	10^4-10^9	0.59	0.25
	10^9-10^{12}	0.13	1/3
Horizontal plates: heated upper surface or cooled lower surface	10^5-2x10^7	0.54	0.25
	$2x10^7-3x10^{10}$	0.14	1/3
Horizontal plates: heated lower surface or cooled upper surface	$3x10^5-3x10^{10}$	0.27	0.25

Fig. 30.5. Coefficients for Eq. (30.42).

of the length and width. For vertical cylinders and plates, L is the height of the surface, not the diameter or width. The reason is that the temperature gradient varies along the fluid flow path which is vertical, not horizontal. Fig. 30.6 is an interferometer photograph showing the natural convection of air along a heated vertical plate. The black and white

Fig. 30.6. Lines of constant temperature along a vertical plate. (Reprinted by permission of Prof. J.P. Holman, Southern Methodist University.)

fringes are lines of constant temperature. Notice that except at the bottom, the lines are nearly parallel, indicating that the temperature gradient is nearly constant. The characteristic dimension L would therefore be expected to have little effect on h. Eq. (30.42) and Fig. 30.5 verify this conclusion. Notice that L is raised to the third power in the Grashof number. For the lower values of $N_{Gr}N_{Pr}$ for which the flow is laminar, the Grashof number for vertical plates is raised to the 0.25 power by k_2 in Eq. (30.42). Since h and L appear to the first power in the Nusselt number, h is proportional to $L^{-1/4}$, and therefore varies only slightly with L. In the higher range of $N_{Gr}N_{Pr}$ in which the flow is turbulent, $k_2 = 1/3$, and L cancels completely out of Eq. (30.42). Then h is not a function of L at all.

A convenient alternative to Eq. (30.42) is

$$N_{Nu} = f(N_{Gr}N_{Pr}) \tag{30.43}$$

for which the functional relationship f is given by an experimental curve. This form can be written as

$$\frac{hL}{k} = f\left(\frac{L^3\rho^2\Delta T\,\beta\, g}{\mu^2}\cdot\frac{\mu c_p}{k}\right) = f(\alpha L^3\Delta T) \tag{30.44}$$

where

$$\alpha = \frac{\rho^2\beta g c_p}{\mu k}\,. \tag{30.45}$$

Fig. 30.7 shows that one curve provides a fair representation of the relationship between N_{Nu}, N_{Gr}, and N_{Pr} for spheres, vertical plates, and vertical and horizontal cylinders in air, water, oil and alcohol. Except for g, each term in α is a property of the fluid, and is evaluated at the average film temperature. If the fluid is air at atmospheric pressure, α and k can be found in Fig. 30.8.

The log-log representation of the variables in Fig. 30.7 makes the deviations from the curve deceptively small. For example, one experimental point lies at log $hL/k = 1.5$, where the curve is at 1.2. The two values of hL/k are 31.6 and 15.8. The experimental value of hL/k is twice that given by the curve. Eq. (30.42) with the values of k_1 and k_2 listed in Fig. 30.5 fits the experimental curve closely over the specified ranges of $N_{Gr}N_{Pr}$. An exception is the formula for heated horizontal plates facing downward:

$$N_{Nu} = 0.27(N_{Gr}N_{Pr})^{0.25}\,, \tag{30.46}$$

which lies below the experimental curve. The reason for this discrepancy can be seen by comparing this configuration with the other four in Fig. 30.5. If one of the latter four bodies is heated, the adjacent fluid is

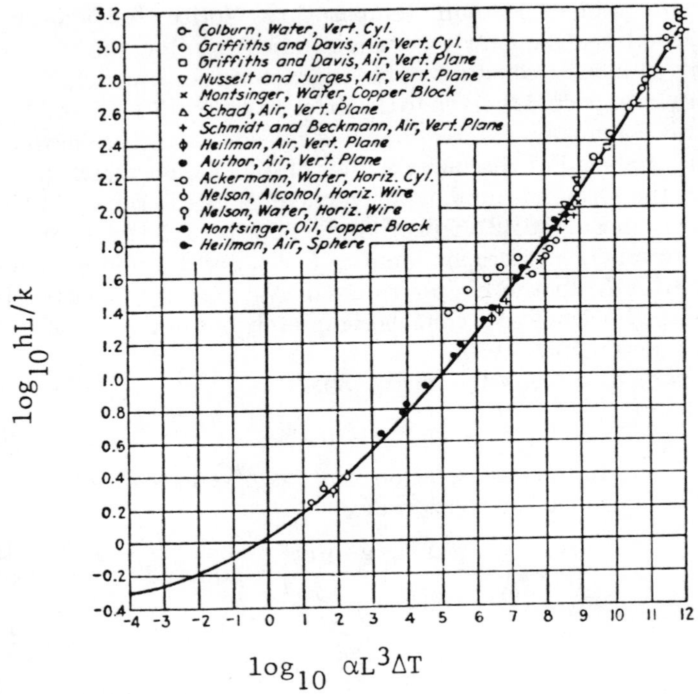

Fig. 30.7. Evaluation of the Nusselt number for free convection. (W.J. King, *Mechanical Engineering*, Volume 54, 1932, page 350.)

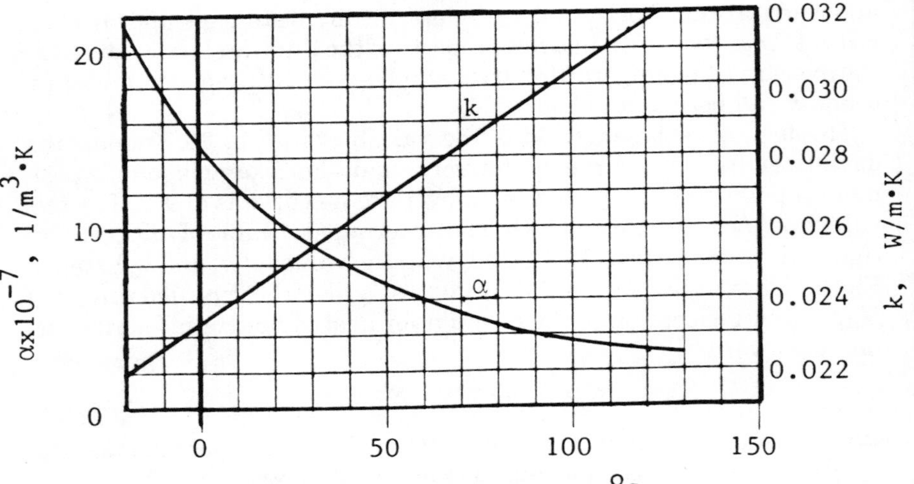

Fig. 30.8. Values of α and k for atmospheric air.

warmed, becomes more buoyant, and rises along the body with little restraint. The fluid under a heated horizontal surface, however, is restricted from rising by the plate. The rate of cooling is reduced, and with it h and the Nusselt number. This discrepancy points out the limitation of dimensional analysis, which is based on two requirements:

1. The formula for the dimensionless products, such as Eq. (30.39), should include all of the physical variables that affect h.

2. The true relationship between the dimensionless products is found by plotting experimental data.

If these requirements had been fulfilled, the relationship determined for N_{Nu}, N_{Gr}, and N_{Pr} would fit every case of free convection exactly. The surprise is not that the results of dimensional analysis are only approximate, but that this procedure of judicious guessing produces results that are useful at all.

30.6 An Example

Fig. 30.7 will be used to calculate the heat lost from a vertical steel hot-water pipe that passes from the floor to the ceiling of a room three meters high, shown in Fig. 30.9. The outside of the pipe has a diameter of 5 cm, an area

$$A = (\pi)(0.05)(3) = 0.471 \text{ m}^2 , \tag{30.47}$$

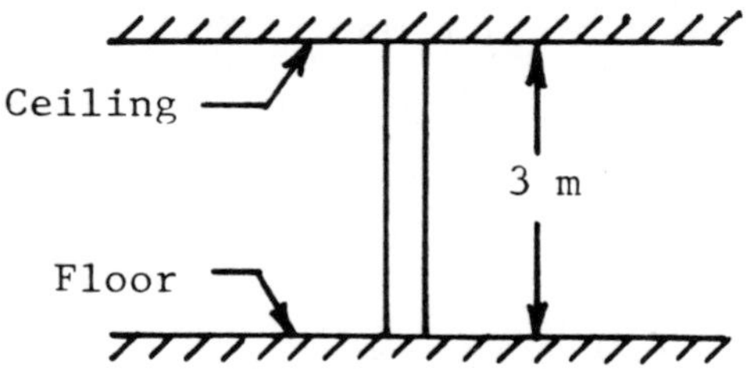

Ceiling

3 m

Floor

Fig. 30.9. A hot-water pipe.

and a temperature T_w of 90°C. The rust on the pipe gives its surface an emissivity ε of 0.79. The temperature T_∞ of the air and the walls of the room is 20°C. The reader is invited to estimate the heat transferred from the pipe to the room by convection and radiation. Which component is larger? The solution starts with a calculation of the average film temperature:

$$T_f = \frac{20 + 90}{2} = 55°\text{C} . \tag{30.48}$$

According to Fig. 30.8, for air at 55°C, $\alpha = 6.5 \times 10^7\ \mathrm{m^{-3}{\cdot}K^{-1}}$ and $k = 0.0273$ W/m·K. The characteristic dimension L of the pipe is its height, 3 m. The temperature difference between the pipe wall and the air is

$$\Delta T = 90 - 20 = 70\ \mathrm{K}\,. \tag{30.49}$$

Then

$$N_{Gr} N_{Pr} = \alpha\, L^3 \Delta T = (6.5 \times 10^7)(3)^3(70) = 1.23 \times 10^{11} \tag{30.50}$$

and

$$\log_{10} \alpha\, L^3 \Delta T = 11.090\,. \tag{30.51}$$

According to Fig. 30.7,

$$\log_{10} \frac{hL}{k} = 2.8\,. \tag{30.52}$$

Then

$$N_{Nu} = \frac{hL}{k} = 631 \tag{30.53}$$

and

$$h = \frac{(631)(0.0273)}{3} = 5.74 \quad \mathrm{W/m^2{\cdot}K}\,. \tag{30.54}$$

The Nusselt number can also be calculated by Eq. (30.42). For a vertical cylinder with $N_{Gr} N_{Pr} = 1.23 \times 10^{11}$,

$$N_{Nu} = 0.13(N_{Gr} N_{Pr})^{1/3} = (0.13)(1.23 \times 10^{11})^{1/3} = 647\,, \tag{30.55}$$

which agrees reasonably well with Eq. (30.53). The power loss by convection from the pipe, according to Eq. (30.3), is

$$q_c = h\, A\, \Delta T = (5.74)(0.471)(70) = 189 \text{ watts.} \tag{30.56}$$

For radiant heat transfer, the pipe constitutes a small body in a large isothermal enclosure. The net radiant power exchanged between the pipe and the room is

$$q_r = \sigma\, A\, \varepsilon\, (T_w^{\,4} - T_\infty^{\,4})$$

$$= (5.669 \times 10^{-8})(0.471)(0.79)(363^4 - 293^4) = 211 \text{ watts}\,, \tag{30.57}$$

which exceeds the power lost by convection from the pipe. Did you predict that the radiant component would be larger?

30.7 Forced Convection Normal to a Pipe

The amount of heat removed from the vertical pipe can be increased considerably by blowing air across it. The heat-transfer coefficient h for forced flow outside of a pipe is a function of the same six variables that determine h for forced flow thru a pipe, listed in Eq. (30.4). The dimensional analysis is the same and leads to Eq. (30.35). Now the characteristic dimension D is the outside diameter of the pipe instead of its length, because the flow of fluid is normal to the pipe, not parallel to it as for natural convection. The Prandtl number $\mu c_p/k$ is a function only of the fluid properties, and for air it varies little over a wide temperature range. If it is assumed to be constant, Eq. (30.36) indicates that N_{Nu} is a function of N_{Re} only. Fig. 30.10 shows the experimentally-observed

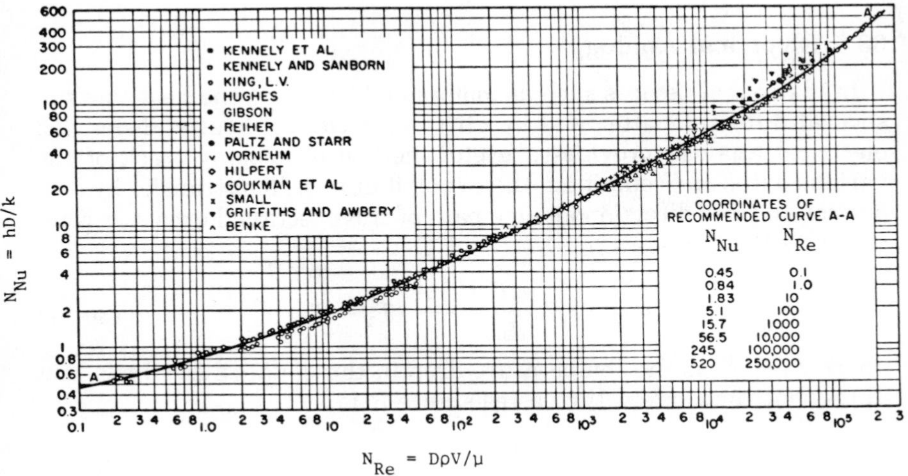

Fig. 30.10. Nusselt number for forced flow of air normal to a cylinder. (From *Heat Transmission*, Third Edition by W.H. McAdams. Copyright 1954 by W.H. McAdams. Used with the permission of McGraw-Hill Book Company.)

function for air blowing normal to a cylinder. The air properties are evaluated at the average film temperature. For air at atmospheric pressure and 55°C,

$$\rho = 1.076 \text{ kg/m}^3 , \qquad \mu = 1.976 \times 10^{-5} \text{ N·s/m}^2 ,$$

$$\text{and} \qquad k = 0.02838 \text{ W/m·K} .$$

If air is blown across the 5-cm pipe at a velocity V of 30 m/s, the Reynolds number is

$$N_{Re} = \frac{D\rho V}{\mu} = \frac{(0.05)(1.076)(30)}{1.976 \times 10^{-5}} = 8.17 \times 10^4 . \qquad (30.58)$$

According to Fig. 30.10, the Nusselt number is

$$N_{Nu} = \frac{hD}{k} = 220 . \qquad (30.59)$$

Therefore

$$h = \frac{220k}{D} = \frac{(220)(0.02838)}{0.05} = 124.9 \qquad \text{W/m}^2\cdot\text{K}\,, \tag{30.60}$$

which is 21.8 times the value with free convection. Forced convection is a great expediter of heat transfer in devices ranging from power transformers to bowls of soup.

30.8 Electrical Analogy

In many real devices such as motors and turbines, the heat flows in several different paths, and by all three modes of heat transfer. An electrical analogy provides a useful method of keeping track of the various paths and combining their contributions. Heat transfer by conduction in the x direction along a path of cross-sectional area A is computed by Fourier's law

$$q = -k\,A\,\frac{dT}{dx} = \frac{k\,A}{L}\,(T_1 - T_2)\,, \tag{30.61}$$

where $T_1 - T_2$ is the temperature drop in the distance L. Ohm's law states that the current thru a resistance R is

$$I = \frac{1}{R}\,(V_1 - V_2)\,, \tag{30.62}$$

where $V_1 - V_2$ is the voltage drop across the resistance. If temperature is analogous to voltage and heat power to current, then L/kA is analogous to electrical resistance. This *thermal resistance* for conduction will also be called R:

$$R = L/kA \qquad \text{kelvins/watt.} \tag{30.63}$$

Newton's law for heat convection is given by Eq. (30.3):

$$q = h\,A\,(T_w - T_\infty)\,. \tag{30.64}$$

The thermal resistance of the film between a solid surface and a moving fluid is therefore

$$R = 1/hA \qquad \text{K/W}\,. \tag{30.65}$$

The Stefan-Boltzmann law for the heat power exchanged by radiation between bodies 1 and 2 is

$$q = \sigma\,A_1F_{12}F_\varepsilon(T_1{}^4 - T_2{}^4)\,, \tag{30.66}$$

$$= \frac{\sigma\,A_1F_{12}F_\varepsilon(T_1{}^4 - T_2{}^4)}{T_1 - T_2}\,(T_1 - T_2)\,. \tag{30.67}$$

The thermal resistance for radiation between the bodies is therefore

$$R = \frac{T_1 - T_2}{\sigma A_1 F_{12} F_\varepsilon (T_1^4 - T_2^4)} . \tag{30.68}$$

This resistance is not constant, but is a nonlinear function of the two temperatures.

The usefulness of the electrical analogy can be illustrated by a re-calculation of the heat lost from the vertical pipe cooled by natural convection. Since $h = 5.74\ \mathrm{W/m^2 \cdot K}$, the thermal resistance representing convection is

$$R_c = \frac{1}{hA} = \frac{1}{(5.74)(0.471)} = 0.3699 \qquad \mathrm{K/W} . \tag{30.69}$$

If the pipe is body 1 and the surroundings are body 2, the thermal resistance representing radiation is

$$R_r = \frac{T_1 - T_2}{\sigma A_1 F_{12} F_\varepsilon (T_1^4 - T_2^4)} = \frac{T_1 - T_2}{\sigma A_1 \varepsilon (T_1^4 - T_2^4)}$$

$$= \frac{70}{(5.669 \times 10^{-8})(0.471)(0.79)(363^4 - 293^4)} = 0.3321 \qquad \mathrm{K/W} . \tag{30.70}$$

The two heat-flow paths are in parallel, and are represented by resistors in parallel as in Fig. 30.11. Their parallel resistance is

$$R = \frac{R_c R_r}{R_c + R_r} , \tag{30.71}$$

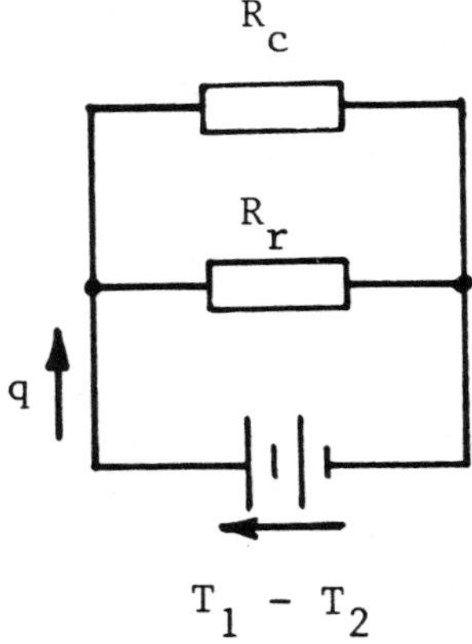

Fig. 30.11. Convection and radiation in parallel.

and the total power lost by the pipe is

$$q = \frac{T_1 - T_2}{R} = \frac{(70)(0.3699 + 0.3321)}{(0.3699)(0.3321)} = 400 \text{ watts} , \qquad (30.72)$$

which of course agrees with the sum of the components computed in Eqs. (30.56) and (30.57).

30.9 Heat Paths in Series

In some devices, paths of radiation and convection are in series, and the temperatures at the terminals of the former are unknown. The thermal resistance for radiation cannot be calculated in one step by Eq. (30.68), but must be determined by iteration. The procedure can be illustrated by returning once more to the vertical steel pipe. This time the pipe is heated by a Calrod unit of 1-cm diameter, concentric with the pipe for its entire length of 3 meters, as shown in Fig. 30.12. The air in

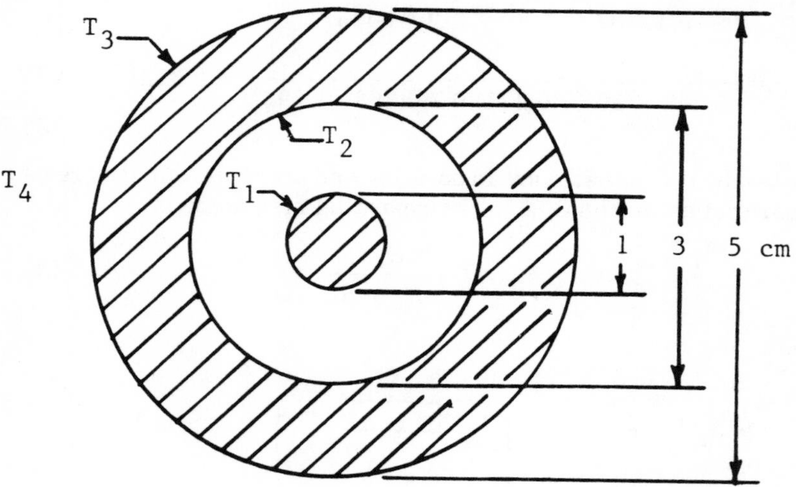

Fig. 30.12. Pipe heated by a Calrod unit.

the annular space has been evacuated. The temperature T_1 of the surface of the Calrod unit is held constant at 300°C. The pipe wall is 1 cm thick and has a thermal conductivity of k of 43 W/m·K. Air at a temperature T_4 of 20°C is blown across the pipe with a velocity of 30 m/s in a room whose walls are also at 20°C. To simplify the solution, assume that

1. The Calrod unit and the inside wall of the pipe are thermally black.

2. The temperatures at the inner and outer diameters of the pipe, T_2 and T_3, are uniform from bottom to top.

3. The small fraction of heat removed from the outer surface of the pipe by radiation is negligible. This assumption will be verified by the results.

The reader is invited to guess T_2, T_3, and the power q consumed by the Calrod unit.

Calculation of these three quantities begins with the analog shown in Fig. 30.13 in which the power q flows across the temperature drop $T_1 - T_4$ thru resistors R_1, R_2, and R_3 representing radiation from the Calrod unit to the inner pipe wall, conduction thru the pipe, and convection to the room air. The dotted resister R_4 represents radiation to the

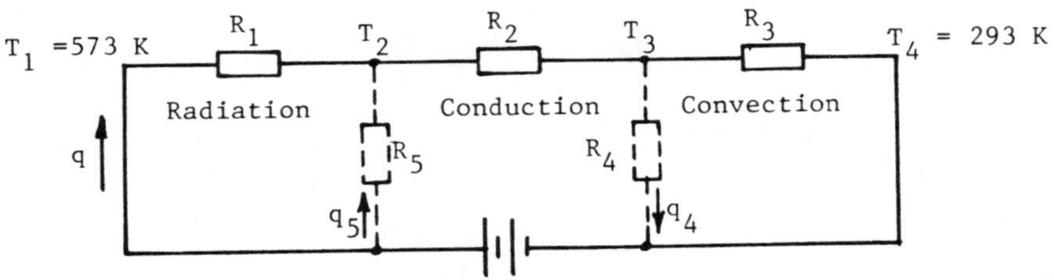

Fig. 30.13. Electrical circuit representing heat flow.

walls of the room, and R_5 represents conduction from the Calrod unit to the pipe ID, which would occur if the air had not been removed. The resistance representing radiation is

$$R_1 = \frac{T_1 - T_2}{\sigma A_1(T_1{}^4 - T_2{}^4)}, \tag{30.73}$$

where A_1 is the surface area of the Calrod unit of diameter d_1 and length L:

$$A = \pi d_1 L \, . \tag{30.74}$$

To compute the resistance R_2 representing conduction thru the pipe, refer to Fig. 30.14. According to Fourier's law, the power passing radially across the cylindrical surface of radius r, length L, area A, and thickness dr is

$$q = -kA\frac{dT}{dr} = -(k)(2\pi rL)\frac{dT}{dr} \, . \tag{30.75}$$

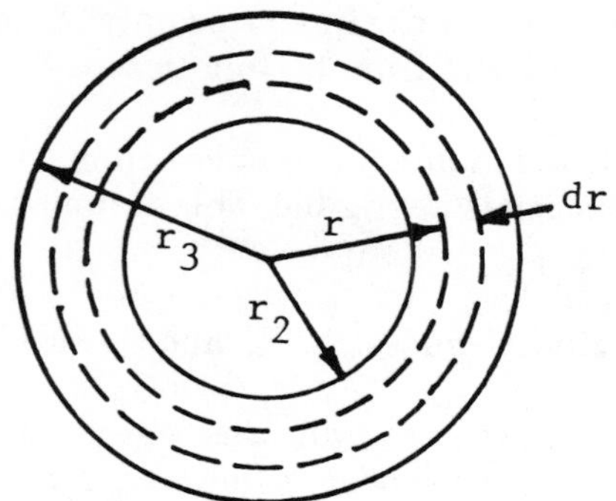

Fig. 30.14. Cross section of the pipe.

Thus

$$dT = -\frac{q}{2\pi kL} \cdot \frac{dr}{r}. \tag{30.76}$$

When the two sides of this equation are integrated, q can be brought outside of the integral sign because it is independent of r:

$$\int_{T_2}^{T_3} dT = -\frac{q}{2\pi kL}\int_{r_2}^{r_3} \frac{dr}{r} \tag{30.77}$$

or

$$T_3 - T_2 = -\frac{q}{2\pi kL}\ln\frac{r_3}{r_2} = -\frac{q}{2\pi kL}\ln\frac{d_3}{d_2}, \tag{30.78}$$

where d_2 and d_3 are the inner and outer diameters of the pipe. Then

$$R_2 = \frac{T_2 - T_3}{q} = \frac{\ln(d_3/d_2)}{2\pi kL}. \tag{30.79}$$

The resistance representing convection is

$$R_3 = 1/hA_3\,, \tag{30.80}$$

where $A_3 = \pi d_3 L$. The value of h found in Eq. (30.60), 124.9 W/m^2·K, will be used although it was calculated for an average film temperature T_f of 55°C. A correction will be made later when the new value of T_f is found.

Now R_2, R_3, T_1, and T_4 are known, but R_1, T_2, and T_3 are not. They can be found by an iterative procedure. Start with the temperature T_2 of the inner pipe wall at the Calrod temperature, 573.15 K. Calculate the power flow q two different ways:

$$q_1 = \frac{T_1 - T_2}{R_1} = \sigma A_1(T_1^4 - T_2^4) \qquad (30.81)$$

and

$$q_2 = \frac{T_2 - T_4}{R_2 + R_3} . \qquad (30.82)$$

If q_2 is greater than q_1, the assumed value of T_2 was too high. Lower T_2 by 10 K and recalculate q_1 and q_2. As T_2 decreases, q_1 increases and q_2 decreases. When q_2 drops below q_1, the calculation has overshot the correct value of T_2. Add 10 K to T_2 to back up, and then proceed in steps of 1 K. The process of overshooting, backing up, and reducing the step size of T_2 can be repeated until q_1 and q_2 are as close together as desired. A BASIC program to make these calculations, and its results, are listed in Fig. 30.15. The run stops when q_1 and q_2 differ by less than $10^{-6}q_1$. The results are

$$\begin{aligned} T_2 &= 29.4°\text{C} \\ T_3 &= 29.0°\text{C} \\ q &= 532 \text{ W} . \end{aligned} \qquad (30.83)$$

Notice that of the three thermal resistances R_1, R_2, and R_3, the first is by far the largest. Most of the temperature drop occurs in the vacuum between the Calrod unit and the inner pipe wall. The temperature drop thru the pipe wall is only 0.34°C.

The value of h used in the calculation of R_3 was based on an average film temperature T_f of 55°C. This temperature turned out to be

$$T_f = \frac{T_3 + T_4}{2} = \frac{29.0 + 20}{2} = 24.5°\text{C} . \qquad (30.84)$$

How much does this discrepancy affect the results? At the new average film temperature the air properties are

$$\rho = 1.187 \text{ kg/m}^3 , \qquad \mu = 1.834 \times 10^{-5} \text{ N·s/m}^2 ,$$

$$k = 0.02604 \text{ W/m·K} .$$

The Reynolds number is now

$$N_{Re} = \frac{D\rho V}{\mu} = \frac{(0.05)(1.187)(30)}{1.834 \times 10^{-5}} = 9.71 \times 10^4 , \qquad (30.85)$$

and according to Fig. 30.10 the Nusselt number is

$$N_{Nu} = \frac{hD}{k} = 250 . \qquad (30.86)$$

```
PIPE           08:49EST     02/17/82

100 READ T1,T2,T4,K,D1,D2,D3,S,L,H,C
120 DATA 573.15,573.15,293.15,43,.01,.03,.05,5.669E-8,3,124.9,10
125 R2=LOG(D3/D2)/(2*PI*K*L)
130 A1=PI*D1*L
140 A3=PI*D3*L
150 R3=1/(H*A3)
155 B=1E-6
160 Q1=S*A1*(T1**4-T2**4)
170 Q2=(T2-T4)/(R2+R3)
190 IF ABS(Q1-Q2)<B*Q1 THEN 260
200 IF Q1>Q2 THEN 230
210 T2=T2-C
220 GO TO 160
230 T2=T2+C
240 C=C/10
250 GO TO 160
260 T3=T4+Q1*R3
270 PRINT "TEMP OF INNER PIPE WALL=";T2-273.15;"DEG C"
280 PRINT "TEMP OF OUTER PIPE WALL=";T3-273.15;"DEG C"
290 PRINT "POWER DISSIPATED IS BETWEEN";Q1;"AND";Q2;"WATTS"
310 PRINT
320 PRINT "R1=";(T1-T2)/Q1;"K/W"
330 PRINT "R2=";R2
340 PRINT "R3=";R3
350 END

READY
RUN

PIPE           08:49EST     02/17/82


TEMP OF INNER PIPE WALL= 29.3708 DEG C
TEMP OF OUTER PIPE WALL= 29.0356 DEG C
POWER DISSIPATED IS BETWEEN 531.818 AND 531.818 WATTS

R1= .508876 K/W
R2= 6.30236E-4
R3= 1.69901E-2
```

Fig. 30.15. Power dissipated by the Calrod unit.

Then

$$h = \frac{250k}{D} = \frac{(250)(0.02604)}{0.05} = 130.2 \qquad \mathrm{W/m^2{\cdot}K}\,. \qquad (30.87)$$

When the program of Fig. 30.15 is rerun, the temperature of the outer pipe wall decreases from 29.0 to 28.7°C, and the temperature drop across the pipe wall remains at 0.34°C. The power dissipated by the pipe increases by only 0.2 watts. These small changes are not significant, since some of the numbers used in the calculations are only approximate. For example, the curve in Fig. 30.10 is a compromise between the results of several experimenters. At $N_{Re} = 4.3 \times 10^4$, the curve lies 40 percent below an experimental point. Certainly another iteration with a new average film temperature of

$$T_f = \frac{28.7 + 20}{2} = 24.4°\text{C} \tag{30.88}$$

is unnecessary.

30.10 The Neglected Heat Paths

According to the third assumption made at the beginning of this analysis, the fraction of heat dissipated from the pipe by radiation to the walls of the room is negligible. This assumption can now be tested. The temperature T_3 of the outer pipe wall given in Fig. 30.15 is 29.04°C or 302.19 K. The radiated power is therefore

$$\begin{aligned} q_4 &= \sigma A_3 \varepsilon (T_3{}^4 - T_4{}^4) = (5.669 \times 10^{-8})(0.471)(0.79)(302.19^4 - 293.15^4) \\ &= 20.1 \text{ watts}, \end{aligned} \tag{30.89}$$

which is only 3.8 percent of the 531 watts dissipated by convection.

A heat-conduction path from the Calrod unit to the inner pipe wall, represented by R_5 in Fig. 30.13, was avoided by specifying that the annular space is evacuated. Without this specification the space would contain air at a mean temperature of about

$$\frac{T_1 + T_2}{2} = \frac{300 + 29.4}{2} = 164.7°\text{C}\,. \tag{30.90}$$

At this temperature the thermal conductivity k of air at atmospheric pressure is 0.03627 W/m·K. According to Eq. (30.79) the resistance representing the conduction path in the air space is

$$R_5 = \frac{\ln(d_2/d_1)}{2\pi kL} = \frac{\ln 3}{(2)(\pi)(0.03627)(3)} = 1.607 \qquad \text{K/W}\,. \tag{30.91}$$

As Fig. 30.13 shows, the resistance R_1 of 0.509 K/W representing radiation from the Calrod unit to the inner pipe wall is in parallel with R_5. The difference between their parallel resistance

$$\frac{(0.509)(1.607)}{0.509 + 1.607} = 0.387 \qquad \text{K/W} \tag{30.92}$$

and R_1 is too great to ignore. The power q_5 conducted thru the annular air space would have to be added to q_1 in Eq. (30.81) before comparison to q_2 obtained in Eq. (30.82).

When a device has two or more significant paths for radiant heat flow, in addition to those for conduction and convection, the analysis is more complicated. Two or more temperatures must be chosen arbitrarily and then adjusted by systematic iteration to balance the various heat flows. The analyst has the problem of writing an efficient program with nested FOR-NEXT or DO loops.

The example of the Calrod unit in a steel pipe is simple enough to solve without a special iterative program. Instead of calculating q_1 and q_2 separately as in Eqs. (30.81) and (30.82) and then comparing them, simply equate them:

$$\sigma A_1(T_1^4 - T_2^4) = \frac{T_2 - T_4}{R_2 + R_3} \tag{30.93}$$

or

$$\sigma A_1 T_2^4 + \frac{1}{R_2 + R_3} T_2 - \left(\sigma A_1 T_1^4 + \frac{T_4}{R_2 + R_3}\right) = 0\,. \tag{30.94}$$

When the values of R_2 and R_3 obtained in Fig. 30.15 are inserted,

$$5.34291 \times 10^{-9} T_2^4 + 56.7526\, T_2 - 17{,}213.6 = 0\,. \tag{30.95}$$

The roots of this polynomial are

$$T_2 = 302.521, \qquad -2291.22, \qquad \text{and} \qquad 994.349 \pm j1912.94\,. \tag{30.96}$$

Only the first root has physical significance. Therefore

$$T_2 = 302.52\ \text{K} = 29.37°\text{C}\,, \tag{30.97}$$

which agrees with the value obtained by the iterative program in Fig. 30.15. Now q and T_3 can be found in two simple steps.

Chapter 31

RIGID-BODY DYNAMICS

31.1 Introduction

Engineers are familiar with the formula $T = I\dot{\omega}$, in which T is the torque applied to a rigid body, I is its moment of inertia, and $\dot{\omega}$ is its angular acceleration. For many practical problems the solution is expedited by expressing torque and angular acceleration as vectors in a rotating coordinate system. Then the formula becomes more complicated. Two useful forms of the torque formula will be derived and used to calculate (1) the pitching torque exerted on an airplane by its propeller during a turn, and (2) the angular velocity of precession of a gyroscope.

31.2 Translation of a Body

Fig. 31.1 shows a body in an xyz coordinate system that is called *inertial* because it does not accelerate or rotate. The position of a particle

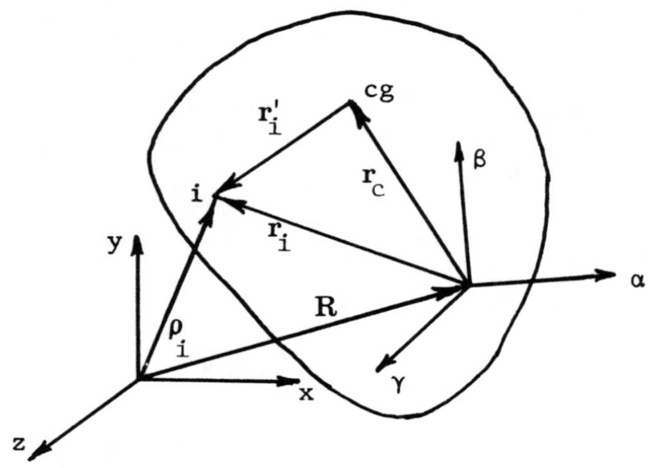

Fig. 31.1. Coordinate systems for a body.

i in the body is denoted by the vector $\boldsymbol{\rho}_i$. Another rectangular coordinate system, $\alpha\beta\gamma$, is located in the body but is not yet required to move with it. As Fig. 31.1 shows, the net force on the particle i of mass m_i is

$$\mathbf{f}_i = m_i \ddot{\boldsymbol{\rho}}_i = m_i(\ddot{\mathbf{R}} + \ddot{\mathbf{r}}_c + \ddot{\mathbf{r}}_i') , \tag{31.1}$$

where $\mathbf{R}$ is the vector out to the origin of the $\alpha\beta\gamma$ axes, $\mathbf{r}_c$ is the position of the body's center of gravity, and $\mathbf{r}'_i$ is the distance from the cg to particle i. The vector $\mathbf{r}_i$ is the distance from the $\alpha\beta\gamma$ origin to particle i. All of these vectors are measured in the inertial xyz coordinates. The vector $\ddot{\mathbf{R}}$ is the acceleration of the $\alpha\beta\gamma$ origin in the inertial coordinate system, and $\ddot{\mathbf{r}}_i$ is the acceleration of particle i relative to the $\alpha\beta\gamma$ origin, also measured in the inertial coordinates. The force on particle i is

$$\mathbf{f}_i = \mathbf{F}_i + \sum_j \mathbf{f}_{ij} , \tag{31.2}$$

where $\mathbf{F}_i$ is any externally-applied force, and $\mathbf{f}_{ij}$ is the force exerted on particle i by particle j of the body. The sum of all forces on all of the particles is

$$\mathbf{F} = \sum_i \mathbf{f}_i = \sum_i \mathbf{F}_i + \sum_i \sum_j \mathbf{f}_{ij} . \tag{31.3}$$

The last term is zero because for every force $\mathbf{f}_{mn}$ there is an equal, opposite force $\mathbf{f}_{nm}$. Combining Eq. (31.3) with (31.1) yields

$$\begin{aligned} \sum_i \mathbf{F}_i &= \sum_i m_i(\ddot{\mathbf{R}} + \ddot{\mathbf{r}}_c + \ddot{\mathbf{r}}'_i) = m(\ddot{\mathbf{R}} + \ddot{\mathbf{r}}_c) + \sum_i m_i \ddot{\mathbf{r}}'_i \\ &= m \frac{d^2}{dt^2} (\mathbf{R} + \mathbf{r}_c) + \frac{d^2}{dt^2} \sum_i m_i \mathbf{r}'_i , \end{aligned} \tag{31.4}$$

where m is the total mass of the body. The last term is zero because $\mathbf{r}'_i$ is measured from the cg of the body. The cg is defined as the point about which the sum of moments is zero:

$$\sum_i m_i \mathbf{r}'_i = 0 . \tag{31.5}$$

Eq. (31.4) becomes

$$\sum_i \mathbf{F}_i = m \frac{d^2}{dt^2} (\mathbf{R} + \mathbf{r}_c) . \tag{31.6}$$

This result is Newton's second law. It states that the sum of external forces on a body is its mass times the acceleration of its cg. Notice that the body does not have to be rigid. It might be a pillow, a cloud of gas, or as in Fig. 31.2, two balls on a pool table. If one of the balls of mass m_o is struck by the force F, its acceleration is F/m_o. The mass of the body is $m = 2m_o$, and its cg is midway between the balls. The acceleration of the body is $F/m = F/2m_o$, or half that of the struck ball.

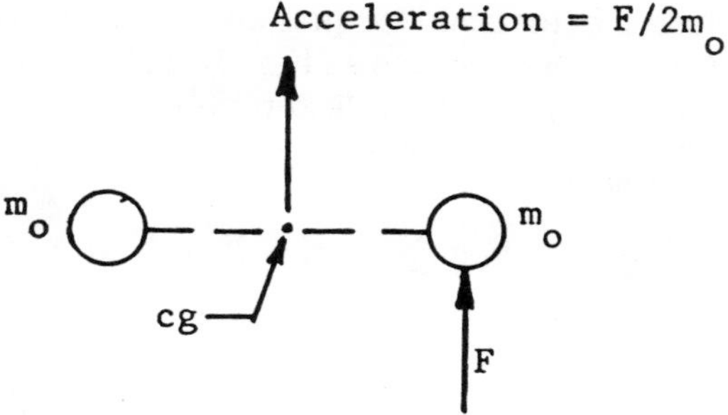

Fig. 31.2. Two pool balls.

31.3 Rotation of a Rigid Body

The next step is to calculate the torque required to produce the rotation of the body in Fig. 31.1. If, as in Fig. 31.3, a force **f** is applied at a

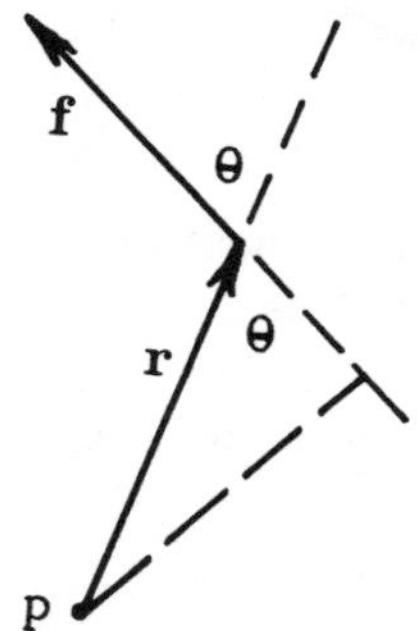

Fig. 31.3. Torque about a point.

distance **r** from a point p, the torque about the point is $\mathbf{r} \times \mathbf{f}$. The net force on particle i in the body of Fig. 31.1 is

$$\mathbf{f}_i = \mathbf{F}_i + \sum_j \mathbf{f}_{ij} = m_i \ddot{\boldsymbol{\rho}}_i = m_i \ddot{\mathbf{R}} + m_i \ddot{\mathbf{r}}_i . \tag{31.7}$$

The torque exerted by this force about the $\alpha\beta\gamma$ origin is

$$\mathbf{r}_i \times \mathbf{f}_i = \mathbf{r}_i \times \mathbf{F}_i + \sum_j \mathbf{r}_i \times \mathbf{f}_{ij} = m_i \mathbf{r}_i \times \ddot{\mathbf{R}} + m_i \mathbf{r}_i \times \ddot{\mathbf{r}}_i . \tag{31.8}$$

The sum of all the torques on all of the particles about the $\alpha\beta\gamma$ origin is

$$\underset{1}{\sum_i \mathbf{r}_i \times \mathbf{F}_i} + \underset{2}{\sum_i \sum_j \mathbf{r}_i \times \mathbf{f}_{ij}} = \sum_i m_i \mathbf{r}_i \times \ddot{\mathbf{R}} + \sum_i m_i \mathbf{r}_i \times \ddot{\mathbf{r}}_i . \tag{31.9}$$

Term 1 is the sum $\mathbf{T}$ of external torques applied to the body, about the $\alpha\beta\gamma$ origin. Term 2 is zero because as Fig. 31.4 shows, for every torque $\mathbf{r}_m \times \mathbf{f}_{mn}$ there is an equal, opposite torque $\mathbf{r}_n \times \mathbf{f}_{nm}$. Since $\mathbf{r}_i = \mathbf{r}_c + \mathbf{r}'_i$, Eq. (31.9) can now be written as

$$\mathbf{T} = \underbrace{\sum_i m_i \, \mathbf{r}_c \times \ddot{\mathbf{R}}}_{1} + \underbrace{\sum_i m_i \, \mathbf{r}'_i \times \ddot{\mathbf{R}}}_{2} + \sum_i m_i \, \mathbf{r}_i \times \ddot{\mathbf{r}}_i \, . \tag{31.10}$$

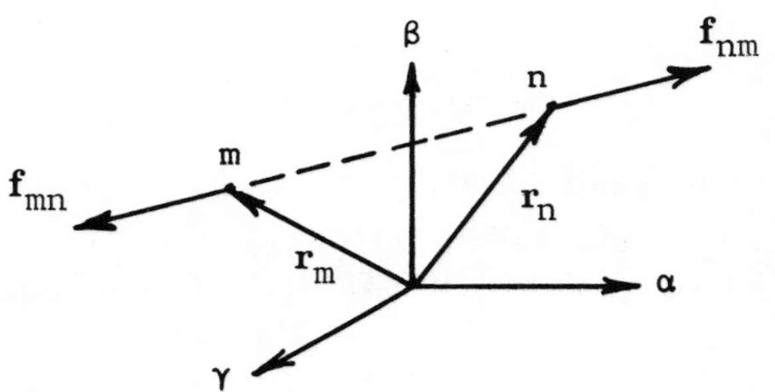

Fig. 31.4. Equal and opposite torques.

Term 1 of this equation can be written as $m \, \mathbf{r}_c \times \ddot{\mathbf{R}}$, where m is the total mass of the body. Term 2 is zero because as Eq. (31.5) shows,

$$\sum_i m_i \, \mathbf{r}'_i = 0 \, . \tag{31.5}$$

Eq. (31.10) reduces to the form

$$\mathbf{T} = \mathbf{r}_c \times m \, \ddot{\mathbf{R}} + \sum_i m_i \, \mathbf{r}_i \times \ddot{\mathbf{r}}_i \, . \tag{31.11}$$

To put the last term of the equation into a more convenient form, observe that

$$\frac{d}{dt} (\mathbf{r}_i \times \dot{\mathbf{r}}_i) = \dot{\mathbf{r}}_i \times \dot{\mathbf{r}}_i + \mathbf{r}_i \times \ddot{\mathbf{r}}_i = \mathbf{r}_i \times \ddot{\mathbf{r}}_i \, . \tag{31.12}$$

Therefore

$$\mathbf{T} = \mathbf{r}_c \times m \, \ddot{\mathbf{R}} + \frac{d}{dt} \sum_i m_i \, \mathbf{r}_i \times \dot{\mathbf{r}}_i \, . \tag{31.13}$$

Until now no restriction has been placed on the structure of the body. From now on it must be a *rigid* body, namely one whose particles remain fixed with respect to each other. The origin of the $\alpha\beta\gamma$ axes will now be fixed at some point in the rigid body, although the coordinate system and the body need not rotate together. All of the particles in the rigid body rotate with the same angular velocity $\boldsymbol{\omega}$. Each particle rotates about the $\alpha\beta\gamma$ origin with a fixed radius $\mathbf{r}_i$. Fig. 31.1 helps to explain that the velocity $\dot{\mathbf{r}}_i$ is the difference between the velocities of the tip and tail of vector $\mathbf{r}_i$, measured in the inertial xyz coordinates. Fig. 31.5 shows that this difference is $\boldsymbol{\omega} \times \mathbf{r}_i$. Therefore

$$\dot{\mathbf{r}}_i = \boldsymbol{\omega} \times \mathbf{r}_i \,, \tag{31.14}$$

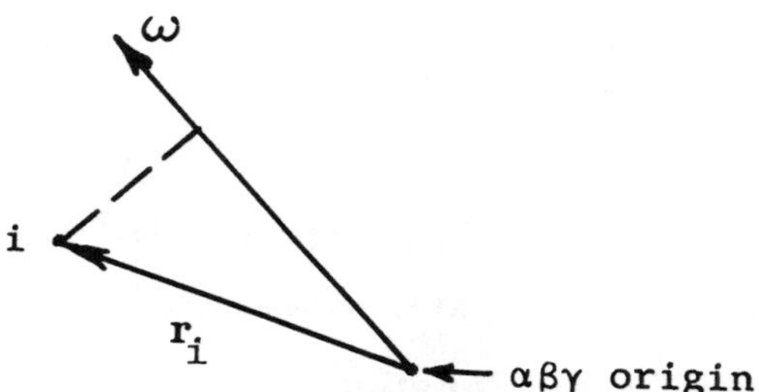

Fig. 31.5. Calculation of velocity $\dot{\mathbf{r}}_i$.

and Eq. (31.13) becomes

$$\mathbf{T} = \mathbf{r}_c \times m\,\ddot{\mathbf{R}} + \frac{d}{dt}\sum_i m_i\,\mathbf{r}_i \times (\boldsymbol{\omega} \times \mathbf{r}_i) \,. \tag{31.15}$$

The *angular momentum* of a rigid body is defined as

$$\mathbf{M} = \sum_i m_i\,\mathbf{r}_i \times (\boldsymbol{\omega} \times \mathbf{r}_i) \,. \tag{31.16}$$

Therefore the net torque applied to a rigid body is

$$\mathbf{T} = \frac{d\mathbf{M}}{dt} + \mathbf{r}_c \times m\,\ddot{\mathbf{R}} \,, \tag{31.17}$$

namely the sum of the rate of change of angular momentum $\mathbf{M}$ and an additional term. Notice that if the $\alpha\beta\gamma$ origin is placed at the cg of the body, $\mathbf{r}_c$ is zero. If the $\alpha\beta\gamma$ origin is not accelerating, $\ddot{\mathbf{R}}$ is zero. Either of these conditions eliminates the additional term. In some practical problems neither condition exists, and both terms of Eq. (31.17) must be evaluated.

Since $\boldsymbol{\omega} \times \mathbf{r}_i = \dot{\mathbf{r}}_i$, the angular momentum given by Eq. (31.16) can be written as

$$\mathbf{M} = \sum_i m_i\,\mathbf{r}_i \times \dot{\mathbf{r}}_i = \sum_i \mathbf{r}_i \times (m_i\,\dot{\mathbf{r}}_i) \,. \tag{31.18}$$

The latter form gives **M** a different interpretation. The vector $m_i \dot{\mathbf{r}}_i$ is the momentum of particle i relative to the $\alpha\beta\gamma$ origin. Fig. 31.6 shows that $\mathbf{r}_i \times (m_i \dot{\mathbf{r}}_i)$ is the moment of $m \dot{\mathbf{r}}_i$ about the $\alpha\beta\gamma$ origin. For this reason **M** is also called the *moment of momentum.*

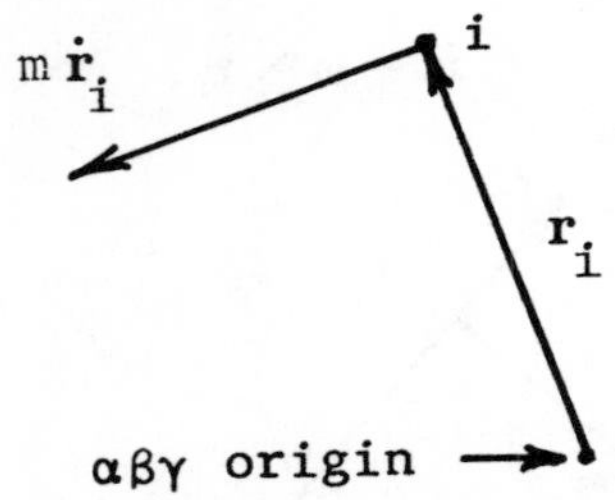

Fig. 31.6. Moment of momentum.

31.4 Euler's Torque Equation

Now the coordinates $\alpha\beta\gamma$ will be used to put the formula for angular momentum, Eq. (31.16), into a form that is useful for solving problems. In these coordinates the vector representing the angular velocity of the body is

$$\boldsymbol{\omega} = \mathbf{l}_\alpha\, \omega_\alpha + \mathbf{l}_\beta\, \omega_\beta + \mathbf{l}_\gamma\, \omega_\gamma\,. \tag{31.19}$$

The distance to particle i in the $\alpha\beta\gamma$ system is

$$\mathbf{r}_i = \mathbf{l}_\alpha\, r_{i\alpha} + \mathbf{l}_\beta\, r_{i\beta} + \mathbf{l}_\gamma\, r_{i\gamma}\,. \tag{31.20}$$

With these two expressions inserted, Eq. (31.16) becomes

$$\begin{aligned}\mathbf{M} = \mathbf{l}_\alpha \sum_i m_i[(r_{i\beta}^2 + r_{i\gamma}^2)\omega_\alpha - r_{i\alpha}\, r_{i\beta}\, \omega_\beta - r_{i\alpha}\, r_{i\gamma}\, \omega_\gamma] \\ + \mathbf{l}_\beta \sum_i m_i[-r_{i\beta}\, r_{i\alpha}\, \omega_\alpha + (r_{i\alpha}^2 + r_{i\gamma}^2)\omega_\beta - r_{i\beta}\, r_{i\gamma}\, \omega_\gamma] \\ + \mathbf{l}_\gamma \sum_i m_i[-r_{i\gamma}\, r_{i\alpha}\, \omega_\alpha - r_{i\gamma}\, r_{i\beta}\, \omega_\beta + (r_{i\alpha}^2 + r_{i\beta}^2)\omega_\gamma]\,.\end{aligned} \tag{31.21}$$

As Fig. 31.7 shows, the term

$$\sum_i m_i(r_{i\beta}^2 + r_{i\gamma}^2)$$

is the moment of inertia of the body about the α axis, called I_α. A term like

$$\sum_i m_i(r_{i\beta}\, r_{i\gamma})$$

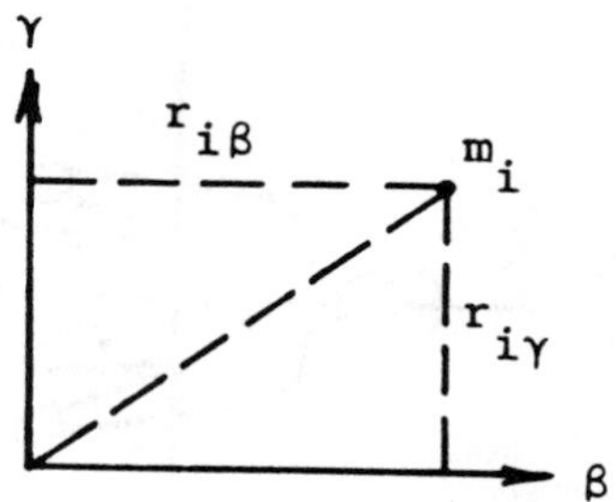

Fig. 31.7. Moment of inertia.

is called a *product of inertia*, $I_{\beta\gamma}$. In terms of moments and products of inertia, Eq. (31.21) can be written as

$$\begin{aligned} \mathbf{M} = {} & \mathbf{1}_\alpha(I_\alpha\,\omega_\alpha - I_{\alpha\beta}\,\omega_\beta - I_{\alpha\gamma}\,\omega_\gamma) \\ & + \mathbf{1}_\beta(-I_{\alpha\beta}\,\omega_\alpha + I_\beta\,\omega_\beta - I_{\beta\gamma}\,\omega_\gamma) \\ & + \mathbf{1}_\gamma(-I_{\alpha\gamma}\,\omega_\alpha - I_{\beta\gamma}\,\omega_\beta + I_\gamma\,\omega_\gamma) \end{aligned} \tag{31.22}$$

or

$$\begin{bmatrix} M_\alpha \\ M_\beta \\ M_\gamma \end{bmatrix} = \begin{bmatrix} I_\alpha & -I_{\alpha\beta} & -I_{\alpha\gamma} \\ -I_{\alpha\beta} & I_\beta & -I_{\beta\gamma} \\ -I_{a\gamma} & -I_{\beta\gamma} & I_\gamma \end{bmatrix} \begin{bmatrix} \omega_\alpha \\ \omega_\beta \\ \omega_\gamma \end{bmatrix}. \tag{31.23}$$

The products of inertia are a nuisance because they couple each component of angular velocity $\boldsymbol{\omega}$ to the other two components of angular momentum $\mathbf{M}$. Fortunately, they can be eliminated by the proper location of the $\alpha\beta\gamma$ axes. Fig. 31.8 shows a body that is symmetrical about the $\alpha\gamma$ plane. The view in the $\alpha\beta$ plane, a small portion of which is enlarged in Fig. 31.9, shows that for every term $m_1\,r_{1\alpha}\,r_{1\beta}$, there is an equal, opposite $m_2\,r_{2\alpha}\,r_{2\beta}$. Therefore $I_{\alpha\beta}$ is zero. The view in the $\beta\gamma$ plane shows that for every term $m_1\,r_{1\beta}\,r_{1\gamma}$, there is an equal and opposite term $m_2\,r_{2\beta}\,r_{2\gamma}$. Accordingly, $I_{\beta\gamma}$ is zero. Notice that $I_{\alpha\gamma}$ is not necessarily zero. If a body is also symmetrical about either the $\alpha\beta$ or $\beta\gamma$ plane, $I_{\alpha\gamma}$ is zero. Thus if a body is symmetrical about any two perpendicular planes, the products of inertia can be eliminated. Choose as axes the intersection of the two planes, and a line in each plane perpendicular to the intersection. Ref. 48 (page 154) shows that at any point in any body a set of orthogonal axes, called *principal axes*, can be found that eliminate the products of inertia. The reader is invited to name a few familiar objects having two planes of symmetry. For these objects, principal axes are easily established.

Previously the $\alpha\beta\gamma$ origin was fixed at some point in the rigid body. Now in addition the $\alpha\beta\gamma$ axes must coincide with principal axes, and

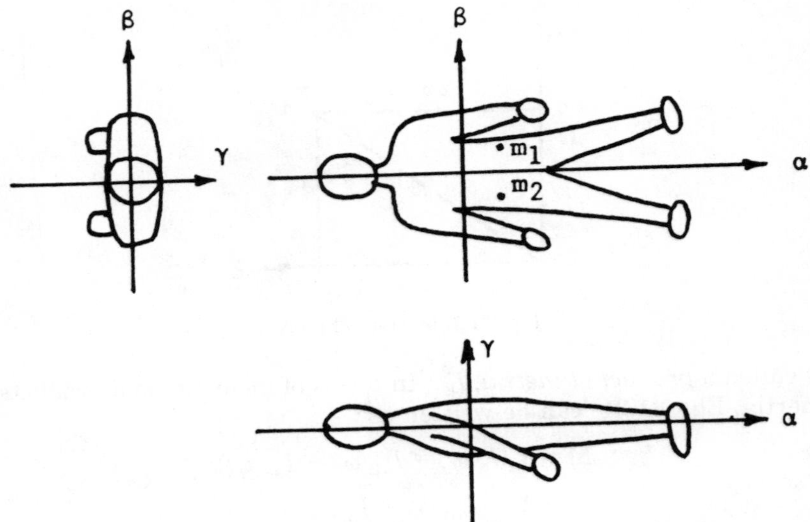

Fig. 31.8. A symmetrical body.

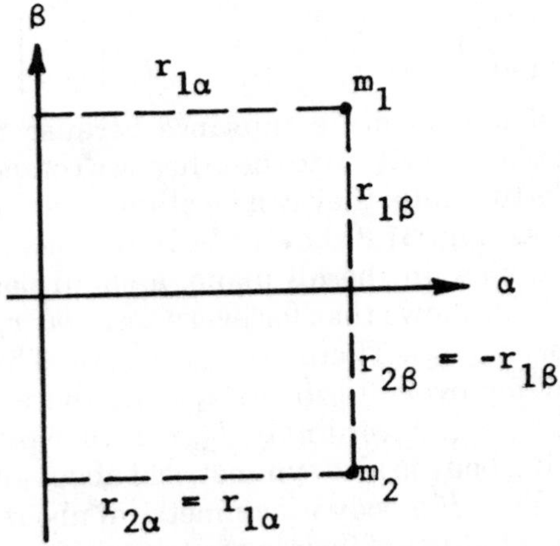

Fig. 31.9. Elimination of a product of inertia.

must rotate with the body at angular velocity $\boldsymbol{\omega}$. Since the products of inertia are zero, the angular momentum of the body given by Eq. (31.22) is simply

$$\mathbf{M} = \mathbf{l}_\alpha I_\alpha \omega_\alpha + \mathbf{l}_\beta I_\beta \omega_\beta + \mathbf{l}_\gamma I_\gamma \omega_\gamma . \tag{31.24}$$

Since the $\alpha\beta\gamma$ axes rotate, their unit vectors have time derivatives. Section 17.4 shows that the derivatives measured with respect to inertial axes are

$$\frac{d\mathbf{l}_\alpha}{dt} = -\mathbf{l}_\gamma\, \omega_\beta + \mathbf{l}_\beta\, \omega_\gamma \tag{31.25}$$

$$\frac{d\mathbf{l}_\beta}{dt} = -\mathbf{l}_\alpha\, \omega_\gamma + \mathbf{l}_\gamma\, \omega_\alpha \tag{31.26}$$

$$\frac{d\mathbf{l}_\gamma}{dt} = \mathbf{l}_\alpha\, \omega_\beta - \mathbf{l}_\beta\, \omega_a \quad . \tag{31.27}$$

A convenient formula for the torque applied to the body can now be obtained by substituting the last four equations into Eq. (31.17). If either $\mathbf{r}_c$ or $\ddot{\mathbf{R}}$ in that equation is zero, it becomes

$$\begin{aligned}\mathbf{T} = {} & \mathbf{l}_\alpha[I_\alpha\, \dot{\omega}_\alpha + (I_\gamma - I_\beta)\omega_\beta\, \omega_\gamma] \\ & + \mathbf{l}_\beta[I_\beta\, \dot{\omega}_\beta + (I_\alpha - I_\gamma)\omega_\alpha\, \omega_\gamma] \\ & + \mathbf{l}_\gamma[I_\gamma\, \dot{\omega}_\gamma + (I_\beta - I_\alpha)\omega_\alpha\, \omega_\beta]\,.\end{aligned} \tag{31.28}$$

This is *Euler's torque equation*. It gives the torque $\mathbf{T}$ required to produce the angular velocity $\boldsymbol{\omega}$ and angular acceleration $\dot{\boldsymbol{\omega}}$ of a rigid body when

1. the $\alpha\beta\gamma$ axes are fixed in the body and rotate with it,
2. the $\alpha\beta\gamma$ axes are principal axes, and
3. the $\alpha\beta\gamma$ origin is the cg of the body or is not accelerating.

Notice that the Euler equation gives the torques about the spinning $\alpha\beta\gamma$ axes. Frequently the torques about another set of axes xyz having the same origin are more useful. The latter torques can be found with the geometric transformation

$$\begin{bmatrix}\mathbf{l}_\alpha \\ \mathbf{l}_\beta \\ \mathbf{l}_\gamma\end{bmatrix} = \begin{bmatrix} c_{\alpha x} & c_{\alpha y} & c_{\alpha z} \\ c_{\beta x} & c_{\beta y} & c_{\beta z} \\ c_{\gamma x} & c_{\gamma y} & c_{\gamma z}\end{bmatrix} \begin{bmatrix}\mathbf{l}_x \\ \mathbf{l}_y \\ \mathbf{l}_z\end{bmatrix} \tag{31.29}$$

where $c_{\alpha x}$ is the cosine of the angle between the α and x axes.

31.5 Example 1. An Airplane Propeller

An example will illustrate the use of Euler's torque equation. Fig. 31.10 shows an airplane whose propeller spins with an angular velocity $\boldsymbol{\omega}_1$ about its shaft. The airplane is turning to the left with an angular velocity $\boldsymbol{\omega}_2$ about a vertical y axis. The torque exerted on the propeller during the turn contains some unexpected components. To calculate

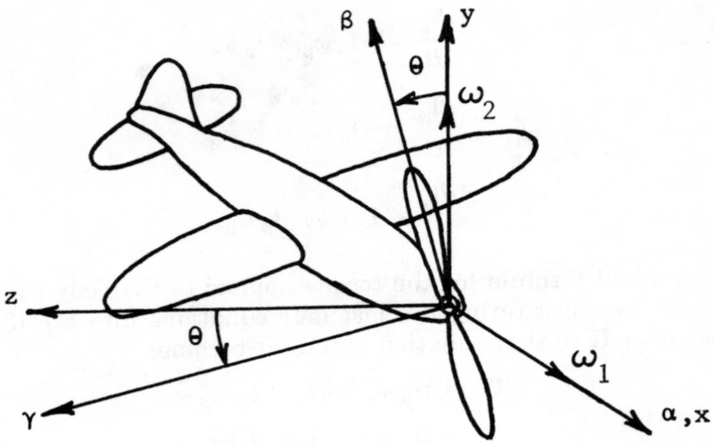

Fig. 31.10. Airplane propeller.

this torque, first orient the $\alpha\beta\gamma$ axes along principal axes of the propeller, with their origin at the propeller's cg. This choice fulfills the three criteria for the use of Euler's torque equation (31.28) As Fig. 31.11 shows,

$$\boldsymbol{\omega}_2 = \mathbf{l}_\beta\, \omega_2 \cos\theta - \mathbf{l}_\gamma\, \omega_2 \sin\theta \,, \tag{31.30}$$

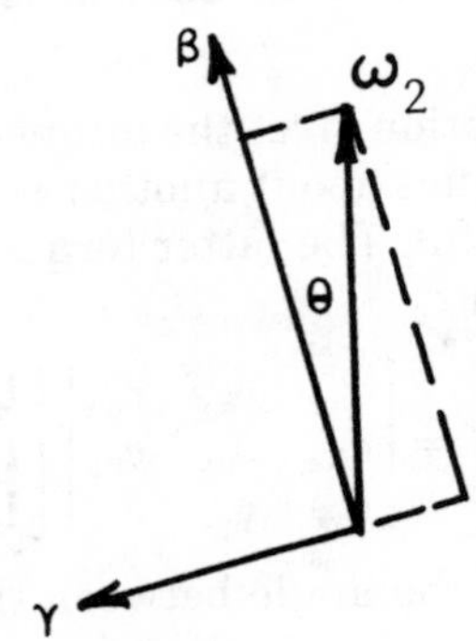

Fig. 31.11. Components of $\boldsymbol{\omega}_2$.

where θ is the angle between the β axis and the vertical y axis. The angular velocity of the propeller and the $\alpha\beta\gamma$ axes is therefore

$$\boldsymbol{\omega} = \boldsymbol{\omega}_1 + \boldsymbol{\omega}_2 = \mathbf{l}_\alpha\, \omega_1 + \mathbf{l}_\beta\, \omega_2 \cos\theta - \mathbf{l}_\gamma\, \omega_2 \sin\theta \,, \tag{31.31}$$

and

$$\omega_\alpha = \omega_1 \,, \qquad \omega_\beta = \omega_2 \cos\theta \,, \qquad \omega_\gamma = -\omega_2 \sin\theta \,. \tag{31.32}$$

Since

$$\omega_1 = \frac{d\theta}{dt}, \tag{31.33}$$

$$\dot{\omega}_\alpha = 0\,, \qquad \dot{\omega}_\beta = -\omega_1\,\omega_2 \sin\theta\,, \qquad \text{and} \qquad \dot{\omega}_\gamma = -\,\omega_1\,\omega_2 \cos\theta\,. \tag{31.34}$$

When these formulas for ω_α, ω_β, ω_γ, and their derivatives are substituted into Eq. (31.28), the result is

$$\begin{aligned}\mathbf{T} = \mathbf{l}_\alpha&[-(I_\gamma - I_\beta)\omega_2^2 \sin\theta \cos\theta] \\ &+ \mathbf{l}_\beta[-I_\beta\,\omega_1\,\omega_2 \sin\theta - (I_\alpha - I_\gamma)\omega_1\,\omega_2 \sin\theta] \\ &+ \mathbf{l}_\gamma[-I_\gamma\,\omega_1\,\omega_2 \cos\theta + (I_\beta - I_\alpha)\omega_1\,\omega_2 \cos\theta]\,.\end{aligned} \tag{31.35}$$

This equation gives the components of torque about the α, β, and γ axes applied to the propeller by the airplane. The effect on the airplane is more easily understood if the torques are expressed about xyz axes that are fixed with respect to the airplane. The x axis coincides with the propeller shaft, and the z axis is horizontal. According to Eq. (31.29),

$$\begin{bmatrix}\mathbf{l}_\alpha \\ \mathbf{l}_\beta \\ \mathbf{l}_\gamma\end{bmatrix} = \begin{bmatrix}1 & 0 & 0 \\ 0 & \cos\theta & \cos(90^\circ - \theta) \\ 0 & \cos(90^\circ + \theta) & \cos\theta\end{bmatrix}\begin{bmatrix}\mathbf{l}_x \\ \mathbf{l}_y \\ \mathbf{l}_z\end{bmatrix}, \tag{31.36}$$

and therefore

$$\left.\begin{aligned}\mathbf{l}_\alpha &= \mathbf{l}_x \\ \mathbf{l}_\beta &= \mathbf{l}_y \cos\theta + \mathbf{l}_z \sin\theta \\ \mathbf{l}_\gamma &= -\mathbf{l}_y \sin\theta + \mathbf{l}_z \cos\theta\quad.\end{aligned}\right\} \tag{31.37}$$

These expressions convert Eq. (31.35) to the form

$$\begin{aligned}\mathbf{T} = \mathbf{l}_x&\left[\frac{\omega_2^2}{2}(I_\beta - I_\gamma)\sin 2\theta\right] \\ &+ \mathbf{l}_y[\omega_1\,\omega_2(I_\gamma - I_\beta)\sin 2\theta] \\ &+ \mathbf{l}_z[-I_\alpha\,\omega_1\,\omega_2 + (I_\beta - I_\gamma)\omega_1\,\omega_2 \cos 2\theta]\,.\end{aligned} \tag{31.38}$$

The negative of **T** is the torque exerted by the propeller on the airplane. Notice that all three components shake the airplane, and in addition a steady z component tends to pitch the airplane upward. For propellers with three or more blades, $I_\beta = I_\gamma$, and the pulsating components of torque are eliminated.

31.6 A Convenient Form of $d\mathbf{M}/dt$

Frequently a problem can be solved more easily by letting the αβγ axes rotate at an angular velocity different from that of the body. Then the formula for torque applied to the body, Eq. (31.17), acquires another useful form. To obtain the new form, observe that the angular momentum of a rigid body is a vector. Measured in the $\alpha\beta\gamma$ coordinates this vector is

$$\mathbf{M} = \mathbf{1}_\alpha M_\alpha + \mathbf{1}_\beta M_\beta + \mathbf{1}_\gamma M_\gamma , \tag{31.39}$$

and its derivative is

$$\frac{d\mathbf{M}}{dt} = \left(\mathbf{1}_\alpha \frac{dM_\alpha}{dt} + \mathbf{1}_\beta \frac{dM_\beta}{dt} + \mathbf{1}_\gamma \frac{dM_\gamma}{dt}\right) + \left(M_\alpha \frac{d\mathbf{1}_\alpha}{dt} + M_\beta \frac{d\mathbf{1}_\beta}{dt} + M_\gamma \frac{d\mathbf{1}_\gamma}{dt}\right) . \tag{31.40}$$

The angular velocity of the body is $\boldsymbol{\omega}$. Let the angular velocity of the $\alpha\beta\gamma$ axes be $\boldsymbol{\Omega}$. The derivatives of the unit vectors are similar to those in Eqs. (31.25) thru (31.27). With respect to inertial axes,

$$\frac{d\mathbf{1}_\alpha}{dt} = -\mathbf{1}_\gamma \Omega_\beta + \mathbf{1}_\beta \Omega_\gamma \tag{31.41}$$

$$\frac{d\mathbf{1}_\beta}{dt} = -\mathbf{1}_\alpha \Omega_\gamma + \mathbf{1}_\gamma \Omega_\alpha \tag{31.42}$$

$$\frac{d\mathbf{1}_\gamma}{dt} = \mathbf{1}_\alpha \Omega_\beta - \mathbf{1}_\beta \Omega_\alpha . \tag{31.43}$$

These three equations reduce Eq. (31.40) to the form

$$\begin{aligned}\frac{d\mathbf{M}}{dt} &= \mathbf{1}_\alpha \left(\frac{dM_\alpha}{dt} - M_\beta \Omega_\gamma + M_\gamma \Omega_\beta\right) \\ &+ \mathbf{1}_\beta \left(\frac{dM_\beta}{dt} + M_\alpha \Omega_\gamma - M_\gamma \Omega_\alpha\right) \\ &+ \mathbf{1}_\gamma \left(\frac{dM_\gamma}{dt} - M_\alpha \Omega_\beta + M_\beta \Omega_\alpha\right) .\end{aligned} \tag{31.44}$$

As seen by an observer rotating with the $\alpha\beta\gamma$ axes, the rate of change of angular momentum is

$$\frac{\delta \mathbf{M}}{\delta t} = \mathbf{1}_\alpha \frac{dM_\alpha}{dt} + \mathbf{1}_\beta \frac{dM_\beta}{dt} + \mathbf{1}_\gamma \frac{dM_\gamma}{dt} . \tag{31.45}$$

Even if the $\alpha\beta\gamma$ axes do not rotate with the body, they can frequently be chosen to eliminate the products of inertia. Then the angular momentum is given by Eq. (31.24):

$$\mathbf{M} = \mathbf{1}_\alpha I_\alpha \omega_\alpha + \mathbf{1}_\beta I_\beta \omega_\beta + \mathbf{1}_\gamma I_\gamma \omega_\gamma . \tag{31.24}$$

Normally the axes are chosen so that neither the moments of inertia I_α, I_β, and I_γ, nor the angular velocities ω_α, ω_β, and ω_γ vary as the axes rotate. Then the observer rotating with the axes sees no change in the vector **M**, and

$$\frac{\delta \mathbf{M}}{\delta t} = 0 . \tag{31.46}$$

This term is not zero if the components of angular velocity change with time. For example, the angular velocity of a spinning top decreases as the top runs down.

Eq. (31.44) can be written in the form

$$\frac{d\mathbf{M}}{dt} = \frac{\delta \mathbf{M}}{\delta t} + \mathbf{\Omega} \times \mathbf{M} . \tag{31.47}$$

The term $\mathbf{\Omega} \times \mathbf{M}$ is called the *gyroscopic torque*. If $\delta\mathbf{M}/\delta t$ is zero, the angular momentum vector **M** is fixed with respect to the $\alpha\beta\gamma$ axes, and rotates with them at the angular velocity $\mathbf{\Omega}$. To produce this motion, the torque $\mathbf{\Omega} \times \mathbf{M}$ must be applied to the body, at right angles to both $\mathbf{\Omega}$ and **M**. If in addition the term $\mathbf{r}_c \times m\, \ddot{\mathbf{R}}$ in Eq. (31.17) is zero, the gyroscopic torque is the entire torque applied to the body.

An example of this motion is the story of the suitcase with a motor-driven flywheel inside, shown in Fig. 31.12. The $\alpha\beta\gamma$ axes are fixed with

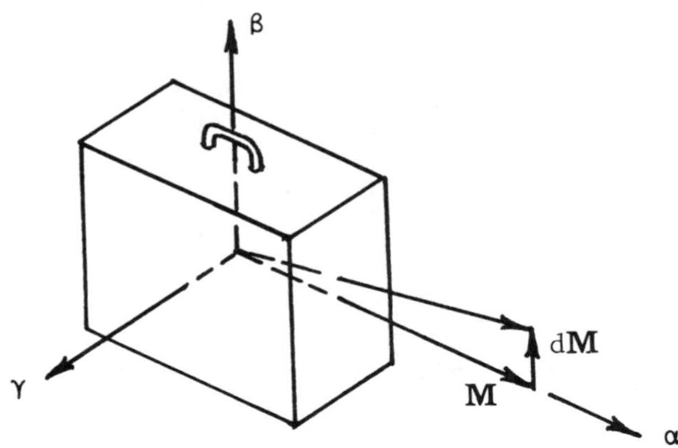

Fig. 31.12. Suitcase with a flywheel inside.

respect to the suitcase. The angular momentum vector of the flywheel is in the α direction. When the porter tries to turn to the left, he exerts a torque

$$\frac{d\mathbf{M}}{dt} = \mathbf{\Omega} \times \mathbf{M} \tag{31.48}$$

in the β direction. This equation shows that $\mathbf{\Omega}$ is in the γ direction. Fig. 31.12 confirms that if the angular momentum vector $\mathbf{M}$ is moved upward by the amount $d\mathbf{M}$, due to the angular velocity $\mathbf{\Omega}$ in the γ direction, the torque required to move it is in the β direction. Instead of turning to the left, the suitcase pitches upward, like the airplane in Example 1. The reader is invited to explain how the porter could make the suitcase turn to the left.

31.7 Example 2. A Gyroscope

Another example will show the usefulness of Eq. (31.47). In Fig. 31.13 is a gyroscope of weight W, spinning with angular velocity $\boldsymbol{\omega}_\alpha$ about its own shaft. The shaft is horizontal, and is precessing with angular velocity $\mathbf{\Omega}$ about a vertical axis located a distance a from the cg of the gyroscope. What is the velocity of precession? The α axis is chosen to coincide with the axis of the shaft, the β axis is horizontal and perpendicular to the shaft, and the γ axis is vertical. Although the αβγ axes do

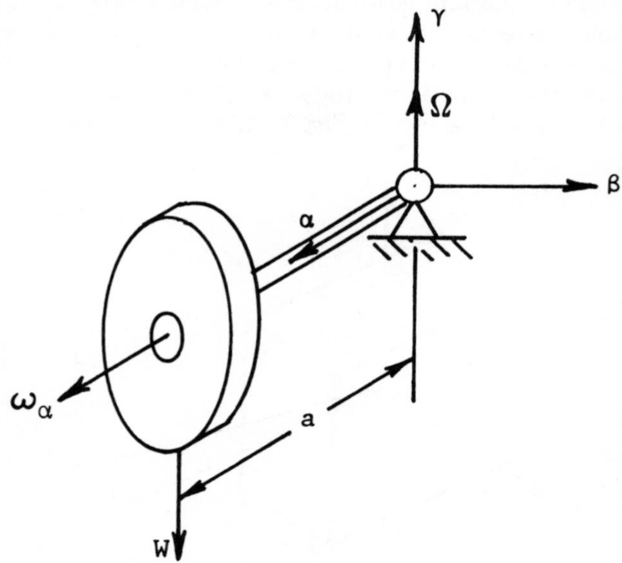

Fig. 31.13. A gyroscope.

not spin with the gyroscope, they remain principal axes as the wheel turns. Because of the symmetry of the wheel, α and any two orthogonal axes in the βγ plane eliminate the products of inertia. The same symmetry makes I_α, I_β, and I_γ remain constant as the wheel turns. The angular velocity of the αβγ axes is $\mathbf{\Omega} = \mathbf{1}_\gamma\Omega$. Since their origin does not accelerate, the term $\mathbf{r}_c \times m\ddot{\mathbf{R}}$ in Eq. (31.17) is zero. The angular velocity of the gyroscope is

$$\boldsymbol{\omega} = \boldsymbol{\omega}_\alpha + \boldsymbol{\Omega} = \mathbf{1}_\alpha\, \omega_\alpha + \mathbf{1}_\gamma\, \Omega\,. \tag{31.49}$$

The angular momentum of the gyroscope is

$$\mathbf{M} = \mathbf{1}_\alpha\, I_\alpha\, \omega_\alpha + \mathbf{1}_\gamma\, I_\gamma\, \Omega\,. \tag{31.50}$$

This vector has a fixed length and rotates with the $\alpha\beta\gamma$ axes. Accordingly,

$$\frac{\delta \mathbf{M}}{\delta t} = 0\,. \tag{31.51}$$

The gyroscopic torque is

$$\boldsymbol{\Omega} \times \mathbf{M} = \begin{vmatrix} \mathbf{1}_\alpha & \mathbf{1}_\beta & \mathbf{1}_\gamma \\ 0 & 0 & \Omega \\ I_\alpha\omega_\alpha & 0 & I_\gamma\Omega \end{vmatrix} = \mathbf{1}_\beta\, I_\alpha\, \omega_\alpha\, \Omega\,. \tag{31.52}$$

According to Eq. (31.17), this is the torque applied to the gyroscope. It is provided by the moment $\mathbf{1}_\beta\, W\, a$. Therefore

$$I_\alpha\, \omega_\alpha\, \Omega = W\, a \tag{31.53}$$

or

$$\Omega = \frac{W\, a}{I_\alpha\, \omega_\alpha}\,. \tag{31.54}$$

This is the angular velocity of precession. When the spin velocity ω_α of a gyroscope slows down, the velocity of precession increases. In an earth satellite where a gyroscope is weightless, it does not precess at all.

The same result can be obtained, with a longer calculation, by the use of Euler's torque equation. The latter, however, would be the better choice if the gyroscope were a rim with two spokes, instead of a solid wheel. Then the $\alpha\beta\gamma$ axes would not be principal axes, the angular momentum could not be expressed by the simple Eq. (31.24), I_β and I_γ would fluctuate as the gyroscope turned, $\delta\mathbf{M}/\delta t$ would not be zero, and the torque required for smooth precession would pulsate. The calculation with Eq. (31.47) would be difficult. Euler's equation, on the other hand, would produce a formula for the pulsating torque as easily as in the example of the propeller.

31.8 Summary

To calculate the torque applied to a rigid body,

1. **Choose the $\alpha\beta\gamma$ axes to coincide with principal axes.**

2. If the $\alpha\beta\gamma$ axes are principal axes that rotate with the body, and their origin is the cg or does not accelerate, use the Euler torque equation (31.28).

3. If the angular velocity $\mathbf{\Omega}$ of the axes is chosen to be different from the angular velocity $\boldsymbol{\omega}$ of the body, write out the α, β, and γ components of each.

4. Using the components of $\boldsymbol{\omega}$ and the moments of inertia about the $\alpha\beta\gamma$ axes, write the angular momentum $\mathbf{M}$ according to Eq. (31.24).

5. Write the components of $d\mathbf{M}/dt$, using Eq. (31.47).

6. If the $\alpha\beta\gamma$ origin is accelerating or is not the cg, add the term $\mathbf{r}_c \times m\,\ddot{\mathbf{R}}$ to $d\mathbf{M}/dt$.

7. The result of step 5 or 6 is $\mathbf{T}$, the torque required to rotate the body, measured in the $\alpha\beta\gamma$ coordinates.

REFERENCES

1. Milton Abramowitz and I.A. Stegun, *Handbook of Mathematical Functions*, National Bureau of Standards Applied Mathematics Series, 1964.
2. N.I. Akhiezer, *The Calculus of Variations*, Blaisdell Publishing Co., 1962.
3. G.A. Bekey and W.J. Karplus, *Hybrid Computation*, John Wiley and Sons, 1968.
4. P.R. Benyon, "A Review of Numerical Methods for Digital Simulation," *Simulation Magazine*, November 1968.
5. R.B. Bird, W.E. Stewart, and E.N. Lightfoot, *Transport Phenomena*, John Wiley and Sons, 1960.
6. H.W. Bode, *Network Analysis and Feedback Amplifier Design*, D. Van Nostrand, 1945.
7. R.E. Bolz and G.L. Tuve, *Handbook of Tables for Applied Engineering Science*, Second Edition, Chemical Rubber Company Press, 1973.
8. P.W. Bridgman, *Dimensional Analysis*, Yale University Press, 1931.
9. R.S. Brodkey, *The Phenomena of Fluid Motions*, Addison-Wesley, 1967.
10. E. Buckingham, "On Physically Similar Systems; Illustrations of the Use of Dimensional Equations," *Physical Review*, Vol. IV, No. 4, 1914, pages 345–376.
11. R.G. Campbell, *Foundations of Fluid Flow Theory*, Addison-Wesley, 1973.
12. Alan Carlson, George Hannauer, Thomas Carey, and P.J. Holsberg, *Handbook of Analog Computation*, Second Edition, Electronic Associates, Inc., 1967.
13. H.S. Carslaw and J.C. Jaeger, *Conduction of Heat in Solids*, Oxford University Press, 1947.
14. D.K. Cheng, *Analysis of Linear Systems*, Addison-Wesley, 1959.
15. P.C. Chou and N.J. Pagano, *Elasticity: Tensor, Dyadic, and Engineering Approaches*, D. Van Nostrand Company, 1967.
16. R.V. Churchill, *Fourier Series and Boundary Value Problems*, Second Edition, McGraw-Hill, 1963.
17. I.G. Currie, *Fundamental Mechanics of Fluids*, McGraw-Hill, 1974.
18. Germund Dahlquist, Ake Bjorck, and Ned Anderson, *Numerical Methods*, Prentice-Hall, 1974.
19. G.B. Dantzig, *Linear Programming and Extensions*, Princeton University Press, 1963.
20. H.T. Davis, *Introduction to Nonlinear Differential and Integral Equations*, United States Atomic Energy Commission, 1960.
21. P.M. DeRusso, R.J. Roy, and C.M. Close, *State Variables for Engineers*, John Wiley and Sons, 1965.
22. R.C. Dorf, *Modern Control Systems*, Addison-Wesley, 1967.
23. R.C. Dorf, *Time-Domain Analysis and Design of Control Systems*, Addison-Wesley, 1965.

24. D.S. Dugdale and C. Ruiz, *Elasticity for Engineers*, McGraw-Hill, London, 1971.
25. *EAI TR-20 Computer Operator's Reference Handbook*, Electronic Associates, Inc., 1966.
26. E.R.G. Eckert, *Introduction to the Transfer of Heat and Mass*, McGraw-Hill, 1950.
27. *Electric Utility Systems and Practices*, Third Edition, Electric Utility Systems Engineering Department, General Electric Company, 1974, Publication No. GEZ-2587B.
28. O.I. Elgerd, *Control Systems Theory*, McGraw-Hill, 1967.
29. J.E. Emswiler and F.L. Schwartz, *Thermodynamics*, Fifth Edition, McGraw-Hill, 1943.
30. O.W. Eshbach, *Handbook of Engineering Fundamentals*, Second Edition, John Wiley and Sons, 1952.
31. V.M. Faires, *Thermodynamics*, Fifth Edition, Macmillan Company, 1970.
32. Enrico Fermi, *Thermodynamics*, Prentice-Hall, 1937, and Dover Publications, 1956.
33. G.A. Fischer, *Static Energy Methods*, unpublished notes, General Electric Co., February 10, 1960.
34. M. Fishenden and O.A. Saunders, *An Introduction to Heat Transfer*, Oxford University Press, 1950.
35. J.W. Forrester, *Industrial Dynamics*, MIT Press and John Wiley and Sons, 1961.
36. J.W. Forrester, *Urban Dynamics*, MIT Press, 1969.
37. J.W. Forrester, *World Dynamics*, Wright-Allen Press, 1971.
38. R.A. Frazer, W.J. Duncan, and A.R. Collar, *Elementary Matrices*, Cambridge University Press, 1938.
39. D.K. Frederick and A.B. Carlson, *Linear Systems in Communication and Control*, John Wiley and Sons, 1971.
40. Herbert Freeman, *Discrete-Time Systems*, John Wiley & Sons, 1965.
41. M.M. Frocht, *Photoelasticity*, Volume I 1941, Volume II 1948, John Wiley and Sons.
42. *Fundamentals of Engineering Analysis*, Volumes I, II, and III, Second Edition, General Electric Company, 1957.
43. S.I. Gass, *Linear Programming*, McGraw-Hill, 1962.
44. C.W. Gear, "The Automatic Integration of Ordinary Differential Equations," *Communications of the ACM* (Association for Computing Machinery), March 1971.
45. C.F. Gerald, *Applied Numerical Analysis*, Addison-Wesley, 1970.
46. J.E. Gibson, *Nonlinear Automatic Control*, McGraw-Hill, 1963.
47. W.H. Giedt, *Principles of Engineering Heat Transfer*, D. Van Nostrand, 1957.

48. Herbert Goldstein, *Classical Mechanics*, Addison-Wesley, 1950.
49. G.A. Goodenough, *Principles of Thermodynamics*, Third Edition, Henry Holt and Company, 1925.
50. Donald Greenspan, *Discrete Numerical Methods in Physics and Engineering*, Academic Press, 1974.
51. G. Hadley, *Linear Programming*, Addison-Wesley, 1962.
52. R.W. Hamming, *Numerical Methods for Scientists and Engineers*, McGraw-Hill, 1962.
53. George Hannauer, *Basics of Parallel Hybrid Computers*, Electronic Associates, Inc., 1968.
54. G.N. Hatsopoulos and J.H. Keenan, *Principles of General Thermodynamics*, John Wiley and Sons, 1965.
55. *Heat Transfer and Fluid Flow Data Books*, Heat Transfer Volume, General Electric Company, Corporate Research and Development Center.
56. F.B. Hildebrand, *Advanced Calculus for Applications*, Prentice-Hall, 1962.
57. F.B. Hildebrand, *Finite-Difference Equations and Simulations*, Prentice-Hall, 1968.
58. F.B. Hildebrand, *Introduction to Numerical Analysis*, McGraw-Hill, 1956.
59. F.B. Hildebrand, *Methods of Applied Mathematics*, Second Edition, Prentice-Hall, 1965.
60. Harry Hochstadt, *Differential Equations, a Modern Approach*, Holt, Rinehart, and Winston, 1964.
61. J.P. Holman, *Heat Transfer*, Fourth Edition, McGraw-Hill, 1976.
62. L. Hoogenboom, "Electrical Analog Model of Two-Dimensional Transient Heat Conduction," ASME Preprint No. 65-HT-66.
63. G.W. Housner and D.E. Hudson, *Applied Mechanics Dynamics*, Second Edition, D. Van Nostrand Company, 1959.
64. J.C. Hsu and A.U. Meyer, *Modern Control Principles and Applications*, McGraw-Hill, 1968.
65. J.C. Hunsaker and B.G. Rightmire, *Engineering Applications of Fluid Mechanics*, McGraw-Hill, 1947.
66. B.L. Hunter, notes on *Conduction Heat Transfer* and *Elasticity* for the Advanced Course in Engineering, General Electric Company.
67. B.W. Imrie, *Compressible Fluid Flow*, John Wiley and Sons, 1973.
68. A.S. Jackson, *Analog Computation*, McGraw-Hill, 1960.
69. Eugene Jahnke and Fritz Emde, *Tables of Functions*, Fourth Edition, Dover Publications, 1945.
70. Max Jakob, *Heat Transfer*, Volume I, John Wiley and Sons, 1949.
71. Alfred Jensen, *Elementary Statics and Strength of Materials*, University of Washington Book Store, 1943.
72. J.B. Jones and G.A Hawkins, *Engineering Thermodynamics*, John Wiley and Sons, 1960.

73. W.M. Kays, *Convective Heat and Mass Transfer*, McGraw-Hill, 1966.
74. J.H. Keenan, *Thermodynamics*, John Wiley and Sons, 1941.
75. W.J. King, "The Basic Laws and Data of Heat Transmission," *Mechanical Engineering*, Vol. 54, 1932, pages 347–353.
76. R.J. Kochenburger, *Computer Simulation of Dynamic Systems*, Prentice-Hall, 1972.
77. Erwin Kreyszig, *Advanced Engineering Mathematics*, Second Edition, John Wiley and Sons, 1967.
78. Horace Lamb, *Hydrodynamics*, Cambridge University Press, 1924.
79. L.D. Landau and E.M. Lifshitz, *Fluid Mechanics*, Pergamon Press, 1959.
80. L.D. Landau and E.M. Lifshitz, *Theory of Elasticity*, Second Edition, Pergamon Press, 1970.
81. H.L. Langhaar, *Dimensional Analysis and Theory of Models*, John Wiley and Sons, 1954.
82. R.B. Leighton, *Principles of Modern Physics*, McGraw-Hill, 1959.
83. M.L. Liou, "A Novel Method of Evaluating Transient Response," *Proceedings of the IEEE*, Vol. 54, No. 1, January 1966.
84. D.R. Mack, *The Decomposition Method of Linear Programming*, General Electric Company TIS Report 67ETE1, 1967.
85. D.R. Mack, *Electrical and Magnetic Fields*, notes for the Advanced Course in Engineering, General Electric Co., 1970.
86. D.R. Mack, "Measurement of Residual Stress in Disks from Turbine-Rotor Forgings," *Experimental Mechanics*, May 1962.
87. D.R. Mack, *A Study of the Large Turbine-Generator Business Using Control Theory*, General Electric Company TIS Report 69ETE2, 1969.
88. W.H. McAdams, *Heat Transmission*, Third Edition, McGraw-Hill, 1954.
89. Ian McCausland, *Introduction to Optimal Control*, John Wiley & Sons, 1969.
90. R.B. McClintock, P.W. Richardson, and R.C. Spencer, *ASME Steam Tables in SI (Metric) Units*, The American Society of Mechanical Engineers, 1977.
91. N.W. McLachlan, *Bessel Functions for Engineers*, Oxford University Press, 1946.
92. Claude McMillan and R.F. Gonzalez, *Systems Analysis*, Richard D. Irwin, Inc., 1968.
93. L.M. Milne-Thompson, *Theoretical Hydrodynamics*, Fifth Edition, Macmillan Company, 1968.
94. Max Morris and O.E. Brown, *Differential Equations*, Prentice-Hall, 1942.
95. P.M. Morse and Herman Feshbach, *Methods of Theoretical Physics*, McGraw-Hill, 1953.
96. Glenn Murphy, *Advanced Mechanics of Materials*, McGraw-Hill, 1946.
97. A.R.M. Noton, *Introduction to Variational Methods in Control Engineering*, Pergamon Press, 1965.

98. Katsuhiko Ogata, *State Space Analysis of Control Systems*, Prentice-Hall, 1967.

99. W.F. Osgood, *Mechanics*, Macmillan Company, 1937.

100. Athanasios Papoulis, *The Fourier Integral and Its Applications*, McGraw-Hill, 1962.

101. R.J.A. Paul, *Fundamental Analogue Techniques*, Macmillan Company, 1965.

102. C.C. Perry and H.R. Lissner, *The Strain Gage Primer*, McGraw-Hill, 1962.

103. L.A. Pipes, *Applied Mathematics for Engineers and Physicists*, Second Edition, McGraw-Hill, 1958.

104. Robert Plonsey and R.E Collin, *Principles and Applications of Electromagnetic Fields*, McGraw-Hill, 1961.

105. L. Prandtl and O.G. Tietjens, *Applied Hydro- and Aeromechanics*, First Edition, McGraw-Hill, 1934.

106. L. Prandtl and O.G. Tietjens, *Fundamentals of Hydro- and Aeromechanics*, First Edition, McGraw-Hill, 1934.

107. A.L. Pugh III, *DYNAMO User's Manual*, Second Edition, MIT Press, 1963.

108. Anthony Ralston, *A First Course in Numerical Analysis*, McGraw-Hill, 1965.

109. Manfred Rauscher, *Introduction to Aeronautical Dynamics*, John Wiley and Sons, 1953.

110. F.E. Relton, *Applied Bessel Functions*, Dover Publications, 1965.

111. J.M. Robertson, *Hydrodynamics in Theory and Application*, Prentice-Hall, 1965.

112. M.J. Romanelli, "Runge-Kutta Methods for the Solution of Ordinary Differential Equations," Chapter 9 of *Mathematical Methods for Digital Computers*, edited by Anthony Ralston and H.S. Wilf, John Wiley and Sons, 1960.

113. A.S. Saada, *Elasticity Theory and Applications*, Pergamon Press, 1974.

114. J.K. Salisbury, *Steam Turbines and Their Cycles*, John Wiley and Sons, 1950.

115. M.G. Salvadori and M.L. Baron, *Numerical Methods of Engineering*, Prentice-Hall, 1952.

116. M. Sasieni, A. Yaspan, and L. Friedman, *Operations Research: Methods and Problems*, John Wiley and Sons, 1959.

117. J.B. Scarborough, *Numerical Mathematical Analysis*, Second Edition, Johns Hopkins Press, 1950.

118. P.J. Schneider, *Conduction Heat Transfer*, Addison-Wesley, 1955.

119. R.J. Schwarz and Bernard Friedland, *Linear Systems*, McGraw-Hill, 1965.

120. F.W. Sears, *Thermodynamics, the Kinetic Theory of Gases, and Statistical Mechanics*, Second Edition, Addison-Wesley, 1953.

121. C.E. Shannon, "Communications in the Presence of Noise," *Proc. IRE*, January 1949.

122. A.H. Shapiro, *The Dynamics and Thermodynamics of Compressible Fluid Flow*, Volume I 1953, Volume II 1954, Ronald Press.
123. J.F. Shelley, notes on *Stress Analysis* for the Advanced Course in Engineering, General Electric Company.
124. Robert Siegel and J.R. Howell, *Thermal Radiation Heat Transfer*, McGraw-Hill, 1972.
125. J.R. Simonson, *An Introduction to Engineering Heat Transfer*, McGraw-Hill, 1967.
126. G.W. Smith and R.C. Wood, *Principles of Analog Computation*, McGraw-Hill, 1959.
127. I.S. Sokolnikoff and R.M. Redheffer, *Mathematics of Physics and Modern Engineering*, Second Edition, McGraw-Hill, 1966.
128. I.S. and E.S. Sokolnikoff, *Higher Mathematics for Engineers and Physicists*, McGraw-Hill, 1934.
129. R.V. Southwell, *An Introduction to the Theory of Elasticity*, Oxford University Press, 1936.
130. E.M. Sparrow and R.D. Cess, *Radiation Heat Transfer*, Brooks/Cole Publishing Co., 1966.
131. R.G. Stanton, *Numerical Methods for Science and Engineering*, Prentice-Hall, 1961.
132. W.M. Swanson, *Fluid Mechanics*, Holt, Rinehart, and Winston, 1970.
133. S. Timoshenko, *Strength of Materials, Part II, Advanced Theory and Problems*, D. Van Nostrand, 1941.
134. S. Timoshenko and J.N. Goodier, *Theory of Elasticity*, McGraw-Hill, 1951.
135. S. Timoshenko and J.M. Lessels, *Applied Elasticity*, Westinghouse Technical Night School Press, 1925.
136. Julius T. Tou, *Modern Control Theory*, McGraw-Hill, 1964.
137. Myron Tribus, *Thermostatics and Thermodynamics*, D. Van Nostrand, 1961.
138. Steven Vajda, *Mathematical Programming*, Addison-Wesley, 1961.
139. G.J. VanWylen and R.E. Sonntag, *Fundamentals of Classical Thermodynamics*, Second Edition, John Wiley and Sons, 1973.
140. J.B. Walsh, *Electromagnetic Theory and Engineering Applications*, Ronald Press, 1960.
141. Kenneth Wark, *Thermodynamics*, McGraw-Hill, 1966.
142. Ernst Weber, *Electromagnetic Theory*, Dover Publications, 1965.
143. D. Welbourne, *Analog Computing Methods*, Pergamon Press, 1965.
144. F.M. White, *Viscous Fluid Flow*, McGraw-Hill, 1974.
145. J.M. Wozencraft and I.M. Jacobs, *Principles of Communication Engineering*, John Wiley and Sons, 1965.
146. W.G. Wright, *Modern Control Theory Course*, Canadian General Electric Co. Technical Data Report DQF-67-AD-15.

147. C.R. Wylie, *Advanced Engineering Mathematics*, Third Edition, McGraw-Hill, 1966.

148. A.M. Yaglom and I.M. Yaglom, *Challenging Mathematical Problems*, Volume II, Holden-Day, 1967.

149. E.E. Zwicky, notes on *Numerical Analysis* for the Advanced Course in Engineering, General Electric Company.

INDEX